# The Cumulative Standardized Normal Distribution (Continued)

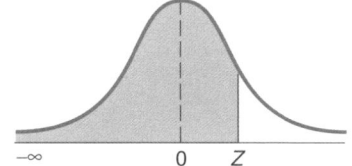

*Entry represents area under the stadardized normal distribution from $-\infty$ to Z*

| Z | 0.00 | 0.01 | 0.02 | 0.03 | 0.04 | 0.05 | 0.06 | 0.07 | 0.08 | 0.09 |
|---|------|------|------|------|------|------|------|------|------|------|
| 0.0 | 0.5000 | 0.5040 | 0.5080 | 0.5120 | 0.5160 | 0.5199 | 0.5239 | 0.5279 | 0.5319 | 0.5359 |
| 0.1 | 0.5398 | 0.5438 | 0.5478 | 0.5517 | 0.5557 | 0.5596 | 0.5636 | 0.5675 | 0.5714 | 0.5753 |
| 0.2 | 0.5793 | 0.5832 | 0.5871 | 0.5910 | 0.5948 | 0.5987 | 0.6026 | 0.6064 | 0.6103 | 0.6141 |
| 0.3 | 0.6179 | 0.6217 | 0.6255 | 0.6293 | 0.6331 | 0.6368 | 0.6406 | 0.6443 | 0.6480 | 0.6517 |
| 0.4 | 0.6554 | 0.6591 | 0.6628 | 0.6664 | 0.6700 | 0.6736 | 0.6772 | 0.6808 | 0.6844 | 0.6879 |
| 0.5 | 0.6915 | 0.6950 | 0.6985 | 0.7019 | 0.7054 | 0.7088 | 0.7123 | 0.7157 | 0.7190 | 0.7224 |
| 0.6 | 0.7257 | 0.7291 | 0.7324 | 0.7357 | 0.7389 | 0.7422 | 0.7454 | 0.7486 | 0.7518 | 0.7549 |
| 0.7 | 0.7580 | 0.7612 | 0.7642 | 0.7673 | 0.7704 | 0.7734 | 0.7764 | 0.7794 | 0.7823 | 0.7852 |
| 0.8 | 0.7881 | 0.7910 | 0.7939 | 0.7967 | 0.7995 | 0.8023 | 0.8051 | 0.8078 | 0.8106 | 0.8133 |
| 0.9 | 0.8159 | 0.8186 | 0.8212 | 0.8238 | 0.8264 | 0.8289 | 0.8315 | 0.8340 | 0.8365 | 0.8389 |
| 1.0 | 0.8413 | 0.8438 | 0.8461 | 0.8485 | 0.8508 | 0.8531 | 0.8554 | 0.8577 | 0.8599 | 0.8621 |
| 1.1 | 0.8643 | 0.8665 | 0.8686 | 0.8708 | 0.8729 | 0.8749 | 0.8770 | 0.8790 | 0.8810 | 0.8830 |
| 1.2 | 0.8849 | 0.8869 | 0.8888 | 0.8907 | 0.8925 | 0.8944 | 0.8962 | 0.8980 | 0.8997 | 0.9015 |
| 1.3 | 0.9032 | 0.9049 | 0.9066 | 0.9082 | 0.9099 | 0.9115 | 0.9131 | 0.9147 | 0.9162 | 0.9177 |
| 1.4 | 0.9192 | 0.9207 | 0.9222 | 0.9236 | 0.9251 | 0.9265 | 0.9279 | 0.9292 | 0.9306 | 0.9319 |
| 1.5 | 0.9332 | 0.9345 | 0.9357 | 0.9370 | 0.9382 | 0.9394 | 0.9406 | 0.9418 | 0.9429 | 0.9441 |
| 1.6 | 0.9452 | 0.9463 | 0.9474 | 0.9484 | 0.9495 | 0.9505 | 0.9515 | 0.9525 | 0.9535 | 0.9545 |
| 1.7 | 0.9554 | 0.9564 | 0.9573 | 0.9582 | 0.9591 | 0.9599 | 0.9608 | 0.9616 | 0.9625 | 0.9633 |
| 1.8 | 0.9641 | 0.9649 | 0.9656 | 0.9664 | 0.9671 | 0.9678 | 0.9686 | 0.9693 | 0.9699 | 0.9706 |
| 1.9 | 0.9713 | 0.9719 | 0.9726 | 0.9732 | 0.9738 | 0.9744 | 0.9750 | 0.9756 | 0.9761 | 0.9767 |
| 2.0 | 0.9772 | 0.9778 | 0.9783 | 0.9788 | 0.9793 | 0.9798 | 0.9803 | 0.9808 | 0.9812 | 0.9817 |
| 2.1 | 0.9821 | 0.9826 | 0.9830 | 0.9834 | 0.9838 | 0.9842 | 0.9846 | 0.9850 | 0.9854 | 0.9857 |
| 2.2 | 0.9861 | 0.9864 | 0.9868 | 0.9871 | 0.9875 | 0.9878 | 0.9881 | 0.9884 | 0.9887 | 0.9890 |
| 2.3 | 0.9893 | 0.9896 | 0.9898 | 0.9901 | 0.9904 | 0.9906 | 0.9909 | 0.9911 | 0.9913 | 0.9916 |
| 2.4 | 0.9918 | 0.9920 | 0.9922 | 0.9925 | 0.9927 | 0.9929 | 0.9931 | 0.9932 | 0.9934 | 0.9936 |
| 2.5 | 0.9938 | 0.9940 | 0.9941 | 0.9943 | 0.9945 | 0.9946 | 0.9948 | 0.9949 | 0.9951 | 0.9952 |
| 2.6 | 0.9953 | 0.9955 | 0.9956 | 0.9957 | 0.9959 | 0.9960 | 0.9961 | 0.9962 | 0.9963 | 0.9964 |
| 2.7 | 0.9965 | 0.9966 | 0.9967 | 0.9968 | 0.9969 | 0.9970 | 0.9971 | 0.9972 | 0.9973 | 0.9974 |
| 2.8 | 0.9974 | 0.9975 | 0.9976 | 0.9977 | 0.9977 | 0.9978 | 0.9979 | 0.9979 | 0.9980 | 0.9981 |
| 2.9 | 0.9981 | 0.9982 | 0.9982 | 0.9983 | 0.9984 | 0.9984 | 0.9985 | 0.9985 | 0.9986 | 0.9986 |
| 3.0 | 0.99865 | 0.99869 | 0.99874 | 0.99878 | 0.99882 | 0.99886 | 0.99889 | 0.99893 | 0.99897 | 0.99900 |
| 3.1 | 0.99903 | 0.99906 | 0.99910 | 0.99913 | 0.99916 | 0.99918 | 0.99921 | 0.99924 | 0.99926 | 0.99929 |
| 3.2 | 0.99931 | 0.99934 | 0.99936 | 0.99938 | 0.99940 | 0.99942 | 0.99944 | 0.99946 | 0.99948 | 0.99950 |
| 3.3 | 0.99952 | 0.99953 | 0.99955 | 0.99957 | 0.99958 | 0.99960 | 0.99961 | 0.99962 | 0.99964 | 0.99965 |
| 3.4 | 0.99966 | 0.99968 | 0.99969 | 0.99970 | 0.99971 | 0.99972 | 0.99973 | 0.99974 | 0.99975 | 0.99976 |
| 3.5 | 0.99977 | 0.99978 | 0.99978 | 0.99979 | 0.99980 | 0.99981 | 0.99981 | 0.99982 | 0.99983 | 0.99983 |
| 3.6 | 0.99984 | 0.99985 | 0.99985 | 0.99986 | 0.99986 | 0.99987 | 0.99987 | 0.99988 | 0.99988 | 0.99989 |
| 3.7 | 0.99989 | 0.99990 | 0.99990 | 0.99990 | 0.99991 | 0.99991 | 0.99992 | 0.99992 | 0.99992 | 0.99992 |
| 3.8 | 0.99993 | 0.99993 | 0.99993 | 0.99994 | 0.99994 | 0.99994 | 0.99994 | 0.99995 | 0.99995 | 0.99995 |
| 3.9 | 0.99995 | 0.99995 | 0.99996 | 0.99996 | 0.99996 | 0.99996 | 0.99996 | 0.99996 | 0.99997 | 0.99997 |
| 4.0 | 0.99996832 | | | | | | | | | |
| 4.5 | 0.99999660 | | | | | | | | | |
| 5.0 | 0.99999971 | | | | | | | | | |
| 5.5 | 0.99999998 | | | | | | | | | |
| 6.0 | 0.99999999 | | | | | | | | | |

# A ROADMAP FOR SELECTING A STATISTICAL METHOD

## TYPE OF DATA

| Type of Analysis | Numerical | Categorical |
|---|---|---|
| Describing a Group or Several Groups | Ordered array, stem-and-leaf display, frequency distribution, relative frequency distribution, percentage distribution, cumulative percentage distribution, histogram, polygon, cumulative percentage polygon (Section 2.2)<br><br>Mean, median, mode, quartiles, geometric mean, range, interquartile range, standard deviation, variance, coefficient of variation, boxplot (Sections 3.1, 3.2, 3.5)<br><br>Index numbers (Section 16.8) | Summary table, bar chart, pie chart, Pareto chart (Section 2.1) |
| Inference about One Group | Confidence Interval Estimate of the Mean (Sections 8.1 and 8.2)<br><br>$t$ Test for the Mean (Section 9.2)<br><br>Chi-Square Test for a Variance (Section 12.5) | Confidence Interval Estimate for the Proportion (Section 8.3)<br><br>$Z$ Test of Hypothesis for the Proportion (Section 9.4) |
| Comparing Two Groups | Tests for the Difference in the Means of Two Independent Populations (Section 10.1)<br><br>Paired $t$ Test (Section 10.2)<br><br>$F$ Test for the Difference in Two Variances (Section 10.4)<br><br>Wilcoxon Rank Sum Test (Section 12.6)<br><br>Wilcoxon Signed Rank Test (Section 12.7) | $Z$ Test for the Difference between Two Proportions (Section 10.3)<br><br>Chi-Square Test for the Difference between Two Proportions (Section 12.1)<br><br>McNemar Test for Two Related Samples (Section 12.4) |
| Comparing More than Two Groups | One-Way Analysis of Variance (Section 11.1)<br><br>Randomized Block Design (Section 11.2)<br><br>Two-Way Analysis of Variance (Section 11.3)<br><br>Kruskal-Wallis Rank Test (Section 12.8)<br><br>Friedman Rank Test (Section 12.9) | Chi-Square Test for Differences among More than Two Proportions (Section 12.2) |
| Analyzing the Relationship between Two Variables | Scatter Plot, Time-Series Plot (Section 2.5)<br><br>Covariance, Coefficient of Correlation (Section 3.6)<br><br>Simple Linear Regression (Chapter 13)<br><br>$t$ Test of Correlation (Section 13.7)<br><br>Time Series Forecasting (Chapter 16) | Contingency Table, Side-by-Side Bar Chart (Section 2.4)<br><br>Chi-Square Test of Independence (Section 12.3) |
| Analyzing the Relationship between Two or More Variables | Multiple Regression (Chapters 14 and 15) | Logistic Regression (Section 14.7) |

# HAVE YOU THOUGHT ABOUT *Customizing* THIS BOOK?

## THE PRENTICE HALL JUST-IN-TIME PROGRAM IN DECISION SCIENCE

You can combine chapters from this book with chapters from any of the Prentice Hall titles listed on the following page to create a text tailored to your specific course needs. You can add your own material or cases from our extensive case collection. By taking a few minutes to look at what is sitting on your bookshelf and the content available on our Web site, you can create your ideal textbook.

### The Just-In-Time program offers:

- **Quality of Material to Choose From**—In addition to the books listed, you also have the option to include any of the cases from Prentice Hall Custom Business Resources, which gives you access to cases (and teaching notes where available) from Darden, Harvard, Ivey, NACRA, and Thunderbird. Most cases can be viewed online at our Web site.

- **Flexibility**—Choose only the material you want, either from one title or several titles (plus cases) and sequence it in whatever way you wish.

- **Instructional Support**—You have access to the text-specific CD-ROM that accompanies the traditional textbook and desk copies of your JIT book.

- **Outside Materials**—There is also the option to include up to 20% of the text from materials outside of Prentice Hall Custom Business Resources.

- **Cost Savings**—Students pay only for material you choose. The base price is $6.00, plus $2.00 for case material, plus $.09 per page. The text can be shrink-wrapped with other Pearson textbooks for a 10% discount. Outside material is priced at $.10 per page plus permission fees.

- **Quality of Finished Product**—Custom cover and title page—including your name, school, department, course title, and section number. Paperback, perfect bound, black-and-white printed text. Customized table of contents. Sequential pagination throughout the text.

**Visit our Web site at www.prenhall.com/custombusiness and create your custom text on our bookbuildsite or download order forms online.**

# THE PRENTICE HALL
## Just-In-Time Program

*Just-In-Time*

 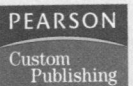

YOU CAN CUSTOMIZE YOUR TEXTBOOK WITH CHAPTERS FROM ANY OF THE FOLLOWING PRENTICE HALL TITLES: *

### BUSINESS STATISTICS
- Berenson/Levine/Krehbiel, BASIC BUSINESS STATISTICS, 11/e
- Groebner/Shannon/Fry/Smith, BUSINESS STATISTICS, 7/e
- Levine/Stephan/Krehbiel/Berenson, STATISTICS FOR MANAGERS USING MICROSOFT EXCEL, 5/e
- Levine/Krehbiel/Berenson, BUSINESS STATISTICS: A FIRST COURSE, 4/e
- Newbold/Carlson/Thorne, STATISTICS FOR BUSINESS AND ECONOMICS, 5/e
- Shannon/Groebner/Fry/Smith, A COURSE IN BUSINESS STATISTICS, 3/e

### PRODUCTION/OPERATIONS MANAGEMENT
- Anupindi/Chopra/Deshmukh/Van Mieghem/Zemel, MANAGING BUSINESS PROCESS FLOWS
- Bozarth/Handfield, INTRODUCTION TO OPERATIONS AND SUPPLY CHAIN MANAGEMENT, 2/e
- Chopra/Meindl, SUPPLY CHAIN MANAGEMENT, 3/e
- Foster, MANAGING QUALITY, 3/e
- Handfield/Nichols, Jr., SUPPLY CHAIN MANAGEMENT
- Heineke/Meile, GAMES AND EXERCISES IN OPERATIONS MANAGEMENT
- Heizer/Render, OPERATIONS MANAGEMENT, 9/e
- Krajewski/Ritzman/Malhotra, OPERATIONS MANAGEMENT, 8/e
- Latona/Nathan, CASES AND READINGS IN POM
- Pinto, PROJECT MANAGEMENT
- Schmenner, PLANT AND SERVICE TOURS IN OPERATIONS MANAGEMENT, 5/e

### MANAGEMENT SCIENCE/SPREADSHEET MODELING
- Render/Stair/Hanna, QUANTITATIVE ANALYSIS FOR MANAGEMENT, 10/e
- Balakrishnan/Render/Stair, MANAGERIAL DECISION MODELING WITH SPREADSHEETS, 2/e
- Render/Stair, CASES AND READINGS IN MANAGEMENT SCIENCE
- Taylor, INTRODUCTION TO MANAGEMENT SCIENCE, 9/e

For more information, or to speak to a customer service representative, contact us at 1-800-777-6872.
**www.prenhall.com/custombusiness**

\* Selection of titles on the JIT program is subject to change

# BASIC BUSINESS STATISTICS

ELEVENTH EDITION

## Concepts and Applications

**MARK L. BERENSON**
*Department of Management and Information Systems*
*School of Business, Montclair State University*

**DAVID M. LEVINE**
*Department of Statistics and Computer Information Systems*
*Zicklin School of Business, Baruch College, City University of New York*

**TIMOTHY C. KREHBIEL**
*Department of Decision Sciences and Management Information Systems*
*Farmer School of Business, Miami University*

PEARSON

Prentice
Hall

Upper Saddle River, New Jersey 07458

**Library of Congress Cataloging-in-Publication Data**

Berenson, Mark L.
    Basic business statistics : concepts and applications / Mark L. Berenson, David M. Levine,
Timothy C. Krehbiel.—11th ed.
        p. cm.
    Includes bibliographical references and index.
    ISBN-13: 978-0-13-603260-1
    ISBN-10: 0-13-603260-5
    1. Commercial statistics. 2. Statistics. I. Levine, David M.,    II. Krehbiel, Timothy C. III.
Title.
    HF1017.B38 2009
    519.5—dc22

                                                    2007045347

**AVP/Executive Editor:** Mark Pfaltzgraff
**AVP/Editor-in-Chief:** Eric Svendsen
**Product Development Manager:** Ashley Santora
**Project Manager:** Susan Abraham
**Editorial Assistant:** Vanessa Bain
**Media Project Manager:** Denise Vaughn
**Marketing Manager:** Anne Fahlgren
**Marketing Assistant:** Susan Osterlitz
**Senior Managing Editor, Production:** Judy Leale
**Production Manager:** Kerri Tomasso
**Permissions Coordinator:** Charles Morris
**Senior Operations Supervisor:** Arnold Vila
**Operations Specialist:** Michelle Klein
**Creative Director:** Leslie Osher

**Senior Art Director:** Janet Slowik
**Cover Designer:** Bobby Starnes/ElectraGraphics, Inc.
**Cover Photo:** Garry Gay/The Image Bank/Getty
    Image
**Director, Image Resource Center:** Melinda Patelli
**Manager, Rights and Permissions:** Zina Arabia
**Manager, Visual Research:** Beth Brenzel
**Manager, Cover Visual Research & Permissions:**
    Karen Sanatar
**Image Permission Coordinator:** Angelique Sharps
**Composition/Full-Service Project Management:**
    GGS Book Services
**Printer/Binder:** Quebecor World Color/Dubuque
**Typeface:** 10.5/12.5 Times New Roman

Credits and acknowledgments borrowed from other sources and reproduced, with permission,
in this textbook appear on appropriate page within the text.

**Photo Credits:** front, page vi, courtesy of Rudy Krehbiel; Chapter 1, page 3, Chuck Savage;
Chapter 2, page 26, Ed Young/Science Photo Library/Photo Researchers, Inc.; Chapter 3,
page 90, Susan Van Ettan Lawson/PhotoEdit Inc.; Chapter 4, page 144, Michael
Newman/PhotoEdit Inc.; Chapter 7, page 258, Chuck Mason/ImageState/International Stock
Photography Ltd.; Chapter 8, page 292, Spencer Grant/PhotoEdit Inc.; Chapter 9, page 342,
Mark Richards/PhotoEdit Inc.; Chapter 10, page 390, Greg Mancuso/Stock Boston; Chapter
11, page 444, Edith G. Haun/Stock Boston; Chapter 12, page 504, Jeff Greenberg/Stock
Boston; Chapter 13, page 574, Jack Star/Getty Images, Inc.—PhotoDisc; Chapter 14, page
636, courtesy of David Levine; Chapter 15, page 692, Rob Crandall/Stock Boston; Chapter
16, page 730, Will & Deni McIntyre/Photo Researchers, Inc.; Chapter 17, page 794, Rick
Gayle/Corbis/Stock Market; Chapter 18, page 824, Jeff Greenberg/PhotoEdit Inc.

Pearson Education LTD., London
Pearson Education Singapore, Pte. Ltd
Pearson Education, Canada, Ltd
Pearson Education–Japan

Pearson Education Australia PTY, Limited
Pearson Education North Asia Ltd
Pearson Educación de Mexico, S.A. de C.V.
Pearson Education Malaysia, Pte. Ltd.
Pearson Education Upper Saddle River, New Jersey

**PEARSON**
Prentice
Hall

                10 9 8 7 6 5 4 3 2 1
        ISBN-13: 978-0-13-603260-1
          ISBN-10: 0-13-603260-5

*To our wives,*
*Rhoda B., Marilyn L., and Patti K.*
*and to our children,*
*Kathy, Lori, Sharyn, Ed, Rudy, and Rhonda*

# ABOUT THE AUTHORS

The textbook authors meet to discuss statistics at Shea Stadium for a Mets v. Phillies game. Shown left to right: David Levine, Mark Berenson, Tim Krehbiel.

**Mark L. Berenson** is Professor of Management and Information Systems at Montclair State University (Montclair, New Jersey) and also Professor Emeritus of Statistics and Computer Information Systems at Bernard M. Baruch College (City University of New York). He currently teaches graduate and undergraduate courses in statistics and in operations management in the School of Business and an undergraduate course in international justice and human rights that he codeveloped in the College of Humanities and Social Sciences.

Berenson received a B.A. in economic statistics and an M.B.A. in business statistics from City College of New York and a Ph.D. in business from the City University of New York.

Berenson's research has been published in *Decision Sciences Journal of Innovative Education, Review of Business Research, The American Statistician, Communications in Statistics, Psychometrika, Educational and Psychological Measurement, Journal of Management Sciences and Applied Cybernetics, Research Quarterly, Stats Magazine, The New York Statistician, Journal of Health Administration Education, Journal of Behavioral Medicine*, and *Journal of Surgical Oncology*. His invited articles have appeared in *The Encyclopedia of Measurement & Statistics* and in *Encyclopedia of Statistical Sciences*. He is coauthor of 11 statistics texts published by Prentice Hall, including *Statistics for Managers using Microsoft Excel, Basic Business Statistics: Concepts and Applications*, and *Business Statistics: A First Course*.

Over the years, Berenson has received several awards for teaching and for innovative contributions to statistics education. In 2005 he was the first recipient of The Catherine A. Becker Service for Educational Excellence Award at Montclair State University.

**David M. Levine** is Professor Emeritus of Statistics and Computer Information Systems at Bernard M. Baruch College (City University of New York). He received B.B.A. and M.B.A. degrees in Statistics from City College of New York and a Ph.D. degree from New York University in Industrial Engineering and Operations Research. He is nationally recognized as a leading innovator in statistics education and is the coauthor of 14 books, including such best-selling statistics textbooks as *Statistics for Managers Using Microsoft Excel, Basic Business Statistics: Concepts and Applications, Business Statistics: A First Course*, and *Applied Statistics for Engineers and Scientists using Microsoft Excel and Minitab.*

He also is the author of *Even You Can Learn Statistics* and *Statistics for Six Sigma Green Belts* published by Financial Times-Prentice-Hall. He is coauthor of *Six Sigma for Green Belts and Champions* and *Design for Six Sigma for Green Belts and Champions*, also published by Financial Times-Prentice-Hall, and *Quality Management, Third Ed.*, McGraw-Hill-Irwin (2005). He is also the author of *Video Review of Statistics* and *Video Review of Probability*, both published by Video Aided Instruction. He has published articles in various journals including *Psychometrika, The*

*American Statistician, Communications in Statistics, Multivariate Behavioral Research, Journal of Systems Management, Quality Progress,* and *The American Anthropologist* and given numerous talks at Decision Sciences, American Statistical Association, and Making Statistics More Effective in Schools of Business conferences. Dr. Levine has also received several awards for outstanding teaching and curriculum development from Baruch College.

**Timothy C. Krehbiel** is Professor of Decision Sciences and Management Information Systems at the Farmer School of Business at Miami University in Oxford, Ohio. He teaches undergraduate and graduate courses in business statistics. In 1996 he received the prestigious Instructional Innovation Award from the Decision Sciences Institute. He has also received the Farmer School of Business Administration Effective Educator Award and the MBA Teaching Excellence Award.

Krehbiel's research interests span many areas of business and applied statistics. His work appears in numerous journals including *Quality Management Journal, Ecological Economics, International Journal of Production Research, Journal of Purchasing and Supply Management, Journal of Applied Business Research, Journal of Marketing Management, Communications in Statistics, Decision Sciences Journal of Innovative Education, Journal of Education for Business, Marketing Education Review,* and *Teaching Statistics.* He is a coauthor of three statistics textbooks published by Prentice Hall: *Business Statistics: A First Course, Basic Business Statistics,* and *Statistics for Managers Using Microsoft Excel.* Krehbiel is also a coauthor of the book *Sustainability Perspectives in Business and Resources.*

Krehbiel graduated *summa cum laude* with a B.A. in history from McPherson College in 1983, and earned an M.S. (1987) and Ph.D. (1990) in statistics from the University of Wyoming.

# BRIEF CONTENTS

## ⊙ CD-ROM TOPICS (.pdf files located on the Student CD-ROM)

# CONTENTS

## 9    FUNDAMENTALS OF HYPOTHESIS TESTING: ONE-SAMPLE TESTS  341

## 12 CHI-SQUARE TESTS AND NONPARAMETRIC TESTS  503

## Educational Philosophy

In our many years of teaching business statistics, we have continually searched for ways to improve the teaching of these courses. Our active participation in a series of Making Statistics More Effective in Schools and Business (MSMESB), Decision Sciences Institute (DSI), and American Statistical Association (ASA) conferences as well as the reality of serving a diverse group of students at large universities have shaped our vision for teaching these courses. Over the years, our vision has come to include these key principles:

1. **Show students the relevance of statistics.** Students need a frame of reference when learning statistics, especially when statistics is not their major. That frame of reference for business students should be the functional areas of business—that is, accounting, finance, information systems, management, and marketing. Each statistical topic needs to be presented in an applied context related to at least one of these functional areas. The focus in teaching each topic should be on its application in business, the interpretation of results, the presentation of assumptions, the evaluation of the assumptions, and the discussion of what should be done if the assumptions are violated.

2. **Familiarize students with business software used in the real world.** Integrating business software into all aspects of an introductory statistics course allows the course to focus on interpretation of results instead of computations. Introductory business statistics courses should recognize that spreadsheet programs and statistical packages are commonly found on a business decision maker's desktop computer, therefore making the *interpretation* of results more important than the tedious hand calculations required to produce them.

3. **Provide guidance to students for using statistical software.** Books should contain clear instructions to help students effectively use the programs that are integrated with the study of statistics, without having those instructions dominating the book or the courses in which they are used.

4. **Give students ample practice in understanding how to apply statistics to business.** Both classroom examples and homework exercises should involve actual or realistic data as much as possible. Students should work with data sets, both small and large, and be encouraged to look beyond the statistical analysis of data to the interpretation of results in a managerial context.

## New to This Edition: Enhanced Statistics Coverage

This eleventh edition of *Basic Business Statistics* enhances the statistical coverage of previous editions in a number of ways:

- *"From the Authors' Desktop"* essays in every chapter provide greater insight to what has just been learned as well as raise important issues about the application of statistical knowledge.
- A new chapter (Chapter 19) discusses real-world data analysis that requires students to apply the statistics they have learned from the previous 18 chapters. The chapter helps students to identify which statistical methods are needed in order to better prepare them for situations they will face in their future careers and everyday life.
- Revised simplified notation for test statistics in hypothesis testing.
- Many new applied examples and exercises with data from *The Wall Street Journal, USA Today*, and other sources have been added to the book.
- Student surveys are included as an integrating theme for exercises across many chapters.
- Even more illustrations of Microsoft Excel and Minitab results, all with cross-references to the appropriate software appendix sections.

## New to This Edition: Expanded Hands-on Software Appendices

This eleventh edition of *Basic Business Statistics* now contains separate and expanded appendices for using Microsoft Excel, Minitab, and PHStat2, the Excel add-in that is included on the Student CD-ROM:

- Totally rewritten Excel appendices contain instructions for using all versions of Excel, including Excel 2007. (Some sections contain two sets of instructions, one for using Excel 97 through Excel 2003, the other for using Excel 2007, when appropriate.)
- Minitab appendices feature the use of Minitab 15, the latest Minitab version, but are also fully compatible with Minitab 14.
- PHStat2 appendices at the end of each chapter identify the PHStat2 procedures that can be used for the chapter's statistical methods.
- New PHStat2 version (2.8) that is Excel 2007 compatible and contains new and enhanced procedures including the separate-variance *t* test, one-way ANOVA, and the *c* chart.

## Chapter-by-Chapter Changes in the Eleventh Edition

Each chapter includes a new opening page that displays the chapter sections and subsections. The following changes have been made to this eleventh edition:

**Chapter 1** has completely new Sections 1.1, 1.2, and 1.6, and includes three *From the Authors' Desktop* essays.

**Chapter 2** has new examples throughout the chapter and a *From the Authors' Desktop* on misusing graphs.

**Chapter 3** has moved quartiles to the section with boxplots (name changed from box-and-whisker), a new mutual fund data set, and a *From the Authors' Desktop* on ethical issues in descriptive statistics.

**Chapter 4** has a revised example throughout the chapter, and a *From the Authors' Desktop* on using Bayes' theorem.

**Chapter 5** has changed notation in the binomial, Poisson, and hypergeometric distributions with *p* changed to $\pi$, and successes changed to items of interest, and a *From the Authors' Desktop* discussing practical applications of the probability distributions discussed in the chapter.

**Chapter 6** has a revised normal distribution table with additional header lines and a *From the Authors' Desktop* on the importance of the normal distribution.

**Chapter 7** has survey sampling and survey worthiness preceding sampling distributions and a *From the Authors' Desktop* on the pros and cons of web-based surveys.

**Chapter 8** has a greatly reduced focus on the confidence interval estimate for the mean with sigma known, revised notation that uses a subscript for distributions that indicates the $\alpha$ level (such as $Z_{\alpha/2}$ or $t_{\alpha/2}$), a *From the Authors' Desktop* on sigma known, and revised normal distribution and *t* distribution tables with additional header lines.

**Chapter 9** has combined previous Sections 9.1 and 9.2 to reduce the emphasis on testing the population mean with sigma known, has moved the *t* test for the mean ahead of the one-tail test, changed notation to use a subscript for distributions to indicate the $\alpha$ level (such as $Z_{\alpha/2}$ or $t_{\alpha/2}$), revised notation that uses subscript STAT with the test statistic (such as $Z_{STAT}$ and $t_{STAT}$), a *From the Authors' Desktop* on sigma known, and revised normal distribution and *t* distribution tables with additional header lines.

**Chapter 10** has revised notation that uses a subscript for distributions to indicate the $\alpha$ level (such as $Z_{\alpha/2}$, $t_{\alpha/2}$, or $F_\alpha$), revised notation that uses subscript STAT with the test statistic (such as $Z_{STAT}$, $t_{STAT}$, and $F_{STAT}$), revised normal distribution, *t*, and *F* distribution tables with additional header lines, revised *F* test for the difference between variances that consists of the larger variance divided by smaller variance, and a *From the Authors' Desktop* that presents a business application of the differences between two means.

**Chapter 11** has revised notation that uses a subscript for distributions to indicate the $\alpha$ level such as $F_\alpha$, revised notation that uses subscript STAT with the test statistic such as $F_{STAT}$, revised *F* distribution tables with additional header lines, a revised example on interaction effects, an additional example for situations in which the interaction is significant, and a *From the Authors' Desktop* on the design of experiments and Six Sigma.

**Chapter 12** has revised notation that uses a subscript for distributions to indicate the $\alpha$ level, revised notation that uses subscript STAT with the test statistic, revised $\chi^2$ distribution tables with additional header lines, a revised McNemar example, *From the Authors' Desktops* on the Kruskal-Wallis test and on the steps involved in using confidence intervals and hypothesis testing, and has moved the Chi-square goodness-of-fit test to the Student CD-ROM.

**Chapter 13** has revised notation that uses the subscript STAT with the test statistic such as $t_{STAT}$, and a *From the Authors' Desktop* on using regression in the business world.

**Chapter 14** has revised notation that uses the subscript STAT with the test statistic such as $t_{STAT}$, and a *From the Authors' Desktop* on logistic regression and data mining.

**Chapter 15** has revised notation that uses the subscript STAT with the test statistic such as $t_{STAT}$, a *From the Authors' Desktop* on multiple regression models and data mining, and has moved influence analysis to the Student CD-ROM.

**Chapter 16** has updated examples throughout the chapter, a *From the Authors' Desktop* about the risks in investing, and has moved Holt-Winters to the Student CD-ROM.

**Chapter 17** has additional decision making criteria, a new marketing example, and a *From the Authors' Desktop* discussing how individual investors are classified by their personal risk tolerance.

**Chapter 18** has control charts preceding total quality management and Six Sigma, has revised sections on total quality management and Six Sigma, and a *From the Authors' Desktop* about different quality improvement systems.

## Hallmark Features

We have continued many of the traditions of past editions and have highlighted some of those features below:

**Using Statistics business scenarios**—Each chapter begins with a Using Statistics example that shows how statistics is used in accounting, finance, information systems, management, or marketing. Each scenario is used throughout the chapter to provide an applied context for the concepts.

**Emphasis on data analysis and interpretation of software results**—We believe that the use of computer software is an integral part of learning statistics. Our focus emphasizes analyzing data by interpreting the results from Microsoft Excel or Minitab while reducing emphasis on doing computations. For example, in the coverage of tables and charts in Chapter 2, the focus is on the interpretation of various charts, not on their construction by hand. In our coverage of hypothesis testing in Chapters 9 through 12, extensive computer results have been included so that the *p*-value approach can be emphasized.

**Pedagogical aides**—An active writing style, boxed numbered equations, set-off examples to provide reinforcement for learning concepts, problems divided into "Learning the Basics" and "Applying the Concepts," key equations, and key terms are included.

**Answers**—Most answers to the even-numbered exercises are provided in an appendix at the end of the book.

**PHStat2**—This add-in, included on the Student CD-ROM, extends the statistical capabilities of Microsoft Excel and executes the low-level menu selection and worksheet entry tasks associated with implementing statistical analysis in Excel. When combined with the Analysis ToolPak add-in, virtually all statistical methods taught in an introductory statistics course can be demonstrated using Microsoft Excel.

**Web Cases**—A chapter-ending Web Case is included for each of the first 17 chapters. By visiting Web sites related to the companies and researching the issues raised in the Using Statistics scenarios that start each chapter, students learn to identify misuses of statistical information. The Web Cases require students to sift through claims and assorted information in order to discover the data most relevant to the case. Students then determine whether the conclusions and claims are supported by the data. (Instructional tips for using the Web Cases and solutions to the Web Cases are included in the Instructor's Solutions Manual.)

**Case studies and team projects**—Detailed case studies are included in numerous chapters. A Managing the *Springville Herald* case is included at the end of most chapters as an integrating theme. A team project relating to mutual funds is included in many chapters as an integrating theme.

**Visual Explorations**—A Microsoft Excel add-in workbook allows students to interactively explore important statistical concepts in descriptive statistics, the normal distribution, sampling distributions, and regression analysis. For example, in descriptive statistics, students observe the effect of changes in the data on the mean, median, quartiles, and standard deviation. With the normal distribution, students see the effect of changes in the mean and standard deviation on the areas under the normal curve. In sampling distributions, students use simulation to explore the effect of sample size on a sampling distribution. In regression analysis, students have the opportunity of fitting a line and observing how changes in the slope and intercept affect the goodness of fit.

## Supplement Package

The supplement package that accompanies this text includes the following:

**Instructor's Solutions Manual**—This manual includes solutions for end-of-section and end-of-chapter problems, answers to case questions, where applicable, and teaching tips for each chapter. Electronic solutions are provided in PDF and Word formats.

**Student Solutions Manual**—This manual provides detailed solutions to virtually all the even-numbered exercises and worked-out solutions to the self-test problems.

**Test Item File**—The Test Item File contains true/false, multiple-choice, fill-in, and problem-solving questions based on the definitions, concepts, and ideas developed in each chapter of the text.

**TestGen software**—A test bank has been designed for use with the TestGen test-generating software. This computerized package allows instructors to custom design, save, and generate classroom tests. The test program permits instructors to edit, add, or delete questions from the test bank; edit existing graphics and create new graphics; analyze test results; and organize a database of tests and student results. This software allows for flexibility and ease of use. It provides many options for organizing and displaying tests, along with a search-and-sort feature. The program can be found online at the Instructor's Resource Center.

**Instructor's Resource Center**—The Instructor's Resource Center contains the electronic files for the complete Instructor's Solutions Manual, the Test Item File, and Lecture PowerPoint presentations (**www.prenhall.com/berenson**).

## Course and Homework Management Tools

**MyBStatLab**—Provides a rich and flexible set of course materials, featuring free-response exercises that are algorithmically generated for unlimited practice and mastery. Students can also use a variety of online tools to independently improve their understanding and performance in the course. Instructors can use MyBStatLab's homework and test manager to select and assign their own online exercises and import TestGen tests for added flexibility.

**WebCT and Blackboard**—With a local installation of either course management system, Prentice Hall provides content designed especially for this textbook to create a complete course suite, tightly integrated with the system's course management tools.

**Companion Web site**—**www.prenhall.com/berenson** contains the following:
- An online study guide with true/false, multiple-choice, and essay questions designed to test students' comprehension of chapter topics
- PowerPoint presentation files with chapter outlines and key equations
- Student data files for text problems in Excel and Minitab format

## Acknowledgments

We are extremely grateful to the Biometrika Trustees, American Cyanimid Company, the RAND Corporation, the American Society for Testing and Materials for their kind permission to publish various tables in Appendix E, and the American Statistical Association for its permission to publish diagrams from the *American Statistician*. Also, we are grateful to Professors George A. Johnson and Joanne Tokle of Idaho State University and Ed Conn, Mountain States Potato Company, for their kind permission to incorporate parts of their work as our Mountain States Potato Company case in Chapter 15.

## A Note of Thanks

We would like to thank Alan Chesen, Wright State University; Alan Chow, University of South Alabama; Stergios Fotopoulos, Washington State University; Kimberly Killmer Hollister, Montclair State University; Carol Markowski, Old Dominion University; Charles McAllister, Southeast Missouri State University; John McKenzie, Babson College; Ram Misra, Montclair State University; Kenneth Paetsch, Cleveland State University; and Susan Pariseau, Merrimack College for their comments, which have made this a better book.

We would especially like to thank Mark Pfaltzgraff, Susie Abraham, Kerri Tomasso, Vanessa Bain, Judy Leale, and Anne Howard of the editorial, marketing, and production teams at Prentice Hall. We would like to thank our statistical reader and accuracy checker Annie Puciloski for her diligence in checking our work; Julie Kennedy for her copyediting; Denne Wesolowski for his proofreading; and Heidi Allgair of GGS Book Services, for their work in the production of this text.

Finally, we would like to thank our parents, wives, and children for their patience, understanding, love, and assistance in making this book a reality. It is to them that we dedicate this book.

## Concluding Remarks

We have gone to great lengths to make this text both pedagogically sound and error free. If you have any suggestions or require clarification about any of the material, or if you find any errors, please contact us at **David_Levine@baruch.cuny.edu** or **Krehbitc@muohio.edu**. Include the phrase "BBS edition 11" in the subject line of your e-mail. For more information or questions about using PHStat2, review Appendix F and the PHStat2 readme file on the Student CD-ROM. For support issues, visit the PHStat2 Web site, **www.prenhall.com/phstat** and the Pearson Customer Technical Support website, **247.pearsoned.com**.

*Mark L. Berenson*
*David M. Levine*
*Timothy C. Krehbiel*

# CHAPTER
# ONE

## INTRODUCTION AND DATA COLLECTION

## LEARNING OBJECTIVES

### This chapter will help you learn:

- How statistics is used in business
- The sources of data used in business
- The types of data used in business
- The basics of Microsoft Excel
- The basics of Minitab

## 1.1    WHY LEARN STATISTICS

People use numbers every day to describe or analyze the world we live in. For example, consider these recent headlines:

- "Why Experts Are Concerned about the Growing Tendency of Employees to Work on Vacation" (K. Stech, *Newsday*, September 4, 2006, p. F4)—Twenty-one percent of employees work sometimes, often, or very often on vacation, and 43% return feeling overwhelmed by all they have to do.
- "Americans Gulping More Bottled Water" (*USA Today*, February 28, 2007, p. 1D)—The annual per capita consumption of bottled water has increased from 18.8 gallons in 2001 to 28.3 gallons in 2006.
- "Paying More with Plastic" (*USA Today*, March 6, 2007, p. 1D)—Consumer payment with credit cards increased from 18% in 1995 to 25% in 2005, while payment in cash decreased to 14% from 21%.
- "The Real Most Valuable Players" (R. Adams, *The Wall Street Journal*, April 14, 2007, pp. P1, P4)—Economists have developed models to predict the real value of player performance and have related it to player salary.

You will make better sense of the numbers in the stories behind these headlines if you understand statistics. **Statistics** is the branch of mathematics that transforms numbers into useful information for decision makers. Statistics provides a way of understanding and then reducing—but not eliminating—the variation that is part of any decision-making process, and also can tell you the known risks associated with making a decision.

Statistics does this by providing a set of methods for analyzing the numbers. These methods help you to find patterns in "the numbers" and enable you to determine whether differences in "the numbers" are just due to chance. As you learn these methods, you will also learn the appropriate conditions for using those methods. And because so many statistical methods must be computerized in order to be of practical benefit, as you learn statistics you also need to learn about the programs that help apply statistics in the business world.

## 1.2    STATISTICS IN THE BUSINESS WORLD

In the business world, statistics has four important applications:

- To summarize business data
- To draw conclusions from that data
- To make reliable forecasts about business activities
- To improve business processes

The field of statistics consists of two branches, descriptive statistics and inferential statistics.

**Descriptive statistics** focuses on collecting, summarizing, presenting and analyzing a set of data. You are probably familiar with presentations such as tables and charts, and statistics such as the mean and median from your previous school experience.

**Inferential statistics** uses data that have been collected from a small group to draw conclusions about a larger group. These methods are used to make decisions about which investment might lead to a higher return and what marketing strategy might lead to increased sales.

Looking at the first bulleted point above, descriptive statistics allows you to create different tables and charts to summarize your data. It also provides statistical measures such as the mean, median, and standard deviation to describe different characteristics of your data.

Drawing conclusions from your data is the heart of inferential statistics. Using these methods enables you to make decisions based on data rather than just on intuition.

Making reliable forecasts involves developing statistical models for prediction. These models enable you to develop more accurate predictions of future activities.

Improving business processes involves using managerial approaches that focus on quality improvement such as Six Sigma. These approaches are data-driven and use statistical methods as an integral part of the quality improvement approach.

To help you develop the necessary skills for making better decisions, every chapter of *Basic Business Statistics* has a Using Statistics scenario. Although the scenarios are fictional, they represent realistic situations in which you will be asked to make decisions while using Microsoft Excel or Minitab to transform data into statistical information. For example, in one chapter, you will be asked to decide the location in a supermarket that best enhances sales of a cola drink, and in another chapter, you will be asked to forecast sales for a clothing store.

## USING STATISTICS @ Good Tunes

Good Tunes, a growing four-store home entertainment systems retailer, seeks to double their number of stores within the next three years. The managers have decided to approach local area banks for the funding needed to underwrite this expansion. They need to prepare an electronic slide show and a formal prospectus that will argue that Good Tunes is a thriving business and a good candidate for expansion.

You have been asked to assist in the process of preparing the slide show and prospectus. What data should you include that will convince bankers to extend the credit that Good Tunes needs? How should you present that data?

In this scenario, you must identify the most relevant data for the bankers. Because Good Tunes is an ongoing business, you can start by reviewing the company's records, which show both its current and past status. Because Good Tunes is a retailer, presenting data about the company's sales seems a reasonable thing to do. You could include the details of every sales transaction that has occurred for the past few years as a way of demonstrating that Good Tunes is a thriving business.

However, presenting the bankers with the thousands of transactions would overwhelm them and not be very useful. As mentioned in Section 1.1, you need to transform the transactions data into information by summarizing the details of each transaction in some useful way that would allow the bankers to (perhaps) uncover a favorable pattern about the sales over time.

One piece of information that the bankers would presumably want to see is the yearly dollar sales totals. Tallying and totaling sales is a common process of transforming data into information. When you tally sales—or any other relevant data about Good Tunes you choose to use— you follow normal business practice and tally by a business period such as by month, quarter, or year. When you do so, you end up with multiple values: sales for this year, sales for last year, sales for the year before that, and so on. How to determine the best way to refer to these multiple values requires learning the basic vocabulary of statistics.

## 1.3 BASIC VOCABULARY OF STATISTICS

Variables are characteristics of items or individuals and are what you analyze when you use a statistical method. For the Good Tunes scenario, sales, expenses by year, and net profit by year are variables that the bankers would want to analyze.

### VARIABLE
A **variable** is a characteristic of an item or individual.

When used in everyday speech, *variable* suggests that something changes or varies, and you would expect the sales, expenses, and net profit to have different values from year to year. These different values are the **data** associated with a variable, and more simply, the "data" to be analyzed.

Variables can differ for reasons other than time. For example, if you conducted an analysis of the composition of a large lecture class, you would probably want to include the variables class standing, gender, and major field of study. These variables would vary, too, because each student in the class is different. One student might be a sophomore, male, economics major, while another may be a junior, female, finance major.

You also need to remember that values are meaningless unless their variables have **operational definitions**. These definitions are universally accepted meanings that are clear to all associated with an analysis. Even though the operational definition for sales per year might seem clear, miscommunication could occur if one person was referring to sales per year for the entire chain of stores and another to sales per year per store. Even individual values for variables sometimes need definition—for the class standing variable, for example, what *exactly* is meant by the words *sophomore* and *junior?* (Perhaps the most famous example of vague definitions was the definition of a valid vote in the state of Florida during the 2000 U.S. presidential election. Vagueness about the operational definitions there ultimately required a U.S. Supreme Court ruling.)

Four other basic vocabulary terms are population, sample, parameter, and statistic.

### POPULATION
A **population** consists of all the items or individuals about which you want to draw a conclusion.

### SAMPLE
A **sample** is the portion of a population selected for analysis.

### PARAMETER
A **parameter** is a numerical measure that describes a characteristic of a population.

### STATISTIC
A **statistic** is a numerical measure that describes a characteristic of a sample.

All the Good Tunes sales transactions for a specific year, all the customers who shopped at Good Tunes this weekend, all the full-time students enrolled in a college, and all the registered voters in Ohio are examples of populations. Examples of samples from these four populations would be 200 Good Tunes sales transactions randomly selected by an auditor for study, 30 Good Tunes customers asked to complete a customer satisfaction survey, 50 full-time students selected for a marketing study, and 500 registered voters in Ohio contacted via telephone for a political poll. In each sample, the transactions or people in the sample represent a portion of the items or individuals that make up the population.

The mean amount spent by all customers who shopped at Good Tunes this weekend is an example of a parameter because the amount spent in the entire population is needed. In contrast, the mean amount spent by the 30 customers completing the customer satisfaction survey is an example of a statistic because the amount spent by only the sample of 30 people is required.

# Coming Attractions

If you are someone who likes to skim quickly through a book to learn a book's organization, you should know that we have organized the chapters of this book according to the four business tasks first listed in Section 1.2. We use those tasks—summarizing business data, drawing conclusions from that data, making reliable forecasts about business activities, and improving business processes—as a way of organizing our chapters.

Chapters 1 through 3 discuss methods of presenting and describing information. Chapters 4 through 12 and Chapter 17 discuss drawing conclusions about populations using sample information. Chapters 13 through 16 provide ways of making reliable forecasts and Chapter 18 introduces you to how you can apply statistical methods to improve business processes.

Don't worry if your instructor does not cover all of these chapters—introductory business statistics courses vary in their scope, length, and number of college credits. Tradi-

tionally, instructors start with descriptive statistics because some of these methods may already be familiar to you from everyday activities and that's the main reason we've put them in the first three chapters. Chapter 4 discusses probability concepts that are needed in Chapters 5 through 7. Chapters 8 through 12 cover inferential statistics. Chapter 8 introduces the confidence interval approach, while Chapter 9 develops the fundamental hypothesis testing concepts that are expanded on in Chapters 10 through 12. Understanding these concepts will allow you to fully answer questions such as "How can you make decisions about the many based on a few?"—a question business people uneducated in statistics often ask when they challenge the use of statistics. Chapters 13 through 16 cover regression and time-series models that are used to make reliable forecasts. Chapter 13 develops the simple regression model, while Chapters 14 through 16 expand the simple model to more complex situations. Chapter 18 provides some

background into the total quality management and Six Sigma quality improvement approaches and introduces statistical methods used in quality improvement.

Remember that the goal of this book is *not* for you to become a statistician. The goal is to help you understand and apply appropriately the statistical methods commonly used in the area of business in which you are most interested—be it accounting, economics, finance, information systems, marketing, or management.

By the way, if you are the type of person who likes to read the last page of a book first, please don't. Introductory business statistics is somewhat cumulative and if you jump to the back of the book, you may find things a bit puzzling if you are only just beginning to learn statistics. So if you have happened to notice things such as strange-looking tables, don't fret—by the time you get to the point in this book where you need to use such tables, you will know how to use them effectively.

## 1.4  DATA COLLECTION

The managers at Good Tunes believe that they will have a stronger argument for expansion if they can show the bankers that the customers of Good Tunes are highly satisfied with the service they received. How could the managers demonstrate that good service was the typical customer experience at Good Tunes?

In the Good Tunes scenario on page 3, sales per year was automatically collected as part of normal business activities. The managers now face the twin challenges to first identify relevant variables for a customer satisfaction study and then devise a method for **data collection**, that is, collecting the values for those variables.

Many different types of circumstances, such as the following, require data collection:

- A marketing research analyst needs to assess the effectiveness of a new television advertisement.
- A pharmaceutical manufacturer needs to determine whether a new drug is more effective than those currently in use.
- An operations manager wants to improve a manufacturing process.
- An auditor wants to review the financial transactions of a company in order to determine whether the company is in compliance with generally accepted accounting principles.

In each of these examples, and for the Good Tunes managers as well, collecting data from every item or individual in the population would be too difficult or too time-consuming. Because this is the typical case, data collection almost always involves collecting data from a sample. (Chapter 7 discusses methods of sample selection.)

Data sources are classified as being either **primary sources** or **secondary sources**. When the data collector is the one using the data for analysis, the source is primary. When the person performing the statistical analysis is not the data collector, the source is secondary. Organizations and individuals that collect and publish data typically use that data as a primary source and then let others use it as a secondary source. For example, the United States federal government collects and distributes data in this way for both public and private purposes. The Bureau of Labor Statistics collects data on employment and also distributes the monthly consumer price index. The Census Bureau oversees a variety of ongoing surveys regarding population, housing, and manufacturing and undertakes special studies on topics such as crime, travel, and health care.

Sources of data fall into one of four categories:

- Data distributed by an organization or an individual
- A designed experiment
- A survey
- An observational study

Market research firms and trade associations distribute data pertaining to specific industries or markets. Investment services such as Mergent (see **www.mergent.com**) provide financial data on a company-by-company basis. Syndicated services such as AC Nielsen provide clients with data that enables the comparison of client products with those of their competitors. Daily newspapers are filled with numerical information regarding stock prices, weather conditions, and sports statistics.

Outcomes of a designed experiment are another data source. These outcomes are the result of an experiment, such as a test of several laundry detergents to compare how well each detergent removes a certain type of stain. Developing proper experimental designs is a subject mostly beyond the scope of this book because such designs often involve sophisticated statistical procedures. However, some of the fundamental experimental design concepts are discussed in Chapters 10 through 12.

Conducting a survey is a third type of data source. People being surveyed are asked questions about their beliefs, attitudes, behaviors, and other characteristics. For example, people could be asked their opinion about which laundry detergent best removes a certain type of stain. (This could lead to a result different from a designed experiment seeking the same answer.)

Conducting an observational study is the fourth important data source. A researcher collects data by directly observing a behavior, usually in a natural or neutral setting. Observational studies are a common tool for data collection in business. For example, market researchers use

**FIGURE 1.1**

Questions about the Good Tunes customer experience

1. How many days did it take from the time you ordered your merchandise to the time you received it?_____

2. Did you buy any merchandise that was featured in the Good Tunes Sunday newspaper sales flyer for the week of your purchase? Yes _____ No_____

3. Was this your first purchase at Good Tunes? Yes _____ No_____

4. Are you likely to buy additional merchandise from Good Tunes in the next 12 months? Yes _____ No_____

5. How much money (in U.S. dollars) do you expect to spend on stereo and consumer electronics equipment in the next 12 months?_____

6. How do you rate the overall service provided by Good Tunes with respect to your recent purchase?

Excellent ☐   Very good ☐   Fair ☐   Poor ☐

7. How do you rate the selection of products offered by Good Tunes with respect to other retailers of home entertainment systems?

Excellent ☐   Very good ☐   Fair ☐   Poor ☐

8. How do you rate the quality of the items you recently purchased from Good Tunes?

Excellent ☐   Very good ☐   Fair ☐   Poor ☐

focus groups to elicit unstructured responses to open-ended questions posed by a moderator to a target audience. Observational study techniques are also used to enhance teamwork or improve the quality of products and services.

Identifying the most appropriate source is a critical task because if biases, ambiguities, or other types of errors flaw the data being collected, even the most sophisticated statistical methods will not produce useful information. For the Good Tunes example, variables relevant to the customer experience could take the form of survey questions related to various aspects of the customer experience, examples of which are shown in Figure 1.1. The survey might also ask questions that seek to classify customers into groups for later analysis.

One good way for Good Tunes to avoid data-collection flaws would be to distribute the questionnaire to a random sample of customers (Chapter 7 explains how to collect a random sample). A poor way would be to rely on a business-rating Web site that allows online visitors to rate a merchant. Such Web sites cannot provide assurance that those who do the ratings are representative of the population of customers, or that they even *are* customers.

# The Buzz about Web Surveys

*From the Authors' Desktop*

Many marketers have become interested in using Web-based surveys and ratings sites to promote their products and services. Although many Internet users visit these sites, they give little thought to the use and misuse of such sites.

Not knowing how the data have been collected makes all of the information on such sites suspect. *The New York Times* has reported that Internet travel sites now closely monitor submitted reviews to avoid fraudulent claims (C. Elliott, "Hotel Reviews Online: In Bed with Hope, Half-Truths and Hype," *The New York Times*, February 7, 2006, pp. C1, C8). However, it's hard to imagine how such sites can offset the influence of offers such as one made by a Key West (Florida) hotel that offered guests a 10% discount if they posted a rave review on a particular travel Web site! Other articles, including one by the travel writer Arthur Frommer, have noted how unscrupulous marketers have manipulated the "buzz" on the Internet to either promote or undermine the reputation of specific travel companies (A. Frommer, "Be Careful about Public Web Site Comments," *Palm Beach Post*, February 25, 2007, p. E3).

Even when shielded from unscrupulous marketers, Web-based surveys can produce suspect results, if the survey is conducted inappropriately. In redesigning Microsoft Office 2007, Microsoft personnel explained that they had been influenced by the anonymous data that an ongoing "customer experience improvement program" had collected. Noting that experienced users usually decline the opportunity to participate in that program, at least one commentator suggested that the data collected were somehow *biased*, unrepresentative of the population of all Microsoft Office users.

Have you ever received a request asking you to rate a business or post an online opinion? Are you more or less likely to do so if asked directly? And would receiving an incentive, as the Key West hotel offered, affect your actions? When writing an early draft of this section, one of the authors received a message from Marriott International that urged all to rate the Marriott travel loyalty program a perfect "10" in the voting for the Freddie Awards sponsored by *InsideFlyer* magazine. Even though he had never heard of the awards or the magazine, he went online and voted. Only later did he learn that the magazine and its awards were targeted to businesspeople who frequently travel. He wondered how his "infrequent flyer" opinion would color the results. (In the end, Marriott International was happy—it won numerous "Freddies" and even sent a note to its customers thanking them for helping in the voting.)

If you do use a rating Web site, be sure to check out the "fine print" on your next visit. How does the Web site collect its ratings? What business relationships does the Web site have with the businesses that are rated on the site? Most Web sites explain their online privacy policy. Perhaps they should also explain their online "data collection policy."

## 1.5  TYPES OF VARIABLES

Statisticians classify variables as either being categorical or numerical and further classify numerical variables as having either discrete or continuous values. Figure 1.2 shows the relationships and provides examples of each type of variable.

**FIGURE 1.2**

Types of variables

| Data Type | | Question Types | Responses |
|---|---|---|---|
| Categorical | → | Do you currently own any stocks or bonds? | Yes ☐   No ☐ |
| Numerical < | Discrete → | To how many magazines do you currently subscribe? | _____ Number |
| | Continuous → | How tall are you? | _____ Inches |

**Categorical variables** (also known as **qualitative variables**) have values that can only be placed into categories, such as yes and no. "Do you currently own stocks and bonds?" and Questions 2 through 4 in Figure 1.1 are examples of categorical variables, all of which have yes or no as their values. Categorical variables can also have more than two possible responses. For example, you could ask customers to indicate the day of the week on which they made their purchases. In Figure 1.1, there are four possible responses to Questions 6 through 8.

**Numerical variables** (also known as **quantitative variables**) have values that represent quantities. For example, Questions 1 and 5 in Figure 1.1 are numerical variables. Numerical variables are further subdivided as discrete or continuous variables.

**Discrete variables** have numerical values that arise from a counting process. "The number of magazines subscribed to" is an example of a discrete numerical variable because the response is one of a finite number of integers. You subscribe to zero, one, two, and so on magazines. The number of items that a customer purchases is also a discrete numerical variable because you are counting the number of items purchased.

**Continuous variables** produce numerical responses that arise from a measuring process. The time you wait for teller service at a bank is an example of a continuous numerical variable because the response takes on any value within a *continuum*, or interval, depending on the precision of the measuring instrument. For example, your waiting time could be 1 minute, 1.1 minutes, 1.11 minutes, or 1.113 minutes, depending on the precision of the measuring device you use.

Theoretically, with sufficient precision of measurement, no two continuous values are identical. As a practical matter, however, most measuring devices are not precise enough to detect small differences, and tied values for a continuous variable (i.e., two or more items or individuals with the same value) are often found in experimental or survey data.

## Levels of Measurement and Measurement Scales

Using levels of measurement is another way of classifying data. There are four widely recognized levels of measurement: nominal, ordinal, interval, and ratio scales.

### Nominal and Ordinal Scales

Data from a categorical variable are measured on a nominal scale or on an ordinal scale. A **nominal scale** (see Figure 1.3) classifies data into distinct categories in which no ranking is implied. In the Good Tunes customer satisfaction survey, the answer to the question "Are you likely to buy additional merchandise from Good Tunes in the next 12 months?" is an example of a nominal scaled variable, as are your favorite soft drink, your political party affiliation, and your gender. Nominal scaling is the weakest form of measurement because you cannot specify any ranking across the various categories.

**FIGURE 1.3**

Examples of nominal scales

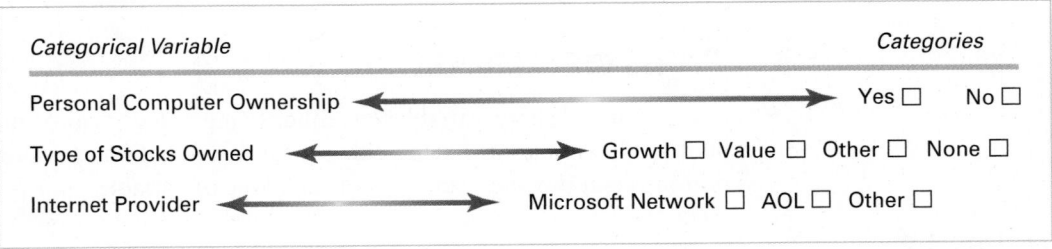

An **ordinal scale** classifies data into distinct categories in which ranking is implied. In the Good Tunes survey, the answers to the question "How do you rate the overall service provided by Good Tunes with respect to your recent purchase?" represent an ordinal scaled variable because the responses "excellent, very good, fair, and poor" are ranked in order of satisfaction level. Figure 1.4 lists other examples of ordinal scaled variables.

**FIGURE 1.4**

Examples of ordinal scales

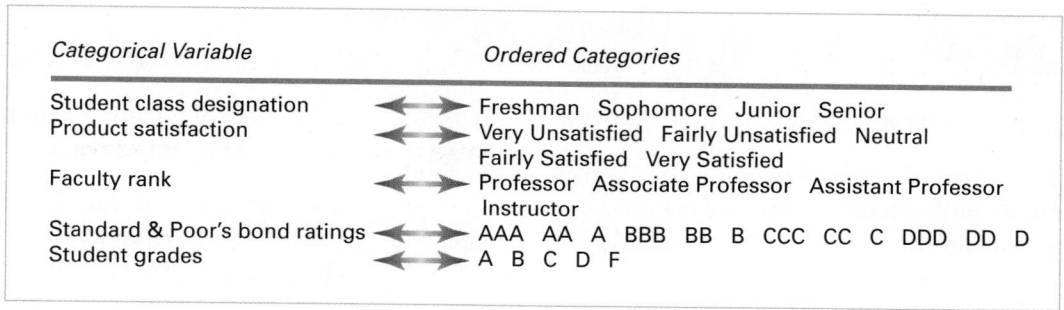

Ordinal scaling is a stronger form of measurement than nominal scaling because an observed value classified into one category possesses more of a property than does an observed value classified into another category. However, ordinal scaling is still a relatively weak form of measurement because the scale does not account for the amount of the differences *between* the categories. The ordering implies only *which* category is "greater," "better," or "more preferred"—not by *how much*.

***Interval and Ratio Scales*** Data from a numerical variable are measured on an interval or a ratio scale. An **interval scale** (see Figure 1.5) is an ordered scale in which the difference between measurements is a meaningful quantity but does not involve a true zero point. For example, a noontime temperature reading of 67 degrees Fahrenheit is 2 degrees warmer than a noontime reading of 65 degrees. In addition, the 2 degrees Fahrenheit difference in the noontime temperature readings is the same as if the two noontime temperature readings were 74 and 76 degrees Fahrenheit because the difference has the same meaning anywhere on the scale.

**FIGURE 1.5**

Examples of interval and ratio scales

A **ratio scale** is an ordered scale in which the difference between the measurements involves a true zero point, as in height, weight, age, or salary measurements. In the Good Tunes customer satisfaction survey, the amount of money (in U.S. dollars) you expect to spend on stereo equipment in the next 12 months is an example of a ratio scaled variable. As another example, a person who weighs 240 pounds is twice as heavy as someone who weighs 120 pounds. Temperature is a trickier case: Fahrenheit and Celsius (centigrade) scales are interval but not ratio scales; the "zero" value is arbitrary, not real. You cannot say that a noontime temperature reading of 4 degrees Fahrenheit is twice as hot as 2 degrees Fahrenheit. But a Kelvin temperature reading, in which zero degrees means no molecular motion, is ratio scaled. In contrast, the Fahrenheit and Celsius scales use arbitrarily selected zero-degree beginning points.

Data measured on an interval scale or on a ratio scale constitute the highest levels of measurement. They are stronger forms of measurement than an ordinal scale because you can determine not only which observed value is the largest but also by how much.

# PROBLEMS FOR SECTION 1.5

## Learning the Basics

**1.1** Three different beverages are sold at a fast-food restaurant—soft drinks, tea, and coffee.
**a.** Explain why the type of beverage sold is an example of a categorical variable.
**b.** Explain why the type of beverage sold is an example of a nominal scaled variable.

**1.2** Soft drinks are sold in three sizes at a fast-food restaurant—small, medium, and large. Explain why the size of the soft drink is an example of an ordinal scaled variable.

**1.3** Suppose that you measure the time it takes to download an MP3 file from the Internet.
**a.** Explain why the download time is a continuous numerical variable.
**b.** Explain why the download time is a ratio scaled variable.

## Applying the Concepts

**✓ SELF Test 1.4** For each of the following variables, determine whether the variable is categorical or numerical. If the variable is numerical, determine whether the variable is discrete or continuous. In addition, determine the level of measurement for each of the following.
**a.** Number of telephones per household
**b.** Length of the longest long-distance call made per month
**c.** Whether someone in the household owns a cell phone
**d.** Whether there is a high-speed Internet connection in the household

**1.5** The following information is collected from students upon exiting the campus bookstore during the first week of classes:
**a.** Amount of time spent shopping in the bookstore
**b.** Number of textbooks purchased
**c.** Academic major
**d.** Gender
Classify each of these variables as categorical or numerical. If the variable is numerical, determine whether the variable is discrete or continuous. In addition, determine the level of measurement for these variables.

**1.6** For each of the following variables, determine whether the variable is categorical or numerical. If the variable is numerical, determine whether the variable is discrete or continuous. In addition, determine the level of measurement for each of the following.
**a.** Name of Internet provider
**b.** Amount of time spent surfing the Internet per week
**c.** Number of e-mails received in a week
**d.** Number of online purchases made in a month

**1.7** For each of the following variables, determine whether the variable is categorical or numerical. If the variable is numerical, determine whether the variable is discrete or continuous. In addition, determine the level of measurement for each of the following.
**a.** Amount of money spent on clothing in the past month
**b.** Favorite department store
**c.** Most likely time period during which shopping for clothing takes place (weekday, weeknight, or weekend)
**d.** Number of pairs of shoes owned

**1.8** Suppose the following information is collected from Robert Keeler on his application for a home mortgage loan at the Metro County Savings and Loan Association:
**a.** Monthly payments: $1,427
**b.** Number of jobs in past 10 years: 1
**c.** Annual family income: $86,000
**d.** Marital status: Married
Classify each of the responses by type of data and level of measurement.

**1.9** One of the variables most often included in surveys is income. Sometimes the question is phrased "What is your income (in thousands of dollars)?" In other surveys, the respondent is asked to "Place an X in the circle corresponding to your income level" and given a number of income ranges from which to choose.
**a.** In the first format, explain why income might be considered either discrete or continuous.
**b.** Which of these two formats would you prefer to use if you were conducting a survey? Why?
**c.** Which of these two formats would likely bring you a greater rate of response? Why?

**1.10** If two students score a 90 on the same examination, what arguments could be used to show that the underlying variable—test score—is continuous?

**1.11** The director of market research at a large department store chain wanted to conduct a survey throughout a metropolitan area to determine the amount of time working women spend shopping for clothing in a typical month.
**a.** Describe both the population and the sample of interest, and indicate the type of data the director might want to collect.
**b.** Develop a first draft of the questionnaire needed in (a) by writing a series of three categorical questions and three numerical questions that you feel are appropriate for this survey.

## 1.6    BUSINESS STATISTICS AND COMPUTERS

During the past 30 years, computerization has made practical the application of new statistical methods that require complex calculations and the collection and analysis of very large sets of data. As the cost of computer processing has dropped over time, the use of these new methods has migrated from those few who were fortunate to have access to specialized "statistical" calculators or large mainframe computers to all those using a typical desktop PC. Statistical functionality is so commonplace today that many simple statistical tasks, once done exclusively with pencil and paper or simple hand calculators, are now done electronically with the assistance of an appropriate computer program.

Minitab and Microsoft Excel are examples of desktop PC programs that people use for statistics. Minitab is an example of a **statistical package**, a program engineered from the ground up to perform statistical analysis as accurately as possible. Microsoft Excel is a general purpose data analysis program found in Microsoft Office that evolved from electronic spreadsheets used in accounting and financial applications. Today Excel is a multifunction data analysis tool. Typical of a general purpose tool, Excel can perform many functions, but none as well as other programs that are more singularly focused (see References 1, 2, and 5). Minitab and Excel are two very different programs and their differences have led to an ongoing debate in business schools about which program is more appropriate for teaching introductory statistics. Adherents of each program point to their program's strengths: Minitab as a complete statistical solution; Excel as a common desktop tool found in many business functional areas (and in many different business school courses).

Although you are probably more familiar with Microsoft Excel than with Minitab, you may be surprised to learn that that both programs share many similarities. This is no coincidence as Minitab was inspired by Omnitab, a mainframe computer program from the 1960s that can be considered an ancestor to all electronic spreadsheet programs. Both Minitab and Excel use **worksheets** (their name for spreadsheets) to store the data you have collected for analysis. Worksheets are tabular arrangements of data, in which the intersections of rows and columns form **cells**, boxes into which you make entries. In Minitab, the data for each variable are placed in individual columns, and this also is the standard practice when using Excel. (The Excel instructions in this book assume this standard practice.) Both Excel and Minitab allow you to save worksheets, programming information, and results in one file, called **workbooks** in Excel and **projects** in Minitab.

Among their differences, Excel uses worksheets to store certain programming information as well as to present results of a statistical analysis whereas Minitab generally displays these things in separate windows. Minitab allows you to save individual worksheets in separate Minitab worksheet (.mtw) files. (The Student CD-ROM packaged with this book contains the data for problems and chapter examples as both Excel workbook files and Minitab worksheet files.)

Because the details of using Microsoft Excel and Minitab differ, you will find at the end of every chapter separate appendices for Microsoft Excel, PHStat2 (the Excel add-in that simplifies your use of Excel as explained in Section P1.1 on page 22), and Minitab. These appendices will help you to re-create the in-chapter examples and help solve the problems listed in the chapter. Should you be new to computing, you can review Appendix C that discusses the minimal computing skills you need to operate Excel (with or without PHStat2) or Minitab effectively. Appendix C also reviews the conventions used to describe computer operations.

If you use the Microsoft Excel appendices, you will occasionally find paired sections—one that gives instructions for Excel 97, 2000, 2002, or 2003; and the other that gives instructions for Excel 2007—that reflect changes Microsoft has made to Office 2007.

Regardless of which program you end up using, be aware that using computer programs to assist in statistical decision making is a necessary and commonplace occurrence in business today.

# Learning to Use Programs *Properly*

When you learn something, you usually get feedback that you use constructively to improve your productivity. Providing feedback is one reason instructors give tests. When you get the results of a test, you can reflect on how well you have properly learned the subject matter. Unfortunately, when learning to use programs such as Microsoft Excel or Minitab while studying business statistics, feedback opportunities can be rare. You either get a usable result (good) or fail to do so (bad). This good–bad, pass–fail type of feedback cannot help you to acquire the skills and good habits you need to use programs effectively. We hope the following checklist will.

You are using programs *properly* if you can:

**1. Understand how to operate the program.** You will not get far if you have not mastered the mechanical tasks of working with a program. These tasks include how to start the program, load or enter data, and select commands or otherwise instruct the program what you want it to do for you.

The end-of-chapter Sections E1, P1, and M1 introduce you to the tasks you need for using either Microsoft Excel or Minitab. Begin with these tasks and don't waste your time teaching yourself every command or trying to memorize every program function. Learn about additional features in a just-in-time fashion, that is, only when you need to use them. In addition, if you own or manage the computer that you use, know how to use the Internet to retrieve and apply program updates and to get technical assistance.

**2. Understand the underlying statistical concepts.** Make sure you understand what a program is doing as it creates its information. As a minimum, be informed about what each menu selection you make does or calculates. Be knowledgeable enough to be able to justify your choice of using a particular statistical method. Don't rely on memorizing keystroke or mouse clicks alone.

**3. Understand how to organize and present information.** Plan how you are going to store and use your data for analysis. Think about how to best arrange and label your data. If using Microsoft Excel, place results on their own worksheets, apart from the worksheet used to store the data to be analyzed. Also think about using worksheet and chart formatting features (see Section E1.1 on page 16 and Section E1.2 on page 17) to enhance the visual presentation and to correct formatting errors that Excel makes. If using Minitab, think about the organization and visual layout of your saved project files.

**4. Know how to review results for errors.** Never assume that any results you create in a program are free of errors. Always review results for obvious errors such as "impossible" results (a mean smaller than any data value). If you have entered formulas into a worksheet, examine them individually, looking for errors.

**5. Make secure and clearly named backups of your work.** Make backup copies of your work on a regular basis. Physically separate the backup copies by writing to a separate disk; two copies of a file on the same disk is not an example of a true backup. Do not name files or backups "file1" or "my file" or other names that do not clearly identify your work.

# SUMMARY

In this chapter, you have been introduced to the role of statistics in turning data into information and the importance of using computer programs such as Microsoft Excel and Minitab. In addition, you have studied data collection and the various types of data used in business. In conjunction with the Using Statistics scenario, you were asked to review the customer survey used by the Good Tunes company (see page 6). The first and fifth questions of the survey shown will produce numerical data. Questions 2 through 4 will produce nominal categorical data. Questions 6 through 8 will produce ordinal categorical data. The responses to the first question (number of days) are discrete, and the responses to the fifth question (amount of money spent) are continuous. In the next two chapters, tables and charts and a variety of descriptive numerical measures that are useful for data analysis are developed.

# KEY TERMS

| | | |
|---|---|---|
| categorical variables   8 | numerical variables   8 | sample   4 |
| cell   11 | operational definition   4 | secondary source   5 |
| continuous variable   8 | ordinal scale   8 | statistic   4 |
| data   4 | parameter   4 | statistical package   11 |
| data collection   5 | population   4 | statistics   2 |
| descriptive statistics   2 | primary source   5 | variable   4 |
| discrete variables   8 | projects   11 | workbooks   11 |
| inferential statistics   2 | qualitative variables   8 | worksheets   11 |
| interval scale   9 | quantitative variables   8 | |
| nominal scale   8 | ratio scale   9 | |

# CHAPTER REVIEW PROBLEMS

## Checking Your Understanding

**1.12** What is the difference between a sample and a population?

**1.13** What is the difference between a statistic and a parameter?

**1.14** What is the difference between descriptive and inferential statistics?

**1.15** What is the difference between a categorical variable and a numerical variable?

**1.16** What is the difference between a discrete variable and a continuous variable?

**1.17** What is an operational definition and why is it so important?

**1.18** What are the four levels of measurement scales?

## Applying the Concepts

**1.19** The Data and Story Library, **lib.stat.cmu.edu/DASL**, is an online library of data files and stories that illustrate the use of basic statistical methods. The stories are classified by method and by topic. Go to this site and click on **List all topics**. Pick a story and summarize how statistics were used in the story.

**1.20** Go to the official Microsoft Excel Web site, **www.microsoft.com/office/excel**, or the official Minitab Web site, **www.minitab.com**. Explain how you think Microsoft Excel or Minitab could be useful in the field of statistics.

**1.21** The Gallup organization releases the results of recent polls at its Web site, **www.galluppoll.com**. Go to this site and read today's top story.
a. Describe the population of interest.
b. Describe the sample that was collected.
c. Describe a parameter of interest.
d. Describe the statistic used to describe the parameter in (c).

**1.22** According to its homepage, "Swivel is a place where curious people explore data—all kinds of data." Go to **www.swivel.com** and explore a data set of interest to you.
a. Which of the four sources of data best describes the source of the data set you selected?
b. Describe a variable in the data set you selected.
c. Is the variable categorical or numerical?
d. If the variable in (c) is numerical, is it discrete or continuous?

**1.23** At the U.S. Census Bureau site, **www.census.gov**, click **Survey of Business Owners** in the "Business & Industry" section and read about The Survey of Business Owners. Click on **Sample SBO-1 Form** to view a survey form.
a. Give an example of a categorical variable found in this survey.
b. Give an example of a numerical variable found in this survey.
c. Is the variable you selected in (b) discrete or continuous?

**1.24** An online survey of almost 53,000 people (N. Hellmich, "Americans Go for the Quick Fix for Dinner," *USA Today*, February 14, 2005, p. B1) indicated that 37% decide what to make for dinner at home at the last minute and that the amount of time to prepare dinner averages 12 minutes, while the amount of time to cook dinner averages 28 minutes.
a. Which of the four categories of data sources listed in Section 1.4 on page 6 do you think were used in this study?
b. Name a categorical variable discussed in this article.
c. Name a numerical variable discussed in this article.

**1.25** Three professors at Northern Kentucky University compared two different approaches to teaching courses in the school of business (M. W. Ford, D. W. Kent, and S. Devoto, "Learning from the Pros: Influence of Web-Based Expert Commentary on Vicarious Learning about Financial Markets," *Decision Sciences Journal of Innovative Education*, January 2007, 5(1), 43–63). At the time of the study, there were 2,100 students in the business school and 96 students were involved in the study. Demographic data collected on these 96 students included class (freshman, sophomore, junior, senior), age, gender, and major.
a. Describe the population of interest.
b. Describe the sample that was collected.
c. For each of the four demographic variables mentioned above, indicate if they are categorical or numerical.
d. For each of the four demographic variables, indicate their level of measurement.

**1.26** A manufacturer of cat food was planning to survey households in the United States to determine purchasing habits of cat owners. Among the questions to be included are those that relate to
1. where cat food is primarily purchased.
2. whether dry or moist cat food is purchased.
3. the number of cats living in the household.
4. whether the cat is pedigreed.
a. Describe the population.
b. For each of the four items listed, indicate whether the variable is categorical or numerical. If it is numerical, is it discrete or continuous?

c. Develop five categorical questions for the survey.
d. Develop five numerical questions for the survey.

## Student Survey Data Base

**1.27**  A sample of 50 undergraduate students answered the following survey.
  1. What is your gender?  Female _____  Male _____
  2. What is your age (*as of last birthday*)? _____
  3. What is your height (*in inches*)? _____
  4. What is your current registered class designation?
     Freshman _____    Sophomore _____
     Junior _____    Senior _____
  5. What is your major area of study?
     Accounting _____  Economics/Finance _____
     Information Systems _____
     International Business _____  Management _____
     Marketing/Retailing _____  Other _____
     Undecided _____
  6. At the present time, do you plan to attend graduate school?  Yes _____  No _____  Not sure _____
  7. What is your current cumulative grade point average?
     _____
  8. What would you expect your starting annual salary (*in $000*) to be if you were to seek employment immediately after obtaining your bachelor's degree?
     _____
  9. What do you anticipate your salary to be (*in $000*) after five years of full-time work experience? _____
  10. What is your current employment status?
      Full-time _____    Part-time _____
      Unemployed _____
  11. How many clubs, groups, organizations, or teams are you currently affiliated with on campus?
  12. How satisfied are you with the student advisement services on campus? _____
      Extremely  1  2  3  4  5  6  7  Extremely
      unsatisfied       Neutral        satisfied
  13. About how much money did you spend this semester for textbooks and supplies? _____
The results of the survey are in the file **Undergradsurvey**.
**a.** Which variables in the survey are categorical?
**b.** Which variables in the survey are numerical?
**c.** Which variables are discrete numerical variables?

**1.28**  A sample of 40 MBA students answered the following survey:
  1. What is your gender?  Female _____  Male _____
  2. What is your age (*as of last birthday*)? _____
  3. What is your height (*in inches*)? _____
  4. What is your current major area of study?
     Accounting _____  Economics/Finance _____
     Information Systems _____
     International Business _____  Management _____
     Marketing/Retailing _____  Other _____
     Undecided _____
  5. What is your graduate cumulative grade point average? _____
  6. What was your undergraduate area of specialization?
     Biological Sciences _____  Business
     Administration _____  Computers or Math _____
     Education _____  Engineering _____
     Humanities _____  Performing Arts _____
     Physical Sciences _____  Social Sciences _____
     Other _____
  7. What was your undergraduate cumulative grade point average? _____
  8. What was your GMAT score? _____
  9. What is your current employment status? _____
     Full-time _____    Part-time _____
     Unemployed _____
  10. How many different full-time jobs have you held in the past 10 years? _____
  11. What do you expect your annual salary (*in $000*) to be immediately after completion of the MBA program? _____
  12. What do you anticipate your salary to be (*in $000*) after five years of full-time work experience following the completion of the MBA program? _____
  13. How satisfied are you with the student advisement services on campus?
      Extremely  1  2  3  4  5  6  7  Extremely
      unsatisfied       Neutral        satisfied
  14. About how much money did you spend this semester for textbooks and supplies? _____
The results of the survey are in the file **Gradsurvey**.
**a.** Which variables in the survey are categorical?
**b.** Which variables in the survey are numerical?
**c.** Which variables are discrete numerical variables?

# END-OF-CHAPTER CASES

At the end of most chapters, you will find a continuing case study that allows you to apply statistics to problems faced by the management of the *Springville Herald*, a daily news-

paper. Complementing this case are a series of Web Cases that extend many of the Using Statistics scenarios that begin each chapter.

References 15

# LEARNING WITH THE WEB CASES

*People use statistical techniques to help communicate and present important information to others both inside and outside their businesses. Every day, as in these examples, people misuse these techniques:*

- A sales manager working with an "easy-to-use" charting program chooses an inappropriate chart that obscures data relationships.
- The editor of an annual report presents a chart of revenues with an abridged *Y*-axis that creates the false impression of greatly rising revenues.
- An analyst generates meaningless statistics about a set of categorical data, using analyses designed for numerical data.

Identifying and preventing misuses of statistics, whether intentional or not, is an important responsibility for all managers. The Web Cases help you develop the skills necessary for this important task.

Web Cases send you to Web sites that are related to the Using Statistics scenarios that begin each chapter. You review internal documents as well as publicly stated claims, seeking to identify and correct the misuses of statistics. Unlike a traditional case study, but much like real-world situations, not all of the information you encounter will be relevant to your task, and you may occasionally discover conflicting information that you need to resolve before continuing with the case.

To assist your learning, the Web Case for each chapter begins with the learning objective and a summary of the problem or issue at hand. Each case directs you to one or more Web pages where you can discover information to answer case questions that help guide your exploration. If you prefer, you can view these pages by opening corresponding HTML files that can be found in the **Web Case** folder on the Student CD-ROM. You can find an index of all files/pages by opening the `SpringvilleCC.htm` file in the **Web Case** folder or by visiting the Springville Chamber of Commerce page, at **www.prenhall.com/Springville/SpringvilleCC.htm**.

## Web Case Example

To illustrate how to learn from a Web Case, open a Web browser and link to **www.prenhall.com/Springville/Good_Tunes.htm**, or open the `Good_Tunes.htm` file in the Student CD-ROM **Web Case** folder. This Web page repre-

sents the home page of Good Tunes, the online retailer mentioned in the Using Statistics scenario in this chapter. Recall that the privately held Good Tunes is seeking financing to expand its business by opening retail locations. Because it is in management's interest to show that Good Tunes is a thriving business, it is not too surprising to discover the "our best sales year ever" claim in the "Good Times at Good Tunes" entry at the top of their home page.

The claim also serves as a hyperlink, so click on **our best sales year ever** to display the page that supports the claim. How would you support such a claim? with a table of numbers? a chart? remarks attributed to a knowledgeable source? Good Tunes has used a chart to present "two years ago" and "latest twelve months" sales data by category. Are there any problems with the choices made on this Web page? *Absolutely*!

First, note that there are no scales for the symbols used, so it is impossible to know what the actual sales volumes are. In fact, as you will learn in Section 2.6, charts that incorporate symbols in this way are considered examples of *chartjunk* and would never be used by people seeking to properly use graphs.

This important point aside, another question that arises is whether the sales data represent the number of units sold or something else. The use of the symbols creates the impression that unit sales data are being presented. If the data are unit sales, does such data best support the claim being made, or would something else, such as dollar volumes, be a better indicator of sales at Good Tunes?

Then there are those curious chart labels. "Latest twelve months" is ambiguous; it could include months from the current year as well as months from one year ago and therefore may not be an equivalent time period to "two years ago." But the business was established in 1997, and the claim being made is "best sales year ever," so why hasn't management included sales figures for *every* year?

Is Good Tunes management hiding something, or are they just unaware of the proper use of statistics? Either way, they have failed to properly communicate a vital aspect of their story.

In subsequent Web Cases, you will be asked to provide this type of analysis, using the open-ended questions of the case as your guide. Not all the cases are as straightforward as this sample, and some cases include perfectly appropriate applications of statistics.

# REFERENCES

1. McCullough, B. D., and B. Wilson, "On the Accuracy of Statistical Procedures in Microsoft Excel 97," *Computational Statistics and Data Analysis*, 31 (1999), 27–37.

2. McCullough, B. D., and B. Wilson, "On the Accuracy of Statistical Procedures in Microsoft Excel 2003," *Computational Statistics and Data Analysis*, 49 (2005), 1244–52.

3. *Microsoft Excel 2007* (Redmond, WA: Microsoft Corporation, 2007).
4. *Minitab Release 15* (State College, PA: Minitab, Inc., 2006).
5. Nash, J. C., "Spreadsheets in Statistical Practice—Another Look," *The American Statistician*, 60 (2006), 287–89.

# Appendix E1
## Introduction to Microsoft Excel

### E1.1 OPENING AND SAVING WORKBOOKS

As discussed in Section 1.6, Microsoft Excel uses worksheets that are stored in workbooks. You open and save workbooks by selecting the storage folder to use and then specifying the file name of the workbook. You begin the process by selecting **File** from the Excel menu bar in Excel 97–2003 or by clicking the **Office Button** in Excel 2007. You then select either **Open** or **Save As**. These selections display nearly identical Open and Save As dialog boxes that vary only slightly owing to the different Excel versions (Figure E1.1 shows the Excel 2007 Save As dialog box).

Inside these dialog boxes, you select the storage folder using the drop-down list at the top of these dialog boxes. You enter, or select from the list box, a file name for the workbook in the **File name** box. You click **Open** or **Save** to complete the task. Sometimes when saving files, you will want to change the file type before you click **Save**. If you use Excel 2007 and want to save your workbook in the format used by earlier Excel versions, select **Excel 97–2003 Workbook (*.xls)** from the **Save as type** drop-down list before you click **Save** (shown in Figure E1.1). If you use any version of Excel and want to save data in a form that can be opened by programs that cannot open Excel workbooks, you might select either **Text (Tab delimited) (*.txt)** or **CSV (Comma delimited) (*.csv)** as the save type.

When you go to open a file and cannot find its name in the list box, verify that the current **Look in** folder is the correct one. If that fails to help, change the file type to **All Files (*.*)** to see all files in the current folder. (This technique will help you discover inadvertent misspellings or missing file extensions that otherwise prevents the file from being displayed.)

Although all versions of Microsoft Excel include a **Save** command, you should avoid this choice until you gain experience. Using Save makes it too easy for you to inad-

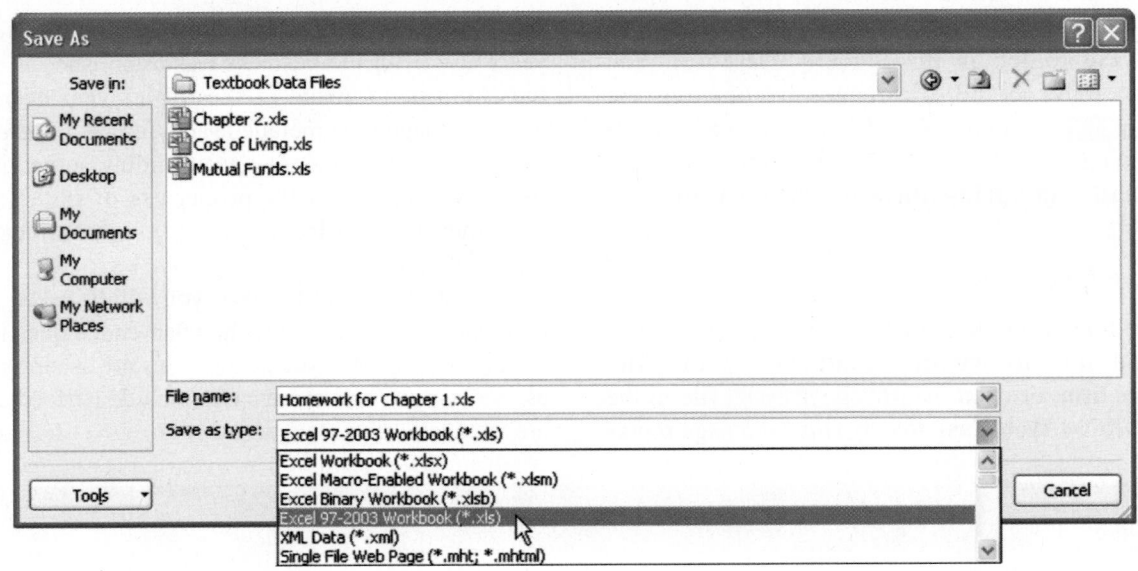

**FIGURE E1.1**
Save As dialog box (Excel 2007 version)

vertently overwrite your work, and in Excel 2007, it saves your workbook in the new **.xlsx** workbook format that cannot be used by earlier Excel versions. If you open a workbook from a nonmodifiable source, such as the Student CD-ROM, Excel will mark the workbook "read-only," so you must use Save As to save any changes you make to the workbook. (Excel will prevent you from using Save in such situations.)

## E1.2 CREATING NEW WORKBOOKS

You create a new workbook through a straightforward process that varies depending on the version of Excel you are using. In Excel 97 or 2000, you select **File → New**. In Excel 2002 (also known as Excel XP) or 2003, you select **File → New** and then click **Blank workbook** in the New Workbook task pane. In Excel 2007, you click **Office Button → New** and in the New Workbook dialog box, you first click **Blank workbook** and then **Create**.

New workbooks are created with a fixed number of worksheets. You can delete extra worksheets or insert more sheets by right-clicking a sheet tab and clicking either **Delete** or **Insert**.

## E1.3 PRINTING WORKSHEETS

When you want to print the contents of a workbook, you should print one sheet at a time to get the best results. You print sheets by first previewing their printed form onscreen and then making any adjustments to the worksheet and/or to the print setup settings.

To print a specific worksheet, you first click on the sheet tab of that worksheet to make the worksheet the currently active one. Then you display the Print Preview window. If you use a version of Excel other than 2007, select **File → Print Preview**. If you use Excel 2007, click **Office Button**, move the mouse pointer over **Print** (do not click) and select **Print Preview** from the Preview and Print gallery.

The Print Preview windows for all Excel versions are similar to one another. Figure E1.2 shows a partial window for Excel 2003 (top) and Excel 2007 (bottom). If the preview contains errors or displays the worksheet in an undesirable manner, click **Close** (or **Close Print Preview** in Excel 2007), make the changes necessary, and reselect the preview command. You can customize your printout by clicking **Setup** (or **Page Setup**) and making the appropriate entries in the Page Setup dialog box, which is similar

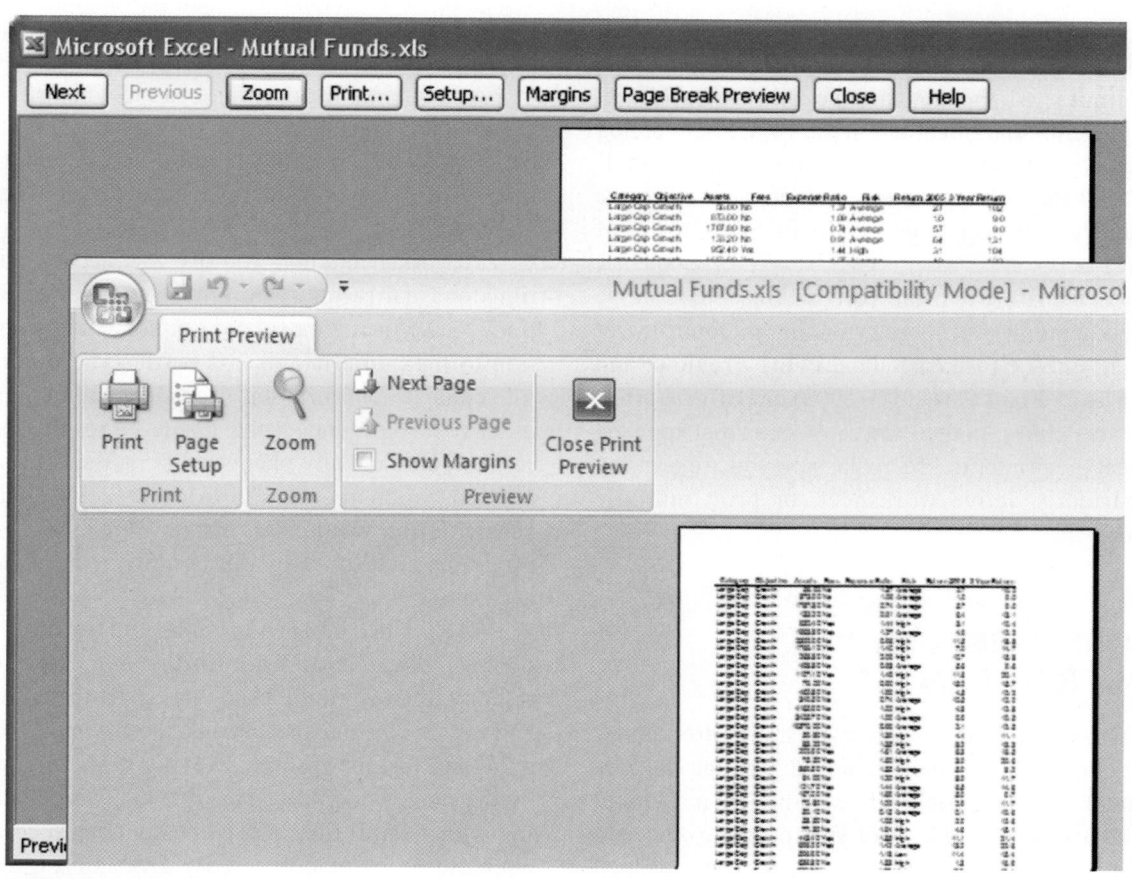

**FIGURE E1.2**

Partial Print Preview windows (Excel 2003 and 2007 versions)

**FIGURE E1.3**
Sheet tab of the Page Setup dialog box (Excel 2003 version)

for all Excel versions. For example, to print your worksheet with grid lines and numbered row and lettered column headings (similar to the appearance of the worksheet onscreen), you click the **Sheet** tab in the Page Setup dialog box and then click **Gridlines** and **Row and column headings** and click **OK** (see Figure E1.3). (You can find more information about using Page Setup in Section F4 of Appendix F.)

When you are ready to print, you can click **Print** in the Print Preview window, but to gain maximum control over your printout, click **Close** (or **Close Print Preview**) and then select **File → Print** (Excel 97–2003) or **Office Button → Print** (Excel 2007). In the Print dialog box that appears, you can select the printer to use, make sure you are printing only the currently active worksheet, or print multiple copies at once.

## E1.4 WORKSHEET ENTRIES AND REFERENCES

As first discussed in Section 1.6, worksheets are tabular arrangements of data in which standard practice dictates that you enter the data for each variable in individual columns. You use the cursor keys or your pointing device to move a **cell pointer** through a worksheet and to select a cell for entry. As you type an entry, it appears in the formula bar, and you place that entry into the cell by either pressing the **Tab** or **Enter** keys or clicking the checkmark button in the formula bar.

As you enter the data for a variable in a column, follow the standard practice of using the row 1 cell to store a name or label for the variable. Should you be entering two or more sets of data, consider placing each set of data in a separate worksheet.

In worksheets that you use for intermediate calculations or final results, you might enter **formulas**, instructions to perform a calculation or some other task, in addition to the numeric and text entries you otherwise make into cells. Proper formulas use values found in one or more other cells to produce a new displayed result. The displayed results automatically change; that is, the formula is recalculated, when the values in other cells change. (Such **recalculation** was the original novel feature of spreadsheet programs and led to such programs being widely used in accounting.)

To refer to a cell in a formula, you use a **cell address** in the form **SheetName!ColumnRow**. For example, **Data!A2** refers to the cell in the Data worksheet that is in column A and row 2. You can also use just the *ColumnRow* portion of a full address, for example, **A2**, if you are referring to a cell on the same worksheet as the one into which you are entering a formula. If the sheet name contains spaces or special characters, for example, **City Data** or **Figure-1.2**, you must enclose the sheet name in a pair of single quotes, as in **'City Data'!A2** or **'Figure-1.2'!A2**.

When you want to refer to a group of cells, for example, to the cells of a column that store the data for a particular variable, you use a **cell range**. A cell range names the upper leftmost cell and the lower rightmost cell of the group using the form ***SheetName!UpperLeftCell:LowerRightCell***. For example, the cell range **Data!B1:B51** identifies the cells in the UndergradSurvey.xls workbook that store the data for the gender variable (with cell B1 storing the variable label "Gender" as explained earlier). Cell ranges can extend over multiple columns; the cell range **Data!B1:E51** in the same workbook would refer to the data for the gender, age, height, and class variables.

As with a single cell reference, you can skip the *SheetName!* part of the reference if you are referring to a cell range on the current worksheet, and, must use a pair of single quotes if a sheet name contains spaces or special characters. However, in many cases in the Excel instructions in this book, including the sheet name will be necessary in a cell reference in order to get the proper results. Because sheet names are used so frequently, you should change the names that Excel assigns to worksheets (names in the form **Sheet1**, **Sheet2**, and so on) to more meaningful words or phrases. To do so, double-click a sheet tab, type the new name, and press **Enter**.

(Although not a form used in this book, cell references can include a workbook name in the form **'[*Workbook Name*]*SheetName*'!*ColumnRow*** or **'[*WorkbookName*] *SheetName*'!*UpperLeftCell:LowerRightCell***. You may discover such references if you inadvertently copy certain types of worksheets or chart sheets from one workbook to another.)

## E1.5 ENTERING FORMULAS INTO WORKSHEETS

You enter formulas by typing the equal sign symbol (=) and then a combination of mathematical or other data-processing operations. For simple formulas, you use the symbols +, −, *, /, and ∧ for the operations addition, subtraction, multiplication, division, and exponentiation (a number raised to a power), respectively. For example, the formula **=Data!B2 + Data!B3 + Data!B4** adds the contents of the cells B2, B3, and B4 of the Data worksheet and displays the sum as the value in the cell containing the formula. You can also use **worksheet functions** in formulas to simplify formulas.

To use a worksheet function in a formula, either type the function as shown in the instructions in this book or use the Excel Function Wizard feature to insert the function. To use this feature, select **Insert → Function** (Excel 97–2003) or **Formulas → Function Wizard** (Excel 2007) and then make entries and selections in one or more dialog boxes.

## E1.6 VERIFYING FORMULAS AND WORKSHEETS

If you use formulas in your worksheets, you should review and verify formulas before you use their results. To view the formulas in a worksheet, press **Ctrl+`** (grave accent key). To restore the original view, the results of the formulas, press **Ctrl+`** a second time.

As you create and use more complicated worksheets, you may want to visually examine the relationships among a formula and the cells it uses (called the precedents) and the cells that use the results of the formula (the dependents). To display arrows that visually show these relationships, use the formula auditing feature of Excel. Select **Tools → Auditing** (Excel 97 or 2000), or **Tools → Formula Auditing** (Excel 2002 or 2003), or **Formulas** (Excel 2007). Then select one of the choices from the **auditing** submenu (Excel 97–2003) or from the **Formula Auditing** group (Excel 2007). When you are finished, selecting **Remove All Arrows** restores your display by removing all auditing arrows.

## E1.7 ENHANCING WORKBOOK PRESENTATION

By formatting the display of individual cells and by rearranging the contents of your workbook, you can enhance the presentation of your workbook.

You can find the most common cell-formatting operations on the Formatting toolbar (Excel 97–2003) or in the Home tab (Excel 2007). Most worksheets shown as illustrations in this book use the **Boldface**, **Fill Color**, **Merge-and-Center**, and **Borders** features to highlight particular cells or cell ranges. Experiment with these features to develop your own style that maximizes the effectiveness of your presentations.

You may also want to rearrange the content of your workbooks. Use the copy-and-paste combination keystroke shortcuts, **Crtl+C** and **Ctrl+V**, to copy content from one cell to another on the same worksheet. Copying cells that contain formulas is not necessarily as straightforward as you might expect. If your formula uses references in the format discussed in Section E1.4, Excel will change to reflect the difference, or offset, between the original (source) cell and the cell into which you are pasting the formula (the target cell). For example, when you copy the formula =A2 + B2 in cell C2 down to cell C3, an offset of one row, Excel pastes the formula =A3 + B3 in C3 to reflect that one-row offset. Cell ranges also get changed, so if you copy the formula =SUM(A1:A4) from cell A5 to cell B5, the formula is changed to =SUM(B1:B4).

You can stop Excel from making such changes by inserting a U.S. dollar symbol ($) before either the column letter or

**FIGURE E1.4**

Move or Copy dialog box (Excel 2007 version)

row number (or both) of a cell reference to form an **absolute reference**, for example, $A$2. Do not confuse the use of the U.S. dollar symbol with the format operation that displays numbers as U.S. currency values. To format cell values for U.S. currency display, you use the **Currency ($)** format button, available on the Formatting toolbar (Excel 97–2003) and in the Number group of **Home** tab (Excel 2007).

Finally, you can also copy entire worksheets for convenience or clarity. To copy a worksheet to a new workbook, you first select the worksheet by clicking its sheet tab. Then you right-click the tab and select **Move or Copy** from the shortcut menu that appears. In the **To book** drop-down list of the Move or Copy dialog box (see Figure E1.4), first select **(new book)** or the name of the preexisting target workbook, and then click **Create a copy** and then click **OK**.

## E1.8 USING ADD-INS

**Add-ins** can simplify the task of creating something to add to a workbook. Add-ins are programming components not included in the main Excel program and may need to be **installed**, or added, to your computer system separately. Add-ins are not always available for you to use because they can be disabled by other users or system security settings. However, the little extra effort you need to ensure that the right add-ins are installed and enabled is well worth the features that add-ins bring to Excel.

As you use Microsoft Excel with this book, you will use the Excel **Analysis ToolPak** add-in for some statistical

tasks. The Analysis ToolPak add-in (which the book simply calls the "ToolPak" from this point forward) adds statistical procedures to Excel, but creates worksheets that do not contain formulas. Should you later change your data, you must repeat the ToolPak procedure to get updated results. Some Excel versions come with the ToolPak preinstalled; others require that you separately install this component from your Microsoft Office or Excel program setup disk. (See Appendix F for additional information about installing the ToolPak.)

As you use Microsoft Excel, you may choose to use **PHStat2**, the Prentice Hall statistics add-in that is included on the Student CD-ROM. If you plan to use PHStat2, you first need to run its setup program, using the instructions found in Appendix F and in the Student CD-ROM PHStat2 readme file. PHStat2 adds a PHStat menu of procedures to the Excel menu bar in Excel 97–2003 and the Add-ins tab in Excel 2007. Unlike the ToolPak, PHStat2 usually creates worksheets that contain formulas and that will produce new results as the underlying data changes. Sometimes, though, PHStat2 asks the ToolPak to create sheets on its behalf, and the resulting sheets are similar to the no-formulas sheets that the ToolPak creates. In many such cases, PHStat2 enhances the sheets it asks the ToolPak to create, correcting errors the ToolPak makes or adding new formula-based calculations. (If you plan to use PHStat2, be sure to read Appendix P1, which immediately follows this appendix.)

In all Excel versions other than Excel 97, all add-ins that you open will be screened by Microsoft Office security components. If you use Excel 2000, 2002, or 2003, you can

**FIGURE E1.5**

Security dialog box (Excel 2003 version)

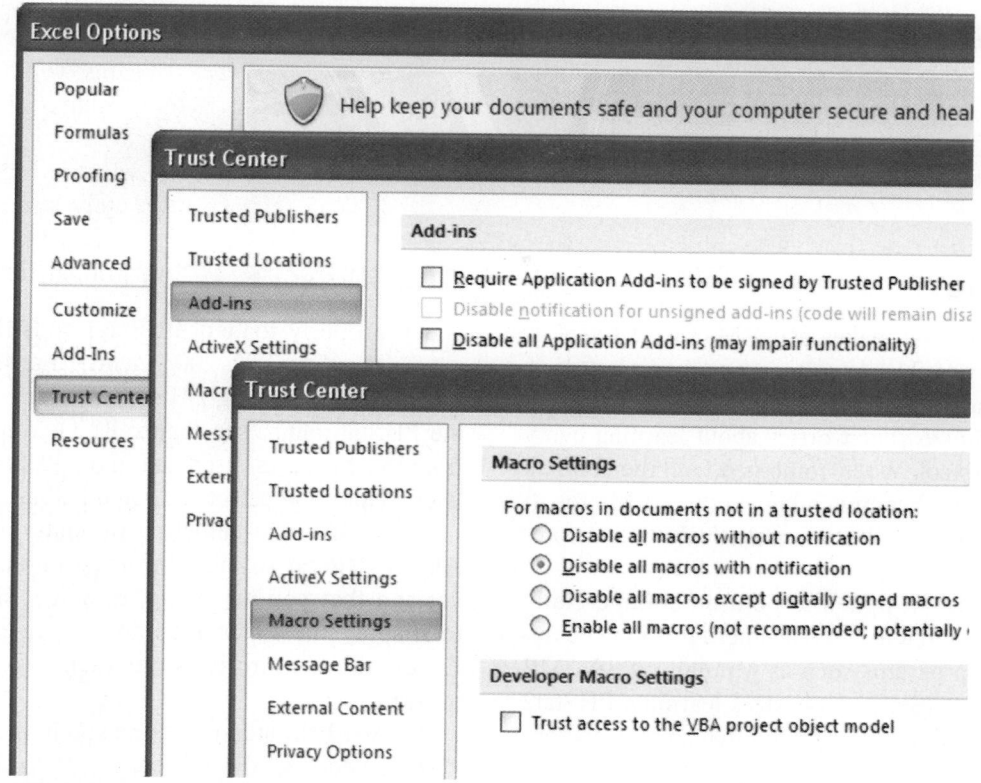

**FIGURE E1.6**
Excel Options and Trust Center panes (Excel 2007)

review and change the security settings by selecting **Tools → Macro → Security** to display a Security dialog box (similar to the one shown in Figure E1.5 for Excel 2003). To use an add-in such as PHStat2 that is "not signed," you would click **Medium** and then click **OK**.

If you use Excel 2007, click the **Office Button**, and then click **Excel Options** in the Office menu. In the Excel Options dialog box (see Figure E1.6) click **Trust Center** in the left pane to display information about security issues. Then click **Trust Center Settings** (obscured in Figure E1.6) to display the Trust Center dialog box. To use an add-in such as PHStat2 that is not signed, click **Add-Ins** in the left pane, and then clear all checkboxes in the right pane (see Figure E1.6). Then click **Macro Settings** in the left pane and click **Disable all macros with notification** in the right pane (see Figure E1.6). On some systems, you may also have to click **Trusted Locations** in the left pane and add the file location of the add-in.

With the Security screen set to an appropriate level, you will see a macro virus warning dialog box when you open an add-in such as PHStat2. Figure E1.7 shows the Excel 2003 and Excel 2007 warning boxes. You click the **Enable Macros** button to allow virus-free add-ins, such as PHStat2, to be opened and used.

**FIGURE E1.7**
Macro warning dialog boxes (Excel 2003 and 2007)

# Appendix P1
## Introduction to PHStat2

## P1.1 OVERVIEW

PHStat2 is software that makes using Microsoft Excel as distraction-free as possible. As a student studying statistics, you can use PHStat2 to maximize your focus on mastering statistics and minimize your worries about learning every little detail about Excel. When combined with the ToolPak add-in, you can use a beginner's knowledge of Microsoft Excel to illustrate nearly all of the statistical methods presented in this book.

PHStat2 was not designed to be used commercially and you should not see it as a replacement for or an equivalent to statistical programs such as Minitab, SPSS, JMP, and SAS. Because PHStat2 emphasizes learning, PHStat2 tries to use the methods of calculation that an introductory statistics student can easily follow, including manual calculation methods presented in this book. In other cases, PHStat2 uses preexisting Microsoft Excel methods to produce results that are too complex to manually calculate or present to the learner. These design choices occasionally produce results that are not as precise or accurate as those produced by commercial programs, which use methods of calculation that are fine-tuned for precision and accuracy. Even though these differences will not be significant for most sets of data and are *not* significant for all data used in chapter examples and problems, they could be if you used PHStat2 with data that happen to have unusual properties.

## P1.2 HOW PHSTAT2 PRESENTS ITS RESULTS

PHStat2 creates new worksheets and chart sheets inserted into the currently active workbook. Cells containing important values and results are highlighted by a light yellow tint and boldface text. These cells and the cells that hold intermediate calculations are usually only minimally numerically formatted. For some procedures, the values in these cells will have an excessive number of seemingly significant digits and you may want to change the numeric formatting for such cells for presentation purposes.

Worksheets that contain cells tinted in light turquoise are designed to be interactive and you can change the numeric values of those cells to produce different results without reselecting the PHStat2 procedure.

## P1.3 USING PHSTAT2

When properly loaded, PHStat2 adds the PHStat menu entry to the Excel 97–2003 menu bar or the Add-Ins tab of Excel 2007. Selecting **PHStat** for either of these displays the PHStat menu (see Figure P1.1). You make selections from this menu, as discussed in the PHStat2 appendices of later chapters, to select and run a PHStat2 procedure.

In addition to selecting procedures, you can select **About PHStat** to view information about the PHStat2 version that you are using, or select **Help for PHStat** to display the PHStat2 help system inside Microsoft Excel (this feature is not available for Windows Vista users).

To use PHStat2, make sure you have read Section E1.8 "Using Add-Ins," the Student CD-ROM **PHStat2 readme file** and the appropriate sections of Appendix F. If you are inexperienced in the task of installing programs on your computer system, you may additionally want to seek assistance from a friend or campus help center if you plan to install PHStat2 on your system. General assistance is also available through the PHStat2 Website, **www.prenhall.com/phstat**.

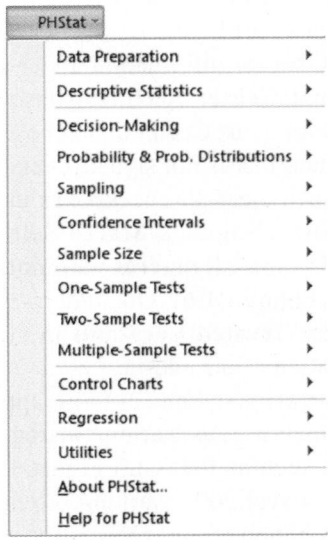

**FIGURE P1.1**

PHStat Menu

# Appendix M1
## Introduction to Minitab

## M1.1 OVERVIEW

Minitab is a statistical program that initially evolved from efforts at the Pennsylvania State University to improve the teaching of statistics. Over the years, Minitab's accuracy and its availability for many different types of computer systems have attracted such corporate customers as the Ford Motor Company, 3M, and General Electric. This combination of having large-scale commercial acceptance and the legacy of being designed for statistics education makes Minitab an attractive program to use in business statistics courses.

As first discussed in Section 1.6, you create Minitab **projects** to store all of your data and results. A project includes several components: a **session area** that contains all your statistical tables; a **Project Manager** that summarizes the project contents; Minitab worksheets that store your data; and graphs of your data. Project components appear as separate windows *inside* the Minitab window. When you start Minitab, you typically see a new project that contains only the session area and one worksheet window. (You can view other components by selecting them in the Minitab **Windows** menu.) You can open and save an entire project or, as is done in this book, open and save individual worksheets.

## M1.2 USING MINITAB WORKSHEETS

You enter data for each variable in individual columns of a Minitab worksheet. Minitab worksheets are organized as numbered rows and columns numbered in the form Cn in which C1 is the first column, C2 is the second column, and so forth. You enter variable labels in a special unnumbered row that precedes row 1. You refer to individual variables either using their column number, such as **C1**, or through their variable labels, such as **Risk**. If a variable label is a phrase such as **Return 2006**, you enter the label with a pair of single quotation marks, for example, as **'Return 2006'**. (In this book, variable labels are generally used to refer to variables, a practice that can minimize errors.)

By default, Minitab names open worksheets serially in the form of Worksheet1, Worksheet2, and so on. Better names are ones that reflect the content of the worksheets, such as Mutual Funds for a worksheet that contains mutual funds data. To give a sheet a descriptive name, open the Project Manager window, right-click the icon for the worksheet, and select **Rename** from the shortcut menu and type in the new name.

## M1.3 OPENING AND SAVING WORKSHEETS AND OTHER COMPONENTS

You open worksheets to use data that have been created by you or others at an earlier time. To open a Minitab worksheet:

1. Select **File → Open Worksheet**.
2. In the Open Worksheet dialog box that appears (see Figure M1.1 on page 24), select the file to be opened and then click **Open**.

If you cannot find your file, you may need to do one or more of the following:

- Use the scroll bars or the slider, if present, to scroll through the entire list of files.
- Select the correct folder from the **Look in** drop-down list at the top of the dialog box.
- Change the **Files of type** value from the drop-down list at the bottom of the dialog box. You should select **Text (*.txt)** from the list to see text files, **Excel (*.xls, *.xlsx)** to see Microsoft Excel files, and so forth. To list every file in the folder, select **All Files(*.*)**.

To save a Minitab worksheet:

1. Select **File → Save Current Worksheet As**.
2. In the Save Worksheet As dialog box that appears (similar to the Open Worksheet dialog box), enter the name for your worksheet in the **File name** box and then click **Save**.

If applicable, you can also do the following:

- Change to another folder by selecting that folder from the **Save in** drop-down list.
- Change the **Save as type** value to something other than the default choice, **Minitab**. "Minitab Portable" or an earlier version of **Minitab**, such as "**Minitab 13**", are commonly chosen alternatives.

After saving your work, you should consider saving your file a second time, using a different name, in order to create a backup copy of your work. Files opened from non-writable disks, such as the Student CD-ROM, cannot be saved to their original files.

To open an entire Minitab Project, select **File → Open Project**. To save a Minitab Project, select **File → Save Project As**. When you use these commands, the dialog box

**FIGURE M1.1**

Open Worksheet dialog box

that appears will contain an **Options** button that you can click to selectively open (or save) parts of your project.

Individual graphs and the session window can also be saved separately by first selecting their windows and then selecting **File → Save Graph As** or **File → Save Session Window As**, as appropriate. Minitab graphs can be saved in either a Minitab graph format or any one of several common graphics formats, and session files can be saved as simple or formatted text files.

## M1.4 PRINTING WORKSHEETS, GRAPHS, AND SESSIONS

To print a specific worksheet, graph, or session:

1. Select the window that contains the worksheet, graph, or session to be printed.
2. Select **File → Print** *object*, where *object* is either **Worksheet**, **Graph**, or **Session Window**, depending on what you seek to print.

If you are printing a graph or a session window, you will then see the Print dialog box. If you are printing a worksheet, you will first see a Data Window Print Options dialog box (Figure M1.2) that allows you to select formatting options for your printout (the default selections should be fine for most of your printouts). Click **OK** in that dialog box to proceed to the Print dialog box.

The Print dialog box contains settings to select the printer to be used, what pages to print, and the number of copies to

produce (1 is the default). If you need to change these settings, change them before clicking **OK** to create your printout.

After printing, you should verify the contents of your printout. Most printing failures will trigger the display of onscreen information that you can use to determine the source of the failure. You can change the paper size or paper orientation of your printout by selecting **File → Print Setup** and then making the appropriate entries in the dialog box that appears. (Click **OK** when you are finished making entries.)

**FIGURE M1.2**

Data Window Print Options dialog box

# CHAPTER
# TWO

## PRESENTING DATA IN TABLES AND CHARTS

## LEARNING OBJECTIVES

### In this chapter, you learn:

- To develop tables and charts for categorical data
- To develop tables and charts for numerical data
- The principles of properly presenting graphs

# USING STATISTICS @ Choice Is Yours, Part I

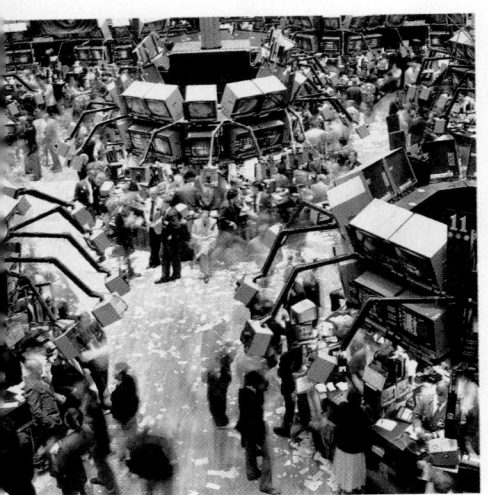

Choice Is Yours is a service that helps customers make wise investment choices. You've been hired to assist investors interested in mutual funds, a market basket of securities. According to **investopedia.com**, "A mutual fund is nothing more than a collection of stocks and/or bonds. You can think of a mutual fund as a company that brings together a group of people and invests their money in stocks, bonds, and other securities. Each investor owns shares, which represent a portion of the holdings of the fund." (You can learn more about mutual funds at **www.investopedia.com/university/mutualfunds/**.)

The Choice Is Yours company previously selected a sample of 868 mutual funds that it believes might be of interest to its customers. You have been asked to present data about these funds in a way that will help customers make good investment choices. What facts about each mutual fund would you collect to help customers compare and contrast the many funds?

A good starting point would be to collect data that would help customers classify mutual funds into various categories. You could research such things as the amount of risk involved in a fund's investment strategy and whether the fund focuses on growth securities, those companies that are expected to grow quickly in the next year, or on value securities, those companies whose stock prices are currently considered undervalued. You might also investigate whether a mutual fund specializes in a certain size company and whether the fund charges management fees that would reduce the percentage return earned by an investor.

Of course, you would want to know how well the fund performed in the past. You would also want to supply the customer with several measures of each fund's past performance. Even though past performance is no assurance of future performance, past data could give customers insight into how well each mutual fund has been managed.

As you further think about your task, you realize that all these data for all 868 mutual funds would be a lot for anyone to review. How could you "get your hands around" such data and explore it in a comprehensible manner?

To *get* your hands around the data described in this chapter's Using Statistics scenario, you need to use methods of descriptive statistics, defined in Chapter 1 as the branch of statistics that collects, summarizes, presents and analyzes data. In this scenario, you need to use descriptive techniques for both categorical variables (to help investors classify the mutual funds) and numerical variables (to help show the return each fund has achieved). Reading this chapter will help you prepare tables and charts that are appropriate for both types of variables. You'll also learn techniques to help answer questions that require two variables, such as "Do growth-oriented mutual funds have lower returns than value mutual funds?" and "Do growth funds tend to be riskier investments than value funds?"

*Many examples in this chapter use a sample of 868 mutual funds, the data for which you can find in the Data worksheet of the* `Mutual Funds.xls` *workbook or in the Minitab worksheet* `Mutual Funds.mtw` *on the Student CD-ROM.*

## 2.1  TABLES AND CHARTS FOR CATEGORICAL DATA

When you have categorical data, you tally responses into categories and then present the frequency or percentage in each category in tables and charts.

### The Summary Table

A **summary table** indicates the frequency, amount, or percentage of items in a set of categories so that you can see differences between categories. A summary table lists the categories in one column and the frequency, amount, or percentage in a different column or columns. Table 2.1 illustrates a summary table based on a recent survey (see the **Banking** file) that asked people where they prefer to do their banking (K. Chu, "Online Banks Launch Checking Accounts," *USA Today*, January 18, 2007, p. 1B). In Table 2.1, the most common choices are in person at branch and on the Internet, followed by drive-through service at branch and ATM. Very few respondents mentioned automated or live telephone.

**TABLE 2.1**

Banking Preference

| Banking Preference | Percentage (%) |
|---|---|
| ATM | 16 |
| Automated or live telephone | 2 |
| Drive-through service at branch | 17 |
| In person at branch | 41 |
| Internet | 24 |

**EXAMPLE 2.1**

SUMMARY TABLE OF LEVELS OF RISK OF MUTUAL FUNDS

The 868 mutual funds that are part of the Using Statistics scenario (see page 26) are classified according to their risk level, categorized as low, average, and high. Construct a summary table of the mutual funds, categorized by risk.

**SOLUTION** From Table 2.2, you can see that fewer than 25% of the funds are low-risk funds. There are more high-risk funds (355, or 40.90%) than low-risk (202, or 23.27%) or average-risk funds (311, or 35.83%). More than 75% of the funds are average risk or high risk.

**TABLE 2.2**

Frequency and Percentage Summary Table Pertaining to Risk Level for 868 Mutual Funds

| Fund Risk Level | Number of Funds | Percentage of Funds (%) |
|---|---|---|
| Low | 202 | 23.27 |
| Average | 311 | 35.83 |
| High | 355 | 40.90 |
| Total | 868 | 100.00 |

### The Bar Chart

In a **bar chart**, a bar shows each category. The length of the bar represents the amount, frequency, or percentage of values falling into a category. Figure 2.1 on page 28 displays the bar chart for where people prefer to do their banking presented in Table 2.1.

Bar charts allow you to compare percentages in different categories. In Figure 2.1, respondents are most likely to bank in person at a branch and on the Internet, followed by drive-through service at a branch and ATM. Very few respondents mentioned automated or live telephone.

**FIGURE 2.1**

Microsoft Excel bar chart for where people prefer to do their banking.

*See Sections E2.4 or P2.3 to create this. (Minitab users, see Section M2.2 to create an equivalent chart.)*

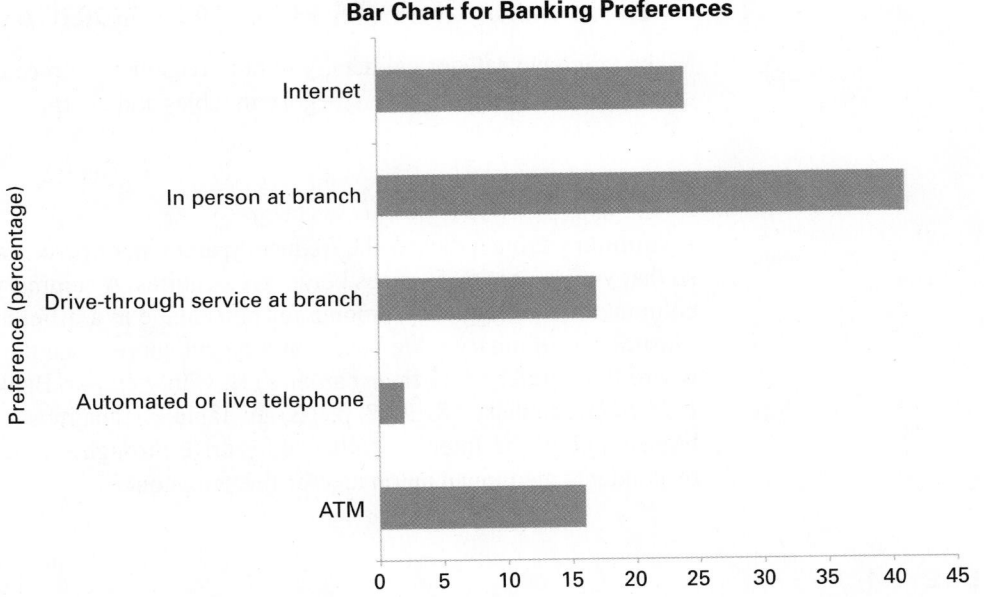

**EXAMPLE 2.2**

BAR CHART OF LEVELS OF RISK OF MUTUAL FUNDS

Construct a bar chart for the levels of risk of mutual funds (based on the information in Table 2.2 on page 27) and interpret the results.

**SOLUTION**  From Figure 2.2, you can see that approximately 200 of the funds are low risk, whereas more than 650 of the 868 funds are either average risk or high risk. There are more high-risk funds than average-risk or low-risk funds.

**FIGURE 2.2**

Microsoft Excel bar chart of the levels of risk of mutual funds

*See Sections E2.4 or P2.3 to create this. (Minitab users, see Section M2.2 to create an equivalent chart.)*

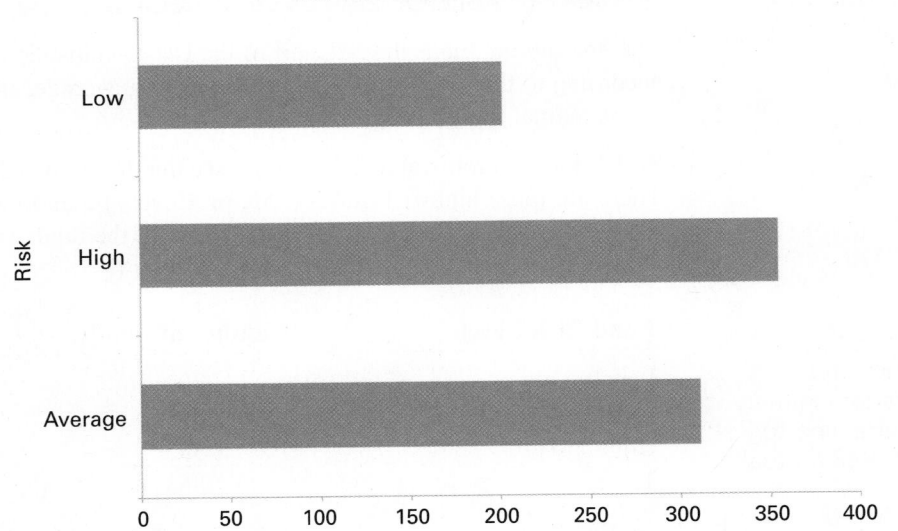

## The Pie Chart

The **pie chart** is a circle broken up into slices that represent categories. The size of each slice of the pie varies according to the percentage in each category. In Table 2.1 on page 27, for example, 41% of the respondents stated that they prefer to bank in person at the branch. Thus, in constructing the pie chart, the 360 degrees that makes up a circle is multiplied by 0.41, resulting in a slice of the pie that takes up 147.6 degrees of the 360 degrees of the circle. From Figure 2.3, you can see that the pie chart lets you visualize the portion of the entire pie that is in each category. In this figure, bank in person at the branch takes 41% of the pie and automated or live telephone takes only 2%.

**FIGURE 2.3**

Microsoft Excel pie chart for where people prefer to do their banking

*See Sections E2.4 or P2.3 to create this. (Minitab users, see Section M2.3 to create an equivalent chart.)*

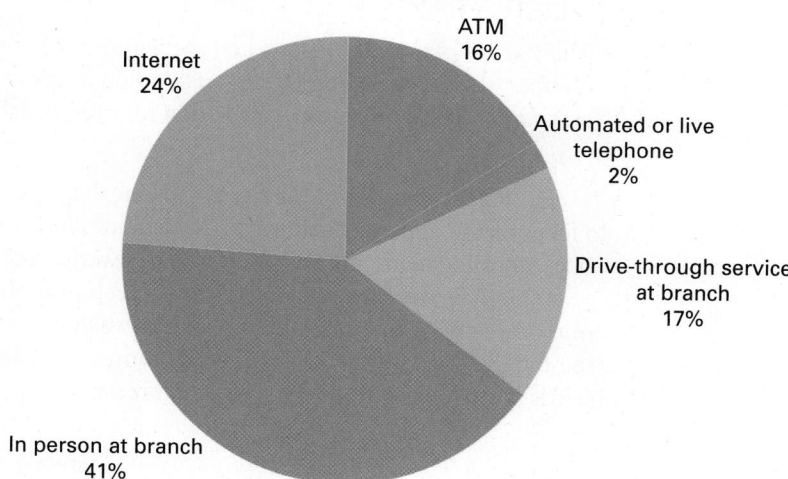

**Pie Chart for Banking Preferences**

ATM 16%

Automated or live telephone 2%

Drive-through service at branch 17%

In person at branch 41%

Internet 24%

Which chart should you use—a bar chart or a pie chart? The selection of a particular chart often depends on your intention. If a comparison of categories is most important, you should use a bar chart. If observing the portion of the whole that is in a particular category is most important, you should use a pie chart.

**EXAMPLE 2.3**

PIE CHART OF LEVELS OF RISK OF MUTUAL FUNDS

Construct a pie chart for the levels of risk of mutual funds (see Table 2.2 on page 27) and interpret the results.

**SOLUTION** From Figure 2.4, you can see that 41% of the funds are high risk, 36% are average risk, and only 23% are low risk.

**FIGURE 2.4**

Microsoft Excel pie chart of the levels of risk of mutual funds

*See Sections E2.4 or P2.3 to create this. (Minitab users, see Section M2.3 to create an equivalent chart.)*

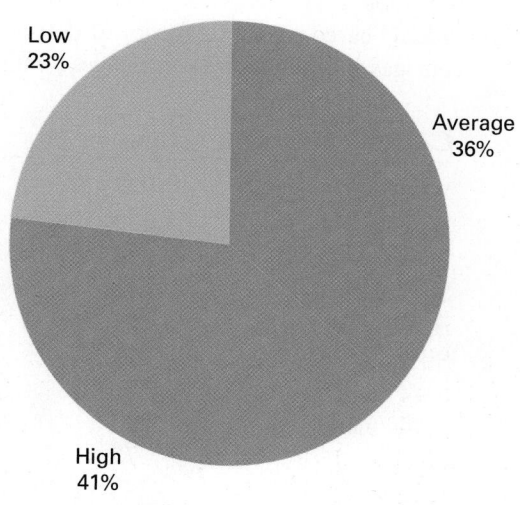

**Pie Chart for Levels of Risk**

Low 23%

Average 36%

High 41%

## The Pareto Chart

In a **Pareto chart**, the responses in the categories are plotted in descending order, according to their frequencies, and are combined with a cumulative percentage line on the same chart. The Pareto chart can identify situations in which the Pareto principle occurs.

PARETO PRINCIPLE

The **Pareto principle** exists when the majority of items in a set of data occur in a small number of categories and the few remaining items are spread out over a large number of categories. These two groups are often referred to as the "vital few" and the "trivial many."

The Pareto chart has the ability to separate the "vital few" from the "trivial many," enabling you to focus on the important categories. In situations in which the data involved consist of defective or nonconforming items, the Pareto chart is a powerful tool for prioritizing improvement efforts.

Table 2.3 presents data for a large injection-molding company that manufactures plastic components used in computer keyboards, washing machines, automobiles, and television sets (see the Keyboard defects file). The data presented in Table 2.3 consist of all computer keyboards with defects produced during a three-month period.

**TABLE 2.3**

Summary Table of Causes of Defects in Computer Keyboards in a Three-Month Period

| Cause | Frequency | Percentage |
|---|---|---|
| Black spot | 413 | 6.53 |
| Damage | 1,039 | 16.43 |
| Jetting | 258 | 4.08 |
| Pin mark | 834 | 13.19 |
| Scratches | 442 | 6.99 |
| Shot mold | 275 | 4.35 |
| Silver streak | 413 | 6.53 |
| Sink mark | 371 | 5.87 |
| Spray mark | 292 | 4.62 |
| Warpage | 1,987 | 31.42 |
| Total | 6,324 | 100.01* |

*Result differs slightly from 100.00 due to rounding.
Source: Extracted from U. H. Acharya and C. Mahesh, "Winning Back the Customer's Confidence: A Case Study on the Application of Design of Experiments to an Injection-Molding Process," Quality Engineering, 11, 1999, pp. 357–363.

Table 2.4 presents a summary table for the computer keyboard data in which the categories are ordered based on the frequency of defects present (rather than arranged alphabetically). The percentages and cumulative percentages for the ordered categories are also included as part of the table.

**TABLE 2.4**

Ordered Summary Table of Causes of Defects in Computer Keyboards in a Three-Month Period

| Cause | Frequency | Percentage | Cumulative Percentage |
|---|---|---|---|
| Warpage | 1,987 | 31.42 | 31.42 |
| Damage | 1,039 | 16.43 | 47.85 |
| Pin mark | 834 | 13.19 | 61.04 |
| Scratches | 442 | 6.99 | 68.03 |
| Black spot | 413 | 6.53 | 74.56 |
| Silver streak | 413 | 6.53 | 81.09 |
| Sink mark | 371 | 5.87 | 86.96 |
| Spray mark | 292 | 4.62 | 91.58 |
| Shot mold | 275 | 4.35 | 95.93 |
| Jetting | 258 | 4.08 | 100.01* |
| Total | 6,324 | 100.01* | |

*Result differs slightly from 100.00 due to rounding.

In Table 2.4, the first category listed is warpage (with 31.42% of the defects), followed by damage (with 16.43%), followed by pin mark (with 13.19%). The two most frequently occurring categories, warpage and damage, account for 47.85% of the defects; the three most frequently occurring categories—warpage, damage, and pin mark—account for 61.04% of the defects, and so on. Figure 2.5 is a Pareto chart based on the results displayed in Table 2.4.

## FIGURE 2.5

Microsoft Excel Pareto chart for the keyboard defects data

*See Sections E2.5 or P2.4 to create this. (Minitab users, see Section M2.4 to create an equivalent chart.)*

Figure 2.5 presents the bars vertically, along with a cumulative percentage line. The cumulative line is plotted at the midpoint of each category, at a height equal to the cumulative percentage. If you follow the line, you see that these first three categories account for about 60% of the defects. Because the categories in the Pareto chart are ordered by the frequency of occurrences, decision makers can see where to concentrate efforts to improve the process. Attempts to reduce defects due to warpage, damage, and pin marks should produce the greatest payoff. Then, efforts can be made to reduce scratches, black spots, and silver streaks.

In order for a Pareto chart to include all categories, even those with few defects, in some situations you need to include a category labeled *Other* or *Miscellaneous*. In these situations, the bar representing these categories should be placed to the right of the other bars.

---

## EXAMPLE 2.4

### PARETO CHART OF BANKING PREFERENCE

Construct a Pareto chart of banking preference (see Table 2.1 on page 27).

**SOLUTION** In Figure 2.6, in person at branch and on the Internet account for 65% of the banking preferences; 98% of the respondents would prefer in person at branch, on the Internet, drive-through at branch, and ATM.

## FIGURE 2.6

Microsoft Excel Pareto chart for banking preference

*See Sections E2.5 or P2.4 to create this. (Minitab users, see Section M2.4 to create an equivalent chart.)*

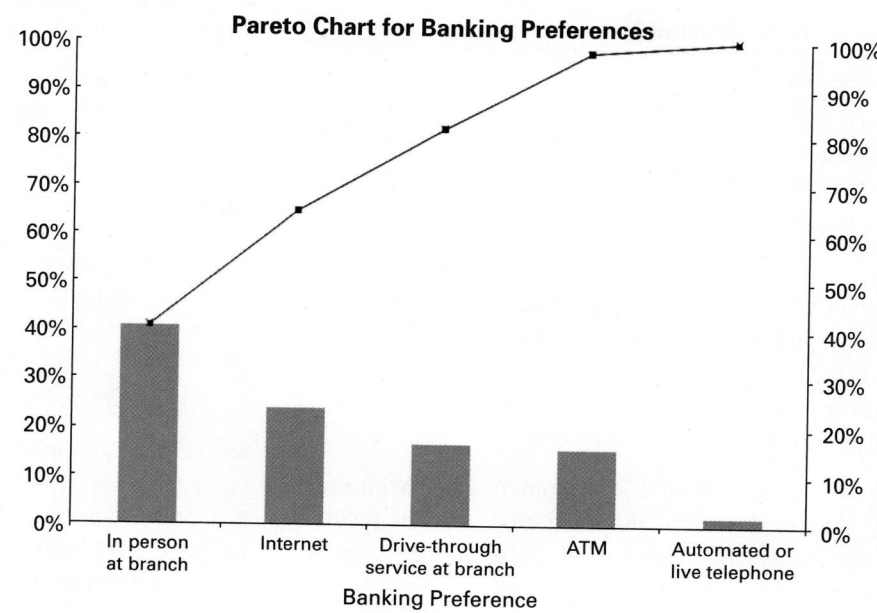

# PROBLEMS FOR SECTION 2.1

## Learning the Basics

**2.1** A categorical variable has three categories with the following frequencies of occurrence:

| Category | Frequency |
|----------|-----------|
| A | 13 |
| B | 28 |
| C | 9 |

a. Compute the percentage of values in each category.
b. Construct a bar chart.
c. Construct a pie chart.
d. Construct a Pareto chart.

**2.2** A categorical variable has four categories with the following percentages of occurrence:

| Category | Percentage | Category | Percentage |
|----------|-----------|----------|-----------|
| A | 12 | C | 35 |
| B | 29 | D | 24 |

a. Construct a bar chart.
b. Construct a pie chart.
c. Construct a Pareto chart.

## Applying the Concepts

**2.3** A survey of 705 workers asked how much they used the Internet at work. The results (*USA Today, Snapshots*, March 21, 2006, p. 1B) were as follows:

| Use of the Internet at Work | % |
|------------------------------|---|
| Too much | 5 |
| More than I should | 4 |
| Within limits | 60 |
| Very little | 5 |
| Do not use | 26 |

a. Construct a bar chart, a pie chart, and a Pareto chart.
b. Which graphical method do you think is best to portray these data?
c. Based on this survey, what conclusions can you reach about the use of the Internet at work?

**2.4** A survey of 1,264 women asked who was their most trusted shopping advisers. The results (*USA Today, Snapshots*, October 19, 2006, p. 1B) were as follows:

| Shopping Advisers | % |
|-------------------|---|
| Advertising | 7 |
| Friends/family | 45 |
| Manufacturer Web sites | 5 |
| News media | 11 |
| Online user reviews | 13 |
| Retail Web sites | 4 |
| Salespeople | 1 |
| Other | 14 |

a. Construct a bar chart, a pie chart, and a Pareto chart.
b. Which graphical method do you think is best to portray these data?
c. What conclusions can you reach concerning women's most trusted shopping advisers?

**2.5** What changes in their compensation package do workers in the United States want most? A survey by Hudson-Index.com indicated the following:

| Perks | % |
|-------|---|
| More money | 42 |
| Better health care | 20 |
| Better retirement | 12 |
| Work/family balance | 10 |
| Other | 16 |

Source: *Adapted from Anne R. Carey and Chad Palmer, "What Workers Want,"* **www.usatoday.com**, *April 9, 2007.*

a. Construct a bar chart, a pie chart, and a Pareto chart.
b. Which graphical method do you think is best to portray these data?
c. What conclusions can you reach concerning which perks workers want most?

**2.6** The following table represents the U.S. sources of electric energy in a recent year:

| Source | % |
|--------|---|
| Coal | 50 |
| Hydropower | 7 |
| Natural gas | 18 |
| Nuclear | 20 |
| Oil | 3 |
| Renewables | 2 |

Source: *International Energy Agency.*

a. Construct a Pareto chart.
b. What percentage of electricity is derived from coal, nuclear energy, or natural gas?

**c.** Construct a pie chart.

**d.** For these data, do you prefer the Pareto chart or the pie chart? Why?

**2.7** An article (K. Delaney, "How Search Engine Rules Cause Sites to Go Missing," *The Wall Street Journal*, March 13, 2007, pp. B1, B4) discussed the amount of Internet search results that Web surfers typically scan before selecting one. The following table represents the results for a sample of 2,369 people:

| Amount of Internet Search Results Scanned | Percentage (%) |
|---|---|
| A few search results | 23 |
| First page of search results | 39 |
| First two pages | 19 |
| First three pages | 9 |
| More than first three pages | 10 |

**a.** Construct a bar chart and a pie chart.

**b.** Which graphical method do you think is best to portray these data?

**c.** What conclusions can you reach concerning how people scan Internet search results?

**2.8** U.S. companies spent more than $250 billion in advertising in 2005 (K. Delaney, "In Latest Deal, Google Steps Further into World of Old Media," *The Wall Street Journal*, January 18, 2006, pp. A1, A6). The spending was as follows:

| Media | Amount ($billions) | Percentage (%) |
|---|---|---|
| Cinema | 0.4 | 0.16 |
| Direct mail | 44.5 | 17.35 |
| Internet | 10.0 | 3.90 |
| Magazines | 23.9 | 9.32 |
| Newspapers | 50.2 | 19.57 |
| Outdoor | 5.7 | 2.22 |
| Radio | 20.6 | 8.03 |
| TV | 55.4 | 21.60 |
| Other | 45.8 | 17.86 |

**a.** Construct a bar chart and a pie chart.

**b.** Which graphical method do you think is best to portray these data?

**c.** What conclusions can you reach concerning how U.S. companies spend their advertising dollars?

**2.9** Medication errors are a serious problem in hospitals. The following data represent the root causes of pharmacy errors at a hospital during a recent time period:

| Reason for Failure | Frequency |
|---|---|
| Additional instructions | 16 |
| Dose | 23 |
| Drug | 14 |
| Duplicate order entry | 22 |
| Frequency | 47 |
| Omission | 21 |
| Order not discontinued when received | 12 |
| Order not received | 52 |
| Patient | 5 |
| Route | 4 |
| Other | 8 |

**a.** Construct a Pareto chart.

**b.** Discuss the "vital few" and "trivial many" reasons for the root causes of pharmacy errors.

**2.10** The following data represent complaints about hotel rooms:

| Reason | Number |
|---|---|
| Room dirty | 32 |
| Room not stocked | 17 |
| Room not ready | 12 |
| Room too noisy | 10 |
| Room needs maintenance | 17 |
| Room has too few beds | 9 |
| Room doesn't have promised features | 7 |
| No special accommodations | 2 |

**a.** Construct a Pareto chart.

**b.** What reasons for complaints do you think the hotel should focus on if it wants to reduce the number of complaints? Explain.

## 2.2    ORGANIZING NUMERICAL DATA

When the number of data values is large, you can organize numerical data into an ordered array or a stem-and-leaf display to help understand the information you have. Suppose you decide to undertake a study that compares the cost of a restaurant meal in an urban area to the cost of a similar meal in the suburbs outside the city. The data file Restaurants contains the data for 50 urban restaurants and 50 suburban restaurants, as shown in Table 2.5. The data are not arranged in order from lowest to highest. This arrangement makes it difficult to arrive at conclusions concerning the price of meals in the two geographical areas.

**TABLE 2.5**

Price per Person at 50 Urban Restaurants and 50 Suburban Restaurants

**Urban**

| | | | | | | | | | |
|---|---|---|---|---|---|---|---|---|---|
| 65 | 48 | 32 | 27 | 47 | 45 | 36 | 55 | 48 | 33 |
| 45 | 46 | 39 | 44 | 45 | 63 | 54 | 20 | 55 | 73 |
| 51 | 34 | 28 | 65 | 44 | 43 | 50 | 29 | 33 | 41 |
| 41 | 52 | 48 | 48 | 38 | 52 | 33 | 40 | 36 | 51 |
| 39 | 38 | 22 | 35 | 35 | 16 | 74 | 57 | 52 | 68 |

**Suburban**

| | | | | | | | | | |
|---|---|---|---|---|---|---|---|---|---|
| 47 | 43 | 44 | 41 | 44 | 48 | 50 | 48 | 38 | 36 |
| 28 | 25 | 44 | 55 | 20 | 36 | 30 | 44 | 24 | 32 |
| 29 | 42 | 53 | 27 | 68 | 34 | 30 | 24 | 61 | 34 |
| 47 | 29 | 26 | 42 | 54 | 51 | 34 | 39 | 39 | 40 |
| 42 | 40 | 61 | 27 | 37 | 37 | 40 | 39 | 43 | 36 |

## The Ordered Array

An **ordered array** is a sequence of data, in rank order, from the smallest value to the largest value. Table 2.6 contains ordered arrays for the cost of meals at urban restaurants and suburban restaurants. From Table 2.6 you can see that the cost of a meal at the urban restaurants is between $16 and $74 and the cost of a meal at the suburban restaurants is between $20 and $68.

**TABLE 2.6**

Ordered Array of Cost per Person at 50 Urban Restaurants and 50 Suburban Restaurants

**Urban**

| | | | | | | | | | |
|---|---|---|---|---|---|---|---|---|---|
| 16 | 20 | 22 | 27 | 28 | 29 | 32 | 33 | 33 | 33 |
| 34 | 35 | 35 | 36 | 36 | 38 | 38 | 39 | 39 | 40 |
| 41 | 41 | 43 | 44 | 44 | 45 | 45 | 45 | 46 | 47 |
| 48 | 48 | 48 | 48 | 50 | 51 | 51 | 52 | 52 | 52 |
| 54 | 55 | 55 | 57 | 63 | 65 | 65 | 68 | 73 | 74 |

**Suburban**

| | | | | | | | | | |
|---|---|---|---|---|---|---|---|---|---|
| 20 | 24 | 24 | 25 | 26 | 27 | 27 | 28 | 29 | 29 |
| 30 | 30 | 32 | 34 | 34 | 34 | 36 | 36 | 36 | 37 |
| 37 | 38 | 39 | 39 | 39 | 40 | 40 | 40 | 41 | 42 |
| 42 | 42 | 43 | 43 | 44 | 44 | 44 | 44 | 47 | 47 |
| 48 | 48 | 50 | 51 | 53 | 54 | 55 | 61 | 61 | 68 |

## The Stem-and-Leaf Display

A **stem-and-leaf display** organizes data into groups (called stems) so that the values within each group (the leaves) branch out to the right on each row. The resulting display allows you to see how the data are distributed and where concentrations of data exist. To see how to construct a stem-and-leaf display, suppose that 15 students from your class eat lunch at a fast-food restaurant. The following data are the amounts ($) spent for lunch:

5.40  4.30  4.80  5.50  7.30  8.50  6.10  4.80  4.90  4.90  5.50  3.50  5.90  6.30  6.60

To form the stem-and-leaf display, you use the units as the stems and round the decimals (the leaves) to one decimal place. For example, the first value is 5.40. Its stem (row) is 5, and its leaf is 4. The second value is 4.30. Its stem (row) is 4, and its leaf is 3. You continue with the remainder of the 15 values and then reorder the leaves within each stem as follows:

```
3 | 5
4 | 38899
5 | 4559
6 | 136
7 | 3
8 | 5
```

**EXAMPLE 2.5**  STEM-AND-LEAF DISPLAY OF THE 2006 RETURN OF THE LOW-RISK MUTUAL FUNDS

In this chapter's Using Statistics scenario, you are interested in studying the past performance of low-risk mutual funds. One measure of past performance is the return in 2006. Construct a stem-and-leaf display of the return in 2006 for the low-risk funds.

**SOLUTION** From Figure 2.7, you can conclude that:

- The lowest return in 2006 was 1.
- The highest return in 2006 was 28.
- The returns in 2006 were concentrated between 14 and 23.
- Only one mutual fund had a 2006 return below 5, and only two low-risk mutual funds had a 2006 return above 25.

Notice that due to the large number of values, Minitab subdivides each stem into five sub-stems containing leaves with 0 and 1, 2 and 3, 4 and 5, 6 and 7, and 8 and 9.

**FIGURE 2.7**

Minitab Stem-and-Leaf Display of the Returns of Low-Risk Mutual Funds in 2006

*See Section M2.5 to create this. (PHStat2 users, see Section P2.5 to create an equivalent display.)*

```
Stem-and-leaf of Return 2006-Low Risk  N  = 202
Leaf Unit = 1.0

    1    0  1
    1    0
    2    0  5
    6    0  6667
   13    0  8888899
   26    1  0000001111111
   33    1  2223333
   66    1  444444444444444455555555555555555555
  (40)   1  6666666666666666666666666667777777777777
   96    1  888888888888888888888888888899999999999999999999999999999999
   38    2  0000000000000001111111111
   13    2  2222223333
    3    2  4
    2    2  6
    1    2  8
```

## PROBLEMS FOR SECTION 2.2

### Learning the Basics

**2.11** Form an ordered array, given the following data from a sample of $n = 7$ midterm exam scores in accounting:

68 94 63 75 71 88 64

**2.12** Form a stem-and-leaf display, given the following data from a sample of $n = 7$ midterm exam scores in finance:

80 54 69 98 93 53 74

**2.13** Form an ordered array, given the following data from a sample of $n = 7$ midterm exam scores in marketing:

88 78 78 73 91 78 85

**2.14** Form an ordered array, given the following stem-and-leaf display from a sample of $n = 7$ midterm exam scores in information systems:

```
5 | 0
6 |
7 | 446
8 | 19
9 | 2
```

### Applying the Concepts

**2.15** The following is a stem-and-leaf display representing the amount of gasoline purchased, in gallons (with leaves in tenths of gallons), for a sample of 25 cars that use a particular service station on the New Jersey Turnpike:

```
 9 | 147
10 | 02238
11 | 12556677
12 | 223489
13 | 02
```

a. Place the data into an ordered array.
b. Which of these two displays seems to provide more information? Discuss.
c. What amount of gasoline (in gallons) is most likely to be purchased?
d. Is there a concentration of the purchase amounts in the center of the distribution?

**2.16** As player salaries have increased, the cost of attending baseball games has increased dramatically. The following data in the file BB2006 (extracted from K. Belson, "Oh Yeah, There's a Ballgame Too," *The New York Times*, October 22, 2006, Business, pp. 1, 7–8) represent the cost of four tickets, two beers, four soft drinks, four hot dogs, two game programs, two baseball caps, and the parking fee for one car for each of the 30 major league baseball teams.

| Team | Cost($) | Team | Cost($) |
|------|---------|------|---------|
| Baltimore | 159 | Chicago Cubs | 219 |
| Boston | 288 | Cincinnati | 157 |
| Chicago White Sox | 191 | Colorado | 141 |
| Cleveland | 158 | Florida | 154 |
| Detroit | 163 | Houston | 192 |
| Kansas City | 120 | Los Angeles | 175 |
| Los Angeles Angels | 134 | Dodgers | |
| Minnesota | 149 | Milwaukee | 132 |
| New York Yankees | 209 | New York Mets | 207 |
| Oakland | 170 | Philadelphia | 194 |
| Seattle | 186 | Pittsburgh | 139 |
| Tampa Bay | 130 | St. Louis | 209 |
| Texas | 134 | San Diego | 180 |
| Toronto | 183 | San Francisco | 202 |
| Arizona | 148 | Washington | 170 |
| Atlanta | 146 | | |

a. Place the data into an ordered array.
b. Construct a stem-and-leaf display for these data.

c. Which of these two displays seems to provide more information? Discuss.
d. Around what value, if any, are the costs of attending a baseball game concentrated? Explain.

**2.17** The file MoviePrices contains data on the price for two tickets, with online service charges, large popcorn, and two medium soft drinks at a sample of six theater chains:

$36.15  $31.00  $35.05  $40.25  $33.75  $43.00

Source: *Extracted from K. Kelly, "The Multiplex Under Siege," The Wall Street Journal, December 24–25, 2005, pp. P1, P5.*

a. Place the data into an ordered array.
b. Construct a stem-and-leaf display for these data.
c. Which of these two displays seems to provide more information? Discuss.
d. Around what value, if any, are the movie prices concentrated? Explain.

**✓SELF Test 2.18** The file Chicken contains data on the total fat, in grams per serving, for a sample of 20 chicken sandwiches from fast-food chains. The data are as follows:

7 8 4 5 16 20 20 24 19 30 23 30 25 19 29 29 30 30 40 56

Source: *Extracted from "Fast Food: Adding Health to the Menu," Consumer Reports, September 2004, pp. 28–31.*

a. Place the data into an ordered array.
b. Construct a stem-and-leaf display.
c. Does the ordered array or the stem-and-leaf display provide more information? Discuss.
d. Around what value, if any, are the total fat amounts concentrated? Explain.

**2.19** The data in the file Batterylife represent the battery life, in shots, for a sample of 12 three pixel digital cameras:

300  180  85  170  380  460  260  35  380  120  110  240

Source: *Extracted from "Cameras: More Features in the Mix," Consumer Reports, July 2005, pp. 14–18.*

a. Place the data into an ordered array.
b. Construct a stem-and-leaf display.
c. Does the ordered array or the stem-and-leaf display provide more information? Discuss.
d. Around what value, if any, is the battery life concentrated? Explain.

## 2.3 TABLES AND CHARTS FOR NUMERICAL DATA

When you have a data set that contains a large number of values, reaching conclusions from an ordered array or a stem-and-leaf display can be difficult. In such circumstances, you need to present data in tables and charts such as the frequency and percentage distributions, histogram, polygon, and cumulative percentage polygon (ogive).

## The Frequency Distribution

The **frequency distribution** is a summary table in which the data are arranged into numerically ordered **classes**. In constructing a frequency distribution, you must give attention to selecting the appropriate *number* of classes for the table, determining a suitable *width* of a class, and establishing the *boundaries* of each **class grouping** to avoid overlapping.

The number of classes you use depends on the number of values in the data. Larger numbers of values allow for a larger number of classes. In general, the frequency distribution should have at least 5 classes but no more than 15. Having too few or too many classes provides little new information.

When developing a frequency distribution, you define each class by class intervals of equal width. To determine the **width of a class interval**, you divide the **range** (highest value − lowest value) of the data by the number of classes desired.

Determining the Width of a Class Interval

$$\text{Width of interval} = \frac{\text{Range}}{\text{number of classes}} \qquad (2.1)$$

Because the urban restaurant data consist of a sample of 50 restaurants, 10 classes are acceptable. From the ordered array in Table 2.6 on page 34, the range of the data is $74 − $16 = $58. Using Equation (2.1), you approximate the width of the class interval as follows:

$$\text{Width of interval} = \frac{58}{10} = 5.8$$

You should choose an interval width that simplifies reading and interpretation. Therefore, instead of using an interval width of $5.80, you should select an interval width of $5.00.

To construct the frequency distribution table, you should establish clearly defined **class boundaries** for each class so that the values can be properly tallied into the classes. You place each value in one and only one class. You must avoid overlapping of classes.

Because you have set the width of each class interval for the restaurant data at $5, you need to establish the boundaries of the various classes so as to include the entire range of values. Whenever possible, you should choose these boundaries to simplify reading and interpretation. Thus, for the urban restaurants, because the cost ranges from $16 to $74, the first class interval ranges from $15 to less than $20, the second from $20 to less than $25, and so on, until they have been tallied into 12 classes. Each class has an interval width of $5, without overlapping. The center of each class, the **class midpoint**, is halfway between the lower boundary of the class and the upper boundary of the class. Thus, the class midpoint for the class from $15 to under $20 is $17.50, the class midpoint for the class from $20 to under $25 is $22.50, and so on. Table 2.7 is a frequency distribution of the cost per meal for the 50 urban restaurants and the 50 suburban restaurants.

**TABLE 2.7**

Frequency Distribution of the Cost per Meal for 50 Urban Restaurants and 50 Suburban Restaurants

| Cost per Meal ($) | Urban Frequency | Suburban Frequency |
|---|---|---|
| 15 but less than 20 | 1 | 0 |
| 20 but less than 25 | 2 | 3 |
| 25 but less than 30 | 3 | 7 |
| 30 but less than 35 | 5 | 6 |
| 35 but less than 40 | 8 | 9 |
| 40 but less than 45 | 6 | 13 |
| 45 but less than 50 | 9 | 4 |
| 50 but less than 55 | 7 | 4 |
| 55 but less than 60 | 3 | 1 |
| 60 but less than 65 | 1 | 2 |
| 65 but less than 70 | 3 | 1 |
| 70 but less than 75 | 2 | 0 |
| Total | 50 | 50 |

The frequency distribution allows you to draw conclusions about the major characteristics of the data. For example, Table 2.7 shows that the cost of meals at urban restaurants is concentrated between $30 and $55, and the cost of meals at suburban restaurants is clustered between $25 and $45.

If the data set does not contain many values, one set of class boundaries may provide a different picture than another set. For example, for the restaurant data, using a class-interval width of 6.0 instead of 5.0 (as was used in Table 2.7) may cause shifts in the way the values distribute among the classes.

You can also get shifts in data concentration when you choose different lower and upper class boundaries. Fortunately, as the sample size increases, alterations in the selection of class boundaries affect the concentration of data less and less.

**EXAMPLE 2.6**

FREQUENCY DISTRIBUTION OF THE 2006 RETURN FOR GROWTH AND VALUE MUTUAL FUNDS

In the Using Statistics scenario, you are interested in comparing the 2006 return of growth and value mutual funds. Construct frequency distributions for the growth funds and the value funds.

**SOLUTION**  The 2006 returns of the growth funds are highly concentrated between 0 and 15, whereas the 2006 returns of the value funds are highly concentrated between 10 and 25 (see Table 2.8). You should not directly compare the frequencies of the growth funds and the value funds because there are 464 growth funds and 404 value funds in the sample. Proportions or relative frequencies and percentages are introduced below.

**TABLE 2.8**

Frequency Distribution of the 2006 Return for Growth and Value Mutual Funds

| 2006 Return | Growth Frequency | Value Frequency |
|---|---|---|
| −10 but less than −5 | 6 | 0 |
| −5 but less than 0 | 21 | 0 |
| 0 but less than 5 | 75 | 1 |
| 5 but less than 10 | 189 | 14 |
| 10 but less than 15 | 121 | 102 |
| 15 but less than 20 | 39 | 208 |
| 20 but less than 25 | 12 | 71 |
| 25 but less than 30 | 1 | 7 |
| 30 but less than 35 | 0 | 0 |
| 35 but less than 40 | 0 | 1 |
| Total | 464 | 404 |

## The Relative Frequency Distribution and the Percentage Distribution

Because you usually want to know the proportion or the percentage of the total that is in each group, the relative frequency distribution or the percentage distribution is preferred to the frequency distribution.

The **proportion** in each group is equal to the number of frequencies in each class divided by the total number of values. The **relative frequency** is another word for the proportion. You then compute the percentage in each group by multiplying the proportion by 100%.

Computing the Proportion or Relative Frequency

The proportion or relative frequency is the number of frequencies in each class divided by the total number of values.

$$\text{Proportion} = \text{Relative Frequency} = \frac{\text{frequency in each class}}{\text{total number of values}} \quad \textbf{(2.2)}$$

Thus, if there are 80 values and the frequency in a certain class is 20, the proportion of frequencies in that class is

$$\frac{20}{80} = 0.25$$

and the percentage is

$$0.25 \times 100\% = 25\%$$

When you are comparing two or more groups that have different sample sizes, you must use either a relative frequency distribution or a percentage distribution. You form the **relative frequency distribution** by first determining the frequency (the number of values) in each class and then dividing by the total number of values. See Equation (2.2). For example, in Table 2.7 on page 37, there are 50 urban restaurants and the cost per meal at 3 of these restaurants is between 25 and 30. Therefore, as shown in Table 2.9, the proportion (or relative frequency) of meals that cost between $25 and $30 at urban restaurants is

$$\frac{6}{50} = 0.12$$

You form the **percentage distribution** by multiplying each proportion (or relative frequency) by 100%. Thus, the proportion of meals at urban restaurants that cost between $50 and $55 is 7 divided by 50, or 0.14, and the percentage is 14%. Table 2.9 presents the relative frequency distribution and percentage distribution of the cost of meals at urban and suburban restaurants.

**TABLE 2.9**

Relative Frequency Distribution and Percentage Distribution of the Cost of Meals at Urban and Suburban Restaurants

| Cost per Meal ($) | Urban Relative Frequency | Urban Percentage | Suburban Relative Frequency | Suburban Percentage |
|---|---|---|---|---|
| 15 but less than 20 | 0.02 | 2.0 | 0.00 | 0.0 |
| 20 but less than 25 | 0.04 | 4.0 | 0.06 | 6.0 |
| 25 but less than 30 | 0.06 | 6.0 | 0.14 | 14.0 |
| 30 but less than 35 | 0.10 | 10.0 | 0.12 | 12.0 |
| 35 but less than 40 | 0.16 | 16.0 | 0.18 | 18.0 |
| 40 but less than 45 | 0.12 | 12.0 | 0.26 | 26.0 |
| 45 but less than 50 | 0.18 | 18.0 | 0.08 | 8.0 |
| 50 but less than 55 | 0.14 | 14.0 | 0.08 | 8.0 |
| 55 but less than 60 | 0.06 | 6.0 | 0.02 | 2.0 |
| 60 but less than 65 | 0.02 | 2.0 | 0.04 | 4.0 |
| 65 but less than 70 | 0.06 | 6.0 | 0.02 | 2.0 |
| 70 but less than 75 | 0.04 | 4.0 | 0.00 | 0.0 |
| Total | 1.00 | 100.0 | 1.00 | 100.0 |

From Table 2.9, you conclude that meals cost more at urban restaurants than at suburban restaurants. Also 18% of the meals cost between $45 and $50 at urban restaurants as compared to 8% of the meals at suburban restaurants; and only 6% of the meals cost between $25 and $30 at urban restaurants as compared to 14% of the meals at suburban restaurants.

**EXAMPLE 2.7**

RELATIVE FREQUENCY DISTRIBUTION AND PERCENTAGE DISTRIBUTION OF THE 2006 RETURN FOR GROWTH AND VALUE MUTUAL FUNDS

In the Using Statistics scenario, you are interested in comparing the 2006 return for growth and value mutual funds. Construct relative frequency distributions and percentage distributions for the growth funds and the value funds.

**SOLUTION**  You conclude (see Table 2.10) that the 2006 return for the growth funds is much lower than for the value funds. 5.82% of growth funds have negative returns, while none of the value funds have negative returns. Of the growth funds, 16.16% have returns between 0 and 5 as compared to only 0.25% of the value funds. Also, more of the value funds have higher returns. For example, 51.49% of the value funds have a return between 15 and 20, whereas only 8.41% of the growth funds have a return between 15 and 20.

**TABLE 2.10**

Relative Frequency Distribution and Percentage Distribution of the 2006 Return for Growth and Value Mutual Funds

| 2006 Return | Growth Proportion | Growth Percentage | Value Proportion | Value Percentage |
|---|---|---|---|---|
| −10 but less than −5 | 0.0129 | 1.29 | 0.0000 | 0.00 |
| −5 but less than 0 | 0.0453 | 4.53 | 0.0000 | 0.00 |
| 0 but less than 5 | 0.1616 | 16.16 | 0.0025 | 0.25 |
| 5 but less than 10 | 0.4073 | 40.73 | 0.0347 | 3.47 |
| 10 but less than 15 | 0.2608 | 26.08 | 0.2525 | 25.25 |
| 15 but less than 20 | 0.0841 | 8.41 | 0.5149 | 51.49 |
| 20 but less than 25 | 0.0259 | 2.59 | 0.1757 | 17.57 |
| 25 but less than 30 | 0.0022 | 0.22 | 0.0173 | 1.73 |
| 30 but less than 35 | 0.0000 | 0.00 | 0.0000 | 0.00 |
| 35 but less than 40 | 0.0000 | 0.00 | 0.0025 | 0.25 |
| Total* | 1.0001 | 100.01 | 1.0001 | 100.01 |

*Error due to rounding*

## The Cumulative Distribution

The **cumulative percentage distribution** provides a way of presenting information about the percentage of items that are less than a certain value. For example, you might want to know what percentage of the urban restaurant meals cost less than $20, less than $30, less than $50, and so on. The percentage distribution is used to form the cumulative percentage distribution. Table 2.11 illustrates how to develop the cumulative percentage distribution for the cost of meals at urban restaurants. This table shows that 0.00% of the meals cost less than $15, 2% cost

**TABLE 2.11**

Developing the Cumulative Percentage Distribution for the Cost of Meals at Urban Restaurants

| Cost per Meal ($) | Percentage | Percentage of Meals Less Than Lower Boundary of Class Interval |
|---|---|---|
| 15 but less than 20 | 2 | 0 |
| 20 but less than 25 | 4 | 2 |
| 25 but less than 30 | 6 | 6 = 2 + 4 |
| 30 but less than 35 | 10 | 12 = 2 + 4 + 6 |
| 35 but less than 40 | 16 | 22 = 2 + 4 + 6 + 10 |
| 40 but less than 45 | 12 | 38 = 2 + 4 + 6 + 10 + 16 |
| 45 but less than 50 | 18 | 50 = 2 + 4 + 6 + 10 + 16 + 12 |
| 50 but less than 55 | 14 | 68 = 2 + 4 + 6 + 10 + 16 + 12 + 18 |
| 55 but less than 60 | 6 | 82 = 2 + 4 + 6 + 10 + 16 + 12 + 18 + 14 |
| 60 but less than 65 | 2 | 88 = 2 + 4 + 6 + 10 + 16 + 12 + 18 + 14 + 6 |
| 65 but less than 70 | 6 | 90 = 2 + 4 + 6 + 10 + 16 + 12 + 18 + 14 + 6 + 2 |
| 70 but less than 75 | 4 | 96 = 2 + 4 + 6 + 10 + 16 + 12 + 18 + 14 + 6 + 2 + 6 |
| 75 but less than 80 | 0 | 100 = 2 + 4 + 6 + 10 + 16 + 12 + 18 + 14 + 6 + 2 + 6 + 4 |

less than $20, 6% cost less than $25 (because 4% of the meals cost between $20 and $25), and so on, until all 100% of the meals cost less than $75.

Table 2.12 summarizes the cumulative percentages of the cost of urban and suburban restaurant meals. The cumulative distribution clearly shows that the cost of meals is lower in suburban restaurants than in urban restaurants. Table 2.12 shows that 20% of the meals at suburban restaurants cost less than $30 as compared to only 12% of the meals at urban restaurants; 32% of the meals at suburban restaurants cost less than $35 as compared to only 22% of the meals at urban restaurants; and 76% of the meals at suburban restaurants cost less than $45 as compared to only 50% of the meals at urban restaurants.

**TABLE 2.12**

Cumulative Percentage Distributions of the Cost of Urban and Suburban Restaurant Meals

| Cost ($) | Urban Percentage of Restaurants with Meals Less Than Indicated Value | Suburban Percentage of Restaurants with Meals Less Than Indicated Value |
|---|---|---|
| 15 | 0 | 0 |
| 20 | 2 | 0 |
| 25 | 6 | 6 |
| 30 | 12 | 20 |
| 35 | 22 | 32 |
| 40 | 38 | 50 |
| 45 | 50 | 76 |
| 50 | 68 | 84 |
| 55 | 82 | 92 |
| 60 | 88 | 94 |
| 65 | 90 | 98 |
| 70 | 96 | 100 |
| 75 | 100 | 100 |

**EXAMPLE 2.8**

CUMULATIVE PERCENTAGE DISTRIBUTION OF THE 2006 RETURN FOR GROWTH AND VALUE MUTUAL FUNDS

In the Using Statistics scenario, you are interested in comparing the 2006 return of growth and value mutual funds. Construct cumulative percentage distributions for the growth funds and the value funds.

**SOLUTION** The cumulative distribution in Table 2.13 indicates that more of the growth funds have lower returns than the value funds. The table shows that 5.82% of the growth funds have negative returns as compared to none of the value funds; 21.98% of the growth funds have returns below 5 as compared to 0.25% of the value funds; and 62.71% of the growth funds have returns below 10 as compared to 3.72% of the value funds.

**TABLE 2.13**

Cumulative Percentage Distributions of the 2006 Return for Growth and Value Funds

| 2006 Return | Growth Fund Percentage Less Than Indicated Value | Value Fund Percentage Less Than Indicated Value |
|---|---|---|
| −10 | 0.00 | 0.00 |
| −5 | 1.29 | 0.00 |
| 0 | 5.82 | 0.00 |
| 5 | 21.98 | 0.25 |
| 10 | 62.71 | 3.72 |
| 15 | 88.79 | 28.97 |
| 20 | 97.20 | 80.46 |
| 25 | 99.79 | 98.03 |
| 30 | 100.00 | 99.76 |
| 35 | 100.00 | 99.76 |
| 40 | 100.01* | 100.01* |

*Error due to rounding.

## The Histogram

A **histogram** is a bar chart for grouped numerical data in which the frequencies or percentages of each group of numerical data are represented as individual vertical bars. In a histogram, there are no gaps between adjacent bars as there is in a bar chart of categorical data. You display the variable of interest along the horizontal ($X$) axis. The vertical ($Y$) axis represents either the frequency or the percentage of values per class interval.

Figure 2.8 displays a Microsoft Excel frequency histogram for the cost of meals at urban restaurants and suburban restaurants. The histogram for urban restaurants indicates that the cost of meals is concentrated between approximately $30 and $55. Very few meals at urban restaurants cost less than $20 or more than $60. The histogram for suburban restaurants shows that the cost of meals is concentrated between $25 and $45. Very few meals at suburban restaurants cost less than $20 or more than $55.

**FIGURE 2.8**

Microsoft Excel histograms for the cost of restaurant meals— Panel A Urban Restaurants and Panel B Suburban Restaurants

*See Sections E2.9 or P2.6 to create this. (Minitab users, see Section M2.6 to create an equivalent chart.)*

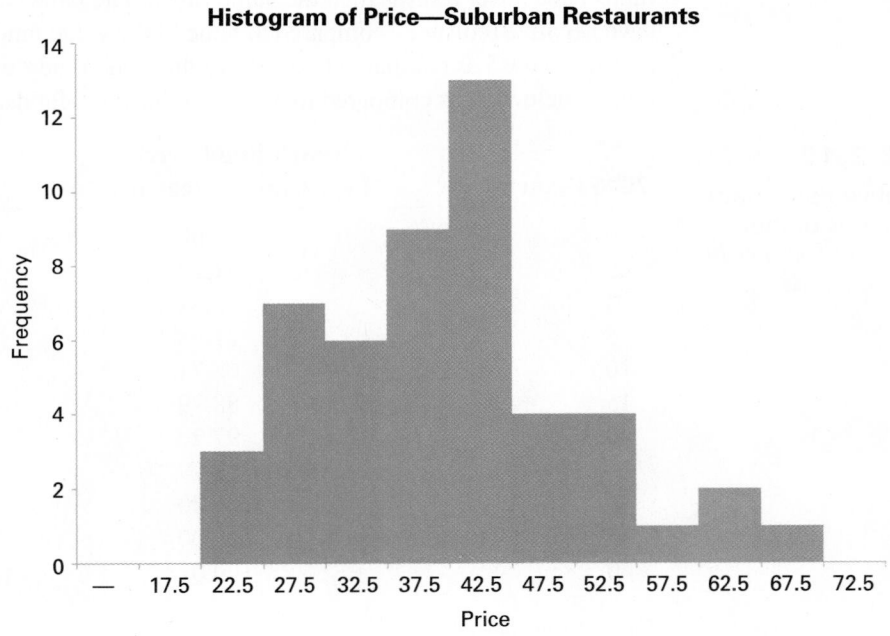

**EXAMPLE 2.9**

## HISTOGRAM OF THE 2006 RETURN FOR GROWTH AND VALUE MUTUAL FUNDS

In the Using Statistics scenario, you are interested in comparing the 2006 return of growth and value mutual funds. Construct histograms for the growth funds and the value funds.

**SOLUTION** Figure 2.9 shows that the distribution of the growth funds has more low returns as compared to the value funds, which have more high returns. The return for growth funds is concentrated between 0 and 15, whereas the return for value funds is concentrated between 10 and 25.

**FIGURE 2.9**

Microsoft Excel Histograms of the 2006 return for growth and value funds

*See Sections E2.9 or P2.6 to create this. (Minitab users, see Section M2.6 to create an equivalent chart.)*

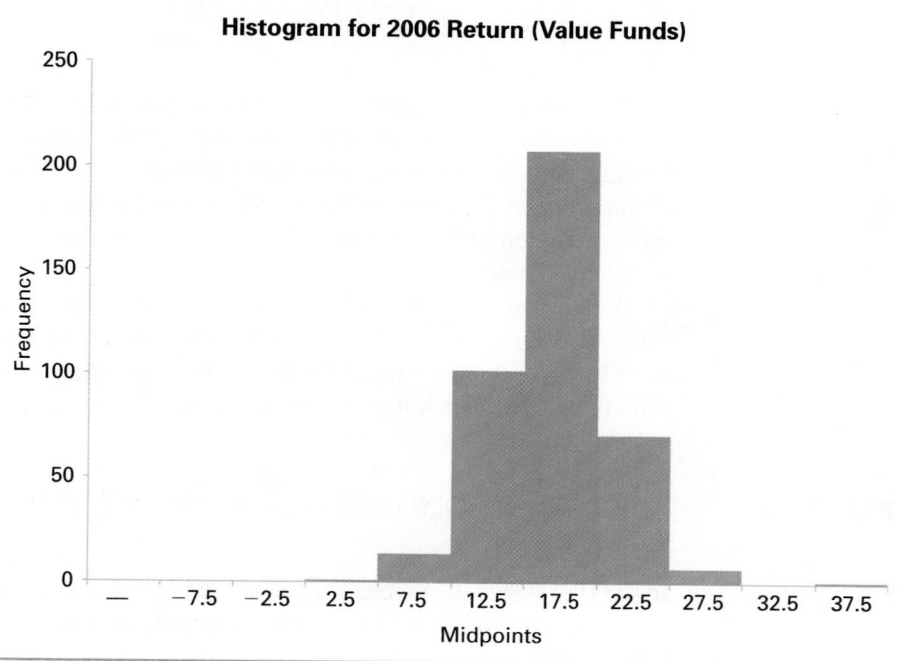

## The Polygon

Constructing multiple histograms on the same graph when comparing two or more sets of data is confusing. Superimposing the vertical bars of one histogram on another histogram makes interpretation difficult. When there are two or more groups, you should use a percentage polygon.

> **PERCENTAGE POLYGON**
>
> A **percentage polygon** is formed by having the midpoint of each class represent the data in that class and then connecting the sequence of midpoints at their respective class percentages.

Figure 2.10 displays percentage polygons for the cost of meals at urban and suburban restaurants. The polygon for the cost of meals at suburban restaurants is concentrated to the left of (corresponding to lower cost) the polygon for the cost of meals at urban restaurants. The highest percentage of meals at the suburban restaurants are for a class midpoint of $42.50, whereas the highest percentage of meals at the urban restaurants are for a class midpoint of $47.50.

**FIGURE 2.10**

Microsoft Excel percentage polygons of the cost of restaurant meals for urban and suburban restaurants

*See Section P2.7 to create this.*

The polygons in Figure 2.10 have points whose values on the $X$ axis represent the midpoint of the class interval. For example, look at the points plotted on the $Y$ axis at 42.5 ($42.50). The point for the cost of meals at suburban restaurants (the higher one) represents the fact that 26% of the meals at these restaurants cost between $40 and $45. The point for the cost of meals at urban restaurants (the lower one) represents the fact that 12% of meals at these restaurants cost between $40 and $45.

When you construct polygons or histograms, the vertical ($Y$) axis should show the true zero, or "origin," so as not to distort the character of the data. The horizontal ($X$) axis does not need to show the zero point for the variable of interest, although the range of the variable should include the major portion of the axis.

---

**EXAMPLE 2.10**    PERCENTAGE POLYGONS OF THE 2006 RETURN FOR GROWTH AND VALUE MUTUAL FUNDS

In the Using Statistics scenario, you are interested in comparing the 2006 return of growth and value mutual funds. Construct percentage polygons for the 2006 return for growth funds and value funds.

**SOLUTION** Figure 2.11 shows that the distribution of the 2006 return of growth funds is lower than the value funds, which has more high returns. The highest percentage of 2006 returns for the growth funds is at 7.5, whereas the highest percentage of 2006 returns for the value funds is at 17.5.

**FIGURE 2.11**

Microsoft Excel percentage polygons of the 2006 return

*See Section P2.7 to create this.*

## The Cumulative Percentage Polygon (Ogive)

The **cumulative percentage polygon**, or **ogive**, displays the variable of interest along the $X$ axis and the cumulative percentages along the $Y$ axis.

Figure 2.12 illustrates the Microsoft Excel cumulative percentage polygons of the cost of meals at urban and suburban restaurants. Most of the curve of the cost of meals at the urban restaurants is located to the right of the curve for the suburban restaurants. This indicates that the urban restaurants have fewer meals that cost below a particular value. For example, 38% of the meals at urban restaurants cost less than $40 as compared to 50% of the meals at suburban restaurants.

**FIGURE 2.12**

Microsoft Excel cumulative percentage polygons of the cost of restaurant meals at urban and suburban restaurants

*See Section P2.7 to create this.*

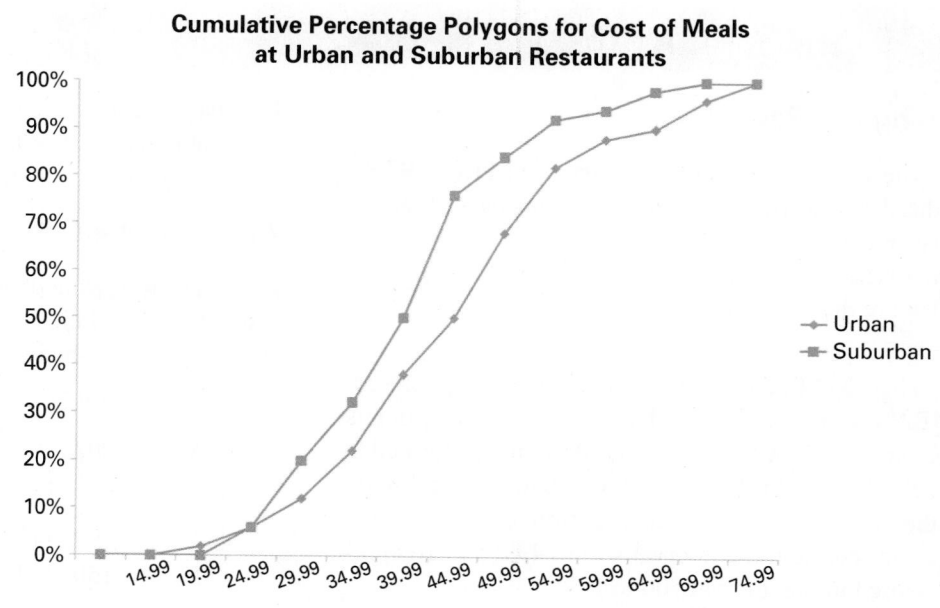

**EXAMPLE 2.11**    CUMULATIVE PERCENTAGE POLYGONS OF THE 2006 RETURN FOR GROWTH AND VALUE MUTUAL FUNDS

In the Using Statistics scenario, you are interested in comparing the 2006 return of growth and value mutual funds. Construct cumulative percentage polygons of the 2006 return for the growth funds and the value funds.

**SOLUTION** Figure 2.13 illustrates the Microsoft Excel cumulative percentage polygons of the 2006 return for growth and value funds. The curve for the 2006 return of value funds is located to the right of the curve for the growth funds. This indicates that the value funds have fewer 2006 returns below a particular value. For example, 88.79% of the growth funds have 2006 returns less than 15 as compared to 28.97% of the value funds. You can conclude that, in general, the value funds outperformed the growth funds in 2006.

**FIGURE 2.13**

Microsoft Excel cumulative percentage polygons of the 2006 return of growth funds and value funds

*See Section P2.7 to create this.*

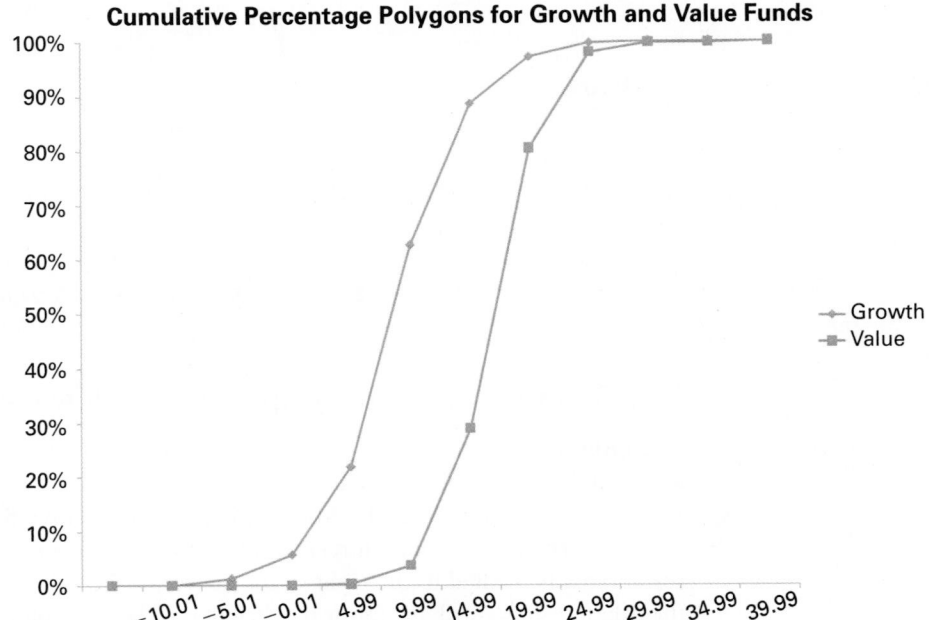

**Cumulative Percentage Polygons for Growth and Value Funds**

---

# PROBLEMS FOR SECTION 2.3

## Learning the Basics

**2.20** The values for a set of data vary from 11.6 to 97.8.
**a.** If these values are grouped into nine classes, indicate the class boundaries.
**b.** What class-interval width did you choose?
**c.** What are the nine class midpoints?

**2.21** The GMAT scores from a sample of 50 applicants to an MBA program indicate that none of the applicants scored below 450. A frequency distribution was formed by choosing class intervals 450 to 499, 500 to 549, and so on, with the last class having an interval from 700 to 749. Two applicants scored in the interval 450 to 499, and 16 applicants scored in the interval 500 to 549.
**a.** What percentage of applicants scored below 500?

**b.** What percentage of applicants scored between 500 and 549?
**c.** What percentage of applicants scored below 550?
**d.** What percentage of applicants scored below 750?

## Applying the Concepts

**2.22** The following data (contained in the file Utility) represent the cost of electricity during July 2007 for a random sample of 50 one-bedroom apartments in a large city:

**Raw Data on Utility Charges ($)**

|    |     |     |     |     |     |     |     |     |     |
|----|-----|-----|-----|-----|-----|-----|-----|-----|-----|
| 96 | 171 | 202 | 178 | 147 | 102 | 153 | 197 | 127 | 82  |
| 157| 185 | 90  | 116 | 172 | 111 | 148 | 213 | 130 | 165 |
| 141| 149 | 206 | 175 | 123 | 128 | 144 | 168 | 109 | 167 |
| 95 | 163 | 150 | 154 | 130 | 143 | 187 | 166 | 139 | 149 |
| 108| 119 | 183 | 151 | 114 | 135 | 191 | 137 | 129 | 158 |

**a.** Form a frequency distribution and a percentage distribution that have class intervals with the upper class boundaries $99, $119, and so on.

**b.** Construct a histogram and a percentage polygon.

**c.** Form a cumulative percentage distribution and plot a cumulative percentage polygon.

**d.** Around what amount does the monthly electricity cost seem to be concentrated?

**2.23** As player salaries have increased, the cost of attending baseball games has increased dramatically. The data in the file BB2006 (extracted from K. Belson, "Oh Yeah, There's a Ballgame Too," *The New York Times*, October 22, 2006, pp. B1, B7–8) represent the cost of four tickets, two beers, four soft drinks, four hot dogs, two game programs, two baseball caps, and the parking fee for one car for each of the 30 major league teams. The following is a histogram created for these data.

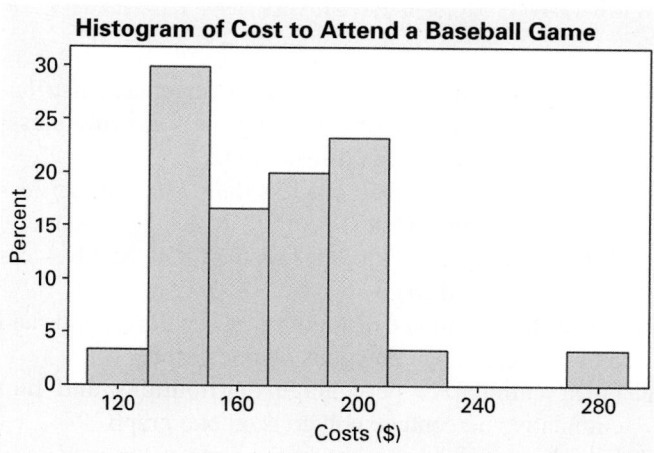

What conclusions can you reach concerning the cost of attending a baseball game at different ballparks?

**2.24** The data in the file PropertyTaxes contains the property taxes per capita for the fifty states and the District of Columbia. The following is a histogram and cumulative percentage polygon created for these data.

What conclusions can you reach concerning the property taxes per capita?

**2.25** One operation of a mill is to cut pieces of steel into parts that will later be used as the frame for front seats in an automobile. The steel is cut with a diamond saw and requires the resulting parts to be within ±0.005 inch of the length specified by the automobile company. The following data (contained in the file Steel) comes from a sample of 100 steel parts. The measurement reported is the difference in inches between the actual length of the steel part, as measured by a laser measurement device, and the specified length of the steel part. For example, the first value, −0.002, represents a steel part that is 0.002 inch shorter than the specified length.

| | | | | |
|---|---|---|---|---|
| −0.002 | 0.002 | 0.0005 | −0.0015 | −0.001 |
| 0.0005 | 0.001 | 0.001 | −0.0005 | −0.001 |
| 0.0025 | 0.001 | 0.0005 | −0.0015 | 0.0005 |
| 0.001 | 0.001 | 0.001 | −0.0005 | −0.0025 |
| 0.002 | −0.002 | 0.0025 | −0.0005 | 0.0025 |
| 0.001 | −0.003 | 0.001 | −0.001 | 0.002 |
| 0.005 | −0.0015 | 0.000 | −0.0015 | 0.0025 |
| −0.002 | −0.0005 | −0.0025 | 0.0025 | −0.002 |
| 0.000 | 0.000 | −0.001 | 0.001 | 0.000 |
| 0.001 | −0.0025 | 0.0035 | 0.0005 | −0.0005 |
| −0.0025 | −0.003 | 0.000 | 0.000 | −0.001 |
| −0.003 | −0.001 | −0.003 | 0.002 | 0.000 |
| 0.001 | 0.002 | −0.002 | −0.0005 | −0.002 |
| −0.0005 | −0.001 | −0.001 | 0.0005 | 0.000 |
| 0.000 | 0.000 | −0.0015 | 0.0005 | 0.000 |
| −0.003 | 0.003 | −0.0015 | 0.000 | 0.0020 |
| −0.001 | 0.0015 | −0.002 | −0.0005 | −0.003 |
| 0.0005 | 0.000 | 0.001 | 0.002 | −0.0005 |
| 0.0025 | 0.000 | −0.0025 | 0.001 | −0.002 |
| −0.0025 | −0.0025 | −0.0005 | −0.0015 | −0.002 |

a. Construct a percentage histogram.
b. Is the steel mill doing a good job in meeting the requirements set by the automobile company? Explain.

**✓SELF Test** **2.26** A manufacturing company produces steel housings for electrical equipment. The main component part of the housing is a steel trough that is made out of a 14-gauge steel coil. It is produced using a 250-ton progressive punch press with a wipe-down operation that puts two 90-degree forms in the flat steel to make the trough. The distance from one side of the form to the other is critical because of weatherproofing in outdoor applications. The company requires that the width of the trough be between 8.31 inches and 8.61 inches. The following (contained in the file **Trough**) are the widths of the troughs, in inches, for a sample of 49 troughs.

8.312 8.343 8.317 8.383 8.348 8.410 8.351 8.373
8.481 8.422 8.476 8.382 8.484 8.403 8.414 8.419
8.385 8.465 8.498 8.447 8.436 8.413 8.489 8.414
8.481 8.415 8.479 8.429 8.458 8.462 8.460 8.444
8.429 8.460 8.412 8.420 8.410 8.405 8.323 8.420
8.396 8.447 8.405 8.439 8.411 8.427 8.420 8.498
8.409

a. Construct a frequency distribution and a percentage distribution.
b. Construct a percentage histogram and a percentage polygon.
c. Plot a cumulative percentage polygon.
d. What can you conclude about the number of troughs that will meet the company's requirements of troughs being between 8.31 and 8.61 inches wide?

**2.27** The manufacturing company in Problem 2.26 also produces electric insulators. If the insulators break when in use, a short circuit is likely to occur. To test the strength of the insulators, destructive testing in high-powered labs is carried out to determine how much *force* is required to break the insulators. Force is measured by observing how many pounds must be applied to the insulator before it breaks. The strengths of 30 insulators (contained in the file **Force**) are as follows:

1,870 1,728 1,656 1,610 1,634 1,784 1,522 1,696
1,592 1,662 1,866 1,764 1,734 1,662 1,734 1,774
1,550 1,756 1,762 1,866 1,820 1,744 1,788 1,688
1,810 1,752 1,680 1,810 1,652 1,736

a. Construct a frequency distribution and a percentage distribution.
b. Construct a percentage histogram and a percentage polygon.
c. Plot a cumulative percentage polygon.

d. What can you conclude about the strength of the insulators if the company requires a force measurement of at least 1,500 pounds before breaking?

**2.28** The ordered arrays in the accompanying table (and contained in the file **Bulbs**) deal with the life (in hours) of a sample of forty 100-watt lightbulbs produced by Manufacturer A and a sample of forty 100-watt lightbulbs produced by Manufacturer B.

| Manufacturer A | | | | | Manufacturer B | | | | |
|---|---|---|---|---|---|---|---|---|---|
| 684 | 697 | 720 | 773 | 821 | 819 | 836 | 888 | 897 | 903 |
| 831 | 835 | 848 | 852 | 852 | 907 | 912 | 918 | 942 | 943 |
| 859 | 860 | 868 | 870 | 876 | 952 | 959 | 962 | 986 | 992 |
| 893 | 899 | 905 | 909 | 911 | 994 | 1,004 | 1,005 | 1,007 | 1,015 |
| 922 | 924 | 926 | 926 | 938 | 1,016 | 1,018 | 1,020 | 1,022 | 1,034 |
| 939 | 943 | 946 | 954 | 971 | 1,038 | 1,072 | 1,077 | 1,077 | 1,082 |
| 972 | 977 | 984 | 1,005 | 1,014 | 1,096 | 1,100 | 1,113 | 1,113 | 1,116 |
| 1,016 | 1,041 | 1,052 | 1,080 | 1,093 | 1,153 | 1,154 | 1,174 | 1,188 | 1,230 |

a. Form a frequency distribution and a percentage distribution for each manufacturer, using the following class-interval widths for each distribution:
   1. Manufacturer A: 650 but less than 750, 750 but less than 850, and so on.
   2. Manufacturer B: 750 but less than 850, 850 but less than 950, and so on.
b. Construct percentage histograms on separate graphs and plot the percentage polygons on one graph.
c. Form cumulative percentage distributions and plot cumulative percentage polygons on one graph.
d. Which manufacturer has bulbs with a longer life—Manufacturer A or Manufacturer B? Explain.

**2.29** The following data (contained in the file **Drink**) represent the amount of soft drink in a sample of fifty 2-liter bottles:

2.109 2.086 2.066 2.075 2.065 2.057 2.052 2.044 2.036 2.038
2.031 2.029 2.025 2.029 2.023 2.020 2.015 2.014 2.013 2.014
2.012 2.012 2.012 2.010 2.005 2.003 1.999 1.996 1.997 1.992
1.994 1.986 1.984 1.981 1.973 1.975 1.971 1.969 1.966 1.967
1.963 1.957 1.951 1.951 1.947 1.941 1.941 1.938 1.908 1.894

a. Construct a frequency distribution and a percentage distribution.
b. Construct a histogram and a percentage polygon.
c. Form a cumulative percentage distribution and plot a cumulative percentage polygon.
d. On the basis of the results of (a) through (c), does the amount of soft drink filled in the bottles concentrate around specific values?

## 2.4  CROSS TABULATIONS

The study of patterns that may exist between two or more categorical variables is common in business. Often, by cross-tabulating the data, these patterns can be explained. You can present **cross tabulations** in tabular form (contingency tables) or graphical form (side-by-side charts).

### The Contingency Table

A **contingency table** presents the results of two categorical variables. The joint responses are classified so that the categories of one variable are located in the rows and the categories of the other variable are located in the columns. The values located at the intersections of the rows and columns are called **cells**. Depending on the type of contingency table constructed, the cells for each row-column combination contain the frequency, the percentage of the overall total, the percentage of the row total, or the percentage of the column total.

Suppose that in the Using Statistics scenario, you want to examine whether there is any pattern or relationship between the level of risk and the objective of the mutual fund (growth versus value). Table 2.14 summarizes this information for all 868 mutual funds.

**TABLE 2.14**

Contingency Table Displaying Fund Objective and Fund Risk

*See Sections E2.11, P2.8, or M2.7 to create this.*

| | RISK LEVEL | | | |
|---|---|---|---|---|
| **OBJECTIVE** | **High** | **Average** | **Low** | **Total** |
| **Growth** | 302 | 140 | 22 | 464 |
| **Value** | 53 | 171 | 180 | 404 |
| **Total** | 355 | 311 | 202 | 868 |

You construct this contingency table by tallying the joint responses for each of the 868 mutual funds with respect to objective and risk into one of the six possible cells in the table. The first fund listed in the Mutual Funds file is classified as a growth fund with a low risk. Thus, you tally this joint response into the cell that is the intersection of the first row and third column. The remaining 867 joint responses are recorded in a similar manner. Each cell contains the frequency for the row-column combination.

In order to further explore any possible pattern or relationship between objective and fund risk, you can construct contingency tables based on percentages. You first convert these results into percentages based on the following three totals:

1. The overall total (i.e., the 868 mutual funds)
2. The row totals (i.e., 464 growth funds and 404 value funds)
3. The column totals (i.e., 355 high, 311 average, and 202 low)

Tables 2.15, 2.16, and 2.17 summarize these percentages.

**TABLE 2.15**

Contingency Table Displaying Fund Objective and Fund Risk, Based on Percentage of Overall Total

| | RISK LEVEL | | | |
|---|---|---|---|---|
| **OBJECTIVE** | **High** | **Average** | **Low** | **Total** |
| **Growth** | 34.79 | 16.13 | 2.53 | 53.46 |
| **Value** | 6.11 | 19.70 | 20.74 | 46.54 |
| **Total** | 40.90 | 35.83 | 23.27 | 100.00 |

**TABLE 2.16**

Contingency Table Displaying Fund Objective and Fund Risk, Based on Percentage of Row Total

| | RISK LEVEL | | | |
|---|---|---|---|---|
| **OBJECTIVE** | **High** | **Average** | **Low** | **Total** |
| **Growth** | 65.09 | 30.17 | 4.74 | 100.00 |
| **Value** | 13.12 | 42.33 | 44.55 | 100.00 |
| **Total** | 40.90 | 35.83 | 23.27 | 100.00 |

**TABLE 2.17**

Contingency Table Displaying Fund Objective and Fund Risk, Based on Percentage of Column Total

| | RISK LEVEL | | | |
| OBJECTIVE | High | Average | Low | Total |
|---|---|---|---|---|
| **Growth** | 85.07 | 45.02 | 10.89 | 53.46 |
| **Value** | 14.93 | 54.98 | 89.11 | 46.54 |
| **Total** | 100.00 | 100.00 | 100.00 | 100.00 |

Table 2.15 shows that 40.9% of the mutual funds sampled are high risk, 53.46% are growth funds, and 34.79% are high-risk funds that are growth funds. Table 2.16 shows that 65.09% of the growth funds are high risk and 4.74% are low risk. Table 2.17 shows that 85.07% of the high-risk funds and only 10.89% of the low-risk funds are growth funds. The tables reveal that growth funds are more likely to be high risk, whereas value funds are more likely to be low risk.

## The Side-by-Side Bar Chart

A useful way to visually display the results of cross-classification data is by constructing a **side-by-side bar chart**. Figure 2.14, which uses the data from Table 2.14 on page 49, is a Microsoft Excel side-by-side bar chart that compares the three fund risk levels, based on their objectives. An examination of Figure 2.14 reveals results consistent with those of Tables 2.15, 2.16, and 2.17: Growth funds are more likely to be high risk, whereas value funds are more likely to be low risk.

**FIGURE 2.14**

Microsoft Excel side-by-side bar chart for fund objective and risk

*See Sections E2.12 or P2.8 to create this. (Minitab users, see Section M2.8 to create an equivalent chart.)*

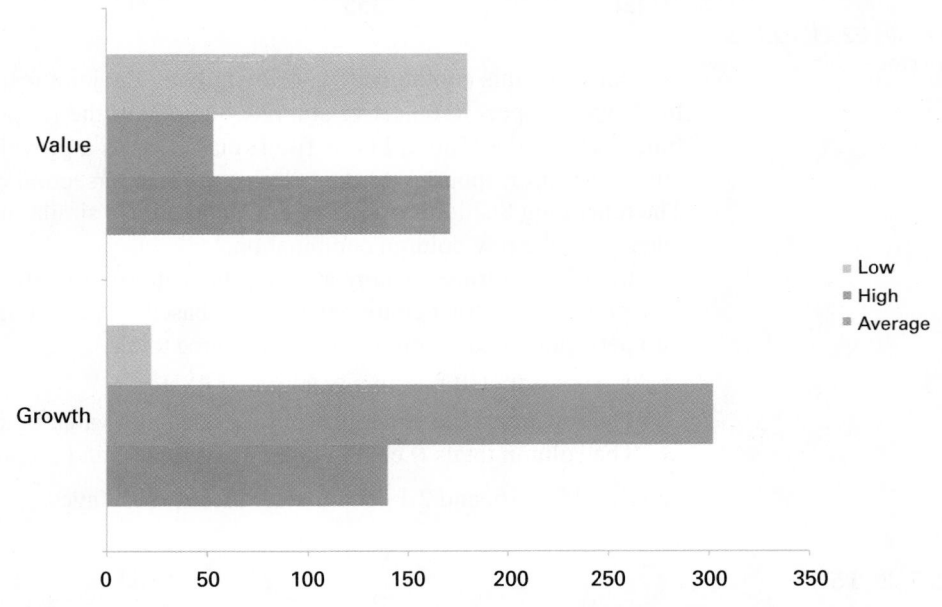

Side-by-Side Chart for Fund Objective and Risk

# PROBLEMS FOR SECTION 2.4

## Learning the Basics

**2.30** The following data represent the responses to two questions asked in a survey of 40 college students majoring in business—What is your gender? (male = M; female = F) and What is your major? (accounting = A; computer information systems = C; marketing = M):

| Gender: | M | M | M | F | M | F | F | M | F | M | F | M | M | M | M | F | F | M | F | F |
|---|---|---|---|---|---|---|---|---|---|---|---|---|---|---|---|---|---|---|---|---|
| Major: | A | C | C | M | A | C | A | A | C | C | A | A | A | M | C | M | A | A | A | C |
| Gender: | M | M | M | M | F | M | F | F | M | M | F | M | M | M | M | F | M | F | M | M |
| Major: | C | C | A | A | M | M | C | A | A | A | C | C | A | A | A | A | C | C | A | C |

**a.** Tally the data into a contingency table where the two rows represent the gender categories and the three columns represent the academic-major categories.

**b.** Form contingency tables based on percentages of all 40 student responses, based on row percentages and based on column percentages.

**c.** Using the results from (a), construct a side-by-side bar chart of gender based on student major.

**2.31** Given the following contingency table, construct a side-by-side bar chart comparing *A* and *B* for each of the three-column categories:

|   | 1 | 2 | 3 | Total |
|---|---|---|---|---|
| A | 20 | 40 | 40 | 100 |
| B | 80 | 80 | 40 | 200 |

## Applying the Concepts

**2.32** The results of a study made as part of a yield improvement effort at a semiconductor manufacturing facility provided defect data for a sample of 450 wafers. The following table presents a summary of the responses to two questions: Was a particle found on the die that produced the wafer? and Is the wafer good or bad?

| QUALITY OF WAFER | CONDITION OF DIE | | |
|---|---|---|---|
| | **No Particles** | **Particles** | **Totals** |
| Good | 320 | 14 | 334 |
| Bad | 80 | 36 | 116 |
| Totals | 400 | 50 | 450 |

Source: *Extracted from S. W. Hall, "Analysis of Defectivity of Semiconductor Wafers by Contingency Table,"* Proceedings Institute of Environmental Sciences, Vol. 1 *(1994), pp. 177–183.*

**a.** Construct contingency tables based on total percentages, row percentages, and column percentages.

**b.** Construct a side-by-side bar chart of quality of wafers based on condition of die.

**c.** What conclusions do you draw from these analyses?

**2.33** Each day at a large hospital, several hundred laboratory tests are performed. The rate at which these tests are done improperly (and therefore need to be redone) seems steady, at about 4%. In an effort to get to the root cause of these nonconformances (i.e., tests that need to be redone), the director of the lab decided to keep records over a period of one week. The laboratory tests were subdivided by the shift of workers who performed the lab tests. The results are as follows:

| LAB TESTS PERFORMED | SHIFT | | |
|---|---|---|---|
| | **Day** | **Evening** | **Total** |
| Nonconforming | 16 | 24 | 40 |
| Conforming | 654 | 306 | 960 |
| Total | 670 | 330 | 1,000 |

**a.** Construct contingency tables based on total percentages, row percentages, and column percentages.

**b.** Which type of percentage—row, column, or total—do you think is most informative for these data? Explain.

**c.** What conclusions concerning the pattern of nonconforming laboratory tests can the laboratory director reach?

**✓SELF Test** **2.34** A sample of 500 shoppers was selected in a large metropolitan area to determine various information concerning consumer behavior. Among the questions asked was "Do you enjoy shopping for clothing?" The results are summarized in the following cross-classification table:

| ENJOY SHOPPING FOR CLOTHING | GENDER | | |
|---|---|---|---|
| | **Male** | **Female** | **Total** |
| Yes | 136 | 224 | 360 |
| No | 104 | 36 | 140 |
| Total | 240 | 260 | 500 |

**a.** Construct contingency tables based on total percentages, row percentages, and column percentages.

**b.** Construct a side-by-side bar chart of enjoying shopping for clothing based on gender.

**c.** What conclusions do you draw from these analyses?

**2.35** As more Americans use cell phones, they question where it is okay to talk on cell phones. The following is a table of results, in percentages, for 2000 and 2006 (extracted from W. Koch, "Businesses Put a Lid on Chatterboxes," *USA Today*, February 7, 2006, p. 3A):

| OK TO TALK ON A CELL PHONE IN A RESTAURANT | YEAR | |
|---|---|---|
| | **2000** | **2006** |
| Yes | 31 | 21 |
| No | 69 | 79 |
| Total | 100 | 100 |

**a.** Construct a side-by-side bar chart.

**b.** Discuss the changes in attitude concerning the use of cell phones in restaurants between 2000 and 2006.

**2.36** An experiment was conducted by James Choi, David Laibson, and Brigitte Madrian to study the choices made in fund selection. When presented with four S&P 500 index funds that were identical except for their fees, undergraduate and MBA students chose the funds as follows (in percentages). Note that because the funds are identical, the best choice is the fund with the lowest fee.

| | Student Group | |
|---|---|---|
| Fund | Undergraduate | MBA |
| Lowest fee | 19 | 19 |
| Second-lowest fee | 37 | 40 |
| Third-lowest fee | 17 | 23 |
| Highest fee | 27 | 18 |

Source: *Extracted from J. Choi, D. Laibson, and B. Madrian, "Why Does the Law of One Practice Fail? An Experiment on Mutual Funds,"* **www.som.yale.edu/faculty/jjc83/fees.pdf**.

**a.** Construct a side-by-side bar chart for the two student groups.

**b.** What do these results tell you about the differences between undergraduate and MBA students in their ability to choose S&P 500 index funds?

**2.37** Where people turn to for news is different for various age groups. A study indicated where different age groups primarily get their news.

| | Age Group | | |
|---|---|---|---|
| Media | Under 36 | 36–50 | 50+ |
| Local TV | 107 | 119 | 133 |
| National TV | 73 | 102 | 127 |
| Radio | 75 | 97 | 109 |
| Local newspaper | 52 | 79 | 107 |
| Internet | 95 | 83 | 76 |

**a.** Construct a side-by-side bar chart for the three age groups.

**b.** What differences are there in the age groups?

## 2.5   SCATTER PLOTS AND TIME-SERIES PLOTS

When analyzing a single numerical variable such as the cost of a restaurant meal or the 2006 return, the appropriate charts to use include histograms, polygons, and cumulative percentage polygons, developed in Section 2.3. This section discusses scatter plots and time-series plots, which are used when you have two numerical variables.

### The Scatter Plot

You use a **scatter plot** to examine possible relationships between two numerical variables. For each observation, you plot one variable on the horizontal $X$ axis and the other variable on the vertical $Y$ axis. For example, a marketing analyst could study the effectiveness of advertising by comparing weekly sales volumes and weekly advertising expenditures. Or a human resources director interested in the salary structure of the company could compare the employees' years of experience with their current salaries.

To demonstrate a scatter plot, you can examine the relationship between the cost of different items in various cities (extracted from K. Spors, "Keeping Up with . . . Yourself," *The Wall Street Journal*, April 11, 2005, p. R4). Table 2.18 provides the cost of a fast-food hamburger meal and the cost of two movie tickets in 10 cities around the world. The Cost of Living file contains the complete data set.

**TABLE 2.18**

Cost of a Fast-Food Hamburger Meal and Cost of Two Movie Tickets in 10 Cities

| City | Hamburger | Movie Tickets |
|---|---|---|
| Tokyo | 5.99 | 32.66 |
| London | 7.62 | 28.41 |
| New York | 5.75 | 20.00 |
| Sydney | 4.45 | 20.71 |
| Chicago | 4.99 | 18.00 |
| San Francisco | 5.29 | 19.50 |
| Boston | 4.39 | 18.00 |
| Atlanta | 3.70 | 16.00 |
| Toronto | 4.62 | 18.05 |
| Rio de Janeiro | 2.99 | 9.90 |

For each city, you plot the cost of a fast-food hamburger meal on the $X$ axis, and the cost of two movie tickets on the $Y$ axis. Figure 2.15 presents a Microsoft Excel scatter plot for these two variables.

**FIGURE 2.15**

Microsoft Excel scatter plot of the cost of a fast-food hamburger meal and the cost of two movie tickets

*See Sections E2.13 or P2.9 to create this. (Minitab users, see Section M2.9 to create an equivalent chart.)*

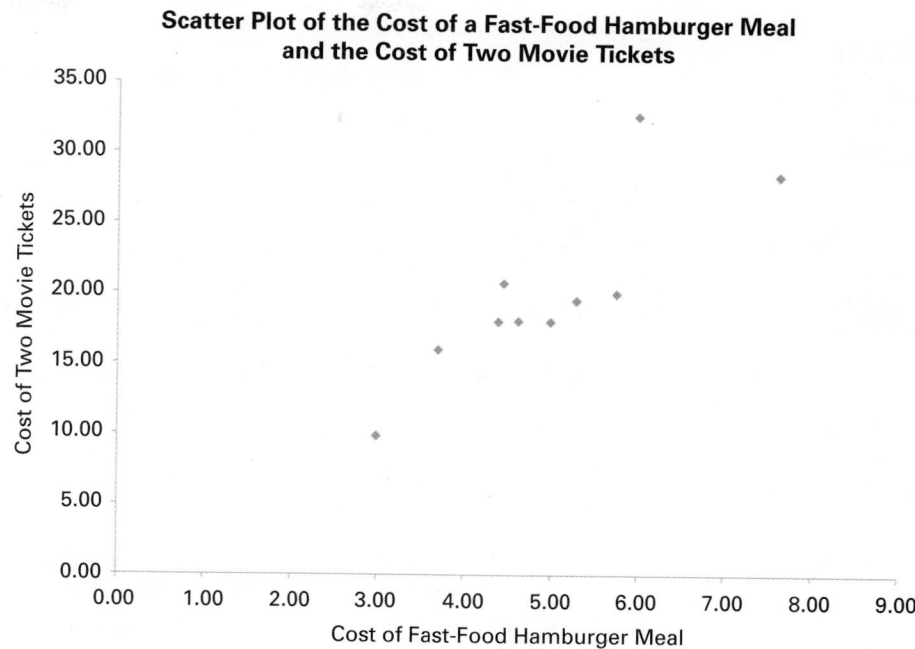

Although there is some variation, there appears to be a clearly increasing (positive) relationship between the cost of a fast-food hamburger meal and the cost of two movie tickets. In other words, cities in which the cost of a fast-food hamburger meal is low seem to also have a low cost of two movie tickets. Other pairs of variables may have a decreasing (negative) relationship in which one variable decreases as the other increases. The scatter plot will be studied again in Chapter 3, when the coefficient of correlation and the covariance are presented, and in Chapter 13, when regression analysis is developed.

## The Time-Series Plot

A **time-series plot** is used to study patterns in the values of a numerical variable over time. Each value is plotted as a point in two dimensions with the time period on the horizontal $X$ axis and the variable of interest on the $Y$ axis.

To demonstrate a time-series plot, you can examine the yearly movie attendance, in billions, from 1999 to 2006 (extracted from C. Passy, "Good Night and Good Luck," *Palm Beach Post*, February 5, 2006, p. 1J and S. Bowles, "Box Office Breaks Its Downward Cycle," *USA Today*, March 7, 2007, p. 1D). Table 2.19 presents the data for the yearly movie attendance (see

**TABLE 2.19**

Movie Attendance, in Billions, from 1999 to 2006

| Year | Attendance |
|------|------------|
| 1999 | 1.47 |
| 2000 | 1.42 |
| 2001 | 1.49 |
| 2002 | 1.63 |
| 2003 | 1.57 |
| 2004 | 1.53 |
| 2005 | 1.41 |
| 2006 | 1.45 |

the file **Movies**). Figure 2.16 is a time-series plot of the movie attendance (in billions) from 1999 to 2006. You can see that although movie attendance increased from 1999 to 2002, it declined from 2003 to 2005, before increasing slightly in 2006. Attendance in 2005 and 2006 was below attendance in 1999.

**FIGURE 2.16**

Microsoft Excel time-series plot of movie attendance from 1999 to 2006

*See Section E2.14 to create this. (Minitab users, see Section M2.9 to create an equivalent chart.)*

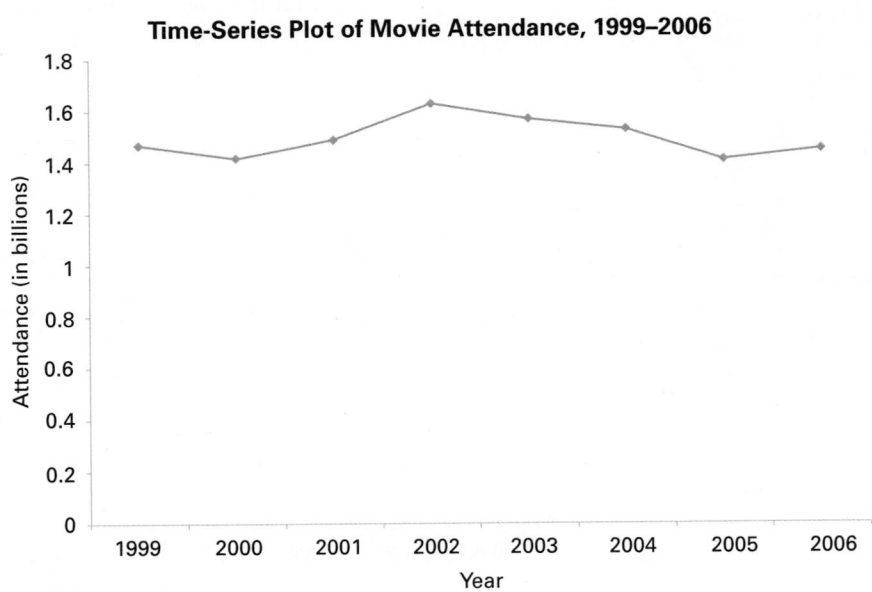

## PROBLEMS FOR SECTION 2.5

### Learning the Basics

**2.38** The following is a set of data from a sample of $n = 11$ items:

$$X \quad 7 \quad 5 \quad 8 \quad 3 \quad 6 \quad 10 \quad 12 \quad 4 \quad 9 \quad 15 \quad 18$$
$$Y \quad 21 \quad 15 \quad 24 \quad 9 \quad 18 \quad 30 \quad 36 \quad 12 \quad 27 \quad 45 \quad 54$$

**a.** Construct a scatter plot.
**b.** Is there a relationship between $X$ and $Y$? Explain.

**2.39** The following is a series of annual sales (in millions of dollars) over an 11-year period (1996 to 2006):

*Year* 1996 1997 1998 1999 2000 2001 2002 2003 2004 2005 2006

*Sales* 13.0 17.0 19.0 20.0 20.5 20.5 20.5 20.0 19.0 17.0 13.0

**a.** Construct a time-series plot.
**b.** Does there appear to be any change in real annual sales over time? Explain.

### Applying the Concepts

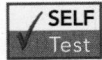 **2.40** There are several methods for calculating fuel economy. The following table (contained in

the file **Mileage**) indicates the mileage as calculated by owners and by current government standards for nine car models:

| Car | Owner | Government |
|---|---|---|
| 2005 Ford F-150 | 14.3 | 16.8 |
| 2005 Chevrolet Silverado | 15.0 | 17.8 |
| 2002 Honda Accord LX | 27.8 | 26.2 |
| 2002 Honda Civic | 27.9 | 34.2 |
| 2004 Honda Civic Hybrid | 48.8 | 47.6 |
| 2002 Ford Explorer | 16.8 | 18.3 |
| 2005 Toyota Camry | 23.7 | 28.5 |
| 2003 Toyota Corolla | 32.8 | 33.1 |
| 2005 Toyota Prius | 37.3 | 56.0 |

Source: *Extracted from J. Healey, "Fuel Economy Calculations to be Altered," USA Today, January 11, 2006, p. 1B.*

**a.** Construct a scatter plot with owner mileage on the $X$ axis and current government standards mileage on the $Y$ axis.
**b.** Does there appear to be a relationship between owner and current government standards mileage? If so, is the relationship positive or negative?

**2.41** The file **Chicken** contains data on the calories and total fat (in grams per serving) for a sample of 20 chicken sandwiches from fast-food chains:

| Sandwich | Calories | Fat |
|---|---|---|
| Wendy's Ultimate Chicken Grill | 360 | 7 |
| Baja Fresh Original Baja Taco with Charbroiled Chicken | 370 | 8 |
| Burger King Smoky BBQ Fire-Grilled Chicken Baguette | 380 | 4 |
| Quiznos Sub Honey Bourbon Chicken on Wheat Bread | 400 | 5 |
| McDonald's Chicken McGrill | 400 | 16 |
| Blimpie Grilled Chicken Hot Sub | 470 | 20 |
| Subway Oven-Roasted Chicken Breast | 470 | 20 |
| Blimpie Buffalo Chicken Hot Sub | 500 | 24 |
| Wendy's Spicy Chicken Fillet | 510 | 19 |
| Taco Bell Ranchero Chicken Soft Taco (two tacos) | 540 | 30 |
| KFC Oven-Roasted Chicken Tender Wrap | 550 | 23 |
| Subway Buffalo Chicken Sub | 550 | 30 |
| Burger King Chicken Whopper | 570 | 25 |
| Au Bon Pain Arizona Chicken | 580 | 19 |
| Boston Market Rotisserie Chicken Carver | 640 | 29 |
| Chipolte Soft Tacos with Chicken (three tacos) | 660 | 29 |
| Cosi Grilled Chicken with Tomato, Basil, and Mozzarella | 720 | 30 |
| Atlanta Bread Company Chargrilled Chicken Pesto Panini | 740 | 30 |
| Corner Bakery Café Chicken Pomodori Panini | 910 | 40 |
| Panera Bread Tuscan Chicken on Rosemary & Onion Focaccia | 950 | 56 |

Source: *Extracted from "Fast food: Adding Health to the Menu," Consumer Reports, September 2004, pp. 28–31.*

a. Construct a scatter plot with calories on the X axis and total fat on the Y axis.
b. What conclusions can you reach about the relationship between the calories and total fat in chicken sandwiches?

**2.42** College basketball is big business, with coaches' salaries, revenues, and expenses in millions of dollars. The file Colleges-Basketball contains the coaches' salary and revenue for college basketball at selected schools in a recent year (extracted from R. Adams, "Pay for Playoffs," *The Wall Street Journal*, March 11–12, 2006, pp. P1, P8).
a. Do you think schools with higher revenues also have higher coaches' salaries?
b. Construct a scatter plot with revenue on the X axis and coaches' salaries on the Y axis.
c. Does the scatter plot confirm or contradict your answer to (a)?

**2.43** College football players trying out for the NFL are given the Wonderlic standardized intelligence test. The file

Wonderlic contains the average Wonderlic scores of football players trying out for the NFL and the graduation rate for football players at selected schools (extracted from S. Walker, "The NFL's Smartest Team," *The Wall Street Journal*, September 30, 2005, pp. W1, W10).
a. Construct a scatter plot with average Wonderlic score on the X axis and graduation rate on the Y axis.
b. What conclusions can you reach about the relationship between the average Wonderlic score and graduation rate?

**2.44** The U.S. Bureau of Labor Statistics compiles data on a wide variety of workforce issues. The following table (contained in the file Unemploy) gives the monthly seasonally adjusted civilian unemployment rate for the United States from 2000 to 2006:

| Month | 2000 | 2001 | 2002 | 2003 | 2004 | 2005 | 2006 |
|---|---|---|---|---|---|---|---|
| January | 4.0 | 4.2 | 5.7 | 5.8 | 5.7 | 5.2 | 4.7 |
| February | 4.1 | 4.2 | 5.7 | 5.9 | 5.6 | 5.4 | 4.8 |
| March | 4.0 | 4.3 | 5.7 | 5.9 | 5.7 | 5.1 | 4.7 |
| April | 3.8 | 4.4 | 5.9 | 6.0 | 5.5 | 5.1 | 4.7 |
| May | 4.0 | 4.3 | 5.8 | 6.1 | 5.6 | 5.1 | 4.6 |
| June | 4.0 | 4.5 | 5.8 | 6.3 | 5.6 | 5.0 | 4.6 |
| July | 4.0 | 4.6 | 5.8 | 6.2 | 5.5 | 5.0 | 4.8 |
| August | 4.1 | 4.9 | 5.7 | 6.1 | 5.4 | 4.9 | 4.7 |
| September | 3.9 | 5.0 | 5.7 | 6.1 | 5.4 | 5.1 | 4.6 |
| October | 3.9 | 5.3 | 5.7 | 6.0 | 5.4 | 4.9 | 4.4 |
| November | 3.9 | 5.5 | 5.9 | 5.9 | 5.4 | 5.0 | 4.5 |
| December | 3.9 | 5.7 | 6.0 | 5.7 | 5.4 | 4.9 | 4.5 |

Source: *"U.S. Bureau of Labor Statistics,"* **www.bls.gov**, *March 30, 2007.*

a. Construct a time-series plot of the U.S. unemployment rate.
b. Does there appear to be any pattern?

**2.45** In 2005, five million people in the United States subscribed to online dating services. The subscribers spent, on average, $99 for the services provided, thus generating nearly $500 million for the online dating companies. The following table (contained in the file Dating) gives the number of subscribers (in millions) to U.S. dating Web sites from 2000 to 2005:

| Year | Number of Subscribers (millions) |
|---|---|
| 2000 | 0.7 |
| 2001 | 1.6 |
| 2002 | 2.8 |
| 2003 | 4.3 |
| 2004 | 4.7 |
| 2005 | 5.0 |

Source: *Extracted from "Making an E-Match,"* National Geographic, *February, 2006, p. 128.*

a. Construct a time-series plot.
b. Do you think the number of subscribers is increasing or decreasing? Do you think the *rate* of growth is increasing or decreasing? Explain.

**2.46** The following table contained in the file `Tvchannels` (extracted from "At Home With More TV Channels," *USA Today*, April 10, 2007, p. A1) shows the average number of TV channels that the U.S. home received from 1985 to 2005:

| Year | Number of TV Channels Received |
|------|-------------------------------|
| 1985 | 18.8 |
| 1990 | 33.2 |
| 1995 | 41.1 |
| 2000 | 61.4 |
| 2005 | 96.4 |

a. Construct a time-series plot for the average number of TV channels that the U.S. home received from 1985 to 2005.
b. What pattern, if any, is present in the data?
c. If you had to make a prediction of the average number of TV channels that the U.S. home will receive in 2010, what would you predict?

**2.47** The following data, contained in the file `Deals`, provide the number of mergers and acquisitions made during January 1 through January 11 of each year from 1995 to 2006 (extracted from "Back of the Envelope," *The New York Times*, January 13, 2006, p. C7):

| Year | Deals |
|------|-------|
| 1995 | 715 |
| 1996 | 865 |
| 1997 | 708 |
| 1998 | 861 |
| 1999 | 931 |
| 2000 | 939 |
| 2001 | 1,031 |
| 2002 | 893 |
| 2003 | 735 |
| 2004 | 759 |
| 2005 | 1,013 |
| 2006 | 622 |

a. Construct a time-series plot.
b. What pattern, if any, is present in the data?
c. If you had to make a prediction of the mergers and acquisitions made during January 1 through January 11, 2007, what would you predict?

## 2.6   MISUSING GRAPHS AND ETHICAL ISSUES

Good graphical displays clearly and unambiguously reveal what the data convey. Unfortunately, many graphs presented in the media (broadcast, print, and online) are incorrect, misleading, or so unnecessarily complicated that they should never be used. To illustrate the misuse of graphs, the chart presented in Figure 2.17 is similar to one that was printed in *Time* magazine as part of an article on increasing exports of wine from Australia to the United States.

In Figure 2.17, the wineglass icon representing the 6.77 million gallons for 1997 does not appear to be almost twice the size of the wineglass icon representing the 3.67 million gallons for 1995, nor does the wineglass icon representing the 2.25 million gallons for 1992 appear to be twice the size of the wineglass icon representing the 1.04 million gallons for 1989. Part of the reason for this is that the three-dimensional wineglass icon is used to represent the two dimensions of exports and time. Although the wineglass presentation may catch the eye, the data should instead be presented in a summary table or a time-series plot.

**FIGURE 2.17**

"Improper" display of Australian wine exports to the United States, in millions of gallons

Source: *Adapted from S. Watterson, "Liquid Gold—Australians Are Changing the World of Wine. Even the French Seem Grateful,"* Time, *November 22, 1999, p. 68.*

**We're drinking more . . .**
Australian wine exports to the U.S. in millions of gallons

1.04   2.25   3.67   6.77

1989   1992   1995   1997

In addition to the type of distortion created by the wineglass icons in the *Time* magazine graph displayed in Figure 2.17, improper use of the vertical and horizontal axes leads to distortions. Figure 2.18 presents another graph used in the same *Time* magazine article.

**FIGURE 2.18**

"Improper" display of amount of land planted with grapes for the wine industry

Source: *Adapted from S. Watterson, "Liquid Gold—Australians Are Changing the World of Wine. Even the French Seem Grateful," Time, November 22, 1999, pp. 68–69.*

There are several problems in this graph. First, there is no zero point on the vertical axis. Second, the acreage of 135,326 for 1949–1950 is plotted above the acreage of 150,300 for 1969–1970. Third, it is not obvious that the difference between 1979–1980 and 1997–1998 (71,569 acres) is approximately 3.5 times the difference between 1979–1980 and 1969–1970 (21,775 acres). Fourth, there are no scale values on the horizontal axis. Years are plotted next to the acreage totals, not on the horizontal axis. Fifth, the values for the time dimension are not properly spaced along the horizontal axis. The value for 1979–1980 is much closer to 1989–1990 than it is to 1969–1970.

Other types of eye-catching displays that you typically see in magazines and newspapers often include information that is not necessary and just adds excessive clutter. Figure 2.19 represents one such display. The graph in Figure 2.19 shows those products with the largest market share for soft drinks in 1999. The graph suffers from too much clutter, although it is designed to show the differences in market share among the soft drinks. The display of the fizz for each soft drink takes up too much of the graph relative to the data. The same information could have been conveyed with a bar chart or pie chart.

**FIGURE 2.19**

"Improper" plot of market share of soft drinks in 1999

Source: *Adapted from Anne B. Carey and Sam Ward, "Coke Still Has Most Fizz," USA Today, May 10, 2000, p. 1B.*

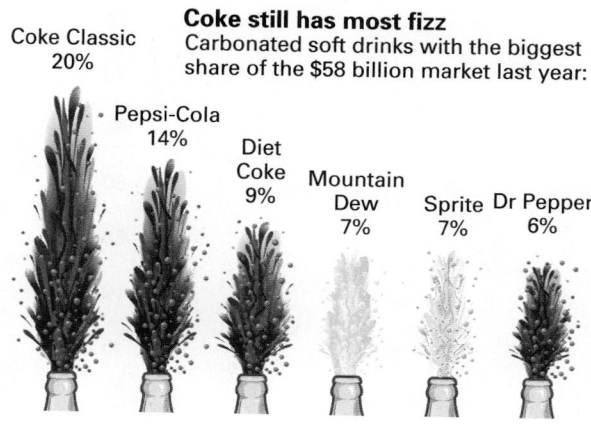

Some guidelines for developing good graphs are as follows:

- The graph should not distort the data.
- The graph should not contain **chartjunk**, unnecessary adornments that convey no useful information.
- Any two-dimensional graph should contain a scale for each axis.
- The scale on the vertical axis should begin at zero.
- All axes should be properly labeled.
- The graph should contain a title.
- The simplest possible graph should be used for a given set of data.

Often these guidelines are unknowingly violated by individuals unaware of how to construct appropriate graphs.

## Ethical Concerns

Inappropriate graphs raise ethical concerns. Such graphs can obscure unfavorable information or create false impressions of data, even if the inappropriate chart was developed naively. Consider the following sets of sales trend charts as shown in Figure 2.20. A casual viewer of these charts might think model B had the best sales trend and that models A and D had similar trends. A more careful examination of these line graphs shows that model B has the weakest sales trend and that model C and D actually have the *same* sales trend. A casual viewer gets misled because of the inconsistent scaling of the Y axis.

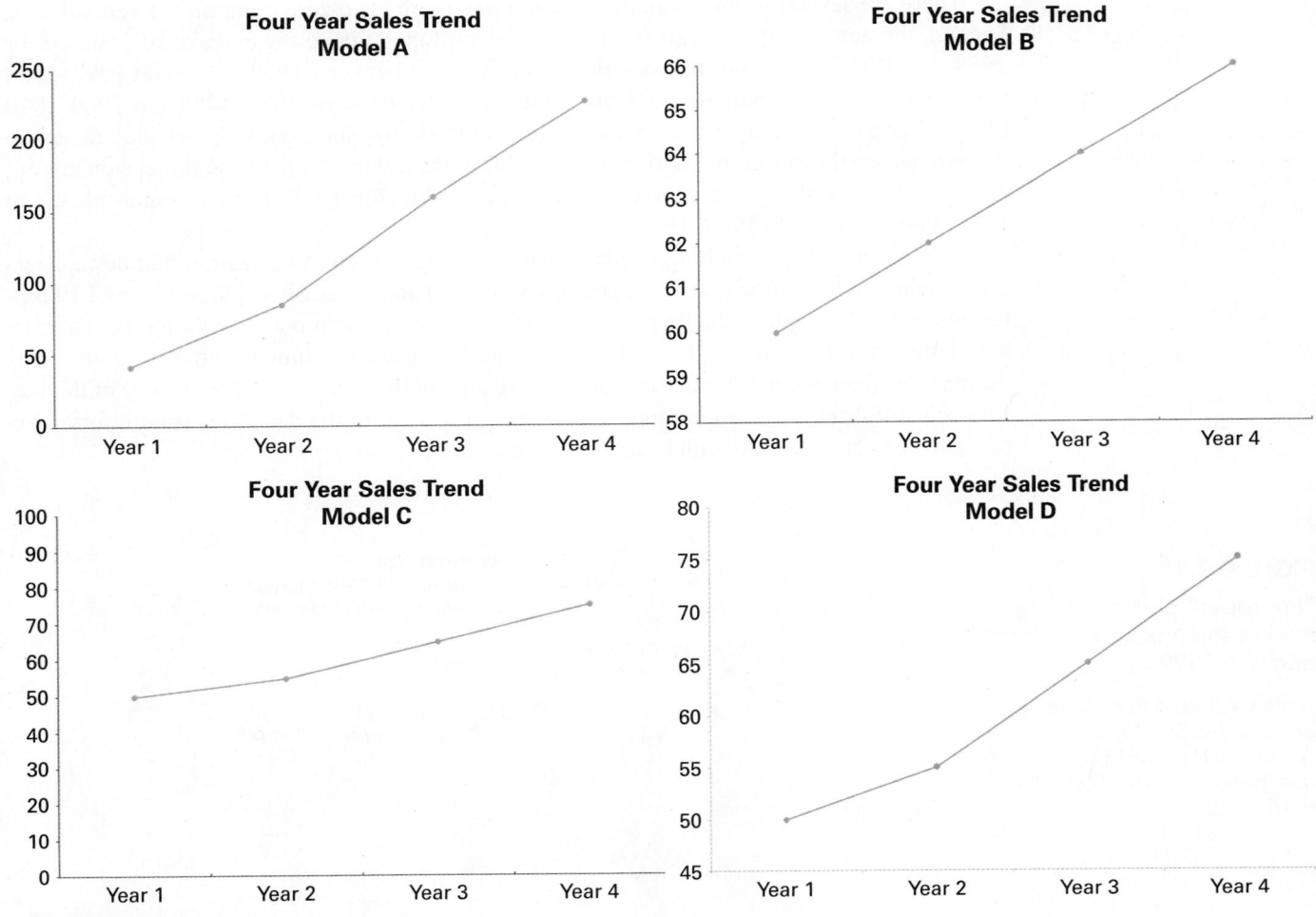

**FIGURE 2.20**  Four sales trend charts

## Pretty, But Not Witty or Wise

*From the Authors' Desktop*

In the Leonard Bernstein and Stephen Sondheim musical, *West Side Story*, the character Maria sings of being "pretty and witty and wise." In the business world, pretty charts are not necessarily smart or witty or wise.

You may get tempted to create pretty charts if you use programs such as Microsoft Excel. Excel allows you to easily create fancy charts that may appear pretty, but are unwise choices. Taking a simple pie chart and making it prettier by adding exploded 3D slices is unwise as this can complicate a viewer's interpretation of the data. Uncommon chart choices such as doughnut, radar, surface, bub-

ble, cone, and pyramid charts may look visually striking, but obscure the data in most cases.

To be smart and wise and effective, try to make sure that the tables and charts you create are simple and clear, so that the information presented can be easily interpreted.

## PROBLEMS FOR SECTION 2.6

### Applying the Concepts

**2.48** **(Student Project)** Bring to class a chart from a Web site, newspaper, or magazine that you believe to be a poorly drawn representation of a numerical variable. Be prepared to submit the chart to the instructor with comments as to why you believe it is inappropriate. Do you believe that the intent of the chart is to purposely mislead the reader? Also, be prepared to present and comment on this in class.

**2.49** **(Student Project)** Bring to class a chart from a Web site, newspaper, or magazine that you believe to be a poorly drawn representation of a categorical variable. Be prepared to submit the chart to the instructor with comments as to why you consider it inappropriate. Do you believe that the intent of the chart is to purposely mislead the reader? Also, be prepared to present and comment on this in class.

**2.50** **(Student Project)** According to its home page, Swivel is "a place where curious people explore data—all kinds of data." Go to **www.swivel.com** and explore the various graphical displays.
a. Select a graphical display that you think does a good job revealing what the data convey. Discuss why you think it is a good graphical display.
b. Select a graphical display that you think needs a lot of improvement. Discuss why you think that it is a poorly constructed graphical display.

**2.51** The following visual display contains an overembellished chart similar to one that appeared in *USA Today*, dealing with the average consumer's Valentine's Day spending ("USA Today Snapshots: The Price of Romance," *USA Today*, February 14, 2007, p. 1B).

a. Describe at least one good feature of this visual display.
b. Describe at least one bad feature of this visual display.
c. Redraw the graph, using the guidelines given on page 58.

**2.52** The following visual display contains an overembellished chart similar to one that appeared in *USA Today*, dealing with the estimated number of hours the typical American will spend using various media ("USA Today Snapshots: Minding Their Media," *USA Today*, March 2, 2007, p. 1B).

**Media Usage**
*Estimated number of hours the typical American will spend using various media this year.*

Listening to music — 175
Reading newspapers — 175
Using Internet — 195
Listening to Radio — 974
Watching TV — 1555

**a.** Describe at least one good feature of this visual display.
**b.** Describe at least one bad feature of this visual display.
**c.** Redraw the graph, using the guidelines given on page 58.

**2.53** The following visual display contains an overembellished chart similar to one that appeared in *USA Today*, dealing with which card is safer to use ("USA Today Snapshots: Credit Card vs. Debit Card," *USA Today*, March 14, 2007, p. 1B).

### Credit Card vs. Debit Card: Which one is safer to use?

Don't Mind 49%
Credit Card 32%
Debit Card 19%

**a.** Describe at least one good feature of this visual display.
**b.** Describe at least one bad feature of this visual display.
**c.** Redraw the graph, using the guidelines given on page 58.

**2.54** An article in *The New York Times* (D. Rosato, "Worried About the Numbers? How About the Charts?" *The New York Times*, September 15, 2002, p. B7) reported on research done on annual reports of corporations by Professor Deanna Oxender Burgess of Florida Gulf Coast University. Professor Burgess found that even slight distortions in a chart changed readers' perception of the information. The article displayed sales information from the annual report of Zale Corporation and showed how results were exaggerated.

Using Internet or library sources, study the most recent annual report of a selected corporation. Find at least one chart in the report that you think needs improvement and develop an improved version of the chart. Explain why you believe the improved chart is better than the one included in the annual report.

**2.55** Figures 2.1, 2.3, and 2.6 consist of a bar chart, a pie chart, and a Pareto chart for where people prefer to do their banking (see pages 28, 30, and 31).
**a.** Use the chart features of Microsoft Excel to construct an exploded pie chart, doughnut chart, a cone chart, and a pyramid chart for where people prefer to do their banking.
**b.** Which graphs do you prefer—the bar chart, pie chart, and Pareto chart or the exploded pie chart, doughnut chart, cone chart, and pyramid chart? Explain.

**2.56** Figures 2.2 and 2.4 consist of a bar chart and a pie chart for the risk level for the mutual fund data (see pages 28 and 29).
**a.** Use the chart features of Microsoft Excel to develop an exploded pie chart, a doughnut chart, a cone chart, and a pyramid chart for the risk level of the mutual funds.
**b.** Do you prefer the bar chart and pie chart, or the exploded pie chart, doughnut chart, cone chart, and pyramid chart? Explain.

# SUMMARY

As you can see in Table 2.20, this chapter discusses data presentation. You have used various tables and charts to draw conclusions about where people prefer to bank, about the cost of restaurant meals in an urban area and its suburbs, and about the set of mutual funds that were first introduced in the Using Statistics scenario at the beginning of the chapter. Now that you have studied tables and charts, in Chapter 3 you will learn about a variety of numerical descriptive measures useful for data analysis and interpretation.

**TABLE 2.20**
Roadmap for Selecting Tables and Charts

| | Type of Data | |
| Type of Analysis | Numerical | Categorical |
| --- | --- | --- |
| Tabulating, organizing, and graphically presenting the values of a variable | Ordered array, stem-and-leaf display, frequency distribution, relative frequency distribution, percentage distribution, cumulative percentage distribution, histogram, polygon, cumulative percentage polygon **(Sections 2.2 and 2.3)** | Summary table, bar chart, pie chart, Pareto chart **(Section 2.1)** |
| Graphically presenting the relationship between two variables | Scatter plot, time-series plot **(Section 2.5)** | Contingency table, side-by-side bar chart **(Section 2.4)** |

# KEY EQUATIONS

**Width of Interval**

$$\text{Width of interval} = \frac{\text{Range}}{\text{number of classes}} \qquad (2.1)$$

**Proportion**

$$\text{Proportion} = \text{Relative Frequency} = \frac{\text{Frequency in each class}}{\text{total number of values}} \qquad (2.2)$$

# KEY TERMS

bar chart    27
cells    49
chartjunk    58
class boundaries    37
class grouping    37
class midpoint    37
classes    37
contingency table    49
cross tabulations    49
cumulative percentage
  distribution    40

cumulative percentage polygon
  (ogive)    45
frequency distribution    37
histogram    42
ogive (cumulative percentage
  polygon)    45
ordered array    34
Pareto chart    30
Pareto principle    30
percentage distribution    39
percentage polygon    44

pie chart    28
proportion    38
range    37
relative frequency    38
relative frequency distribution    39
scatter plot    52
side-by-side bar chart    50
stem-and-leaf display    34
summary table    27
time-series plot    53
width of a class interval    37

# CHAPTER REVIEW PROBLEMS

## Checking Your Understanding

**2.57** How do histograms and polygons differ in terms of construction and use?

**2.58** Why would you construct a summary table?

**2.59** What are the advantages and/or disadvantages of using a bar chart, a pie chart, or a Pareto chart?

**2.60** Compare and contrast the bar chart for categorical data with the histogram for numerical data.

**2.61** What is the difference between a time-series plot and a scatter plot?

**2.62** Why is it said that the main feature of the Pareto chart is its ability to separate the "vital few" from the "trivial many"? Discuss.

**2.63** What are the three different ways to break down the percentages in a contingency table?

## Applying the Concepts

**2.64** The following data represent the breakdown of the price of a new college textbook:

| Revenue Categories | Percentage | |
|---|---|---|
| Publisher | 64.8 | |
| Manufacturing costs | | 32.3 |
| Marketing and promotion | | 15.4 |
| Administrative costs and taxes | | 10.0 |
| After-tax profit | | 7.1 |
| Bookstore | 22.4 | |
| Employee salaries and benefits | | 11.3 |
| Operations | | 6.6 |
| Pretax profit | | 4.5 |
| Author | 11.6 | |
| Freight | 1.2 | |

Source: *Extracted from T. Lewin, "When Books Break the Bank,"* The New York Times, *September 16, 2003, pp. B1, B4.*

**a.** Using the four categories publisher, bookstore, author, and freight, construct a bar chart, a pie chart, and a Pareto chart.
**b.** Using the four subcategories of publisher and three subcategories of bookstore along with the author and freight categories, construct a Pareto chart.
**c.** Based on the results of (a) and (b), what conclusions can you reach concerning who gets the revenue from the sales of new college textbooks? Do any of these results surprise you? Explain.

**2.65** The following data represent the global market share for plasma TVs and LCD TVs in the fourth quarter of 2005:

| Company | Plasma TVs (%) | Company | LCD TVs (%) |
|---|---|---|---|
| Hitachi | 7.3 | LGE | 6.5 |
| LGE | 15.4 | Phillips/Magnavox | 14.2 |
| Panasonic | 26.0 | Samsung | 11.6 |
| Phillips | 13.3 | Sharp | 13.6 |
| Samsung | 14.4 | Sony | 14.6 |
| Others | 23.6 | Others | 39.5 |

Source: *Extracted from Y. Kkageyama, "Flat-Panel TVs Proving Savior of Japanese Electronics Makers,"* The Palm Beach Post, *April 23, 2006, p. F3.*

**a.** For plasma TVs and LCD TVs, separately construct a bar chart, a pie chart, and a Pareto chart.
**b.** Based on the results of (a), explain how the market share of plasma TVs differs from the market share of LCD TVs.

**2.66** The following data represent energy consumption and renewable energy consumption in the United States in 2005:

| Energy Source | %* | Renewable Energy Source | %* |
|---|---|---|---|
| Coal | 23.0 | Ethanol | 10.1 |
| Hydroelectric power | 2.7 | Geothermal | 10.8 |
| Natural gas | 22.2 | Solar | 1.9 |
| Nuclear electric power | 8.1 | Waste | 17.1 |
| Petroleum | 40.5 | Wind | 4.5 |
| Renewable fuels | 3.3 | Wood | 55.5 |

*Percentages do not add to 100% due to rounding.
Source: *Energy Information Administration, 2006.*

*Percentages do not add to 100% due to rounding.
Source: *Energy Information Administration, 2006.*

**a.** For energy consumption and renewable energy consumption, separately construct a bar chart, a pie chart, and a Pareto chart.
**b.** Based on the results of (a), what conclusions can you reach about energy consumption and renewable energy consumption in the United States in 2005?

**2.67** The following data represent proven conventional oil reserves, in billions of barrels, subdivided by region and country:

| Region and Country | Proven Conventional Reserves (Billions of Barrels) | |
|---|---|---|
| *North America* | 54.8 | |
| Mexico | | 28.3 |
| United States | | 21.8 |
| Canada | | 4.7 |
| *Central and South America* | 95.2 | |
| Venezuela | | 76.9 |
| Brazil | | 8.1 |
| Other Central and South America | | 10.2 |
| *Western Europe* | 17.2 | |
| Norway | | 9.5 |
| Britain | | 5.0 |
| Other Western Europe | | 2.7 |
| *Africa* | 74.9 | |
| Libya | | 29.5 |
| Nigeria | | 22.5 |
| Algeria | | 9.2 |
| Angola | | 5.4 |
| Other Africa | | 8.3 |
| *Middle East* | 683.6 | |
| Saudi Arabia | | 259.2 |
| Iraq | | 112.5 |
| United Arab Emirates | | 97.8 |
| Kuwait | | 94.0 |
| Iran | | 89.7 |
| Qatar | | 13.2 |
| Oman | | 5.5 |
| Other Middle East | | 11.7 |
| *Far East and Oceania* | 44.0 | |
| China | | 24.0 |
| Indonesia | | 5.0 |
| India | | 4.7 |
| Other Far East and Oceania | | 10.3 |
| *Eastern Europe and Former USSR* | 59.0 | |
| Russia | | 48.6 |
| Kazakhstan | | 5.4 |
| Other Eastern Europe and Former USSR | | 5.0 |

Source: *U.S. Department of Energy.*

a. Using the set of countries, construct a bar chart, a pie chart, and a Pareto chart.

b. Using the set of regions, construct a bar chart, a pie chart, and a Pareto chart.

c. Which graphical method do you think is best to portray these data?

d. Based on the results of (a) and (b), what conclusions can you make concerning the proven conventional oil reserves for the different countries and regions?

**2.68** People conduct hundreds of millions of search queries every day. In response, businesses are estimated to spend almost $20 billion annually on online ad spending (K. J. Delaney, "The New Benefits of Web-Search Queries," *The Wall Street Journal*, February 6, 2007, p. B3). The following represents the categories of online ad spending and the results of a Yahoo! keyword tool for searches related to sneakers.

**Estimated 2007 U.S. Online Ad Spending**

| Type | Spending ($billions) |
|---|---|
| Classified | 3.32 |
| Display ads | 3.90 |
| Paid search | 8.29 |
| Rich media/video | 2.15 |
| Other | 1.85 |
| Total | 19.51 |

**Results of a Yahoo! Keyword Tool for Searches Related to "Sneakers"**

| Search result | Number of Occurrences |
|---|---|
| Jordan sneaker | 13,240 |
| Nike sneaker | 8,139 |
| Puma sneaker | 6,768 |
| Sneaker | 58,995 |
| Sneaker pimps* | 15,357 |

*Sneaker pimps is a British electropop band.

a. For type of online ad spending, construct a bar chart, a pie chart, and a Pareto chart.

b. Which graphical method do you think is best to portray these data?

c. For the results of "sneakers" searches, construct a bar chart, a pie chart, and a Pareto chart.

d. Which graphical method do you think is best to portray these data?

e. What conclusions can you reach concerning online ad spending and the results of "sneakers" searches?

**2.69** The owner of a restaurant serving Continental-style entrées is interested in studying patterns of patron demand for the Friday-to-Sunday weekend time period. Records are maintained that indicate the type of entrée ordered. The data are as follows:

| Type of Entrée | Number Served |
|---|---|
| Beef | 187 |
| Chicken | 103 |
| Duck | 25 |
| Fish | 122 |
| Pasta | 63 |
| Shellfish | 74 |
| Veal | 26 |

**a.** Construct a percentage summary table for the types of entrées ordered.

**b.** Construct a bar chart, a pie chart, and a Pareto chart for the types of entrées ordered.

**c.** Do you prefer a Pareto chart or a pie chart for these data? Why?

**d.** What conclusions can the restaurant owner reach concerning demand for different types of entrées?

**2.70** Suppose that the owner of the restaurant in Problem 2.69 is also interested in studying the demand for dessert during the same time period. She decided that two other variables, along with whether a dessert was ordered, are to be studied: the gender of the individual and whether a beef entrée is ordered. The results are as follows:

|  | GENDER | | |
| --- | --- | --- | --- |
| **DESSERT ORDERED** | **Male** | **Female** | **Total** |
| **Yes** | 96 | 40 | 136 |
| **No** | 224 | 240 | 464 |
| **Total** | 320 | 280 | 600 |

|  | BEEF ENTRÉE | | |
| --- | --- | --- | --- |
| **DESSERT ORDERED** | **Yes** | **No** | **Total** |
| **Yes** | 71 | 65 | 136 |
| **No** | 116 | 348 | 464 |
| **Total** | 187 | 413 | 600 |

**a.** For each of the two contingency tables, construct a contingency table of row percentages, column percentages, and total percentages.

**b.** Which type of percentage (row, column, or total) do you think is most informative for each gender? for beef entrée? Explain.

**c.** What conclusions concerning the pattern of dessert ordering can the owner of the restaurant reach?

**2.71** The following data (extracted from R. Wolf, "Paper-Trail Voting Gets Organized Opposition," *USA Today*, April 24, 2007, p. 2A) represent the method for recording votes in the November 2006 election, broken down by percentage of counties in the United States using each method and the number of counties using each method in 2000 and 2006.

| Method | Percentage of Counties Using Method |
| --- | --- |
| Electronic | 36.6 |
| Hand-counted paper ballots | 1.8 |
| Lever | 2.0 |
| Mixed | 3.0 |
| Optically scanned paper ballots | 56.2 |
| Punch card | 0.4 |

|  | Number of Counties | |
| --- | --- | --- |
| **Method** | **2000** | **2006** |
| Electronic | 309 | 1,142 |
| Hand-counted paper ballots | 370 | 57 |
| Lever | 434 | 62 |
| Mixed | 149 | 92 |
| Optically scanned paper ballots | 1,279 | 1,752 |
| Punch card | 572 | 13 |

**a.** Construct a pie chart and a Pareto chart for the percentage of counties using the various methods.

**b.** Construct side-by-side bar charts, by year, for the number of counties using the various methods.

**c.** Which type of graphical display is more helpful in depicting the data? Explain.

**d.** What conclusions can you reach concerning the type of voting method used in November 2006?

**e.** What differences are there in the methods used in 2000 and 2006?

**2.72** In summer 2000, a growing number of warranty claims on Firestone tires sold on Ford SUVs prompted Firestone and Ford to issue a major recall. An analysis of warranty-claims data helped identify which models to recall. A breakdown of 2,504 warranty claims based on tire size is given in the following table:

| Tire Size | Warranty Claims |
| --- | --- |
| 23575R15 | 2,030 |
| 311050R15 | 137 |
| 30950R15 | 82 |
| 23570R16 | 81 |
| 331250R15 | 58 |
| 25570R16 | 54 |
| Others | 62 |

Source: *Extracted from Robert L. Simison, "Ford Steps Up Recall Without Firestone,"* The Wall Street Journal, *August 14, 2000, p. A3.*

The 2,030 warranty claims for the 23575R15 tires can be categorized into ATX models and Wilderness models. The type of incident leading to a warranty claim, by model type, is summarized in the following table:

| Incident | ATX Model Warranty Claims | Wilderness Warranty Claims |
| --- | --- | --- |
| Tread separation | 1,365 | 59 |
| Blowout | 77 | 41 |
| Other/unknown | 422 | 66 |
| Total | 1,864 | 166 |

Source: *Extracted from Robert L. Simison, "Ford Steps Up Recall Without Firestone,"* The Wall Street Journal, *August 14, 2000, p. A3.*

a. Construct a Pareto chart for the number of warranty claims by tire size. What tire size accounts for most of the claims?

b. Construct a pie chart to display the percentage of the total number of warranty claims for the 23575R15 tires that come from the ATX model and Wilderness model. Interpret the chart.

c. Construct a Pareto chart for the type of incident causing the warranty claim for the ATX model. Does a certain type of incident account for most of the claims?

d. Construct a Pareto chart for the type of incident causing the warranty claim for the Wilderness model. Does a certain type of incident account for most of the claims?

**2.73** One of the major measures of the quality of service provided by any organization is the speed with which the organization responds to customer complaints. A large family-held department store selling furniture and flooring, including carpet, had undergone a major expansion in the past several years. In particular, the flooring department had expanded from 2 installation crews to an installation supervisor, a measurer, and 15 installation crews. During a recent year, the company got 50 complaints concerning carpet installation. The following data (contained in the file Furniture) represent the number of days between the receipt of the complaint and the resolution of the complaint:

```
54   5  35 137   31 27 152   2 123 81 74 27
11  19 126 110  110 29   61 35  94 31 26   5
12   4 165  32   29 28   29 26  25  1 14 13
13  10   5  27    4 52   30 22  36 26 20 23
33  68
```

a. Construct a frequency distribution and a percentage distribution.

b. Construct a histogram and a percentage polygon.

c. Form a cumulative percentage distribution and plot a cumulative percentage polygon (ogive).

d. On the basis of the results of (a) through (c), if you had to tell the president of the company how long a customer should expect to wait to have a complaint resolved, what would you say? Explain.

**2.74** Data concerning 71 of the best-selling domestic beers in the United States are located in the file Domesticbeer. The values for three variables are included: percentage alcohol, number of calories per 12 ounces, and number of carbohydrates (in grams) per 12 ounces.

Source: *Extracted from* **www.Beer100.com**, *May 4, 2007.*

a. Construct a percentage histogram for each of the three variables.

b. Construct three scatter plots: percentage alcohol versus calories, percentage alcohol versus carbohydrates, and calories versus carbohydrates.

c. Discuss the information you learned from studying the graphs in (a) and (b).

**2.75** The data in the file Spending are the federal *per capita* spending, in thousands of dollars, for each state in 2004.
a. Develop an ordered array.
b. Plot a percentage histogram.
c. What conclusions can you reach about the differences in federal per-capita spending between the states?

**2.76** The data in the file Savings are the yields for a money market account, a one-year certificate of deposit (CD), and a five-year CD for 37 banks in south Florida, as of March 9, 2007 (extracted from **www.Bankrate.com**, March 9, 2007).
a. Construct a percentage histogram for each of the three variables.
b. Construct three scatter plots: money market account versus one-year CD, money market account versus five-year CD, and one-year CD versus five-year CD.
c. Discuss the information you learned from studying the graphs in (a) and (b).

**2.77** The data in the file Ceo represent the total compensation (in $millions) of CEOs of the 150 large public companies that filed proxies by March 31, 2007, by revenue (extracted from "C.E.O. Pay: The New Rules," *The New York Times*, April 8, 2007, pp. 10B, 11B).
a. Construct a frequency distribution and a percentage distribution.
b. Construct a histogram and a percentage polygon.
c. Construct a cumulative percentage distribution and plot a cumulative percentage polygon (ogive).
d. Based on (a) through (c), what conclusions can you reach concerning CEO compensation in 2006?
e. Are there any companies whose CEO has a total compensation below $500,000? If so, go to the company's Web site and see if you can find out a reason why the CEO has a total compensation below $500,000.

**2.78** Studies conducted by a manufacturer of "Boston" and "Vermont" asphalt shingles have shown product weight to be a major factor in customers' perception of quality. Moreover, the weight represents the amount of raw materials being used and is therefore very important to the company from a cost standpoint. The last stage of the assembly line packages the shingles before the packages are placed on wooden pallets. When a pallet is full (a pallet for most brands holds 16 squares of shingles), it is weighed, and the measurement is recorded. The company expects pallets of its "Boston" brand-name shingles to weigh at least 3,050 pounds but less than 3,260 pounds. For the company's "Vermont" brand-name shingles, pallets should weigh at least 3,600 pounds but less than 3,800. The file Pallet contains the weights (in pounds) from a sample of 368 pallets of "Boston" shingles and 330 pallets of "Vermont" shingles.

a. For the "Boston" shingles, construct a frequency distribution and a percentage distribution having eight class intervals, using 3,015, 3,050, 3,085, 3,120, 3,155, 3,190, 3,225, 3,260, and 3,295 as the class boundaries.

b. For the "Vermont" shingles, construct a frequency distribution and a percentage distribution having seven class intervals, using 3,550, 3,600, 3,650, 3,700, 3,750, 3,800, 3,850, and 3,900 as the class boundaries.

c. Construct percentage histograms for the "Boston" shingles and for the "Vermont" shingles.

d. Comment on the distribution of pallet weights for the "Boston" and "Vermont" shingles. Be sure to identify the percentage of pallets that are underweight and overweight.

**2.79** The data in the file `States` represent the results of the American Community Survey, a sampling of households taken in all states during the 2000 U.S. Census. For each of the variables average travel-to-work time in minutes, percentage of homes with eight or more rooms, median household income, and percentage of mortgage-paying homeowners whose housing costs exceed 30% of income:

a. Construct a frequency distribution and a percentage distribution.

b. Construct a histogram and a percentage polygon.

c. Construct a cumulative percentage distribution and plot a cumulative percentage polygon.

d. What conclusions about these four variables can you make based on the results of (a) through (c)?

**2.80** The data in the file `Protein` indicate calorie and cholesterol information concerning popular protein foods (fresh red meats, poultry, and fish).

Source: U.S. Department of Agriculture.

a. Construct a percentage histogram for the amount of calories.

b. Construct a percentage histogram for the amount of cholesterol.

c. What conclusions can you reach from your analyses in (a) and (b)?

**2.81** In Figure 2.15 on page 53, a scatter plot of the relationship between the cost of a fast-food hamburger meal and the cost of movie tickets in 10 different cities was constructed. The file `Cost of Living` also includes the overall cost index, the monthly rent for a two-bedroom apartment, the cost of a cup of coffee with service, the cost of dry-cleaning a men's blazer, and the cost of toothpaste.

a. Construct six separate scatter plots. For each, use the overall cost index as the Y axis. Use the monthly rent for a two-bedroom apartment, the costs of a cup of coffee with service, a fast-food hamburger meal, dry-cleaning a men's blazer, toothpaste, and movie tickets as the X axis.

b. What conclusions can you reach about the relationship of the overall cost index to these six variables?

**2.82** In Problem 2.41 on page 54, using the data in the file `Chicken`, you constructed a scatter plot of calories with the total fat content of chicken sandwiches.

a. Construct a scatter plot of calories on the Y axis and carbohydrates on the X axis.

b. Construct a scatter plot of calories on the Y axis and sodium on the X axis.

c. Which variable (total fat, carbohydrates, or sodium) seems to be most closely related to calories? Explain.

**2.83** The file `Gas` contains the weekly average price of gasoline in the United States from January 3, 2005, to April 2, 2007. Prices are in dollars per gallon.

Source: "U.S. Department of Energy," **www.eia.doe.gov**, April 3, 2007.

a. Construct a time-series plot.

b. What pattern, if any, is present in the data?

**2.84** The data contained in the file `Drink` represent the amount of soft drink filled in a sample of 50 consecutive 2-liter bottles. The results are listed horizontally in the order of being filled:

2.109 2.086 2.066 2.075 2.065 2.057 2.052 2.044 2.036 2.038

2.031 2.029 2.025 2.029 2.023 2.020 2.015 2.014 2.013 2.014

2.012 2.012 2.012 2.010 2.005 2.003 1.999 1.996 1.997 1.992

1.994 1.986 1.984 1.981 1.973 1.975 1.971 1.969 1.966 1.967

1.963 1.957 1.951 1.951 1.947 1.941 1.941 1.938 1.908 1.894

a. Construct a time-series plot for the amount of soft drink on the Y axis and the bottle number (going consecutively from 1 to 50) on the X axis.

b. What pattern, if any, is present in these data?

c. If you had to make a prediction of the amount of soft drink filled in the next bottle, what would you predict?

d. Based on the results of (a) through (c), explain why it is important to construct a time-series plot and not just a histogram, as was done in Problem 2.29 on page 48.

**2.85** The S&P 500 Index tracks the overall movement of the stock market by considering the stock prices of 500 large corporations. The data file `Stocks2006` contains weekly data for this index as well as the weekly closing stock price for three companies during 2006. The variables included are:

    WEEK—Week ending on date given
    S&P—Weekly closing value for the S&P 500 Index
    GE—Weekly closing stock price for General Electric
    TARGET—Weekly closing stock price for Target
    SARA LEE—Weekly closing stock price for Sara Lee

Source: Extracted from **finance.yahoo.com**, April 3, 2007.

a. Construct a time-series plot for the weekly closing values of the S&P 500 Index, General Electric, Target, and Sara Lee.

**b.** Explain any patterns present in the plots.

**c.** Write a short summary of your findings.

**2.86** **(Class Project)** Let each student in the class respond to the question "Which carbonated soft drink do you most prefer?" so that the teacher can tally the results into a summary table.

**a.** Convert the data to percentages and construct a Pareto chart.

**b.** Analyze the findings.

**2.87** **(Class Project)** Let each student in the class be cross-classified on the basis of gender (male, female) and current employment status (yes, no) so that the teacher can tally the results.

**a.** Construct a table with either row or column percentages, depending on which you think is more informative.

**b.** What would you conclude from this study?

**c.** What other variables would you want to know regarding employment in order to enhance your findings?

## Report Writing Exercises

**2.88** Referring to the results from Problem 2.78 on page 65 concerning the weight of "Boston" and "Vermont" shingles, write a report that evaluates whether the weight of the pallets of the two types of shingles are what the company expects. Be sure to incorporate tables and charts into the report.

**2.89** Referring to the results from Problem 2.72 on page 64 concerning the warranty claims on Firestone tires, write a report that evaluates warranty claims on Firestone tires sold on Ford SUVs. Be sure to incorporate tables and charts into the report.

## Team Project

The data file **Mutual Funds** contains information regarding nine variables from a sample of 868 mutual funds. The variables are:

Category—Type of stocks comprising the mutual fund (small cap, mid cap, large cap)

Objective—Objective of stocks comprising the mutual fund (growth or value)

Assets—In millions of dollars

Fees—Sales charges (no or yes)

Expense ratio—Ratio of expenses to net assets in percentage

2006 return—Twelve-month return in 2006

Three-year return—Annualized return, 2004–2006

Five-year return—Annualized return, 2002–2006

Risk—Risk-of-loss factor of the mutual fund (low, average, or high)

**2.90** For the expense ratio:

**a.** Construct a percentage histogram.

**b.** Plot percentage polygons of the expense ratio for mutual funds that have fees and mutual funds that do not have fees on the same graph.

**c.** What conclusions about the expense ratio can you reach based on the results of (a) and (b)?

**2.91** For the three-year annualized return from 2004 to 2006:

**a.** Construct a percentage histogram.

**b.** Plot percentage polygons of the three-year annualized return from 2004 to 2006 for growth mutual funds and value mutual funds on the same graph.

**c.** What conclusions about the three-year annualized return from 2004 to 2006 can you reach based on the results of (a) and (b)?

**2.92** For the five-year annualized return from 2002 to 2006:

**a.** Construct a percentage histogram.

**b.** Plot percentage polygons of the five-year annualized return from 2004 to 2006 for growth mutual funds and value mutual funds on the same graph.

**c.** What conclusions about the five-year annualized return from 2004 to 2006 can you reach based on the results of (a) and (b)?

## Student Survey Database

**2.93** Problem 1.27 on page 14 describes a survey of 50 undergraduate students (see the file **Undergradsurvey**). For these data, construct all the appropriate tables and charts and write a report summarizing your conclusions.

**2.94** Problem 1.27 on page 14 describes a survey of 50 undergraduate students (see the file **Undergradsurvey**).

**a.** Select a sample of 50 undergraduate students at your school and conduct a similar survey for those students.

**b.** For the data collected in (a), construct all the appropriate tables and charts and write a report summarizing your conclusions.

**c.** Compare the results of (b) to those of Problem 2.93.

**2.95** Problem 1.28 on page 14 describes a survey of 40 MBA students (see the file **Gradsurvey**). For these data, construct all appropriate tables and charts and write a report summarizing your conclusions.

**2.96** Problem 1.28 on page 14 describes a survey of 40 MBA students (see the file **Gradsurvey**).

**a.** Select a sample of 40 MBA students in your MBA program and conduct a similar survey for those students.

**b.** For the data collected in (a), construct all the appropriate tables and charts and write a report summarizing your conclusions.

**c.** Compare the results of (b) to those of Problem 2.95.

# MANAGING THE *SPRINGVILLE HERALD*

Advertising fees are an important source of revenue for any newspaper. In an attempt to boost these revenues and to minimize costly errors, the management of the *Herald* has established a task force charged with improving customer service in the advertising department. Open a Web browser and link to **www.prenhall.com/HeraldCase/Ad_Errors.htm** (or open the `Ad_Errors.htm` file in the Student CD-ROM's Herald Case folder) to review the task force's data collec-

tion. Identify the data that are important in describing the customer service problems. For each set of data you identify, construct the graphical presentation you think is most appropriate for the data and explain your choice. Also, suggest what other information concerning the different types of errors would be useful to examine. Offer possible courses of action for either the task force or management to take that would support the goal of improving customer service.

# WEB CASE

*In the Using Statistics scenario, you were asked to gather information to help make wise investment choices. Sources for such information include brokerage firms and investment counselors. Apply your knowledge about the proper use of tables and charts in this Web Case about the claims of foresight and excellence by a Springville financial services firm.*

Visit the EndRun Financial Services Web site at **www.prenhall.com/Springville/EndRun.htm** (or open the `EndRun.htm` file in the Student CD-ROM's Web Case folder). Review the company's investment claims and supporting data and then answer the following.

1. How does the presentation of the general information about EndRun on its home page affect your perception of the business?

2. Is EndRun's claim about having more winners than losers a fair and accurate reflection of the quality of its investment service? If you do not think that the claim is a fair and accurate one, provide an alternate presentation that you think is fair and accurate.

3. EndRun's "Big Eight" mutual funds are part of the sample found in the `Mutual Funds` worksheet. Is there any other relevant data from that file that could have been included in the Big Eight table? How would that new data alter your perception of EndRun's claims?

4. EndRun is proud that all Big Eight funds have gained in value over the past five years. Do you agree that EndRun should be proud of its selections? Why or why not?

# REFERENCES

1. Huff, D., *How to Lie with Statistics* (New York: Norton, 1954).
2. *Microsoft Excel 2007* (Redmond, WA: Microsoft Corporation, 2007).
3. *Minitab for Windows Version 15* (State College, PA: Minitab, Inc., 2006).
4. Tufte, E. R., *Beautiful Evidence* (Cheshire, CT: Graphics Press, 2006).
5. Tufte, E. R., *Envisioning Information* (Cheshire, CT: Graphics Press, 1990).
6. Tufte, E. R., *The Visual Display of Quantitative Information*, 2nd ed. (Cheshire, CT: Graphics Press, 2002).
7. Tufte, E. R., *Visual Explanations* (Cheshire, CT: Graphics Press, 1997).
8. Wainer, H., *Visual Revelations: Graphical Tales of Fate and Deception from Napoleon Bonaparte to Ross Perot* (New York: Copernicus/Springer-Verlag, 1997).

# Appendix E2
## Using Microsoft Excel for Tables and Charts

## E2.1 INTRODUCTION

This appendix describes how to use Microsoft Excel to create tables and charts. If you plan to use PHStat2 with Microsoft Excel, read Appendix P2 "Using PHStat2 for Tables and Charts." Because Excel 2007 changes many table and chart features, some appendix sections contain paired sets of instructions, such as Sections E2.2A and E2.2B, one for use with Excel 97–2003, the other for use with Excel 2007. Use only the set of instructions that applies to the Excel version that you have.

Before continuing, you should review the material in Appendix E1 and Appendix C if you have not done so already.

Occasionally PHStat2 will be the only reasonable way to accomplish a task using Microsoft Excel. In such cases, an Excel appendix section will refer you to the appropriate PHStat2 appendix section.

## E2.2 CREATING SUMMARY TABLES

To create a summary table from unsummarized data, you create a PivotTable. To create a summary table from data already summarized in table form, enter the contents of the table into a blank worksheet, using row 1 cells for column headings.

You create a PivotTable by dragging the variable names of the unsummarized data into a form or template. Because the process differs between Excel 97–2003 and Excel 2007, use the instructions of either Sections E2.2A or E2.2B to complete this task.

## E2.2A CREATING PIVOTTABLES (EXCEL 97–2003)

To create a PivotTable in Excel 97–2003, open to the worksheet that contains your unsummarized data and select **Data → PivotTable Report** (Excel 97) or **Data → PivotTable and PivotChart Report** (Excel 2000–2003). When you make these selections you start the PivotTable Wizard, a sequence of three dialog boxes (four in Excel 97) that step you through the process of creating a PivotTable. Figure E2.1 shows the dialog boxes for Excel 2003. (Other versions have similar dialog boxes; Excel 97 uses four dialog boxes, breaking the third box into two.)

You step through these dialog boxes by clicking **Next** to advance to the next dialog box or **Back** to move back to a previous one. At any point, you can click **Cancel** to stop creating a PivotTable or click **Finish** to end the wizard and create a PivotTable. To create a summary table, make the following entries in the Wizard Step dialog boxes:

**Wizard Step 1**   Click **Microsoft Excel list or database** as the source data and **PivotTable** as the report type. (You do not select a report type in Microsoft Excel 97; PivotTable is assumed.)

**Wizard Step 2**   Enter the cell range of the data to be summarized in the PivotTable. This cell range must contain variable labels (column headings) in the first row of the range because the wizard, in Step 3, will use the cells in the first row as the names for your variables.

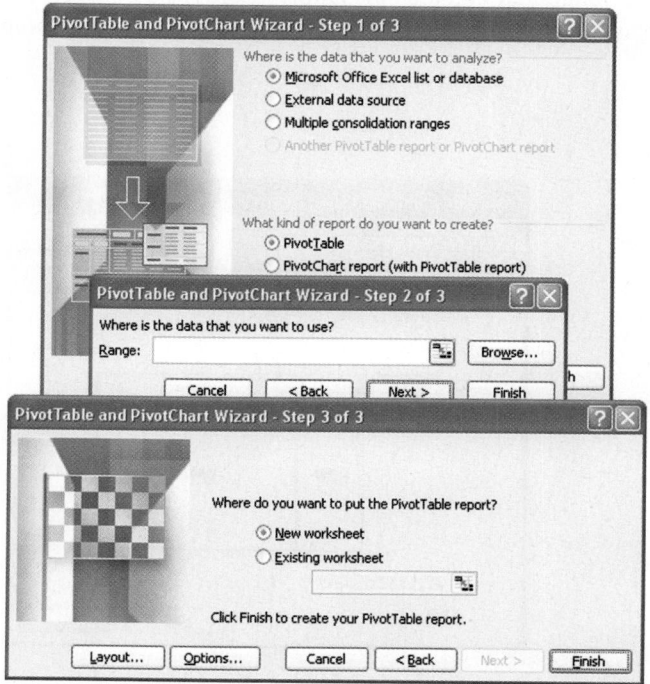

**FIGURE E2.1** PivotTable Wizard steps (Excel 2003)

**Wizard Step 3**   First, click the **New worksheet** option as the location for your PivotTable. Then click **Layout** to display the Layout dialog box (see Figure E2.2). Design your table using the instructions in the next paragraph and then click **OK** to return to the Step 3 box. Then, click **Options** to display the PivotTable Options dialog box (see Figure E2.2). Enter **0** as the **For empty cells, show** value and click **OK** to return to the Wizard Step 3 dialog box. Then, click **Finish** to create the PivotTable.

(If you use Excel 97, the Layout dialog box appears as the Step 3 dialog box. When you click **Next** in this box, you then see a Step 4 dialog box that contains location options. There is no Options button in either the Step 3 or Step 4 dialog boxes in Excel 97.)

In the Layout dialog box of Step 3, drag the label of the variable to be summarized and drop it in the ROW area. Drag a second copy of this same label and drop it in the DATA area. This second label changes to **Count of variable** name to indicate that a count, or tally, of the occurrences of each category will be shown in the DATA area.

After Excel creates the PivotTable, close any floating PivotTable toolbar windows. Enter a title in cell A1 of the new worksheet that contains your PivotTable. Also, rename the new worksheet, using a descriptive name. In cell C4, enter **Percentage** and in cell C5, enter the formula in the form $=B5/B\$n$, in which $n$ is the row that contains the Grand Total. (If you do not understand the significance of the $ symbol, you can review Section E1.7.) For example, if the Grand Total row is row 8, enter $=B5/B\$8$. Copy this formula down through all the category rows and format the cell range that contains these formulas for percentage display. Further adjust the table display as is necessary, using

Section E1.7 as your guide. (You may also need to adjust the width of columns by dragging the column rules at the top of the worksheet.)

## E2.2B CREATING PIVOTTABLES (EXCEL 2007)

To create a PivotTable in Excel 2007, open to the worksheet that contains your unsummarized data and select **Insert → PivotTable**. In the Create PivotTable dialog box (see Figure E2.3), leave the **Select a table or range** option selected and change, if necessary, the **Table/Range** cell range. (In Figure E2.3, the cell range is for the mutual funds data found in the Data worksheet of **Mutual Funds.xls**.) Select the **New Worksheet** option and click **OK**.

In the PivotTable Field List task pane, drag the label of the variable to be summarized and drop it in the **Row Labels** box. Drag a second copy of this same label and drop it in the **Σ Values** box. This second label changes to **Count of variable name** to indicate that a count, or tally, of the occurrences of each category will be shown in the DATA area.

Right-click the PivotTable and click **Table Options** in the shortcut menu that appears. In the PivotTable Options dialog box (a reorganized version of the older one shown in Figure E2.2), click the **Layout & Format** tab, check **For empty cells show**, enter **0** as its value, and then click **OK**. Close the PivotTable Field List task pane. Enter a title in cell A1 of the new worksheet that contains your PivotTable. Also, rename the new worksheet, using a descriptive name.

In cell C4, enter **Percentage** and in cell C5, enter the formula in the form $=B5/B\$n$, in which $n$ is the row that

**FIGURE E2.2** PivotTable Layout and Options dialog boxes (Excel 2000–2003)

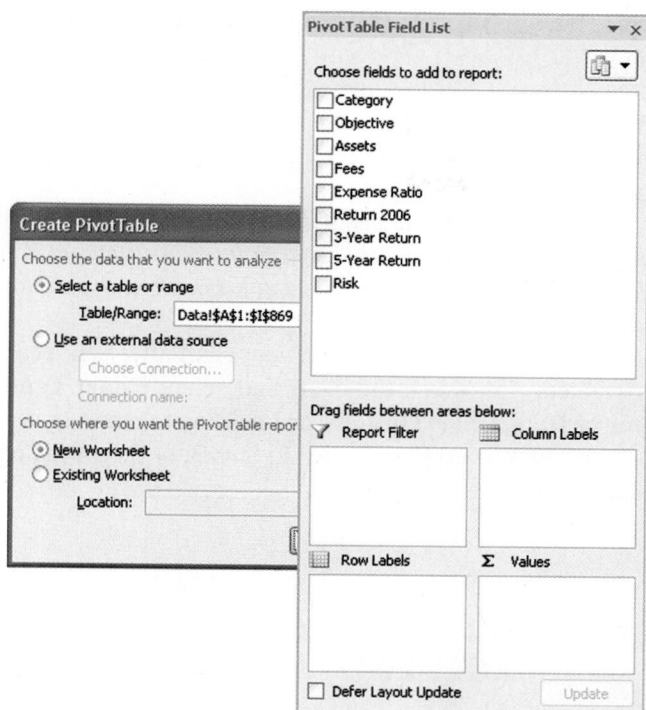

**FIGURE E2.3** Create PivotTable dialog box and PivotTable Field List task pane (Excel 2007)

contains the Grand Total. (If you do not understand the significance of the $ symbol, you can review Section E1.7.) For example, if the Grand Total row is row 8, enter =B5/B$8. Copy this formula down through all the category rows and format the cell range that contains these formulas for percentage display. Further adjust the table display as is necessary, using Section E1.7 as your guide. (You may also need to adjust the width of columns by dragging the column rules at the top of the worksheet.)

## E2.3 CREATING CHARTS: OVERVIEW

Although Microsoft Excel contains many features that create tables and charts, you can easily get improper results or otherwise get frustrated if you do not properly organize your worksheet data first. In Excel, charts are linked to sets of worksheet data, and the arrangement of that data influences the chart Excel creates. For example, when creating a scatter plot, Excel will always consider the first column of data as the $X$ variable data. If you wanted to create the scatter plot of the cost of a fast-food hamburger meal and the cost of two movie tickets (Figure 2.15 on page 53), you would want to place the meal costs in a column to the left of the column containing the ticket costs.

The best way to avoid arrangement errors is to place your data on a separate worksheet using consecutive columns starting with column A. (Data worksheets in the Student CD-ROM Excel workbook files have this arrangement.) If you are using Microsoft Excel 2007, you should also select your data by dragging the mouse over your data, as explained in Appendix C, to prevent Excel 2007 from making a "bad" guess as to the table or chart you seek.

With these simple steps you will eliminate the most common errors that occur when using Excel charting features. However, creating a chart using Excel charting features does not necessarily end your task. Many charts will need minor reformatting to pass the strictest presentation standards. Illustrations in this book reflect such formatting and appendix sections throughout the book include reformatting instructions when appropriate.

Some charts, especially those created in Excel 97–2003, contain colored backgrounds (typically gray) that can interfere with clear printing or displaying of the chart. To remove the background in an Excel 97–2003 chart, right-click the background and click **Format Plot Area** in the shortcut menu. In the dialog box that appears, click the **None** option of the **Area** group and click **OK**. (This was done for all the charts shown in this book.) To remove a background in Excel 2007, right-click the chart background and select **Layout → Plot Area** and select **None** in the Plot Area gallery.

Occasionally, you may open to a chart sheet and see only part of a (too-large) chart or see a (too-small) chart surrounded by a too-large frame mat. To display an optimally sized chart in Excel 97–2003, open to the chart sheet and press **Esc**. Select **View → Zoom** and then, in the Zoom dialog box, select the **Fit selection** option and click **OK**. To display an optimally sized chart in Excel 2007, use the Zoom slider on the lower right of the Excel window frame or click the chart and then select **Format** and use the items in the Size group. Finally, if the symbols, captions, and/or legends and titles prove too big or too small for you, you can usually change these elements by right-clicking over them and clicking the shortcut menu choice that contains the word **Format**.

If you use PHStat2, the charts created by PHStat2 will generally include these minor reformatting and enhancements discussed above.

## E2.3A CREATING CHARTS (EXCEL 97–2003)

To create a chart in Excel 97–2003, open to the worksheet containing your unsummarized data and select **Insert → Chart** to begin the Chart Wizard, a sequence of four dialog boxes that step you through the process of creating a chart. (Figure E2.4 shows these dialog boxes for Excel 2003. Excel 97, 2000, and 2002 have similar sets of dialog boxes.) To create a chart, make the following entries in the Wizard Step dialog boxes:

**Wizard Step 1** Choose the chart type from either the **Standard Types** or **Custom Types** tab. Most of the charts you create in this text are chart types found in the Standard Types tab.

**Wizard Step 2** Enter the cell range of the data to be charted in the **Data Range** tab. For some types of charts, you also enter the cell range or ranges that contain chart labeling information in the **Series** tab. Cell ranges in the Series tab must always be entered with their worksheet names as a formula, in the form =*SheetName*!*CellRange*.

**Wizard Step 3** Enter titles and select formatting options for your chart in the various tabs of this dialog box. Unless told otherwise in later instructions, make the following entries and selections:

In the **Titles** tab, enter a title and enter axis labels if appropriate. In the **Axes** tab, click both the (X) axis and (Y) axis check boxes and click **Automatic** under the (X) axis check box. In the **Gridlines** tab, clear all the check boxes. In the **Legend** tab, clear the **Show legend** check box. In the **Data Labels** tab, click the **None** option under the **Data labels** heading. In the **Data Table** tab, clear the **Show data table** check box. (Not all tabs are displayed for all chart types. If a tab is not displayed, skip the instructions for the tab.)

**Wizard Step 4** Click the **As new sheet** option to place the chart on its own chart sheet. Then click **Finish** to create the chart.

*Because the Wizard Step 4 dialog box instructions never vary, they are not explicitly listed in later instructions. You should always click **As new sheet** and **Finish** in this dialog box when you create a chart.*

If you discover a mistake in your chart after your chart is created, right-click the chart and select **Chart Type, Source Data, Chart Options**, or **Location** to return to versions of the Wizard Step 1, Step 2, Step 3, or Step 4 dialog boxes, respectively.

## E2.3B CREATING CHARTS (EXCEL 2007)

To create a chart in Excel 2007, open to the worksheet that contains your unsummarized data. Select the cell range of the data to be charted. If your cell range contains two non-

**FIGURE E2.4** Chart Wizard dialog boxes (Excel 2003)

**FIGURE E2.5** Selecting a chart sub-type (Excel 2007)

adjacent areas, hold down the **Ctrl** key as you drag and select each area. Select **Insert** and in the **Charts** group, click the chart type. From the drop-down gallery that appears, click the chart sub-type you want. To help distinguish sub-types, move the mouse pointer over a sub-type and wait for a description to be displayed. In Figure E2.5, the description for the bar chart "clustered bar" sub-type is displayed.

Customize your chart by clicking the chart and selecting the **Layout** tab of the Chart Tools ribbon group (or PivotChart Tools, if the chart is based on a PivotTable). Review the settings for the members of the **Labels** and **Axes** groups in this tab. Unless told otherwise in later instructions, make the following entries and selections (for a given chart type, some of these items may be disabled and not available):

Click **Chart Title** and choose either **Centered Overlay Title** or **Above Chart**. Click **Axes Titles → Primary Horizontal Axis Title → Title Below Axis**. Click **Axes Titles → Primary Vertical Axis Title → Rotated Title**. (For charts with secondary axes, select **Title Below Axis** as the **Secondary Horizontal Axis Title** and **None** as the **Secondary Vertical Axis Title**.) Click **Data Labels → None** and click **Data Table → None**.

Click **Axes → Primary Horizontal Title → Show Left to Right Axis**. Click **Axes → Primary Vertical Title → Show Default Axis**. Some charts have secondary axes; for such charts, select **None** as the **Secondary Horizontal**

**Axis Title** and **Show Default Axis** as the **Secondary Vertical Axis Title.** Click **Gridlines.** Select **None** for both the **Primary Horizontal Gridlines** and **Primary Vertical Gridlines**. Also select **None** for secondary gridlines, if the chart contains those as well.

Excel 2007 creates charts on worksheets. To move a chart to its own chart sheet (recommended), right-click the chart frame and click **Move Chart** in the shortcut menu that appears. In the Move Chart dialog box that appears, select the **New sheet** option and click **OK**.

## E2.4 CREATING BAR AND PIE CHARTS: OVERVIEW

You create bar and pie charts from summary tables such as PivotTables using Excel charting features. You cannot create bar and pie charts directly from unsummarized data using Excel unless you use PHStat2.

## E2.4A CREATING BAR AND PIE CHARTS (EXCEL 97–2003)

Open to the worksheet that contains your summary table. If your summary table is a PivotTable, click a cell that is outside your PivotTable. Select **Insert → Chart** to begin the

Chart Wizard and make the following entries in the Wizard Step dialog boxes:

**Wizard Step 1**   Click the **Standard Types** tab. For a bar chart, click **Bar** as the **Chart type** and then click the first **Chart sub-type** choice, labeled **Clustered Bar** when selected. For a pie chart, click **Pie** as the **Chart type** and then click the first **Chart sub-type** choice, labeled **Pie** when selected.

**Wizard Step 2**   Click the **Data Range** tab and enter the cell range of the category labels and the frequency counts as the **Data range**. If you used the instructions in Section E2.2 to create your summary table, this range will always start with cell A4 and end with a cell in column B. (You do not include the column C cells that contain the percentages.) Click the **Columns** option if it is visible. In some Excel versions the model chart shown in the dialog box contains additional boxed labels that you can ignore for now.

**Wizard Step 3**   Click the **Titles** tab. Enter a title as the **Chart title** and, if you are creating a bar chart, enter appropriate values for the **Category (X) axis** and **Value (Y) axis** titles. For a bar chart, click, in turn, the **Axes**, **Gridlines**, **Legend**, **Data Labels**, and **Data Table** tabs and adjust the settings, as discussed in Section E2.3A on page 72. For a pie chart, click the **Legend** tab and clear **Show legend** and then click the **Data Labels** tab. If you are using Excel 97 or Excel 2000, click the **Show label and percent** option; otherwise, click **Category name** and **Percentage**.

If the chart created contains the additional boxed labels, such as "Drop Page Fields Here," that you ignored in the Step 2 dialog box, right-click the category drop-down list on the chart sheet and click **Hide PivotChart Field Buttons**. This eliminates the clutter and makes your chart look more like the ones throughout Chapter 2.

## E2.4B CREATING BAR AND PIE CHARTS (EXCEL 2007)

Open to the worksheet that contains your summary table. Click a cell inside your table and then select **Insert**. For a bar chart, click **Column** in the Charts group, and then click **Clustered Column** in the chart gallery. For a pie chart, click **Pie** in the Charts group, and then click **Pie** in the chart gallery. Adjust chart settings as discussed in Section E2.3B on page 73.

## E2.5 CREATING PARETO CHARTS: OVERVIEW

You create a Pareto chart from a modified summary table by using Excel charting features. You modify your summary table by adding a column for cumulative percentage. If you have used the Section E2.2 instructions to create a PivotTable, enter the heading **Cumulative Pctage** in cell D4 and enter the formula =C5 in cell D5. In cell D6, enter the formula =C6+D5 and copy this formula down through all the category rows of the summary table. Format the column D cell range that contains formulas for percentage display. Adjust the number of decimals displayed and the width of column D as necessary.

If you use Excel 2007, click cell B5 (the first frequency) and select **Home → Sort & Filter** (in the Editing group) → **Sort Largest to Smallest**. If you use Excel 97–2003, right-click cell A4 and click **Field Settings** in the shortcut menu (**Field**, if using Microsoft Excel 97). In the PivotTable Field dialog box that appears (see Figure E2.6), click **Advanced**. In the PivotTable Field Advanced Options dialog box that appears (also see Figure E2.4), select the **Descending** option and **Count of *variable*** from the **Using field** drop-down list. Click **OK** to return to the PivotTable Field dialog box and then click **OK** in that dialog box to return to the worksheet. (These last steps reorder the category rows in the table in descending order.)

With these changes, you can proceed to creating the actual Pareto chart using the instructions appropriate for the Excel version you use.

**FIGURE E2.6** PivotTable Field and PivotTable Field Advanced Options dialog boxes (Excel 97–2003)

## E2.5A CREATING A PARETO CHART (EXCEL 97–2003)

With your workbook opened to the worksheet that contains the modified summary table, click a cell that is outside the summary table. Select **Insert → Chart** to begin the Chart Wizard and make the following entries in the Wizard Step dialog boxes:

**Wizard Step 1** Click the **Custom Types** tab. Click **Built-in** and then click **Line - Column on 2 Axes** as the **Chart type**.

**Wizard Step 2** Click the **Data Range** tab. Enter the cell range of the percentage and cumulative percentage frequencies, without their column headings, in the **Data range** edit box. This range will always start with cell C4 and end with a cell in column D. Click the **Columns** option in the **Series in** group and then click the **Series** tab. Enter as a **formula** the column A cell range that contains the category labels as the **Category (X) axis labels**. Leave the **Second category (X) axis labels** box blank, if it appears.

**Wizard Step 3** Click the **Titles** tab. Enter a title as the **Chart title**, the name of the variable in the **Category (X) axis** edit box, and **Percentage** in the **Value (Y) axis** edit box. Leave the other two boxes blank. Click, in turn, the **Gridlines**, **Legend**, **Data Labels**, and **Data Table** tabs and use the settings discussed in Section E2.3A.

The Pareto chart that the wizard creates contains a secondary (right) *Y*-axis scale that improperly extends past 100%. To correct this error, right-click that axis (you will see the popup message **Secondary Value Axis** when your mouse is properly positioned) and click **Format Axis** in the shortcut menu. In the **Scale** tab of the Format Axis dialog box, change the **Maximum** value to **1** and click **OK**. Right-click the primary (left) axis and repeat these instructions if the left axis needs rescaling too (you will see the popup message **Value Axis** when your mouse is properly positioned).

## E2.5B CREATING A PARETO CHART (EXCEL 2007)

Select the cell range of the data to be charted. (This range will begin with cell C4, if you used the Section E2.2B instructions to create a PivotTable.) Select **Insert → Column** (in the Charts group) and select the first sub-type, identified as **Clustered Column** when you move the mouse pointer over that sub-type and pause. Select **Format**

**FIGURE E2.7** The Select Data Source dialog box (Excel 2007)

and select the cumulative percentage series from the drop-down list in the Current Selection group. Then select **Format Selection** (from the same group) and in the Format Data Series dialog box select the **Secondary Axis** in the **Series Options** panel and click **Close**. With the cumulative percentage series still selected in the Current Selection group, select **Design → Change Chart Type**, and in the **Change Chart Type** gallery, select the line chart identified as **Line with Markers** and click **OK**.

If your chart contains extraneous plots—for example, a plot of percentage frequencies—delete such plots one series at a time by doing the following: Select **Format** and then select an extraneous series from the drop-down list in the Current Selection group. Select **Design → Select Data**. In the Select Data Source dialog box (see Figure E2.7), select the extraneous **Legend Entries** series (**Percentage** in Figure E2.7) and click **Remove** and then **OK**.

Relocate your chart to a chart sheet and customize your chart, using the instructions in Section E.2.3B. If the secondary (right) *Y*-axis scale improperly extends past 100%, right-click the axis and click **Format Axis** in the shortcut menu. In the **Scale** tab of the Format Axis dialog box, change the value in the **Maximum** edit box to **1** and click **Close**. Right-click the primary (left) axis and repeat these instructions if the left axis needs rescaling too.

## E2.6 CREATING ORDERED ARRAYS

To create an ordered array, first organize your worksheet so that each variable appears in its own column, enter a variable column heading in row 1, and enter the values for the variable starting in row 2. Select the data to be sorted. If you use Excel 97–2003, select **Data ➔ Sort**. In the Sort dialog box, select the variable to be sorted from the Sort by drop-down list. Click the **Ascending** option button, click **Header row**, and click **OK**. If you use Excel 2007, select **Home ➔ Sort & Filter** (in the Editing group) ➔ **Sort Smallest to Largest**.

## E2.7 CREATING STEM-AND-LEAF DISPLAYS

No Microsoft Excel features directly create stem-and-leaf displays. Use PHStat2 Section P2.5 to create a stem-and-leaf display in Excel.

## E2.8 CREATING BINS FOR FREQUENCY DISTRIBUTIONS

To create frequency distributions using Excel features, you must first translate your class groupings into what Excel calls **bins**.

Bins are numbers in an ordered list that define ranges for each row of a frequency distribution or each bar of a histogram. Unlike class groupings, which have well-defined lower and upper boundary values, the boundary values of each bin are implied. For a particular bin number, the range defined is all values that are less than or equal to the bin number and that are greater than the previous bin number, which must be a lesser value.

In Chapter 2, Tables 2.7– 2.11 use class groupings in the form *valueA but less than valueB*. You can translate class groupings in this form into nearly equivalent bins by creating a list of bin numbers that are slightly less than each *valueB* that appears in the class groupings. For example, the Table 2.7 class groupings on page 37 could be translated into nearly equivalent bins by using this list of bin numbers: 14.99 ("slightly less" than 15.0), 19.99, 24.99, 29.99, 34.99, 39.99, 44.99, 49.99, 54.99, 59.99, 64.99, 69.99, and 74.99).

If you have class groupings in the form "all values from *valueA* to *valueB*," such as the set 0.0 through 4.9, 5.0 through 9.9, 10.0 through 14.9, and 15.0 through 19.9, you can approximate each class grouping by choosing a bin number slightly more than each *valueB*, as in this list of bin numbers: 4.99 (slightly more than 4.9), 9.99, 14.99, and 19.99.

Because the first bin number always represents a range with no explicit lower boundary (other than negative infinity), a first bin can never have a midpoint. (You may have noticed in this chapter that in the charts in which midpoints are used as labels, the first bin is labeled with – and not with a midpoint.) To enter a list of bin numbers, use a blank column in the worksheet that contains your unsummarized data, entering the column heading "Bins" in the row 1 cell.

Unlike the frequency distributions shown in Tables 2.8, 2.10, and 2.13, you typically include frequency, percentage frequency, and cumulative percentage frequencies as columns of one table and not as separate tables. Also, unlike what is done in Chapter 2, in Excel, you create frequency distributions for individual categories, one at a time (e.g., growth funds or value funds) and not frequency distributions that contain two categories (e.g., growth and value funds). To create multiple category tables, such as Tables 2.8, 2.10, and 2.13, you must combine columns from the individual tables using copy-and-paste operations.

## E2.9 CREATING FREQUENCY DISTRIBUTIONS AND HISTOGRAMS

To create frequency distributions and histograms from unsummarized data, use the ToolPak **Histogram** procedure. This procedure requires that you first translate your class groupings into bins, as explained in the previous section.

Open to the worksheet that contains the unsummarized data and verify that bin values have been placed in their own column. Begin the ToolPak add-in and select **Histogram** from the **Analysis Tools** list and then click **OK**. In the Histogram dialog box (see Figure E2.8), enter the cell range of the data to be summarized as the **Input Range**. Enter the cell range of the list of bin numbers (including the column heading "Bins") as the **Bin Range**. (If you leave Bin Range blank, the procedure creates a set of bins for you, but such bins are often not as well chosen as the ones you can specify yourself.) Click **Labels** to indicate that the first cells of the Input Range and Bin Range contain a label. Click **New Worksheet Ply** and **Cumulative Percentage**, and then click **Chart Output** (if you want to create a histogram). Click **OK** to create the frequency distribution (and histogram) on a new worksheet.

**FIGURE E2.8** The Data Analysis Histogram dialog box

The frequency distribution that the ToolPak creates improperly contains an open-ended bin labeled **More**. To eliminate the More class, first manually add the frequency count of the More row to the count of the preceding bin and set the cumulative percentage of the preceding bin to 100%. Then, select the entire row containing the More row. Next, select **Edit → Delete** in Excel 97–2003 or right-click the selected row in Excel 2007. In the Delete dialog box, click **Shift cells up** and then click **OK**.

As you correct your frequency distribution, your histogram also changes, and the bar representing the incorrect More group disappears. However, the histogram will still contain these errors: There are gaps between the bars, the bins are labeled with their maximum bin values and not with their midpoint values, and the secondary *Y*-axis scale exceeds 100%.

**To eliminate the gaps between bars**, right-click inside one of the histogram bars. (You will see a popup message that begins with **Series 'Frequency'** when your mouse is properly positioned.) Click **Format Data Series** in the shortcut menu to display the Format Data Series dialog box. If you use Excel 97–2003, click the **Options** tab, change the value of **Gap width** to **0**, and click **OK**. If you use Excel 2007, move the **Gap Width** slider to **No Gap** in the **Series Options** panel of this dialog box.

**To change the bin labels**, enter the list of midpoint values in column D of the worksheet. Cell D2 should contain the heading **Midpoints** and cell D3 should contain – – – (which you should enter as '– to avoid an error). Right-click the tinted background of the chart. (You will see the ToolTip **Plot Area** when your mouse is properly positioned.) Click **Source Data** (Excel 97–2003) or **Select Data** (Excel 2007) in the shortcut menu. If you use Excel 97–2003, select the **Series** tab in the Source Data dialog box and enter the cell range of the midpoints as a formula, in the form =*SheetName*!*CellRange*, in the **Category (X) axis labels** box. Then delete the entry for the **Second category(X) axis labels** and click **OK**. If you use Excel 2007, click the **Edit** button under the **Horizontal (Categories) Axis Labels** heading in the Select Data Source dialog box. In the Axis Labels dialog box, enter the cell range of the midpoints as a formula, in the form =*SheetName*!*CellRange*, and click **OK**. (This range should start with the first midpoint value and not with the midpoint column heading.) Click **OK** a second time (in the original dialog box) to complete the task.

**To rescale the secondary *Y*-axis**, right-click on the secondary (right) *Y*-axis. (You will see a popup message that includes the words **Secondary** and **Axis** when your mouse is properly positioned.) Click **Format Axis** in the shortcut menu. If you use Excel 97–2003, change the **Maximum** in the **Scale** tab of the Format Axis dialog box to **1** and click **OK**. If you use Excel 2007, select the **Fixed** option for **Maximum** and enter **1** as the maximum value in

the **Axis Options** panel of the Format Axis dialog box, and then click **OK**.

If you want to add a percentage frequency column to the frequency distribution, select column C and then select **Insert → Columns**. In the new column C, enter the heading **Percentage** in cell C2. Enter the formula =**B3/SUM(B:B)** in cell C3 and copy the formula down the column through the rest of the frequency distribution. Format column C for percentage display to complete the column.

## E2.10 CREATING PERCENTAGE AND CUMULATIVE PERCENTAGE POLYGONS

No Microsoft Excel features directly create percentage or cumulative percentage polygons. Use PHStat2 Section P2.7 to create a polygon in Excel.

## E2.11 CREATING CONTINGENCY TABLES: OVERVIEW

You create a contingency table from unsummarized data by creating a PivotTable using instructions adapted from Section E2.2. To create a contingency table from data already summarized in table form, enter the contents of the table into a blank worksheet, using the column A and row 1 cells for row and column headings.

## E2.11A CREATING CONTINGENCY TABLES (EXCEL 97–2003)

Adapt the instructions of Section E2.2A, "Creating PivotTables (Excel 97–2003)." When you get to the Step 3 instructions, modify them as follows. In the Layout dialog box in Step 3, first drag the label of the first variable to be summarized and drop it in the ROW area. Drag a second copy of this same label and drop it in the DATA area. (The label changes to **Count of variable name**.) Then drag the label of the second variable and drop it in the COLUMN area. In the PivotTable Options dialog box, also in Step 3, verify that both **Grand total for columns** and **Grand totals for rows** are checked (they should be) and that you have entered **0** as the **For empty cells, show** value. (Excel 97 does not contain this options dialog box.)

## E2.11B CREATING CONTINGENCY TABLES (EXCEL 2007)

Adapt the instructions of Section E2.2B, "Creating PivotTables (Excel 2007)." When you get to the instructions for using the PivotTable Field List task pane, modify them as follows. In the PivotTable Field List task pane, drag the label of the variable to be summarized and drop it in the **Row Labels** box. Drag a second copy of this same label and drop it in the **Σ Values** box. (This second label changes to **Count of variable name**.) Then drag the label of the second variable and drop it in the **Column Labels** area. When you later right-click the PivotTable, click **Pivot Table Options** in the shortcut menu. In the **Total & Filters** tab of the PivotTable Options dialog box, verify that both **Show grand totals for columns** and **Show grand totals for rows** are checked. Also, as stated in Section E2.2B, click the **Layout & Format** tab, check **For empty cells show**, and enter **0** as its value, and then click **OK**.

## E2.12 CREATING SIDE-BY-SIDE CHARTS

You use Excel charting features to create a side-by-side chart from a contingency table of two categorical variables.

### E2.12A CREATING SIDE-BY-SIDE CHARTS (EXCEL 97–2003)

To create a side-by-side chart, open to the worksheet containing the contingency table. First, click a cell that is outside the contingency table. Then, select **Insert ➔ Chart** to begin the Chart Wizard and make the following entries in the Wizard Step dialog boxes:

**Wizard Step 1** Click **Bar** from the **Standard Types Chart type** box and leave the first **Chart sub-type** selected.

**Wizard Step 2** If you are using a PivotTable, click the PivotTable when the **Data range** box is selected to have Excel fill in the proper cell range. If you are using a manually entered contingency table, enter the rectangular range that excludes the total row and the total column but that includes the row and column headings.

**Wizard Step 3** Click the **Titles** tab. Enter a title as the **Chart title** and appropriate values for the **Category (X) axis** and **Value (Y) axis** titles. (Unlike other charts, Excel considers the horizontal axis to be the *Value (Y) axis* and the vertical axis of this chart to be the *Category (X) axis*, which is different from what you might otherwise expect.) Click the **Legend** tab and click **Show legend**. Use the formatting settings for **Axes**, **Gridlines**, **Data Labels**, and **Data Table** tabs that are given in Section E2.3A on page 72.

If field buttons appear on the chart, right-click any button and click **Hide PivotChart Field Buttons** in the shortcut menu.

### E2.12B CREATING SIDE-BY-SIDE CHARTS (EXCEL 2007)

To create a side-by-side chart, open to the worksheet that contains the contingency table. If your contingency table is also a PivotTable, click a cell inside the PivotTable; otherwise, select the cell range of the contingency table, including row and column headings, but excluding the total row and total column.

Select **Insert ➔ Bar** and click the **Clustered Bar** gallery choice. If your chart contains reversed row and column variables and is not based on a PivotTable, right-click the chart and click **Select Data** in the shortcut menu. In the Select Data Source dialog box, click **Switch Row/Column** and then click **OK**. If your chart has reversed variables and is based on a PivotTable, you have to reorder your variables in the PivotTable in order to get the correct chart. Finish by relocating your chart to a chart sheet and customizing your chart, using the instructions in Section E.2.3B on page 73, with this exception: When you click **Legend**, select **Show Legend at Right**.

## E2.13 CREATING SCATTER PLOTS: OVERVIEW

You use Excel charting features to create scatter plots. To create a scatter plot, the variable columns to be plotted must be arranged $X$ variable column first, then $Y$ variable column, reading left-to-right. (If your data are arranged $Y$ then $X$, first cut and paste the $Y$ variable column so it appears to the right of the $X$ variable column before continuing.)

### E2.13A CREATING SCATTER PLOTS (EXCEL 97–2003)

Open to the worksheet containing the properly arranged columns. Select **Insert ➔ Chart** (to begin the Chart Wizard) and make the following entries in the Wizard Step dialog boxes:

**Wizard Step 1** Click **XY (Scatter)** from the Standard Types Chart type box and click the first Chart sub-type.

**Wizard Step 2** Enter the cell range of the two variables in the **Data range** box and select the **Columns** option. If the two variables are in nonadjacent columns, first type or point to the cell range of the first variable, then type a comma, then type or point to the cell range of the second variable, and then press **Enter**. Do not make any entries in the **Series** tab of this dialog box.

**Wizard Step 3**   Click the **Titles** tab. Enter a title as the **Chart title** and enter appropriate values for the **Value (X) axis** and **Value (Y) axis** titles. Click, in turn, the **Axes**, **Gridlines**, **Legend**, and **Data Labels** tabs and use the formatting settings given in Section E2.3A on page 72.

## E2.13B CREATING SCATTER PLOTS (EXCEL 2007)

Open to the worksheet containing the properly arranged columns. Select **Insert → Scatter** and click the **Scatter with only Markers** gallery choice. Finish by relocating your chart to a chart sheet and customizing your chart using the instructions in Section E.2.3B on page 73.

## E2.14 CREATING TIME-SERIES PLOTS

You create time-series plots by using Excel charting features with a time-series worksheet in which the time periods have been entered into columns. If your data are arranged with the numerical variable before the time variable, first cut and paste the numerical variable column so it appears to the right of the time variable column before continuing.

## E2.14A CREATING A TIME-SERIES PLOT (EXCEL 97–2003)

Open to the worksheet containing the properly arranged columns. Select **Insert → Chart** to begin the Chart Wizard

and make the following entries in the Wizard Step dialog boxes:

**Wizard Step 1**   Click **Line** from the Standard Types Chart type box and select the first Chart sub-type in the second row, identified as **Line with markers displayed at each data value**.

**Wizard Step 2**   Enter the cell range of the two variables in the **Data range** box and select the **Columns** option. If the variables are in nonadjacent columns, first type or point to the cell range of the first variable, then type a comma, then type or point to the cell range of the second variable, and then press **Enter**. Do not make any entries in the **Series** tab of this dialog box.

**Wizard Step 3**   Click the **Titles** tab. Enter a title as the **Chart title** and enter appropriate values for the **Value (X) axis** and **Value (Y) axis** titles. Click, in turn, the **Axes**, **Gridlines**, **Legend**, **Data Labels**, and **Data Table** tabs and use the formatting settings that are given in Section E2.3A on page 72.

## E2.14B CREATING A TIME-SERIES PLOT (EXCEL 2007)

Open to the worksheet containing the properly arranged columns. In the Select Data Source dialog box, select **Insert → XY (Scatter) → Scatter with Straight Lines and Markers**. Finish by relocating your chart to a chart sheet and customizing your chart using the instructions in Section E.2.3B on page 73.

# Appendix P2
## Using PHStat2 for Tables and Charts

## P2.1 INTRODUCTION

Before continuing, you should review the material in Appendix P1 that presents a general introduction to using PHStat2. You should also review Appendix F and the

PHStat2 readme file on the Student CD-ROM if you plan to install PHStat2 on your computer system. Note that for some tasks that are straightforward to do in Excel, there is no equivalent PHStat2 procedure (use the appropriate Excel appendix section for such tasks).

## P2.2 CREATING SUMMARY TABLES

To create summary charts, use **PHStat → Descriptive Statistics → One-Way Tables & Charts**. This procedure accepts either unsummarized data (**Raw Categorical Data**) or data in the form of categories that have already been tallied (**Table of Frequencies**). In both cases, the procedure uses the Excel PivotTable feature to create a summary table.

## P2.3 CREATING CHARTS

To create summary charts, use various Output Options of the **PHStat → Descriptive Statistics → One-Way Tables & Charts** procedure discussed in the previous section. The options use Excel charting features to create a percentage column, bar, pie, or Pareto chart. (The charts are created with the custom formatting discussed in Sections E2.3 and E2.5.)

## P2.4 CREATING PARETO CHARTS

To create summary charts, use the **Pareto Chart** Output Options of the **PHStat → Descriptive Statistics → One-Way Tables & Charts** procedure discussed in Section P2.2.

## P2.5 CREATING STEM-AND-LEAF DISPLAYS

To create a stem-and-leaf display, use **PHStat → Descriptive Statistics → Stem-and-Leaf Display**. This procedure creates a stem-and-leaf display from the unsummarized data in the **Variable Cell Range**. The stem-and-leaf display

appears as a series of formatted worksheet labels in a new worksheet. If you click **Summary Statistics**, a table of summary statistics is included on that new worksheet.

The **Set stem unit as** option should be used sparingly and, if you use this option, the stem unit you specify must be a power of ten. Only use this option if **Autocalculate stem unit** creates a display that has too few or too many stems.

## P2.6 CREATING FREQUENCY DISTRIBUTIONS AND HISTOGRAMS

To create a frequency distribution and histogram from unsummarized data, use **PHStat → Descriptive Statistics → Histogram & Polygons**. This procedure accepts data either for a single group or multiple groups as either unstacked data (column by column) or stacked data (one column). If you use the **Multiple Groups – Stacked** option, you will also need to enter the **Grouping Variable Cell Range**.

This procedure silently uses the ToolPak Histogram procedure but corrects several errors made by the ToolPak procedure. Because the ToolPak is used silently, you must specify a cell range for bins (and not class groupings). Because the first bin will always be open-ended towards negative infinity, this bin will never have a true midpoint. Therefore, the command expects that your **Midpoints Cell Range** will be one cell smaller than your **Bins Cell Range** and will assign the first midpoint to the second class. (Review Section E2.8 "Creating Bins for Frequency Distributions" on page 76 if you are not familiar with the Excel bins concept.)

## P2.8 CREATING CONTINGENCY TABLES AND SIDE-BY-SIDE CHARTS

To create a contingency table and, optionally, a side-by-side chart from unsummarized data, use **PHStat → Descriptive Statistics → Two-Way Tables & Charts**. This procedure uses the Excel PivotTable feature to create a contingency table. Click **Side-by-Side Bar Chart** to optionally create the side-by-side chart.

## P2.7 CREATING PERCENTAGE AND CUMULATIVE PERCENTAGE POLYGONS

To create percentage and cumulative percentage polygons, use the Output Options of the **PHStat → Descriptive Statistics → Histogram & Polygons** procedure discussed in the previous section. The options use Excel charting features to create a percentage polygon and/or cumulative percentage polygon, as well as a frequency polygon.

## P2.9 CREATING SCATTER PLOTS

To create a scatter plot, use the **Scatter Diagram** Output Option of the **PHStat → Regression → Simple Linear Regression** procedure. For full information about using this procedure, see Section P13.2 on page 632.

# Appendix M2
## Using Minitab for Tables and Charts

You can use Minitab to create many of the tables and charts discussed in this chapter. If you are new to Minitab, make sure to review Appendix M1, "Introduction to Minitab," that starts on page 23, before continuing.

## M2.1 UNSTACKING DATA

Data are usually arranged so that all of the values of a variable are stacked vertically down a column. In many cases, you need to separately analyze different subgroups in terms of a numerical variable of interest. For example, in the mutual fund data, you may want to analyze the 2006 percentage return for the growth funds separately from the 2006 percentage return for the value funds. This can be accomplished by unstacking the 2006 percentage return variable so that the 2006 percentage returns for the growth funds are located in one column and the 2006 percentage returns for the value funds are located in a different column.

To unstack the growth and value funds data:

1. Open the `Mutual Funds.mtw` worksheet.
2. Select **Data → Unstack Columns**.

In the Unstack Columns dialog box (see Figure M2.1):

3. Enter **'Return 2006'** in the **Unstack the data in** box and **Objective** in the **Using subscripts in** box.
4. Click the **After last column in use** option and **Name the columns containing the unstacked data**.
5. Click **OK**.

**FIGURE M2.1** Minitab Unstack Columns dialog box

The new variables Return2006_Growth and Return2006_Value appear in columns C10 and C11. (You can change these variable names by editing their values in the cell at the top of these columns.)

## M2.2 CREATING BAR CHARTS

To create the bar chart in Figure 2.1 on page 28:

1. Open the `Banking.mtw` worksheet.
2. Select **Graph → Bar Chart**.

In the Bar Charts dialog box (see Figure M2.2):

3. Select **Values from a table** from the **Bars represent** drop-down list. (Make this selection because the fre-

**FIGURE M2.2** Minitab Bar Charts dialog box

quencies in each category are provided. If you are using raw data such as is found in the `Mutual Funds.mtw` worksheet, select **Counts of unique values** instead.)

4. In the gallery of choices, click **Simple**.
5. Click **OK**.

In the Bar Chart - Values from a table, One column of values, Simple dialog box (see Figure M2.3):

6. Enter **'Percentage (%)'** in the **Graph variables** box.
7. Enter **'Banking Preference'** in the **Categorical variable** box.
8. Click **OK** (to create the chart).

To modify the bar chart by changing the colors for the bars and borders in the bar chart:

1. Right-click one of the bars of the bar chart.
2. Select **Edit Bars** from the shortcut menu.

In the **Attributes** tab of the Edit Bars dialog box:

3. Click **Custom** under the **Fill Pattern** heading and make selections from the **Type** and **Background color** drop-down lists.
4. Click **Custom** under the **Border and Fill Lines** heading and make selections from the **Type**, **Color**, and **Size** drop-down lists.
5. At the bottom of the dialog box, click **OK**.

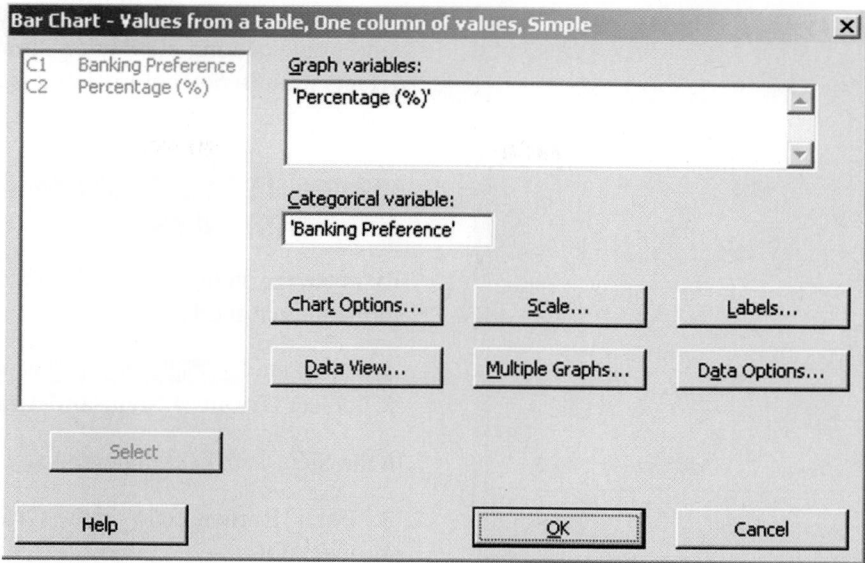

**FIGURE M2.3** Minitab Bar Chart - Values from a table, One column of values, Simple dialog box

## M2.3 CREATING PIE CHARTS

To create a pie chart similar to Figure 2.4 on page 29:

1. Open the Mutual Funds.mtw worksheet.
2. Select **Graph → Pie Chart**.

In the Pie Chart dialog box (see Figure M2.4):

3. Click **Chart counts of unique values.**

(If you used a worksheet such as Banking.mtw that contained the frequencies in each category, you would click

**Chart values from a table** and not **Chart counts of unique values.**)

4. Enter **Risk** in the **Categorical variables** box.
5. Click **Labels**.

In the Pie Chart - Labels dialog box (see Figure M2.5):

6. Click the **Slice Labels** tab.
7. Click **Category name** and **Percent**.
8. Click **OK** (to return to the original Pie Chart dialog box).
9. Back in the original Pie Chart dialog box, click **OK**.

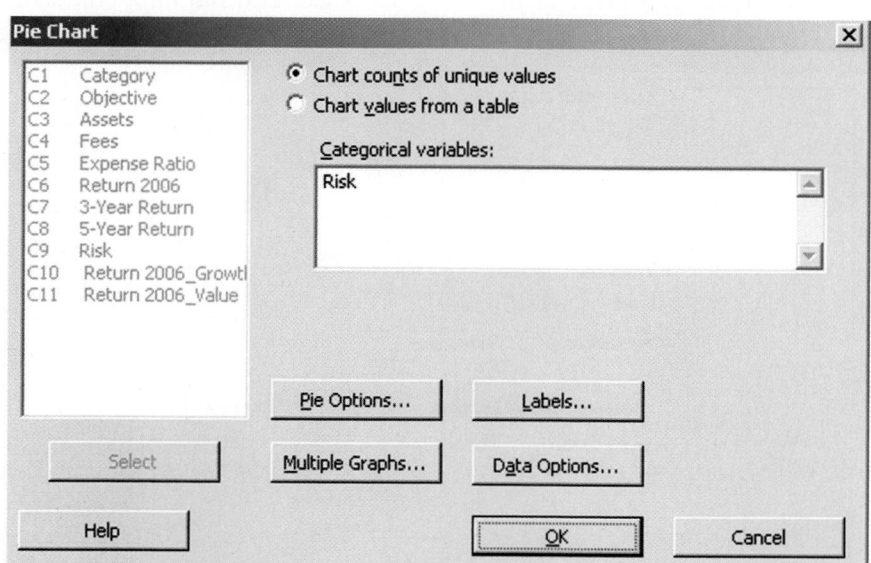

**FIGURE M2.4** Minitab Pie Chart dialog box

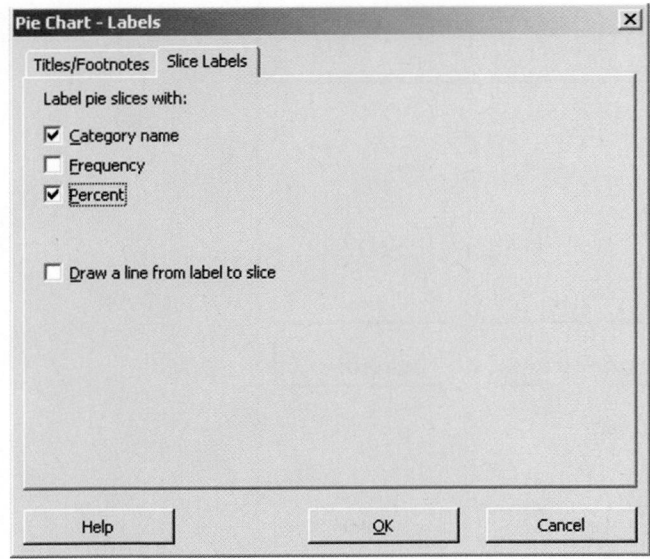

**FIGURE M2.5** Minitab Pie Charts - Labels dialog box

## M2.4 CREATING PARETO CHARTS

To create the Pareto chart of Figure 2.5 on page 31:

1. Open the Keyboard Defects.mtw worksheet. (This worksheet contains the causes of the defects in column C1 and the frequency of defects in column C2.)
2. Select **Stat → Quality Tools → Pareto Chart**.

In the Pareto Chart dialog box (see Figure M2.6):

3. Click **Chart defects table**.
4. Enter **Defect** in the **Labels in** box.
5. Enter **Frequency** in the **Frequencies in** box.
6. Click **Do not combine**.
7. Click **OK**.

If the variable of interest was located in a single column and is in raw form with each row indicating a type of error,

you would click **Charts defects data in** and enter the appropriate column number or variable name in the **Chart defects data in** box before doing steps 6 and 7.

## M2.5 CREATING STEM-AND-LEAF DISPLAYS

To create the stem-and-leaf display of the 2006 returns for all the mutual funds:

1. Open the Mutual Funds.mtw worksheet.
2. Select **Graph → Stem-and-Leaf**.

In the Stem-and-Leaf dialog box (see Figure M2.7):

3. Enter **'Return 2006'** in the **Graph variables** box.
4. Click **OK**.

## M2.6 CREATING HISTOGRAMS

To create the histogram of the 2006 returns for all the mutual funds:

1. Open the Mutual Funds.mtw worksheet.
2. Select **Graph → Histogram**.
3. In the gallery of the Histograms dialog box (see Figure M2.8), click **Simple** and then click **OK**.
4. In the Histogram-Simple dialog box (see Figure M2.9), enter **'Return 2006'** in the **Graph variables** box and then click **OK** (to create the chart).

To modify the histogram by changing the colors for the bars and borders in the histogram:

1. Right-click one of the bars of the histogram.
2. Select **Edit Bars** from the shortcut menu.

**FIGURE M2.6** Minitab Pareto Chart dialog box

**FIGURE M2.7**
Minitab Stem-and-Leaf
dialog box

**FIGURE M2.8**
Minitab Histograms
dialog box

**FIGURE M2.9**
Minitab Histogram-
Simple dialog box

In the **Attributes** tab of the Edit Bars dialog box:

3. Click **Custom** under the **Fill Pattern** heading and make selections from the **Type** and **Background color** drop-down lists.
4. Click **Custom** under the **Border and Fill Lines** heading and make selections from the **Type**, **Color**, and **Size** drop-down lists.
5. In the **Binning** tab of the same dialog box, click **Midpoint** to specify midpoints or click **Cutpoint** to specify class limits. Then click **Midpoint/Cutpoint positions** and enter the set of midpoint or cutpoints values in the box.
6. Click **OK** (to complete the modifications).

If you wish to create separate histograms for the growth and value funds similar to Figure 2.9 on page 43, do the following:

7. Enter **'Return2006_Growth'** and **'Return2006_Value'** in the **Graph variables** box.
8. Select **Multiple Graphs**.
9. In the By Variables tab, select the **On separate graphs** button and then click **OK**.
10. Click **OK** again to construct the graphs.

## M2.7 CREATING CROSS-TABULATION TABLES

To create cross-tabulation tables similar to Tables 2.14 through 2.17 on pages 49–50:

1. Open the Mutual Funds.mtw worksheet.
2. Select **Stat → Tables → Cross Tabulation and Chi-Square**.

In the Cross Tabulation and Chi-Square dialog box (see Figure M2.10):

3. Enter **Objective** in the **For rows** box.
4. Enter **Risk** in the **For columns** box.
5. Click **Counts**, **Row percents**, **Column percents**, and **Total percents**.
6. Click **OK**.

## M2.8 CREATING SIDE-BY-SIDE BAR CHARTS

To create a side-by-side bar chart similar to Figure 2.14 on page 50:

1. Open the Mutual Funds.mtw worksheet.
2. Select **Graph → Bar Chart**

In the Bar Charts dialog box (similar to Figure M2.2 on page 82):

3. Select **Counts of unique values** from the **Bars represent** drop-down list (because you are using raw data).
4. In the gallery of choices, click **Cluster**.
5. Click **OK**.

In the Bar Chart-Counts of unique values, Cluster dialog box (see Figure M2.11):

6. Enter **Objective** and **Risk** in the **Categorical variables (2–4, outermost first)** box.
7. Click **OK**.

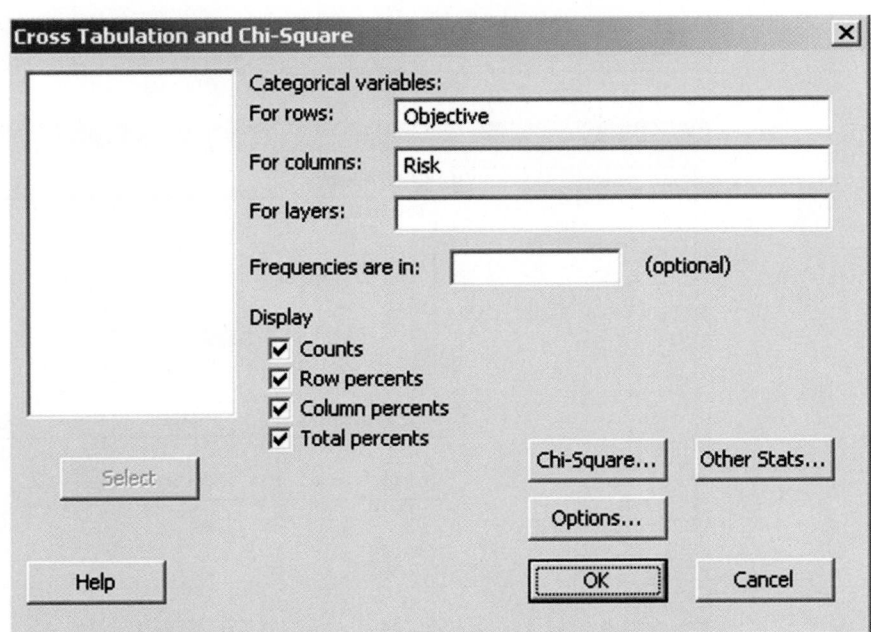

**FIGURE M2.10** Minitab Cross Tabulation and Chi-Square dialog box

**FIGURE M2.11**
Minitab Bar Chart -
Counts of unique
values, Cluster dialog
box

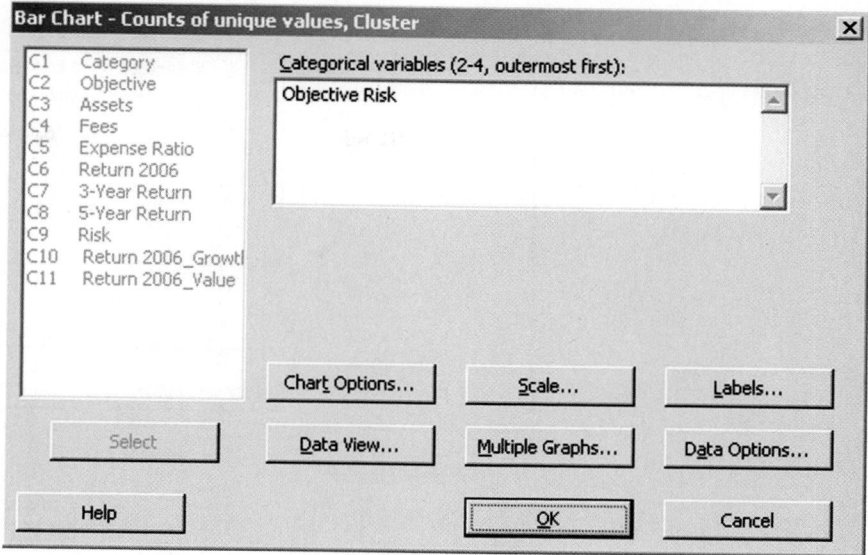

## M2.9 CREATING SCATTER PLOT AND TIME-SERIES PLOTS

To create the scatter plot of the cost of a hamburger and the cost of movie tickets (see Figure 2.15 on page 53):

1.  Open the `Cost of Living.mtw` worksheet.
2.  Select **Graph → Scatterplot**.

In the Scatterplots dialog box (see Figure M2.12):

3.  In the gallery, click **Simple**.
4.  Click **OK**.

In the Scatterplot - Simple dialog box (see Figure M2.13 on page 88):

5.  Enter **'Movie Tickets'** in the row 1 **Y variables** cell.
6.  Enter **Hamburger** in the row 1 **X variables** cell.
7.  Click **OK (** to create the chart).

To create a time-series plot, use the same eight-step process, entering the variable of interest in step 5 and the time period variable in step 6.

**FIGURE M2.12**
Minitab Scatterplots
dialog box

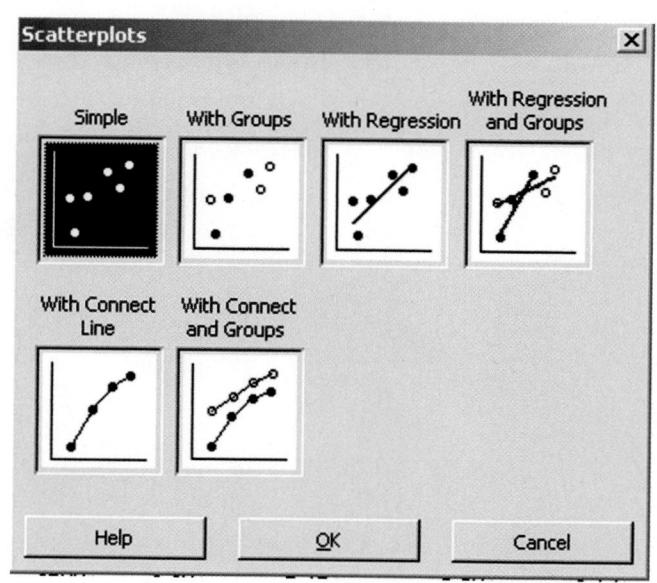

**FIGURE M2.13**
Minitab Scatterplot -
Simple dialog box

# CHAPTER
# THREE

## NUMERICAL DESCRIPTIVE MEASURES

# LEARNING OBJECTIVES

## In this chapter, you learn:

- To describe the properties of central tendency, variation, and shape in numerical data
- To calculate descriptive summary measures for a population
- To calculate descriptive summary measures from frequency distribution
- To construct and interpret a boxplot
- To describe the covariance and the coefficient of correlation

# USING STATISTICS @ Choice Is Yours, Part II

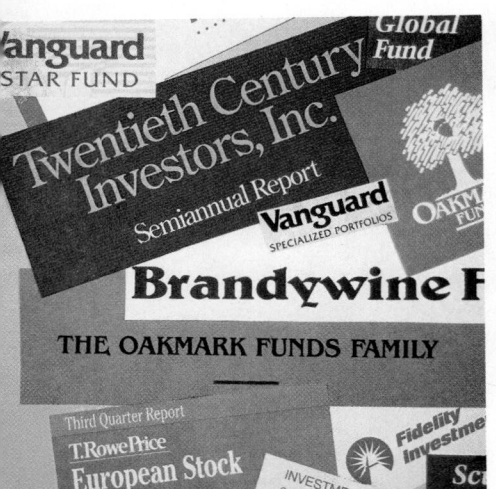

The tables and charts you prepared for the sample of 868 mutual funds has proved useful to the customers of the Choice Is Yours service. However, customers have become frustrated trying to evaluate mutual fund performance. Although they know how the 2006 returns are distributed, they have no idea what a typical 2006 rate of return would be for a particular category of mutual funds, such as low-risk funds, nor do they know how that typical value compares to the typical values of other categories. They also have no idea of the extent of the variability in the 2006 rate of return. Are all the values relatively similar, or do they include very small and very large values? Are there a lot of small values and a few large ones, or vice versa, or are there a similar number of small and large values?

How could you help the customers get answers to these questions so that they could better evaluate the mutual funds?

The customers in the Using Statistics scenario are asking questions about numerical variables. When summarizing and describing numerical variables, you need to do more than just prepare the tables and charts discussed in Chapter 2. You need to consider the central tendency, variation, and shape of each numerical variable.

> CENTRAL TENDENCY
>
> The **central tendency** is the extent to which all the data values group around a typical or central value.
>
> VARIATION
>
> The **variation** is the amount of dispersion, or scattering, of values away from a central value.
>
> SHAPE
>
> The **shape** is the pattern of the distribution of values from the lowest value to the highest value.

This chapter discusses ways you can measure the central tendency, variation, and shape of a variable. You will also learn about the covariance and the coefficient of correlation, which help measure the strength of the association between two numerical variables. Using these measures would give the customers of the Choice Is Yours service the answers they seek.

## 3.1   MEASURES OF CENTRAL TENDENCY

Most sets of data show a distinct tendency to group around a central point. When people talk about an "average value" or the "middle value" or the "most frequent value," they are talking informally about the mean, median, and mode—three measures of central tendency.

### The Mean

The **arithmetic mean** (typically referred to as the **mean**) is the most common measure of central tendency. The mean is the only common measure in which all the values play an equal role. The mean serves as a "balance point" in a set of data (like the fulcrum on a seesaw). You calculate the mean by adding together all the values in a data set and then dividing that sum by the number of values in the data set.

The symbol $\bar{X}$, called *X-bar*, is used to represent the mean of a sample. For a sample containing $n$ values, the equation for the mean of a sample is written as

$$\bar{X} = \frac{\text{sum of the values}}{\text{number of values}}$$

Using the series $X_1, X_2, \ldots, X_n$ to represent the set of $n$ values and $n$ to represent the number of values in the sample, the equation becomes:

$$\bar{X} = \frac{X_1 + X_2 + \cdots + X_n}{n}$$

By using summation notation (discussed fully in Appendix B), you replace the numerator $X_1 + X_2 + \cdots + X_n$ by the term $\sum_{i=1}^{n} X_i$, which means sum all the $X_i$ values from the first $X$ value, $X_1$, to the last $X$ value, $X_n$, to form Equation (3.1), a formal definition of the sample mean.

---

**Sample Mean**

The **sample mean** is the sum of the values divided by the number of values.

$$\bar{X} = \frac{\sum_{i=1}^{n} X_i}{n} \tag{3.1}$$

where

$$\bar{X} = \text{sample mean}$$

$$n = \text{number of values or sample size}$$

$$X_i = i\text{th value of the variable } X$$

$$\sum_{i=1}^{n} X_i = \text{summation of all } X_i \text{ values in the sample}$$

---

Because all the values play an equal role, a mean is greatly affected by any value that is greatly different from the others in the data set. When you have such extreme values, you should avoid using the mean as a measure of central tendency.

The mean can suggest a typical or central value for a data set. For example, if you knew the typical time it takes you to get ready in the morning, you might be able to better plan your morning and minimize any excessive lateness (or earliness) going to your destination. Suppose you define the time to get ready as the time (rounded to the nearest minute) from when you get out of bed to when you leave your home. You collect the times shown below for 10 consecutive workdays (stored in the data file Times ):

| Day: | 1 | 2 | 3 | 4 | 5 | 6 | 7 | 8 | 9 | 10 |
|---|---|---|---|---|---|---|---|---|---|---|
| Time (minutes): | 39 | 29 | 43 | 52 | 39 | 44 | 40 | 31 | 44 | 35 |

The mean time is 39.6 minutes, computed as follows:

$$\bar{X} = \frac{\text{sum of the values}}{\text{number of values}}$$

$$\bar{X} = \frac{\sum_{i=1}^{n} X_i}{n}$$

$$\bar{X} = \frac{39 + 29 + 43 + 52 + 39 + 44 + 40 + 31 + 44 + 35}{10}$$

$$= \frac{396}{10} = 39.6$$

Even though no one day in the sample actually had the value 39.6 minutes, allotting about 40 minutes to get ready would be a good rule for planning your mornings. The mean is a good measure of central tendency in this case because the data set does not contain any exceptionally small or large values.

Consider a case in which the value on Day 4 is 102 minutes instead of 52 minutes. This extreme value causes the mean to rise to 44.6 minutes, as follows:

$$\bar{X} = \frac{\text{sum of the values}}{\text{number of values}}$$

$$\bar{X} = \frac{\sum_{i=1}^{n} X_i}{n}$$

$$\bar{X} = \frac{446}{10} = 44.6$$

The one extreme value has increased the mean by more than 10%, from 39.6 to 44.6 minutes. In contrast to the original mean that was in the "middle" (i.e., greater than 5 of the getting-ready times and less than the 5 other times), the new mean is greater than 9 of the 10 getting-ready times. Because of the extreme value, now the mean is not a good measure of central tendency.

---

**EXAMPLE 3.1**

THE MEAN CALORIES FOR COFFEE DRINKS

The data in the file CoffeeDrink represent the calories of 16-ounce iced coffee drinks at Dunkin' Donuts and Starbucks:

| Product | Calories |
|---------|----------|
| Dunkin' Donuts Iced Mocha Swirl latte (whole milk) | 240 |
| Starbucks Coffee Frappuccino blended coffee | 260 |
| Dunkin' Donuts Coffee Coolatta (cream) | 350 |
| Starbucks Iced Coffee Mocha Expresso (whole milk and whipped cream) | 350 |
| Starbucks Mocha Frappuccino blended coffee (whipped cream) | 420 |
| Starbucks Chocolate Brownie Frappuccino blended coffee (whipped cream) | 510 |
| Starbucks Chocolate Frappuccino Blended Crème (whipped cream) | 530 |

Source: *Extracted from "Coffee as Candy at Dunkin' Donuts and Starbucks,"* Consumer Reports, *June 2004, p. 9.*

Compute the mean number of calories for the iced coffee drinks.

**SOLUTION** The mean number of calories is 380, calculated as follows:

$$\bar{X} = \frac{\text{sum of the values}}{\text{number of values}}$$

$$\bar{X} = \frac{\displaystyle\sum_{i=1}^{n} X_i}{n}$$

$$= \frac{2660}{7} = 380$$

## The Median

The **median** is the middle value in a set of data that has been ranked from smallest to largest. Half the values are smaller than or equal to the median, and half the values are larger than or equal to the median. The median is not affected by extreme values, so you can use the median when extreme values are present.

To calculate the median for a set of data, you first rank the values from smallest to largest and then use Equation (3.2) to compute the rank of the value that is the median.

Median

$$\text{Median} = \frac{n+1}{2} \text{ ranked value} \qquad \textbf{(3.2)}$$

You compute the median value by following one of two rules:

- **Rule 1** If there are an *odd* number of values in the data set, the median is the middle-ranked value.
- **Rule 2** If there are an *even* number of values in the data set, then the median is the *average* of the two middle-ranked values.

To compute the median for the sample of 10 times to get ready in the morning, you rank the daily times as follows:

Ranked values:

$$29 \quad 31 \quad 35 \quad 39 \quad 39 \quad 40 \quad 43 \quad 44 \quad 44 \quad 52$$

Ranks:

$$1 \quad 2 \quad 3 \quad 4 \quad 5 \quad 6 \quad 7 \quad 8 \quad 9 \quad 10$$

$$\uparrow$$

$$\text{Median} = 39.5$$

Because the result of dividing $n + 1$ by 2 is $(10 + 1)/2 = 5.5$ for this sample of 10, you must use Rule 2 and average the fifth and sixth ranked values, 39 and 40. Therefore, the median is 39.5. The median of 39.5 means that for half the days, the time to get ready is less than or equal to 39.5 minutes, and for half the days, the time to get ready is greater than or equal to 39.5 minutes. In this case, the median time to get ready of 39.5 minutes is very close to the mean time to get ready of 39.6 minutes.

**EXAMPLE 3.2**   COMPUTING THE MEDIAN FROM AN ODD-SIZED SAMPLE

The data in the file `CoffeeDrink` (see Example 3.1 on page 92) represent the calories of 16-ounce iced coffee drinks at Dunkin' Donuts and Starbucks. Compute the median number of calories for the iced coffee drinks at Dunkin' Donuts and Starbucks.

**SOLUTION** Because the result of dividing $n + 1$ by 2 is $(7 + 1)/2 = 4$ for this sample of seven, using Rule 1, the median is the fourth ranked value. The number of calories of 16-ounce iced coffee drinks at Dunkin' Donuts and Starbucks are ranked from the smallest to the largest:

Ranked values:

$$240 \quad 260 \quad 350 \quad 350 \quad 420 \quad 510 \quad 530$$

Ranks:

$$1 \quad 2 \quad 3 \quad 4 \quad 5 \quad 6 \quad 7$$
$$\uparrow$$
$$\text{Median} = 350$$

The median number of calories is 350. Half the drinks had equal to or less than 350 calories, and half the drinks had equal to or more than 350 calories.

## The Mode

The **mode** is the value in a set of data that appears most frequently. Like the median and unlike the mean, extreme values do not affect the mode. Often, there is no mode or there are several modes in a set of data. For example, consider the time-to-get-ready data shown below:

$$29 \quad 31 \quad 35 \quad 39 \quad 39 \quad 40 \quad 43 \quad 44 \quad 44 \quad 52$$

There are two modes, 39 minutes and 44 minutes, because each of these values occurs twice.

**EXAMPLE 3.3**   DETERMINING THE MODE

A systems manager in charge of a company's network keeps track of the number of server failures that occur in a day. Determine the mode for the following data, which represents the number of server failures in a day for the past two weeks:

$$1 \quad 3 \quad 0 \quad 3 \quad 26 \quad 2 \quad 7 \quad 4 \quad 0 \quad 2 \quad 3 \quad 3 \quad 6 \quad 3$$

**SOLUTION** The ordered array for these data is

$$0 \quad 0 \quad 1 \quad 2 \quad 2 \quad 3 \quad 3 \quad 3 \quad 3 \quad 3 \quad 4 \quad 6 \quad 7 \quad 26$$

Because 3 appears five times, more times than any other value, the mode is 3. Thus, the systems manager can say that the most common occurrence is having three server failures in a day. For this data set, the median is also equal to 3, and the mean is equal to 4.5. The extreme value 26 is an outlier. For these data, the median and the mode better measure central tendency than the mean.

A set of data has no mode if none of the values is "most typical." Example 3.4 presents a data set with no mode.

**EXAMPLE 3.4**

DATA WITH NO MODE

The bounced check fees ($) for a sample of 10 banks was

$$26 \quad 28 \quad 20 \quad 21 \quad 22 \quad 25 \quad 18 \quad 23 \quad 15 \quad 30$$

Compute the mode.

**SOLUTION**  These data have no mode. None of the values is most typical because each value appears once.

## The Geometric Mean

The **geometric mean** measures the rate of change of a variable over time. Equation (3.3) defines the geometric mean.

> **Geometric Mean**
> The geometric mean is the $n$th root of the product of $n$ values.
>
> $$\bar{X}_G = (X_1 \times X_2 \times \cdots \times X_n)^{1/n} \qquad \text{(3.3)}$$

The **geometric mean rate of return** measures the average percentage return of an investment over time. Equation (3.4) defines the geometric mean rate of return.

> **Geometric Mean Rate of Return**
>
> $$\bar{R}_G = [(1 + R_1) \times (1 + R_2) \times \cdots \times (1 + R_n)]^{1/n} - 1 \qquad \text{(3.4)}$$
>
> where $R_i$ is the rate of return in time period $i$

To illustrate these measures, consider an investment of $100,000 that declined to a value of $50,000 at the end of Year 1 and then rebounded back to its original $100,000 value at the end of Year 2. The rate of return for this investment for the two-year period is 0 because the starting and ending value of the investment is unchanged. However, the arithmetic mean of the yearly rates of return of this investment is

$$\bar{X} = \frac{(-0.50) + (1.00)}{2} = 0.25 \text{ or } 25\%$$

because the rate of return for Year 1 is

$$R_1 = \left( \frac{50,000 - 100,000}{100,000} \right) = -0.50 \text{ or } -50\%$$

and the rate of return for Year 2 is

$$R_2 = \left( \frac{100{,}000 - 50{,}000}{50{,}000} \right) = 1.00 \text{ or } 100\%$$

Using Equation (3.4), the geometric mean rate of return for the two years is

$$
\begin{aligned}
\bar{R}_G &= [(1 + R_1) \times (1 + R_2)]^{1/n} - 1 \\
&= [(1 + (-0.50)) \times (1 + (1.0))]^{1/2} - 1 \\
&= [(0.50) \times (2.0)]^{1/2} - 1 \\
&= [1.0]^{1/2} - 1 \\
&= 1 - 1 = 0
\end{aligned}
$$

Thus, the geometric mean rate of return more accurately reflects the (zero) change in the value of the investment for the two-year period than does the arithmetic mean.

---

**EXAMPLE 3.5**      COMPUTING THE GEOMETRIC MEAN RATE OF RETURN

The percentage change in the Russell 2000 Index of the stock prices of 2,000 small companies was +4.55% in 2005 and +17.00% in 2006. Compute the geometric rate of return.

**SOLUTION**  Using Equation (3.4), the geometric mean rate of return in the Russell 2000 Index for the two years is

$$
\begin{aligned}
\bar{R}_G &= [(1 + R_1) \times (1 + R_2)]^{1/n} - 1 \\
&= [(1 + (0.0455)) \times (1 + (0.1700))]^{1/2} - 1 \\
&= [(1.0455) \times (1.1700)]^{1/2} - 1 \\
&= [1.223235]^{1/2} - 1 \\
&= 1.106 - 1 = 0.106
\end{aligned}
$$

The geometric mean rate of return in the Russell 2000 Index for the two years is 10.6%.

---

## 3.2  VARIATION AND SHAPE

In addition to central tendency, every data set can be characterized by its variation and shape. Variation measures the **spread**, or **dispersion**, of values in a data set. One simple measure of variation is the range, the difference between the largest and smallest values. More commonly used in statistics are the standard deviation and variance, two measures explained later in this section. The shape of a data set represents a pattern of all the values, from the lowest to highest value. As you will learn later in this section, many data sets have a pattern that looks approximately like a bell, with a peak of values somewhere in the middle.

## The Range

The **range** is the simplest numerical descriptive measure of variation in a set of data.

> ### Range
> The range is equal to the largest value minus the smallest value.
>
> $$\text{Range} = X_{\text{largest}} - X_{\text{smallest}} \qquad \qquad (3.5)$$

To determine the range of the times to get ready in the morning, you rank the data from smallest to largest:

29    31    35    39    39    40    43    44    44    52

Using Equation (3.5), the range is 52 – 29 = 23 minutes. The range of 23 minutes indicates that the largest difference between any two days in the time to get ready in the morning is 23 minutes.

---

**EXAMPLE 3.6**    COMPUTING THE RANGE IN THE CALORIES IN ICED COFFEE DRINKS

The data in the file `CoffeeDrink` (see Example 3.1 on page 92) represent the calories of 16-ounce iced coffee drinks at Dunkin' Donuts and Starbucks. Compute the range in the number of calories for the iced coffee drinks at Dunkin' Donuts and Starbucks.

**SOLUTION**  Ranked from smallest to largest, the number of calories for the seven iced coffee drinks are

240    260    350    350    420    510    530

Therefore, using Equation (3.5), the range = 530 – 240 = 290. The largest difference in the number of calories between any two iced coffee drinks is 290.

---

The range measures the *total spread* in the set of data. Although the range is a simple measure of the total variation in the data, it does not take into account *how* the data are distributed between the smallest and largest values. In other words, the range does not indicate whether the values are evenly distributed throughout the data set, clustered near the middle, or clustered near one or both extremes. Thus, using the range as a measure of variation when at least one value is an extreme value is misleading.

## The Variance and the Standard Deviation

Although the range is a simple measure of variation, it does not take into consideration how the values distribute or cluster between the extremes. Two commonly used measures of variation that take into account how all the values in the data are distributed are the **variance** and the **standard deviation**. These statistics measure the "average" scatter around the mean—how larger values fluctuate above it and how smaller values distribute below it.

A simple measure of variation around the mean might take the difference between each value and the mean and then sum these differences. However, if you did that, you would find that because the mean is the balance point in a set of data, for *every* set of data, these differences would sum to zero. One measure of variation that differs from data set to data set *squares* the difference between each value and the mean and then sums these squared differences. In statistics, this quantity is called a **sum of squares** (or **SS**). This sum is then divided by the number of values minus 1 (for sample data) to get the sample variance ($S^2$). The square root of the sample variance is the sample standard deviation ($S$).

Because the sum of squares is a sum of squared differences that by the rules of arithmetic will always be nonnegative, *neither the variance nor the standard deviation can ever be negative.* For virtually all sets of data, the variance and standard deviation will be a positive value, although both of these statistics will be zero if there is no variation at all in a set of data and each value in the sample is the same.

For a sample containing $n$ values, $X_1, X_2, X_3, \ldots, X_n$, the sample variance (given by the symbol $S^2$) is

$$S^2 = \frac{(X_1 - \bar{X})^2 + (X_2 - \bar{X})^2 + \cdots + (X_n - \bar{X})^2}{n-1}$$

Equation (3.6) expresses the sample variance using summation notation, and Equation (3.7) expresses the sample standard deviation.

### Sample Variance

The **sample variance** is the sum of the squared differences around the mean divided by the sample size minus one.

$$S^2 = \frac{\sum_{i=1}^{n} (X_i - \bar{X})^2}{n-1} \qquad (3.6)$$

where

$\bar{X}$ = mean

$n$ = sample size

$X_i$ = $i$th value of the variable $X$

$\sum_{i=1}^{n} (X_i - \bar{X})^2$ = summation of all the squared differences between the $X_i$ values and $\bar{X}$

### Sample Standard Deviation

The **sample standard deviation** is the square root of the sum of the squared differences around the mean divided by the sample size minus one.

$$S = \sqrt{S^2} = \sqrt{\frac{\sum_{i=1}^{n} (X_i - \bar{X})^2}{n-1}} \qquad (3.7)$$

If the denominator were $n$ instead of $n - 1$, Equation (3.6) [and the inner term in Equation (3.7)] would calculate the average of the squared differences around the mean. However, $n - 1$ is used because of certain desirable mathematical properties possessed by the statistic $S^2$ that make it appropriate for statistical inference (which is discussed in Chapter 7). As the sample size increases, the difference between dividing by $n$ and by $n - 1$ becomes smaller and smaller.

You will most likely use the sample standard deviation as your measure of variation [defined in Equation (3.7)]. Unlike the sample variance, which is a squared quantity, the standard deviation is always a number that is in the same units as the original sample data. The standard deviation helps you to know how a set of data clusters or distributes around its mean. For almost all sets of data, the majority of the observed values lie within an interval of plus and minus one standard deviation above and below the mean. Therefore, knowledge of the mean and the standard deviation usually helps define where at least the majority of the data values are clustering.

To hand-calculate the sample variance, $S^2$, and the sample standard deviation, $S$, do the following:

1. Compute the difference between each value and the mean.
2. Square each difference.
3. Add the squared differences.
4. Divide this total by $n - 1$ to get the sample variance.
5. Take the square root of the sample variance to get the sample standard deviation.

Table 3.1 shows the first four steps for calculating the variance and standard deviation for the getting-ready-times data with a mean ($\bar{X}$) equal to 39.6. (See page 92 for the calculation of the mean.) The second column of Table 3.1 shows step 1. The third column of Table 3.1 shows step 2. The sum of the squared differences (step 3) is shown at the bottom of Table 3.1. This total is then divided by $10 - 1 = 9$ to compute the variance (step 4).

**TABLE 3.1**

Computing the Variance of the Getting-Ready Times

$\bar{X} = 39.6$

| Time (X) | Step 1: $(X_i - \bar{X})$ | Step 2: $(X_i - \bar{X})^2$ |
|---|---|---|
| 39 | −0.60 | 0.36 |
| 29 | −10.60 | 112.36 |
| 43 | 3.40 | 11.56 |
| 52 | 12.40 | 153.76 |
| 39 | −0.60 | 0.36 |
| 44 | 4.40 | 19.36 |
| 40 | 0.40 | 0.16 |
| 31 | −8.60 | 73.96 |
| 44 | 4.40 | 19.36 |
| 35 | −4.60 | 21.16 |
| | Step 3: Sum: | Step 4: Divide by (n − 1): |
| | 412.40 | 45.82 |

You can also calculate the variance by substituting values for the terms in Equation (3.6):

$$S^2 = \frac{\sum_{i=1}^{n}(X_i - \bar{X})^2}{n-1}$$

$$= \frac{(39 - 39.6)^2 + (29 - 39.6)^2 + \cdots + (35 - 39.6)^2}{10 - 1}$$

$$= \frac{412.4}{9}$$

$$= 45.82$$

Because the variance is in squared units (in squared minutes, for these data), to compute the standard deviation, you take the square root of the variance. Using Equation (3.7) on page 98, the sample standard deviation, S, is

$$S = \sqrt{S^2} = \sqrt{\frac{\sum_{i=1}^{n}(X_i - \bar{X})^2}{n-1}} = \sqrt{45.82} = 6.77$$

This indicates that the getting-ready times in this sample are clustering within 6.77 minutes around the mean of 39.6 minutes (i.e., clustering between $\bar{X} - 1S = 32.83$ and $\bar{X} + 1S = 46.37$). In fact, 7 out of 10 getting-ready times lie within this interval.

Using the second column of Table 3.1, you can also calculate the sum of the differences between each value and the mean to be zero. For any set of data, this sum will always be zero:

$$\sum_{i=1}^{n}(X_i - \bar{X}) = 0 \text{ for all sets of data}$$

This property is one of the reasons that the mean is used as the most common measure of central tendency.

---

**EXAMPLE 3.7**

COMPUTING THE VARIANCE AND STANDARD DEVIATION OF THE NUMBER OF CALORIES IN ICED COFFEE DRINKS

The data in the file CoffeeDrink (see Example 3.1 on page 92) represent the calories of 16-ounce iced coffee drinks at Dunkin' Donuts and Starbucks. Compute the variance and standard deviation of the calories in 16-ounce iced coffee drinks.

**SOLUTION** Table 3.2 illustrates the computation of the variance and standard deviation for the calories in 16-ounce iced coffee drinks.

**TABLE 3.2**

Computing the Variance of the Calories in 16-ounce Iced Coffee Drinks

$\bar{X} = 380$

| Calories | Step 1: $(X_i - \bar{X})$ | Step 2: $(X_i - \bar{X})^2$ |
|---|---|---|
| 240 | −140 | 19,600 |
| 260 | −120 | 14,400 |
| 350 | −30 | 900 |
| 350 | −30 | 900 |
| 420 | 40 | 1600 |
| 510 | 130 | 16,900 |
| 530 | 150 | 22,500 |
| | Step 3: Sum: | Step 4: Divide by $(n-1)$: |
| | 76,800 | 12,800 |

Using Equation (3.6) on page 98:

$$S^2 = \frac{\sum_{i=1}^{n}(X_i - \bar{X})^2}{n-1}$$
$$= \frac{(240-380)^2 + (260-380)^2 + \cdots + (530-380)^2}{7-1}$$
$$= \frac{76,800}{6}$$
$$= 12,800$$

Using Equation (3.7) on page 98, the sample standard deviation, $S$, is

$$S = \sqrt{S^2} = \sqrt{\frac{\sum_{i=1}^{n}(X_i - \bar{X})^2}{n-1}} = \sqrt{12,800} = 113.1371$$

The standard deviation of 113.1371 indicates that the calories in the iced coffee drinks are clustering within 113.1371 around the mean of 380 (i.e., clustering between $\bar{X} - 1S = 266.8629$ and $\bar{X} + 1S = 493.1371$). In fact, 42.9% (3 out of 7) of the calories lie within this interval.

The following summarizes the characteristics of the range, variance, and standard deviation:

- The more the data are spread out or dispersed, the larger the range, variance, and standard deviation.
- The more the data are concentrated or homogeneous, the smaller the range, variance, and standard deviation.
- If the values are all the same (so that there is no variation in the data), the range, variance, and standard deviation will all equal zero.
- None of the measures of variation (the range, standard deviation, and variance) can *ever* be negative.

## The Coefficient of Variation

Unlike the previous measures of variation presented, the **coefficient of variation** is a *relative measure* of variation that is always expressed as a percentage rather than in terms of the units of the particular data. The coefficient of variation, denoted by the symbol $CV$, measures the scatter in the data relative to the mean.

Coefficient of Variation

The coefficient of variation is equal to the standard deviation divided by the mean, multiplied by 100%.

$$CV = \left(\frac{S}{\bar{X}}\right)100\% \qquad \text{(3.8)}$$

where

$$S = \text{sample standard deviation}$$

$$\bar{X} = \text{sample mean}$$

For the sample of 10 getting-ready times, because $\bar{X} = 39.6$ and $S = 6.77$, the coefficient of variation is

$$CV = \left(\frac{S}{\bar{X}}\right)100\% = \left(\frac{6.77}{39.6}\right)100\% = 17.10\%$$

For the getting-ready times, the standard deviation is 17.1% of the size of the mean.

    The coefficient of variation is very useful when comparing two or more sets of data that are measured in different units, as Example 3.8 illustrates.

**EXAMPLE 3.8**    COMPARING TWO COEFFICIENTS OF VARIATION WHEN TWO VARIABLES HAVE DIFFERENT UNITS OF MEASUREMENT

The operations manager of a package delivery service is deciding whether to purchase a new fleet of trucks. When packages are stored in the trucks in preparation for delivery, you need to consider two major constraints—the weight (in pounds) and the volume (in cubic feet) for each item.

    The operations manager samples 200 packages and finds that the mean weight is 26.0 pounds, with a standard deviation of 3.9 pounds, and the mean volume is 8.8 cubic feet, with a standard deviation of 2.2 cubic feet. How can the operations manager compare the variation of the weight and the volume?

**SOLUTION**  Because the measurement units differ for the weight and volume constraints, the operations manager should compare the relative variability in the two types of measurements. For weight, the coefficient of variation is

$$CV_W = \left(\frac{3.9}{26.0}\right)100\% = 15\%$$

For volume, the coefficient of variation is

$$CV_V = \left(\frac{2.2}{8.8}\right)100\% = 25\%$$

Thus, relative to the mean, the package volume is much more variable than the package weight.

## Z Scores

An **extreme value** or **outlier** is a value located far away from the mean. $Z$ scores are useful in identifying outliers. The larger the $Z$ score, the greater the distance from the value to the mean. The **Z score** is the difference between the value and the mean, divided by the standard deviation.

Z Scores

$$Z = \frac{X - \bar{X}}{S} \tag{3.9}$$

For the time-to-get-ready data, the mean is 39.6 minutes, and the standard deviation is 6.77 minutes. The time to get ready on the first day is 39.0 minutes. You compute the $Z$ score for Day 1 by using Equation (3.9):

$$Z = \frac{X - \bar{X}}{S}$$
$$= \frac{39.0 - 39.6}{6.77}$$
$$= -0.09$$

Table 3.3 shows the $Z$ scores for all 10 days. The largest $Z$ score is 1.83 for Day 4, on which the time to get ready was 52 minutes. The lowest $Z$ score was $-1.57$ for Day 2, on which the time to get ready was 29 minutes. As a general rule, a $Z$ score is considered an outlier if it is less than $-3.0$ or greater than $+3.0$. None of the times met that criterion to be considered outliers.

**TABLE 3.3**

Z Scores for the 10 Getting-Ready Times

| | Time (X) | Z Score |
|---|---|---|
| | 39 | -0.09 |
| | 29 | -1.57 |
| | 43 | 0.50 |
| | 52 | 1.83 |
| | 39 | -0.09 |
| | 44 | 0.65 |
| | 40 | 0.06 |
| | 31 | -1.27 |
| | 44 | 0.65 |
| | 35 | -0.68 |
| **Mean** | 39.6 | |
| **Standard deviation** | 6.77 | |

**EXAMPLE 3.9**

COMPUTING THE Z SCORES OF THE NUMBER OF CALORIES IN ICED COFFEE DRINKS

The data in the file **CoffeeDrink** (see Example 3.1 on page 92) represent the calories of 16-ounce iced coffee drinks at Dunkin' Donuts and Starbucks. Compute the $Z$ scores of the calories of 16-ounce iced coffee drinks.

**SOLUTION** Table 3.4 illustrates the $Z$ scores of the calories of 16-ounce iced coffee drinks. The largest $Z$ score is 1.33, for an iced coffee drink with 530 calories. The lowest $Z$ score is $-1.24$, for an iced coffee drink with 240 calories. There are no apparent outliers in these data because none of the $Z$ scores are less than $-3$ or greater than $+3$.

**TABLE 3.4**

Z Scores of the Number of Calories in Iced Coffee Drinks

| | Calories | Z Scores |
|---|---|---|
| | 240 | -1.24 |
| | 260 | -1.06 |
| | 350 | -0.27 |
| | 350 | -0.27 |
| | 420 | 0.35 |
| | 510 | 1.15 |
| | 530 | 1.33 |
| **Mean** | 380 | |
| **Standard Deviation** | 113.1371 | |

## Shape

Shape is the pattern of the distribution of data values throughout the entire range of all the values. A distribution is either symmetrical or skewed. In a **symmetrical** distribution, the values below the mean are distributed exactly as the values above the mean. In this case, the low and high values balance each other out. In a **skewed** distribution, the values are not symmetrical around the mean. This skewness results in an imbalance of low values or high values.

Shape influences the relationship of the mean to the median in the following ways:

- Mean < median: negative, or left-skewed
- Mean = median: symmetric, or zero skewness
- Mean > median: positive, or right-skewed

Figure 3.1 depicts three data sets, each with a different shape.

**FIGURE 3.1**

A comparison of three data sets differing in shape

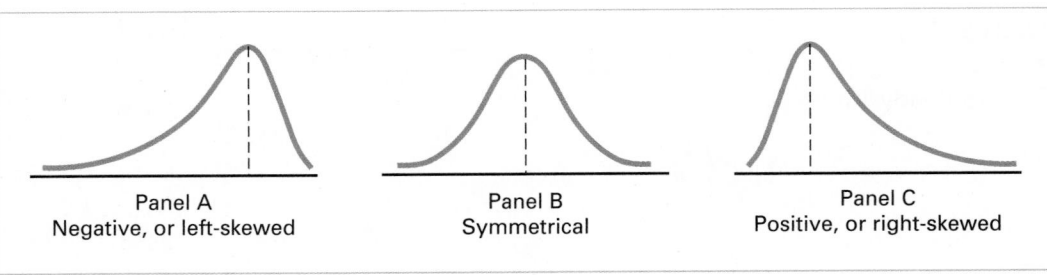

|  |  |  |
|---|---|---|
| Panel A | Panel B | Panel C |
| Negative, or left-skewed | Symmetrical | Positive, or right-skewed |

The data in Panel A are negative, or **left-skewed**. In this panel, most of the values are in the upper portion of the distribution. A long tail and distortion to the left is caused by some extremely small values. These extremely small values pull the mean downward so that the mean is less than the median.

The data in Panel B are symmetrical. Each half of the curve is a mirror image of the other half of the curve. The low and high values on the scale balance, and the mean equals the median.

The data in Panel C are positive, or **right-skewed**. In this panel, most of the values are in the lower portion of the distribution. A long tail on the right is caused by some extremely large values. These extremely large values pull the mean upward so that the mean is greater than the median.

## Microsoft Excel ToolPak Descriptive Statistics Results

The Microsoft Excel ToolPak Descriptive Statistics procedure (see Appendix E3.1) computes the mean, median, mode, standard deviation, variance, range, minimum, maximum, and count (sample size) and displays these statistics on a new worksheet. In addition, the procedure calculates and displays the standard error, the kurtosis, and skewness, three statistics not discussed previously in this section. The standard error, discussed in Chapter 7, is the standard deviation divided by the square root of the sample size. Skewness measures the lack of symmetry in the data. A skewness value of zero indicates a symmetrical distribution. A positive value indicates right-skewness whereas a negative value indicates left-skewness. Kurtosis measures the relative concentration of values in the center of the distribution, as compared with the tails. A kurtosis value of zero indicates a bell-shaped distribution. A negative value indicates a distribution that is flatter than a bell-shaped distribution. A positive value indicates a distribution with a sharper peak than a bell-shaped distribution.

Figure 3.2 shows the results of using the Descriptive Statistics procedure to calculate separate descriptive summary measures for growth and value mutual funds. (The procedure was used twice, and the results that appeared on two separate worksheets were consolidated on one sheet.)

**FIGURE 3.2**

ToolPak descriptive statistics for growth and value funds 2006 return

*See Section E3.1 to create this.*

| | A | B | C |
|---|---|---|---|
| 1 | *Descriptive Statistics for Return 2006* | | |
| 2 | | Growth | Value |
| 3 | Mean | 8.7103 | 16.8829 |
| 4 | Standard Error | 0.2515 | 0.1968 |
| 5 | Median | 8.6000 | 16.8500 |
| 6 | Mode | 7.5000 | 16.6000 |
| 7 | Standard Deviation | 5.4178 | 3.9553 |
| 8 | Sample Variance | 29.3524 | 15.6446 |
| 9 | Kurtosis | 0.7390 | 1.4329 |
| 10 | Skewness | -0.0118 | 0.0371 |
| 11 | Range | 37.5 | 32.2 |
| 12 | Minimum | -9.0 | 2.8 |
| 13 | Maximum | 28.5 | 35.0 |
| 14 | Sum | 4041.6 | 6820.7 |
| 15 | Count | 464 | 404 |

In examining the results, there are large differences in the 2006 return for the growth and value funds. The value funds had a mean 2006 return of 16.8829 and a median return of 16.85. This compares to a mean of 8.7103 and a median of 8.6 for the growth funds. This means that half of the value funds had returns of 16.85 or better, and half the growth funds had returns of only 8.6 or better. The growth funds had a larger standard deviation than the value funds. Neither the growth nor the value funds showed any skewness because their measures of skewness were very close to 0. Both the growth and value funds exhibited positive kurtosis, meaning that the distribution of the returns had a sharper peak than a bell-shaped distribution.

## Minitab Descriptive Statistics Results

As shown in Figure 3.3, for descriptive statistics, Minitab computes the sample size (labeled as N), the mean, the standard deviation (labeled as StDev), the coefficient of variation (labeled as CoefVar), first and third quartiles (see Section 3.5), median, maximum, range, and the interquartile range (labeled as IQR—see Section 3.5). In addition, Minitab computes skewness and kurtosis statistics. A skewness value of zero indicates a symmetrical distribution. A positive value indicates right-skewness whereas a negative value indicates left-skewness. Kurtosis measures the relative concentration of values in the center of the distribution, as compared with the tails. A kurtosis value of zero indicates a bell-shaped distribution. A negative value indicates a distribution that is flatter than a bell-shaped distribution. A positive value indicates a distribution with a sharper peak than a bell-shaped distribution.

**FIGURE 3.3**

Minitab descriptive statistics of the 2006 returns for growth and value funds

*See Section M3.1 to create this.*

### Descriptive Statistics: Return 2006

| Variable | Objective | N | Mean | StDev | CoefVar | Minimum | Q1 | Median |
|---|---|---|---|---|---|---|---|---|
| Return 2006 | Growth | 464 | 8.710 | 5.418 | 62.20 | -9.000 | 5.325 | 8.600 |
| | Value | 404 | 16.883 | 3.955 | 23.43 | 2.800 | 14.500 | 16.850 |

| Variable | Objective | Q3 | Maximum | Range | IQR | Skewness | Kurtosis |
|---|---|---|---|---|---|---|---|
| Return 2006 | Growth | 12.400 | 28.500 | 37.500 | 7.075 | -0.01 | 0.74 |
| | Value | 19.500 | 35.000 | 32.200 | 5.000 | 0.04 | 1.43 |

In examining the results, there are large differences in the 2006 return for the growth and value funds. The value funds had a mean 2006 return of 16.883 and a median return of 16.85. This compares to a mean of 8.7103 and a median of 8.60 for the growth funds. This means that half of the value funds had returns of 16.85 or better, and half the growth funds had returns of only 8.60 or better. The growth funds had a larger standard deviation than the value funds. Neither the growth nor the value funds showed any skewness because their skewness statistics were very close to 0. Both the growth and value funds exhibited positive kurtosis, meaning that the distribution of the returns had a sharper peak than a bell-shaped distribution.

# VISUAL EXPLORATIONS: Exploring Descriptive Statistics

You can use the Visual Explorations Descriptive Statistics procedure to see the effect of changing data values on measures of central tendency, variation, and shape. Open the `visual explorations.xla` add-in workbook (see Appendix D) and select **VisualExplorations → Descriptive Statistics** (Excel 97–2003) or **Add-ins → VisualExplorations → Descriptive Statistics** (Excel 2007) from the Microsoft Excel menu bar. Read the instructions in the pop-up box (see illustration below) and click **OK** to examine a dot-scale diagram for the

sample of 10 getting-ready times used throughout this chapter. (Review Section E1.8 on page 20 for more information on using add-ins, if necessary.)

Experiment by entering an extreme value such as 10 minutes into one of the tinted cells of column A. Which measures are affected by this change? Which ones are not? You can flip between the "before" and "after" diagrams by repeatedly pressing **Ctrl + Z** (undo) followed by **Ctrl + Y** (redo) to help see the changes the extreme value caused in the diagram.

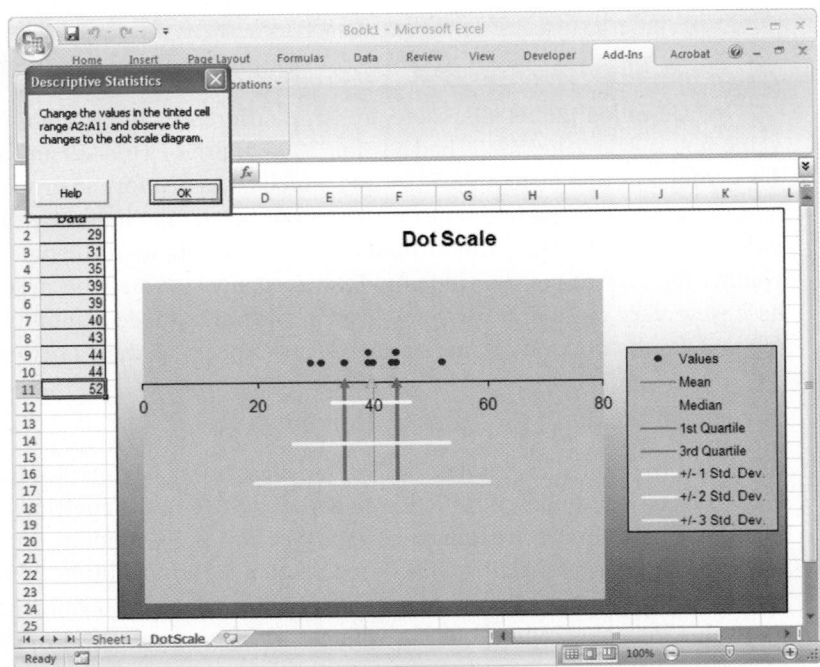

# PROBLEMS FOR SECTIONS 3.1 AND 3.2

## Learning the Basics

**3.1** The following is a set of data from a sample of $n = 5$:

$$7 \quad 4 \quad 9 \quad 8 \quad 2$$

a. Compute the mean, median, and mode.
b. Compute the range, variance, standard deviation, and coefficient of variation.
c. Compute the $Z$ scores. Are there any outliers?
d. Describe the shape of the data set.

**3.2** The following is a set of data from a sample of $n = 6$:

$$7 \quad 4 \quad 9 \quad 7 \quad 3 \quad 12$$

a. Compute the mean, median, and mode.
b. Compute the range, variance, standard deviation, and coefficient of variation.
c. Compute the $Z$ scores. Are there any outliers?
d. Describe the shape of the data set.

**3.3** The following set of data is from a sample of $n = 7$:

$$12 \quad 7 \quad 4 \quad 9 \quad 0 \quad 7 \quad 3$$

a. Compute the mean, median, and mode.
b. Compute the range, variance, standard deviation, and coefficient of variation.
c. Compute the Z scores. Are there any outliers?
d. Describe the shape of the data set.

**3.4** The following is a set of data from a sample of $n = 5$:

$$7 \quad -5 \quad -8 \quad 7 \quad 9$$

a. Compute the mean, median, and mode.
b. Compute the range, variance, standard deviation, and coefficient of variation.
c. Compute the Z scores. Are there any outliers?
d. Describe the shape of the data set.

**3.5** Suppose the rate of return for a particular stock during the past two years was 10% and 30%. Compute the geometric mean rate of return. (*Note:* A rate of return of 10% is recorded as 0.10, and a rate of return of 30% is recorded as 0.30.)

## Applying the Concepts

**3.6** The operations manager of a plant that manufactures tires wants to compare the actual inner diameters of two grades of tires, each of which is expected to be 575 millimeters. A sample of five tires of each grade was selected, and the results representing the inner diameters of the tires, ranked from smallest to largest, are as follows:

| Grade X | Grade Y |
|---|---|
| 568 570 575 578 584 | 573 574 575 577 578 |

a. For each of the two grades of tires, compute the mean, median, and standard deviation.
b. Which grade of tire is providing better quality? Explain.
c. What would be the effect on your answers in (a) and (b) if the last value for grade Y were 588 instead of 578? Explain.

**3.7** According to the U.S. Census Bureau, in February 2007 the median sales price of new houses was $250,000 and the mean sales price was $331,000 (U.S. Census Bureau News, **www.census.gov**, March 26, 2007).
a. Interpret the median sales price.
b. Interpret the mean sales price.
c. Discuss the shape of the price of new houses.

**SELF Test 3.8** The data in the file **Movieprices** contain the price for two tickets with online service charges, large popcorn, and two medium soft drinks at a sample of six theater chains:

$36.15  $31.00  $35.05  $40.25  $33.75  $43.00

Source: *Extracted from K. Kelly, "The Multiplex Under Siege," The Wall Street Journal, December 24–25, 2005, pp. P1, P5.*

a. Compute the mean and median.
b. Compute the variance, standard deviation, range, and coefficient of variation.
c. Are the data skewed? If so, how?
d. Based on the results of (a) through (c), what conclusions can you reach concerning the cost of going to the movies?

**3.9** The data in the file **Sedans** represent the overall miles per gallon (MPG) of 2007 family sedans (4 cylinder).

| Model | MPG | Model | MPG |
|---|---|---|---|
| Volkswagen Passat | 24 | Mazda | 23 |
| Nissan Altima | 25 | Ford Fusion | 23 |
| Toyota Camry Hybrid | 34 | Mercury Milan | 23 |
| Honda Accord | 24 | Toyota Prius | 44 |
| Kia Optima | 23 | Chevrolet Malibu | 24 |
| Toyota Camry LE | 24 | Mitsubishi Galant | 23 |
| Subaru Legacy | 18 | Pontiac G6 | 22 |
| Hyundai Sonata | 23 | Chrysler Sebring | 23 |

Source: *Extracted from "Vehicle Ratings," Consumer Reports, April 2007, pp. 36–37.*

a. Compute the mean, median, and mode.
b. Compute the variance, standard deviation, range, coefficient of variation, and Z scores.
c. Are the data skewed? If so, how?
d. Compare the results of (a) through (c) to those of Problem 3.10 (a) through (c) that refer to the miles per gallon of small SUVs.

**3.10** The data in the file **SUV** represent the overall miles per gallon (MPG) of 2007 small SUVs.

| Model | MPG | Model | MPG |
|---|---|---|---|
| Toyota RAV4 6-cyl | 22 | Mercury Mariner Luxury | 18 |
| Hyundai Santa Fe | 18 | Mazda Tribute | 18 |
| Toyota RAV4 4-cyl | 23 | Nissan Xterra | 17 |
| Subaru Forester Sports 2.5 XT | 20 | Honda Element | 21 |
| Honda CR-V | 21 | Suzuki Grand Vitara | 18 |
| Subaru Forester Sports 2.5 X | 22 | Chevrolet Equinox | 18 |
| | | Pontiac Torrent | 18 |
| Mitsubishi Outlander | 19 | Jeep Compass | 22 |
| Hyundai Tucson | 18 | Saturn Vue | 19 |
| Kia Sportage | 18 | Saturn Vue Hybrid | 24 |
| Ford Escape Hybrid | 26 | Kia Sorento | 15 |
| Mercury Mariner Hybrid | 26 | Jeep Liberty | 15 |
| | | Toyota FJ Cruiser | 17 |
| Suzuki XL-7 | 17 | Dodge Nitro | 16 |
| Ford Escape | 18 | Jeep Wrangler | 15 |

Source: *Extracted from "Vehicle Ratings," Consumer Reports, April 2007, pp.42–43.*

a. Compute the mean, median, and mode.

**b.** Compute the variance, standard deviation, range, coefficient of variation, and $Z$ scores.

**c.** Are the data skewed? If so, how?

**d.** Compare the results of (a) through (c) to those of Problem 3.9 (a) through (c) that refer to the miles per gallon of 4-cylinder family sedans.

**3.11** The data in the file Chicken contain the total fat, in grams per serving, for a sample of 20 chicken sandwiches from fast-food chains. The data are as follows:

7 8 4 5 16 20 20 24 19 30 23 30 25 19 29 29 30 30 40 56

Source: *Extracted from "Fast Food: Adding Health to the Menu,"* Consumer Reports, *September 2004, pp. 28–31.*

**a.** Compute the mean, median, and mode.

**b.** Compute the variance, standard deviation, range, coefficient of variation, and $Z$ scores. Are there any outliers? Explain.

**c.** Are the data skewed? If so, how?

**d.** Based on the results of (a) through (c), what conclusions can you reach concerning the total fat of chicken sandwiches?

**3.12** The data in the file Batterylife represent the battery life (in shots) for a sample of 12 three-pixel digital cameras:

300 180 85 170 380 460 260 35 380 120 110 240

Source: *Extracted from "Cameras: More Features in the Mix,"* Consumer Reports, *July 2005, pp. 14–18.*

**a.** Compute the mean, median, and mode.

**b.** Compute the variance, standard deviation, range, coefficient of variation, and $Z$ scores. Are there any outliers? Explain.

**c.** Are the data skewed? If so, how?

**d.** Based on the results of (a) through (c), what conclusions can you reach concerning the battery life (in shots) for three-pixel digital cameras?

**3.13** Is there a difference in the variation of the yields of different types of investments between banks? The data in the file Bankyield represent the nationwide highest yields for money market accounts and five-year CDs as of March 12, 2007:

| Money Market | Five-Year CD |
| --- | --- |
| 5.35 | 5.95 |
| 5.31 | 5.89 |
| 5.30 | 5.83 |
| 5.30 | 5.83 |
| 5.25 | 5.79 |

Source: *Extracted from www.Bankrate.com, March 12, 2007.*

**a.** For money market accounts and five-year CDs, separately compute the variance, standard deviation, range, and coefficient of variation.

**b.** Based on the results of (a), do money market accounts or five-year CDs have more variation in the highest yields offered? Explain.

**3.14** The data in the file Themeparks contain the starting admission price (in $) for one-day tickets to 10 theme parks in the United States:

58  63  41  42  29  50  62  43  40  40

Source: *Extracted from C. Jackson and E. Gamerman, "Rethinking the Thrill Factor,"* The Wall Street Journal, *April 15–16, 2006, pp. P1, P4.*

**a.** Compute the mean, median, and mode.

**b.** Compute the range, variance, and standard deviation.

**c.** Based on the results of (a) and (b), what conclusions can you reach concerning the starting admission price for one-day tickets.

**d.** Suppose that the first value was 98 instead of 58. Repeat (a) through (c), using this value. Comment on the difference in the results.

**3.15** A bank branch located in a commercial district of a city has developed an improved process for serving customers during the noon-to-1:00 p.m. lunch period. The waiting time, in minutes (defined as the time the customer enters the line to when he or she reaches the teller window), of a sample of 15 customers during this hour is recorded over a period of one week. The results are contained in the data file Bank1 and are listed below:

4.21 5.55 3.02 5.13 4.77 2.34 3.54 3.20 4.50
6.10 0.38 5.12 6.46 6.19 3.79

**a.** Compute the mean and median.

**b.** Compute the variance, standard deviation, range, coefficient of variation, and $Z$ scores. Are there any outliers? Explain.

**c.** Are the data skewed? If so, how?

**d.** As a customer walks into the branch office during the lunch hour, she asks the branch manager how long she can expect to wait. The branch manager replies, "Almost certainly less than five minutes." On the basis of the results of (a) through (c), evaluate the accuracy of this statement.

**3.16** Suppose that another branch, located in a residential area, is also concerned with the noon-to-1 p.m. lunch hour. The waiting time, in minutes (defined as the time the customer enters the line to when he or she reaches the teller window), of a sample of 15 customers during this hour is recorded over a period of one week. The results are contained in the data file Bank2 and are listed below:

9.66 5.90 8.02 5.79 8.73 3.82 8.01 8.35 10.49
6.68 5.64 4.08 6.17 9.91 5.47

**a.** Compute the mean and median.

**b.** Compute the variance, standard deviation, range, coefficient of variation and $Z$ scores. Are there any outliers? Explain.

**c.** Are the data skewed? If so, how?

**d.** As a customer walks into the branch office during the lunch hour, he asks the branch manager how long he can expect to wait. The branch manager replies, "Almost certainly less than five minutes." On the basis of the results of (a) through (c), evaluate the accuracy of this statement.

**3.17** General Electric (GE) is one of the world's largest companies; it develops, manufactures, and markets a wide range of products, including medical diagnostic imaging devices, jet engines, lighting products, and chemicals. Through its affiliate, NBC Universal, GE produces and delivers network television and motion pictures. In 2004, GE's stock price rose 20.6%, but in 2005, the price dropped 1.4%.

Source: *Extracted from* ***www.finance.yahoo.com****, April 17, 2006.*

**a.** Compute the geometric mean rate of increase for the two-year period 2004–2005. (*Hint:* Denote an increase of 20.6% as $R_1 = 0.206$.)

**b.** If you purchased $1,000 of GE stock at the start of 2004, what was its value at the end of 2005?

**c.** Compare the result of (b) to that of Problem 3.18(b).

**d.** In 2006, GE's stock price increased by 6.2%. Compute the geometric mean rate of increase for the three-year period 2004–2006.

**3.18** TASER International, Inc., develops, manufactures, and sells nonlethal self-defense devices known as tasers. Marketing primarily to law enforcement, corrections institutions, and the military, TASER's popularity has enjoyed a roller-coaster ride. The stock price in 2004 increased 361.4%, but in 2005, it decreased 78.0%.

Source: *Extracted from* ***finance.yahoo.com****, April 17, 2006.*

**a.** Compute the geometric mean rate of increase for the two-year period 2004–2005. (*Hint:* Denote an increase of 361.4% as $R_1 = 3.614$.)

**b.** If you purchased $1,000 of TASER stock at the start of 2004, what was its value at the end of 2005?

**c.** Compare the result of (b) to that of Problem 3.17(b).

**d.** In 2006, TASER's stock price increased by 9.3%. Compute the geometric mean rate of increase for the three-year period 2004–2006.

**3.19** In 2002, all the major stock market indexes decreased dramatically as the attacks on 9/11 drove stock prices spiraling downward. Stocks soon rebounded, but what type of mean return did investors experience over the five-year period from 2002 to 2006? The data in the following table (contained in the data file **Indices**) represent the total rate of return (in percentage) for the Dow Jones Industrial Average (DJIA), the Standard & Poor's 500 (S&P 500), and the technology-heavy NASDAQ Composite (Nasdaq).

| Year | DJIA | S&P 500 | Nasdaq |
|------|------|---------|--------|
| 2006 | 16.3 | 13.6 | 9.5 |
| 2005 | −0.6 | 2.9 | 1.4 |
| 2004 | 3.4 | 9.1 | 8.6 |
| 2003 | 30.0 | 26.4 | 50.0 |
| 2002 | −16.8 | −24.2 | −31.5 |

Source: *Extracted from* ***finance.yahoo.com****, April 26, 2007.*

**a.** Calculate the geometric mean rate of return for the DJIA, S&P 500, and Nasdaq.

**b.** What conclusions can you reach concerning the geometric rates of return of the three market indexes?

**c.** Compare the results of (b) to those of Problem 3.20(b).

**3.20** In 2002–2006, precious metals changed rapidly in value. The data in the following table (contained in the data file **Metals**) represent the total rate of return (in percentage) for platinum, gold, and silver:

| Year | Platinum | Gold | Silver |
|------|----------|------|--------|
| 2006 | 15.9 | 23.2 | 46.1 |
| 2005 | 12.3 | 17.8 | 29.5 |
| 2004 | 5.7 | 4.6 | 14.2 |
| 2003 | 36.0 | 19.9 | 27.8 |
| 2002 | 24.6 | 25.6 | 3.3 |

Source: *Extracted from* ***kitco.com****, April 26, 2007.*

**a.** Calculate the geometric mean rate of return for platinum, gold, and silver.

**b.** What conclusions can you reach concerning the geometric rates of return of the three precious metals?

**c.** Compare the results of (b) to those of Problem 3.19(b).

## 3.3 NUMERICAL DESCRIPTIVE MEASURES FOR A POPULATION

Sections 3.1 and 3.2 present various statistics that described the properties of central tendency and variation for a sample. If your data set represents numerical measurements for an entire population, you need to calculate and interpret parameters, summary measures for a population. In this section, you will learn about three descriptive population parameters: the population mean, population variance, and population standard deviation.

To help illustrate these parameters, first review Table 3.5, which contains the one-year return for the five largest bond funds (in terms of total assets) as of March 29, 2007. (The data are contained in the file **Largest bonds**.)

**TABLE 3.5**

One-Year Return for the Population Consisting of the Five Largest Bond Funds

| Bond Fund | One-Year Return |
|---|---|
| Pimco: Total Rtn; Inst | 6.1 |
| Vanguard Tot Bd; Inv | 6.2 |
| American Funds Bond; A | 7.2 |
| Franklin CA TF Inc; A | 5.9 |
| Vanguard GNMA; Inv | 5.5 |

Source: *Extracted from* The Wall Street Journal, *March 29, 2007, p. C4.*

## The Population Mean

The **population mean** is represented by the symbol $\mu$, the Greek lowercase letter mu. Equation (3.10) defines the population mean.

### Population Mean

The population mean is the sum of the values in the population divided by the population size $N$.

$$\mu = \frac{\displaystyle\sum_{i=1}^{N} X_i}{N} \tag{3.10}$$

where

$\mu$ = population mean

$X_i$ = $i$th value of the variable $X$

$\displaystyle\sum_{i=1}^{N} X_i$ = summation of all $X_i$ values in the population

To compute the mean one-year return for the population of bond funds given in Table 3.5, use Equation (3.10):

$$\mu = \frac{\displaystyle\sum_{i=1}^{N} X_i}{N} = \frac{6.1+6.2+7.2+5.9+5.5}{5} = \frac{30.9}{5} = 6.18$$

Thus, the mean percentage return for these bond funds is 6.18.

## The Population Variance and Standard Deviation

The **population variance** and the **population standard deviation** measure variation in a population. Like the related sample statistics, the population standard deviation is the square root of the population variance. The symbol $\sigma^2$, the Greek lowercase letter sigma squared, represents the population variance, and the symbol $\sigma$, the Greek lowercase letter sigma, represents the population standard deviation. Equations (3.11) and (3.12) define these parameters. The denominators for the right-side terms in these equations use $N$ and not the $(n-1)$ term that is used in the equations for the sample variance and standard deviation [see Equations (3.6) and (3.7) on page 98].

## Population Variance

The population variance is the sum of the squared differences around the population mean divided by the population size $N$.

$$\sigma^2 = \frac{\sum_{i=1}^{N}(X_i - \mu)^2}{N}$$

(3.11)

where

$\mu$ = population mean

$X_i$ = $i$th value of the variable $X$

$\sum_{i=1}^{N}(X_i - \mu)^2$ = summation of all the squared differences between the $X_i$ values and $\mu$

## Population Standard Deviation

$$\sigma = \sqrt{\frac{\sum_{i=1}^{N}(X_i - \mu)^2}{N}}$$

(3.12)

To compute the population variance for the data of Table 3.5, you use Equation (3.11):

$$\sigma^2 = \frac{\sum_{i=1}^{N}(X_i - \mu)^2}{N}$$

$$= \frac{(6.1-6.18)^2 + (6.2-6.18)^2 + (7.2-6.18)^2 + (5.9-6.18)^2 + (5.5-6.18)^2}{5}$$

$$= \frac{0.0064 + 0.0004 + 1.0444 + 0.0784 + 0.4624}{5}$$

$$= \frac{1.588}{5} = 0.3176$$

Thus, the variance of the one-year returns is 0.3176 squared percentage return. The squared units make the variance hard to interpret. You should use the standard deviation that is expressed in the original units of the data (percentage return). From Equation (3.12),

$$\sigma = \sqrt{\sigma^2} = \sqrt{\frac{\sum_{i=1}^{N}(X_i - \mu)^2}{N}} = \sqrt{0.3176} = 0.5636$$

Therefore, the typical percentage return differs from the mean of 6.18 by approximately 0.56. This small amount of variation suggests that these large bond funds produce results that do not differ greatly.

## The Empirical Rule

In most data sets, a large portion of the values tend to cluster somewhere near the median. In right-skewed data sets, this clustering occurs to the left of the mean—that is, at a value less than the mean. In left-skewed data sets, the values tend to cluster to the right of the mean—that is, greater than the mean. In symmetrical data sets, where the median and mean are the same, the values often tend to cluster around the median and mean, producing a bell-shaped distribution. You can use the **empirical rule** to examine the variability in bell-shaped distributions:

- Approximately 68% of the values are within a distance of ±1 standard deviation from the mean.
- Approximately 95% of the values are within a distance of ±2 standard deviations from the mean.
- Approximately 99.7% of the values are within a distance of ±3 standard deviations from the mean.

The empirical rule helps you measure how the values distribute above and below the mean and can help you identify outliers. The empirical rule implies that for bell-shaped distributions, only about 1 out of 20 values will be beyond two standard deviations from the mean in either direction. As a general rule, you can consider values not found in the interval $\mu \pm 2\sigma$ as potential outliers. The rule also implies that only about 3 in 1,000 will be beyond three standard deviations from the mean. Therefore, values not found in the interval $\mu \pm 3\sigma$ are almost always considered outliers.

**EXAMPLE 3.10**

USING THE EMPIRICAL RULE

A population of 12-ounce cans of cola is known to have a mean fill-weight of 12.06 ounces and a standard deviation of 0.02. The population is known to be bell-shaped. Describe the distribution of fill-weights. Is it very likely that a can will contain less than 12 ounces of cola?

**SOLUTION**
$$\mu \pm \sigma = 12.06 \pm 0.02 = (12.04, 12.08)$$
$$\mu \pm 2\sigma = 12.06 \pm 2(0.02) = (12.02, 12.10)$$
$$\mu \pm 3\sigma = 12.06 \pm 3(0.02) = (12.00, 12.12)$$

Using the empirical rule, approximately 68% of the cans will contain between 12.04 and 12.08 ounces, approximately 95% will contain between 12.02 and 12.10 ounces, and approximately 99.7% will contain between 12.00 and 12.12 ounces. Therefore, it is highly unlikely that a can will contain less than 12 ounces.

For heavily skewed data sets, or those not appearing bell-shaped for any other reason, the Chebyshev rule discussed next should be applied instead of the empirical rule.

## The Chebyshev Rule

The **Chebyshev rule** (reference 1) states that for any data set, regardless of shape, the percentage of values that are found within distances of $k$ standard deviations from the mean must be at least

$$(1 - 1/k^2) \times 100\%$$

You can use this rule for any value of $k$ greater than 1. Consider $k = 2$. The Chebyshev rule states that at least $[1 - (1/2)^2] \times 100\% = 75\%$ of the values must be found within ±2 standard deviations of the mean.

The Chebyshev rule is very general and applies to any type of distribution. The rule indicates *at least* what percentage of the values fall within a given distance from the mean. However, if the data set is approximately bell-shaped, the empirical rule will more accurately reflect the greater concentration of data close to the mean. Table 3.6 compares the Chebyshev and empirical rules.

| | | **% of Values Found in Intervals Around the Mean** | |
|---|---|---|---|
| **TABLE 3.6**<br>How Data Vary Around<br>the Mean | **Interval** | **Chebyshev**<br>**(any distribution)** | **Empirical Rule**<br>**(bell-shaped distribution)** |
| | $(\mu - \sigma, \mu + \sigma)$ | At least 0% | Approximately 68% |
| | $(\mu - 2\sigma, \mu + 2\sigma)$ | At least 75% | Approximately 95% |
| | $(\mu - 3\sigma, \mu + 3\sigma)$ | At least 88.89% | Approximately 99.7% |

**EXAMPLE 3.11**     USING THE CHEBYSHEV RULE

As in Example 3.10, a population of 12-ounce cans of cola is known to have a mean fill-weight of 12.06 ounces and a standard deviation of 0.02. However, the shape of the population is unknown, and you cannot assume that it is bell-shaped. Describe the distribution of fill-weights. Is it very likely that a can will contain less than 12 ounces of cola?

**SOLUTION**     $\mu \pm \sigma = 12.06 \pm 0.02 = (12.04, 12.08)$

$$\mu \pm 2\sigma = 12.06 \pm 2(0.02) = (12.02, 12.10)$$

$$\mu \pm 3\sigma = 12.06 \pm 3(0.02) = (12.00, 12.12)$$

Because the distribution may be skewed, you cannot use the empirical rule. Using the Chebyshev rule, you cannot say anything about the percentage of cans containing between 12.04 and 12.08 ounces. You can state that at least 75% of the cans will contain between 12.02 and 12.10 ounces and at least 88.89% will contain between 12.00 and 12.12 ounces. Therefore, between 0 and 11.11% of the cans will contain less than 12 ounces.

You can use these two rules for understanding how data are distributed around the mean when you have sample data. In each case, you use the value you calculated for $\bar{X}$ in place of $\mu$ and the value you calculated for $S$ in place of $\sigma$. The results you compute using the sample statistics are *approximations* because you used sample statistics $(\bar{X}, S)$ and not population parameters $(\mu, \sigma)$.

## PROBLEMS FOR SECTION 3.3

### Learning the Basics

**3.21** The following is a set of data for a population with $N = 10$:

    7  5  11  8  3  6  2  1  9  8

**a.** Compute the population mean.
**b.** Compute the population standard deviation.

**3.22** The following is a set of data for a population with $N = 10$:

    7  5  6  6  6  4  8  6  9  3

**a.** Compute the population mean.
**b.** Compute the population standard deviation.

### Applying the Concepts

**3.23** The data in the file `Tax` represent the quarterly sales tax receipts (in thousands of dollars) submitted to the comptroller of the Village of Fair Lake for the period ending March 2007 by all 50 business establishments in that locale:

| | | | | |
|---|---|---|---|---|
| 10.3 | 11.1 | 9.6 | 9.0 | 14.5 |
| 13.0 | 6.7 | 11.0 | 8.4 | 10.3 |
| 13.0 | 11.2 | 7.3 | 5.3 | 12.5 |
| 8.0 | 11.8 | 8.7 | 10.6 | 9.5 |
| 11.1 | 10.2 | 11.1 | 9.9 | 9.8 |
| 11.6 | 15.1 | 12.5 | 6.5 | 7.5 |
| 10.0 | 12.9 | 9.2 | 10.0 | 12.8 |
| 12.5 | 9.3 | 10.4 | 12.7 | 10.5 |
| 9.3 | 11.5 | 10.7 | 11.6 | 7.8 |
| 10.5 | 7.6 | 10.1 | 8.9 | 8.6 |

**a.** Compute the mean, variance, and standard deviation for this population.

**b.** What percentage of these businesses have quarterly sales tax receipts within ±1, ±2, or ±3 standard deviations of the mean?

**c.** Compare and contrast your findings with what would be expected on the basis of the empirical rule. Are you surprised at the results in (b)?

**3.24** Consider a population of 1,024 mutual funds that primarily invest in large companies. You have determined that μ, the mean one-year total percentage return achieved by all the funds, is 8.20 and that σ, the standard deviation, is 2.75. According to the empirical rule, what percentage of these funds is expected to be

**a.** within ±1 standard deviation of the mean?

**b.** within ±2 standard deviations of the mean?

**c.** According to the Chebyshev rule, what percentage of these funds are expected to be within ±1, ±2, or ±3 standard deviations of the mean?

**d.** According to the Chebyshev rule, at least 93.75% of these funds are expected to have one-year total returns between what two amounts?

**3.25** The file Collegetuition contains the tuition and fees for public four-year colleges in each of the 50 states for the 2006–2007 school year. The amounts do not include room and board. The file also contains the percentage increase in tuition and fees from 2005–2006 to 2006–2007 (extracted from Sandra Block, "Rising Costs Make Climb to Higher Education Steeper," **usatoday.com**, January 12, 2007).

**a.** Compute the population mean and population standard deviation for tuition and fees.

**b.** Interpret the parameters in (a).

**c.** Compute the population mean and population standard deviation for the percentage increase from 2005–2006 to 2006–2007.

**d.** Interpret the parameters in (c).

**3.26** The data in the file Energy contains the per-capita energy consumption, in kilowatt hours, for each of the 50 states and the District of Columbia during a recent year.

**a.** Compute the mean, variance, and standard deviation for the population.

**b.** What proportion of these states has average per-capita energy consumption within ±1 standard deviation of the mean, within ±2 standard deviations of the mean, and within ±3 standard deviations of the mean?

**c.** Compare and contrast your findings versus what would be expected based on the empirical rule. Are you surprised at the results in (b)?

**d.** Repeat (a) through (c) with the District of Columbia removed. How have the results changed?

**3.27** Thirty companies comprise the DJIA. Just how big are these companies? One common method to measure the size of a company is to use its market capitalization, which is computed by taking the number of stock shares multiplied by the price of a share of stock. On April 25, 2007, the market capitalization of these companies ranged from General Motors's $17.4 billion to Exxon-Mobil's $453.9 billion. The entire population of market capitalization values is recorded in the file Dowmarketcap.

Source: *Extracted from* **money.cnn.com**, *April 25, 2007.*

**a.** Calculate the mean and standard deviation of the market capitalization for this population of 30 companies.

**b.** Interpret the parameters calculated in (a).

## 3.4  COMPUTING NUMERICAL DESCRIPTIVE MEASURES FROM A FREQUENCY DISTRIBUTION

Sometimes you have only a frequency distribution, not the raw data. When this occurs, you can compute approximations to the mean and the standard deviation.

When you have data from a sample that has been summarized into a frequency distribution, you can compute an approximation of the mean by assuming that all values within each class interval are located at the midpoint of the class.

Approximating the Mean from a Frequency Distribution

$$\bar{X} = \frac{\sum_{j=1}^{c} m_j f_j}{n} \tag{3.13}$$

where

$$\bar{X} = \text{sample mean}$$

$$n = \text{number of values or sample size}$$

$$c = \text{number of classes in the frequency distribution}$$

$$m_j = \text{midpoint of the } j\text{th class}$$

$$f_j = \text{number of values in the } j\text{th class}$$

To calculate the standard deviation from a frequency distribution, you assume that all values within each class interval are located at the midpoint of the class.

**Approximating the Standard Deviation From a Frequency Distribution**

$$S = \sqrt{\frac{\sum_{j=1}^{c}(m_j - \bar{X})^2 f_j}{n-1}} \qquad (3.14)$$

Example 3.12 illustrates the computation of the mean and the standard deviation from a frequency distribution.

**EXAMPLE 3.12**

APPROXIMATING THE MEAN AND STANDARD DEVIATION FROM A FREQUENCY DISTRIBUTION

Consider the frequency distribution of the 2006 return of value funds (Table 3.7). Compute the mean and standard deviation.

**TABLE 3.7**

Frequency Distribution of the 2006 Return for Value Mutual Funds

| 2006 Return | Frequency |
|---|---|
| 0 to under 5 | 1 |
| 5 to under 10 | 14 |
| 10 to under 15 | 102 |
| 15 to under 20 | 208 |
| 20 to under 25 | 71 |
| 25 to under 30 | 7 |
| 30 to under 35 | 0 |
| 35 to under 40 | 1 |
| Total | 404 |

**SOLUTION** The computations that you need to calculate the approximations of the mean and standard deviation of the 2006 return for value mutual funds are summarized in Table 3.8 on page 116. Using Equation (3.13) on page 114,

$$\bar{X} = \sqrt{\frac{\sum_{j=1}^{c} m_j f_j}{n}}$$

$$\bar{X} = \frac{6,850.0}{404} = 16.9554$$

**TABLE 3.8**
Computations Needed for Approximating the Mean and Standard Deviation of the 2006 return for Value Mutual Funds

| Percentage Return | Frequency ($f_j$) | Midpoint ($m_j$) | $m_j f_j$ | $(m_j - \bar{X})$ | $(m_j - \bar{X})^2$ | $(m_j - \bar{X})^2 f_j$ |
|---|---|---|---|---|---|---|
| 0 to under 5 | 1 | 2.5 | 2.5 | −14.45545 | 208.9599 | 208.9599 |
| 5 to under 10 | 14 | 7.5 | 105.0 | −9.45545 | 89.4055 | 1,251.6763 |
| 10 to under 15 | 102 | 12.5 | 1,275.0 | −4.45545 | 19.8510 | 2,024.8015 |
| 15 to under 20 | 208 | 17.5 | 3,640.0 | 0.54455 | 0.2965 | 61.6802 |
| 20 to under 25 | 71 | 22.5 | 1,597.5 | 5.54455 | 30.7421 | 2,182.6880 |
| 25 to under 30 | 7 | 27.5 | 192.5 | 10.54455 | 111.1876 | 778.3134 |
| 30 to under 35 | 0 | 32.5 | 0.0 | 15.54455 | 241.6332 | 0.0000 |
| 35 to under 40 | 1 | 37.5 | 37.5 | 20.54455 | 422.0787 | 422.0787 |
|  | 404 |  | 6,850.0 |  |  | 6,930.1980 |

and using Equation (3.14) on page 115

$$S = \sqrt{\frac{\sum_{i=1}^{c}(m_j - \bar{X})^2 f_j}{n-1}}$$

$$S = \sqrt{\frac{6930.198}{404 - 1}}$$

$$= \sqrt{17.196521}$$

$$= 4.1469$$

## PROBLEMS FOR SECTION 3.4

### Learning the Basics

**3.28** Given the following frequency distribution for $n = 100$:

| Class Intervals | Frequency |
|---|---|
| 0—Under 10 | 10 |
| 10—Under 20 | 20 |
| 20—Under 30 | 40 |
| 30—Under 40 | 20 |
| 40—Under 50 | 10 |
|  | 100 |

Approximate
a. the mean.
b. the standard deviation.

**3.29** Given the following frequency distribution for $n = 100$:

| Class Intervals | Frequency |
|---|---|
| 0—Under 10 | 40 |
| 10—Under 20 | 25 |
| 20—Under 30 | 15 |
| 30—Under 40 | 15 |
| 40—Under 50 | 5 |
|  | 100 |

Approximate
a. the mean.
b. the standard deviation.

### Applying the Concepts

**3.30** A wholesale appliance distributing firm wished to study its accounts receivable for two successive months. Two independent samples of 50 accounts were selected for each of the two months. The results are summarized in the following table:

| Amount | March Frequency | April Frequency |
|---|---|---|
| $0 to under $2,000 | 6 | 10 |
| $2,000 to under $4,000 | 13 | 14 |
| $4,000 to under $6,000 | 17 | 13 |
| $6,000 to under $8,000 | 10 | 10 |
| $8,000 to under $10,000 | 4 | 0 |
| $10,000 to under $12,000 | 0 | 3 |
| Total | 50 | 50 |

For each month, approximate the
**a.** mean.
**b.** standard deviation.
**c.** On the basis of (a) and (b), do you think the mean and the standard deviation of the accounts receivable have changed substantially from March to April? Explain.

**3.31** The following table contains the cumulative frequency distributions and cumulative percentage distributions of braking distance (in feet) at 80 miles per hour for a sample of 25 U.S.-manufactured automobile models and for a sample of 72 foreign-made automobile models in a recent year:

| Braking Distance (in Ft) | U.S.-Made Automobile Models "Less Than" Indicated Values | | Foreign-Made Automobile Models "Less Than" Indicated Values | |
|---|---|---|---|---|
| | Number | Percentage | Number | Percentage |
| 210 | 0 | 0.0 | 0 | 0.0 |
| 220 | 1 | 4.0 | 1 | 1.4 |
| 230 | 2 | 8.0 | 4 | 5.6 |
| 240 | 3 | 12.0 | 19 | 26.4 |
| 250 | 4 | 16.0 | 32 | 44.4 |
| 260 | 8 | 32.0 | 54 | 75.0 |
| 270 | 11 | 44.0 | 61 | 84.7 |

*(continued)*

| Braking Distance (in Ft) | U.S.-Made Automobile Models "Less Than" Indicated Values | | Foreign-Made Automobile Models "Less Than" Indicated Values | |
|---|---|---|---|---|
| | Number | Percentage | Number | Percentage |
| 280 | 17 | 68.0 | 68 | 94.4 |
| 290 | 21 | 84.0 | 68 | 94.4 |
| 300 | 23 | 92.0 | 70 | 97.2 |
| 310 | 25 | 100.0 | 71 | 98.6 |
| 320 | 25 | 100.0 | 72 | 100.0 |

For U.S.- and foreign-made automobiles:
**a.** Construct a frequency distribution for each group.
**b.** On the basis of the results of (a), approximate the mean of the braking distance.
**c.** On the basis of the results of (a), approximate the standard deviation of the braking distance.
**d.** On the basis of the results of (b) and (c), do U.S.- and foreign-made automobiles seem to differ in their braking distance? Explain.

**3.32** The following data represent the distribution of the ages of employees within two different divisions of a publishing company.

| Age of Employees (Years) | A Frequency | B Frequency |
|---|---|---|
| 20—Under 30 | 8 | 15 |
| 30—Under 40 | 17 | 32 |
| 40—Under 50 | 11 | 20 |
| 50—Under 60 | 8 | 4 |
| 60—Under 70 | 2 | 0 |

For each of the two divisions (*A* and *B*), approximate the
**a.** mean.
**b.** standard deviation.
**c.** On the basis of the results of (a) and (b), do you think there are differences in the age distribution between the two divisions? Explain.

## 3.5   QUARTILES AND THE BOXPLOT

Sections 3.1 through 3.3 discuss measures of central tendency, variation, and shape. Another way of describing numerical data is through an exploratory data analysis that includes the quartiles, the five-number summary, and the boxplot (references 4 and 5).

### Quartiles

**Quartiles** split a set of data into four equal parts—the **first quartile, $Q_1$**, divides the smallest 25.0% of the values from the other 75.0% that are larger. The **second quartile, $Q_2$**, is the median—50.0% of the values are smaller than the median and 50.0% are larger. The **third**

[1] The $Q_1$, median, and $Q_3$
are also the 25th, 50th,
and 75th percentiles,
respectively. Equations (3.2),
(3.15), and (3.16) can be
expressed generally in
terms of finding percentiles:
(p × 100)th percentile =
p × (n + 1) ranked value.

**quartile, $Q_3$,** divides the smallest 75.0% of the values from the largest 25.0%. Equations (3.15) and (3.16) define the first and third quartiles.[1]

### First Quartile, $Q_1$

25.0% of the values are smaller than or equal to $Q_1$, the first quartile, and 75.0% are larger than or equal to the first quartile, $Q_1$.

$$Q_1 = \frac{n+1}{4} \text{ ranked value} \qquad (3.15)$$

### Third Quartile, $Q_3$

75.0% of the values are smaller than or equal to the third quartile, $Q_3$, and 25.0% are larger than or equal to the third quartile, $Q_3$.

$$Q_3 = \frac{3(n+1)}{4} \text{ ranked value} \qquad (3.16)$$

Use the following rules to calculate the quartiles from a set of ranked values:

- **Rule 1** If the ranked value is a whole number, then the quartile is equal to that ranked value. For example, if the sample size $n = 7$, the first quartile, $Q_1$, is equal to the $(7 + 1)/4 =$ second ranked value.
- **Rule 2** If the ranked value is a fractional half (2.5, 4.5, etc.), then the quartile is equal to the average of the corresponding ranked values. For example, if the sample size $n = 9$, the first quartile, $Q_1$, is equal to the $(9 + 1)/4 = 2.5$ ranked value, halfway between the second ranked value and the third ranked value.
- **Rule 3** If the ranked value is neither a whole number nor a fractional half, you round the result to the nearest integer and select that ranked value. For example, if the sample size $n = 10$, the first quartile, $Q_1$, is equal to the $(10 + 1)/4 = 2.75$ ranked value. Round 2.75 to 3 and use the third ranked value.

To illustrate the computation of the quartiles for the time-to-get-ready data, rank the following data from smallest to largest:

Ranked values:

29   31   35   39   39   40   43   44   44   52

Ranks:

1    2    3    4    5    6    7    8    9    10

The first quartile is the $(n + 1)/4 = (10 + 1)/4 = 2.75$ ranked value. Using Rule 3, you round up to the third ranked value. The third ranked value for the time-to-get-ready data is 35 minutes. You interpret the first quartile of 35 to mean that on 25% of the days, the time to get ready is less than or equal to 35 minutes, and on 75% of the days, the time to get ready is greater than or equal to 35 minutes.

The third quartile is the $3(n + 1)/4 = 3(10 + 1)/4 = 8.25$ ranked value. Using Rule 3 for quartiles, you round this down to the eighth ranked value. The eighth ranked value is 44 minutes. Thus, on 75% of the days, the time to get ready is less than or equal to 44 minutes, and on 25% of the days, the time to get ready is greater than or equal to 44 minutes.

**EXAMPLE 3.13**    COMPUTING THE QUARTILES

The data in the file `CoffeeDrink` (see Example 3.1 on page 92) represent the calories of 16-ounce iced coffee drinks at Dunkin' Donuts and Starbucks. Compute the first quartile ($Q_1$) and third quartile ($Q_3$) number of calories for the iced coffee drinks at Dunkin' Donuts and Starbucks.

**SOLUTION**  Ranked from smallest to largest, the number of calories for the seven iced coffee drinks are:

Ranked values:

$$240 \quad 260 \quad 350 \quad 350 \quad 420 \quad 510 \quad 530$$

Ranks:

$$1 \quad 2 \quad 3 \quad 4 \quad 5 \quad 6 \quad 7$$

For these data

$$Q_1 = \frac{(n+1)}{4} \text{ ranked value}$$

$$= \frac{7+1}{4} \text{ ranked value} = 2\text{nd ranked value}$$

Therefore, using Rule 1, $Q_1$ is the second ranked value. Because the second ranked value is 260, the first quartile, $Q_1$, is 260.

To find the third quartile, $Q_3$:

$$Q_3 = \frac{3(n+1)}{4} \text{ ranked value}$$

$$= \frac{3(7+1)}{4} \text{ ranked value} = 6\text{th ranked value}$$

Therefore, using Rule 1, $Q_3$ is the sixth ranked value. Because the sixth ranked value is 510, $Q_3$ is 510.

The first quartile of 260 indicates that 25% of the iced coffee drinks have calories that are below or equal to 260 and 75% are greater than or equal to 260. The third quartile of 510 indicates that 75% of the iced coffee drinks have calories that are below or equal to 510 and 25% are greater than or equal to 510.

## The Interquartile Range

The **interquartile range** (also called **midspread**) is the difference between the third and first quartiles in a set of data.

Interquartile Range

The interquartile range is the difference between the third quartile and the first quartile.

$$\text{Interquartile range} = Q_3 - Q_1 \qquad\qquad \textbf{(3.17)}$$

The interquartile range measures the spread in the middle 50% of the data. Therefore, it is not influenced by extreme values. To determine the interquartile range of the times to get ready

$$29 \quad 31 \quad 35 \quad 39 \quad \quad 39 \quad 40 \quad 43 \quad 44 \quad 44 \quad 52$$

you use Equation (3.17) and the earlier results on page 118, $Q_1 = 35$ and $Q_3 = 44$:

$$\text{Interquartile range} = 44 - 35 = 9 \text{ minutes}$$

Therefore, the interquartile range in the time to get ready is 9 minutes. The interval 35 to 44 is often referred to as the *middle fifty*.

---

**EXAMPLE 3.14**

COMPUTING THE INTERQUARTILE RANGE FOR THE NUMBER OF CALORIES IN ICED COFFEE DRINKS

The data in the file **CoffeeDrink** (see Example 3.1 on page 92) represent the calories of 16-ounce iced coffee drinks at Dunkin' Donuts and Starbucks. Compute the interquartile range of the number of calories of 16-ounce iced coffee drinks.

**SOLUTION**   Ranked from smallest to largest, the number of calories for the seven iced coffee drinks are:

$$240 \quad 260 \quad 350 \quad 350 \quad 420 \quad 510 \quad 530$$

Using Equation (3.17) and the earlier results on page 119, $Q_1 = 260$ and $Q_3 = 510$:

$$\text{Interquartile range} = 510 - 260 = 250$$

Therefore, the interquartile range of the number of calories of 16-ounce iced coffee drinks is 250 calories.

---

Because the interquartile range does not consider any value smaller than $Q_1$ or larger than $Q_3$, it cannot be affected by extreme values. Summary measures such as the median, $Q_1$, $Q_3$, and the interquartile range, which cannot be influenced by extreme values, are called **resistant measures**.

### The Five-Number Summary

A **five-number summary** that consists of

$$X_{\text{smallest}} \quad Q_1 \quad \text{Median} \quad Q_3 \quad X_{\text{largest}}$$

provides a way to determine the shape of a distribution. Table 3.9 explains how the relationships among the "five numbers" allows you to recognize the shape of a data set.

For the sample of 10 getting-ready times, the smallest value is 29 minutes and the largest value is 52 minutes (see page 91). Calculations done on pages 93 and 119 show that the median = 39.5, $Q_1 = 35$, and $Q_3 = 44$. Therefore, the five-number summary is

$$29 \quad 35 \quad 39.5 \quad 44 \quad 52$$

The distance from $X_{\text{smallest}}$ to the median ($39.5 - 29 = 10.5$) is slightly less than the distance from the median to $X_{\text{largest}}$ ($52 - 39.5 = 12.5$). The distance from $X_{\text{smallest}}$ to $Q_1$ ($35 - 29 = 6$) is slightly less than the distance from $Q_3$ to $X_{\text{largest}}$ ($52 - 44 = 8$). Therefore, the getting-ready times are slightly right-skewed.

## TABLE 3.9

Relationships Among the Five-Number Summary and the Type of Distribution

| Comparison | Type of Distribution | | |
| --- | --- | --- | --- |
| | Left-Skewed | Symmetric | Right-Skewed |
| The distance from $X_{smallest}$ to the median versus the distance from the median to $X_{largest}$. | The distance from $X_{smallest}$ to the median is greater than the distance from the median to $X_{largest}$. | Both distances are the same. | The distance from $X_{smallest}$ to the median is less than the distance from the median to $X_{largest}$. |
| The distance from $X_{smallest}$ to $Q_1$ versus the distance from $Q_3$ to $X_{largest}$. | The distance from $X_{smallest}$ to $Q_1$ is greater than the distance from $Q_3$ to $X_{largest}$. | Both distances are the same. | The distance from $X_{smallest}$ to $Q_1$ is less than the distance from $Q_3$ to $X_{largest}$. |
| The distance from $Q_1$ to the median versus the distance from the median to $Q_3$. | The distance from $Q_1$ to the median is greater than the distance from the median to $Q_3$. | Both distances are the same. | The distance from $Q_1$ to the median is less than the distance from the median to $Q_3$. |

**EXAMPLE 3.15**  COMPUTING THE FIVE-NUMBER SUMMARY OF THE NUMBER OF CALORIES IN ICED COFFEE DRINKS

The data in the file **CoffeeDrink** (see Example 3.1 on page 92) represent the calories of 16-ounce iced coffee drinks at Dunkin' Donuts and Starbucks. Compute the five-number summary of the number of calories of 16-ounce iced coffee drinks.

**SOLUTION**  From previous computations for the calories of 16-ounce iced coffee drinks (see pages 94 and 119), the median = 350, $Q_1 = 260$, and $Q_3 = 510$. In addition, the smallest value in the data set is 240, and the largest value is 530. Therefore, the five-number summary is

$$240 \quad 260 \quad 350 \quad 510 \quad 530$$

The three comparisons listed in Table 3.9 are used to evaluate skewness. The distance from $X_{smallest}$ to the median ($350 - 240 = 110$) is less than the distance ($530 - 350 = 180$) from median to $X_{largest}$. The distance from $X_{smallest}$ to $Q_1$ ($260 - 240 = 20$) is the same as the distance from $Q_3$ to $X_{largest}$ ($530 - 510 = 20$). The distance from $Q_1$ to the median ($350 - 260 = 90$) is less than the distance from the median to $Q_3$ ($510 - 350 = 160$). Two comparisons indicate a right-skewed distribution whereas the other indicates a symmetric distribution. Therefore, you can conclude that the number of calories in iced coffee drinks is right-skewed.

### The Boxplot

A **boxplot** provides a graphical representation of the data based on the five-number summary. Figure 3.4 on page 122 illustrates the boxplot for the getting-ready times. The vertical line drawn within the box represents the median. The vertical line at the left side of the box represents the location of $Q_1$, and the vertical line at the right side of the box represents the location of $Q_3$. Thus, the box contains the middle 50% of the values. The lower 25% of the data are represented by a line connecting the left side of the box to the location of the smallest value, $X_{smallest}$. Similarly, the upper 25% of the data are represented by a line connecting the right side of the box to $X_{largest}$.

**FIGURE 3.4**

Boxplot for the getting
ready times

*See Appendix E3.3 or P3.1
to create this. (Use Section
M3.2 to create the Minitab
equivalent.)*

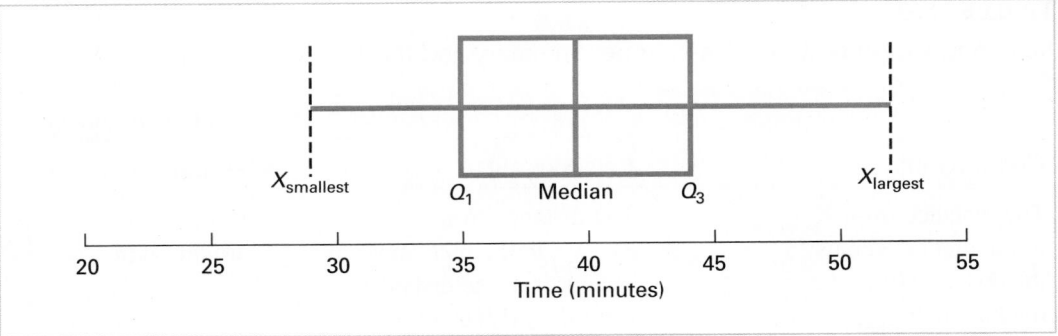

The boxplot of the getting-ready times in Figure 3.4 indicates very slight right-skewness because the distance between the median and the highest value is slightly greater than the distance between the lowest value and the median. Also, the right tail is slightly longer than the left tail.

**EXAMPLE 3.16**

THE BOXPLOTS OF THE 2006 RETURNS OF GROWTH AND VALUE MUTUAL FUNDS

The 868 mutual funds ( Mutual Funds ) that are part of the Using Statistics scenario (see page 90) are classified according to whether the mutual funds are growth or value funds. Construct the boxplot of the 2006 returns for growth and value mutual funds.

**SOLUTION** Figure 3.5 shows the PHStat2 boxplot of the 2006 return for the growth and value mutual funds and Figure 3.6 is a Minitab boxplot. The median return, the quartiles, and the minimum and maximum return are much higher for the value funds than for the growth funds. Both the growth and value funds appear to be fairly symmetrical between the quartiles, but the value funds seem to have more extremely high returns.

**FIGURE 3.5**

PHStat2 boxplots of the
2006 return for growth
and value mutual funds

*See Appendix E3.3 or P3.1
to create this.*

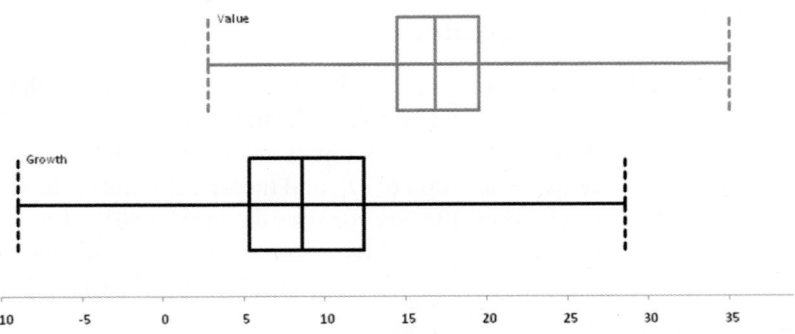

Boxplots for the Growth and Value Funds
2006 Return

**FIGURE 3.6**

Minitab boxplots of the 2006 return for growth and value mutual funds

*See Appendix M3.2 to create this.*

Notice that in Figure 3.6, several * appear in the boxplots. This indicates outliers that are more than 1.5 times the interquartile range beyond the quartiles.

Figure 3.7 demonstrates the relationship between the boxplot and the polygon for four different types of distributions. (*Note:* The area under each polygon is split into quartiles corresponding to the five-number summary for the boxplot.)

**FIGURE 3.7**

Boxplots and corresponding polygons for four distributions

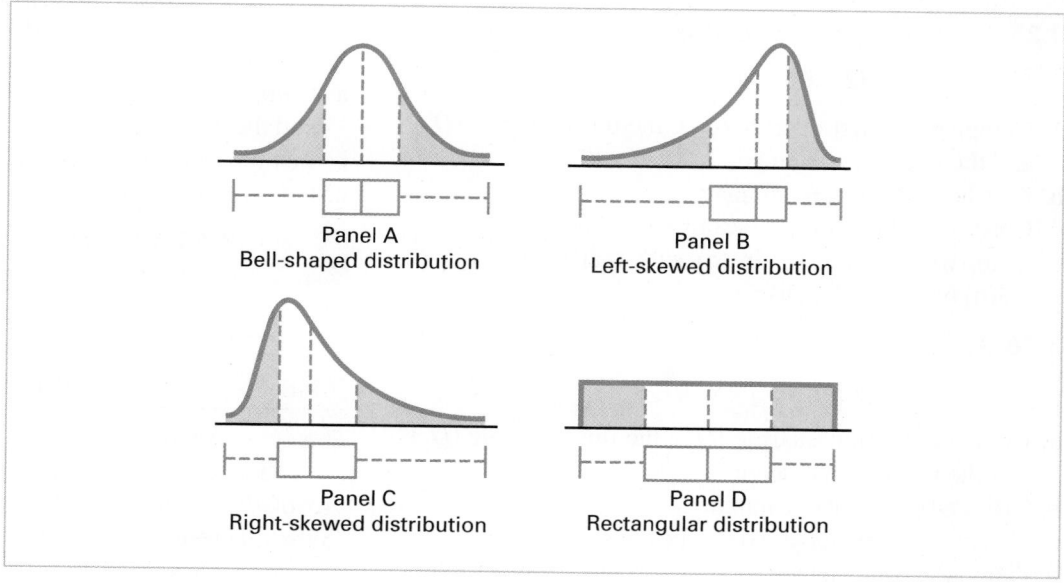

Panels A and D of Figure 3.7 are symmetrical. In these distributions, the mean and median are equal. In addition, the length of the left tail is equal to the length of the right tail, and the median line divides the box in half.

Panel B of Figure 3.7 is left-skewed. The few small values distort the mean toward the left tail. For this left-skewed distribution, there is a heavy clustering of values at the high end of the scale (i.e., the right side); 75% of all values are found between the left edge of the box ($Q_1$) and the end of the right tail ($X_{largest}$). There is a long left tail that contains the smallest 25% of the values, demonstrating the lack of symmetry in this data set.

Panel C of Figure 3.7 is right-skewed. The concentration of values is on the low end of the scale (i.e., the left side of the boxplot). Here, 75% of all data values are found between the beginning of the left tail ($X_{smallest}$) and the right edge of the box ($Q_3$). There is a long right tail that contains the largest 25% of the values, demonstrating the lack of symmetry in this data set.

## PROBLEMS FOR SECTION 3.5

### Learning the Basics

**3.33** The following is a set of data from a sample of $n = 5$:

$$7 \quad 4 \quad 9 \quad 8 \quad 2$$

a. Compute the first quartile ($Q_1$), the third quartile ($Q_3$), and the interquartile range.
b. List the five-number summary.
c. Construct a boxplot and describe the shape.
d. Compare your answer in (c) with that from Problem 3.1(d) on page 106. Discuss.

**3.34** The following is a set of data from a sample of $n = 6$:

$$7 \quad 4 \quad 9 \quad 7 \quad 3 \quad 12$$

a. Compute the first quartile ($Q_1$), the third quartile ($Q_3$), and the interquartile range.
b. List the five-number summary.
c. Construct a boxplot and describe the shape.
d. Compare your answer in (c) with that from Problem 3.2(d) on page 106. Discuss.

**3.35** The following is a set of data from a sample of $n = 7$:

$$12 \quad 7 \quad 4 \quad 9 \quad 0 \quad 7 \quad 3$$

a. Compute the first quartile ($Q_1$), the third quartile ($Q_3$), and the interquartile range.
b. List the five-number summary.
c. Construct a boxplot and describe the shape.
d. Compare your answer in (c) with that from Problem 3.3(d) on page 107. Discuss.

**3.36** The following is a set of data from a sample of $n = 5$:

$$7 \quad -5 \quad -8 \quad 7 \quad 9$$

a. Compute the first quartile ($Q_1$), the third quartile ($Q_3$), and the interquartile range.
b. List the five-number summary.
c. Construct a boxplot and describe the shape.
d. Compare your answer in (c) with that from Problem 3.4(d) on page 107. Discuss.

### Applying the Concepts

**3.37** The data file Chicken contains the total fat, in grams per serving, for a sample of 20 chicken sandwiches from fast-food chains. The data are as follows:

$$7 \quad 8 \quad 4 \quad 5 \quad 16 \quad 20 \quad 20 \quad 24 \quad 19 \quad 30$$
$$23 \quad 30 \quad 25 \quad 19 \quad 29 \quad 29 \quad 30 \quad 30 \quad 40 \quad 56$$

Source: *Extracted from "Fast Food: Adding Health to the Menu,"* Consumer Reports, *September 2004, pp. 28–31.*

a. Compute the first quartile ($Q_1$), the third quartile ($Q_3$), and the interquartile range.

b. List the five-number summary.
c. Construct a boxplot and describe the shape.

**3.38** The data in the file Batterylife represent the battery life (in shots) for a sample of three-pixel digital cameras:

$$300 \quad 180 \quad 85 \quad 170 \quad 380 \quad 460 \quad 260 \quad 35 \quad 380 \quad 120 \quad 110 \quad 240$$

Source: *Extracted from "Cameras: More Features in the Mix,"* Consumer Reports, *July 2005, pp. 14–18.*

a. Compute the first quartile ($Q_1$), the third quartile ($Q_3$), and the interquartile range.
b. List the five-number summary.
c. Construct a boxplot and describe the shape.

**3.39** The data file Themeparks contains data on the starting admission price (in $) for one-day tickets to 10 theme parks in the United States:

$$58 \quad 63 \quad 41 \quad 42 \quad 29 \quad 50 \quad 62 \quad 43 \quad 40 \quad 40$$

Source: *Extracted from C. Jackson and E. Gamerman, "Rethinking the Thrill Factor,"* The Wall Street Journal, *April 15–16, 2006, pp. P1, P4.*

a. Compute the first quartile ($Q_1$), the third quartile ($Q_3$), and the interquartile range.
b. List the five-number summary.
c. Construct a boxplot and describe the shape.

**✓ SELF Test** **3.40** The data in the file SUV represent the overall miles per gallon (MPG) of 2007 small SUVs.

| Model | MPG | Model | MPG |
|---|---|---|---|
| Toyota RAV4 6-cyl | 22 | Mazda Tribute | 18 |
| Hyundai Santa Fe | 18 | Mercury Mariner | 18 |
| Toyota RAV4 4-cyl | 23 | Luxury | |
| Subaru Forester | 20 | Nissan Xterra | 17 |
| Sports 2.5 XT | | Honda Element | 21 |
| Honda CR-V | 21 | Suzuki Grand Vitara | 18 |
| Subaru Forester | 22 | Chevrolet Equinox | 18 |
| Sports 2.5 X | | Pontiac Torrent | 18 |
| Mitsubishi Outlander | 19 | Jeep Compass | 22 |
| Hyundai Tucson | 18 | Saturn Vue | 19 |
| Kia Sportage | 18 | Saturn Vue Hybrid | 24 |
| Ford Escape Hybrid | 26 | Kia Sorento | 15 |
| Mercury Mariner | 26 | Jeep Liberty | 15 |
| Hybrid | | Toyota FJ Cruiser | 17 |
| Suzuki XL-7 | 17 | Dodge Nitro | 16 |
| Ford Escape | 18 | Jeep Wrangler | 15 |

Source: *Extracted from "Vehicle Ratings,"* Consumer Reports, *April 2007, pp. 42–43.*

**a.** Compute the first quartile ($Q_1$), the third quartile ($Q_3$), and the interquartile range.

**b.** List the five-number summary.

**c.** Construct a boxplot and describe the shape.

**3.41** The data in the file `Savings` are the yields for a money market account, a one-year certificate of deposit (CD), and a five-year CD for 37 banks in South Florida as of March 9, 2007 (extracted from **Bankrate.com**, March 9, 2007).

**a.** List the five-number summary for the yield of the money market account, one-year CD, and a five-year CD.

**b.** Construct a boxplot for the yield of the money market account, one-year CD, and a five-year CD.

**c.** What similarities and differences are there in the distributions for the yield of the money market account, one-year CD, and a five-year CD?

**3.42** A bank branch located in a commercial district of a city has developed an improved process for serving customers during the noon-to-1:00 p.m. lunch period. The waiting time, in minutes (defined as the time the customer enters the line to when he or she reaches the teller window), of a sample of 15 customers during this hour is recorded over a period of one week. The results are contained in the data file `Bank1` and are listed below:

4.21  5.55  3.02  5.13  4.77  2.34  3.54  3.20
4.50  6.10  0.38  5.12  6.46  6.19  3.79

Another branch, located in a residential area, is also concerned with the noon-to-1 p.m. lunch hour. The waiting time, in minutes (defined as the time the customer enters the line to when he or she reaches the teller window), of a sample of 15 customers during this hour is recorded over a period of one week. The results are contained in the data file `Bank2` and are listed below:

9.66  5.90  8.02  5.79  8.73  3.82  8.01  8.35
10.49  6.68  5.64  4.08  6.17  9.91  5.47

**a.** List the five-number summaries of the waiting times at the two bank branches.

**b.** Construct boxplots and describe the shape of the distribution for the two bank branches.

**c.** What similarities and differences are there in the distributions of the waiting time at the two bank branches?

## 3.6  THE COVARIANCE AND THE COEFFICIENT OF CORRELATION

In Section 2.5, you used scatter plots to visually examine the relationship between two numerical variables. This section presents two numerical measures of the relationship between two numerical variables: the covariance and the coefficient of correlation.

### The Covariance

The **covariance** measures the strength of the linear relationship between two numerical variables ($X$ and $Y$). Equation (3.18) defines the **sample covariance**, and Example 3.17 illustrates its use.

The Sample Covariance

$$\text{cov}(X,Y) = \frac{\sum_{i=1}^{n}(X_i - \bar{X})(Y_i - \bar{Y})}{n-1} \qquad (3.18)$$

---

**EXAMPLE 3.17**  COMPUTING THE SAMPLE COVARIANCE

In Figure 2.15 on page 53, you examined the relationship between the cost of a fast-food hamburger meal and the cost of two movie tickets in 10 cities around the world (extracted from K. Spors, "Keeping Up with . . . Yourself," *The Wall Street Journal*, April 11, 2005, p. R4). The data file `Cost of living` contains the complete data set. Compute the sample covariance.

**SOLUTION** Table 3.10 provides the cost of a fast-food hamburger meal and the cost of two movie tickets in 10 cities around the world.

**TABLE 3.10**

Cost of a Fast-Food
Hamburger Meal and
Cost of Two Movie
Tickets in 10 Cities

| City | Hamburger | Movie Tickets |
|---|---|---|
| Tokyo | 5.99 | 32.66 |
| London | 7.62 | 28.41 |
| New York | 5.75 | 20.00 |
| Sydney | 4.45 | 20.71 |
| Chicago | 4.99 | 18.00 |
| San Francisco | 5.29 | 19.50 |
| Boston | 4.39 | 18.00 |
| Atlanta | 3.70 | 16.00 |
| Toronto | 4.62 | 18.05 |
| Rio de Janeiro | 2.99 | 9.90 |

Figure 3.8 contains a Microsoft Excel worksheet that calculates the covariance for these data. The Calculations area of Figure 3.8 breaks down Equation (3.18) into a set of smaller calculations. From cell C20, or by using Equation (3.18) directly, you find that the covariance is 6.8378:

$$\text{cov}(X,Y) = \frac{61.5399}{10-1}$$
$$= 6.8378$$

**FIGURE 3.8**

Microsoft Excel
worksheet for the
covariance between the
cost of a fast-food
hamburger meal and
the cost of two movie
tickets in 10 cities

*See Appendix E3.4 to
create this.*

| | A | B | C | |
|---|---|---|---|---|
| 1 | **Covariance Analysis** | | | |
| 2 | | | | |
| 3 | **Hamburger Meal** | **Movie Ticket** | **(X-XBar)(Y-YBar)** | |
| 4 | 5.99 | 32.66 | 12.6749 | =(A4 - $C$16) * (B4 - $C$17) |
| 5 | 7.62 | 28.41 | 21.8860 | =(A5 - $C$16) * (B5 - $C$17) |
| 6 | 5.75 | 20.00 | -0.0948 | =(A6 - $C$16) * (B6 - $C$17) |
| 7 | 4.45 | 20.71 | -0.3105 | =(A7 - $C$16) * (B7 - $C$17) |
| 8 | 4.99 | 18.00 | -0.0234 | =(A8 - $C$16) * (B8 - $C$17) |
| 9 | 5.29 | 19.50 | -0.1938 | =(A9 - $C$16) * (B9 - $C$17) |
| 10 | 4.39 | 18.00 | 1.2504 | =(A10 - $C$16) * (B10 - $C$17) |
| 11 | 3.70 | 16.00 | 5.2733 | =(A11 - $C$16) * (B11 - $C$17) |
| 12 | 4.62 | 18.05 | 0.7442 | =(A12 - $C$16) * (B12 - $C$17) |
| 13 | 2.99 | 9.90 | 20.3335 | =(A13 - $C$16) * (B13 - $C$17) |
| 14 | | | | |
| 15 | | **Calculations** | | |
| 16 | | XBar | 4.9790 | =AVERAGE(A4:A13) |
| 17 | | YBar | 20.1230 | =AVERAGE(B4:B13) |
| 18 | | n-1 | 9 | =COUNT(A4:A13) - 1 |
| 19 | | Sum | 61.5399 | =SUM(C4:C13) |
| 20 | | Covariance | 6.8378 | =C19 / C18 |

The covariance has a major flaw as a measure of the linear relationship between two numerical variables. Because the covariance can have any value, you are unable to determine the relative strength of the relationship. In other words, you cannot tell whether the value 6.8378 is an indication of a strong relationship or a weak relationship. To better determine the relative strength of the relationship, you need to compute the coefficient of correlation.

### The Coefficient of Correlation

The **coefficient of correlation** measures the relative strength of a linear relationship between two numerical variables. The values of the coefficient of correlation range from −1 for a perfect negative correlation to +1 for a perfect positive correlation. Perfect means that if the points were plotted in a scatter plot, all the points could be connected with a straight line. When dealing with population data for two numerical variables, the Greek letter ρ is used as the symbol for the coefficient of correlation. Figure 3.9 illustrates three different types of association between two variables.

**FIGURE 3.9**

Types of association between variables

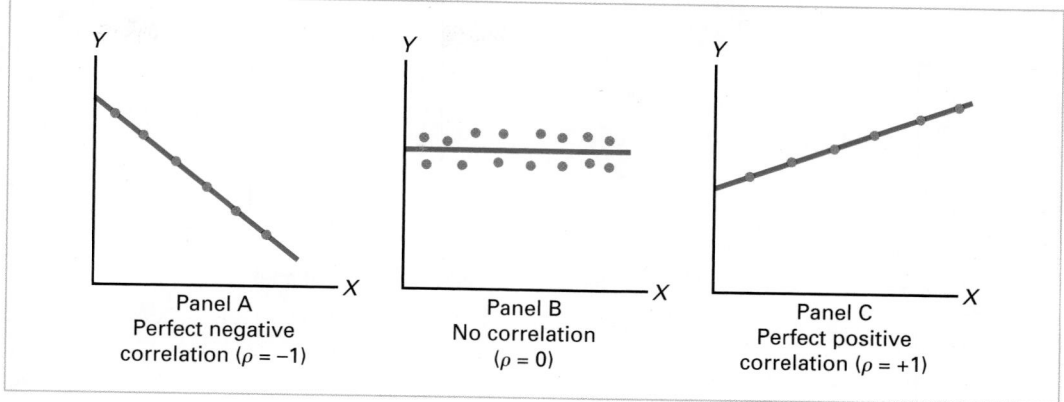

In Panel A of Figure 3.9, there is a perfect negative linear relationship between $X$ and $Y$. Thus, the coefficient of correlation, $\rho$, equals $-1$, and when $X$ increases, $Y$ decreases in a perfectly predictable manner. Panel B shows a situation in which there is no relationship between $X$ and $Y$. In this case, the coefficient of correlation, $\rho$, equals 0, and as $X$ increases, there is no tendency for $Y$ to increase or decrease. Panel C illustrates a perfect positive relationship where $\rho$ equals $+1$. In this case, $Y$ increases in a perfectly predictable manner when $X$ increases.

Correlation alone cannot prove that there is a causation effect—that is, that the change in the value of one variable caused the change in the other variable. A strong correlation can be produced simply by chance, by the effect of a third variable not considered in the calculation of the correlation, or by a cause-and-effect relationship. You would need to perform additional analysis to determine which of these three situations actually produced the correlation. Therefore, you can say that causation implies correlation, but correlation alone does not imply causation.

Equation (3.19) defines the **sample coefficient of correlation**, $r$.

The Sample Coefficient of Correlation

$$r = \frac{\text{cov}(X,Y)}{S_X S_Y} \tag{3.19}$$

where

$$\text{cov}(X, Y) = \frac{\sum_{i=1}^{n}(X_i - \bar{X})(Y_i - \bar{Y})}{n-1}$$

$$S_X = \sqrt{\frac{\sum_{i=1}^{n}(X_i - \bar{X})^2}{n-1}}$$

$$S_Y = \sqrt{\frac{\sum_{i=1}^{n}(Y_i - \bar{Y})^2}{n-1}}$$

When you have sample data, you calculate the sample coefficient of correlation, $r$. When using sample data, you are unlikely to have a sample coefficient of exactly $+1$, 0, or $-1$. Figure 3.10 presents scatter plots along with their respective sample coefficients of correlation, $r$, for six data sets, each of which contains 100 values of $X$ and $Y$.

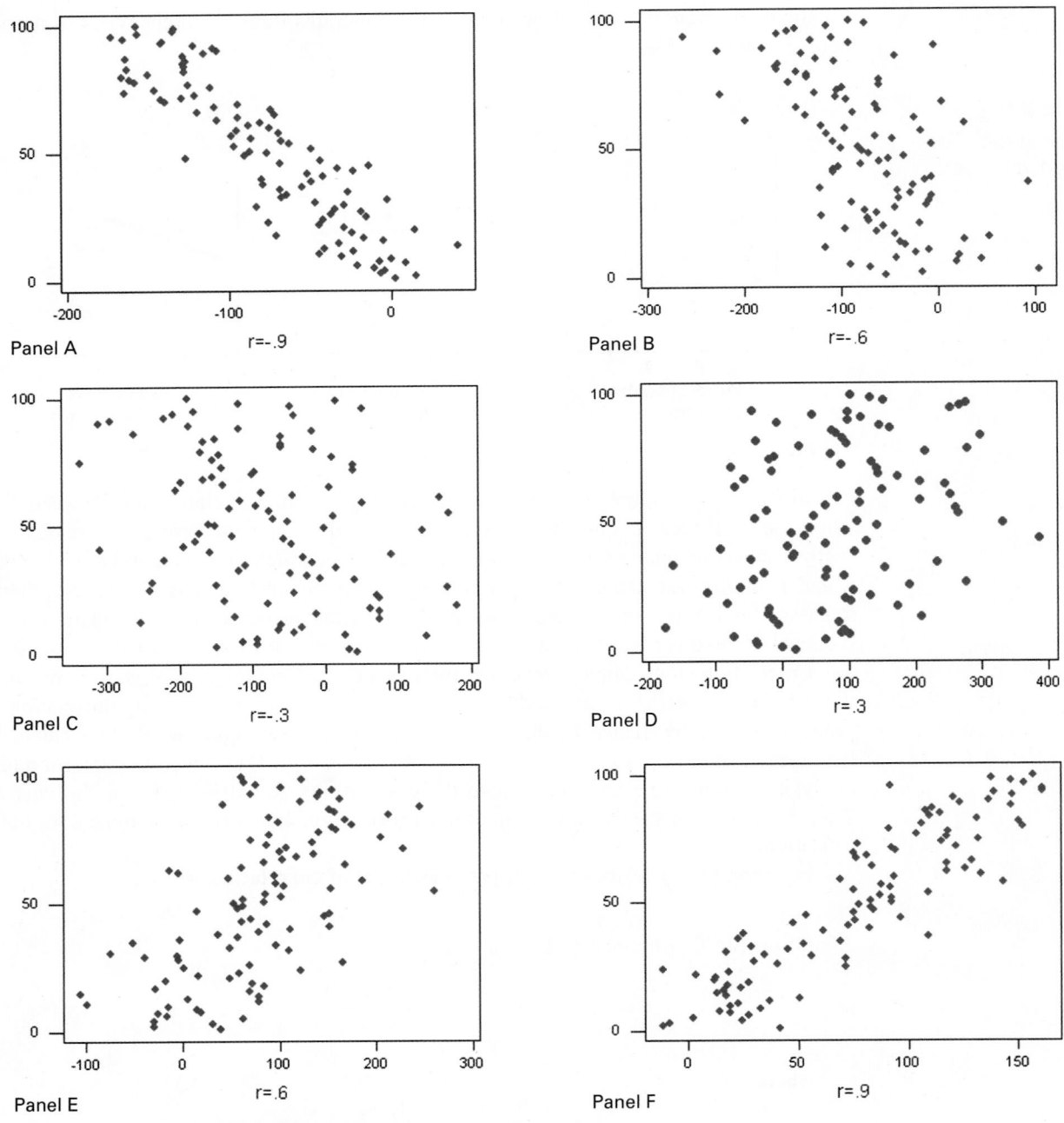

**FIGURE 3.10**

Six Minitab scatter plots and their sample coefficients of correlation, *r*

In Panel A, the coefficient of correlation, *r*, is −0.9. You can see that for small values of *X*, there is a very strong tendency for *Y* to be large. Likewise, the large values of *X* tend to be paired with small values of *Y*. The data do not all fall on a straight line, so the association between *X* and *Y* cannot be described as perfect. The data in Panel B have a coefficient of correlation equal to −0.6, and the small values of *X* tend to be paired with large values of *Y*. The linear relationship between *X* and *Y* in Panel B is not as strong as that in Panel A. Thus, the coefficient of correlation in Panel B is not as negative as that in Panel A. In Panel C, the linear relationship between *X* and *Y* is very weak, *r* = −0.3, and there is only a slight tendency for the small values of *X* to be paired with the larger values of *Y*. Panels D through F depict data sets that have positive coefficients of correlation because small values of *X* tend to be paired with small values of *Y*, and the large values of *X* tend to be associated with large values of *Y*.

**EXAMPLE 3.18**    COMPUTING THE SAMPLE COEFFICIENT OF CORRELATION

Consider the cost of a fast-food hamburger meal and the cost of two movie tickets in 10 cities around the world (see Table 3.10 on page 126). From Figure 3.11 and Equation (3.19), compute the sample coefficient of correlation.

**SOLUTION**    $r = \dfrac{\text{cov}(X,Y)}{S_X S_Y}$

$= \dfrac{6.8378}{(1.2925)(6.337)}$

$= 0.8348$

**FIGURE 3.11**

Microsoft Excel worksheet for the sample coefficient of correlation, $r$, between the cost of a fast-food hamburger meal and two movie tickets

See Appendix E3.5 to create this. (Use Section M3.3 to create the Minitab equivalent.)

| | A | B | C | D | E |
|---|---|---|---|---|---|
| 1 | Hamburger Meal | Movie Ticket | (X-XBar)² | (Y-YBar)² | (X-XBar)(Y-YBar) |
| 2 | 5.99 | 32.66 | 1.0221 | 157.1764 | 12.6749 |
| 3 | 7.62 | 28.41 | 6.9749 | 68.6744 | 21.8860 |
| 4 | 5.75 | 20.00 | 0.5944 | 0.0151 | -0.0948 |
| 5 | 4.45 | 20.71 | 0.2798 | 0.3446 | -0.3105 |
| 6 | 4.99 | 18.00 | 0.0001 | 4.5071 | -0.0234 |
| 7 | 5.29 | 19.50 | 0.0967 | 0.3881 | -0.1938 |
| 8 | 4.39 | 18.00 | 0.3469 | 4.5071 | 1.2504 |
| 9 | 3.70 | 16.00 | 1.6358 | 16.9991 | 5.2733 |
| 10 | 4.62 | 18.05 | 0.1289 | 4.2973 | 0.7442 |
| 11 | 2.99 | 9.90 | 3.9561 | 104.5097 | 20.3335 |
| 12 | | Sums: | 15.03589 | 361.41901 | 61.5399 |
| 13 | | | | | |
| 14 | | | | Calculations | |
| 15 | | | | XBar | 4.979 | =AVERAGE(A2:A11) |
| 16 | | | | YBar | 20.123 | =AVERAGE(B2:B11) |
| 17 | | | | n-1 | 9 | =COUNT(A2:A11)-1 |
| 18 | | | | Covariance | 6.83777 | =E12 / E17 |
| 19 | | | | Sₓ | 1.2925 | =SQRT(C12 / E17) |
| 20 | | | | Sᵧ | 6.3370 | =SQRT(D12 / E17) |
| 21 | | | | r | 0.8348 | =CORREL(A2:A11, B2:B11) |

The cost of a fast-food hamburger meal and the cost of two movie tickets are positively correlated. Those cities with the lowest cost of a fast-food hamburger meal tend to be associated with the lowest cost of two movie tickets. Those cities with the highest cost of a fast-food hamburger meal tend to be associated with the highest cost of two movie tickets. This relationship is strong, as indicated by a coefficient of correlation, $r = 0.8348$.

You cannot assume that having a low cost of a fast-food hamburger meal caused the low cost of two movie tickets. You can only say that this is what tended to happen in the sample.

In summary, the coefficient of correlation indicates the linear relationship, or association, between two numerical variables. When the coefficient of correlation gets closer to $+1$ or $-1$, the linear relationship between the two variables is stronger. When the coefficient of correlation is near 0, little or no linear relationship exists. The sign of the coefficient of correlation indicates whether the data are positively correlated (i.e., the larger values of $X$ are typically paired with the larger values of $Y$) or negatively correlated (i.e., the larger values of $X$ are typically paired with the smaller values of $Y$). The existence of a strong correlation does not imply a causation effect. It only indicates the tendencies present in the data.

# PROBLEMS FOR SECTION 3.6

## Learning the Basics

**3.43** The following is a set of data from a sample of $n = 11$ items:

| $X$ | 7 | 5 | 8 | 3 | 6 | 10 | 12 | 4 | 9 | 15 | 18 |
| $Y$ | 21 | 15 | 24 | 9 | 18 | 30 | 36 | 12 | 27 | 45 | 54 |

a. Compute the covariance.
b. Compute the coefficient of correlation.
c. How strong is the relationship between $X$ and $Y$? Explain.

## Applying the Concepts

**3.44** An article (P. Lim, "An Around-the-World Ticket for Your Portfolio," *The New York Times*, June 3, 2007, p. B5) that discussed investment in foreign stocks (over the last five years) stated that the coefficient of correlation between the return on investment of U.S. stocks (as expressed by the S & P 500) and the German stock market was 0.89, U.S. stocks (as expressed by the S & P 500) and Brazilian stock market was 0.68, and U.S. stocks (as expressed by the S & P 500) and the Japanese stock market was 0.29. What conclusions can you make about the strength of the relationship between the return on investment of U.S. stocks and each of these three other types of investments?

**3.45** According to the Mortgage Bankers Association, home mortgage applications were rising as lower loan rates fostered home purchases and refinancings ("Mortgage Applications Creep Up as Rates Fall," **www.usatoday.com**, April 25, 2007).
a. Is the article implying that the number of home mortgages and loan rates are positively correlated, negatively correlated, or independent?
b. If you believe that the article is implying that the number of home mortgages and loan rates are correlated, do you believe that there is a cause-and-effect relationship? Discuss.

**√SELF Test** **3.46** The data in the file `CoffeeDrink` represent the calories and fat, in grams, of 16-ounce iced coffee drinks at Dunkin' Donuts and Starbucks:

| Product | Calories | Fat |
|---|---|---|
| Dunkin' Donuts Iced Mocha Swirl latte (whole milk) | 240 | 8.0 |
| Starbucks Coffee Frappuccino blended coffee | 260 | 3.5 |
| Dunkin' Donuts Coffee Coolatta (cream) | 350 | 22.0 |
| Starbucks Iced Coffee Mocha Expresso (whole milk and whipped cream) | 350 | 20.0 |
| Starbucks Mocha Frappuccino blended coffee (whipped cream) | 420 | 16.0 |
| Starbucks Chocolate Brownie Frappuccino blended coffee (whipped cream) | 510 | 22.0 |
| Starbucks Chocolate Frappuccino Blended Crème (whipped cream) | 530 | 19.0 |

Source: *Extracted from "Coffee as Candy at Dunkin' Donuts and Starbucks,"* Consumer Reports, *June 2004, p. 9.*

a. Compute the covariance.
b. Compute the coefficient of correlation.
c. Which do you think is more valuable in expressing the relationship between calories and fat—the covariance or the coefficient of correlation? Explain.
d. What conclusions can you reach about the relationship between calories and fat?

**3.47** There are several methods for calculating fuel economy. The following table (contained in the file `Mileage`) indicates the mileage, as calculated by owners and by current government standards:

| Car | Owner | Government |
|---|---|---|
| 2005 Ford F-150 | 14.3 | 16.8 |
| 2005 Chevrolet Silverado | 15.0 | 17.8 |
| 2002 Honda Accord LX | 27.8 | 26.2 |
| 2002 Honda Civic | 27.9 | 34.2 |
| 2004 Honda Civic Hybrid | 48.8 | 47.6 |
| 2002 Ford Explorer | 16.8 | 18.3 |
| 2005 Toyota Camry | 23.7 | 28.5 |
| 2003 Toyota Corolla | 32.8 | 33.1 |
| 2005 Toyota Prius | 37.3 | 56.0 |

Source: *Extracted from J. Healey, "Fuel Economy Calculations to Be Altered,"* USA Today, *January 11, 2006, p. 1B.*

a. Compute the covariance.
b. Compute the coefficient of correlation.
c. Which do you think is more valuable in expressing the relationship between owner and current government standards mileage—the covariance or the coefficient of correlation? Explain.
d. What conclusions can you reach about the relationship between owner and current government standards mileage?

**3.48** College basketball is big business, with coaches' salaries, revenues, and expenses in millions of dollars. The data file `Colleges-basketball` contains the coaches' salaries

and revenue for college basketball at selected schools in a recent year (extracted from R. Adams, "Pay for Playoffs," *The Wall Street Journal*, March 11–12, 2006, pp. P1, P8).
a. Compute the covariance.
b. Compute the coefficient of correlation.
c. What conclusions can you reach about the relationship between a coach's salary and revenue?

**3.49** College football players trying out for the NFL are given the Wonderlic standardized intelligence test. The data

in the file **Wonderlic** contains the average Wonderlic score of football players trying out for the NFL and the graduation rate for football players at selected schools (extracted from S. Walker, "The NFL's Smartest Team," *The Wall Street Journal*, September 30, 2005, pp. W1, W10).
a. Compute the covariance.
b. Compute the coefficient of correlation.
c. What conclusions can you reach about the relationship between the average Wonderlic score and graduation rate?

# Presenting Descriptive Statistics: Pitfalls and Ethical Issues

*From the Authors' Desktop*

This chapter describes how a set of numerical data can be characterized by the statistics that measure the properties of central tendency, variation, and shape. In business, descriptive statistics such as the ones you have learned about are frequently included in summary reports that are prepared periodically.

The volume of information available on the Internet, in newspapers, and in magazines has produced much skepticism about the objectivity of data. When you are reading information that contains descriptive statis-

tics, you should keep in mind the quip often attributed to the famous nineteenth-century British statesman Benjamin Disraeli: "There are three kinds of lies: lies, damned lies, and statistics."

For example, in examining statistics that are provided, you need to compare the mean and the median. Are they similar or are they very different? Or, is only the mean provided? The answers to these questions will enable you to know whether the data are skewed or symmetrical and whether the median might be a better measure of central tendency than the mean. In addition, you should look to see

whether the standard deviation has been included in the statistics provided. Without the standard deviation, it is difficult to determine the amount of variation that exists in the data.

Ethical considerations arise when you are deciding what results to include in a report. You should document both good and bad results. In addition, when making oral presentations and presenting written reports, you need to give results in a fair, objective, and neutral manner. Unethical behavior occurs when you selectively fail to report pertinent findings that are detrimental to the support of a particular position.

# SUMMARY

In this and the previous chapter, you studied descriptive statistics—how data are presented in tables and charts, and then summarized, described, analyzed, and interpreted. When dealing with the mutual fund data, you were able to present useful information through the use of pie charts, histograms, and other graphical methods. You explored characteristics of past performance, such as central tendency, variability, and shape, using numerical descriptive

measures, such as the mean, median, quartiles, range, standard deviation, and coefficient of correlation. Table 3.11 provides a list of the numerical descriptive measures covered in this chapter.

In the next chapter, the basic principles of probability are presented in order to bridge the gap between the subject of descriptive statistics and the subject of inferential statistics.

| **TABLE 3.11** | **Type of Analysis** | **Numerical Data** |
|---|---|---|
| Summary of Numerical Descriptive Measures | Describing central tendency, variation, and shape of a numerical variable | Mean, median, mode, quartiles, geometric mean, range, interquartile range, variance, standard deviation, coefficient of variation, $Z$ scores, boxplot **(Sections 3.1, 3.2, 3.5)** |
| | Describing the relationship between two numerical variables | Covariance, coefficient of correlation **(Section 3.6)** |

# KEY EQUATIONS

**Sample Mean**

$$\bar{X} = \frac{\sum_{i=1}^{n} X_i}{n} \qquad (3.1)$$

**Median**

$$\text{Median} = \frac{n+1}{2} \text{ ranked value} \qquad (3.2)$$

**Geometric Mean**

$$\bar{X}_G = (X_1 \times X_2 \times \cdots \times X_n)^{1/n} \qquad (3.3)$$

**Geometric Mean Rate of Return**

$$\bar{R}_G = [(1+R_1) \times (1+R_2) \times \cdots \times (1+R_n)]^{1/n} - 1 \qquad (3.4)$$

**Range**

$$\text{Range} = X_{\text{largest}} - X_{\text{smallest}} \qquad (3.5)$$

**Sample Variance**

$$S^2 = \frac{\sum_{i=1}^{n} (X_i - \bar{X})^2}{n-1} \qquad (3.6)$$

**Sample Standard Deviation**

$$S = \sqrt{S^2} = \sqrt{\frac{\sum_{i=1}^{n} (X_i - \bar{X})^2}{n-1}} \qquad (3.7)$$

**Coefficient of Variation**

$$CV = \left(\frac{S}{\bar{X}}\right) 100\% \qquad (3.8)$$

**Z Scores**

$$Z = \frac{X - \bar{X}}{S} \qquad (3.9)$$

**Population Mean**

$$\mu = \frac{\sum_{i=1}^{N} X_i}{N} \qquad (3.10)$$

**Population Variance**

$$\sigma^2 = \frac{\sum_{i=1}^{N} (X_i - \mu)^2}{N} \qquad (3.11)$$

**Population Standard Deviation**

$$\sigma = \sqrt{\frac{\sum_{i=1}^{N} (X_i - \mu)^2}{N}} \qquad (3.12)$$

**Mean of a Frequency Distribution**

$$\bar{X} = \frac{\sum_{j=1}^{c} m_j f_j}{n} \qquad (3.13)$$

**Standard Deviation of a Frequency Distribution**

$$S = \sqrt{\frac{\sum_{j=1}^{c} (m_j - \bar{X})^2 f_j}{n-1}} \qquad (3.14)$$

**First Quartile $Q_1$**

$$Q_1 = \frac{n+1}{4} \text{ ranked value} \qquad (3.15)$$

**Third Quartile $Q_3$**

$$Q_3 = \frac{3(n+1)}{4} \text{ ranked value} \qquad (3.16)$$

**Interquartile Range**

$$\text{Interquartile range} = Q_3 - Q_1 \qquad (3.17)$$

**Sample Covariance**

$$\text{cov}(X,Y) = \frac{\sum_{i=1}^{n}(X_i - \bar{X})(Y_i - \bar{Y})}{n-1} \qquad \text{(3.18)}$$

**Sample Coefficient of Correlation**

$$r = \frac{\text{cov}(X,Y)}{S_X S_Y} \qquad \text{(3.19)}$$

# KEY TERMS

arithmetic mean   90
boxplot   121
central tendency   90
Chebyshev rule   112
coefficient of correlation   126
coefficient of variation   101
covariance   125
dispersion   96
empirical rule   112
extreme value   102
five-number summary   120
geometric mean   95
geometric mean rate of return   95
interquartile range   119
left-skewed   104

mean   90
median   93
midspread   119
mode   94
outlier   102
population mean   110
population standard deviation   110
population variance   110
$Q_1$: first quartile   117
$Q_2$: second quartile   117
$Q_3$: third quartile   117
quartiles   117
range   97
resistant measure   120
right-skewed   104

sample coefficient of correlation   127
sample covariance   125
sample mean   91
sample standard deviation   98
sample variance   98
shape   90
skewed   104
spread   96
standard deviation   97
sum of squares (*SS*)   98
symmetrical   104
variance   97
variation   90
*Z* score   102

# CHAPTER REVIEW PROBLEMS

## Checking Your Understanding

**3.50** What are the properties of a set of numerical data?

**3.51** What is meant by the property of central tendency?

**3.52** What are the differences among the mean, median, and mode, and what are the advantages and disadvantages of each?

**3.53** How do you interpret the first quartile, median, and third quartile?

**3.54** What is meant by the property of variation?

**3.55** What does the *Z* score measure?

**3.56** What are the differences among the various measures of variation, such as the range, interquartile range, variance, standard deviation, and coefficient of variation, and what are the advantages and disadvantages of each?

**3.57** How does the empirical rule help explain the ways in which the values in a set of numerical data cluster and distribute?

**3.58** How do the empirical rule and the Chebyshev rule differ?

**3.59** What is meant by the property of shape?

**3.60** How do the covariance and the coefficient of correlation differ?

## Applying the Concepts

**3.61** The American Society for Quality (ASQ) conducted a salary survey of all its members. ASQ members work in all areas of manufacturing and service-related institutions, with a common theme of an interest in quality. For the U.S. survey, e-mails were sent to 70,645 members, and 10,848 valid responses were received. The two most common job titles were manager and quality engineer. Another title is Master Black Belt, who is a person who takes a leadership role as the keeper of the Six Sigma process (see Section 18.8). Descriptive statistics concerning salaries for these three titles are given on page 134 (extracted from M. Edmund, "Elevation Almost Everywhere," *Quality Progress*, December 2006, pp. 21–48). Compare the salaries of managers, quality engineers, and Master Black Belts.

| Title | Sample Size | Minimum | Maximum | Standard Deviation | Mean | Median |
|---|---|---|---|---|---|---|
| Manager | 2,615 | 25,000 | 178,000 | 22,266 | 80,837 | 80,000 |
| Quality Engineer | 1,617 | 25,000 | 160,000 | 17,316 | 68,028 | 66,000 |
| Master Black Belt | 155 | 46,000 | 200,000 | 25,010 | 106,617 | 105,000 |

**3.62** In New York State, savings banks are permitted to sell a form of life insurance called savings bank life insurance (SBLI). The approval process consists of underwriting, which includes a review of the application, a medical information bureau check, possible requests for additional medical information and medical exams, and a policy compilation stage during which the policy pages are generated and sent to the bank for delivery. The ability to deliver approved policies to customers in a timely manner is critical to the profitability of this service to the bank. During a period of one month, a random sample of 27 approved policies was selected, and the following total processing times in days were recorded; the data are contained in the file **Insurance**:

73  19  16  64  28  28  31  90  60  56  31  56  22  18

45  48  17  17  17  91  92  63  50  51  69  16  17

**a.** Compute the mean, median, first quartile, and third quartile.
**b.** Compute the range, interquartile range, variance, standard deviation, and coefficient of variation.
**c.** Construct a boxplot. Are the data skewed? If so, how?
**d.** What would you tell a customer who enters the bank to purchase this type of insurance policy and asks how long the approval process takes?

**3.63** One of the major measures of the quality of service provided by any organization is the speed with which it responds to customer complaints. A large family-held department store selling furniture and flooring, including carpet, had undergone a major expansion in the past several years. In particular, the flooring department had expanded from 2 installation crews to an installation supervisor, a measurer, and 15 installation crews. A sample of 50 complaints concerning carpet installation was selected during a recent year. The data in the file **Furniture** represent the number of days between the receipt of a complaint and the resolution of the complaint:

54    5   35  137  31  27  152   2  123  81  74  27  11

19  126  110  110  29  61   35  94   31  26   5  12   4

165  32  29   28  29  26   25   1   14  13  13  10   5

27    4  52   30  22  36   26  20   23  33  68

**a.** Compute the mean, median, first quartile, and third quartile.

**b.** Compute the range, interquartile range, variance, standard deviation, and coefficient of variation.
**c.** Construct a boxplot. Are the data skewed? If so, how?
**d.** On the basis of the results of (a) through (c), if you had to tell the president of the company how long a customer should expect to wait to have a complaint resolved, what would you say? Explain.

**3.64** A manufacturing company produces steel housings for electrical equipment. The main component part of the housing is a steel trough that is made out of a 14-gauge steel coil. It is produced using a 250-ton progressive punch press with a wipe-down operation, putting two 90-degree forms in the flat steel to make the trough. The distance from one side of the form to the other is critical because of weatherproofing in outdoor applications. The company requires that the width of the trough be between 8.31 inches and 8.61 inches. The data file **Trough** contains the widths of the troughs, in inches, for a sample of $n = 49$:

8.312 8.343 8.317 8.383 8.348 8.410 8.351 8.373 8.481 8.422

8.476 8.382 8.484 8.403 8.414 8.419 8.385 8.465 8.498 8.447

8.436 8.413 8.489 8.414 8.481 8.415 8.479 8.429 8.458 8.462

8.460 8.444 8.429 8.460 8.412 8.420 8.410 8.405 8.323 8.420

8.396 8.447 8.405 8.439 8.411 8.427 8.420 8.498 8.409

**a.** Calculate the mean, median, range, and standard deviation for the width. Interpret these measures of central tendency and variability.
**b.** List the five-number summary.
**c.** Construct a boxplot and describe its shape.
**d.** What can you conclude about the number of troughs that will meet the company's requirement of troughs being between 8.31 and 8.61 inches wide?

**3.65** The manufacturing company in Problem 3.64 also produces electric insulators. If the insulators break when in use, a short circuit is likely to occur. To test the strength of the insulators, destructive testing is carried out to determine how much force is required to break the insulators. Force is measured by observing how many pounds must be applied to the insulator before it breaks. The data from 30 insulators from this experiment are contained in the file **Force**:

1,870 1,728 1,656 1,610 1,634 1,784 1,522 1,696 1,592 1,662

1,866 1,764 1,734 1,662 1,734 1,774 1,550 1,756 1,762 1,866

1,820 1,744 1,788 1,688 1,810 1,752 1,680 1,810 1,652 1,736

**a.** Calculate the mean, median, range, and standard deviation for the force needed to break the insulator.
**b.** Interpret the measures of central tendency and variability in (a).
**c.** Construct a boxplot and describe its shape.

**d.** What can you conclude about the strength of the insulators if the company requires a force measurement of at least 1,500 pounds before breakage?

**3.66** The data contained in the file `Tuition2006` consist of the in-state tuition and fees and the out-of-state tuition and fees for four-year colleges with the highest percentage of students graduating within six years.

Source: *U.S. Department of Education, 2006.*

For each variable:

**a.** Compute the mean, median, first quartile, and third quartile.
**b.** Compute the range, interquartile range, variance, standard deviation, and coefficient of variation.
**c.** Construct a boxplot. Are the data skewed? If so, how?
**d.** Compute the coefficient of correlation between the in-state tuition and fees and the out-of-state tuition and fees.
**e.** What conclusions can you reach concerning the in-state tuition and fees and the out-of-state tuition and fees?

**3.67** A quality characteristic of interest for a tea-bag-filling process is the weight of the tea in the individual bags. If the bags are underfilled, two problems arise. First, customers may not be able to brew the tea to be as strong as they wish. Second, the company may be in violation of the truth-in-labeling laws. For this product, the label weight on the package indicates that, on average, there are 5.5 grams of tea in a bag. If the mean amount of tea in a bag exceeds the label weight, the company is giving away product. Getting an exact amount of tea in a bag is problematic because of variation in the temperature and humidity inside the factory, differences in the density of the tea, and the extremely fast filling operation of the machine (approximately 170 bags per minute). The data in the file `Teabags` shown below provide the weight, in grams, of a sample of 50 tea bags produced in one hour by a single machine:

5.65 5.44 5.42 5.40 5.53 5.34 5.54 5.45 5.52 5.41

5.57 5.40 5.53 5.54 5.55 5.62 5.56 5.46 5.44 5.51

5.47 5.40 5.47 5.61 5.53 5.32 5.67 5.29 5.49 5.55

5.77 5.57 5.42 5.58 5.58 5.50 5.32 5.50 5.53 5.58

5.61 5.45 5.44 5.25 5.56 5.63 5.50 5.57 5.67 5.36

**a.** Compute the mean, median, first quartile, and third quartile.
**b.** Compute the range, interquartile range, variance, standard deviation, and coefficient of variation.
**c.** Interpret the measures of central tendency and variation within the context of this problem. Why should the company producing the tea bags be concerned about the central tendency and variation?
**d.** Construct a boxplot. Are the data skewed? If so, how?

**e.** Is the company meeting the requirement set forth on the label that, on average, there are 5.5 grams of tea in a bag? If you were in charge of this process, what changes, if any, would you try to make concerning the distribution of weights in the individual bags?

**3.68** The manufacturer of Boston and Vermont asphalt shingles provides its customers with a 20-year warranty on most of its products. To determine whether a shingle will last as long as the warranty period, accelerated-life testing is conducted at the manufacturing plant. Accelerated-life testing exposes the shingle to the stresses it would be subject to in a lifetime of normal use via an experiment in a laboratory setting that takes only a few minutes to conduct. In this test, a shingle is repeatedly scraped with a brush for a short period of time, and the shingle granules removed by the brushing are weighed (in grams). Shingles that experience low amounts of granule loss are expected to last longer in normal use than shingles that experience high amounts of granule loss. In this situation, a shingle should experience no more than 0.8 gram of granule loss if it is expected to last the length of the warranty period. The data file `Granule` contains a sample of 170 measurements made on the company's Boston shingles and 140 measurements made on Vermont shingles.

**a.** List the five-number summary for the Boston shingles and for the Vermont shingles.
**b.** Construct side-by-side boxplots for the two brands of shingles and describe the shapes of the distributions.
**c.** Comment on the shingles' ability to achieve a granule loss of 0.8 gram or less.

**3.69** A study conducted by Zagat Survey concluded that many first-rate restaurants are located in hotels across the United States. Travelers can find quality food, service, and décor without leaving their hotels. The top-rated hotel restaurant is The French Room, located in The Adolphus Hotel in Dallas, Texas. The estimated price for dinner, including one drink and tip, at The French Room is $80. The highest price reported is $179 at Alain Ducasse, located in the Jumeirah Essex House in New York City (extracted from Gary Stoller, "Top Restaurants Check into Luxury Hotels," *USA Today*, April 11, 2006, p. 5B). The file `Bestrest` contains the top 100 hotel restaurants in the United States and the variables state, city, restaurant, hotel, cost (estimated price of dinner including one drink and tip), and rating (1 to 100, with 1 the top-rated restaurant).

**a.** Construct the five-number summary of dinner price.
**b.** Construct a boxplot of dinner price and interpret the distribution of dinner prices.
**c.** Calculate and interpret the correlation coefficient of the rating and dinner price.

**3.70** The data in the file `Chicken` contains the characteristics for a sample of 20 chicken sandwiches from fast-food chains.

**a.** Compute the correlation coefficient between calories and carbohydrates.

**b.** Compute the correlation coefficient between calories and sodium.

**c.** Compute the correlation coefficient between calories and total fat.

**d.** Which variable (total fat, carbohydrates, or sodium) seems to be most closely related to calories? Explain.

**3.71** In Example 3.18 on page 129, the correlation coefficient between the cost of a fast-food hamburger meal and the cost of movie tickets in 10 different cities was computed. The data file **Cost of living** also includes the overall cost index, the monthly rent for a two-bedroom apartment, and the costs of a cup of coffee with service, dry cleaning for a men's blazer, and toothpaste.

**a.** Compute the correlation coefficient between the overall cost index and the monthly rent for a two-bedroom apartment, the cost of a cup of coffee with service, the cost of a fast-food hamburger meal, the cost of dry-cleaning a men's blazer, the cost of toothpaste, and the cost of movie tickets. (There will be six separate correlation coefficients.)

**b.** What conclusions can you reach about the relationship of the overall cost index to each of these six variables?

**3.72** The data in the file **Spending** is the per-capita spending, in thousands of dollars, for each state in 2004.

**a.** Compute the mean, median, first quartile, and third quartile.

**b.** Compute the range, interquartile range, variance, standard deviation, and coefficient of variation.

**c.** Construct a boxplot. Are the data skewed? If so, how?

**d.** What conclusions can you reach concerning per-capita spending, in thousands of dollars, for each state in 2004?

**3.73** The data in the file **CEO** represent the total compensation (in $millions) of CEOs of the 100 largest companies, by revenue (extracted from "Special Report: Executive Compensation," *USA Today*, April 10, 2006, pp. 3B, 4B).

**a.** Compute the mean, median, first quartile, and third quartile.

**b.** Compute the range, interquartile range, variance, standard deviation, and coefficient of variation.

**c.** Construct a boxplot. Are the data skewed? If so, how?

**d.** What conclusions can you draw concerning the total compensation (in $millions) of CEOs?

**3.74** You are planning to study for your statistics examination with a group of classmates, one of whom you particularly want to impress. This individual has volunteered to use Microsoft Excel or Minitab to get the needed summary information, tables, and charts for a data set containing several numerical and categorical variables assigned by the instructor for study purposes. This person comes over to you with the printout and exclaims, "I've got it all–the means, the medians, the standard deviations, the boxplots, the pie charts—for all our variables. The problem is, some of the output looks weird—like the boxplots for gender and for major and the pie charts for grade point index and for height. Also, I can't understand why Professor Krehbiel said we can't get the descriptive stats for some of the variables—I got them for everything! See, the mean for height is 68.23, the mean for grade point index is 2.76, the mean for gender is 1.50, the mean for major is 4.33." What is your reply?

## Report Writing Exercises

**3.75** Data concerning 71 of the best-selling domestic beers in the United States are located in the file **Domesticbeer**. The values for three variables are included: percentage alcohol, number of calories per 12 ounces, and number of carbohydrates (in grams) per 12 ounces.

Source: *Extracted from **www.Beer100.com**, May 4, 2007.*

Your task is to write a report based on a complete descriptive evaluation of each of the numerical variables—percentage alcohol, number of calories per 12 ounces, and number of carbohydrates (in grams) per 12 ounces. Appended to your report should be all appropriate tables, charts, and numerical descriptive measures.

## Team Projects

The data file **Mutual Funds** contains information regarding nine variables from a sample of 868 mutual funds:

Category—Type of stocks comprising the mutual fund (small cap, mid cap, large cap)

Objective—Objective of stocks comprising the mutual fund (growth or value)

Assets—In millions of dollars

Fees—Sales charges (no or yes)

Expense ratio—Ratio of expenses to net assets in percentage

Risk—Risk-of-loss factor of the mutual fund (low, average, high)

2006 return—Twelve-month return in 2006

Three-year return—Annualized return, 2004–2006

Five-year return—Annualized return, 2002–2006

**3.76** For expense ratio in percentage, three-year return, and five-year return,

**a.** Compute the mean, median, first quartile, and third quartile.

**b.** Compute the range, interquartile range, variance, standard deviation, and coefficient of variation.

**c.** Construct a boxplot. Are the data skewed? If so, how?

**d.** What conclusions can you reach concerning these variables?

**3.77** You wish to compare mutual funds that have fees to those that do not have fees. For each of these two groups, for the variables expense ratio in percentage, 2006 return, three-year return, and five-year return,

**a.** Compute the mean, median, first quartile, and third quartile.

**b.** Compute the range, interquartile range, variance, standard deviation, and coefficient of variation.

**c.** Construct a boxplot. Are the data skewed? If so, how?

**d.** What conclusions can you reach about differences between mutual funds that have fees and those that do not have fees?

**3.78** You wish to compare mutual funds that have a growth objective to those that have a value objective. For each of these two groups, for the variables expense ratio in percentage, three-year return, and five-year return,

**a.** Compute the mean, median, first quartile, and third quartile.

**b.** Compute the range, interquartile range, variance, standard deviation, and coefficient of variation.

**c.** Construct a boxplot. Are the data skewed? If so, how?

**d.** What conclusions can you reach about differences between mutual funds that have a growth objective and those that have a value objective?

**3.79** You wish to compare small cap, mid cap, and large cap mutual funds. For each of these three groups, for the variables expense ratio in percentage, 2006 return, three-year return, and five-year return,

**a.** Compute the mean, median, first quartile, and third quartile.

**b.** Compute the range, interquartile range, variance, standard deviation, and coefficient of variation.

**c.** Construct a boxplot. Are the data skewed? If so, how?

**d.** What conclusions can you reach about differences between small cap, mid cap, and large cap mutual funds?

## Student Survey Data Base

**3.80** Problem 1.27 on page 14 describes a survey of 50 undergraduate students (see the file Undergradsurvey ). For these data, for each numerical variable,

**a.** Compute the mean, median, first quartile, and third quartile.

**b.** Compute the range, interquartile range, variance, standard deviation, and coefficient of variation.

**c.** Construct a boxplot. Are the data skewed? If so, how?

**d.** Write a report summarizing your conclusions.

**3.81** Problem 1.27 on page 14 describes a survey of 50 undergraduate students (see the file Undergradsurvey ).

**a.** Select a sample of 50 undergraduate students at your school and conduct a similar survey for those students.

**b.** For the data collected in (a), repeat (a) through (d) of Problem 3.80.

**c.** Compare the results of (b) to those of Problem 3.80.

**3.82** Problem 1.28 on page 14 describes a survey of 40 MBA students (see the file Gradsurvey ). For these data, for each numerical variable,

**a.** Compute the mean, median, first quartile, and third quartile.

**b.** Compute the range, interquartile range, variance, standard deviation, and coefficient of variation.

**c.** Construct a boxplot. Are the data skewed? If so, how?

**d.** Write a report summarizing your conclusions.

**3.83** Problem 1.28 on page 14 describes a survey of 40 MBA students (see the file Gradsurvey ).

**a.** Select a sample of 40 graduate students from your MBA program and conduct a similar survey for those students.

**b.** For the data collected in (a), repeat (a) through (d) of Problem 3.82.

**c.** Compare the results of (b) to those of Problem 3.82.

# MANAGING THE *SPRINGVILLE HERALD*

For what variable in the Chapter 2 "Managing the *Springville Herald*" case (see page 68) are numerical descriptive measures needed? For the variable you identify:

1. Compute the appropriate numerical descriptive measures, and construct a boxplot.

2. Identify another graphical display that might be useful and construct it. What conclusions can you form from that plot that cannot be made from the boxplot?

3. Summarize your findings in a report that can be included with the task force's study.

# WEB CASE

Apply your knowledge about the proper use of numerical descriptive measures in this continuing Web Case from Chapter 2.

Visit EndRun Financial Services, at **www.prenhall.com/Springville/EndRun.htm** (or open the `EndRun.htm` file in the Student CD-ROM Web Case folder) a second time and reexamine their supporting data and then answer the following:

1. Can descriptive measures be computed for any variables? How would such summary statistics support EndRun's claims? How would those summary statistics affect your perception of EndRun's record?

2. Evaluate the methods EndRun used to summarize the results of its customer survey (see **www.prenhall.com/Springville/ER_Survey.htm** or the `ER_Survey.htm` file on the Student CD-ROM Web Case folder). Is there anything you would do differently to summarize these results?

3. Note that the last question of the survey has fewer responses than the other questions. What factors may have limited the number of responses to that question?

# REFERENCES

1. Kendall, M. G., A. Stuart, and J. K. Ord, *Kendall's Advanced Theory of Statistics, Volume 1: Distribution Theory*, 6th ed. (New York: Oxford University Press, 1994).
2. *Microsoft Excel 2007* (Redmond, WA: Microsoft Corporation, 2007).
3. *Minitab for Windows Version 15* (State College, PA: Minitab, Inc., 2006).
4. Tukey, J., *Exploratory Data Analysis* (Reading, MA: Addison-Wesley, 1977).
5. Velleman, P. F., and D. C. Hoaglin, *Applications, Basics, and Computing of Exploratory Data Analysis* (Boston: Duxbury Press, 1981).

# Appendix E3
## Using Microsoft Excel for Descriptive Statistics

### E3.1 Computing Measures of Central Tendency, Variation, and Shape

You compute measures of central tendency, variation, and shape by either using the ToolPak Descriptive Statistics procedure or by using worksheet functions. Use the ToolPak procedure when you want to create a list of summary statistics similar to the one shown in Figure 3.2 on page 105. Use worksheet functions when you want to add one or a few descriptive measures to a worksheet (as is done in Figure 3.8 on page 126).

### Using ToolPak Descriptive Statistics

Open to the worksheet containing your data to be summarized. Select **Tools → Data Analysis** (Excel 97–2003) or **Data → Data Analysis** (Excel 2007). In the Data Analysis dialog box, select **Descriptive Statistics** from the **Analysis Tools** list and then click **OK**. In the Descriptive Statistics dialog box (shown in Figure E3.1), enter the cell range of the data as the **Input Range**. Click the **Columns** option and **Labels in first row**. Finish by clicking **New Worksheet Ply**, **Summary statistics**, **Kth Largest**, and **Kth Smallest**, and then **OK**.

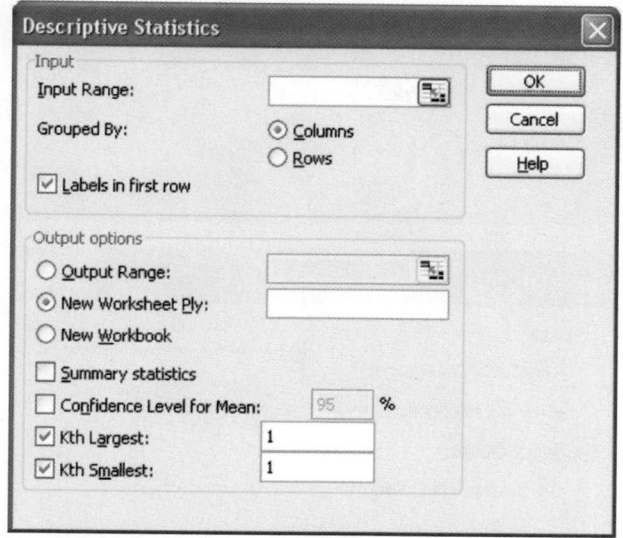

**FIGURE E3.1**

ToolPak Descriptive Statistics dialog box

To compute descriptive statistics for a variable by subgroups, as was done in Figure 3.2 on page 105 for the growth and value subgroups, first sort your data by the categorical variable to which the subgroups belong. Next, repeat the instructions given on page 138 for each subgroup using the cell range of the subgroup and the New Worksheet Ply option each time. Then copy and paste the results found in the second and subsequent worksheets to this first sheet to create a multiple column table similar to the one shown in Figure 3.2.

## Using Worksheet Functions

You use the worksheet functions SUM, COUNT, AVERAGE (for mean), MEDIAN, MODE, QUARTILE, or GEOMEAN to compute measures of central tendency or STDEV, VAR, MIN, MAX, LARGE, or SMALL to compute measures of shape and variation. For all but QUARTILE, enter a formula in the form =*WorksheetFunction(cell range of data to be summarized)*. For QUARTILE enter the formula in the form = *WorksheetFunction(cell range of data to be summarized, quartile number)*. Use 1 as the *quartile number* to compute the first quartile, 2 to compute the second quartile (the median), or 3 to compute the third quartile. In Excel versions earlier than Excel 2003, you may encounter some minor errors in results when using the QUARTILE function.

## E3.2 Computing Measures for a Population

To compute the population variance and standard deviation use the worksheet functions VARP and STDEVP. To use either function, enter a formula into a blank cell in the form =*WorksheetFunction(cell range of data to be summarized)*.

## E3.3 Creating Boxplots

You create boxplots by entering a five-number summary into the tinted cell range B2:B6 of the **Plot** worksheet of the Boxplot.xls workbook. The workbook uses the contents of this range to create a boxplot on the Plot worksheet.

## E3.4 Computing the Covariance

You compute the covariance by making entries in the **Covariance** worksheet of the Covariance.xls workbook, shown in Figure 3.8 on page 126. If you want to use this worksheet with other pairs of variables, follow the instructions in the worksheet for modifying the table area. The worksheet gains its flexibility by the cell C18 formula that uses the COUNT function to determine the sample size $n$. This allows the worksheet to always use the proper value of $n - 1$ for the covariance calculation when you change the size of the table area.

## E3.5 Computing the Coefficient of Correlation

You compute the correlation coefficient by making entries in the **Correlation** worksheet of the Correlation.xls workbook, shown in Figure 3.11 on page 129. If you want to use this worksheet with other pairs of variables, follow the instructions in the worksheet for modifying the table area. This worksheet shares some of the design of the covariance worksheet discussed in the previous section.

This worksheet uses the CORREL function in the formula =**CORREL(A2:A11, B2:B11)** in cell E21 to compute the correlation coefficient. Because the covariance, $S_X$, and $S_Y$ are computed elsewhere in this worksheet, the formula =E18/(E19 * E20) could also be used to compute the correlation coefficient statistic.

# Appendix P3
## Using PHStat2 for Descriptive Statistics

### P3.1 Creating Boxplots

To create boxplots, use **PHStat → Descriptive Statistics → Boxplot**. This procedure accepts data for a single group or multiple groups as either unstacked data (column by column) or stacked data (one column). If you use the **Multiple Groups-Stacked** option, you will also need to enter the **Grouping Variable Cell Range**.

The procedure creates a custom worksheet and then uses Excel charting features to create a boxplot from the data of that worksheet. If you click **Five-Number Summary**, a five-number summary appears on a separate worksheet.

# Appendix M3
## Using Minitab for Descriptive Statistics

### M3.1 Computing Descriptive Statistics

To create descriptive statistics for the 2006 return for different objectives shown in Figure 3.3 on page 106:

1. Open the Mutual Funds.mtw worksheet.
2. Select **Stat → Basic Statistics → Display Descriptive Statistics**.

In the Display Descriptive Statistics dialog box (see Figure M3.1):

3. Enter **'Return 2006'** in the **Variables** box.
4. Enter **Objective** in the **By variables (optional)** box.
5. Click **Statistics**.
6. In the Display Descriptive Statistics - Statistics dialog box (see Figure M3.2), select **Mean, Standard deviation, Coefficient of variation, First quartile, Median, Third quartile, Interquartile range, Minimum, Maximum, Range, Skewness, Kurtosis,**

**FIGURE M3.1**

Minitab Display Descriptive Statistics dialog box

**FIGURE M3.2**

Minitab Display Descriptive Statistics - Statistics dialog box

and **N total** and then click **OK** to return to the Display Descriptive Statistics dialog box.

7. Back in the Display Descriptive Statistics dialog box, click **OK**.

## M3.2 Creating Boxplots

To create a boxplot for the 2006 return for different objectives shown in Figure 3.6 on page 123:

1. Open the Mutual Funds.mtw worksheet.
2. Select **Graph → Boxplot**.

In the Boxplots dialog box (see Figure M3.3):

3. Click **With Groups** in the **One Y** gallery. (You would click **Simple** in the **One Y** gallery if you were creating a boxplot for one group.)
4. Click **OK**.

In the Boxplot - One Y, With Groups dialog box (see Figure M3.4):

5. Enter **'Return 2006'** in the **Graph variables** box.
6. Enter **Objective** in the **Categorical variables** box.
7. Click the **Scale** button.
8. Select the **Transpose value and category scales** box.
9. Click **OK**.
10. Click **OK** (to create the boxplot).

**FIGURE M3.3**

Minitab Boxplots dialog box

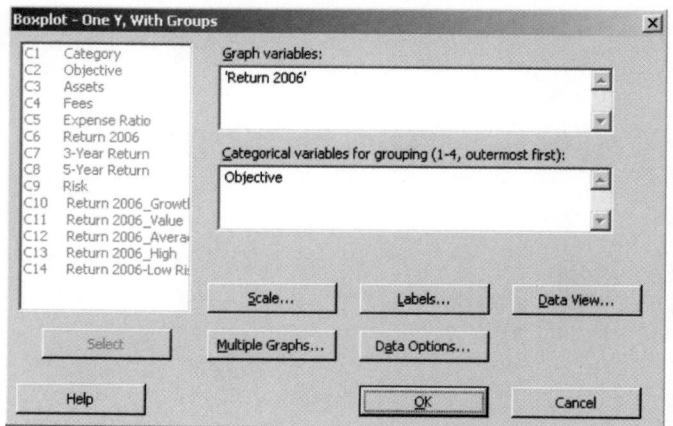

**FIGURE M3.4**

Minitab Boxplots - One Y, With Groups dialog box

## M3.3 Computing the Coefficient of Correlation

To compute the coefficient of correlation for the cost of a fast-food hamburger meal and the cost of two movie tickets in ten cities (see Table 3.10 on page 126):

1. Open the `Cost of Living.mtw` worksheet.
2. Select **Stat → Basic Statistics → Correlation**.

In the Correlation dialog box (see Figure M3.5):

3. Enter **Hamburger** and **'Movie Tickets'** in the **Variables** box.
4. Click **OK**.

**FIGURE M3.5**

Minitab Correlation dialog box

# CHAPTER
# FOUR

## BASIC PROBABILITY

**USING STATISTICS @** M&R Electronics World

# LEARNING OBJECTIVES

## In this chapter, you learn:

- Basic probability concepts
- Conditional probability
- To use Bayes' theorem to revise probabilities
- Various counting rules

# USING STATISTICS @ M&R Electronics World

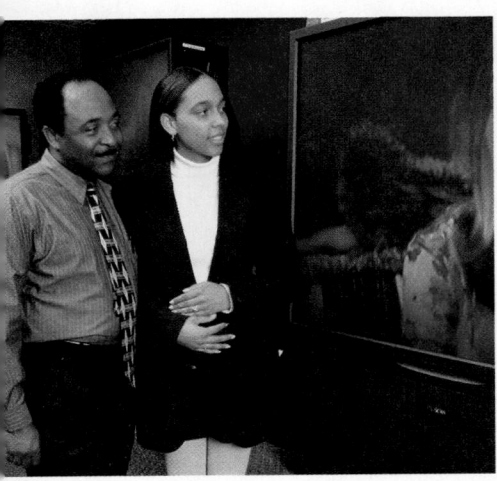

As the marketing manager for M&R Electronics World, you are analyzing the survey results of an intent-to-purchase study. This study asked the heads of 1,000 households about their intentions to purchase a big-screen television (defined as 36 inches or larger) sometime during the next 12 months. Investigations of this type are known as *intent-to-purchase studies*. As a follow-up, you plan to survey the same people 12 months later to see whether such a television was purchased. In addition, for households purchasing big-screen televisions, you would like to know whether the television they purchased was a plasma screen, whether they also purchased a digital video recorder (DVR) in the past 12 months, and whether they were satisfied with their purchase of the big-screen television.

You are expected to use the results of this survey to plan a new marketing strategy that will enhance sales and better target those households likely to purchase multiple or more expensive products. What questions can you ask in this survey? How can you express the relationships among the various intent-to-purchase responses of individual households?

In previous chapters, you learned descriptive methods to summarize categorical and numerical variables. In this chapter, you will learn about probability to answer questions such as the following:

- What is the probability that a household is planning to purchase a big-screen television in the next year?
- What is the probability that a household will actually purchase a big-screen television?
- What is the probability that a household is planning to purchase a big-screen television and actually purchases the television?
- Given that the household is planning to purchase a big-screen television, what is the probability that the purchase is made?
- Does knowledge of whether a household *plans* to purchase the television change the likelihood of predicting whether the household *will* purchase the television?
- What is the probability that a household that purchases a big-screen television will purchase a plasma-screen television?
- What is the probability that a household that purchases a big-screen television with a plasma screen will also purchase a DVR?
- What is the probability that a household that purchases a big-screen television will be satisfied with the purchase?

With answers to questions such as these, you can begin to make decisions about your marketing strategy. Should your strategy for selling more big-screen televisions target those households that have indicated an intent to purchase? Should you concentrate on selling plasma screens? Is it likely that households that purchase big-screen televisions with plasma screens can be easily persuaded to also purchase DVRs?

The principles of probability help bridge the worlds of descriptive statistics and inferential statistics. Reading this chapter will help you learn about different types of probabilities, how to compute probabilities, and how to revise probabilities in light of new information. Probability principles are the foundation for the probability distribution, the concept of mathematical expectation, and the binomial, hypergeometric, and Poisson distributions, topics that are discussed in Chapter 5.

## 4.1  BASIC PROBABILITY CONCEPTS

What is meant by the word *probability*? A **probability** is the numeric value representing the chance, likelihood, or possibility a particular event will occur, such as the price of a stock increasing, a rainy day, a defective product, or the outcome five in a single toss of a die. In all these instances, the probability involved is a proportion or fraction whose value ranges between 0 and 1, inclusive. An event that has no chance of occurring (i.e., the **impossible event**) has a probability of 0. An event that is sure to occur (i.e., the **certain event**) has a probability of 1.

There are three types of probability:

- *A priori*
- Empirical
- Subjective

In *a priori* **probability**, the probability of success is based on prior knowledge of the process involved. In the simplest case, where each outcome is equally likely, the chance of occurrence of the event is defined in Equation (4.1).

Probability of Occurrence

$$\text{Probability of occurrence} = \frac{X}{T} \qquad (4.1)$$

where

$X$ = number of ways in which the event occurs

$T$ = total number of possible outcomes

Consider a standard deck of cards that has 26 red cards and 26 black cards. The probability of selecting a black card is 26/52 = 0.50 because there are $X$ = 26 black cards and $T$ = 52 total cards. What does this probability mean? If each card is replaced after it is selected, does it mean that 1 out of the next 2 cards selected will be black? No, because you cannot say for certain what will happen on the next several selections. However, you can say that in the long run, if this selection process is continually repeated, the proportion of black cards selected will approach 0.50.

**EXAMPLE 4.1**  FINDING *A PRIORI* PROBABILITIES

A standard six-sided die has six faces. Each face of the die contains either one, two, three, four, five, or six dots. If you roll a die, what is the probability that you will get a face with five dots?

**SOLUTION** Each face is equally likely to occur. Because there are six faces, the probability of getting a face with five dots is $\frac{1}{6}$.

The preceding examples use the *a priori* probability approach because the number of ways the event occurs and the total number of possible outcomes are known from the composition of the deck of cards or the faces of the die.

In the **empirical probability** approach, the outcomes are based on observed data, not on prior knowledge of a process. Surveys are often used to generate empirical probabilities. Examples of this type of probability are the proportion of individuals in the Using Statistics scenario who actually purchase a big-screen television, the proportion of registered voters who prefer a certain political candidate, and the proportion of students who have part-time jobs. For example, if you take a survey of students, and 60% state that they have part-time jobs, then there is a 0.60 probability that an individual student has a part-time job.

The third approach to probability, **subjective probability**, differs from the other two approaches because subjective probability differs from person to person. For example, the development team for a new product may assign a probability of 0.6 to the chance of success for the product, even though the president of the company may be less optimistic and assign a probability of 0.3. The assignment of subjective probabilities to various outcomes is usually based on a combination of an individual's past experience, personal opinion, and analysis of a particular situation. Subjective probability is especially useful in making decisions in situations in which you cannot use *a priori* probability or empirical probability.

## Events and Sample Spaces

The basic elements of probability theory are the individual outcomes of a variable under study. You need the following definitions to understand probabilities.

### EVENT

Each possible outcome of a variable is referred to as an **event**.
A **simple event** is described by a single characteristic.

For example, when you toss a coin, the two possible outcomes are heads and tails. Each of these represents a simple event. When you roll a standard six-sided die in which the six faces of the die contain either one, two, three, four, five, or six dots, there are six possible simple events. An event can be any one of these simple events, a set of them, or a subset of all of them. For example, the event of an *even number of dots* consists of three simple events (i.e., two, four, or six dots).

### JOINT EVENT

A **joint event** is an event that has two or more characteristics.

Getting two heads on the toss of two coins is an example of a joint event because it consists of heads on the toss of the first coin and heads on the toss of the second coin.

### COMPLEMENT

The **complement** of event $A$ (represented by the symbol $A'$) includes all events that are not part of $A$.

The complement of a head is a tail because that is the only event that is not a head. The complement of face five is not getting face five. Not getting face five consists of getting face one, two, three, four, or six.

### SAMPLE SPACE

The collection of all the possible events is called the **sample space**.

The sample space for tossing a coin consists of heads and tails. The sample space when rolling a die consists of one, two, three, four, five, and six dots. Example 4.2 demonstrates events and sample spaces.

**EXAMPLE 4.2**

EVENTS AND SAMPLE SPACES

The Using Statistics scenario on page 144 concerns M&R Electronics World. Table 4.1 presents the results of the sample of 1,000 households in terms of purchase behavior for big-screen televisions.

**TABLE 4.1**

Purchase Behavior for Big-Screen Televisions

| PLANNED TO PURCHASE | ACTUALLY PURCHASED | | |
|---|---|---|---|
| | Yes | No | Total |
| Yes | 200 | 50 | 250 |
| No | 100 | 650 | 750 |
| Total | 300 | 700 | 1,000 |

What is the sample space? Give examples of simple events and joint events.

**SOLUTION**  The sample space consists of the 1,000 respondents. Simple events are "planned to purchase," "did not plan to purchase," "purchased," and "did not purchase." The complement of the event "planned to purchase" is "did not plan to purchase." The event "planned to purchase and actually purchased" is a joint event because the respondent must plan to purchase the television *and* actually purchase it.

## Contingency Tables and Venn Diagrams

There are several ways in which you can view a particular sample space. One way involves assigning the appropriate events to a **contingency table** (see Section 2.4) such as the one displayed in Table 4.1. You get the values in the cells of the table by subdividing the sample space of 1,000 households according to whether someone planned to purchase and actually purchased the big-screen television set. For example, 200 of the respondents planned to purchase a big-screen television set and subsequently did purchase the big-screen television set.

A second way to present the sample space is by using a **Venn diagram**. This diagram graphically represents the various events as "unions" and "intersections" of circles. Figure 4.1 on page 148 presents a typical Venn diagram for a two-variable situation, with each variable having only two events ($A$ and $A'$, $B$ and $B'$). The circle on the left (the red one) represents all events that are part of $A$. The circle on the right (the yellow one) represents all events that are part of $B$. The area contained within circle $A$ and circle $B$ (center area) is the intersection of $A$ and $B$ (written as $A \cap B$), because it is part of $A$ and also part of $B$. The total area of the two circles is the union of $A$ and $B$ (written as $A \cup B$) and contains all outcomes that are just part of event $A$, just part of event $B$, or part of both $A$ and $B$. The area in the diagram outside of $A \cup B$ contains outcomes that are neither part of $A$ nor part of $B$.

You must define $A$ and $B$ in order to develop a Venn diagram. You can define either event as $A$ or $B$, as long as you are consistent in evaluating the various events. For the large-screen television example, you can define the events as follows:

$$A = \text{planned to purchase} \qquad B = \text{actually purchased}$$
$$A' = \text{did not plan to purchase} \quad B' = \text{did not actually purchase}$$

In drawing the Venn diagram (see Figure 4.2 on page 148), you must determine the value of the intersection of $A$ and $B$ so that the sample space can be divided into its parts. $A \cap B$ consists of all 200 households who planned to purchase and actually purchased a big-screen television set. The remainder of event $A$ (planned to purchase) consists of the 50 households who planned to purchase a big-screen television set but did not actually purchase one. The remainder of event

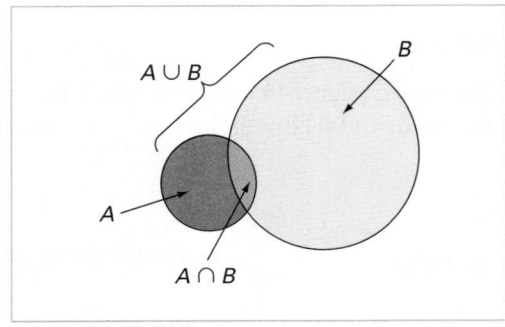

**FIGURE 4.1**
Venn diagram for events *A* and *B*

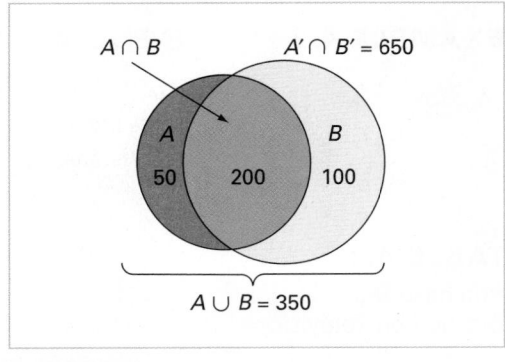

**FIGURE 4.2**
Venn diagram for the M&R Electronics
World example

*B* (actually purchased) consists of the 100 households who did not plan to purchase a big-screen television set but actually purchased one. The remaining 650 households represent those who neither planned to purchase nor actually purchased a big-screen television set.

## Simple Probability

Now you can answer some of the questions posed in the Using Statistics scenario. Because the results are based on data collected in a survey (refer to Table 4.1), you can use the empirical probability approach.

As stated previously, the most fundamental rule for probabilities is that they range in value from 0 to 1. An impossible event has a probability of 0, and an event that is certain to occur has a probability of 1.

**Simple probability** refers to the probability of occurrence of a simple event, $P(A)$. A simple probability in the Using Statistics scenario is the probability of planning to purchase a big-screen television. How can you determine the probability of selecting a household that planned to purchase a big-screen television? Using Equation (4.1) on page 145:

$$\text{Probability of occurrence} = \frac{X}{T}$$

$$P(\text{Planned to purchase}) = \frac{\text{Number who planned to purchase}}{\text{Total number of households}}$$

$$= \frac{250}{1,000} = 0.25$$

Thus, there is a 0.25 (or 25%) chance that a household planned to purchase a big-screen television. Example 4.3 illustrates another application of simple probability.

---

**EXAMPLE 4.3**    COMPUTING THE PROBABILITY THAT THE BIG-SCREEN TELEVISION PURCHASED IS A PLASMA SCREEN

In the Using Statistics follow-up survey, additional questions were asked of the 300 households that actually purchased big-screen televisions. Table 4.2 indicates the consumers' responses to whether the television purchased was a plasma screen and whether they also purchased a DVR in the past 12 months.

Find the probability that if a household that purchased a big-screen television is randomly selected, the television purchased is a plasma screen.

**TABLE 4.2**

Purchase Behavior
Regarding Plasma-
Screen Televisions and
DVR

| | PURCHASED DVR | | |
| PURCHASED PLASMA SCREEN | Yes | No | Total |
| --- | --- | --- | --- |
| Plasma screen | 38 | 42 | 80 |
| Not plasma screen | 70 | 150 | 220 |
| Total | 108 | 192 | 300 |

**SOLUTION**  Using the following definitions:

$A$ = purchased a plasma screen          $B$ = purchased a DVR

$A'$ = did not purchase a plasma screen    $B'$ = did not purchase a DVR

$$P(\text{Plasma screen}) = \frac{\text{Number of plasma-screen televisions}}{\text{Total number of televisions}}$$

$$= \frac{80}{300} = 0.267$$

There is a 26.7% chance that a randomly selected big-screen television purchase is a purchase of a plasma-screen television.

## Joint Probability

Whereas simple or marginal probability refers to the probability of occurrence of simple events, **joint probability** refers to the probability of an occurrence involving two or more events. An example of joint probability is the probability that you will get heads on the first toss of a coin and heads on the second toss of a coin.

Referring to Table 4.1 on page 147, those individuals who planned to purchase and actually purchased a big-screen television consist only of the outcomes in the single cell "yes—planned to purchase *and* yes—actually purchased." Because this group consists of 200 households, the probability of picking a household that planned to purchase *and* actually purchased a big-screen television is

$$P(\text{Planned to purchase } and \text{ actually purchased}) = \frac{\text{Planned to purchase } and \text{ actually purchased}}{\text{Total number of respondents}}$$

$$= \frac{200}{1,000} = 0.20$$

Example 4.4 also demonstrates how to determine joint probability.

**EXAMPLE 4.4**

DETERMINING THE JOINT PROBABILITY THAT A BIG-SCREEN TELEVISION CUSTOMER PURCHASED A PLASMA-SCREEN TELEVISION AND A DVR

In Table 4.2, the purchases are cross-classified as plasma screen or not plasma screen and whether or not the household purchased a DVR. Find the probability that a randomly selected household that purchased a big-screen television also purchased a plasma-screen television and a DVR.

**SOLUTION** Using Equation (4.1) on page 145,

$$P(\text{Plasma screen } and \text{ DVR}) = \frac{\text{Number that purchased a plasma screen } and \text{ a DVR}}{\text{Total number of big-screen television purchasers}}$$

$$= \frac{38}{300} = 0.127$$

Therefore, there is a 12.7% chance that a randomly selected household that purchased a big-screen television purchased a plasma-screen television and a DVR.

## Marginal Probability

The **marginal probability** of an event consists of a set of joint probabilities. You can determine the marginal probability of a particular event by using the concept of joint probability just discussed. For example, if $B$ consists of two events, $B_1$ and $B_2$, then $P(A)$, the probability of event $A$, consists of the joint probability of event $A$ occurring with event $B_1$ and the joint probability of event $A$ occurring with event $B_2$. You use Equation (4.2) to compute marginal probabilities.

Marginal Probability

$$P(A) = P(A \text{ and } B_1) + P(A \text{ and } B_2) + \cdots + P(A \text{ and } B_k) \qquad \textbf{(4.2)}$$

where $B_1, B_2, \ldots, B_k$ are $k$ mutually exclusive and collectively exhaustive events, defined as follows:

Two events are **mutually exclusive** if both the events cannot occur simultaneously.
A set of events is **collectively exhaustive** if one of the events must occur.

Heads and tails in a coin toss are mutually exclusive events. The result of a coin toss cannot simultaneously be a head and a tail. Heads and tails in a coin toss are also collectively exhaustive events. One of them must occur. If heads does not occur, tails must occur. If tails does not occur, heads must occur. Being male and being female are mutually exclusive and collectively exhaustive events. No one is both (the two are mutually exclusive), and everyone is one or the other (the two are collectively exhaustive).

You can use Equation (4.2) to compute the marginal probability of "planned to purchase" a big-screen television:

$$P(\text{Planned to purchase}) = P(\text{Planned to purchase } and \text{ purchased})$$
$$+ P(\text{Planned to purchase } and \text{ did not purchase})$$

$$= \frac{200}{1,000} + \frac{50}{1,000}$$

$$= \frac{250}{1,000} = 0.25$$

You get the same result if you add the number of outcomes that make up the simple event "planned to purchase."

## General Addition Rule

How do you find the probability of event "*A or B*"? You need to consider the occurrence of either event $A$ or event $B$ or both $A$ and $B$. For example, how can you determine the probability that a household planned to purchase *or* actually purchased a big-screen television? The event "planned to purchase *or* actually purchased" includes all households that planned to purchase and all households that actually purchased the big-screen television. You examine each cell of the contingency table (Table 4.1 on page 147) to determine whether it is part of this event. From Table 4.1, the cell "planned to purchase *and* did not actually purchase" is part of the event because it includes respondents who planned to purchase. The cell "did not plan to purchase *and* actually purchased" is included because it contains respondents who actually purchased. Finally, the cell "planned to purchase *and* actually purchased" has both characteristics of interest. Therefore, one way to calculate the probability of "planned to purchase *or* actually purchased" is:

$$P(\text{Planned to purchase } or \text{ actually purchased}) = P(\text{Planned to purchase } and \text{ did not actually purchase}) + P(\text{Did not plan to purchase } and \text{ actually purchased}) + P(\text{Planned to purchase } and \text{ actually purchased})$$

$$= \frac{50}{1,000} + \frac{100}{1,000} + \frac{200}{1,000} = \frac{350}{1,000} = 0.35$$

Often, it is easier to determine $P(A \text{ or } B)$, the probability of the event $A$ or $B$, by using the **general addition rule**, defined in Equation (4.3).

**General Addition Rule**

The probability of $A$ or $B$ is equal to the probability of $A$ plus the probability of $B$ minus the probability of $A$ and $B$.

$$P(A \text{ or } B) = P(A) + P(B) - P(A \text{ and } B) \qquad \textbf{(4.3)}$$

Applying Equation (4.3) to the previous example produces the following result:

$$P(\text{Planned to purchase } or \text{ actually purchased}) = P(\text{Planned to purchase}) + P(\text{Actually purchased}) - P(\text{Planned to purchase } and \text{ actually purchased})$$

$$= \frac{250}{1,000} + \frac{300}{1,000} - \frac{200}{1,000}$$

$$= \frac{350}{1,000} = 0.35$$

The general addition rule consists of taking the probability of $A$ and adding it to the probability of $B$ and then subtracting the probability of the joint event $A$ *and* $B$ from this total because the joint event has already been included in computing both the probability of $A$ and the probability of $B$. Referring to Table 4.1 on page 147, if the outcomes of the event "planned to purchase" are added to those of the event "actually purchased," the joint event "planned to purchase *and* actually purchased" has been included in each of these simple events. Therefore, because this joint event has been double-counted, you must subtract it to provide the correct result. Example 4.5 illustrates another application of the general addition rule.

---

**EXAMPLE 4.5**    USING THE GENERAL ADDITION RULE FOR THE HOUSEHOLDS THAT PURCHASED BIG-SCREEN TELEVISIONS

In Example 4.3 on page 148, the purchases were cross-classified in Table 4.2 on page 149 as a plasma screen or not a plasma screen and whether or not the household purchased a DVR. Find the probability that among households that purchased a big-screen television, they purchased a plasma-screen television or a DVR.

**SOLUTION**  Using Equation (4.3),

$$P(\text{Plasma screen } or \text{ DVR}) = P(\text{Plasma screen}) + P(\text{DVR}) - P(\text{Plasma screen } and \text{ DVR})$$

$$= \frac{80}{300} + \frac{108}{300} - \frac{38}{300}$$

$$= \frac{150}{300} = 0.50$$

Therefore, there is a 50.0% chance that a randomly selected household that purchased a big-screen television purchased a plasma-screen television or a DVR.

# PROBLEMS FOR SECTION 4.1

## Learning the Basics

**4.1**  Two coins are tossed.
**a.** Give an example of a simple event.
**b.** Give an example of a joint event.
**c.** What is the complement of a head on the first toss?

**4.2**  An urn contains 12 red balls and 8 white balls. One ball is to be selected from the urn.
**a.** Give an example of a simple event.
**b.** What is the complement of a red ball?

**4.3**  Given the following contingency table:

|      | $B$ | $B'$ |
|------|-----|------|
| $A$  | 10  | 20   |
| $A'$ | 20  | 40   |

What is the probability of
**a.** event $A$?
**b.** event $A'$?
**c.** event $A$ and $B$?
**d.** event $A$ or $B$?

**4.4**  Given the following contingency table:

|      | $B$ | $B'$ |
|------|-----|------|
| $A$  | 10  | 30   |
| $A'$ | 25  | 35   |

What is the probability of
**a.** event $A'$?
**b.** event $A$ and $B$?
**c.** event $A'$ and $B'$?
**d.** event $A'$ or $B'$?

## Applying the Concepts

**4.5**  For each of the following, indicate whether the type of probability involved is an example of *a priori* probability, empirical probability, or subjective probability.
**a.** The next toss of a fair coin will land on heads.
**b.** Italy will win soccer's World Cup the next time the competition is held.
**c.** The sum of the faces of two dice will be seven.
**d.** The train taking a commuter to work will be more than 10 minutes late.

**4.6**  For each of the following, state whether the events created are mutually exclusive and collectively exhaustive. If they are not mutually exclusive and collectively exhaustive, either reword the categories to make them mutually exclusive and collectively exhaustive or explain why that would not be useful.
**a.** Registered voters in the United States were asked whether they registered as Republicans or Democrats.
**b.** Each respondent was classified by the type of car he or she drives: American, European, Japanese, or none.
**c.** People were asked, "Do you currently live in (i) an apartment or (ii) a house?"
**d.** A product was classified as defective or not defective.

**4.7**  Which of the following events occur with a probability of zero? For each, state why or why not.
**a.** A voter in the United States who is registered as a Republican and a Democrat
**b.** A voter in the United States who is female and registered as a Republican
**c.** An automobile that is a Ford and a Toyota
**d.** An automobile that is a Toyota and was manufactured in the United States

**4.8**  According to an Ipsos poll, the perception of unfairness in the U.S. tax code is spread fairly evenly across income groups, age groups, and education levels. In an April 2006 survey of 1,005 adults, Ipsos reported that almost 60% of all people said the code is unfair, whereas slightly more than 60% of those making more than $50,000 viewed the code as unfair ("People Cry Unfairness," *The Cincinnati Enquirer*, April 16, 2006, p. A8). Suppose that the following contingency table represents the specific breakdown of responses:

| U.S. TAX CODE | INCOME LEVEL | | |
|---|---|---|---|
| | **Less Than $50,000** | **More Than $50,000** | **Total** |
| **Fair** | 225 | 180 | 405 |
| **Unfair** | 280 | 320 | 600 |
| **Total** | 505 | 500 | 1,005 |

**a.** Give an example of a simple event.
**b.** Give an example of a joint event.
**c.** What is the complement of "tax code is fair"?
**d.** Why is "tax code is fair *and* makes less than $50,000" a joint event?

**4.9** Referring to the contingency table in Problem 4.8, if a respondent is selected at random, what is the probability that he or she
**a.** thinks the tax code is unfair?
**b.** thinks the tax code is unfair *and* makes less than $50,000?
**c.** thinks the tax code is unfair *or* makes less than $50,000?
**d.** Explain the difference in the results in (b) and (c).

✓ **SELF** **4.10** A yield improvement study at a semicon-
  Test    ductor manufacturing facility provided defect data for a sample of 450 wafers. The following table presents a summary of the responses to two questions: "Was a particle found on the die that produced the wafer?" and "Is the wafer good or bad?"

| QUALITY OF WAFER | CONDITION OF DIE | | |
|---|---|---|---|
| | **No Particles** | **Particles** | **Totals** |
| **Good** | 320 | 14 | 334 |
| **Bad** | 80 | 36 | 116 |
| **Totals** | 400 | 50 | 450 |

Source: *Extracted from S. W. Hall, "Analysis of Defectivity of Semiconductor Wafers by Contingency Table,"* Proceedings Institute of Environmental Sciences, Vol. 1, *1994, pp. 177–183.*

**a.** Give an example of a simple event.
**b.** Give an example of a joint event.
**c.** What is the complement of a good wafer?
**d.** Why is a "good wafer" and a die "with particles" a joint event?

**4.11** Referring to the contingency table in Problem 4.10, if a wafer is selected at random, what is the probability that

**a.** it was produced from a die with no particles?
**b.** it is a bad wafer *and* was produced from a die with no particles?
**c.** it is a bad wafer *or* was produced from a die with no particles?
**d.** Explain the difference in the results in (b) and (c).

**4.12** An experiment was conducted to study the choices made in mutual fund selection. Undergraduate and MBA students were presented with different S&P 500 Index funds that were identical except for fees. Suppose 100 undergraduate students and 100 MBA students were selected. Partial results are shown in the following table:

| FUND | STUDENT GROUP | |
|---|---|---|
| | **Undergraduate** | **MBA** |
| **Highest-cost fund** | 27 | 18 |
| **Not highest-cost fund** | 73 | 82 |

Source: *Extracted from J. J. Choi, D. Laibson, and B. C. Madrian,* Why Does the Law of One Price Fail? ***www.som.yale.edu/faculty/jjc83/fees.pdf.***

If a student is selected at random, what is the probability that he or she
**a.** selected the highest-cost fund?
**b.** selected the highest-cost fund *and* is an undergraduate?
**c.** selected the highest-cost fund *or* is an undergraduate?
**d.** Explain the difference in the results in (b) and (c).

**4.13** Where people turn to for news is different for various age groups. Suppose that a study conducted on this issue (extracted from P. Johnson, "Young People Turn to the Web for News," *USA Today*, March 23, 2006, p. 9D) was based on 200 respondents who were between the ages of 36 and 50, and 200 respondents who were over age 50. Of the 200 respondents who were between the ages of 36 and 50, 82 got their news primarily from newspapers. Of the 200 respondents who were over age 50, 104 got their news primarily from newspapers. Construct a contingency table or a Venn diagram to evaluate the probabilities. If a respondent is selected at random, what is the probability that he or she
**a.** got news primarily from newspapers?
**b.** got news primarily from newspapers and is over 50 years old?
**c.** got news primarily from newspapers or is over 50 years old?
**d.** Explain the difference in the results in (b) and (c).

**4.14** A sample of 500 respondents was selected in a large metropolitan area to study consumer behavior. Among the questions asked was "Do you enjoy shopping for clothing?" Of 240 males, 136 answered yes. Of 260 females, 224 answered yes. Construct a contingency table or a Venn diagram to evaluate the probabilities. What is the probability that a respondent chosen at random

**a.** enjoys shopping for clothing?

**b.** is a female *and* enjoys shopping for clothing?

**c.** is a female *or* enjoys shopping for clothing?

**d.** is a male *or* a female?

**4.15** Each year, ratings are compiled concerning the performance of new cars during the first 90 days of use. Suppose that the cars have been categorized according to whether the car needs warranty-related repair (yes or no) and the country in which the company manufacturing the car is based (United States or not United States). Based on the data collected, the probability that the new car needs warranty repair is 0.04, the probability that the car was manufactured by a U.S.-based company is 0.60, and the probability that the new car needs a warranty repair *and* was manufactured by a U.S.-based company is 0.025. Construct a contingency table or a Venn diagram to evaluate the probabilities of a warranty-related repair. What is the probability that a new car selected at random

**a.** needs a warranty repair?

**b.** needs a warranty repair *and* was manufactured by a U.S.-based company?

**c.** needs a warranty repair *or* was manufactured by a U.S.-based company?

**d.** needs a warranty repair *or* was not manufactured by a U.S.-based company?

## 4.2   CONDITIONAL PROBABILITY

Each example in Section 4.1 involves finding the probability of an event when sampling from the entire sample space. How do you determine the probability of an event if certain information about the events involved is already known?

### Computing Conditional Probabilities

**Conditional probability** refers to the probability of event $A$, given information about the occurrence of another event $B$.

Conditional Probability

The probability of $A$ given $B$ is equal to the probability of $A$ *and* $B$ divided by the probability of $B$.

$$P(A \mid B) = \frac{P(A \text{ and } B)}{P(B)} \qquad \textbf{(4.4a)}$$

The probability of $B$ given $A$ is equal to the probability of $A$ *and* $B$ divided by the probability of $A$.

$$P(B \mid A) = \frac{P(A \text{ and } B)}{P(A)} \qquad \textbf{(4.4b)}$$

where

$$P(A \text{ and } B) = \text{joint probability of } A \text{ and } B$$

$$P(A) = \text{marginal probability of } A$$

$$P(B) = \text{marginal probability of } B$$

Referring to the Using Statistics scenario involving the purchase of big-screen televisions, suppose you were told that a household planned to purchase a big-screen television. Now, what is the probability that the household actually purchased the television? In this example, the objective is to find $P$(Actually purchased | Planned to purchase). Here you are given the information that the household planned to purchase the big-screen television. Therefore, the sample space does not consist of all 1,000 households in the survey. It consists of only those households that planned to purchase the big-screen television. Of 250 such households, 200 actually purchased the big-screen television. Therefore, based on Table 4.1 on page 147, the probability that a household actually purchased the big-screen television given that he or she planned to purchase is

$$P(\text{Actually purchased} \mid \text{Planned to purchase}) = \frac{\text{Planned to purchase } and \text{ actually purchased}}{\text{Planned to purchase}}$$

$$= \frac{200}{250} = 0.80$$

You can also use Equation (4.4b) to compute this result:

$$P(B \mid A) = \frac{P(A \text{ and } B)}{P(A)}$$

where

$$A = \text{planned to purchase}$$
$$B = \text{actually purchased}$$

then

$$P(\text{Actually purchased} \mid \text{Planned to purchase}) = \frac{200/1,000}{250/1,000}$$

$$= \frac{200}{250} = 0.80$$

Example 4.6 further illustrates conditional probability.

---

**EXAMPLE 4.6**

FINDING A CONDITIONAL PROBABILITY OF PURCHASING A DVR

Table 4.2 on page 149 is a contingency table for whether the household purchased a plasma-screen television and whether the household purchased a DVR. If a household purchased a plasma-screen television, what is the probability that it also purchased a DVR?

**SOLUTION** Because you know that the household purchased a plasma-screen television, the sample space is reduced to 80 households. Of these 80 households, 38 also purchased a DVR. Therefore, the probability that a household purchased a DVR, given that the household purchased a plasma-screen television, is:

$$P(\text{Purchased DVR} \mid \text{Purchased plasma screen}) = \frac{\text{Number purchasing plasma screen } and \text{ DVR}}{\text{Number purchasing plasma screen}}$$

$$= \frac{38}{80} = 0.475$$

If you use Equation (4.4b) on page 154:

$$A = \text{Purchased plasma-screen television} \quad B = \text{Purchased DVR}$$

then

$$P(B \mid A) = \frac{P(A \text{ and } B)}{P(A)} = \frac{38/300}{80/300} = 0.475$$

Therefore, given that the household purchased a plasma-screen television, there is a 47.5% chance that the household also purchased a DVR. You can compare this conditional probability to the marginal probability of purchasing a DVR, which is 108/300 = 0.36, or 36%. These results tell you that households that purchased plasma-screen televisions are more likely to purchase DVRs than are households that purchased big-screen televisions that are not plasma-screen televisions.

## Decision Trees

In Table 4.1 on page 147, households are classified according to whether they planned to purchase and whether they actually purchased big-screen televisions. A **decision tree** is an alternative to the contingency table. Figure 4.3 represents the decision tree for this example.

**FIGURE 4.3**

Decision tree for M&R Electronics World example

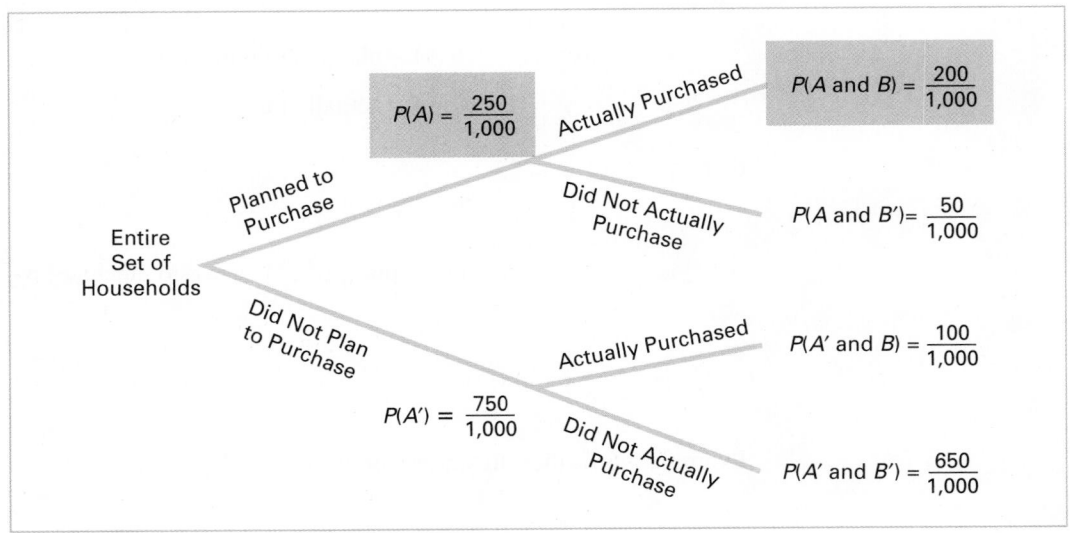

In Figure 4.3, beginning at the left with the entire set of households, there are two "branches" for whether or not the household planned to purchase a big-screen television. Each of these branches has two subbranches, corresponding to whether the household actually purchased or did not actually purchase the big-screen television. The probabilities at the end of the initial branches represent the marginal probabilities of $A$ and $A'$. The probabilities at the end of each of the four subbranches represent the joint probability for each combination of events $A$ and $B$. You compute the conditional probability by dividing the joint probability by the appropriate marginal probability.

For example, to compute the probability that the household actually purchased, given that the household planned to purchase the big-screen television, you take $P$(Planned to purchase *and* actually purchased) and divide by $P$(Planned to purchase). From Figure 4.3:

$$P(\text{Actually purchased} \mid \text{Planned to purchase}) = \frac{200/1,000}{250/1,000}$$

$$= \frac{200}{250} = 0.80$$

Example 4.7 illustrates how to construct a decision tree.

**EXAMPLE 4.7**      FORMING THE DECISION TREE FOR THE HOUSEHOLDS THAT PURCHASED
BIG-SCREEN TELEVISIONS

Using the cross-classified data in Table 4.2 on page 149, construct the decision tree. Use the
decision tree to find the probability that a household purchased a DVR, given that the household purchased a plasma-screen television.

**SOLUTION**  The decision tree for purchased a DVR and a plasma-screen television is displayed in Figure 4.4. Using Equation (4.4b) on page 154 and the following definitions,

$$A = \text{Purchased plasma-screen television}$$

$$B = \text{Purchased DVR}$$

$$P(B \mid A) = \frac{P(A \text{ and } B)}{P(A)} = \frac{38/300}{80/300} = 0.475$$

**FIGURE 4.4**

Decision tree for
purchased a DVR and a
plasma-screen
television

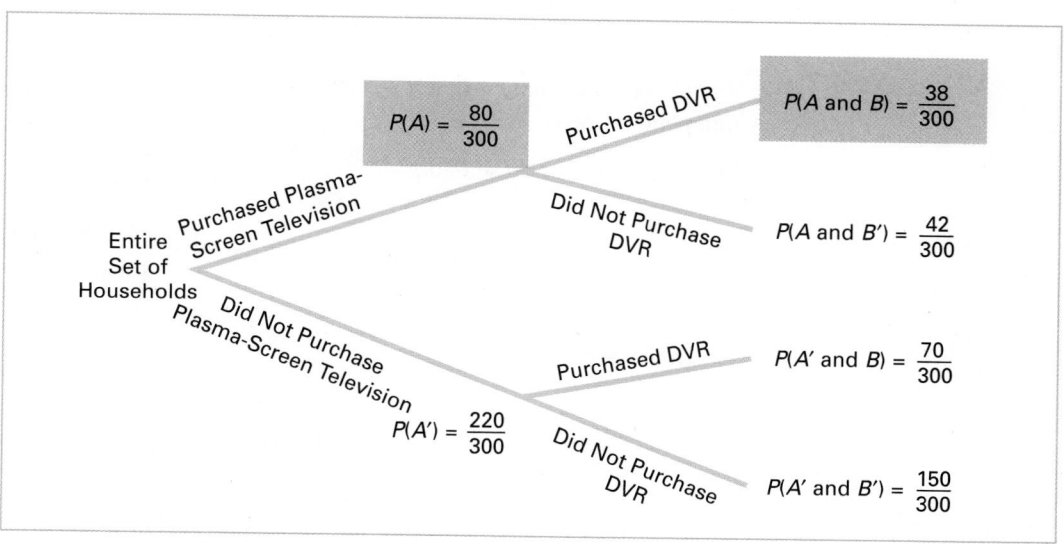

## Independence

In the example concerning the purchase of big-screen televisions, the conditional probability is
$200/250 = 0.80$ that the selected household actually purchased the big-screen television, given
that the household planned to purchase. The simple probability of selecting a household that actually purchased is $300/1,000 = 0.30$. This result shows that the prior knowledge that the household
planned to purchase affected the probability that the household actually purchased the television.
In other words, the outcome of one event is *dependent* on the outcome of a second event.

When the outcome of one event does *not* affect the probability of occurrence of another event,
the events are said to be independent. **Independence** can be determined by using Equation (4.5).

Independence
Two events, $A$ and $B$, are independent if and only if

$$P(A \mid B) = P(A) \tag{4.5}$$

where

$$P(A \mid B) = \text{conditional probability of } A \text{ given } B$$

$$P(A) = \text{marginal probability of } A$$

Example 4.8 demonstrates the use of Equation (4.5).

---

**EXAMPLE 4.8**

DETERMINING INDEPENDENCE

In the follow-up survey of the 300 households that actually purchased big-screen televisions, the households were asked if they were satisfied with their purchases. Table 4.3 cross-classifies the responses to the satisfaction question with the responses to whether the television was a plasma-screen television.

**TABLE 4.3**

Satisfaction with Purchase of Big-Screen Televisions

| | SATISFIED WITH PURCHASE? | | |
|---|---|---|---|
| **TYPE OF TELEVISION** | **Yes** | **No** | **Total** |
| **Plasma screen** | 64 | 16 | 80 |
| **Not plasma screen** | 176 | 44 | 220 |
| **Total** | 240 | 60 | 300 |

Determine whether being satisfied with the purchase and type of television purchased are independent.

**SOLUTION**  For these data,

$$P(\text{Satisfied} \mid \text{Plasma screen}) = \frac{64/300}{80/300} = \frac{64}{80} = 0.80$$

which is equal to

$$P(\text{Satisfied}) = \frac{240}{300} = 0.80$$

Thus, being satisfied with the purchase and type of television purchased are independent. Knowledge of one event does not affect the probability of the other event.

---

## Multiplication Rules

By manipulating the formula for conditional probability, you can determine the joint probability $P(A \text{ and } B)$ from the conditional probability of an event. The **general multiplication rule** is derived using Equation (4.4a) on page 154:

$$P(A \mid B) = \frac{P(A \text{ and } B)}{P(B)}$$

and solving for the joint probability $P(A \text{ and } B)$.

> **General Multiplication Rule**
> The probability of A and B is equal to the probability of A given B times the probability of B.
>
> $$P(A \text{ and } B) = P(A \mid B)P(B) \qquad (4.6)$$

Example 4.9 demonstrates the use of the general multiplication rule.

**EXAMPLE 4.9**     USING THE MULTIPLICATION RULE

Consider the 80 households that purchased plasma-screen televisions. In Table 4.3 on page 158 you see that 64 households are satisfied with their purchase and 16 households are dissatisfied. Suppose two households are randomly selected from the 80 customers. Find the probability that both households are satisfied with their purchase.

**SOLUTION**  Here you can use the multiplication rule in the following way. If:

$$A = \text{second household selected is satisfied}$$
$$B = \text{first household selected is satisfied}$$

then, using Equation (4.6),

$$P(A \text{ and } B) = P(A \mid B)P(B)$$

The probability that the first household is satisfied with the purchase is 64/80. However, the probability that the second household is also satisfied with the purchase depends on the result of the first selection. If the first household is not returned to the sample after the satisfaction level is determined (i.e., sampling without replacement), the number of households remaining is 79. If the first household is satisfied, the probability that the second is also satisfied is 63/79 because 63 satisfied households remain in the sample. Therefore,

$$P(A \text{ and } B) = \left(\frac{63}{79}\right)\left(\frac{64}{80}\right) = 0.6380$$

There is a 63.80% chance that both of the households sampled will be satisfied with their purchase.

---

The **multiplication rule for independent events** is derived by substituting $P(A)$ for $P(A \mid B)$ in Equation (4.6).

> **Multiplication Rule for Independent Events**
>
> If $A$ and $B$ are independent, the probability of $A$ and $B$ is equal to the probability of $A$ times the probability of $B$.
>
> $$P(A \text{ and } B) = P(A)P(B) \qquad \textbf{(4.7)}$$

If this rule holds for two events, $A$ and $B$, then $A$ and $B$ are independent. Therefore, there are two ways to determine independence:

1. Events $A$ and $B$ are independent if, and only if, $P(A \mid B) = P(A)$.
2. Events $A$ and $B$ are independent if, and only if, $P(A \text{ and } B) = P(A)P(B)$.

## Marginal Probability Using the General Multiplication Rule

In Section 4.1, marginal probability was defined using Equation (4.2) on page 150. You can state the equation for marginal probability by using the general multiplication rule. If

$$P(A) = P(A \text{ and } B_1) + P(A \text{ and } B_2) + \cdots + P(A \text{ and } B_k)$$

then, using the general multiplication rule, Equation (4.8) defines the marginal probability.

> **Marginal Probability Using the General Multiplication Rule**
> $$P(A) = P(A \mid B_1)P(B_1) + P(A \mid B_2)P(B_2) + \cdots + P(A \mid B_k)P(B_k) \quad (4.8)$$
>
> where $B_1, B_2, \ldots, B_k$ are $k$ mutually exclusive and collectively exhaustive events.

To illustrate this equation, refer to Table 4.1 on page 147. Let

$$P(A) = \text{probability of "planned to purchase"}$$
$$P(B_1) = \text{probability of "actually purchased"}$$
$$P(B_2) = \text{probability of "did not actually purchase"}$$

Then, using Equation (4.8), the probability of planned to purchase is:

$$P(A) = P(A \mid B_1)P(B_1) + P(A \mid B_2)P(B_2)$$

$$= \left(\frac{200}{300}\right)\left(\frac{300}{1,000}\right) + \left(\frac{50}{700}\right)\left(\frac{700}{1,000}\right)$$

$$= \frac{200}{1,000} + \frac{50}{1,000} = \frac{250}{1,000} = 0.25$$

## PROBLEMS FOR SECTION 4.2

### Learning the Basics

**4.16** Given the following contingency table:

|      | $B$ | $B'$ |
|------|-----|------|
| $A$  | 10  | 20   |
| $A'$ | 20  | 40   |

What is the probability of
a. $A \mid B$?
b. $A \mid B'$?
c. $A' \mid B'$?
d. Are events $A$ and $B$ independent?

**4.17** Given the following contingency table:

|      | $B$ | $B'$ |
|------|-----|------|
| $A$  | 10  | 30   |
| $A'$ | 25  | 35   |

What is the probability of
a. $A \mid B$?
b. $A' \mid B'$?
c. $A \mid B'$?
d. Are events $A$ and $B$ independent?

**4.18** If $P(A \text{ and } B) = 0.4$ and $P(B) = 0.8$, find $P(A \mid B)$.

**4.19** If $P(A) = 0.7$, $P(B) = 0.6$, and $A$ and $B$ are independent, find $P(A \text{ and } B)$.

**4.20** If $P(A) = 0.3$, $P(B) = 0.4$, and $P(A \text{ and } B) = 0.2$, are $A$ and $B$ independent?

### Applying the Concepts

**4.21** Where people turn to for news is different for various age groups. Suppose that a study conducted on this issue (extracted from P. Johnson, "Young People Turn to the Web for News," *USA Today*, March 23, 2006, p. 9D) was based on 200 respondents who were between the ages of 36 and 50 and 200 respondents who were over age 50. Of the 200 respondents who were between the ages of 36 and 50, 82 got their news primarily from newspapers. Of the 200 respondents who were over age 50, 104 got their news primarily from newspapers.
a. Given that a respondent is over age 50, what then is the probability that he or she gets news primarily from newspapers?
b. Given that a respondent gets news primarily from newspapers, what is the probability that he or she is over age 50?
c. Explain the difference in the results in (a) and (b).
d. Are the two events, whether the respondent is over age 50 and whether he or she gets news primarily from newspapers, independent?

**4.22** A yield improvement study at a semiconductor manufacturing facility provided defect data for a sample of 450 wafers. The following table presents a summary of the responses to two questions: "Were particles found on the die that produced the wafer?" and "Is the wafer good or bad?"

| QUALITY OF WAFER | CONDITION OF DIE | | |
|---|---|---|---|
| | **No Particles** | **Particles** | **Totals** |
| **Good** | 320 | 14 | 334 |
| **Bad** | 80 | 36 | 116 |
| **Totals** | 400 | 50 | 450 |

Source: *Extracted from S. W. Hall, "Analysis of Defectivity of Semiconductor Wafers by Contingency Table,"* Proceedings Institute of Environmental Sciences, Vol. 1, *1994, pp. 177–183.*

**a.** Suppose you know that a wafer is bad. What is the probability that it was produced from a die that had particles?

**b.** Suppose you know that a wafer is good. What is the probability that it was produced from a die that had particles?

**c.** Are the two events, a good wafer and a die with no particles, independent? Explain.

**4.23** According to an Ipsos poll, the perception of unfairness in the U.S. tax code is spread fairly evenly across income groups, age groups, and education levels. In an April 2006 survey of 1,005 adults, Ipsos reported that almost 60% of all people said the code is unfair, whereas slightly more than 60% of those making more than $50,000 viewed the code as unfair ("People Cry Unfairness," *The Cincinnati Enquirer*, April 16, 2006, p. A8). Suppose that the following contingency table represents the specific breakdown of responses:

| | INCOME LEVEL | | |
|---|---|---|---|
| | **Less Than $50,000** | **More Than $50,000** | **Total** |
| **Fair** | 225 | 180 | 405 |
| **Unfair** | 280 | 320 | 600 |
| **Total** | 505 | 500 | 1,005 |

**a.** Given that a respondent earns less than $50,000, what is the probability that he or she said that the tax code is fair?

**b.** Given that a respondent earns more than $50,000, what is the probability that he or she said that the tax code is fair?

**c.** Is income level independent of attitude about whether the tax code is fair? Explain.

**4.24** An experiment was conducted to study the choices made in mutual fund selection. Undergraduate and MBA students were presented with different S&P 500 Index funds that were identical except for fees. Suppose 100 undergraduate students and 100 MBA students were selected. Partial results are shown in the following table:

| FUND | STUDENT GROUP | |
|---|---|---|
| | **Undergraduate** | **MBA** |
| **Highest-cost fund** | 27 | 18 |
| **Not highest-cost fund** | 73 | 82 |

Source: *Extracted from J. J. Choi, D. Laibson, and B. C. Madrian,* Why Does the Law of One Price Fail? ***www.som.yale.edu/faculty/jjc83/fees.pdf.***

**a.** Given that a student is an undergraduate, what is the probability that he or she selected the highest-cost fund?

**b.** Given that a student selected the highest-cost fund, what is the probability that he or she is an undergraduate?

**c.** Explain the difference in the results in (a) and (b).

**d.** Are the two events "student group" and "fund selected" independent? Explain.

**4.25** A sample of 500 respondents was selected in a large metropolitan area to study consumer behavior, with the following results:

| ENJOYS SHOPPING FOR CLOTHING | GENDER | | |
|---|---|---|---|
| | **Male** | **Female** | **Total** |
| **Yes** | 136 | 224 | 360 |
| **No** | 104 | 36 | 140 |
| **Total** | 240 | 260 | 500 |

**a.** Suppose the respondent chosen is a female. What is the probability that she does not enjoy shopping for clothing?

**b.** Suppose the respondent chosen enjoys shopping for clothing. What is the probability that the individual is a male?

**c.** Are enjoying shopping for clothing and the gender of the individual independent? Explain.

**4.26** Each year, ratings are compiled concerning the performance of new cars during the first 90 days of use. Suppose that the cars have been categorized according to whether the car needs warranty-related repair (yes or no) and the country in which the company manufacturing the car is based (United States or not United States). Based on the data collected, the probability that the new car needs a warranty repair is 0.04, the probability that the car is manufactured by a U.S.-based company is 0.60, and the probability that the new car needs a warranty repair *and* was manufactured by a U.S.-based company is 0.025.

**a.** Suppose you know that a company based in the United States manufactured a particular car. What is the probability that the car needs warranty repair?

**b.** Suppose you know that a company based in the United States did not manufacture a particular car. What is the probability that the car needs warranty repair?

**c.** Are need for warranty repair and location of the company manufacturing the car independent?

**4.27** In 36 of the 57 years from 1950 through 2006, the S&P 500 finished higher after the first 5 days of trading. In 31 of those 36 years, the S&P 500 finished higher for the year. Is a good first week a good omen for the upcoming year? The following table gives the first-week and annual performance over this 57-year period:

**S&P 500'S ANNUAL PERFORMANCE**

| FIRST WEEK | Higher | Lower |
|---|---|---|
| **Higher** | 31 | 5 |
| **Lower** | 11 | 10 |

**a.** If a year is selected at random, what is the probability that the S&P 500 finished higher for the year?
**b.** Given that the S&P 500 finished higher after the first five days of trading, what is the probability that it finished higher for the year?
**c.** Are the two events "first-week performance" and "annual performance" independent? Explain.
**d.** Look up the performance after the first five days of 2007 and the 2007 annual performance of the S&P 500 at **finance.yahoo.com**. Comment on the results.

**4.28** A standard deck of cards is being used to play a game. There are four suits (hearts, diamonds, clubs, and spades), each having 13 faces (ace, 2, 3, 4, 5, 6, 7, 8, 9, 10, jack, queen, and king), making a total of 52 cards. This complete deck is thoroughly mixed, and you will receive the first 2 cards from the deck without replacement.
**a.** What is the probability that both cards are queens?
**b.** What is the probability that the first card is a 10 and the second card is a 5 or 6?
**c.** If you were sampling with replacement, what would be the answer in (a)?
**d.** In the game of blackjack, the picture cards (jack, queen, king) count as 10 points, and the ace counts as either 1 or 11 points. All other cards are counted at their face value. Blackjack is achieved if 2 cards total 21 points. What is the probability of getting blackjack in this problem?

**4.29** A box of nine gloves contains two left-handed gloves and seven right-handed gloves.
**a.** If two gloves are randomly selected from the box without replacement, what is the probability that both gloves selected will be right-handed?
**b.** If two gloves are randomly selected from the box without replacement, what is the probability there will be one right-handed glove and one left-handed glove selected?
**c.** If three gloves are selected with replacement, what is the probability that all three will be left-handed?
**d.** If you were sampling with replacement, what would be the answers to (a) and (b)?

## 4.3   BAYES' THEOREM

**Bayes' theorem** is used to revise previously calculated probabilities based on new information. Developed by Thomas Bayes in the eighteenth century (see references 1, 2, and 5), Bayes' theorem is an extension of what you previously learned about conditional probability.

You can apply Bayes' theorem to the situation in which M&R Electronics World is considering marketing a new model of television. In the past, 40% of the televisions introduced by the company have been successful, and 60% have been unsuccessful. Before introducing the television to the marketplace, the marketing research department conducts an extensive study and releases a report, either favorable or unfavorable. In the past, 80% of the successful televisions had received favorable market research reports, and 30% of the unsuccessful televisions had received favorable reports. For the new model of television under consideration, the marketing research department has issued a favorable report. What is the probability that the television will be successful?

Bayes' theorem is developed from the definition of conditional probability. To find the conditional probability of $B$ given $A$, consider Equation (4.4b) [originally presented on page 154 and shown below]:

$$P(B \mid A) = \frac{P(A \text{ and } B)}{P(A)} = \frac{P(A \mid B)P(B)}{P(A)}$$

Bayes' theorem is derived by substituting Equation (4.8) on page 160 for $P(A)$ in the denominator of Equation (4.4b).

**Bayes' Theorem**

$$P(B_i \mid A) = \frac{P(A \mid B_i)P(B_i)}{P(A \mid B_1)P(B_1) + P(A \mid B_2)P(B_2) + \cdots + P(A \mid B_k)P(B_k)} \qquad \textbf{(4.9)}$$

where $B_i$ is the $i$th event out of $k$ mutually exclusive and collectively exhaustive events.

To use Equation (4.9) for the television-marketing example, let

$$\text{event } S = \text{successful television} \qquad \text{event } F = \text{favorable report}$$
$$\text{event } S' = \text{unsuccessful television} \qquad \text{event } F' = \text{unfavorable report}$$

and

$$P(S) = 0.40 \qquad P(F \mid S) = 0.80$$
$$P(S') = 0.60 \qquad P(F \mid S') = 0.30$$

Then, using Equation (4.9),

$$P(S \mid F) = \frac{P(F \mid S)P(S)}{P(F \mid S)P(S) + P(F \mid S')P(S')}$$

$$= \frac{(0.80)(0.40)}{(0.80)(0.40) + (0.30)(0.60)}$$

$$= \frac{0.32}{0.32 + 0.18} = \frac{0.32}{0.50}$$

$$= 0.64$$

The probability of a successful television, given that a favorable report was received, is 0.64. Thus, the probability of an unsuccessful television, given that a favorable report was received, is $1 - 0.64 = 0.36$. Table 4.4 summarizes the computation of the probabilities, and Figure 4.5 presents the decision tree.

**TABLE 4.4**

Bayes' Theorem Calculations for the Television-Marketing Example

| Event $S_i$ | Prior Probability $P(S_i)$ | Conditional Probability $P(F \mid S_i)$ | Joint Probability $P(F \mid S_i)P(S_i)$ | Revised Probability $P(S_i \mid F)$ |
|---|---|---|---|---|
| $S$ = successful television | 0.40 | 0.80 | 0.32 | $P(S \mid F) = 0.32/0.50$ <br> $= 0.64$ |
| $S'$ = unsuccessful television | 0.60 | 0.30 | $\dfrac{0.18}{0.50}$ | $P(S' \mid F) = 0.18/0.50$ <br> $= 0.36$ |

**FIGURE 4.5**

Decision tree for marketing a new television

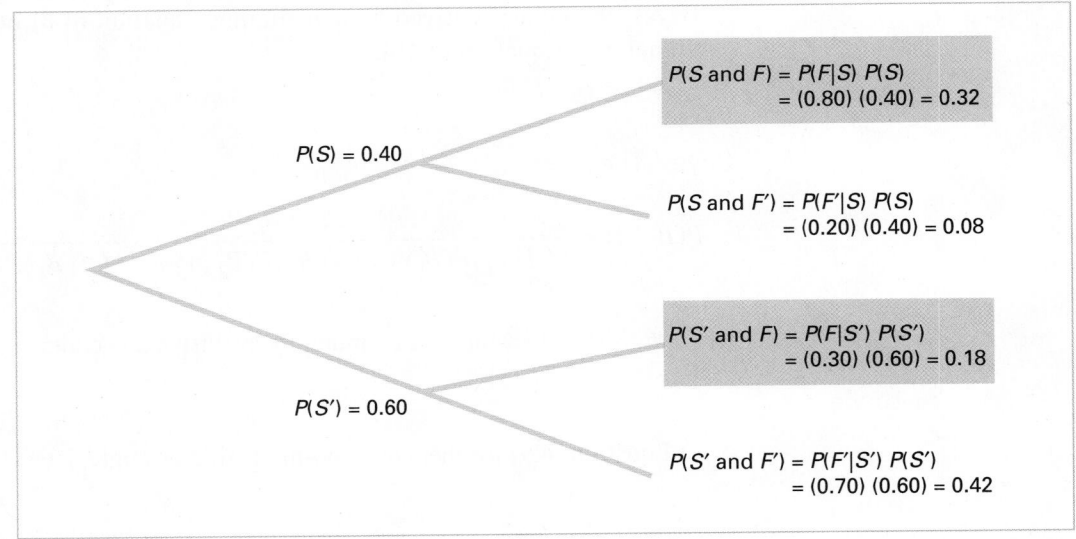

Example 4.10 applies Bayes' theorem to a medical diagnosis problem.

**EXAMPLE 4.10**    USING BAYES' THEOREM IN A MEDICAL DIAGNOSIS PROBLEM

The probability that a person has a certain disease is 0.03. Medical diagnostic tests are available to determine whether the person actually has the disease. If the disease is actually present, the probability that the medical diagnostic test will give a positive result (indicating that the disease is present) is 0.90. If the disease is not actually present, the probability of a positive test result (indicating that the disease is present) is 0.02. Suppose that the medical diagnostic test has given a positive result (indicating that the disease is present). What is the probability that the disease is actually present? What is the probability of a positive test result?

**SOLUTION**  Let

$$\text{event } D = \text{has disease} \qquad \text{event } T = \text{test is positive}$$
$$\text{event } D' = \text{does not have disease} \qquad \text{event } T' = \text{test is negative}$$

and

$$P(D) = 0.03 \qquad P(T \mid D) = 0.90$$
$$P(D') = 0.97 \qquad P(T \mid D') = 0.02$$

Using Equation (4.9) on page 163,

$$P(D \mid T) = \frac{P(T \mid D)P(D)}{P(T \mid D)P(D) + P(T \mid D')P(D')}$$

$$= \frac{(0.90)(0.03)}{(0.90)(0.03) + (0.02)(0.97)}$$

$$= \frac{0.0270}{0.0270 + 0.0194} = \frac{0.0270}{0.0464}$$

$$= 0.582$$

The probability that the disease is actually present, given that a positive result has occurred (indicating that the disease is present), is 0.582. Table 4.5 summarizes the computation of the probabilities, and Figure 4.6 presents the decision tree.

**TABLE 4.5**

Bayes' Theorem Calculations for the Medical Diagnosis Problem

| Event $D_i$ | Prior Probability $P(D_i)$ | Conditional Probability $P(T \mid D_i)$ | Joint Probability $P(T \mid D_i)P(D_i)$ | Revised Probability $P(D_i \mid T)$ |
|---|---|---|---|---|
| $D$ = has disease | 0.03 | 0.90 | 0.0270 | $P(D \mid T) = 0.0270/0.0464$ <br> $= 0.582$ |
| $D'$ = does not have disease | 0.97 | 0.02 | 0.0194 <br><br> 0.0464 | $P(D' \mid T) = 0.0194/0.0464$ <br> $= 0.418$ |

**FIGURE 4.6**

Decision tree for the medical diagnosis problem

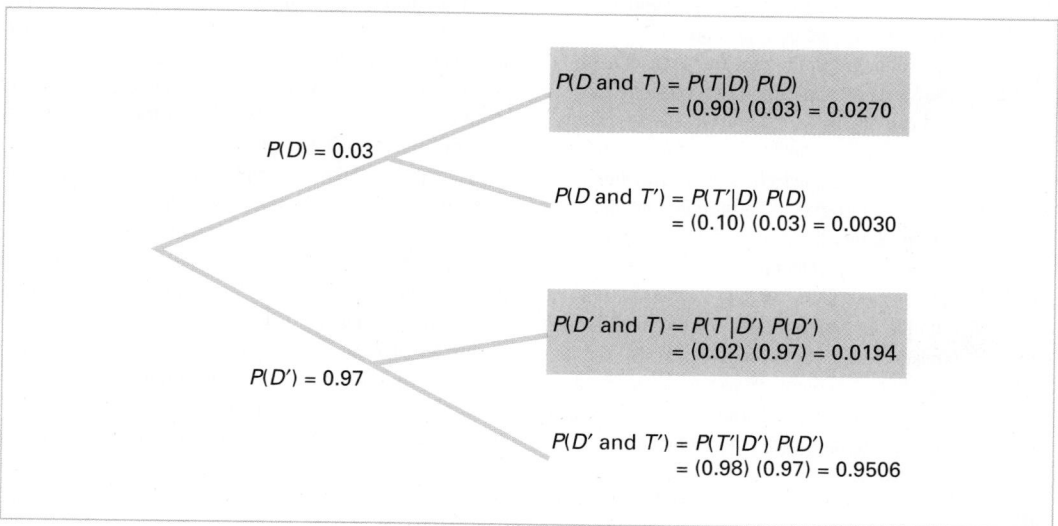

$P(D) = 0.03$

$P(D \text{ and } T) = P(T|D)\ P(D)$
$= (0.90)\ (0.03) = 0.0270$

$P(D \text{ and } T') = P(T'|D)\ P(D)$
$= (0.10)\ (0.03) = 0.0030$

$P(D') = 0.97$

$P(D' \text{ and } T) = P(T|D')\ P(D')$
$= (0.02)\ (0.97) = 0.0194$

$P(D' \text{ and } T') = P(T'|D')\ P(D')$
$= (0.98)\ (0.97) = 0.9506$

The denominator in Bayes' theorem represents $P(T)$, the probability of a positive test result, which in this case is 0.0464, or 4.64%.

# Divine Providence and Spam

*From The Authors' Desktop*

Would you guess that the author of *Divine Benevolence: Or, An Attempt to Prove That the Principal End of the Divine Providence and Government Is the Happiness of His Creatures* also wrote *An Essay Towards Solving a Problem in the Doctrine of Chances*? Probably not, but, in fact, both essays were written by Thomas Bayes, who was a minister and theologian by training. Don't feel bad if you made a wrong guess—later in this passage you will see how your wrong guess illustrates a modern-day application of Bayesian statistics—spam, or junk mail, filters.

*An Essay Towards Solving . . .* introduced Bayes' theorem, discussed in Section 4.3. After writing the essay, Bayes put it aside, and we only know about the paper because a friend published it after Bayes' death in 1763. His friend thought the essay proved the existence of God; Bayes, himself, was more modest about the essay, noting "so far as mathe-matics do not tend to make men more sober and rational thinkers . . . they are only to be considered as an amusement, which ought not to take us off from serious business." *(Please do not use this as an excuse for not doing your statistics homework.)*

In spite of his friend's enthusiasm, Bayes' theorem was soon dismissed by the majority of mathematicians, who felt, among other reasons, that establishing the prior probabilities needed by the theorem would ultimately be nothing more than an example of setting subjective probabilities. Others, who had a more accepting view, noted that the prior probabilities would need to be constantly updated and therefore were concerned about the impossibility of keeping track of all the results that would be needed in order to constantly update those probabilities (to better reflect current experience).

Although always championed by a minority of statisticians, and notably, a number of nonstatisticians, Bayes' theorem remained at the fringes of respectable statistics for more than 150 years. The theorem began its long return from statistical exile when *An Essay Towards . . .* was republished in 1940, with commentary by W. Edwards Deming. (Ironically, like Bayes' theorem, many of Deming's own ideas would also be ignored, only to be widely accepted later on, as Chapter 18 explains.) But it took the data-processing power of modern computer systems to bring Bayesian statistics into the mainstream of research.

Today, applications of Bayesian statistics are allowing computer programs to "mine" large databases in order to discover hidden patterns. Your favorite Internet search engine may use some Bayesian techniques, as well, to deliver Internet links most likely to be relevant to your search. But of all the Bayesian applications in use, the one you've most likely experienced involves spam, the unwanted junk mail that clogs your e-mail inbox.

Return to the question that opens this *From The Authors' Desktop*. Implicit in this question is the expectation that word frequencies vary by subject matter. A statistics book would very likely contain the word *statistics* as well as words such as *chance, problem,* and *solving.* An eighteenth-century book about theology and religion would be more likely to contain the uppercase forms of *Divine* and *Providence.* Likewise, there are words very unlikely to appear in either book, such as the words *sedimentary, igneous,* and *metamorphic* (types of rocks), and there are words that are likely to appear in both such as the common words *a, an,* and *the.*

That the words are either likely or unlikely suggests an application of probability theory. Of course, likely and unlikely are fuzzy concepts, and we could never be completely sure if we had classified a book correctly. After all, a book about the underground film director John Waters (of *Hairspray* fame) might talk about him traveling with the late star of many of his movies, *Divine,* to see *Providence* (as in Rhode Island). Still, we would probably not mistake such a book for an eighteenth-century book on theology if we considered other words, such as *film* and *movie,* which are unlikely to be found in an eighteenth-century publication.

Classifying books into one of several categories creates complications too difficult to explain here, but what if we looked at the simpler problem of trying to classify a newly arrived e-mail message as either spam or a legitimate message (sometimes called "ham" in this context)? More specifically, what if we focused on all the e-mails sent to one address? And what if we added something to that person's e-mail program that would track word frequencies associated with spam and ham messages in order to constantly update the prior probabilities that Bayes' theorem needs? When researchers realized all this was possible, Bayesian spam filters got their start.

These filters ask, "What is the probability that an e-mail is spam, given the presence of a certain word?" Using Bayes' theorem, the filters can calculate this probability by multiplying the probability of finding the word in a spam e-mail, $P(A|B)$ in Equation (4.9), by the probability that the e-mail is spam, $P(B)$, and dividing by the probability of finding the word in an e-mail, the denominator in Equation (4.9).

Bayesian spam filters quickly proved superior to simple keyword filters in both identifying spam and avoiding labeling a ham message as spam. Most Bayesian spam filters ignore common words found in both ham and spam e-mails. These filters also take shortcuts by focusing on a small set of words that have a high probability of being found in a spam e-mail and on words that have a low probability of being found in a spam e-mail.

As spammers (people who sent junk e-mail) learned of these new filters, they tried to outfox them. Having learned that Bayesian filters might be assigning a high $P(A|B)$ value to words like Viagra, commonly found in early spam messages, spammers thought they could fool the filter by misspelling the word as Vi@gr@ or V1agra. What they failed to realize was that the misspelled variants were even more likely to be found in a spam message than the original word. Thus, the misspelled variants made the job even easier for the Bayesian filters. Of course, through all the e-mails, the filters are constantly being retrained—that is, updating probabilities and noting when the user indicates a particular e-mail marked as ham is really spam. So, the initial Vi@agr@ e-mails were mismarked as ham, but the filter quickly learns to treat such messages as spam. (Don't worry about filters marking a ham message as spam; most filters are set up with a bias in their probabilities that minimizes such occurrences.)

Other spammers, reading a little bit about filters, decided to add "good" words, words that would have a very low $P(A|B)$ value, or "rare" words, words not frequently encountered in e-mails. This, they thought, should change the result as the filter evaluated the text of an e-mail and led the filter to enable their spam messages to be viewed as ham messages. But these spammers overlooked the fact that the conditional probabilities are constantly updated and that words once considered "good" would be discarded by the filter as their $P(A|B)$ value increased. They also failed to realize that, as "rare" words started to show up in spam messages (and yet still rarely in ham messages), those words acted like the misspelled variants they had tried earlier.

After these attacks were beaten back by Bayesian filters, spammers apparently started learning more about Bayesian statistics. Some figured that they could "break" Bayesian filters by inserting random words in their messages. Those random words would affect the filter by causing it to see many words whose $P(A|B)$ value would be low. The Bayesian filter would begin to label many spam messages as ham and end up being of no practical use. Because the Internet still contains some Web pages and posts that triumph this approach, we will leave it to you to figure out why this method of attack cannot succeed in the long run and why this method is not as initially successful as some would claim.

Today, spammers are still trying to outwit Bayesian filters. Some spammers have decided to eliminate all or most of the words in their messages and replace them with graphics so that Bayesian filters will have very few words with which to work. But this approach will fail too, as Bayesian filters are rewritten to consider things other than words in a message. After all, Bayes' theorem is all about events, and "graphics present with no text" is as valid an event as "*some word* present in e-mail."

In truth, for a variety of reasons, including expediency, most e-mail filters today use a combination of techniques that includes applying Bayesian statistics. And although the war against Bayesian filters will escalate over time, it's a war that statistics dooms spammers to lose in the long run.

Bayesian spam filters illustrate how applications of statistics can show up in your life in very unexpected ways and how a knowledge of statistics is an important component of being a well-educated person. You will discover more unexpected examples as you read through the rest of this book.

# PROBLEMS FOR SECTION 4.3

## Learning the Basics

**4.30** If $P(B) = 0.05$, $P(A \mid B) = 0.80$, $P(B') = 0.95$, and $P(A \mid B') = 0.40$, find $P(B \mid A)$.

**4.31** If $P(B) = 0.30$, $P(A \mid B) = 0.60$, $P(B') = 0.70$, and $P(A \mid B') = 0.50$, find $P(B \mid A)$.

## Applying the Concepts

**4.32** In Example 4.10 on page 164, suppose that the probability that a medical diagnostic test will give a positive result if the disease is not present is reduced from 0.02 to 0.01. Given this information,

**a.** if the medical diagnostic test has given a positive result (indicating that the disease is present), what is the probability that the disease is actually present?

**b.** if the medical diagnostic test has given a negative result (indicating that the disease is not present), what is the probability that the disease is not present?

**4.33** An advertising executive is studying television viewing habits of married men and women during prime-time hours. Based on past viewing records, the executive has determined that during prime time, husbands are watching television 60% of the time. When the husband is watching television, 40% of the time the wife is also watching. When the husband is not watching television, 30% of the time the wife is watching television. Find the probability that

**a.** if the wife is watching television, the husband is also watching television.

**b.** the wife is watching television in prime time.

**SELF Test** **4.34** Olive Construction Company is determining whether it should submit a bid for a new shopping center. In the past, Olive's main competitor, Base Construction Company, has submitted bids 70% of the time. If Base Construction Company does not bid on a job, the probability that Olive Construction Company will get the job is 0.50. If Base Construction Company bids on a job, the probability that Olive Construction Company will get the job is 0.25.

**a.** If Olive Construction Company gets the job, what is the probability that Base Construction Company did not bid?

**b.** What is the probability that Olive Construction Company will get the job?

**4.35** Laid-off workers who become entrepreneurs because they cannot find meaningful employment with another company are known as *entrepreneurs by necessity*. *The Wall Street Journal* reports that these entrepreneurs by necessity are less likely to grow into large businesses than are *entrepreneurs by choice* (J. Bailey, "Desire—More Than Need—Builds a Business," *The Wall Street Journal*, May 21, 2001, p. B4). This article states that 89% of the entrepreneurs in the United States are entrepreneurs by choice and 11% are entrepreneurs by necessity. Only 2% of entrepreneurs by necessity expect their new business to employ 20 or more people within five years, whereas 14% of entrepreneurs by choice expect to employ at least 20 people within five years.

**a.** If an entrepreneur is selected at random, and that individual expects that his or her new business will employ 20 or more people within five years, what is the probability that this individual is an entrepreneur by choice?

**b.** Discuss several possible reasons why entrepreneurs by choice are more likely to believe that they will grow their businesses.

**4.36** The editor of a textbook publishing company is trying to decide whether to publish a proposed business statistics textbook. Information on previous textbooks published indicates that 10% are huge successes, 20% are modest successes, 40% break even, and 30% are losers. However, before a publishing decision is made, the book will be reviewed. In the past, 99% of the huge successes received favorable reviews, 70% of the moderate successes received favorable reviews, 40% of the break-even books received favorable reviews, and 20% of the losers received favorable reviews.

**a.** If the proposed textbook receives a favorable review, how should the editor revise the probabilities of the various outcomes to take this information into account?

**b.** What proportion of textbooks receives favorable reviews?

**4.37** A municipal bond service has three rating categories (*A*, *B*, and *C*). Suppose that in the past year, of the municipal bonds issued throughout the United States, 70% were rated *A*, 20% were rated *B*, and 10% were rated *C*. Of the municipal bonds rated *A*, 50% were issued by cities, 40% by suburbs, and 10% by rural areas. Of the municipal bonds rated *B*, 60% were issued by cities, 20% by suburbs, and 20% by rural areas. Of the municipal bonds rated *C*, 90% were issued by cities, 5% by suburbs, and 5% by rural areas.

**a.** If a new municipal bond is to be issued by a city, what is the probability that it will receive an *A* rating?

**b.** What proportion of municipal bonds are issued by cities?

**c.** What proportion of municipal bonds are issued by suburbs?

## 4.4  COUNTING RULES

In Equation (4.1) on page 145, the probability of occurrence of an outcome was defined as the number of ways the outcome occurs, divided by the total number of possible outcomes. In many instances, there are a large number of possible outcomes and determining the exact number can be difficult. In these circumstances, rules for counting the number of possible outcomes have been developed. This section presents five different counting rules.

**Counting Rule 1**

If any one of $k$ different mutually exclusive and collectively exhaustive events can occur on each of $n$ trials, the number of possible outcomes is equal to

$$k^n \tag{4.10}$$

---

**EXAMPLE 4.11**    COUNTING RULE 1

Suppose you toss a coin five times. What is the number of different possible outcomes (the sequences of heads and tails)?

**SOLUTION**  If you toss a coin (having two sides) five times, using Equation (4.10), the number of outcomes is $2^5 = 2 \times 2 \times 2 \times 2 \times 2 = 32$.

---

**EXAMPLE 4.12**    ROLLING A DIE TWICE

Suppose you roll a die twice. How many different possible outcomes can occur?

**SOLUTION**  If a die (having six sides) is rolled twice, using Equation (4.10), the number of different outcomes is $6^2 = 36$.

---

The second counting rule is a more general version of the first and allows for the number of possible events to differ from trial to trial.

**Counting Rule 2**

If there are $k_1$ events on the first trial, $k_2$ events on the second trial, . . . , and $k_n$ events on the $n$th trial, then the number of possible outcomes is

$$(k_1)(k_2) \cdots (k_n) \tag{4.11}$$

---

**EXAMPLE 4.13**    COUNTING RULE 2

A state motor vehicle department would like to know how many license plate numbers are available if the license plates consist of three letters followed by three numbers (0 through 9).

**SOLUTION**  Using Equation (4.11), if a license plate consists of three letters followed by three numbers, the total number of possible outcomes is $(26)(26)(26)(10)(10)(10) = 17,576,000$.

---

**EXAMPLE 4.14**    DETERMINING THE NUMBER OF DIFFERENT DINNERS

A restaurant menu has a price-fixed complete dinner that consists of an appetizer, entrée, beverage, and dessert. You have a choice of five appetizers, ten entrées, three beverages, and six desserts. Determine the total number of possible dinners.

**SOLUTION**  Using Equation (4.11), the total number of possible dinners is $(5)(10)(3)(6) = 900$.

The third counting rule involves computing the number of ways that a set of items can be arranged in order.

---

**Counting Rule 3**

The number of ways that all $n$ items can be arranged in order is

$$n! = (n)(n-1)\cdots(1) \qquad (4.12)$$

where $n!$ is called $n$ *factorial* and 0! is defined as 1.

---

**EXAMPLE 4.15**    COUNTING RULE 3

If a set of six books is to be placed on a shelf, in how many ways can the six books be arranged?

**SOLUTION**  To begin, you must realize that any of the six books could occupy the first position on the shelf. Once the first position is filled, there are five books to choose from in filling the second position. You continue this assignment procedure until all the positions are occupied. The number of ways that you can arrange six books is

$$n! = 6! = (6)(5)(4)(3)(2)(1) = 720$$

In many instances you need to know the number of ways in which a subset of the entire group of items can be arranged in *order*. Each possible arrangement is called a **permutation**.

---

**Counting Rule 4**

*Permutations:* The number of ways of arranging $X$ objects selected from $n$ objects in order is

$$_{n}P_{X} = \frac{n!}{(n-X)!} \qquad (4.13)$$

where

$n$ = the total number of objects

$X$ = the number of objects to be arranged

$n!$ = $n$ factorial = $n(n-1)\cdots(1)$

$P$ is the symbol for permutations.[1]

[1] On many scientific calculators, there is a button labeled nPr that allows you to compute permutations. The symbol r is used instead of X.

---

**EXAMPLE 4.16**    COUNTING RULE 4

Modifying Example 4.15, if you have six books, but there is room for only four books on the shelf, in how many ways can you arrange these books on the shelf?

**SOLUTION**  Using Equation (4.13), the number of ordered arrangements of four books selected from six books is equal to

$$_{n}P_{X} = \frac{n!}{(n-X)!} = \frac{6!}{(6-4)!} = \frac{(6)(5)(4)(3)(2)(1)}{(2)(1)} = 360$$

In many situations you are not interested in the *order* of the outcomes, but only in the number of ways that $X$ items can be selected from $n$ items, *irrespective of order*. Each possible selection is called a **combination**.

---

**Counting Rule 5**

*Combinations:* The number of ways of selecting $X$ objects from $n$ objects, irrespective of order, is equal to

$$_nC_X = \frac{n!}{X!(n-X)!} \qquad\qquad (4.14)$$

where

$n$ = the total number of objects

$X$ = the number of objects to be arranged

$n!$ = $n$ factorial = $n(n-1)\ldots(1)$

$C$ is the symbol for combinations.[2]

---

[2]*On many scientific calculators, there is a button labeled nCr that allows you to compute combinations. The symbol r is used instead of X.*

Comparing this rule to the previous one, you see that it differs only in the inclusion of a term $X!$ in the denominator. When permutations were used, all of the arrangements of the $X$ objects are distinguishable. With combinations, the $X!$ possible arrangements of objects are irrelevant.

---

**EXAMPLE 4.17**    COUNTING RULE 5

Modifying Example 4.16, if the order of the books on the shelf is irrelevant, in how many ways can you arrange these books on the shelf?

**SOLUTION**   Using Equation (4.14), the number of combinations of four books selected from six books is equal to

$$_nC_X = \frac{n!}{X!(n-X)!} = \frac{6!}{4!(6-4)!} = \frac{(6)(5)(4)(3)(2)(1)}{(4)(3)(2)(1)(2)(1)} = 15$$

---

# PROBLEMS FOR SECTION 4.4

## Applying the Concepts

**4.38** If there are ten multiple-choice questions on an exam, each having three possible answers, how many different sequences of answers are there?

**4.39** A lock on a bank vault consists of three dials, each with 30 positions. In order for the vault to open, each of the three dials must be in the correct position.
**a.** How many different possible "dial combinations" are there for this lock?

**b.** What is the probability that if you randomly select a position on each dial, you will be able to open the bank vault?

**c.** Explain why "dial combinations" are not mathematical combinations expressed by Equation (4.14).

**4.40 a.** If a coin is tossed seven times, how many different outcomes are possible?

**b.** If a die is tossed seven times, how many different outcomes are possible?

**c.** Discuss the differences in your answers to (a) and (b).

**4.41** A particular brand of women's jeans is available in seven different sizes, three different colors, and three different styles. How many different jeans does the store manager need to order to have one pair of each type?

**4.42** ✓ SELF Test You would like to make a salad that consists of lettuce, tomato, cucumber, and peppers. You go to the supermarket intending to purchase one variety of each of these ingredients. You discover that there are eight varieties of lettuce, four varieties of tomatoes, three varieties of cucumbers, and three varieties of peppers for sale at the supermarket. How many different salads can you make?

**4.43** If each letter is used once, how many different four-letter "words" can be made from the letters E, L, O, and V?

**4.44** ✓ SELF Test In Major League Baseball, there are five teams in the Eastern Division of the National League: Atlanta, Florida, New York, Philadelphia, and Washington. How many different orders of finish are there for these five teams? (Assume that there are no ties in the standings.) Do you believe that all these orders are equally likely? Discuss.

**4.45** Referring to Problem 4.44, how many different orders of finish are possible for the first four positions?

**4.46** A gardener has six rows available in his vegetable garden to place tomatoes, eggplant, peppers, cucumbers, beans, and lettuce. Each vegetable will be allowed one and only one row. How many ways are there to position these vegetables in his garden?

**4.47** The Trifecta at the local racetrack consists of picking the correct order of finish of the first three horses in the ninth race. If there are 12 horses entered in today's ninth race, how many Trifecta outcomes are there?

**4.48** ✓ SELF Test The Quinella at the local racetrack consists of picking the horses that will place first and second in a race *irrespective* of order. If eight horses are entered in a race, how many Quinella combinations are there?

**4.49** A student has seven books that she would like to place in her backpack. However, there is only room for four books. Regardless of the arrangement, how many ways are there of placing four books into her backpack?

**4.50** A daily lottery is conducted in which two winning numbers are selected out of 100 numbers. How many different combinations of winning numbers are possible?

**4.51** A reading list for a course contains 20 articles. How many ways are there to choose three articles from this list?

## 4.5 ETHICAL ISSUES AND PROBABILITY

Ethical issues can arise when any statements related to probability are presented to the public, particularly when these statements are part of an advertising campaign for a product or service. Unfortunately, many people are not comfortable with numerical concepts (see reference 4) and tend to misinterpret the meaning of the probability. In some instances, the misinterpretation is not intentional, but in other cases, advertisements may unethically try to mislead potential customers.

One example of a potentially unethical application of probability relates to advertisements for state lotteries. When purchasing a lottery ticket, the customer selects a set of numbers (such as 6) from a larger list of numbers (such as 54). Although virtually all participants know that they are unlikely to win the lottery, they also have very little idea of how unlikely it is for them to select all 6 winning numbers from the list of 54 numbers. They have even less idea of the probability of winning a consolation prize by selecting either 4 or 5 winning numbers.

Given this background, you might consider a recent commercial for a state lottery that stated, "We won't stop until we have made everyone a millionaire" to be deceptive and possibly unethical. Do you think the state has any intention of ever stopping the lottery, given the fact that the state relies on it to bring millions of dollars into the treasury? Is it possible that the lottery can make everyone a millionaire? Is it ethical to suggest that the purpose of the lottery is to make everyone a millionaire?

Another example of a potentially unethical application of probability relates to an investment newsletter promising a 90% probability of a 20% annual return on investment. To make the claim in the newsletter an ethical one, the investment service needs to (a) explain the basis on which this probability estimate rests, (b) provide the probability statement in another format, such as 9 chances in 10, and (c) explain what happens to the investment in the 10% of the cases in which a 20% return is not achieved (e.g., is the entire investment lost?).

## PROBLEMS FOR SECTION 4.5

### Applying the Concepts

**4.52** Write an advertisement for the state lottery that ethically describes the probability of winning a certain prize.

**4.53** Write an advertisement for the investment newsletter that ethically states the probability of a 20% return on an investment.

## SUMMARY

This chapter develops concepts concerning basic probability, conditional probability, and Bayes' theorem. In the next chapter, important discrete probability distributions such as the binomial, hypergeometric, and Poisson distributions are developed.

## KEY EQUATIONS

**Probability of Occurrence**

$$\text{Probability of occurrence} = \frac{X}{T} \quad \text{(4.1)}$$

**Marginal Probability**

$$P(A) = P(A \text{ and } B_1) + P(A \text{ and } B_2) + \cdots + P(A \text{ and } B_k) \quad \text{(4.2)}$$

**General Addition Rule**

$$P(A \text{ or } B) = P(A) + P(B) - P(A \text{ and } B) \quad \text{(4.3)}$$

**Conditional Probability**

$$P(A \mid B) = \frac{P(A \text{ and } B)}{P(B)} \quad \text{(4.4a)}$$

$$P(B \mid A) = \frac{P(A \text{ and } B)}{P(A)} \quad \text{(4.4b)}$$

**Independence**

$$P(A \mid B) = P(A) \quad \text{(4.5)}$$

**General Multiplication Rule**

$$P(A \text{ and } B) = P(A \mid B)P(B) \quad \text{(4.6)}$$

**Multiplication Rule for Independent Events**

$$P(A \text{ and } B) = P(A)P(B) \quad \text{(4.7)}$$

**Marginal Probability Using the General Multiplication Rule**

$$P(A) = P(A \mid B_1)P(B_1) + P(A \mid B_2)P(B_2) + \cdots + P(A \mid B_k)P(B_k) \quad \text{(4.8)}$$

**Bayes' Theorem**

$$P(B_i \mid A) = \frac{P(A \mid B_i)P(B_i)}{P(A \mid B_1)P(B_1) + P(A \mid B_2)P(B_2) + \cdots + P(A \mid B_k)P(B_k)} \quad \text{(4.9)}$$

**Counting Rule 1**

$$k^n \quad \text{(4.10)}$$

**Counting Rule 2**

$$(k_1)(k_2) \cdots (k_n) \quad \text{(4.11)}$$

**Counting Rule 3**

$$n! = (n)(n-1) \cdots (1) \quad \text{(4.12)}$$

**Permutations**

$$_nP_X = \frac{n!}{(n-X)!} \quad \text{(4.13)}$$

**Combinations**

$$_nC_X = \frac{n!}{X!(n-X)!} \quad \text{(4.14)}$$

# KEY TERMS

*a priori* probability   145
Bayes' theorem   162
certain event   145
collectively exhaustive   150
combination   170
complement   146
conditional probability   154
contingency table   147
decision tree   156
empirical probability   145

event   146
general addition rule   151
general multiplication rule   158
impossible event   145
independence   157
joint event   146
joint probability   149
marginal probability   150
multiplication rule for independent
   events   159

mutually exclusive   150
permutation   169
probability   145
sample space   146
simple event   146
simple probability   148
subjective probability   146
Venn diagrams   147

# CHAPTER REVIEW PROBLEMS

## Checking Your Understanding

**4.54** What are the differences between *a priori* probability, empirical probability, and subjective probability?

**4.55** What is the difference between a simple event and a joint event?

**4.56** How can you use the general addition rule to find the probability of occurrence of event *A* or *B*?

**4.57** What is the difference between mutually exclusive events and collectively exhaustive events?

**4.58** How does conditional probability relate to the concept of independence?

**4.59** How does the multiplication rule differ for events that are and are not independent?

**4.60** How can you use Bayes' theorem to revise probabilities in light of new information?

**4.61** In Bayes' theorem, how does the prior probability differ from the revised probability?

## Applying the Concepts

**4.62** From April 2 to April 5, 2007, Gallup poll conducted a nationwide telephone survey with randomly selected adults. Each respondent was asked, "In politics, as of today, do you consider yourself a Republican, a Democrat, or an Independent?" Of the 1008 responses received, 36% considered themselves Independents, 34% Democrats, and 30% Republicans ("Party Affiliation," **www.galluppoll.com**, April 17, 2007). Suppose that at this time you randomly selected three adults in the United States.
**a.** What is the probability that all three consider themselves Republican?
**b.** What is the probability that all three consider themselves Democrats?
**c.** What is the probability that all three consider themselves Independents?

**d.** What is the probability that you select one Republican, one Democrat, and one Independent?
**e.** Is the approach you used in (a) through (d) an example of *a priori*, empirical, or subjective probability?

**4.63** A survey of 500 men and 500 women, designed to study financial tensions between couples, asked how likely each was to hide purchases, cash, or investments from his or her partner. The following table summarizes the results.

| TYPE | LIKELY TO HIDE | |
|---|---|---|
| | **Men** | **Women** |
| **Auto-related** | 66 | 36 |
| **Cash** | 126 | 133 |
| **Clothes** | 62 | 116 |
| **Electronics** | 79 | 56 |
| **Entertainment** | 96 | 76 |
| **Food** | 74 | 94 |
| **Investments** | 76 | 52 |
| **Travel** | 53 | 39 |

Source: *Extracted from L. Wei, "Your Money Manager as Financial Therapist,"* The Wall Street Journal, *November 5–6, 2005, p. B4.*

For each type of purchase, construct a contingency table or a Venn diagram of likely to hide (yes or no) with gender. If a respondent is chosen at random, what is the probability that
**a.** he or she is likely to hide a clothing purchase?
**b.** he or she is likely to hide investments?
**c.** the person is a male and is likely to hide auto-related purchases?
**d.** the person is a female and is likely to hide clothing purchases?
**e.** Given that the person hides investments, what is the probability that the person is a male?
**f.** Are any of the types of things that couples hide independent of the gender of the respondent? Explain.

**4.64** A survey by the Pew Research Center ("Snapshots: Goals of 'Gen next' vs. 'Gen X'," *USA Today*, March 27, 2007, p. 1A) indicated that 81% of 18- to 25-year-olds had getting rich as a goal as compared to 62% of 26- to 40-year-olds. Suppose that the survey was based on 500 respondents from each of the two groups.

a. Form a contingency table or a Venn diagram.

b. Give an example of a simple event and a joint event.

c. What is the probability that a randomly selected respondent has a goal of getting rich?

d. What is the probability that a randomly selected respondent has a goal of getting rich and is in the 26- to 40-year-old group?

e. Are the events "age group" and "has getting rich as a goal" independent? Explain.

**4.65** The owner of a restaurant serving Continental-style entrées was interested in studying ordering patterns of patrons for the Friday-to-Sunday weekend time period. Records were maintained that indicated the demand for dessert during the same time period. The owner decided to study two other variables, along with whether a dessert was ordered: the gender of the individual and whether a beef entrée was ordered. The results are as follows:

|                     | GENDER |        |       |
| ------------------- | ------ | ------ | ----- |
| **DESSERT ORDERED** | **Male** | **Female** | **Total** |
| Yes                 | 96     | 40     | 136   |
| No                  | 224    | 240    | 464   |
| Total               | 320    | 280    | 600   |

|                     | BEEF ENTRÉE |        |       |
| ------------------- | ------ | ------ | ----- |
| **DESSERT ORDERED** | **Yes** | **No** | **Total** |
| Yes                 | 71     | 65     | 136   |
| No                  | 116    | 348    | 464   |
| Total               | 187    | 413    | 600   |

A waiter approaches a table to take an order. What is the probability that the first customer to order at the table

a. orders a dessert?

b. orders a dessert *or* a beef entrée?

c. is a female *and* does not order a dessert?

d. is a female *or* does not order a dessert?

e. Suppose the first person that the waiter takes the dessert order from is a female. What is the probability that she does not order dessert?

f. Are gender and ordering dessert independent?

g. Is ordering a beef entrée independent of whether the person orders dessert?

**4.66** Unsolicited commercial e-mail messages containing product advertisements, commonly referred to as spam, are routinely deleted before being read by more than 80%

of all e-mail users. Furthermore, a small percentage of those reading the spam actually follow through and purchase items. Yet many companies use these unsolicited e-mail advertisements because of the extremely low cost involved. Movies Unlimited, a mail-order video and DVD business in Philadelphia, is one of the more successful companies in terms of generating sales through this form of e-marketing. Ed Weiss, general manager of Movies Unlimited, estimates that somewhere from 15% to 20% of the company's e-mail recipients read the advertisements. Moreover, approximately 15% of those who read the advertisements place orders (S. Forster, "E-Marketers Look to Polish Spam's Rusty Image," *The Wall Street Journal*, May 20, 2002, p. D2).

a. Using Mr. Weiss's lower estimate that the probability a recipient will read the advertisement is 0.15, what is the probability that a recipient will read the advertisement and place an order?

b. Movies Unlimited uses a 175,000-customer database to send e-mail advertisements. If an e-mail advertisement is sent to everyone in its customer database, how many customers do you expect will read the advertisement and place an order?

c. If the probability a recipient will read the advertisement is 0.20, what is the probability that a recipient will read the advertisement and place an order?

d. What is your answer to (b) if the probability that a recipient will read the advertisement is 0.20?

**4.67** An experiment was conducted by James Choi, David Laibson, and Brigitte Madrian to study the choices made in fund selection. Suppose 100 undergraduate students and 100 MBA students were selected. When presented with four S&P 500 Index funds that were identical except for their fees, undergraduate and MBA students chose the funds as follows:

|                          | STUDENT GROUP |        |
| ------------------------ | ------------- | ------ |
| **FUND**                 | **Undergraduate** | **MBA** |
| **Lowest-cost fund**        | 19            | 19     |
| **Second-lowest-cost fund** | 37            | 40     |
| **Third-lowest-cost fund**  | 17            | 23     |
| **Highest-cost fund**       | 27            | 18     |

Source: *Extracted from J. J. Choi, D. Laibson, and B. C. Madrian, Why Does the Law of One Price Fail?* ***www.som.yale.edu/faculty/jjc83/fees.pdf***.

If a student is selected at random, what is the probability that he or she

a. selected the lowest- or second-lowest cost fund?

b. selected the lowest-cost fund and is an undergraduate?

c. selected the lowest-cost fund or is an undergraduate?

d. Given that the student is an undergraduate, what is the probability that he or she selected the highest-cost fund?

e. Do you think undergraduate students and graduate students differ in their fund selection? Explain.

**4.68** Sport utility vehicles (SUVs), vans, and pickups are generally considered to be more prone to roll over than cars. In 1997, 24.0% of all highway fatalities involved rollovers; 15.8% of all fatalities in 1997 involved SUVs, vans, and pickups, given that the fatality involved a rollover. Given that a rollover was not involved, 5.6% of all fatalities involved SUVs, vans, and pickups (A. Wilde Mathews, "Ford Ranger, Chevy Tracker Tilt in Test," *The Wall Street Journal*, July 14, 1999, p. A2). Consider the following definitions:

$A$ = fatality involved an SUV, van, or pickup

$B$ = fatality involved a rollover

a. Use Bayes' theorem to find the probability that a fatality involved a rollover, given that the fatality involved an SUV, a van, or a pickup.
b. Compare the result in (a) to the probability that a fatality involved a rollover and comment on whether SUVs, vans, and pickups are generally more prone to rollover accidents than other vehicles.

**4.69** Enzyme-linked immunosorbent assay (ELISA) is the most common type of screening test for detecting the HIV virus. A positive result from an ELISA indicates that the HIV virus is present. For most populations, ELISA has a high degree of sensitivity (to detect infection) and specificity (to detect noninfection). (See HIVInsite, at **HIVInsite.ucsf.edu**.) Suppose that the probability a person is infected with the HIV virus for a certain population is 0.015. If the HIV virus is actually present, the probability that the ELISA test will give a positive result is 0.995. If the HIV virus is not actually present, the probability of a positive result from an ELISA is 0.01. If the ELISA has given a positive result, use Bayes' theorem to find the probability that the HIV virus is actually present.

## Team Project

The data file **Mutual Funds** contains information regarding four categorical variables from a sample of 868 mutual funds. The variables are:

Category—Type of stocks comprising the mutual fund (small cap, mid cap, large cap)

Objective—Objective of stocks comprising the mutual fund (growth or value)

Fees—Sales charges (no or yes)

Risk—Risk-of-loss factor of the mutual fund (low, average, high)

**4.70** Construct contingency tables of category and objective, category and fees, category and risk, objective and fees, and fees and risk.
a. For each of these contingency tables, compute all the conditional and marginal probabilities.

b. Based on (a), what conclusions can you reach about whether these variables are independent?

## Student Survey Data Base

**4.71** Problem 1.27 on page 14 describes a survey of 50 undergraduate students (see the file **Undergradsurvey**). For these data, construct contingency tables of gender and major, gender and graduate school intention, gender and employment status, class and graduate school intention, class and employment status, major and graduate school intention, and major and employment status.
a. For each of these contingency tables, compute all the conditional and marginal probabilities.
b. Based on (a), what conclusions can you reach about whether these variables are independent?

**4.72** Problem 1.27 on page 14 describes a survey of 50 undergraduate students (see the file **Undergradsurvey**).
a. Select a sample of 50 undergraduate students at your school and conduct a similar survey for those students.
b. For these data, construct contingency tables of gender and major, gender and graduate school intention, gender and employment status, class and graduate school intention, class and employment status, major and graduate school intention, and major and employment status. For each of these contingency tables, compute all the conditional and marginal probabilities.
c. Based on (b), what conclusions can you reach about whether these variables are independent?
d. Compare the results of (c) to those of Problem 4.71(b).

**4.73** Problem 1.28 on page 14 describes a survey of 40 MBA students (see the file **Gradsurvey**). For these data, construct contingency tables of gender and graduate major, gender and undergraduate major, gender and employment status, graduate major and undergraduate major, and graduate major and employment status.
a. For each of these contingency tables, compute all the conditional and marginal probabilities.
b. Based on (b), what conclusions can you reach about whether these variables are independent?

**4.74** Problem 1.28 on page 14 describes a survey of 40 MBA students (see the file **Gradsurvey**).
a. Select a sample of 40 MBA students from your MBA program and conduct a similar survey for those students.
b. For these data, construct contingency tables of gender and graduate major, gender and undergraduate major, gender and employment status, graduate major and undergraduate major, and graduate major and employment status. For each of these contingency tables, compute all the conditional and marginal probabilities.
c. Based on (b), what conclusions can you reach about whether these variables are independent?
d. Compare the results of (c) to those of Problem 4.73(b).

# WEB CASE

*Apply your knowledge about contingency tables and the proper application of simple and joint probabilities in this continuing Web Case from Chapter 3.*

Visit the EndRun Guaranteed Investment Package (GIP) Web page, at **www.prenhall.com/Springville/ ER_Guaranteed.htm** or open this Web page file from the Student CD-ROM Web Case folder. Read the claims and examine the supporting data. Then answer the following:

1. How accurate is the claim of the probability of success for EndRun's GIP? In what ways is the claim mislead-

ing? How would you calculate and state the probability of having an annual rate of return not less than 15%?

2. What mistake was made in reporting the 7% probability claim? Using the table found on the "Winning Probabilities" Web page, `ER_Guaranteed3.htm`, compute the proper probabilities for the group of investors.

3. Are there any probability calculations that would be appropriate for rating an investment service? Why or why not?

# REFERENCES

1. Bellhouse, D. R., "The Reverend Thomas Bayes, FRS: A Biography to Celebrate the Tercentenary of His Birth," *Statistical Science* 19 (2004), 3–43.

2. Lowd, D., and C. Meek, "Good Word Attacks on Statistical Spam Filters," presented at the Second Conference on Email and Anti-Spam, CEAS 2005.

3. *Microsoft Excel 2007* (Redmond, WA: Microsoft Corp., 2007).

4. Paulos, J. A., *Innumeracy* (New York: Hill and Wang, 1988).

5. Silberman, S., "The Quest for Meaning," *Wired 8.02*, February 2000.

6. T. Zeller, "The Fight Against V1@gra (and Other Spam)," *The New York Times*, May 21, 2006, pp. B1, B6.

# Appendix E4
## Using Microsoft Excel for Basic Probability

## E4.1 Computing Basic Probabilities (all Excel versions)

To compute basic probabilities, open to the **Probabilities** worksheet of the `Probabilities.xls` workbook. Enter event labels and counts in the tinted cells in rows 3 through 6. Figure E4.1 shows a completed worksheet for the "Purchase Behavior for Big-Screen Television" data of Table 4.1 on page 147. Also shown offset in Figure E4.1 are the formulas this worksheet uses to compute the various probabilities.

The worksheet also "computes" the *labels* for the probabilities table with formulas that use the ampersand (**&**) operator to combine parts of a label. For example, the cell A10 formula **="P(" & B5 & ")"** asks Excel to combine the contents of B5 (**Yes**) to the label **"P("** to get **"P(Yes"** and then to "add" **")"** to get **"P(Yes)"** and form the formula **="P(Yes)"**—a novel, but acceptable, way of entering the label value **P(Yes)** in a cell.

**FIGURE E4.1**

Probabilities worksheet

## E4.2 Using Bayes' Theorem (all Excel versions)

You calculate probabilities using Bayes' theorem by making entries in the cell range B5:C6 of the **Bayes** worksheet of the `Bayes.xls` workbook. Figure E4.2 shows a completed worksheet for the television-marketing example shown in Table 4.4 on page 163.

**FIGURE E4.2**

Bayes' theorem worksheet

# Appendix P4
## Using PHStat2 for Basic Probability

## P4.1 Computing Basic Probabilities

To compute basic probabilities, use **PHStat → Probability & Prob. Distributions → Simple & Joint Probabilities**.

This procedure inserts a **Basic Probabilities** worksheet similar to Figure E4.1 on page 176 into the current workbook. To use the worksheet, fill in the Sample Space area with your data. (Unlike most PHStat2 procedures, this procedure does *not* display a dialog box.)

# CHAPTER
# FIVE

## SOME IMPORTANT DISCRETE PROBABILITY DISTRIBUTIONS

## LEARNING OBJECTIVES

### In this chapter, you learn:

- The properties of a probability distribution
- To compute the expected value and variance of a probability distribution
- To calculate the covariance and understand its use in finance
- To compute probabilities from binomial, Poisson, and hypergeometric distributions
- How to use the binomial, Poisson, and hypergeometric distributions to solve business problems

# USING STATISTICS @ Saxon Home Improvement

axon Home Improvement

Home > Online Store > Shopping Cart

**Shopping Cart**

Listed below are the items you have added to your shopping cart. Please review, then select a Checkout Option below to purchase your items.

Want to retrieve a previous shopping list or order? Click here to Retrieve Shopping List. Would you like to save the items in your cart as a shopping list? Click here to Save Shopping List.

Return to shopping

| Check out | Express checkout | Subtotal: $104.94 |

| Name | Price | Qty | Extended Price | Remove |
|---|---|---|---|---|
| Chromecraft Chrome Adjustable Spray Showerhead CC2601 | $14.97 | 1 | $14.97 | Remove |
| Gamma Chrome Single Handle Lavatory Faucet | $84.00 | 1 | $84.00 | Remove |

Accounting information systems collect, process, store, transform, and distribute financial information to decision makers both internal and external to a business organization (see reference 7). These systems continuously audit accounting information, looking for errors or incomplete or improbable information. For example, when customers of the Saxon Home Improvement Company submit online orders, the company's accounting information system reviews the order forms for possible mistakes. Any questionable invoices are *tagged* and included in a daily *exceptions report*. Recent data collected by the company show that the likelihood is 0.10 that an order form will be tagged. Saxon would like to determine the likelihood of finding a certain number of tagged forms in a sample of a specific size. For example, what would be the likelihood that none of the order forms are tagged in a sample of four forms? That one of the order forms is tagged?

How could the Saxon Home Improvement Company determine the solution to this type of probability problem? One way is to use a model, or small-scale representation, that approximates the process. By using such an approximation, Saxon managers could make inferences about the actual order process. Model building is a difficult task for some endeavors, and, in this case, the Saxon managers can use *probability distributions*, mathematical models suited for solving the type of probability problems the managers are facing. Reading this chapter will help you learn about characteristics of a probability distribution and how to specifically apply the binomial, Poisson, and hypergeometric distributions to business problems.

## 5.1 THE PROBABILITY DISTRIBUTION FOR A DISCRETE RANDOM VARIABLE

In Section 1.5, a *numerical variable* was defined as a variable that yielded numerical responses, such as the number of magazines you subscribe to or your height. Numerical variables are classified as *discrete* or *continuous*. Continuous numerical variables produce outcomes that come from a measuring process (e.g., your height). Discrete numerical variables produce outcomes that come from a counting process (e.g., the number of magazines you subscribe to). This chapter deals with probability distributions that represent discrete numerical variables.

PROBABILITY DISTRIBUTION FOR A DISCRETE RANDOM VARIABLE

A **probability distribution for a discrete random variable** is a mutually exclusive listing of all the possible numerical outcomes along with the probability of occurrence of each outcome.

For example, Table 5.1 gives the distribution of the number of mortgages approved per week at the local branch office of a bank. The listing in Table 5.1 is collectively exhaustive because all possible outcomes are included. Thus, the probabilities sum to 1. Figure 5.1 is a graphical representation of Table 5.1.

**TABLE 5.1**

Probability Distribution of the Number of Home Mortgages Approved per Week

| Home Mortgages Approved per Week | Probability |
|---|---|
| 0 | 0.10 |
| 1 | 0.10 |
| 2 | 0.20 |
| 3 | 0.30 |
| 4 | 0.15 |
| 5 | 0.10 |
| 6 | 0.05 |

**FIGURE 5.1**

Probability distribution of the number of home mortgages approved per week

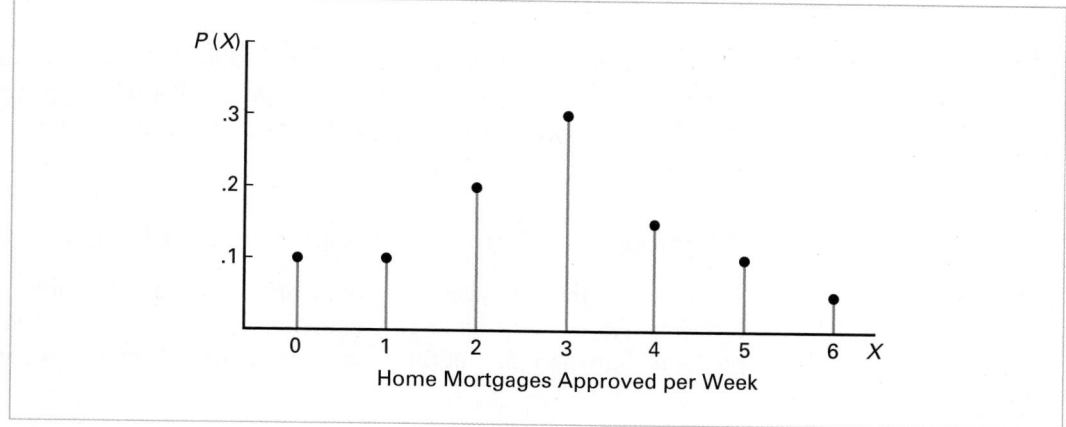

## Expected Value of a Discrete Random Variable

The mean, $\mu$, of a probability distribution is the **expected value** of its random variable. To calculate the expected value, you multiply each possible outcome, $X$, by its corresponding probability, $P(X)$, and then sum these products.

Expected Value, $\mu$, of a Discrete Random Variable

$$\mu = E(X) = \sum_{i=1}^{N} X_i P(X_i) \tag{5.1}$$

where

$X_i$ = the $i$th outcome of the discrete random variable $X$

$P(X_i)$ = probability of occurrence of the $i$th outcome of $X$

For the probability distribution of the number of home mortgages approved per week (Table 5.1), the expected value is computed below using Equation (5.1) and is also shown in Table 5.2.

$$\mu = E(X) = \sum_{i=1}^{N} X_i P(X_i)$$

$$= (0)(0.1) + (1)(0.1) + (2)(0.2) + (3)(0.3) + (4)(0.15) + (5)(0.1) + (6)(0.05)$$

$$= 0 + 0.1 + 0.4 + 0.9 + 0.6 + 0.5 + 0.3$$

$$= 2.8$$

**TABLE 5.2**

Computing the
Expected Value of the
Number of Home
Mortgages Approved
per Week

| Home Mortgages Approved per Week ($X_i$) | $P(X_i)$ | $X_i P(X_i)$ |
|:---:|:---:|:---:|
| 0 | 0.10 | (0)(0.10) = 0.0 |
| 1 | 0.10 | (1)(0.10) = 0.1 |
| 2 | 0.20 | (2)(0.20) = 0.4 |
| 3 | 0.30 | (3)(0.30) = 0.9 |
| 4 | 0.15 | (4)(0.15) = 0.6 |
| 5 | 0.10 | (5)(0.10) = 0.5 |
| 6 | 0.05 | (6)(0.05) = 0.3 |
|   | 1.00 | $\mu = E(X) = 2.8$ |

The expected value is 2.8. The expected value of 2.8 for the number of mortgages approved is not a possible outcome because the actual number of mortgages approved in a given week must be an integer value. The expected value represents the *mean* number of mortgages approved per week.

## Variance and Standard Deviation of a Discrete Random Variable

You compute the variance of a probability distribution by multiplying each possible squared difference $[X_i - E(X)]^2$ by its corresponding probability, $P(X_i)$, and then summing the resulting products. Equation (5.2) defines the **variance of a discrete random variable**.

Variance of a Discrete Random Variable

$$\sigma^2 = \sum_{i=1}^{N} [X_i - E(X)]^2 P(X_i) \tag{5.2}$$

where

$$X_i = \text{the } i\text{th outcome of the discrete random variable } X$$
$$P(X_i) = \text{probability of occurrence of the } i\text{th outcome of } X$$

Equation (5.3) defines the **standard deviation of a discrete random variable**.

Standard Deviation of a Discrete Random Variable

$$\sigma = \sqrt{\sigma^2} = \sqrt{\sum_{i=1}^{N} [X_i - E(X)]^2 P(X_i)} \tag{5.3}$$

The variance and the standard deviation of the number of home mortgages approved per week are computed below and in Table 5.3, using Equations (5.2) and (5.3):

$$\sigma^2 = \sum_{i=1}^{N} [X_i - E(X)]^2 P(X_i)$$

$$= (0 - 2.8)^2 (0.10) + (1 - 2.8)^2 (0.10) + (2 - 2.8)^2 (0.20) + (3 - 2.8)^2 (0.30)$$

$$+ (4 - 2.8)^2 (0.15) + (5 - 2.8)^2 (0.10) + (6 - 2.8)^2 (0.05)$$

$$= 0.784 + 0.324 + 0.128 + 0.012 + 0.216 + 0.484 + 0.512$$

$$= 2.46$$

**TABLE 5.3**

Computing the Variance and Standard Deviation of the Number of Home Mortgages Approved per Week

| Home Mortgages Approved per Week $(X_i)$ | $P(X_i)$ | $X_i P(X_i)$ | $[X_i - E(X)]^2 P(X_i)$ |
|---|---|---|---|
| 0 | 0.10 | $(0)(0.10) = 0.0$ | $(0 - 2.8)^2(0.10) = 0.784$ |
| 1 | 0.10 | $(1)(0.10) = 0.1$ | $(1 - 2.8)^2(0.10) = 0.324$ |
| 2 | 0.20 | $(2)(0.20) = 0.4$ | $(2 - 2.8)^2(0.20) = 0.128$ |
| 3 | 0.30 | $(3)(0.30) = 0.9$ | $(3 - 2.8)^2(0.30) = 0.012$ |
| 4 | 0.15 | $(4)(0.15) = 0.6$ | $(4 - 2.8)^2(0.15) = 0.216$ |
| 5 | 0.10 | $(5)(0.10) = 0.5$ | $(5 - 2.8)^2(0.10) = 0.484$ |
| 6 | 0.05 | $(6)(0.05) = 0.3$ | $(6 - 2.8)^2(0.05) = 0.512$ |
| | 1.00 | $\mu = E(X) = 2.8$ | $\sigma^2 = 2.46$ |

and

$$\sigma = \sqrt{\sigma^2} = \sqrt{2.46} = 1.57$$

Thus, the mean number of mortgages approved per week is 2.8, the variance is 2.46, and the standard deviation is 1.57.

# PROBLEMS FOR SECTION 5.1

## Learning the Basics

**5.1** Given the following probability distributions:

| Distribution A | | Distribution B | |
|---|---|---|---|
| X | P(X) | X | P(X) |
| 0 | 0.50 | 0 | 0.05 |
| 1 | 0.20 | 1 | 0.10 |
| 2 | 0.15 | 2 | 0.15 |
| 3 | 0.10 | 3 | 0.20 |
| 4 | 0.05 | 4 | 0.50 |

a. Compute the expected value for each distribution.
b. Compute the standard deviation for each distribution.
c. Compare the results of distributions $A$ and $B$.

**5.2** Given the following probability distributions:

| Distribution C | | Distribution D | |
|---|---|---|---|
| X | P(X) | X | P(X) |
| 0 | 0.20 | 0 | 0.10 |
| 1 | 0.20 | 1 | 0.20 |
| 2 | 0.20 | 2 | 0.40 |
| 3 | 0.20 | 3 | 0.20 |
| 4 | 0.20 | 4 | 0.10 |

a. Compute the expected value for each distribution.
b. Compute the standard deviation for each distribution.
c. Compare the results of distributions $C$ and $D$.

## Applying the Concepts

**5.3** How many credit cards do you have in your wallet? According to a survey by Ipsos, a large survey research company, 26% of adults in the United States reported having no credit cards; 38% reported having one or two; 20% three or four; 15% five or more; and 1% reported "not sure" ("Snapshots," **www.usatoday.com**, April 18, 2006). Suppose that the following table contains the complete probability distribution for the number of credit cards owned by adults in the United States:

| Number of Credit Cards $(X)$ | $P(X)$ |
|---|---|
| 0 | 0.26 |
| 1 | 0.22 |
| 2 | 0.16 |
| 3 | 0.12 |
| 4 | 0.08 |
| 5 | 0.06 |
| 6 | 0.04 |
| 7 | 0.03 |
| 8 | 0.02 |
| 9 | 0.01 |

a. Compute the mean number of credit cards owned by a U.S. adult.
b. Compute the standard deviation.

✓ SELF Test **5.4** The following table contains the probability distribution for the number of traffic accidents daily in a small city:

| Number of Accidents Daily (X) | P(X) |
|---|---|
| 0 | 0.10 |
| 1 | 0.20 |
| 2 | 0.45 |
| 3 | 0.15 |
| 4 | 0.05 |
| 5 | 0.05 |

**a.** Compute the mean number of accidents per day.
**b.** Compute the standard deviation.

**5.5** The manager of a large computer network has developed the following probability distribution of the number of interruptions per day:

| Interruptions (X) | P(X) |
|---|---|
| 0 | 0.32 |
| 1 | 0.35 |
| 2 | 0.18 |
| 3 | 0.08 |
| 4 | 0.04 |
| 5 | 0.02 |
| 6 | 0.01 |

**a.** Compute the expected number of interruptions per day.
**b.** Compute the standard deviation.

**5.6** In the carnival game Under-or-Over-Seven, a pair of fair dice is rolled once, and the resulting sum determines whether the player wins or loses his or her bet. For example, the player can bet $1 that the sum will be under 7—that is, 2, 3, 4, 5, or 6. For this bet, the player wins $1 if the result is under 7 and loses $1 if the outcome equals or is greater than 7. Similarly, the player can bet $1 that the sum will be over 7—that is, 8, 9, 10, 11, or 12. Here, the player wins $1 if the result is over 7 but loses $1 if the result is 7 or under. A third method of play is to bet $1 on the outcome 7. For this bet, the player wins $4 if the result of the roll is 7 and loses $1 otherwise.
**a.** Construct the probability distribution representing the different outcomes that are possible for a $1 bet on under 7.

**b.** Construct the probability distribution representing the different outcomes that are possible for a $1 bet on over 7.
**c.** Construct the probability distribution representing the different outcomes that are possible for a $1 bet on 7.
**d.** Show that the expected long-run profit (or loss) to the player is the same, no matter which method of play is used.

**5.7** The number of arrivals per minute at a bank located in the central business district of a large city was recorded over a period of 200 minutes with the following results:

| Arrivals | Frequency |
|---|---|
| 0 | 14 |
| 1 | 31 |
| 2 | 47 |
| 3 | 41 |
| 4 | 29 |
| 5 | 21 |
| 6 | 10 |
| 7 | 5 |
| 8 | 2 |

**a.** Compute the expected number of arrivals per day.
**b.** Compute the standard deviation.

**5.8** The manager of a commercial mortgage department of a large bank has collected data during the past two years concerning the number of commercial mortgages approved per week. The results from these two years (104 weeks) indicated the following:

| Number of Commercial Mortgages Approved | Frequency |
|---|---|
| 0 | 13 |
| 1 | 25 |
| 2 | 32 |
| 3 | 17 |
| 4 | 9 |
| 5 | 6 |
| 6 | 1 |
| 7 | 1 |

**a.** Compute the expected number of mortgages approved per week.
**b.** Compute the standard deviation.

## 5.2  COVARIANCE AND ITS APPLICATION IN FINANCE

In Section 5.1, the expected value, variance, and standard deviation of a discrete random variable of a probability distribution were discussed. In this section, the covariance between two variables is introduced and applied to portfolio management, a topic of great interest to financial analysts.

## Covariance

The **covariance**, $\sigma_{XY}$, measures the strength of the relationship between two numerical random variables, $X$ and $Y$. A positive covariance indicates a positive relationship. A negative covariance indicates a negative relationship. A covariance of 0 indicates that the two variables are independent. Equation (5.4) defines the covariance.

Covariance

$$\sigma_{XY} = \sum_{i=1}^{N}[X_i - E(X)][Y_i - E(Y)]P(X_iY_i) \qquad (5.4)$$

where

$$X = \text{discrete random variable } X$$
$$X_i = i\text{th outcome of } X$$
$$Y = \text{discrete random variable } Y$$
$$Y_i = i\text{th outcome of } Y$$
$$P(X_iY_i) = \text{probability of occurrence of the } i\text{th outcome of } X \text{ and the } i\text{th outcome of } Y$$
$$i = 1, 2, \ldots, N$$

To illustrate the covariance, suppose that you are deciding between two alternative investments for the coming year. The first investment is a mutual fund that consists of the stocks that comprise the Dow Jones Industrial Average. The second investment is a mutual fund that is expected to perform best when economic conditions are weak. Table 5.4 summarizes your estimate of the returns (per $1,000 investment) under three economic conditions, each with a given probability of occurrence.

**TABLE 5.4**

Estimated Returns for Each Investment Under Three Economic Conditions

| | | | Investment | |
|---|---|---|---|---|
| $P(X_iY_i)$ | **Economic Condition** | | **Dow Jones Fund** | **Weak-Economy Fund** |
| 0.2 | Recession | | −$100 | +$200 |
| 0.5 | Stable economy | | +$100 | +50 |
| 0.3 | Expanding economy | | +$250 | −100 |

The expected value and standard deviation for each investment and the covariance of the two investments are computed as follows:

$$\text{Let } X = \text{Dow Jones fund, and } Y = \text{weak-economy fund}$$
$$E(X) = \mu_X = (-100)(0.2) + (100)(0.5) + (250)(0.3) = \$105$$
$$E(Y) = \mu_Y = (+200)(0.2) + (50)(0.5) + (-100)(0.3) = \$35$$
$$Var(X) = \sigma_X^2 = (-100-105)^2(0.2) + (100-105)^2(0.5) + (250-105)^2(0.3)$$
$$= 14,725$$
$$\sigma_X = \$121.35$$

$$Var(Y) = \sigma_Y^2 = (200-35)^2(0.2) + (50-35)^2(0.5) + (-100-35)^2(0.3)$$

$$= 11,025$$

$$\sigma_Y = \$105.00$$

$$\sigma_{XY} = (-100-105)(200-35)(0.2) + (100-105)(50-35)(0.5)$$

$$+ (250-105)(-100-35)(0.3)$$

$$= -6,765 - 37.5 - 5,872.5$$

$$= -12,675$$

Thus, the Dow Jones fund has a higher expected value (i.e., larger expected return) than the weak-economy fund but also has a higher standard deviation (i.e., more risk). The covariance of −12,675 between the two investments indicates a negative relationship in which the two investments are varying in the *opposite* direction. Therefore, when the return on one investment is high, typically, the return on the other is low.

## Expected Value, Variance, and Standard Deviation of the Sum of Two Random Variables

Equations (5.1) through (5.3) defined the expected value, variance, and standard deviation of a probability distribution and Equation (5.4) defined the covariance between two variables, $X$ and $Y$. The **expected value of the sum of two random variables** is equal to the sum of the expected values. The **variance of the sum of two random variables** is equal to the sum of the variances plus twice the covariance. The **standard deviation of the sum of two random variables** is the square root of the variance of the sum of two random variables.

Expected Value of the Sum of Two Random Variables

$$E(X+Y) = E(X) + E(Y) \tag{5.5}$$

Variance of the Sum of Two Random Variables

$$Var(X+Y) = \sigma_{X+Y}^2 = \sigma_X^2 + \sigma_Y^2 + 2\sigma_{XY} \tag{5.6}$$

Standard Deviation of the Sum of Two Random Variables

$$\sigma_{X+Y} = \sqrt{\sigma_{X+Y}^2} \tag{5.7}$$

To illustrate the expected value, variance, and standard deviation of the sum of two random variables, consider the two investments previously discussed. If $X$ = Dow Jones fund and $Y$ = weak-economy fund, using Equations (5.5), (5.6), and (5.7),

$$E(X+Y) = E(X) + E(Y) = 105 + 35 = \$140$$

$$\sigma_{X+Y}^2 = \sigma_X^2 + \sigma_Y^2 + 2\sigma_{XY}$$

$$= 14,725 + 11,025 + (2)(-12,675)$$

$$= 400$$

$$\sigma_{X+Y} = \$20$$

The expected value of the sum of the Dow Jones fund and the weak-economy fund is $140, with a standard deviation of $20. The standard deviation of the sum of the two investments is much less than the standard deviation of either single investment because there is a large negative covariance between the investments.

## Portfolio Expected Return and Portfolio Risk

Now that the covariance and the expected value and standard deviation of the sum of two random variables have been defined, these concepts can be applied to the study of a group of assets referred to as a **portfolio**. Investors combine assets into portfolios to reduce their risk (see references 1 and 2). Often, the objective is to maximize the return while minimizing the risk. For such portfolios, rather than studying the sum of two random variables, each investment is weighted by the proportion of assets assigned to that investment. Equations (5.8) and (5.9) define the **portfolio expected return** and **portfolio risk**.

### Portfolio Expected Return

The portfolio expected return for a two-asset investment is equal to the weight assigned to asset $X$ multiplied by the expected return of asset $X$ plus the weight assigned to asset $Y$ multiplied by the expected return of asset $Y$.

$$E(P) = wE(X) + (1 - w)E(Y) \tag{5.8}$$

where

$E(P)$ = portfolio expected return

$w$ = proportion of the portfolio value assigned to asset $X$

$(1 - w)$ = proportion of the portfolio value assigned to asset $Y$

$E(X)$ = expected return of asset $X$

$E(Y)$ = expected return of asset $Y$

### Portfolio Risk

$$\sigma_p = \sqrt{w^2\sigma_X^2 + (1-w)^2\sigma_Y^2 + 2w(1-w)\sigma_{XY}} \tag{5.9}$$

In the previous example, you evaluated the expected return and risk of two different investments, a Dow Jones fund and a weak-economy fund. You also computed the covariance of the two investments. Now, suppose that you wish to form a portfolio of these two investments that consists of an equal investment in each of these two funds. To compute the portfolio expected return and the portfolio risk, using Equations (5.8) and (5.9), with $w = 0.50$, $E(X) = \$105$, $E(Y) = \$35$, $\sigma_X^2 = 14{,}725$, $\sigma_Y^2 = 11{,}025$, and $\sigma_{XY} = -12{,}675$,

$$E(P) = (0.5)(105) + (1 - 0.5)(35) = \$70$$

$$\sigma_p = \sqrt{(0.5)^2(14{,}725) + (1 - 0.5)^2(11{,}025) + 2(0.5)(1 - 0.5)(-12{,}675)}$$

$$= \sqrt{100} = \$10$$

Thus, the portfolio has an expected return of $70 for each $1,000 invested (a return of 7%) and has a portfolio risk of $10. The portfolio risk here is small because there is a large negative covariance between the two investments. The fact that each investment performs best under different circumstances reduces the overall risk of the portfolio.

## PROBLEMS FOR SECTION 5.2

### Learning the Basics

**5.9** Given the following probability distributions for variables $X$ and $Y$:

| $P(X_iY_i)$ | $X$ | $Y$ |
|---|---|---|
| 0.4 | 100 | 200 |
| 0.6 | 200 | 100 |

Compute
a. $E(X)$ and $E(Y)$.
b. $\sigma_X$ and $\sigma_Y$.
c. $\sigma_{XY}$.
d. $E(X + Y)$.

**5.10** Given the following probability distributions for variables $X$ and $Y$:

| $P(X_iY_i)$ | $X$ | $Y$ |
|---|---|---|
| 0.2 | −100 | 50 |
| 0.4 | 50 | 30 |
| 0.3 | 200 | 20 |
| 0.1 | 300 | 20 |

Compute
a. $E(X)$ and $E(Y)$.
b. $\sigma_X$ and $\sigma_Y$.
c. $\sigma_{XY}$.
d. $E(X + Y)$.

**5.11** Two investments, $X$ and $Y$, have the following characteristics:

$$E(X) = \$50, \ E(Y) = \$100, \ \sigma_X^2 = 9,000,$$

$$\sigma_Y^2 = 15,000, \ \text{and} \ \sigma_{XY} = 7,500.$$

If the weight of portfolio assets assigned to investment $X$ is 0.4, compute the
a. portfolio expected return.
b. portfolio risk.

### Applying the Concepts

**5.12** The process of being served at a bank consists of two independent parts—the time waiting in line and the time it takes to be served by the teller. Suppose that the time waiting in line has an expected value of 4 minutes, with a standard deviation of 1.2 minutes, and the time it takes to be served by the teller has an expected value of 5.5 minutes, with a standard deviation of 1.5 minutes. Compute the
a. expected value of the total time it takes to be served at the bank.
b. standard deviation of the total time it takes to be served at the bank.

**5.13** In the portfolio example in this section (see page 187), half the portfolio assets are invested in the Dow Jones fund and half in a weak-economy fund. Recalculate the portfolio expected return and the portfolio risk if
a. 30% of the portfolio assets are invested in the Dow Jones fund and 70% in a weak-economy fund.
b. 70% of the portfolio assets are invested in the Dow Jones fund and 30% in a weak-economy fund.
c. Which of the three investment strategies (30%, 50%, or 70% in the Dow Jones fund) would you recommend? Why?

**5.14** You are trying to develop a strategy for ✓ SELF investing in two different stocks. The anticipated Test annual return for a $1,000 investment in each stock under four different economic conditions has the following probability distribution:

| Probability | Economic Condition | Returns Stock X | Stock Y |
|---|---|---|---|
| | | **Returns** | |
| 0.1 | Recession | −100 | 50 |
| 0.3 | Slow growth | 0 | 150 |
| 0.3 | Moderate growth | 80 | −20 |
| 0.3 | Fast growth | 150 | −100 |

Compute the
a. expected return for stock $X$ and for stock $Y$.
b. standard deviation for stock $X$ and for stock $Y$.
c. covariance of stock $X$ and stock $Y$.
d. Would you invest in stock $X$ or stock $Y$? Explain.

**5.15** Suppose that in Problem 5.14 you wanted to create a portfolio that consists of stock $X$ and stock $Y$. Compute the portfolio expected return and portfolio risk for each of the following percentages invested in stock $X$:

a. 30%
b. 50%
c. 70%
d. On the basis of the results of (a) through (c), which portfolio would you recommend? Explain.

**5.16** You are trying to develop a strategy for investing in two different stocks. The anticipated annual return for a $1,000 investment in each stock under four different economic conditions has the following probability distribution:

| | | Returns | |
|---|---|---|---|
| Probability | Economic Condition | Stock $X$ | Stock $Y$ |
| 0.1 | Recession | −50 | −100 |
| 0.3 | Slow growth | 20 | 50 |
| 0.4 | Moderate growth | 100 | 130 |
| 0.2 | Fast growth | 150 | 200 |

Compute the
a. expected return for stock $X$ and for stock $Y$.
b. standard deviation for stock $X$ and for stock $Y$.
c. covariance of stock $X$ and stock $Y$.
d. Would you invest in stock $X$ or stock $Y$? Explain.

**5.17** Suppose that in Problem 5.16 you wanted to create a portfolio that consists of stock $X$ and stock $Y$. Compute the portfolio expected return and portfolio risk for each of the following percentages invested in stock $X$:
a. 30%
b. 50%
c. 70%
d. On the basis of the results of (a) through (c), which portfolio would you recommend? Explain.

**5.18** You plan to invest $1,000 in a corporate bond fund or in a common stock fund. The following information about the annual return (per $1,000) of each of these investments under different economic conditions is available, along with the probability that each of these economic conditions will occur:

| Probability | Economic Condition | Corporate Bond Fund | Common Stock Fund |
|---|---|---|---|
| 0.10 | Recession | −30 | −150 |
| 0.15 | Stagnation | 50 | −20 |
| 0.35 | Slow growth | 90 | 120 |
| 0.30 | Moderate growth | 100 | 160 |
| 0.10 | High growth | 110 | 250 |

Compute the
a. expected return for the corporate bond fund and for the common stock fund.
b. standard deviation for the corporate bond fund and for the common stock fund.
c. covariance of the corporate bond fund and the common stock fund.
d. Would you invest in the corporate bond fund or the common stock fund? Explain.

**5.19** Suppose that in Problem 5.18 you wanted to create a portfolio that consists of the corporate bond fund and the common stock fund. Compute the portfolio expected return and portfolio risk for each of the following situations:
a. $300 in the corporate bond fund and $700 in the common stock fund.
b. $500 in each fund.
c. $700 in the corporate bond fund and $300 in the common stock fund.
d. On the basis of the results of (a) through (c), which portfolio would you recommend? Explain.

## 5.3  BINOMIAL DISTRIBUTION

This section and the three that follow use mathematical models to solve business problems.

MATHEMATICAL MODEL
A **mathematical model** is a mathematical expression that represents a variable of interest.

When a mathematical expression is available, you can compute the exact probability of occurrence of any particular outcome of the variable.

The **binomial distribution** is one of the most useful mathematical models. You use the binomial distribution when the discrete random variable is the number of events of interest in a sample of $n$ observations. The binomial distribution has four basic properties:

•  The sample consists of a fixed number of observations, $n$.
•  Each observation is classified into one of two mutually exclusive and collectively exhaustive categories.

- The probability of an observation being classified as the event of interest, $\pi$, is constant from observation to observation. Thus, the probability of an observation being classified as not being the event of interest, $1 - \pi$, is constant over all observations.
- The outcome of any observation is independent of the outcome of any other observation. To ensure independence, the observations can be randomly selected either from an *infinite population without replacement* or from a *finite population with replacement*.

Returning to the Using Statistics scenario presented on page 180 concerning the accounting information system, suppose the event of interest is defined as a tagged order form. You are interested in the number of tagged order forms in a given sample of orders.

What results can occur? If the sample contains four orders, there could be none, one, two, three, or four tagged order forms. The binomial random variable, the number of tagged order forms, cannot take on any other value because the number of tagged order forms cannot be more than the sample size, $n$, and cannot be less than zero. Therefore, the binomial random variable has a range from 0 to $n$.

Suppose that you observe the following result in a sample of four orders:

| First Order | Second Order | Third Order | Fourth Order |
|---|---|---|---|
| Tagged | Tagged | Not tagged | Tagged |

What is the probability of having three tagged order forms in a sample of four orders in this particular sequence? Because the historical probability of a tagged order is 0.10, the probability that each order occurs in the sequence is

| First Order | Second Order | Third Order | Fourth Order |
|---|---|---|---|
| $\pi = 0.10$ | $\pi = 0.10$ | $1 - \pi = 0.90$ | $\pi = 0.10$ |

Each outcome is independent of the others because the order forms were selected from an extremely large or practically infinite population without replacement. Therefore, the probability of having this particular sequence is

$$\pi\pi(1-\pi)\pi = \pi^3(1-\pi)^1$$

$$= (0.10)(0.10)(0.10)(0.90)$$

$$= (0.10)^3(0.90)^1$$

$$= 0.0009$$

This result indicates only the probability of three tagged order forms (events of interest) from a sample of four order forms in a *specific sequence*. To find the number of ways of selecting $X$ objects from $n$ objects, *irrespective of sequence*, you use the **rule of combinations** given in Equation (5.10) below and previously defined in Equation (4.14) on page 170.

---

Combinations

The number of combinations[1] of selecting $X$ objects out of $n$ objects is given by

$$_nC_X = \frac{n!}{X!(n-X)!} \tag{5.10}$$

where

$n! = (n)(n-1)\cdots(1)$ is called $n$ factorial. By definition, $0! = 1$.

[1]On many scientific calculators, there is a button labeled $_nC_r$ that allows you to compute the number of combinations. The symbol r is used instead of X.

With $n = 4$ and $X = 3$, there are

$$_nC_X = \frac{n!}{X!(n-X)!} = \frac{4!}{3!(4-3)!} = \frac{4 \times 3 \times 2 \times 1}{(3 \times 2 \times 1)(1)} = 4$$

such sequences. The four possible sequences are:

Sequence 1 = *tagged, tagged, tagged, not tagged*, with probability
$$\pi\pi\pi(1 - \pi) = \pi^3(1 - \pi)^1 = 0.0009$$

Sequence 2 = *tagged, tagged, not tagged, tagged*, with probability
$$\pi\pi(1 - \pi)\pi = \pi^3(1 - \pi)^1 = 0.0009$$

Sequence 3 = *tagged, not tagged, tagged, tagged*, with probability
$$\pi(1 - \pi)\pi\pi = \pi^3(1 - \pi)^1 = 0.0009$$

Sequence 4 = *not tagged, tagged, tagged, tagged*, with probability
$$(1 - \pi)\pi\pi\pi = \pi^3(1 - \pi)^1 = 0.0009$$

Therefore, the probability of three tagged order forms is equal to

(Number of possible sequences) $\times$ (Probability of a particular sequence)
$$= (4) \times (0.0009) = 0.0036$$

You can make a similar, intuitive derivation for the other possible outcomes of the random variable—zero, one, two, and four tagged order forms. However, as $n$, the sample size, gets large, the computations involved in using this intuitive approach become time-consuming. Equation (5.11) is the mathematical model that provides a general formula for computing any binomial probability from the binomial distribution with the number of events of interest, $X$, given the values of $n$ and $\pi$.

**Binomial Distribution**

$$P(X) = \frac{n!}{X!(n-X)!} \pi^X (1-\pi)^{n-X} \qquad \textbf{(5.11)}$$

where

$P(X)$ = probability of $X$ events of interest, given $n$ and $\pi$

$n$ = number of observations

$\pi$ = probability of an event of interest

$1 - \pi$ = probability of not having an event of interest

$X$ = number of events of interest in the sample ($X = 0, 1, 2, \ldots, n$)

Equation (5.11) restates what you had intuitively derived. The binomial variable $X$ can have any integer value $X$ from 0 through $n$. In Equation (5.11), the product

$$\pi^X(1 - \pi)^{n-X}$$

represents the probability of exactly $X$ events of interest from $n$ observations in a *particular sequence*.

The term

$$\frac{n!}{X!(n-X)!}$$

represents the number of *combinations* of the $X$ events of interest from the $n$ observations that are possible. Hence, given the number of observations, $n$, and the probability of an event of interest, $\pi$, the probability of $X$ events of interest is:

$$P(X) = (\text{Number of possible sequences}) \times (\text{Probability of a particular sequence})$$

$$= \frac{n!}{X!(n-X)!} \pi^X (1-\pi)^{n-X}$$

Example 5.1 illustrates the use of Equation (5.11).

---

**EXAMPLE 5.1**    DETERMINING $P(X = 3)$, GIVEN $n = 4$ AND $\pi = 0.1$

If the likelihood of a tagged order form is 0.1, what is the probability that there are three tagged order forms in the sample of four?

**SOLUTION**  Using Equation (5.11) on page 191, the probability of three tagged orders from a sample of four is

$$P(X = 3) = \frac{4!}{3!(4-3)!}(0.1)^3(1-0.1)^{4-3}$$

$$= \frac{4!}{3!(4-3)!}(0.1)^3(0.9)^1$$

$$= 4(0.1)(0.1)(0.1)(0.9) = 0.0036$$

---

Examples 5.2 and 5.3 show the computations for other values of $X$.

---

**EXAMPLE 5.2**    DETERMINING $P(X \geq 3)$, GIVEN $n = 4$ AND $\pi = 0.1$

If the likelihood of a tagged order form is 0.1, what is the probability that there are three or more (i.e., at least three) tagged order forms in the sample of four?

**SOLUTION**  In Example 5.1, you found that the probability of *exactly* three tagged order forms from a sample of four is 0.0036. To compute the probability of *at least* three tagged order forms, you need to add the probability of three tagged order forms to the probability of four tagged order forms. The probability of four tagged order forms is

$$P(X = 4) = \frac{4!}{4!(4-4)!}(0.1)^4(1-0.1)^{4-4}$$

$$= \frac{4!}{4!(0)!}(0.1)^4(0.9)^0$$

$$= 1(0.1)(0.1)(0.1)(0.1) = 0.0001$$

Thus, the probability of at least three tagged order forms is

$$P(X \geq 3) = P(X = 3) + P(X = 4)$$

$$= 0.0036 + 0.0001$$

$$= 0.0037$$

There is a 0.37% chance that there will be at least three tagged order forms in a sample of four.

**EXAMPLE 5.3**

DETERMINING $P(X < 3)$, GIVEN $n = 4$ AND $\pi = 0.1$

If the likelihood of a tagged order form is 0.1, what is the probability that there are less than three tagged order forms in the sample of four?

**SOLUTION** The probability that there are less than three tagged order forms is

$$P(X < 3) = P(X = 0) + P(X = 1) + P(X = 2)$$

Using Equation (5.11) on page 191, these probabilities are

$$P(X = 0) = \frac{4!}{0!(4-0)!}(0.1)^0(1-0.1)^{4-0} = 0.6561$$

$$P(X = 1) = \frac{4!}{1!(4-1)!}(0.1)^1(1-0.1)^{4-1} = 0.2916$$

$$P(X = 2) = \frac{4!}{2!(4-2)!}(0.1)^2(1-0.1)^{4-2} = 0.0486$$

Therefore, $P(X < 3) = 0.6561 + 0.2916 + 0.0486 = 0.9963$. $P(X < 3)$ could also be calculated from its complement, $P(X \geq 3)$, as follows:

$$P(X < 3) = 1 - P(X \geq 3)$$
$$= 1 - 0.0037 = 0.9963$$

Computations such as those in Example 5.3 can become tedious, especially as $n$ gets large. To avoid computational drudgery, you can find many binomial probabilities directly from Table E.6 (in Appendix E), a portion of which is reproduced in Table 5.5. Table E.6 provides binomial probabilities for $X = 0, 1, 2, \ldots, n$ for various selected combinations of $n$ and $\pi$. For example, to find the probability of exactly two events of interest in a sample of four when the probability of an event is 0.1, you first find $n = 4$ and then look in the row $X = 2$ and column $\pi = 0.10$. The result is 0.0486.

**TABLE 5.5**

Finding a Binomial Probability for $n = 4$, $X = 2$, and $\pi = 0.1$

| | | | | $\pi$ | |
|---|---|---|---|---|---|
| $n$ | $X$ | 0.01 | 0.02 | .... | 0.10 |
| 4 | 0 | 0.9606 | 0.9224 | .... | 0.6561 |
| | 1 | 0.0388 | 0.0753 | .... | 0.2916 |
| | 2 | 0.0006 | 0.0023 | .... | 0.0486 |
| | 3 | 0.0000 | 0.0000 | .... | 0.0036 |
| | 4 | 0.0000 | 0.0000 | .... | 0.0001 |

Source: *Table E.6.*

You can also compute the binomial probabilities given in Table E.6 by using Microsoft Excel or Minitab as shown in Figures 5.2 and 5.3 (note that Minitab uses the letter p instead of $\pi$ to denote the probability of an event of interest).

**FIGURE 5.2**

Microsoft Excel
worksheet for
computing binomial
probabilities

*See Section E5.3 or P5.2 to
create this.*

|  | A | B |  |
|---|---|---|---|
| 1 | Tagged Orders | | |
| 2 | | | |
| 3 | Data | | |
| 4 | Sample size | 4 | |
| 5 | Probability of an event of interest | 0.1 | |
| 6 | | | |
| 7 | Statistics | | |
| 8 | Mean | 0.4 | =B4 * B5 |
| 9 | Variance | 0.36 | =B8 * (1 - B5) |
| 10 | Standard deviation | 0.6 | =SQRT(B9) |
| 11 | | | |
| 12 | Binomial Probabilities Table | | |
| 13 | X | P(X) | |
| 14 | 0 | 0.6561 | =BINOMDIST(A14, $B$4, $B$5, FALSE) |
| 15 | 1 | 0.2916 | =BINOMDIST(A15, $B$4, $B$5, FALSE) |
| 16 | 2 | 0.0486 | =BINOMDIST(A16, $B$4, $B$5, FALSE) |
| 17 | 3 | 0.0036 | =BINOMDIST(A17, $B$4, $B$5, FALSE) |
| 18 | 4 | 0.0001 | =BINOMDIST(A18, $B$4, $B$5, FALSE) |

**FIGURE 5.3**

Minitab results for
computing binomial
probabilities

*See Section M5.1 to create
this.*

```
        Binomial with n = 4 and p = 0.1

   x   P( X = x )
   0      0.6561
   1      0.2916
   2      0.0486
   3      0.0036
   4      0.0001
```

The shape of a binomial probability distribution depends on the values of $n$ and $\pi$. Whenever $\pi = 0.5$, the binomial distribution is symmetrical, regardless of how large or small the value of $n$. When $\pi \neq 0.5$, the distribution is skewed. The closer $\pi$ is to 0.5 and the larger the number of observations, $n$, the less skewed the distribution becomes. For example, the distribution of the number of tagged order forms is highly skewed to the right because $\pi = 0.1$ and $n = 4$ (see Figure 5.4).

**FIGURE 5.4**

Microsoft Excel
histogram of the
binomial probability
distribution with $n = 4$
and $\pi = 0.1$

*See Section E5.3 and E2.9
or P5.2 to create this.*

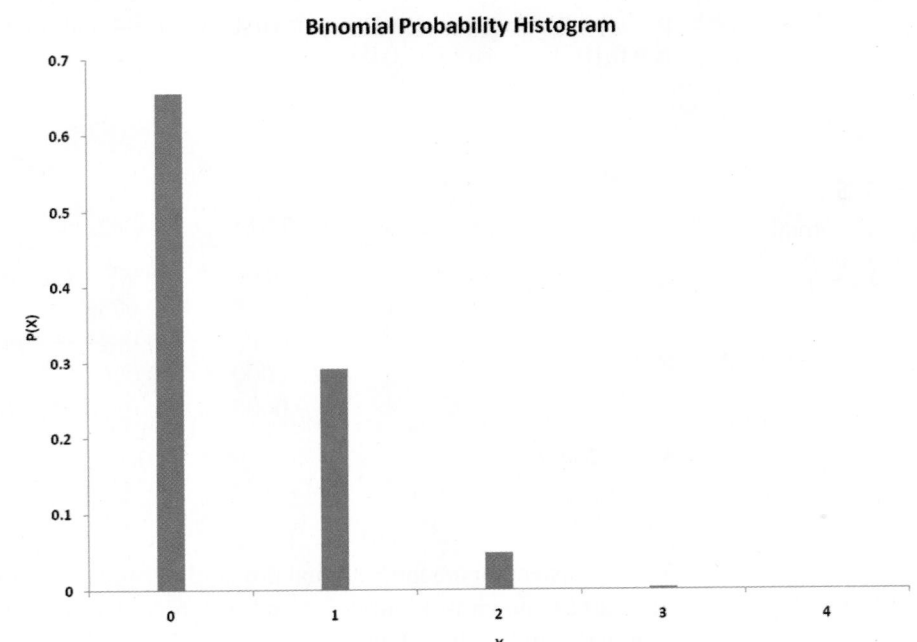

**Binomial Probability Histogram**

The mean (or expected value) of the binomial distribution is equal to the product of $n$ and $\pi$. Instead of using Equation (5.1) on page 181 to compute the mean of the probability distribution, you use Equation (5.12) to compute the mean for variables that follow the binomial distribution.

---

**Mean of the Binomial Distribution**

The mean, $\mu$, of the binomial distribution is equal to the sample size, $n$, multiplied by the probability of an event of interest, $\pi$.

$$\mu = E(X) = n\pi \tag{5.12}$$

---

On the average, over the long run, you theoretically expect $\mu = E(X) = n\pi = (4)(0.1) = 0.4$ tagged order form in a sample of four orders.

The standard deviation of the binomial distribution is calculated using Equation (5.13).

---

**Standard Deviation of the Binomial Distribution**

$$\sigma = \sqrt{\sigma^2} = \sqrt{Var(X)} = \sqrt{n\pi(1-\pi)} \tag{5.13}$$

---

The standard deviation of the number of tagged order forms is

$$\sigma = \sqrt{4(0.1)(0.9)} = 0.60$$

You get the same result if you use Equation (5.3) on page 182.

Example 5.4 applies the binomial distribution to service at a fast-food restaurant.

---

**EXAMPLE 5.4**    COMPUTING BINOMIAL PROBABILITIES

Accuracy in taking orders at a drive-through window is important for fast-food chains. Each month, *QSR Magazine*, **www.qsrmagazine.com**, publishes the results of its surveys. Accuracy is measured as the percentage of orders that are filled correctly. In a recent month, the percentage of orders filled correctly at McDonald's was approximately 91%. If a sample of three orders is taken, what are the mean and standard deviation of the binomial distribution for the number of orders filled correctly? Suppose that you go to the drive-through window at McDonald's and place an order. Two friends of yours independently place orders at the drive-through window at the same McDonald's. What are the probabilities that all three, that none of the three, and that at least two of the three orders will be filled correctly?

**SOLUTION** Because there are three orders and the probability of a correct order is 0.91, $n = 3$ and $\pi = 0.91$. Using Equations (5.12) and (5.13),

$$\mu = E(X) = n\pi = 3(0.91) = 2.73$$

$$\sigma = \sqrt{\sigma^2} = \sqrt{Var(X)} = \sqrt{n\pi(1-\pi)}$$

$$= \sqrt{3(0.91)(0.09)}$$

$$= \sqrt{0.2457} = 0.4957$$

Using Equation (5.11) on page 191,

$$P(X=3) = \frac{3!}{3!(3-3)!}(0.91)^3(1-0.91)^{3-3}$$

$$= \frac{3!}{3!(3-3)!}(0.91)^3(0.09)^0$$

$$= 1(0.91)(0.91)(0.91)(1) = 0.7536$$

$$P(X=0) = \frac{3!}{0!(3-0)!}(0.91)^0(1-0.91)^{3-0}$$

$$= \frac{3!}{0!(3-0)!}(0.91)^0(0.09)^3$$

$$= 1(1)(0.09)(0.09)(0.09) = 0.0007$$

$$P(X=2) = \frac{3!}{2!(3-2)!}(0.91)^2(1-0.91)^{3-2}$$

$$= \frac{3!}{2!(3-2)!}(0.91)^2(0.09)^1$$

$$= 3(0.91)(0.91)(0.09) = 0.2236$$

$$P(X \geq 2) = P(X=2) + P(X=3)$$

$$= 0.2236 + 0.7536$$

$$= 0.9772$$

The mean number of orders filled correctly in a sample of three orders is 2.73, and the standard deviation is 0.4957. The probability that all three orders are filled correctly is 0.7536, or 75.36%. The probability that none of the orders are filled correctly is 0.0007, or 0.07%. The probability that at least two orders are filled correctly is 0.9772, or 97.72%.

In this section, you have been introduced to the binomial distribution. The binomial distribution is an important mathematical model in many business situations.

# PROBLEMS FOR SECTION 5.3

## Learning the Basics

**5.20** Determine the following:
**a.** For $n = 4$ and $\pi = 0.12$, what is $P(X = 0)$?
**b.** For $n = 10$ and $\pi = 0.40$, what is $P(X = 9)$?
**c.** For $n = 10$ and $\pi = 0.50$, what is $P(X = 8)$?
**d.** For $n = 6$ and $\pi = 0.83$, what is $P(X = 5)$?

**5.21** If $n = 5$ and $\pi = 0.40$, what is the probability that
**a.** $X = 4$?
**b.** $X \leq 3$?
**c.** $X < 2$?
**d.** $X > 1$?

**5.22** Determine the mean and standard deviation of the random variable $X$ in each of the following binomial distributions:
**a.** $n = 4$ and $\pi = 0.10$
**b.** $n = 4$ and $\pi = 0.40$
**c.** $n = 5$ and $\pi = 0.80$
**d.** $n = 3$ and $\pi = 0.50$

## Applying the Concepts

**5.23** The increase or decrease in the price of a stock between the beginning and the end of a trading day is assumed to be an equally likely random event. What is the probability that a stock will show an increase in its closing price on five consecutive days?

**5.24** A recent article in *Quality Progress* (Dennis R. Owens, "The Probability of Reoccurrence: P(r)," April 2007, 40, p. 88) discusses a manufacturing company assessing the chance that its product will fail. The article identifies six independent events that can cause a failure. The probability of each of these events failing is quite low, 0.05, but for a product to ultimately be a success, it must not experience a failure in any of the six events.

**a.** Use the binomial probability distribution to calculate the probability that a product will ultimately be successful (i.e., that if will not fail).

**b.** If the probabilities of the six events are not all equal, how could you calculate the probability in (a)?

**5.25** A student is taking a multiple-choice exam in which each question has four choices. Assuming that she has no knowledge of the correct answers to any of the questions, she has decided on a strategy in which she will place four balls (marked *A*, *B*, *C*, and *D*) into a box. She randomly selects one ball for each question and replaces the ball in the box. The marking on the ball will determine her answer to the question. There are five multiple-choice questions on the exam. What is the probability that she will get

**a.** five questions correct?

**b.** at least four questions correct?

**c.** no questions correct?

**d.** no more than two questions correct?

✓ SELF Test  **5.26** In Example 5.4 on page 195, you and two friends decided to go to McDonald's. Instead, suppose that you went to KFC, which last month filled 87.8% of the orders correctly. What is the probability that

**a.** all three orders will be filled correctly?

**b.** none of the three will be filled correctly?

**c.** at least two of the three will be filled correctly?

**d.** What are the mean and standard deviation of the binomial distribution used in (a) through (c)? Interpret these values.

**5.27** In February 2007, The Gallup Poll surveyed adults living in the United States. When asked about the current state of the job market, 45% indicated that now is a good time to be looking for a quality job. The remainder answered no opinion or that now is a bad time to be looking for a quality job. The results were more positive than survey results taken in 2003, but down from the boom years of the late 1990s (Gallup Poll News Service, "Consumer Views of the Economy," **www.galluppoll.com**, April 30, 2007). Suppose that you select a random sample of 10 adults and survey them concerning the current state of the job market. Assume that 45% of the adults in the United States still think that now is a "good time" to be looking for a quality job, and further assume that the number of the 10 adults thinking that now is a "good time" is distributed as a binomial random variable.

**a.** What are the mean and standard deviation of this distribution?

**b.** What is the probability that exactly three think that now is a "good time"?

**c.** What is the probability that three or less think that now is a "good time"?

**d.** If three adults in your survey indicate that now is a "good time," do you think that 45% of the adults in the United States still think that now is a good time to look for a quality job?

**5.28** An article reported that 29% of the home mortgage loans made by Washington Mutual Inc. in 2006 were

high-cost loans, mainly subprime loans made to those with weak credit histories or high debt in relation to income (J. R. Hagerty and A. Carrns, "WaMu Leads in Risky Type of Lending," *The Wall Street Journal*, April 17, 2007, p. A8). If you were to examine five home mortgage loans made by Washington Mutual Inc. in 2006, what is the probability that

**a.** none are high-cost loans?

**b.** all five are high-cost loans?

**c.** at least two are high-cost loans?

**d.** The article also reported that 15% of the home mortgage loans made by Washington Mutual Inc. in 2006 were granted to second-home owners or investors. Do a similar analysis for this type of loans you did for high-cost loans in (a) through (c)—find the probability that none, all five, and at least two loans were granted to second-home owners or investors. Compare the results for these loans to those of the high-cost loans you computed in (a) through (c).

**5.29** When a customer places an order with Rudy's On-Line Office Supplies, a computerized accounting information system (AIS) automatically checks to see if the customer has exceeded his or her credit limit. Past records indicate that the probability of customers exceeding their credit limit is 0.05. Suppose that, on a given day, 20 customers place orders. Assume that the number of customers that the AIS detects as having exceeded their credit limit is distributed as a binomial random variable.

**a.** What are the mean and standard deviation of the number of customers exceeding their credit limits?

**b.** What is the probability that 0 customers will exceed their limits?

**c.** What is the probability that 1 customer will exceed his or her limit?

**d.** What is the probability that 2 or more customers will exceed their limits?

**5.30** In a survey conducted by the Society for Human Resource Management, 68% of workers said that employers have the right to monitor their telephone use ("Snapshots," **usatoday.com**, April 18, 2006). Suppose that a random sample of 20 workers is selected, and they are asked if employers have the right to monitor telephone use. What is the probability that

**a.** 5 or less of the workers agree?

**b.** 10 or less of the workers agree?

**c.** 15 or less of the workers agree?

**5.31** Referring to Problem 5.30, when the same workers were asked if employers have the right to monitor their cellphone use, the percentage dropped to 52%. Suppose that the 20 workers are asked if employers have the right to monitor cellphone use. What is the probability that

**a.** 5 or less of the workers agree?

**b.** 10 or less of the workers agree?

**c.** 15 or less of the workers agree?

**d.** Compare the results of (a) through (c) to those for Problem 5.30.

## 5.4   POISSON DISTRIBUTION

Many studies are based on counts of the times a particular event occurs in a given *area of opportunity*. An **area of opportunity** is a continuous unit or interval of time, volume, or any physical area in which there can be more than one occurrence of an event. Examples are the surface defects on a new refrigerator, the number of network failures in a day, the number of people arriving at a bank, and the number of fleas on the body of a dog. You can use the **Poisson distribution** to calculate probabilities in situations such as these if the following properties hold:

- You are interested in counting the number of times a particular event occurs in a given area of opportunity. The area of opportunity is defined by time, length, surface area, and so forth.
- The probability that an event occurs in a given area of opportunity is the same for all the areas of opportunity.
- The number of events that occur in one area of opportunity is independent of the number of events that occur in any other area of opportunity.
- The probability that two or more events will occur in an area of opportunity approaches zero as the area of opportunity becomes smaller.

Consider the number of customers arriving during the lunch hour at a bank located in the central business district in a large city. You are interested in the number of customers that arrive each minute. Does this situation match the four properties of the Poisson distribution given above? First, the *event* of interest is a customer arriving, and the *given area of opportunity* is defined as a 1-minute interval. Will zero customers arrive, one customer arrive, two customers arrive, and so on? Second, it is reasonable to assume that the probability that a customer arrives during a 1-minute interval is the same as the probability for all the other 1-minute intervals. Third, the arrival of one customer in any 1-minute interval has no effect on (i.e., is independent of) the arrival of any other customer in any other 1-minute interval. Finally, the probability that two or more customers will arrive in a given time period approaches zero as the time interval becomes small. For example, the probability is virtually zero that two customers will arrive in a time interval of 0.01 second. Thus, you can use the Poisson distribution to determine probabilities involving the number of customers arriving at the bank in a 1-minute time interval during the lunch hour.

The Poisson distribution has one parameter, called $\lambda$ (the Greek lowercase letter *lambda*), which is the mean or expected number of events per unit. The variance of a Poisson distribution is also equal to $\lambda$, and the standard deviation is equal to $\sqrt{\lambda}$. The number of events, $X$, of the Poisson random variable ranges from 0 to infinity ($\infty$).

Equation (5.14) presents the mathematical expression for the Poisson distribution for computing the probability of $X$ events, given that $\lambda$ events are expected.

---

Poisson Distribution

$$P(X) = \frac{e^{-\lambda}\lambda^{X}}{X!}$$   (5.14)

where

$P(X)$ = the probability of $X$ events in an area of opportunity

$\lambda$ = expected number of events

$e$ = mathematical constant approximated by 2.71828

$X$ = number of events ($X = 0, 1, 2, \ldots, \infty$)

---

To demonstrate the Poisson distribution, suppose that the mean number of customers who arrive per minute at the bank during the noon-to-1 p.m. hour is equal to 3.0. What is the probability that in a given minute, exactly two customers will arrive? And what is the probability that more than two customers will arrive in a given minute?

Using Equation (5.14) and $\lambda = 3$, the probability that in a given minute exactly two customers will arrive is

$$P(X=2) = \frac{e^{-3.0}(3.0)^2}{2!} = \frac{9}{(2.71828)^3(2)} = 0.2240$$

To determine the probability that in any given minute more than two customers will arrive,

$$P(X>2) = P(X=3) + P(X=4) + \cdots + P(X=\infty)$$

Because in a probability distribution, all the probabilities must sum to 1, the terms on the right side of the equation $P(X>2)$ also represent the complement of the probability that $X$ is less than or equal to 2 [i.e., $1 - P(X \le 2)$]. Thus,

$$P(X>2) = 1 - P(X \le 2) = 1 - [P(X=0) + P(X=1) + P(X=2)]$$

Now, using Equation (5.14),

$$P(X>2) = 1 - \left[\frac{e^{-3.0}(3.0)^0}{0!} + \frac{e^{-3.0}(3.0)^1}{1!} + \frac{e^{-3.0}(3.0)^2}{2!}\right]$$

$$= 1 - [0.0498 + 0.1494 + 0.2240]$$

$$= 1 - 0.4232 = 0.5768$$

Thus, there is a 57.68% chance that more than two customers will arrive in the same minute.

To avoid drudgery involved in these computations, you can find Poisson probabilities directly from Table E.7 (in Appendix E), a portion of which is reproduced in Table 5.6. Table E.7 provides the probabilities that the Poisson random variable takes on values of $X = 0, 1, 2, \ldots$, for selected values of the parameter $\lambda$. To find the probability that exactly two customers will arrive in a given minute when the mean number of customers arriving is 3.0 per minute, you can read the probability corresponding to the row $X = 2$ and column $\lambda = 3.0$ from the table. The result is 0.2240, as demonstrated in Table 5.6.

You can also compute the Poisson probabilities given in Table E.7 by using Microsoft Excel or Minitab, as illustrated in Figures 5.5 and 5.6.

**TABLE 5.6**

Finding a Poisson Probability for $\lambda = 3$

| $X$ | 2.1 | 2.2 | .... | 3.0 |
|---|---|---|---|---|
| 0 | .1225 | .1108 | .... | .0498 |
| 1 | .2572 | .2438 | .... | .1494 |
| 2 | .2700 | .2681 | .... | .2240 |
| 3 | .1890 | .1966 | .... | .2240 |
| 4 | .0992 | .1082 | .... | .1680 |
| 5 | .0417 | .0476 | .... | .1008 |
| 6 | .0146 | .0174 | .... | .0504 |
| 7 | .0044 | .0055 | .... | .0216 |
| 8 | .0011 | .0015 | .... | .0081 |
| 9 | .0003 | .0004 | .... | .0027 |
| 10 | .0001 | .0001 | .... | .0008 |
| 11 | .0000 | .0000 | .... | .0002 |
| 12 | .0000 | .0000 | .... | .0001 |

Source: *Table E.7.*

**FIGURE 5.5**

Microsoft Excel worksheet for computing Poisson probabilities with $\lambda = 3$

*See Section E5.4 or P5.3 to create this.*

|    | A | B | C | D | E |
|----|---|---|---|---|---|
| 1  | **Customer Arrivals Analysis** | | | | |
| 2  | | | | | |
| 3  | | **Data** | | | |
| 4  | **Mean/Expected number of events of interest:** | | | | 3 |
| 5  | | | | | |
| 6  | **Poisson Probabilities Table** | | | | |
| 7  | **X** | **P(X)** | | | |
| 8  | 0 | 0.049787 | =POISSON(A8, \$E\$4, FALSE) | | |
| 9  | 1 | 0.149361 | =POISSON(A9, \$E\$4, FALSE) | | |
| 10 | 2 | 0.224042 | =POISSON(A10, \$E\$4, FALSE) | | |
| 11 | 3 | 0.224042 | =POISSON(A11, \$E\$4, FALSE) | | |
| 12 | 4 | 0.168031 | =POISSON(A12, \$E\$4, FALSE) | | |
| 13 | 5 | 0.100819 | =POISSON(A13, \$E\$4, FALSE) | | |
| 14 | 6 | 0.050409 | =POISSON(A14, \$E\$4, FALSE) | | |
| 15 | 7 | 0.021604 | =POISSON(A15, \$E\$4, FALSE) | | |
| 16 | 8 | 0.008102 | =POISSON(A16, \$E\$4, FALSE) | | |
| 17 | 9 | 0.002701 | =POISSON(A17, \$E\$4, FALSE) | | |
| 18 | 10 | 0.000810 | =POISSON(A18, \$E\$4, FALSE) | | |
| 19 | 11 | 0.000221 | =POISSON(A19, \$E\$4, FALSE) | | |
| 20 | 12 | 0.000055 | =POISSON(A20, \$E\$4, FALSE) | | |
| 21 | 13 | 0.000013 | =POISSON(A21, \$E\$4, FALSE) | | |
| 22 | 14 | 0.000003 | =POISSON(A22, \$E\$4, FALSE) | | |
| 23 | 15 | 0.000001 | =POISSON(A23, \$E\$4, FALSE) | | |
| 24 | 16 | 0.000000 | =POISSON(A24, \$E\$4, FALSE) | | |
| 25 | 17 | 0.000000 | =POISSON(A25, \$E\$4, FALSE) | | |
| 26 | 18 | 0.000000 | =POISSON(A26, \$E\$4, FALSE) | | |
| 27 | 19 | 0.000000 | =POISSON(A27, \$E\$4, FALSE) | | |
| 28 | 20 | 0.000000 | =POISSON(A28, \$E\$4, FALSE) | | |

**FIGURE 5.6**

Minitab results for computing Poisson probabilities with $\lambda = 3$

*See Section M5.2 to create this.*

```
             Poisson with mean = 3

        x    P( X = x )
        0     0.049787
        1     0.149361
        2     0.224042
        3     0.224042
        4     0.168031
        5     0.100819
        6     0.050409
        7     0.021604
        8     0.008102
        9     0.002701
       10     0.000810
       11     0.000221
       12     0.000055
       13     0.000013
       14     0.000003
       15     0.000001
```

**EXAMPLE 5.5**   COMPUTING POISSON PROBABILITIES

The number of work-related injuries per month in a manufacturing plant is known to follow a Poisson distribution with a mean of 2.5 work-related injuries a month. What is the probability that in a given month no work-related injuries occur? That at least one work-related injury occurs?

**SOLUTION** Using Equation (5.14) on page 198 with $\lambda = 2.5$ (or using Table E.7 or Microsoft Excel or Minitab), the probability that in a given month no work-related injuries occur is

$$P(X = 0) = \frac{e^{-2.5}(2.5)^0}{0!} = \frac{1}{(2.71828)^{2.5}(1)} = 0.0821$$

The probability that there will be no work-related injuries in a given month is 0.0821 or 8.21%. Thus,

$$P(X \geq 1) = 1 - P(X = 0)$$
$$= 1 - 0.0821$$
$$= 0.9179$$

The probability that there will be at least one work-related injury is 0.9179 or 91.79%.

## PROBLEMS FOR SECTION 5.4

### Learning the Basics

**5.32** Assume a Poisson distribution.
**a.** If $\lambda = 2.5$, find $P(X = 2)$.
**b.** If $\lambda = 8.0$, find $P(X = 8)$.
**c.** If $\lambda = 0.5$, find $P(X = 1)$.
**d.** If $\lambda = 3.7$, find $P(X = 0)$.

**5.33** Assume a Poisson distribution.
**a.** If $\lambda = 2.0$, find $P(X \geq 2)$.
**b.** If $\lambda = 8.0$, find $P(X \geq 3)$.
**c.** If $\lambda = 0.5$, find $P(X \leq 1)$.
**d.** If $\lambda = 4.0$, find $P(X \geq 1)$.
**e.** If $\lambda = 5.0$, find $P(X \leq 3)$.

**5.34** Assume a Poisson distribution with $\lambda = 5.0$. What is the probability that
**a.** $X = 1$?
**b.** $X < 1$?
**c.** $X > 1$?
**d.** $X \leq 1$?

### Applying the Concepts

**5.35** Assume that the number of network errors experienced in a day on a local area network (LAN) is distributed as a Poisson random variable. The mean number of network errors experienced in a day is 2.4. What is the probability that in any given day
**a.** zero network errors will occur?
**b.** exactly one network error will occur?
**c.** two or more network errors will occur?
**d.** less than three network errors will occur?

**SELF Test** **5.36** The quality control manager of Marilyn's Cookies is inspecting a batch of chocolate-chip cookies that has just been baked. If the production process is in control, the mean number of chip parts per cookie is 6.0. What is the probability that in any particular cookie being inspected
**a.** less than five chip parts will be found?
**b.** exactly five chip parts will be found?
**c.** five or more chip parts will be found?
**d.** either four or five chip parts will be found?

**5.37** Refer to Problem 5.36. How many cookies in a batch of 100 should the manager expect to discard if company policy requires that all chocolate-chip cookies sold have at least four chocolate-chip parts?

**5.38** The U.S. Department of Transportation maintains statistics for mishandled bags per 1,000 airline passengers. In 2005, Jet Blue had 4.06 mishandled bags per 1,000 passengers (extracted from M. Mullins, "Out of Place," *USA Today*, March 24, 2006, p. 10A). What is the probability that in the next 1,000 passengers, Jet Blue will have
**a.** no mishandled bags?
**b.** at least one mishandled bag?
**c.** at least two mishandled bags?
**d.** Compare the results in (a) through (c) to those of Delta in Problem 5.39(a) through (c).

**5.39** The U.S. Department of Transportation maintains statistics for mishandled bags per 1,000 airline passengers. In 2005, Delta had 7.09 mishandled bags per 1,000 passengers (extracted from M. Mullins, "Out of Place," *USA*

*Today*, March 24, 2006, p. 10A). What is the probability that in the next 1,000 passengers, Delta will have
a. no mishandled bags?
b. at least one mishandled bag?
c. at least two mishandled bags?
d. Compare the results in (a) through (c) to those of Jet Blue in Problem 5.38(a) through (c).

**5.40** Based on past experience, it is assumed that the number of flaws per foot in rolls of grade 2 paper follows a Poisson distribution with a mean of 1 flaw per 5 feet of paper (0.2 flaw per foot). What is the probability that in a
a. 1-foot roll, there will be at least 2 flaws?
b. 12-foot roll, there will be at least 1 flaw?
c. 50-foot roll, there will be greater than or equal to 5 flaws and less than or equal to 15 flaws?

**5.41** J.D. Power and Associates calculates and publishes various statistics concerning car quality. The initial quality score measures the number of problems per new car sold. For 2007 model cars, Ford had 1.27 problems per car. Dodge had 1.32 problems per car (S. Carty, "Ford Moves Up in Quality Survey," *USA Today*, June 7, 2007, p. 3B). Let the random variable *X* be equal to the number of problems with a newly purchased 2007 Ford.
a. What assumptions must be made in order for *X* to be distributed as a Poisson random variable? Are these assumptions reasonable?
Making the assumptions as in (a), if you purchased a 2007 Ford, what is the probability that the new car will have
b. zero problems?
c. two or less problems?
d. Give an operational definition for *problem*. Why is the operational definition important in interpreting the initial quality score?

**5.42** Refer to Problem 5.41. If you purchased a 2007 Dodge, what is the probability that the new car will have

a. zero problems?
b. two or less problems?
c. Compare your answers in (a) and (b) to those for the Ford in Problem 5.41(b) and (c).

**5.43** Refer to Problem 5.41. The same article reported that in 2006, Ford had 1.20 problems per car, and Dodge had 1.56 problems per car. If you purchased a 2006 Ford, what is the probability that the new car will have
a. zero problems?
b. two or less problems?
c. Compare your answers in (a) and (b) to those for the 2007 Ford in Problem 5.41(b) and (c).

**5.44** Refer to Problem 5.43. If you purchased a 2006 Dodge, what is the probability that the new car will have
a. zero problems?
b. two or less problems?
c. Compare your answers in (a) and (b) to those for the 2007 Dodge in Problem 5.42(a) and (b).

**5.45** A toll-free phone number is available from 9 a.m. to 9 p.m. for your customers to register complaints about a product purchased from your company. Past history indicates that an average of 0.4 calls are received per minute.
a. What properties must be true about the situation described here in order to use the Poisson distribution to calculate probabilities concerning the number of phone calls received in a 1-minute period?
Assuming that this situation matches the properties discussed in (a), what is the probability that during a 1-minute period
b. zero phone calls will be received?
c. three or more phone calls will be received?
d. What is the maximum number of phone calls that will be received in a 1-minute period 99.99% of the time?

## 5.5   HYPERGEOMETRIC DISTRIBUTION

Both the binomial distribution and the **hypergeometric distribution** are concerned with the number of events of interest in a sample containing *n* observations. One of the differences in these two probability distributions is in the way that the samples are selected. For the binomial distribution, the sample data are selected *with* replacement from a *finite* population or *without* replacement from an *infinite* population. Thus, the probability of an event of interest, π, is constant over all observations, and the outcome of any particular observation is independent of any other. For the hypergeometric distribution, the sample data are selected *without* replacement from a *finite* population. Thus, the outcome of one observation is dependent on the outcomes of the previous observations.

Consider a population of size *N*. Let *A* represent the total number of events of interest in the population. The hypergeometric distribution is then used to find the probability of *X* events of interest in a sample of size *n*, selected without replacement. Equation (5.15) presents the mathematical expression of the hypergeometric distribution for finding the probability of *X* events of interest, given a knowledge of *n*, *N*, and *A*.

Hypergeometric Distribution

$$P(X) = \frac{\binom{A}{X}\binom{N-A}{n-X}}{\binom{N}{n}}$$  (5.15)

where

$P(X)$ = the probability of $X$ events of interest, given knowledge of $n$, $N$, and $A$

$n$ = sample size

$N$ = population size

$A$ = number of events of interest in the population

$N - A$ = number of events that are not of interest in the population

$X$ = number of events of interest in the sample

$\binom{A}{X} = {}_AC_X$ [see Equation (5.10) on p. 190]

The number of events of interest in the sample, represented by $X$, cannot be greater than the number of events of interest in the population, $A$, or the sample size, $n$. Thus, the range of the hypergeometric random variable is limited to the sample size or to the number of events of interest in the population, whichever is smaller.

Equation (5.16) defines the mean of the hypergeometric distribution, and Equation (5.17) defines the standard deviation.

Mean of the Hypergeometric Distribution

$$\mu = E(X) = \frac{nA}{N}$$  (5.16)

Standard Deviation of the Hypergeometric Distribution

$$\sigma = \sqrt{\frac{nA(N-A)}{N^2}}\sqrt{\frac{N-n}{N-1}}$$  (5.17)

In Equation (5.17), the expression $\sqrt{\frac{N-n}{N-1}}$ is a **finite population correction factor** that results from sampling without replacement from a finite population.

To illustrate the hypergeometric distribution, suppose that you are forming a team of 8 managers from different departments within your company. Your company has a total of 30 managers, and 10 of these people are from the finance department. If members of the team are to be selected at random, what is the probability that the team will contain 2 managers from the finance department? Here, the population of $N = 30$ managers within the company is finite. In addition, $A = 10$ are from the finance department. A team of $n = 8$ members is to be selected.

Using Equation (5.15),

$$P(X = 2) = \frac{\binom{10}{2}\binom{20}{6}}{\binom{30}{8}}$$

$$= \frac{\dfrac{10!}{2!(8)!}\dfrac{(20)!}{(6)!(14)!}}{\dfrac{30!}{8!(22)!}}$$

$$= 0.298$$

Thus, the probability that the team will contain two members from the finance department is 0.298, or 29.8%.

Such computations can become tedious, especially as $N$ gets large. However, you can compute hypergeometric probabilities by using Microsoft Excel or Minitab. Figures 5.7 and 5.8 present Microsoft Excel and Minitab results for the team-formation example, where the number of managers from the finance department (i.e., the number of events of interest in the sample) can be equal to 0, 1, 2, . . . , 8. (Note that Minitab uses the letter M instead of A to represent the number of events of interest in the population.)

**FIGURE 5.7**

Microsoft Excel worksheet for the team member example

*See Section E5.5 or P5.4 to create this.*

**FIGURE 5.8**

Minitab results for the team member example

*See Section M5.3 to create this.*

```
Hypergeometric with N = 30, M = 10, and n = 8

x    P( X = x )
0    0.021523
1    0.132447
2    0.298005
3    0.317872
4    0.173836
5    0.049083
6    0.006817
7    0.000410
8    0.000008
```

# PROBLEMS FOR SECTION 5.5

## Learning the Basics

**5.46** Determine the following:
**a.** If $n = 4$, $N = 10$, and $A = 5$, find $P(X = 3)$.
**b.** If $n = 4$, $N = 6$, and $A = 3$, find $P(X = 1)$.
**c.** If $n = 5$, $N = 12$, and $A = 3$, find $P(X = 0)$.
**d.** If $n = 3$, $N = 10$, and $A = 3$, find $P(X = 3)$.

**5.47** Referring to Problem 5.46, compute the mean and standard deviation for the hypergeometric distributions described in (a) through (d).

## Applying the Concepts

**SELF Test** **5.48** An auditor for the Internal Revenue Service is selecting a sample of 6 tax returns for an audit. If 2 or more of these returns are "improper," the entire population of 100 tax returns will be audited. What is the probability that the entire population will be audited if the actual number of improper returns in the population is
**a.** 25?
**b.** 30?
**c.** 5?
**d.** 10?
**e.** Discuss the differences in your results, depending on the actual number of improper returns in the population.

**5.49** The dean of a business school wishes to form an executive committee of 5 from among the 40 tenured faculty members at the school. The selection is to be random, and at the school there are 8 tenured faculty members in accounting. What is the probability that the committee will contain

**a.** none of them?
**b.** at least 1 of them?
**c.** not more than 1 of them?
**d.** What is your answer to (a) if the committee consists of 7 members?

**5.50** From a shipment of 30 cars being sent to a local automobile dealer, 4 are SUVs. What is the probability that if 4 cars arrive at a particular dealership,
**a.** all 4 are SUVs?
**b.** none are SUVs?
**c.** at least 1 is an SUV?
**d.** What are your answers to (a) through (c) if 6 cars being shipped are SUVs?

**5.51** A state lottery is conducted in which 6 winning numbers are selected from a total of 54 numbers. What is the probability that if 6 numbers are randomly selected,
**a.** all 6 numbers will be winning numbers?
**b.** 5 numbers will be winning numbers?
**c.** none of the numbers will be winning numbers?
**d.** What are your answers to (a) through (c) if the 6 winning numbers are selected from a total of 40 numbers?

**5.52** In a shipment of 15 sets of golf clubs, 3 are left-handed. If 4 sets of golf clubs are selected, what is the probability that
**a.** exactly 1 is left-handed?
**b.** at least 1 is left-handed?
**c.** no more than 2 are left-handed?
**d.** What is the mean number of left-handed sets of golf clubs that you would expect to find in the sample of 4 sets of golf clubs?

## 5.6  ◉ (CD-ROM TOPIC) USING THE POISSON DISTRIBUTION TO APPROXIMATE THE BINOMIAL DISTRIBUTION

Under certain circumstances, the Poisson distribution can be used to approximate the binomial distribution. To study this topic, go to the `section5.6.pdf` file located on the Student CD-ROM that accompanies this book.

# SUMMARY

In this chapter, you have studied mathematical expectation, the covariance, and the binomial, Poisson, and hypergeometric distributions. In the Using Statistics scenario, you

learned how to calculate probabilities from the binomial distribution concerning the observation of tagged invoices in the accounting information system used by the Saxon

Home Improvement Company. In the following chapter, you will study several important continuous distributions including the normal distribution.

To help decide what probability distribution to use for a particular situation, you need to ask the following questions:

* Is there a fixed number of observations, $n$, each of which is classified as an event of interest or not an event of interest? Or is there an area of opportunity? If there is a fixed number of observations, $n$, each of which is classified as an event of interest or not an event of interest, you use the binomial or hypergeometric distribution. If there is an area of opportunity, you use the Poisson distribution.

* In deciding whether to use the binomial or hypergeometric distribution, is the probability of an event of interest constant over all trials? If yes, you can use the binomial distribution. If no, you can use the hypergeometric distribution.

# Probability Distributions—More Likely Than You Think

*From the Authors' Desktop*

At first glance, probability distributions seem so abstract as to be not applicable in your daily life. Although the theory behind these distributions is perhaps the single most challenging topic in this book, the applications of probability distributions are a lot more accessible than you might first realize.

Taking the topics in the order in which they appeared in the chapter, the covariance and portfolio risk represents the foundation for what you need to know in order to develop portfolios in finance. Of course, to keep things simple, the example in the chapter examined only two alternatives. In developing an actual portfolio, many different alternative investments would be considered.

The binomial distribution, originally developed back in the eighteenth century for games of chance, finds applications today in the securities marketplace (to some, the ultimate game of chance!). Some examples include the relationship between the S & P index during the first five days of the year and the entire year (see Problem 5.70 on page 210), the likelihood

of equaling the record of 14 consecutive daily increases in the Dow Jones Industrial Average set in 1897 (E. S. Browning, "Dow Ends Run at History," *The Wall Street Journal*, April 12, 2007, p. C1), and the possible relationship between the winner of the National Football League Super Bowl and the performance of the Dow Jones Industrial Average (see Problem 5.71 on page 210).

Even though the Poisson distribution might sound a bit fishy (*poisson* is the French word for fish), you may have crossed paths with this distribution waiting in line at a bank, a toll plaza, and yes, waiting to buy a Filet-O-Fish sandwich or other item at a local McDonald's. If you ever wondered why there is only one line (or why there is a separate line for each server) and how the bank, toll authority, or restaurant determined how many servers should be available at a certain time, you have discovered applications of waiting line or queuing theory. Queuing theory depends on the Poisson distribution for the distribution of the arrivals and depends on the exponential distribution (to be covered in Section 6.5) for

the distribution of how long it takes to be served.

Don't like to wait in lines? How about the chance that you will have a certain number of problems with your new car or that an airline will lose a piece of luggage that you checked, or that you will lose more than a certain number of balls in an 18-hole round of golf? Answers to these types of questions also depend on the Poisson distribution.

Finally, you might one day "take a chance" on the hypergeometric distribution, if you play *Powerball* or other lottery-type games. If you really want to know more than "your chance of winning may vary," you can use the hypergeometric distribution to compute the probability of winning a prize in the lottery (see Problem 5.74 on page 210 for one example) or the probability that the lottery ticket you purchased won't be worth anything.

So keep your eyes and ears open, and something related to probability distributions is bound to enter your work life or everyday life.

# KEY EQUATIONS

**Expected Value, $\mu$, of a Discrete Random Variable**

$$\mu = E(X) = \sum_{i=1}^{N} X_i P(X_i) \tag{5.1}$$

**Variance of a Discrete Random Variable**

$$\sigma^2 = \sum_{i=1}^{N} [X_i - E(X)]^2 P(X_i) \tag{5.2}$$

**Standard Deviation of a Discrete Random Variable**

$$\sigma = \sqrt{\sigma^2} = \sqrt{\sum_{i=1}^{N} [X_i - E(X)]^2 P(X_i)} \tag{5.3}$$

**Covariance**

$$\sigma_{XY} = \sum_{i=1}^{N} [X_i - E(X)][Y_i - E(Y)] P(X_i Y_i) \tag{5.4}$$

**Expected Value of the Sum of Two Random Variables**

$$E(X+Y) = E(X) + E(Y) \qquad (5.5)$$

**Variance of the Sum of Two Random Variables**

$$Var(X+Y) = \sigma_{X+Y}^2 = \sigma_X^2 + \sigma_Y^2 + 2\sigma_{XY} \qquad (5.6)$$

**Standard Deviation of the Sum of Two Random Variables**

$$\sigma_{X+Y} = \sqrt{\sigma_{X+Y}^2} \qquad (5.7)$$

**Portfolio Expected Return**

$$E(P) = wE(X) + (1-w)E(Y) \qquad (5.8)$$

**Portfolio Risk**

$$\sigma_p = \sqrt{w^2\sigma_X^2 + (1-w)^2\sigma_Y^2 + 2w(1-w)\sigma_{XY}} \qquad (5.9)$$

**Combinations**

$$_nC_X = \frac{n!}{X!(n-X)!} \qquad (5.10)$$

**Binomial Distribution**

$$P(X) = \frac{n!}{X!(n-X)!}\pi^X(1-\pi)^{n-X} \qquad (5.11)$$

**Mean of the Binomial Distribution**

$$\mu = E(X) = n\pi \qquad (5.12)$$

**Standard Deviation of the Binomial Distribution**

$$\sigma = \sqrt{\sigma^2} = \sqrt{Var(X)} = \sqrt{n\pi(1-\pi)} \qquad (5.13)$$

**Poisson Distribution**

$$P(X) = \frac{e^{-\lambda}\lambda^X}{X!} \qquad (5.14)$$

**Hypergeometric Distribution**

$$P(X) = \frac{\binom{A}{X}\binom{N-A}{n-X}}{\binom{N}{n}} \qquad (5.15)$$

**Mean of the Hypergeometric Distribution**

$$\mu = E(X) = \frac{nA}{N} \qquad (5.16)$$

**Standard Deviation of the Hypergeometric Distribution**

$$\sigma = \sqrt{\frac{nA(N-A)}{N^2}}\sqrt{\frac{N-n}{N-1}} \qquad (5.17)$$

# KEY TERMS

area of opportunity   198
binomial distribution   189
covariance, $\sigma_{XY}$   185
expected value of the sum of two random variables   186
expected value, $\mu$, of a discrete random variable   181
finite population correction factor   203
hypergeometric distribution   202
mathematical model   189
Poisson distribution   198
portfolio   187
portfolio expected return   187
portfolio risk   187
probability distribution for a discrete random variable   180
rule of combinations   190
standard deviation of a discrete random variable   182
standard deviation of the sum of two random variables   186
variance of a discrete random variable   182
variance of the sum of two random variables   186

# CHAPTER REVIEW PROBLEMS

## Checking Your Understanding

**5.53** What is the meaning of the expected value of a probability distribution?

**5.54** What are the four properties that must be present in order to use the binomial distribution?

**5.55** What are the four properties that must be present in order to use the Poisson distribution?

**5.56** When do you use the hypergeometric distribution instead of the binomial distribution?

## Applying the Concepts

**5.57** Event insurance allows promoters of sporting and entertainment events to protect themselves from financial losses due to uncontrollable circumstances such as rainouts. For example, each spring, Cincinnati's Downtown Council puts on the Taste of Cincinnati. This is a rainy time of year in Cincinnati, and the chance of receiving an inch or more of rain during a spring weekend is about one out of four. An article in the *Cincinnati Enquirer*, by Jim Knippenberg ("Chicken Pox Means 3 Dog Night Remedy," *Cincinnati Enquirer*, May 28, 1997, p. E1), gave the details for an insurance policy purchased by the Downtown Council. The policy would pay $100,000 if it rained more than an inch during the weekend festival. The cost of the policy was reported to be $6,500.
**a.** Determine whether you believe that these dollar amounts are correct. (*Hint:* Calculate the expected value of the profit to be made by the insurance company.)
**b.** Assume that the dollar amounts are correct. Is this policy a good deal for Cincinnati's Downtown Council?

**5.58** Between 1872 and 2000, stock prices rose in 74% of the years (M. Hulbert, "The Stock Market Must Rise in 2002? Think Again," *The New York Times*, December 6, 2001, Business, p. 6). Based on this information, and assuming a binomial distribution, what do you think the probability is that the stock market will rise
**a.** next year?
**b.** the year after next?
**c.** in four of the next five years?
**d.** in none of the next five years?
**e.** For this situation, what assumption of the binomial distribution might not be valid?

**5.59** The mean cost of a phone call handled by an automated customer-service system is $0.45. The mean cost of a phone call passed on to a "live" operator is $5.50. However, as more and more companies have implemented automated systems, customer annoyance with such systems has grown. Many customers are quick to leave the automated system when given an option such as "Press zero to talk to a customer-service representative." According to the Center for Client Retention, 40% of all callers to automated customer-service systems automatically opt to go to a live operator when given the chance (J. Spencer, "In Search of the Operator," *The Wall Street Journal*, May 8, 2002, p. D1).

If 10 independent callers contact an automated customer-service system, what is the probability that
**a.** 0 will automatically opt to talk to a live operator?
**b.** exactly 1 will automatically opt to talk to a live operator?
**c.** 2 or less will automatically opt to talk to a live operator?
**d.** all 10 will automatically opt to talk to a live operator?
**e.** If all 10 automatically opt to talk to a live operator, do you think that the 40% figure given in the article applies to this particular system? Explain.

**5.60** One theory concerning the Dow Jones Industrial Average is that it is likely to increase during U.S. presidential election years. From 1964 through 2004, the Dow Jones Industrial Average increased in 9 of the 11 U.S. presidential election years. Assuming that this indicator is a random event with no predictive value, you would expect that the indicator would be correct 50% of the time.
**a.** What is the probability of the Dow Jones Industrial Average increasing in 9 or more of the 11 U.S. presidential election years if the true probability of an increase in the Dow Jones Industrial Average is 0.50?
**b.** Read Problem 5.58 and note that the Dow Jones Industrial Average increased in 74% of the years studied. What is the probability of the Dow Jones Industrial Average increasing in 9 or more of the 11 U.S. presidential election years if the probability of an increase in the Dow Jones Industrial Average is 0.74?

**5.61** Priority Mail is the U.S. Postal Service's alternative to commercial express mail companies such as FedEx. An article in *The Wall Street Journal* presented some interesting conclusions comparing Priority Mail shipments with the much less expensive first-class shipments (R. Brooks, "New Data Reveal 'Priority Mail' Is Slower Than a Stamp," *The Wall Street Journal*, May 29, 2002, p. D1). When comparing shipments intended for delivery in three days, first-class deliveries failed to deliver on time 19% of the time, whereas Priority Mail failed 33% of the time. Note that at the time of the article, first-class deliveries started as low as $0.34, and Priority Mail started at $3.50.

If 10 items are to be shipped first-class to 10 different destinations claimed to be in a three-day delivery location, what is the probability that
**a.** 0 items will take more than three days?
**b.** exactly 1 item will take more than three days?

**c.** 2 or more will take more than three days?
**d.** What are the mean and the standard deviation of the probability distribution?

**5.62** Refer to Problem 5.61. If the shipments are made using Priority Mail, what is the probability that
**a.** 0 items will take more than three days?
**b.** exactly 1 will take more than three days?
**c.** 2 or more will take more than three days?
**d.** What are the mean and the standard deviation of the probability distribution?
**e.** Compare the results of (a) through (c) to those of Problem 5.61(a) through (c).

**5.63** Cinema advertising is increasing. Normally 60 to 90 seconds long, these advertisements are longer and more extravagant, and they tend to have more captive audiences than television advertisements. Thus, it is not surprising that the recall rates for viewers of cinema advertisements are higher than those for television advertisements. According to survey research conducted by the ComQUEST division of BBM Bureau of Measurement in Toronto, the probability a viewer will remember a cinema advertisement is 0.74, whereas the probability a viewer will remember a 30-second television advertisement is 0.37 (N. Hendley, "Cinema Advertising Comes of Age," *Marketing Magazine*, May 6, 2002, p. 16).
**a.** Is the 0.74 probability reported by the BBM Bureau of Measurement best classified as *a priori* probability, empirical probability, or subjective probability?
**b.** Suppose that 10 viewers of a cinema advertisement are randomly sampled. Consider the random variable defined by the number of viewers who recall the advertisement. What assumptions must be made in order to assume that this random variable is distributed as a binomial random variable?
**c.** Assuming that the number of viewers who recall the cinema advertisement is a binomial random variable, what are the mean and standard deviation of this distribution?
**d.** Based on your answer to (c), if none of the viewers can recall the ad, what can be inferred about the 0.74 probability given in the article?

**5.64** Refer to Problem 5.63. Compute the probability that of the 10 viewers of the cinema advertisement,
**a.** exactly 0 can recall the advertisement.
**b.** all 10 can recall the advertisement.
**c.** more than half can recall the advertisement.
**d.** 8 or more can recall the advertisement.

**5.65** Refer to Problem 5.63. For television advertisements, using the given probability of recall, 0.37, compute the probability that of the 10 viewers,
**a.** exactly 0 can recall the advertisement.
**b.** all 10 can recall the advertisement.
**c.** more than half can recall the advertisement.

**d.** 8 or more can recall the advertisement.
**e.** Compare the results of (a) through (d) to those of Problem 5.64(a) through (d).

**5.66** A survey conducted by Neilsen/Net Ratings (J. Angwin and K. Delaney, "My Space's Pact with Google Hits a Snag," *The Wall Street Journal*, February 7, 2007, p. B3) it indicated that 51% of the searches conducted in the United States used Google as the search engine. Suppose that you are to randomly call 10 Internet users in the United States and ask them to name the search engine they used. Using the results of the Neilsen/Net Ratings study, what is the probability that
**a.** all 10 will have used Google as the search engine?
**b.** exactly 5 will have used Google as the search engine?
**c.** at least 5 will have used Google as the search engine?
**d.** less than 5 will have used Google as the search engine?
**e.** What is the expected number of people who have used Google as the search engine? Explain the practical meaning of this number.

**5.67** A study by the Center for Financial Services Innovation showed that in 2004 only 64% of U.S. income earners aged 15 and older had a bank account (A. Carrns, "Banks Court a New Client," *The Wall Street Journal*, March 16, 2007, p. D1).
If a random sample of 20 U.S. income earners aged 15 and older is selected, what is the probability that
**a.** all 20 have a bank account?
**b.** no more than 15 have a bank account?
**c.** more than 10 have a bank account?
**d.** What assumptions did you have to make to answer (a) through (c)?

**5.68** One of the retail industry's biggest frustrations is customers who abuse the return and exchange policies (S. Kang, "New Return Policy: Retailers Say 'No' to Serial Exchangers," *The Wall Street Journal*, November 29, 2004, pp. B1, B3). In a recent year, returns were 13% of sales in department stores. Consider a sample of 20 customers who make a purchase at a department store. Use the binomial model to answer the following questions:
**a.** What is the expected value, or mean, of the binomial distribution?
**b.** What is the standard deviation of the binomial distribution?
**c.** What is the probability that none of the 20 customers will make a return?
**d.** What is the probability that no more than 2 of the customers will make a return?
**e.** What is the probability that 3 or more of the customers will make a return?

**5.69** Refer to Problem 5.68. In the same year, returns were 1% of sales in grocery stores.
**a.** What is the expected value, or mean, of the binomial distribution?

b. What is the standard deviation of the binomial distribution?

c. What is the probability that none of the 20 customers will make a return?

d. What is the probability that no more than 2 of the customers will make a return?

e. What is the probability that 3 or more of the customers will make a return?

f. Compare the results of (a) through (e) to those of Problem 5.68(a) through (e).

**5.70** One theory concerning the S&P 500 index is that if it increases during the first five trading days of the year, it is likely to increase during the entire year. From 1950 through 2006, the S&P 500 index had these early gains in 37 years. In 31 of these 37 years, the S&P 500 index increased. Assuming that this indicator is a random event with no predictive value, you would expect that the indicator would be correct 50% of the time. What is the probability of the S&P 500 index increasing in 31 or more years if the true probability of an increase in the S&P 500 index is

a. 0.50?

b. 0.70?

c. 0.90?

d. Based on the results of (a) through (c), what do you think is the probability that the S&P 500 index will increase if there is an early gain in the first five trading days of the year? Explain.

**5.71** *Spurious correlation* refers to the apparent relationship between variables that either have no true relationship or are related to other variables that have not been measured. One widely publicized stock market indicator in the United States that is an example of spurious correlation is the relationship between the winner of the National Football League Super Bowl and the performance of the Dow Jones Industrial Average in that year. The indicator states that when a team representing the National Football Conference wins the Super Bowl, the Dow Jones Industrial Average will increase in that year. When a team representing the American Football Conference wins the Super Bowl, the Dow Jones Industrial Average will decline in that year. Since the first Super Bowl was held in 1967 through 2006, the indicator has been correct 32 out of 40 times. Assuming that this indicator is a random event with no predictive value, you would expect that the indicator would be correct 50% of the time.

a. What is the probability that the indicator would be correct 32 or more times in 40 years?

b. What does this tell you about the usefulness of this indicator?

**5.72** Worldwide golf ball sales total more than $1 billion annually. One reason for such a large number of golf ball purchases is that golfers lose them at a rate of 4.5 per 18-hole round ("Snapshots," **www.usatoday.com**, January 29,

2004). Assume that the number of golf balls lost in an 18-hole round is distributed as a Poisson random variable.

a. What assumptions need to be made so that the number of golf balls lost in an 18-hole round is distributed as a Poisson random variable?

Making the assumptions given in (a), what is the probability that

b. 0 balls will be lost in an 18-hole round?

c. 5 or less balls will be lost in an 18-hole round?

d. 6 or more balls will be lost in an 18-hole round?

**5.73** According to a Virginia Tech survey, college students make an average of 11 calls per day on their cellphone. Moreover, 80% of the students surveyed indicated that their parents pay their cellphone expenses (Jean Elliot, "Professor Researches Cell Phone Usage among Students," **www.physorg.com**, February 26, 2007).

a. What distribution can you use to model the number of calls a student makes in a day?

b. If you select a student at random, what is the probability that he or she makes more than 10 calls in a day? More than 15? More than 20?

c. If you select a random sample of 10 students, what distribution can you use to model the proportion of students who have parents that pay their cellphone expenses?

d. Using the distribution selected in (c), what is the probability that all 10 have parents that pay their cellphone expenses? At least 9? At least 8?

**5.74** Mega Millions is one of the most popular lottery games in the United States. Participating states in Mega Millions are Georgia, Illinois, Maryland, Massachusetts, Michigan, New Jersey, New York, Ohio, and Virginia. Rules for playing and the list of prizes are given below ("Win Megamoney Playing Ohio's Biggest Jackpot Game," Ohio Lottery Headquarters, 2002):

*Rules:*
- Select five numbers from a pool of numbers from 1 to 52 and one Mega Ball number from a second pool of numbers from 1 to 52.
- Each wager costs $1.

*Prizes:*
- Match all five numbers + Mega Ball—win jackpot (minimum of $10,000,000)
- Match all five numbers—win $175,000
- Match four numbers + Mega Ball—win $5,000
- Match four numbers—win $150
- Match three numbers + Mega Ball—win $150
- Match two numbers + Mega Ball—win $10
- Match three numbers—win $7
- Match one number + Mega Ball—win $3
- Match Mega Ball—win $2

Find the probability of winning
**a.** the jackpot.
**b.** the $175,000 prize. (Note that this requires matching all five numbers but not matching the Mega Ball.)
**c.** $5,000.
**d.** $150.
**e.** $10.
**f.** $7.
**g.** $3.
**h.** $2.
**i.** nothing.
**j.** All stores selling Mega Millions tickets are required to have a brochure that gives complete game rules and probabilities of winning each prize (the probability of having a losing ticket is not given). The slogan for all lottery games in the state of Ohio is "Play Responsibly. Odds Are, You'll Have Fun." Do you think Ohio's slogan and the requirement of making available complete game rules and probabilities of winning is an ethical approach to running the lottery system?

# MANAGING THE *SPRINGVILLE HERALD*

The *Herald* marketing department is seeking to increase home-delivery sales through an aggressive direct-marketing campaign that includes mailings, discount coupons, and telephone solicitations. Feedback from these efforts indicates that getting their newspapers delivered early in the morning is a very important factor for both prospective as well as existing subscribers. After several brainstorming sessions, a team consisting of members from the marketing and circulation departments decided that guaranteeing newspaper delivery by a specific time could be an important selling point in retaining and getting new subscribers. The team concluded that the *Herald* should offer a guarantee that customers will receive their newspapers by a certain time or else that day's issue is free.

To assist the team in setting a guaranteed delivery time, Al Leslie, the research director, determined that the circulation department had data that showed the percentage of newspapers yet undelivered every quarter hour from 6 a.m. to 8 a.m. Jan Shapiro remembered that customers were asked on their subscription forms at what time they would be looking for their copy of the *Herald* to be delivered. These data were subsequently combined and posted on an internal *Herald* Web page. (See `Circulation_Data.htm` in the Herald Case folder on the Student CD-ROM or go to **www.prenhall.com/HeraldCase/Circulation_Data.htm**).

## EXERCISES

Review the internal data and propose a reasonable time (to the nearest quarter hour) to guarantee delivery. To help explore the effects of your choice, calculate the following probabilities:

**SH5.1** If a sample of 50 customers is selected on a given day, what is the probability, given your selected delivery time, that
  **a.** less than 3 customers will receive a free newspaper?
  **b.** 2, 3, or 4 customers will receive a free newspaper?
  **c.** more than 5 customers will receive a free newspaper?

**SH5.2** Consider the effects of improving the newspaper delivery process so that the percentage of newspapers that go undelivered by your guaranteed delivery time decreases by 2%. If a sample of 50 customers is selected on a given day, what is the probability, given your selected delivery time (and the delivery improvement), that
  **a.** less than 3 customers will receive a free newspaper?
  **b.** 2, 3, or 4 customers will receive a free newspaper?
  **c.** more than 5 customers will receive a free newspaper?

# WEB CASE

*Apply your knowledge about expected value and the covariance in this continuing Web Case from Chapters 3 and 4.*

Visit the EndRun Bulls and Bears Web page, at **www.prenhall.com/Springville/ER_BullsandBears.htm** (or open the Web page file from the Student CD-ROM Web Case folder), read the claims, and examine the supporting data. Then answer the following:

**1.** Are there any "catches" about the claims the Web site makes for the rate of return of Happy Bull and Worried Bear Funds?

**2.** What subjective data influence the rate-of-return analyses of these funds? Could EndRun be accused of making false and misleading statements? Why or why not?

**3.** The expected-return analysis seems to show that the Worried Bear Fund has a greater expected return than the Happy Bull Fund. Should a rational investor never invest in the Happy Bull Fund? Why or why not?

# REFERENCES

1. Bernstein, P. L., *Against the Gods: The Remarkable Story of Risk* (New York: Wiley, 1996).
2. Emery, D. R., J. D. Finnerty, and J. D. Stowe, *Corporate Financial Management*, 3rd ed. (Upper Saddle River, NJ: Prentice Hall, 2007).
3. Kirk, R. L., ed., *Statistical Issues: A Reader for the Behavioral Sciences* (Belmont, CA: Wadsworth, 1972).
4. Levine, D. M., P. Ramsey, and R. Smidt, *Applied Statistics for Engineers and Scientists Using Microsoft Excel and Minitab* (Upper Saddle River, NJ: Prentice Hall, 2001).
5. *Microsoft Excel 2007* (Redmond, WA: Microsoft Corp., 2007).
6. *Minitab Version 15* (State College, PA: Minitab, Inc., 2006).
7. Moscove, S. A., M. G. Simkin, and A. Bagranoff, *Core Concepts of Accounting Information Systems*, 10th ed. (New York: Wiley, 2007).

# Appendix E5
## Using Microsoft Excel for Discrete Probability Distributions

## E5.1 Computing the Expected Value of a Discrete Random Variable

You compute the expected value of a discrete random variable by making entries in the **Discrete** worksheet of the Expected Value.xls workbook. This worksheet uses the SUM and SQRT (square root) functions to calculate its statistics.

Figure E5.1 shows a completed worksheet using the mortgage probability distribution of Table 5.1 on page 181. To adapt this worksheet to other problems that have more or less than seven outcomes, first select the cell range **A5:E5**. To add table rows, right-click and click **Insert**. (If a box of options appears, click **Shift cells down** and then click **OK**.) Then, copy the formulas in cell range C4:E4 down through the new table rows and enter the new *X* and *P(X)* values in columns A and B.

To delete table rows, right-click and click **Delete**. (If a box of options appears, click **Shift cells up** and then click **OK**.) Enter a corrected list of *X* values starting with **1** in cell A5 in column A and enter the new *P(X)* values in column B.

## E5.2 Computing Portfolio Expected Return and Portfolio Risk

You compute the portfolio expected return and the portfolio risk of two investments by opening to the **Portfolio** worksheet of the Portfolio.xls workbook (see Figure E5.2). This worksheet already contains the entries for the estimated returns for the investment data of Table 5.4 on page 185. To adapt this worksheet to other problems, change the probabilities and outcomes table data and the **Weight Assigned to X** value. If your problem does not have three

| | A | B | C | D | E | F | G | H |
|---|---|---|---|---|---|---|---|---|
| 1 | Discrete Random Variable Probability Distribution | | | | | | | |
| 2 | | | | | | | Statistics | |
| 3 | X | P(X) | X*P(X) | [X-E(X)]^2 | [X-E(X)]^2*P(X) | | Expected value | 2.8 | =SUM(C:C) |
| 4 | 0 | 0.10 | 0 | 7.84 | 0.784 | | Variance | 2.46 | =SUM(E:E) |
| 5 | 1 | 0.10 | 0.1 | 3.24 | 0.324 | | Standard deviation | 1.57 | =SQRT(H4) |
| 6 | 2 | 0.20 | 0.4 | 0.64 | 0.128 | | | | |
| 7 | 3 | 0.30 | 0.9 | 0.04 | 0.012 | | X*P(X) | [X - E(X)]^2 | [X - E(X)]^2*P(X) |
| 8 | 4 | 0.15 | 0.6 | 1.44 | 0.216 | | =A4 * B4 | =(A4 - $H$3)^2 | =D4 * B4 |
| 9 | 5 | 0.10 | 0.5 | 4.84 | 0.484 | | =A5 * B5 | =(A5 - $H$3)^2 | =D5 * B5 |
| 10 | 6 | 0.05 | 0.3 | 10.24 | 0.512 | | =A6 * B6 | =(A6 - $H$3)^2 | =D6 * B6 |
| | | | | | | | =A7 * B7 | =(A7 - $H$3)^2 | =D7 * B7 |
| | | | | | | | =A8 * B8 | =(A8 - $H$3)^2 | =D8 * B8 |
| | | | | | | | =A9 * B9 | =(A9 - $H$3)^2 | =D9 * B9 |

**FIGURE E5.1**
Discrete worksheet

| | A | B | C | D |
|---|---|---|---|---|
| 1 | **Portfolio Expected Return and Risk** | | | |
| 2 | | | | |
| 3 | **Probabilities & Outcomes:** | P | X | Y |
| 4 | | 0.2 | -100 | 200 |
| 5 | | 0.5 | 100 | 50 |
| 6 | | 0.3 | 250 | -100 |
| 7 | | | | |
| 8 | **Weight Assigned to X** | 0.5 | | |
| 9 | | | | |
| 10 | **Statistics** | | | |
| 11 | E(X) | 105 | =SUMPRODUCT(B4:B6, C4:C6) | |
| 12 | E(Y) | 35 | =SUMPRODUCT(B4:B6, D4:D6) | |
| 13 | Variance(X) | 14725 | =SUMPRODUCT(B4:B6, H4:H6) | |
| 14 | Standard Deviation(X) | 121.3466 | =SQRT(B13) | |
| 15 | Variance(Y) | 11025 | =SUMPRODUCT(B4:B6, I4:I6) | |
| 16 | Standard Deviation(Y) | 105 | =SQRT(B15) | |
| 17 | Covariance(XY) | -12675 | =SUMPRODUCT(B4:B6, J4:J6) | |
| 18 | Variance(X+Y) | 400 | =B13 + B15 + 2 * B17 | |
| 19 | Standard Deviation(X+Y) | 20 | =SQRT(B18) | |
| 20 | | | | |
| 21 | **Portfolio Management** | | | |
| 22 | **Weight Assigned to X** | 0.5 | =B8 | |
| 23 | **Weight Assigned to Y** | 0.5 | =1 - B22 | |
| 24 | **Portfolio Expected Return** | 70 | =B22 * B11 + B23 * B12 | |
| 25 | **Portfolio Risk** | 10 | =SQRT(B22^2 * B13 + B23^2 * B15 + 2 * B22 * B23 * B17) | |

**FIGURE E5.2**

Portfolio worksheet

outcomes, first select **row 5** and then add or delete rows one at a time by right-clicking row 5 and clicking either **Insert** or **Delete**. (If you inserted rows, you will also have to copy formulas down to those new rows.)

The worksheet features the **SUMPRODUCT(*cell range 1, cell range 2*)** function, which computes the sum of the products of corresponding elements of two cell ranges (or arrays, in mathematical terms). In this worksheet, the first array/cell range is always the set of $P(X_iY_i)$ probabilities. To compute the variance, standard deviation, and covariance, the worksheet uses a calculation area in rows F through J (not shown in Figure E5.2).

## E5.3 Computing Binomial Probabilities

You compute binomial probabilities by making entries in the **Binomial** worksheet of the `Binomial.xls` workbook. This worksheet (shown in Figure 5.2 on page 194) already contains the entries for the tagged orders example of Section 5.3. To adapt this worksheet to other problems, change the **Sample size** and **Probability of an event of interest** values in cells B4 and B5. If your problem has a sample size other than 4, first select **row 15** and then add or delete rows one at a time by right-clicking row 15 and clicking either **Insert** or **Delete** and adjusting the X values in column A. (If you inserted rows, you will also have to copy formulas down to those new rows.)

The worksheet features the **BINOMDIST(*X, n, π, cumulative*)** function in which X is the number of events of interest, n is the sample size, π is the probability of an event

of interest, and *cumulative* is a True or False value. When *cumulative* is **True**, the function computes the probability of X or fewer events of interest; when *cumulative* is **False**, the function computes the probability of exactly X events of interest.

## E5.4 Computing Poisson Probabilities

You compute Poisson probabilities by making entries in the **Poisson** worksheet of the `Poisson.xls` workbook. This worksheet (shown in Figure 5.5 on page 200) already contains the entries for the bank customer arrivals problem of Section 5.4. To adapt this worksheet to other problems, change the **Mean/Expected number of events of interest** value in cell **E4**.

The worksheet features the **POISSON(*X, lambda, cumulative*)** function in which X is the number of events of interest, *lambda* is the average or expected number of events of interest, and *cumulative* is a True or False value. When *cumulative* is **True**, the function computes the probability of X or fewer events of interest; when *cumulative* is **False**, the function computes the probability of exactly X events of interest.

## E5.5 Computing Hypergeometric Probabilities

You compute Hypergeometric probabilities by making entries in the **Hypergeometric** worksheet of the `Hypergeometric.xls` workbook. This worksheet (shown in Figure 5.7 on page 204) already contains the entries for the team formation problem of Section 5.5. To adapt this worksheet to other problems, change the **Sample size**, **No. of events of interest in population**, and **Population size** in the cell range **B4:B6**. If your problem has a sample size other than 8, first select **row 11**, then right-click and click either **Insert** (or **Delete**) to add (or delete) rows one at a time. Finish by adjusting the $X$ values in column A. (If you inserted rows, you will also have to copy formulas down to those new rows.)

The worksheet features the **HYPERGEOMDIST($X$, $n$, $A$, $N$)** function in which $X$ is the number of events of interest, $n$ is the sample size, $A$ is the number of events of interest in the population, and $N$ is the population size. When *cumulative* is **False**, the function computes the probability of exactly $X$ events of interest.

# Appendix P5
## Using PHStat2 for Discrete Probability Distributions

### P5.1 Computing Portfolio Expected Return & Portfolio Risk

To compute the portfolio expected return and the portfolio risk of two investments, use **PHStat → Decision-Making → Covariance and Portfolio Analysis**. This procedure creates a covariance (and portfolio analysis) worksheet into which you add the probabilities and outcomes. Click **Portfolio Management Analysis** to include the portfolio analysis section on the worksheet and create a worksheet similar to Figure E5.2 on page 213.

194 using the sample size, probability of an event of interest, and an outcomes range that you specify. If you click **Cumulative Probabilities**, the binomial table will include additional columns for $P(<=X)$, $P(<X)$, $P(>X)$, and $P(>=X)$. If you click **Histogram**, the procedure uses Excel charting features to create a histogram on a separate sheet.

### P5.2 Computing Binomial Probabilities

To compute binomial probabilities, use **PHStat → Probability & Prob. Distributions → Binomial**. This procedure creates a worksheet similar to Figure 5.2 on page

### P5.3 Computing Poisson Probabilities

To compute Poisson probabilities, use **PHStat → Probability & Prob. Distributions → Poisson**. This procedure creates a worksheet similar to Figure 5.5 on page 200 using the mean or expected number of events of interest that you specify. If you select the **Cumulative Probabilities** check box, the Poisson table will include additional columns for $P(<=X)$, $P(<X)$, $P(>X)$, and $P(>=X)$. If you click **Histogram**, the procedure uses Excel charting features to create a histogram on a separate sheet.

page 204 using the sample size, number of events of interest in the population, and population size that you specify. If you click **Histogram**, the procedure uses Excel charting features to create a histogram on a separate sheet.

## P5.4 Computing Hypergeometric Probabilities

To compute hypergeometric probabilities, use **PHStat → Probability & Prob. Distributions → Hypergeometric**. This procedure creates a worksheet similar to Figure 5.7 on

# Appendix M5
## Using Minitab for Discrete Probability Distributions

### M5.1 Computing Binomial Probabilities

To compute binomial probabilities for the Section 5.3 accounting information system example, shown in Figure 5.3 on page 194:

1. Open to a new, blank worksheet.
2. Enter the values **0, 1, 2, 3**, and **4** in rows 1 to 5 of column C1, leaving the unnumbered variable label cell at the top of the column empty.
3. Select **Calc → Probability Distributions → Binomial**.

In the Binomial Distribution dialog box (see Figure M5.1 on page 216):

4. Click **Probability** (to compute the probabilities of exactly $X$ events of interest for all values of $X$).

5. Enter **4** (the sample size) in the **Number of trials** box.
6. Enter **.1** in the **Event probability** box.
7. Click **Input column** and enter **C1** in its box.
8. Click **OK**.

### M5.2 Computing Poisson Probabilities

To compute Poisson probabilities for the Section 5.4 bank customer arrival example, shown in Figure 5.6 on page 200:

1. Open to a new, blank worksheet.
2. Enter the values **0** through **15** in rows 1 to 16 of column C1, leaving the unnumbered variable label cell at the top of the column empty.
3. Select **Calc → Probability Distributions → Poisson**.

**FIGURE M5.1**

Minitab Binomial Distribution dialog box

In the Poisson Distribution dialog box (see Figure M5.2 below):

4. Click **Probability** (to compute the probabilities of exactly *X* events for all values of *X*).
5. Enter **3** (the $\lambda$ value) in the **Mean** box.
6. Click **Input column** and enter **C1** in its box.
7. Click **OK**.

**FIGURE M5.2**

Minitab Poisson Distribution dialog box

## M5.3 Computing Hypergeometric Probabilities

To compute hypergeometric probabilities for the Section 5.5 team formation example, shown in Figure 5.8 on page 204:

1. Open to a new, blank worksheet.
2. Enter the values **0, 1, 2, 3, 4, 5, 6, 7,** and **8** in rows 1 to 9 of column C1, leaving the unnumbered variable label cell at the top of the column empty.
3. Select **Calc → Probability Distributions → Hypergeometric**.

In the Hypergeometric Distribution dialog box (see Figure M5.3):

4. Click **Probability** (to compute the probability of exactly *X* events for all values of *X*).
5. Enter **30** (the population size) in the **Population size (N)** box.
6. Enter **10** in the **Event count in population (M)** box.
7. Enter **8** (the sample size) in the **Sample size (n)** box.
8. Click **Input column** and enter **C1** in its box.
9. Click **OK**.

**FIGURE M5.3**

Minitab Hypergeometric Distribution dialog box

# CHAPTER SIX

## THE NORMAL DISTRIBUTION AND OTHER CONTINUOUS DISTRIBUTIONS

## LEARNING OBJECTIVES

### In this chapter, you learn:

- To compute probabilities from the normal distribution
- To use the normal probability plot to determine whether a set of data is approximately normally distributed
- To compute probabilities from the uniform distribution
- To compute probabilities from the exponential distribution
- To approximate binomial probabilities using the normal distribution

# USING STATISTICS @ OurCampus!

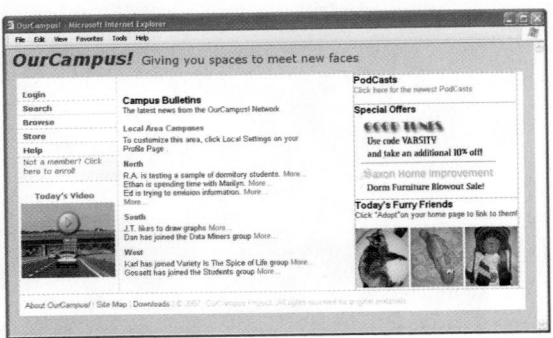

You are a designer for the OurCampus! Web site, which targets college students. To attract and retain customers, you need to make sure that the home page downloads quickly. Both the design of the home page and the load on the company's Web servers affect the download time. To check how fast the home page loads, you open a Web browser on a PC at the corporate offices of OurCampus! and measure the download time—the amount of time in seconds that pass from first linking to the Web site until the home page is fully displayed.

Past data indicate that the mean download time is 7 seconds and that the standard deviation is 2 seconds. Approximately two-thirds of the download times are between 5 and 9 seconds, and about 95% of the download times are between 3 and 11 seconds. In other words, the download times are distributed as a bell-shaped curve, with a clustering around the mean of 7 seconds. How could you use this information to answer questions about the download times of the current home page?

In Chapter 5, Saxon Home Improvement Company managers wanted to be able to solve problems about the number of tagged items in a given sample size. As an OurCampus! Web designer, you face a different task, one that involves a continuous measurement because a download time could be any value and not just a whole number. How can you answer questions about this *continuous numerical variable*, such as:

- What proportion of the home page downloads take more than 10 seconds?
- How many seconds elapse before 10% of the downloads are complete?
- How many seconds elapse before 99% of the downloads are complete?
- How would redesigning the home page to download faster affect the answers to these questions?

As in Chapter 5, you can use a probability distribution as a model. Reading this chapter will help you learn about characteristics of continuous probability distributions and how to use the normal, uniform, and exponential distributions to solve business problems.

## 6.1 CONTINUOUS PROBABILITY DISTRIBUTIONS

A **continuous probability density function** is the mathematical expression that defines the distribution of the values for a continuous random variable. Figure 6.1 graphically displays the three continuous probability density functions discussed in this chapter.

**FIGURE 6.1**

Three continuous distributions

Panel A depicts a normal distribution. The normal distribution is symmetrical and bell shaped, implying that most values tend to cluster around the mean, which, due to the distribution's symmetrical shape, is equal to the median. Although the values in a normal distribution can range from negative infinity to positive infinity, the shape of the distribution makes it very unlikely that extremely large or extremely small values will occur.

Panel B depicts a uniform distribution where each value has an equal probability of occurrence anywhere in the range between the smallest value, *a*, and the largest value, *b*. Sometimes referred to as the rectangular distribution, the uniform distribution is symmetrical and therefore the mean equals the median.

Panel C illustrates an exponential distribution. This distribution is skewed to the right, making the mean larger than the median. The range for an exponential distribution is zero to positive infinity, but the distribution's shape makes the occurrence of extremely large values unlikely.

## 6.2   THE NORMAL DISTRIBUTION

The **normal distribution** (sometimes referred to as the *Gaussian distribution*) is the most common continuous distribution used in statistics. The normal distribution is vitally important in statistics for three main reasons:

- Numerous continuous variables common in business have distributions that closely resemble the normal distribution.
- The normal distribution can be used to approximate various discrete probability distributions.
- The normal distribution provides the basis for *classical statistical inference* because of its relationship to the *Central Limit Theorem* (which is discussed in Section 7.4).

The normal distribution is represented by the classic bell shape shown in Panel A of Figure 6.1. In the normal distribution, you can calculate the probability that various values occur within certain ranges or intervals. However, the *exact* probability of a *particular value* from a continuous distribution such as the normal distribution is zero. This property distinguishes continuous variables, which are measured, from discrete variables, which are counted. As an example, time (in seconds) is measured and not counted. Therefore, you can determine the probability that the download time for a home page on a Web browser is between 7 and 10 seconds, or the probability that the download time is between 8 and 9 seconds, or the probability that the download time is between 7.99 and 8.01 seconds. However, the probability that the download time is *exactly* 8 seconds is zero.

The normal distribution has several important theoretical properties:

- It is symmetrical and thus its mean and median are equal.
- It is bell shaped in its appearance.
- Its interquartile range is equal to 1.33 standard deviations. Thus, the middle 50% of the values are contained within an interval of two-thirds of a standard deviation below the mean and two-thirds of a standard deviation above the mean.
- It has an infinite range $(-\infty < X < \infty)$.

In practice, many variables have distributions that closely resemble the theoretical properties of the normal distribution. The data in Table 6.1 on page 220 represent the thickness (in inches) of 10,000 brass washers manufactured by a large company. The continuous variable of interest, thickness, can be approximated by the normal distribution. The measurements of the thickness of the 10,000 brass washers cluster in the interval 0.0190 to 0.0192 inch and distribute symmetrically around that grouping, forming a bell-shaped pattern.

Figure 6.2 shows the relative frequency histogram and polygon for the distribution of the thickness of 10,000 brass washers. For these data, the first three theoretical properties of the normal distribution are approximately satisfied. However, the fourth one, having an infinite range, does not hold. The thickness of the washer cannot possibly be zero or below, nor can a washer be so thick that it becomes unusable. From Table 6.1, you see that only 48 out of every

**TABLE 6.1**

Thickness of 10,000 Brass Washers

| Thickness (inches) | Relative Frequency |
|---|---|
| < 0.0180 | 48/10,000 = 0.0048 |
| 0.0180 < 0.0182 | 122/10,000 = 0.0122 |
| 0.0182 < 0.0184 | 325/10,000 = 0.0325 |
| 0.0184 < 0.0186 | 695/10,000 = 0.0695 |
| 0.0186 < 0.0188 | 1,198/10,000 = 0.1198 |
| 0.0188 < 0.0190 | 1,664/10,000 = 0.1664 |
| 0.0190 < 0.0192 | 1,896/10,000 = 0.1896 |
| 0.0192 < 0.0194 | 1,664/10,000 = 0.1664 |
| 0.0194 < 0.0196 | 1,198/10,000 = 0.1198 |
| 0.0196 < 0.0198 | 695/10,000 = 0.0695 |
| 0.0198 < 0.0200 | 325/10,000 = 0.0325 |
| 0.0200 < 0.0202 | 122/10,000 = 0.0122 |
| 0.0202 or above | 48/10,000 = 0.0048 |
| Total | 1.0000 |

**FIGURE 6.2**

Relative frequency histogram and polygon of the thickness of 10,000 brass washers

*Source: Data are taken from Table 6.1.*

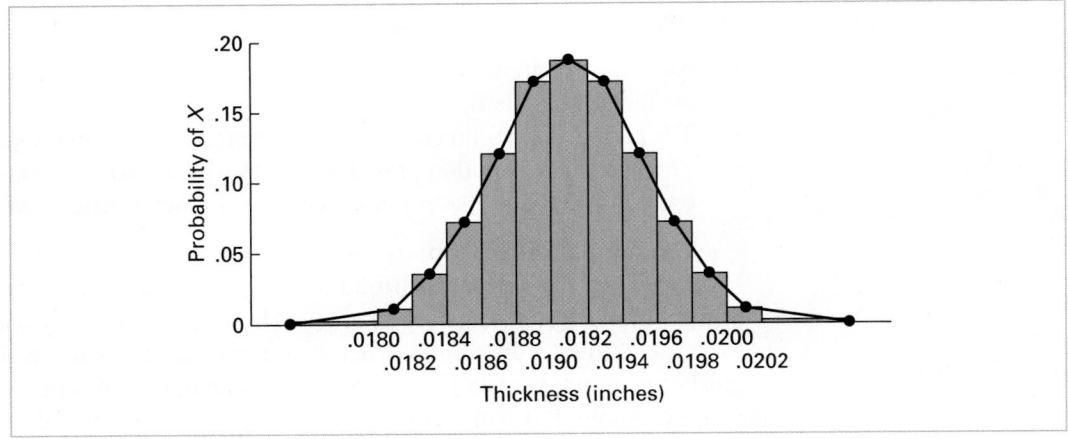

10,000 brass washers manufactured are expected to have a thickness of 0.0202 inch or more, whereas an equal number are expected to have a thickness under 0.0180 inch. Thus, the chance of randomly getting a washer so thin or so thick is 0.0048 + 0.0048 = 0.0096, less than 1 in 100.

The mathematical expression representing a continuous probability density function is denoted by the symbol $f(X)$. For the normal distribution, the **normal probability density function** is given in Equation (6.1).

Normal Probability Density Function

$$f(X) = \frac{1}{\sqrt{2\pi\sigma}} e^{-(1/2)[(X-\mu)/\sigma]^2}$$

(6.1)

where

$e$ = the mathematical constant approximated by 2.71828

$\pi$ = the mathematical constant approximated by 3.14159

$\mu$ = the mean

$\sigma$ = the standard deviation

$X$ = any value of the continuous variable, where $-\infty < X < \infty$

Because $e$ and $\pi$ are mathematical constants, the probabilities of the random variable $X$ are dependent only on the two parameters of the normal distribution—the mean, $\mu$, and the standard deviation, $\sigma$. Every time you specify a *particular combination* of $\mu$ and $\sigma$, a *different* normal probability distribution is generated. Figure 6.3 illustrates three different normal distributions.

**FIGURE 6.3**

Three normal distributions

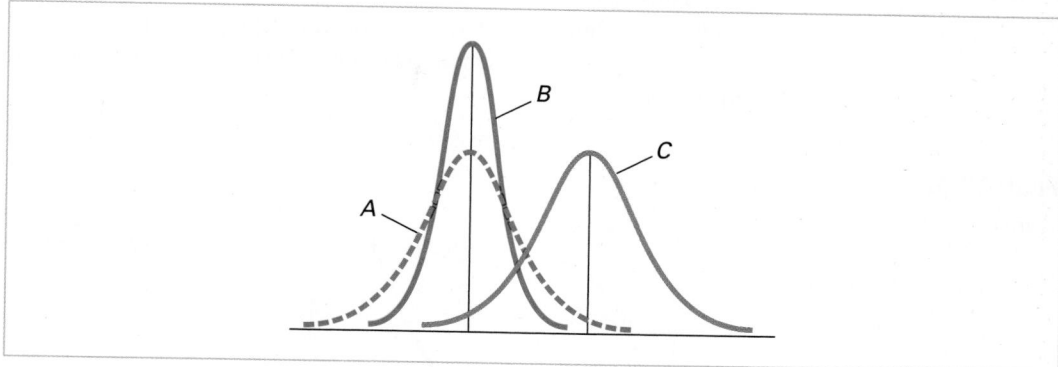

Distributions $A$ and $B$ have the same mean ($\mu$) but have different standard deviations. Distributions $A$ and $C$ have the same standard deviation ($\sigma$) but have different means. Distributions $B$ and $C$ differ with respect to both $\mu$ and $\sigma$.

The mathematical expression in Equation (6.1) is computationally tedious and requires integral calculus. Fortunately, normal probability tables are available, and you *never* need to use Equation (6.1) to make computations of normal distribution probabilities. The first step in finding normal probabilities is to use the **transformation formula**, given in Equation (6.2), to convert any normal random variable, $X$, to a **standardized normal random variable**, $Z$.

Transformation Formula

The $Z$ value is equal to the difference between $X$ and the mean, $\mu$, divided by the standard deviation, $\sigma$.

$$Z = \frac{X - \mu}{\sigma} \qquad \text{(6.2)}$$

Although the original data for the random variable $X$ had mean $\mu$ and standard deviation $\sigma$, the standardized random variable, $Z$, will always have mean $\mu = 0$ and standard deviation $\sigma = 1$.

Any set of normally distributed values can be converted to its standardized form. Then you can determine the desired probabilities by using Table E.2, the **cumulative standardized normal distribution**. To see how the transformation formula is applied and the results are used to find probabilities from Table E.2, recall from the Using Statistics scenario on page 218 that past data indicate that the time to download the Web page is normally distributed, with a mean, $\mu = 7$ seconds and a standard deviation, $\sigma = 2$ seconds. From Figure 6.4 on page 222, you see that every measurement, $X$, has a corresponding standardized measurement, $Z$, computed from the transformation formula [Equation (6.2)]. Therefore, a download time of 9 seconds is equivalent to 1 standardized unit (i.e., 1 standard deviation above the mean) because

$$Z = \frac{9 - 7}{2} = +1$$

A download time of 1 second is equivalent to 3 standardized units (3 standard deviations) below the mean because

$$Z = \frac{1-7}{2} = -3$$

Thus, the standard deviation is the unit of measurement. In other words, a time of 9 seconds is 2 seconds (i.e., 1 standard deviation) higher, or *slower*, than the mean time of 7 seconds. Similarly, a time of 1 second is 6 seconds (i.e., 3 standard deviations) lower, or *faster*, than the mean time.

**FIGURE 6.4**

Transformation of scales

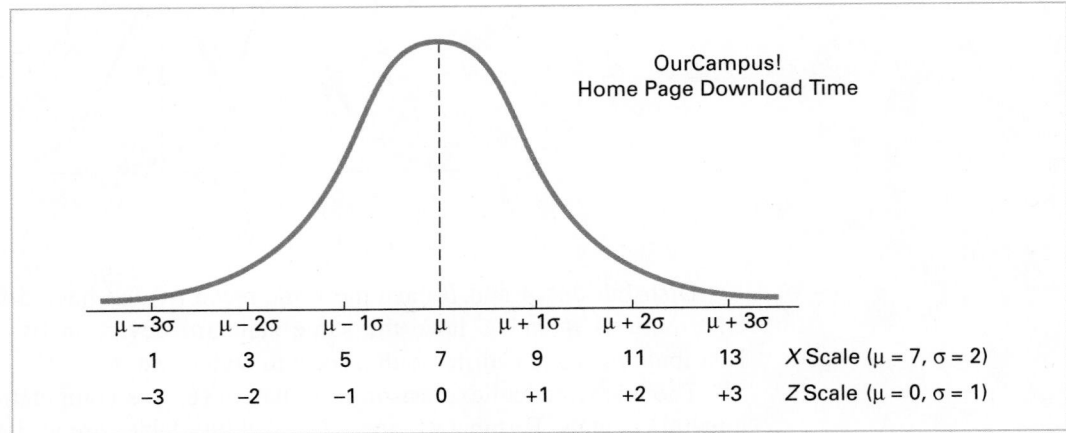

To further illustrate the transformation formula, suppose that the home page of another Web site has a download time that is normally distributed, with a mean, $\mu = 4$ seconds, and a standard deviation, $\sigma = 1$ second. This distribution is illustrated in Figure 6.5.

**FIGURE 6.5**

A different transformation of scales

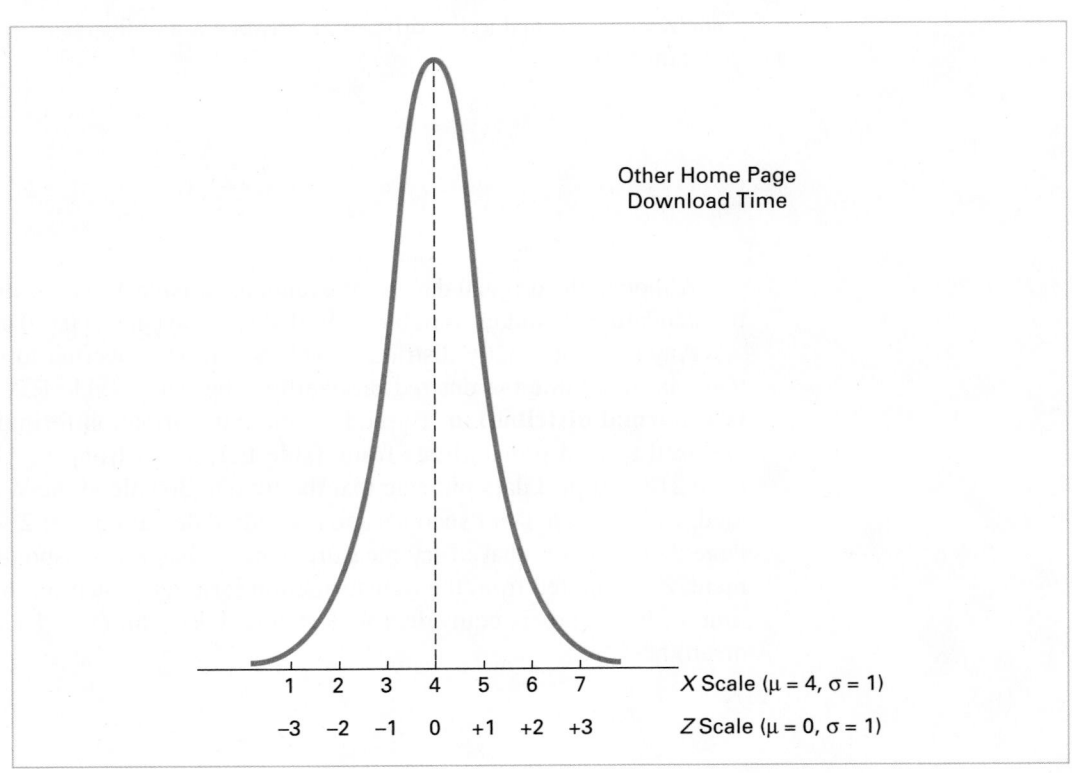

Comparing these results with those of the OurCampus! Web site, you see that a download time of 5 seconds is 1 standard deviation above the mean download time because

$$Z = \frac{5-4}{1} = +1$$

A time of 1 second is 3 standard deviations below the mean download time because

$$Z = \frac{1-4}{1} = -3$$

Suppose you wanted to find the probability that the download time for the OurCampus! site is less than 9 seconds. First, you use Equation (6.2) on page 221 to transform $X = 9$ to standardized $Z$ units. Because $X = 9$ is one standard deviation above the mean, $Z = +1.00$. Next, you use Table E.2 to find the cumulative area under the normal curve less than (i.e., to the left of) $Z = +1.00$. To read the probability or area under the curve less than $Z = +1.00$, you scan down the $Z$ column from Table E.2 until you locate the $Z$ value of interest (in 10ths) in the $Z$ row for 1.0. Next, you read across this row until you intersect the column that contains the 100ths place of the $Z$ value. Therefore, in the body of the table, the tabulated probability for $Z = 1.00$ corresponds to the intersection of the row $Z = 1.0$ with the column $Z = .00$, as shown in Table 6.2, which is extracted from Table E.2. This probability is 0.8413. As illustrated in Figure 6.6, there is an 84.13% chance that the download time will be less than 9 seconds.

**TABLE 6.2**

Finding a Cumulative Area Under the Normal Curve

| Z | **.00** | .01 | .02 | .03 | .04 | .05 | .06 | .07 | .08 | .09 |
|---|---|---|---|---|---|---|---|---|---|---|
| 0.0 | .5000 | .5040 | .5080 | .5120 | .5160 | .5199 | .5239 | .5279 | .5319 | .5359 |
| 0.1 | .5398 | .5438 | .5478 | .5517 | .5557 | .5596 | .5636 | .5675 | .5714 | .5753 |
| 0.2 | .5793 | .5832 | .5871 | .5910 | .5948 | .5987 | .6026 | .6064 | .6103 | .6141 |
| 0.3 | .6179 | .6217 | .6255 | .6293 | .6331 | .6368 | .6406 | .6443 | .6480 | .6517 |
| 0.4 | .6554 | .6591 | .6628 | .6664 | .6700 | .6736 | .6772 | .6808 | .6844 | .6879 |
| 0.5 | .6915 | .6950 | .6985 | .7019 | .7054 | .7088 | .7123 | .7157 | .7190 | .7224 |
| 0.6 | .7257 | .7291 | .7324 | .7357 | .7389 | .7422 | .7454 | .7486 | .7518 | .7549 |
| 0.7 | .7580 | .7612 | .7642 | .7673 | .7704 | .7734 | .7764 | .7794 | .7823 | .7852 |
| 0.8 | .7881 | .7910 | .7939 | .7967 | .7995 | .8023 | .8051 | .8078 | .8106 | .8133 |
| 0.9 | .8159 | .8186 | .8212 | .8238 | .8264 | .8289 | .8315 | .8340 | .8365 | .8389 |
| 1.0 | .8413 | .8438 | .8461 | .8485 | .8508 | .8531 | .8554 | .8577 | .8599 | .8621 |

Source: *Extracted from Table E.2.*

**FIGURE 6.6**

Determining the area less than $Z$ from a cumulative standardized normal distribution

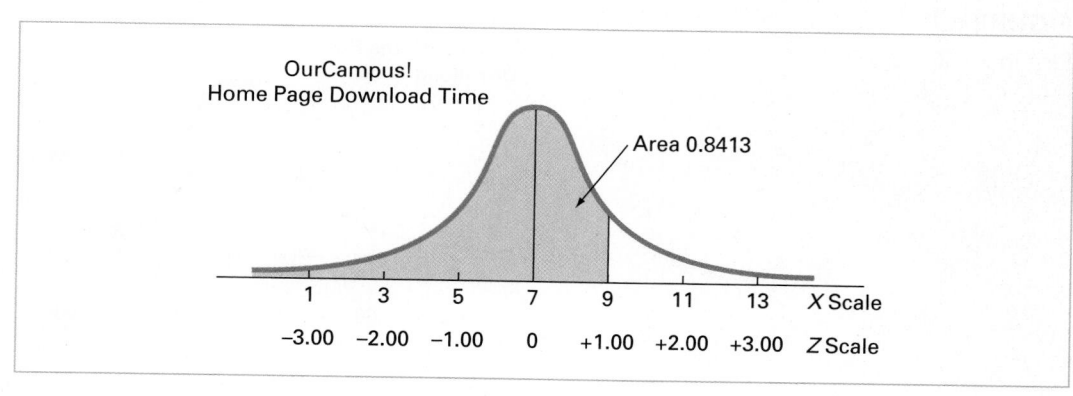

OurCampus! Home Page Download Time

Area 0.8413

However, for the other home page, you see that a time of 5 seconds is 1 standardized unit above the mean time of 4 seconds. Thus, the probability that the download time will be less than 5 seconds is also 0.8413. Figure 6.7 shows that regardless of the value of the mean, $\mu$, and standard deviation, $\sigma$, of a normally distributed variable, Equation (6.2) can transform the problem to $Z$ values.

**FIGURE 6.7**

Demonstrating a transformation of scales for corresponding cumulative portions under two normal curves

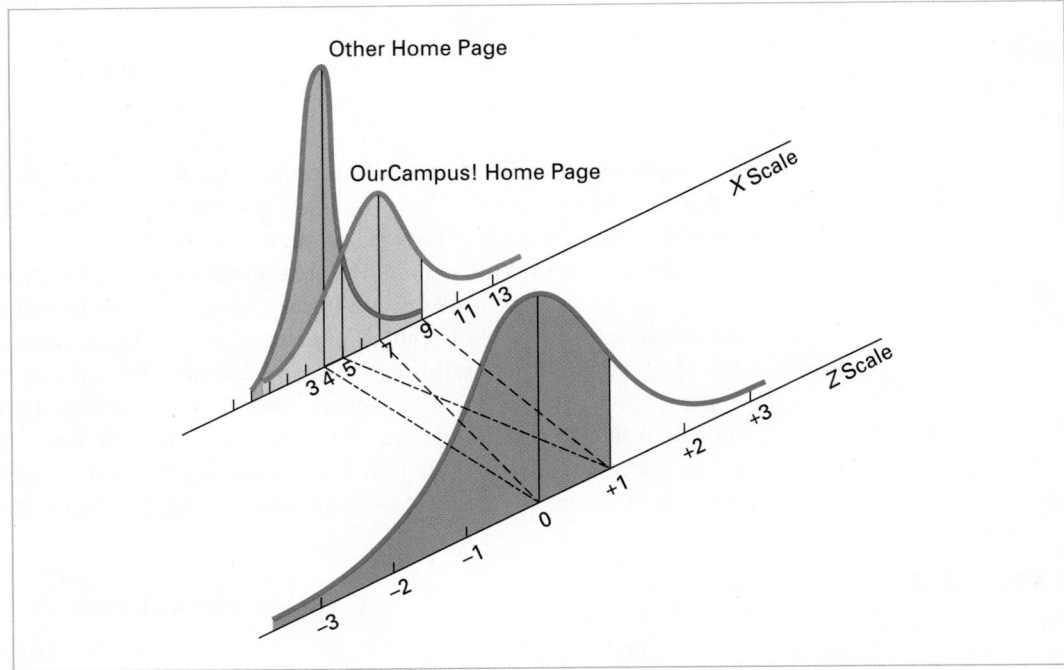

Now that you have learned to use Table E.2 with Equation (6.2), you can answer many questions related to the OurCampus! home page, using the normal distribution.

**EXAMPLE 6.1**

FINDING $P(X > 9)$

What is the probability that the download time will be more than 9 seconds?

**SOLUTION** The probability that the download time will be less than 9 seconds is 0.8413 (see Figure 6.6 on page 223). Thus, the probability that the download time will be more than 9 seconds is the *complement* of less than 9 seconds, $1 - 0.8413 = 0.1587$. Figure 6.8 illustrates this result.

**FIGURE 6.8**

Finding $P(X > 9)$

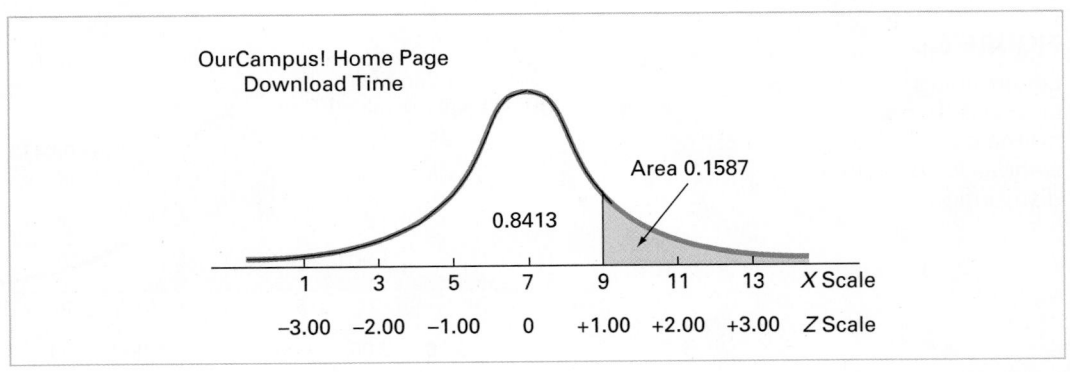

**EXAMPLE 6.2**

FINDING $P(7 < X < 9)$

What is the probability that the download time will be between 7 and 9 seconds?

**SOLUTION** From Figure 6.6 on page 223, you can see that the probability that a download time is less than 9 seconds is 0.8413. Now you must determine the probability that the download time will be under 7 seconds and subtract this from the probability that the download time is under 9 seconds. Figure 6.9 illustrates this result.

**FIGURE 6.9**

Finding $P(7 < X < 9)$

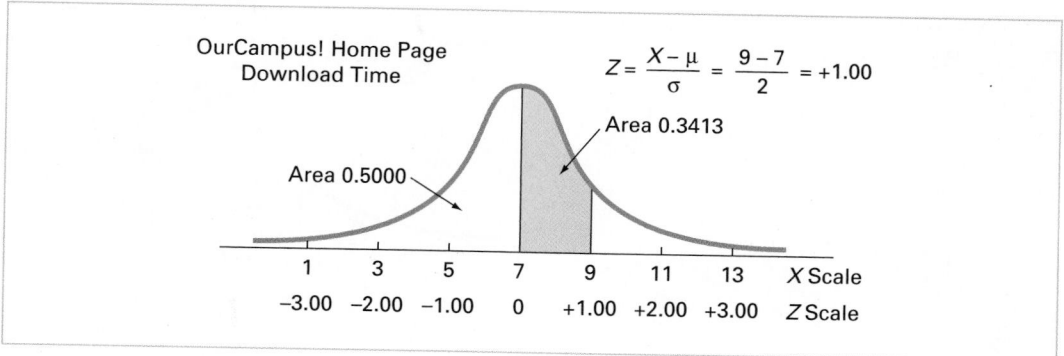

Using Equation (6.2) on page 221,

$$Z = \frac{7-7}{2} = 0.00$$

Using Table E.2 or Table 6.2, the area under the normal curve less than the mean of $Z = 0.00$ is 0.5000. (Because the mean and the median are the same for normally distributed data, 50% of the download times are less than 7 seconds.) Hence, the area under the curve between $Z = 0.00$ and $Z = 1.00$ is $0.8413 - 0.5000 = 0.3413$.

**EXAMPLE 6.3**

FINDING $P(X < 7 \text{ OR } X > 9)$

What is the probability that the download time will be under 7 seconds or over 9 seconds?

**SOLUTION** From Figure 6.9, the probability that the download time is between 7 and 9 seconds is 0.3413. The probability that the download time is under 7 seconds or over 9 seconds is its complement, $1 - 0.3413 = 0.6587$.

Another way to view this problem, is to separately calculate the probability of a download time of less than 7 seconds and the probability of a download time of greater than 9 seconds and then add these two probabilities together. Figure 6.10 illustrates this result. Because the mean is seven seconds, 50% of download times are under 7 seconds. From Example 6.1, the probability that the download time is greater than 9 seconds is 0.1587. Hence, the probability that a download time is under 7 or over 9 seconds, $P(X < 7 \text{ or } X > 9)$, is $0.5000 + 0.1587 = 0.6587$.

**FIGURE 6.10**

Finding $P(X < 7$ or $X > 9)$

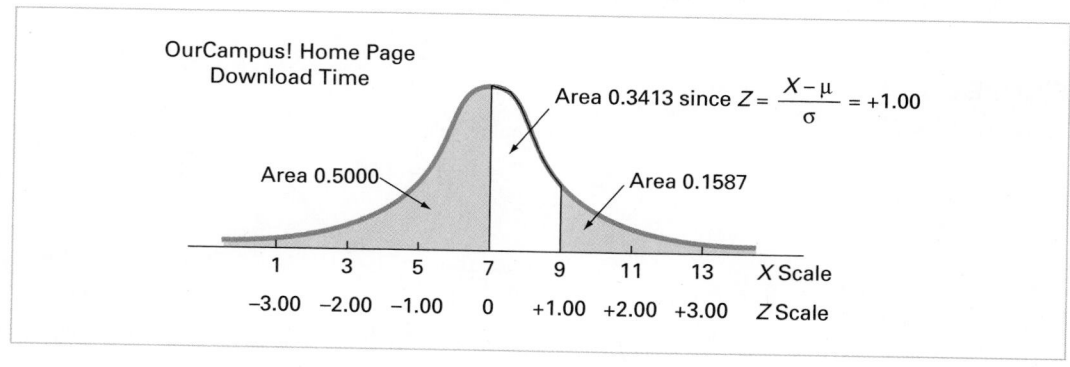

**EXAMPLE 6.4**

FINDING $P(5 < X < 9)$

What is the probability that the download time will be between 5 and 9 seconds—that is, $P(5 < X < 9)$?

**SOLUTION**  In Figure 6.11, you can see that the area of interest is located between two values, 5 and 9.

**FIGURE 6.11**

Finding $P(5 < X < 9)$

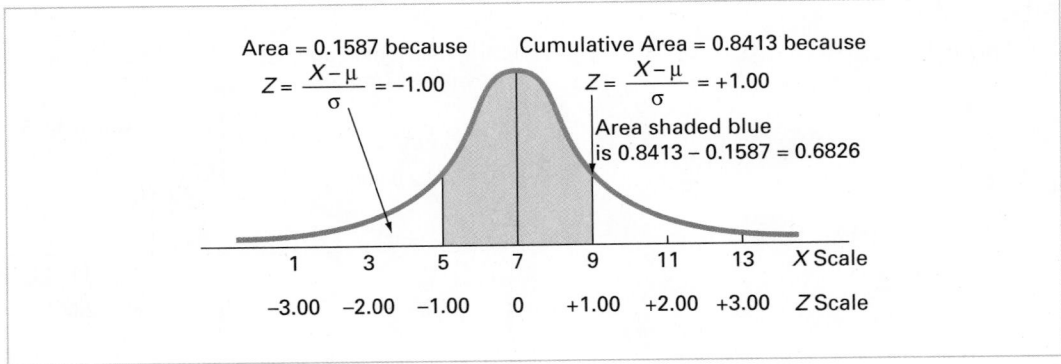

In Example 6.1 on page 224, you already found that the area under the normal curve less than 9 seconds is 0.8413. To find the area under the normal curve less than 5 seconds,

$$Z = \frac{5-7}{2} = -1.00$$

Using Table E.2, you look up $Z = -1.00$ and find 0.1587. Thus, the probability that the download time will be between 5 and 9 seconds is $0.8413 - 0.1587 = 0.6826$, as displayed in Figure 6.11.

The result of Example 6.4 enables you to state that for any normal distribution, 68.26% of the values will fall within ±1 standard deviation of the mean. From Figure 6.12, 95.44% of the values will fall within ±2 standard deviations of the mean. Thus, 95.44% of the download times are between 3 and 11 seconds. From Figure 6.13, 99.73% of the values are within ±3 standard deviations above or below the mean. Thus, 99.73% of the download times are between 1 and 13 seconds. Therefore, it is unlikely (0.0027, or only 27 in 10,000) that a download time will be so fast or so slow that it will take under 1 second or more than 13 seconds. In general, you can use $6\sigma$ (that is, 3 standard deviations below the mean to 3 standard deviations above the mean) as a practical approximation of the range for normally distributed data.

**FIGURE 6.12**

Finding $P(3 < X < 11)$

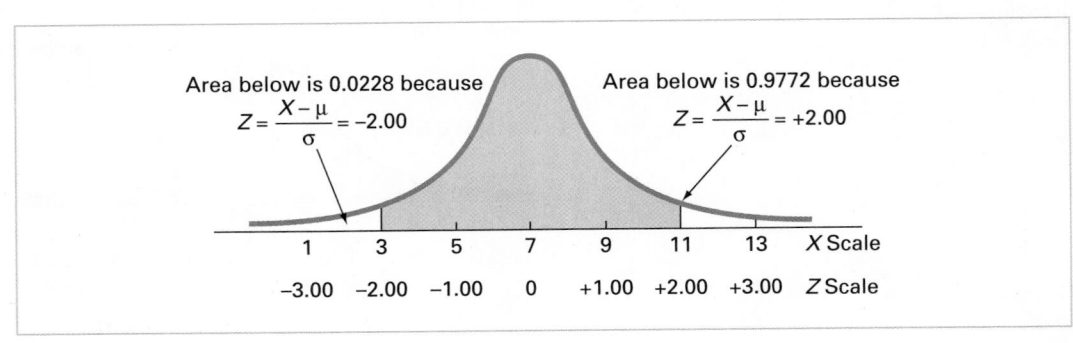

**FIGURE 6.13**

Finding $P(1 < X < 13)$

Figures 6.11, 6.12, and 6.13 illustrate how the values of a normal distribution cluster near the mean. For any normal distribution:

- Approximately 68.26% of the values fall within ±1 standard deviation of the mean.
- Approximately 95.44% of the values fall within ±2 standard deviations of the mean.
- Approximately 99.73% of the values fall within ±3 standard deviations of the mean.

This result is the justification for the empirical rule presented on page 112. The accuracy of the empirical rule improves as a data set follows the normal distribution more closely.

**EXAMPLE 6.5**

FINDING $P(X < 3.5)$

What is the probability that a download time will be under 3.5 seconds?

**SOLUTION** To calculate the probability that a download time will be under 3.5 seconds, you need to examine the shaded lower-left tail region of Figure 6.14.

**FIGURE 6.14**

Finding $P(X < 3.5)$

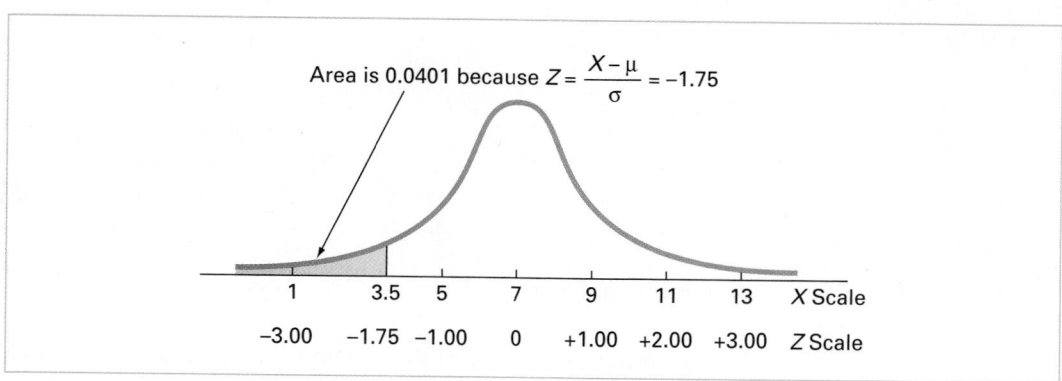

To determine the area under the curve below 3.5 seconds, you first calculate

$$Z = \frac{X - \mu}{\sigma} = \frac{3.5 - 7}{2} = -1.75$$

You then look up the $Z$ value of $-1.75$ by matching the appropriate $Z$ row $(-1.7)$ with the appropriate $Z$ column $(.05)$, as shown in Table 6.3 on page 228 (which is extracted from Table E.2). The resulting probability or area under the curve less than $-1.75$ standard deviations below the mean is 0.0401.

**TABLE 6.3**

Finding a Cumulative Area Under the Normal Curve

| | | | | | Cumulative Probabilities | | | | | |
|---|---|---|---|---|---|---|---|---|---|---|
| **Z** | **.00** | **.01** | **.02** | **.03** | **.04** | **.05** | **.06** | **.07** | **.08** | **.09** |
| . | . | . | . | . | . | . | . | . | . | . |
| . | . | . | . | . | . | . | . | . | . | . |
| . | . | . | . | . | . | . | . | . | . | . |
| −1.7 | .0446 | .0436 | .0427 | .0418 | .0409 | .0401 | .0392 | .0384 | .0375 | .0367 |
| −1.6 | .0548 | .0537 | .0526 | .0516 | .0505 | .0495 | .0485 | .0475 | .0465 | .0455 |

Source: *Extracted from Table E.2.*

Examples 6.1 through 6.5 require you to use the normal table to find an area under the normal curve that corresponds to a specific $X$ value. There are many circumstances in which you want to find the $X$ value that corresponds to a specific area. Examples 6.6 and 6.7 illustrate such situations.

**EXAMPLE 6.6**

FINDING THE $X$ VALUE FOR A CUMULATIVE PROBABILITY OF 0.10

How much time (in seconds) will elapse before 10% of the downloads are complete?

**SOLUTION** Because 10% of the home pages are expected to download in under $X$ seconds, the area under the normal curve less than this value is 0.1000. Using the body of Table E.2, you search for the area or probability of 0.1000. The closest result is 0.1003, as shown in Table 6.4 (which is extracted from Table E.2).

**TABLE 6.4**

Finding a $Z$ Value Corresponding to a Particular Cumulative Area (0.10) Under the Normal Curve

| | | | | | Cumulative Probabilities | | | | | |
|---|---|---|---|---|---|---|---|---|---|---|
| **Z** | **.00** | **.01** | **.02** | **.03** | **.04** | **.05** | **.06** | **.07** | **.08** | **.09** |
| . | . | . | . | . | . | . | . | . | . | . |
| . | . | . | . | . | . | . | . | . | . | . |
| . | . | . | . | . | . | . | . | . | . | . |
| −1.5 | .0668 | .0655 | .0643 | .0630 | .0618 | .0606 | .0594 | .0582 | .0571 | .0559 |
| −1.4 | .0808 | .0793 | .0778 | .0764 | .0749 | .0735 | .0721 | .0708 | .0694 | .0681 |
| −1.3 | .0968 | .0951 | .0934 | .0918 | .0901 | .0885 | .0869 | .0853 | .0838 | .0823 |
| −1.2 | .1151 | .1131 | .1112 | .1093 | .1075 | .0156 | .0138 | .1020 | .1003 | .0985 |

Source: *Extracted from Table E.2.*

Working from this area to the margins of the table, the $Z$ value corresponding to the particular $Z$ row (−1.2) and $Z$ column (.08) is −1.28 (see Figure 6.15).

**FIGURE 6.15**

Finding $Z$ to determine $X$

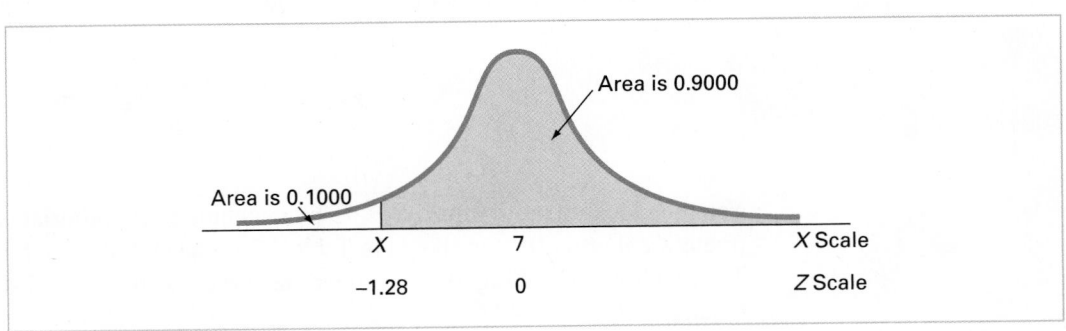

Once you find $Z$, you use the transformation formula Equation (6.2) on page 221 to determine the $X$ value, as follows. Let

$$Z = \frac{X - \mu}{\sigma}$$

then

$$X = \mu + Z\sigma$$

Substituting $\mu = 7$, $\sigma = 2$, and $Z = -1.28$,

$$X = 7 + (-1.28)(2) = 4.44 \text{ seconds}$$

Thus, 10% of the download times are 4.44 seconds or less.

In general, you use Equation (6.3) for finding an $X$ value.

**Finding An $X$ Value Associated with Known Probability**

The $X$ value is equal to the mean $\mu$ plus the product of the $Z$ value and the standard deviation $\sigma$.

$$X = \mu + Z\sigma \qquad \textbf{(6.3)}$$

To find a *particular* value associated with a known probability, follow these steps:

1. Sketch the normal curve and then place the values for the mean and $X$ on the $X$ and $Z$ scales.
2. Find the cumulative area less than $X$.
3. Shade the area of interest.
4. Using Table E.2, determine the $Z$ value corresponding to the area under the normal curve less than $X$.
5. Using Equation (6.3), solve for $X$:

$$X = \mu + Z\sigma$$

**EXAMPLE 6.7**

FINDING THE $X$ VALUES THAT INCLUDE 95% OF THE DOWNLOAD TIMES

What are the lower and upper values of $X$, symmetrically distributed around the mean, that include 95% of the download times?

**SOLUTION**  First, you need to find the lower value of $X$ (called $X_L$). Then you find the upper value of $X$ (called $X_U$). Because 95% of the values are between $X_L$ and $X_U$, and because $X_L$ and $X_U$ are equally distant from the mean, 2.5% of the values are below $X_L$ (see Figure 6.16).

**FIGURE 6.16**

Finding $Z$ to determine $X_L$

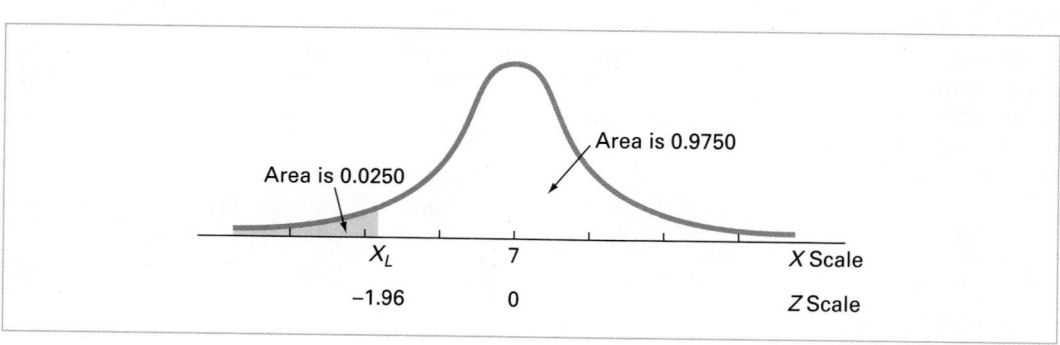

Although $X_L$ is not known, you can find the corresponding $Z$ value because the area under the normal curve less than this $Z$ is 0.0250. Using the body of Table 6.5, you search for the probability 0.0250.

**TABLE 6.5**

Finding a Z Value Corresponding to a Cumulative Area of 0.025 Under the Normal Curve

| | | | | | Cumulative Area | | | | | |
|---|---|---|---|---|---|---|---|---|---|---|
| Z | .00 | .01 | .02 | .03 | .04 | .05 | .06 | .07 | .08 | .09 |
| . | . | . | . | . | . | . | . | . | . | . |
| . | . | . | . | . | . | . | . | . | . | . |
| . | . | . | . | . | . | . | . | . | . | . |
| −2.0 | .0228 | .0222 | .0217 | .0212 | .0207 | .0202 | .0197 | .0192 | .0188 | .0183 |
| −1.9 | .0287 | .0281 | .0274 | .0268 | .0262 | .0256 | .0250 | .0244 | .0239 | .0233 |
| −1.8 | .0359 | .0351 | .0344 | .0336 | .0329 | .0232 | .0314 | .0307 | .0301 | .0294 |

Source: *Extracted from Table E.2.*

Working from the body of the table to the margins of the table, you see that the $Z$ value corresponding to the particular $Z$ row (−1.9) and $Z$ column (.06) is −1.96.

Once you find $Z$, the final step is to use Equation (6.3) on page 229 as follows:

$$X = \mu + Z\sigma$$
$$= 7 + (-1.96)(2)$$
$$= 7 - 3.92$$
$$= 3.08 \text{ seconds}$$

You use a similar process to find $X_U$. Because only 2.5% of the home page downloads take longer than $X_U$ seconds, 97.5% of the home page downloads take less than $X_U$ seconds. From the symmetry of the normal distribution, the desired $Z$ value, as shown in Figure 6.17, is +1.96 (because $Z$ lies to the right of the standardized mean of 0). You can also extract this $Z$ value from Table 6.6. You can see that 0.975 is the area under the normal curve less than the $Z$ value of +1.96.

**FIGURE 6.17**

Finding Z to determine $X_U$

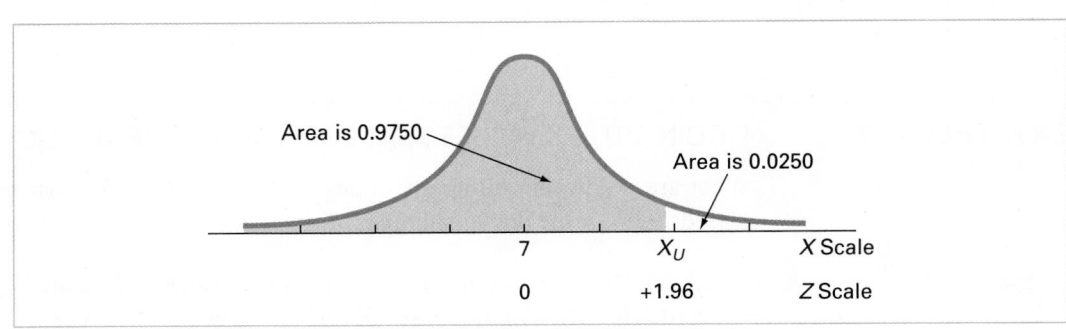

Area is 0.9750
Area is 0.0250

| 7 | $X_U$ | X Scale |
| 0 | +1.96 | Z Scale |

**TABLE 6.6**

Finding a Z Value Corresponding to a Cumulative Area of 0.975 Under the Normal Curve

| | | | | | Cumulative Area | | | | | |
|---|---|---|---|---|---|---|---|---|---|---|
| Z | .00 | .01 | .02 | .03 | .04 | .05 | .06 | .07 | .08 | .09 |
| . | . | . | . | . | . | . | . | . | . | . |
| . | . | . | . | . | . | . | . | . | . | . |
| . | . | . | . | . | . | . | . | . | . | . |
| +1.8 | .9641 | .9649 | .9656 | .9664 | .9671 | .9678 | .9686 | .9693 | .9699 | .9706 |
| +1.9 | .9713 | .9719 | .9726 | .9732 | .9738 | .9744 | .9750 | .9756 | .9761 | .9767 |
| +2.0 | .9772 | .9778 | .9783 | .9788 | .9793 | .9798 | .9803 | .9808 | .9812 | .9817 |

Source: *Extracted from Table E.2.*

Using Equation (6.3) on page 229,

$$X = \mu + Z\sigma$$
$$= 7 + (+1.96)(2)$$
$$= 7 + 3.92$$
$$= 10.92 \text{ seconds}$$

Therefore, 95% of the download times are between 3.08 and 10.92 seconds.

# VISUAL EXPLORATIONS: Exploring the Normal Distribution

You can use the Visual Explorations Normal Distribution procedure to see the effects of changes in the mean and standard deviation on the area under a normal distribution curve.

Open the Visual Explorations.xla add-in workbook and select **VisualExplorations → Normal Distribution** (Excel 97-2003) or **Add-Ins → VisualExplorations → Normal Distribution** (Excel 2007). You will see a normal curve for the Using Statistics home page download example and a floating control panel that allows you to adjust the shape of the curve and the shaded area under the curve (see illustration below). Use the control panel spinner but-

tons to change the values for the mean, standard deviation, and $X$ value, while noting their effects on the probability of $X \leq$ value and the corresponding shaded area under the curve (see illustration below). If you prefer, you can select the **Z Values** option button to see the normal curve labeled with $Z$ values.

Click the **Reset** button to reset the control panel values or click **Help** for additional information about the problem. Click **Finish** when you are done exploring. (Review Section E1.8 on page 20 for more information on using add-ins, if necessary.)

You can also use Microsoft Excel or Minitab to compute normal probabilities. Figure 6.18 illustrates a Microsoft Excel worksheet for Examples 6.5 and 6.6 and Figure 6.19 illustrates Minitab results for Examples 6.1 and 6.6.

**FIGURE 6.18**

Microsoft Excel worksheet for computing normal probabilities

*See Section E6.1 or P6.1 to create this.*

| | A | B | |
|---|---|---|---|
| 1 | **Normal Probabilities** | | |
| 2 | | | |
| 3 | **Common Data** | | |
| 4 | **Mean** | 7 | |
| 5 | **Standard Deviation** | 2 | |
| 6 | | | |
| 7 | **Probability for X <=** | | |
| 8 | **X Value** | 3.5 | |
| 9 | **Z Value** | -1.75 | =STANDARDIZE(B8, B4, B5) |
| 10 | **P(X<=3.5)** | 0.0401 | =NORMDIST(B8, B4, B5, TRUE) |
| 11 | | | |
| 12 | **Find X and Z Given Cum. Pctage.** | | |
| 13 | **Cumulative Percentage** | 10.00% | |
| 14 | **Z Value** | -1.2816 | =NORMSINV(B13) |
| 15 | **X Value** | 4.4369 | =NORMINV(B13, B4, B5) |

**FIGURE 6.19**

Minitab results for normal probabilities

*See Section M6.1 to create this.*

**Cumulative Distribution Function**

```
Normal with mean = 7 and standard deviation = 2

x    P( X <= x )
9       0.841345
```

**Inverse Cumulative Distribution Function**

```
Normal with mean = 7 and standard deviation = 2

P( X <= x )          x
       0.1    4.43690
```

# (The Not-So-Normal Story of) How the Normal Distribution Got Its Name

*From the Authors' Desktop*

You've already read that the normal distribution is a very important one in statistics. The name "normal" might suggest that other probability distributions are somehow abnormal. This is not the case. In fact, if anything is abnormal, it is the story of how the normal distribution got its name.

The story starts with Abraham de Moivre who, in the early eighteenth century, was computing binomial probabilities for various games of chance and writing such papers as *The Doctrine of Chances*. (A problem in this paper is what led Thomas Bayes to write *An Essay Towards Solving a Problem in the Doctrine of Chances* discussed in the *From the Authors' Desktop* on page 165.) With no computers around at the time, de Moivre had to laboriously hand calculate those probabilities

using the equivalent of Equation 5.11 on page 191 for each solution. As he worked out his solutions for all cases for a certain type of problem, he began to notice that a histogram of his binomial results suggested the trace of a bell-shaped curve. (The normal approximation to the binomial distribution is covered in Section 6.6.)

For this discovery, you might expect that de Moivre would have the distribution named for him. (After all, in Chapter 5 you already have read about a distribution named after its discoverer, Siméon-Denis Poisson.) But no! If anything, the distribution is sometimes called the Gaussian distribution, after the German Carl Frederick Gauss, who, about a century later than de Moivre, used the normal distribution to describe the distribution of errors in measurements made by astronomers. Because

of this application, the normal distribution became known as the Error Curve.

Over time, other researchers discovered that when they measured other things, the same pattern of errors occurred. By the late nineteenth century, some began to conclude that the Error Curve was a fundamental universal law that governed *all* measurements of *any* natural phenomena.

Today we know that not all things conform to the normal distribution, although many do, and that nonnormal distributions are not any less natural than normal ones. For this understanding, we probably have to thank Karl Pearson.

Pearson was a mathematician interested in questions of biological inheritance and evolution. Pearson believed that individuals in populations could show true variability, independent of the variability caused by errors in measurement that astronomers and Gauss had recognized. Although Pearson's concept of individual variability underlies most of the concepts taught in this book, his point of view was radical to some of his contemporaries who saw the world so standardized and "normal." Pearson changed minds by showing that some populations are naturally skewed (coining that word in passing) and he helped put to rest the notion that the normal distribution underlies all phenomena.

Ironically, it was Pearson who did the most to popularize the name "normal" for the distribution discussed in this chapter. Starting with an 1894 paper, Pearson standardized the use of the term *normal* even as he was collecting and describing data that showed how

measurements of phenomena do not naturally or "normally" conform to the "Error Curve."

Today, more than a century after Pearson first published his thoughts, people still make the type of mistakes that Pearson refuted. One of us recalls the story about a upper-level college seminar class of three in which the professor announced one student would get an A, one would get a B, and one would get a C "because grades need to be normally distributed." (That the professor was describing a uniform distribution was a double irony.)

As a student you have probably heard many discussions about grade inflation (undoubtedly a phenomena at many schools). But, have you ever realized that an argument offered as "proof" of this inflation—that there are "too few" low grades because

grades are *skewed* towards A's and B's—wrongly implies that grades should be "normally" distributed. (By the time you finish reading this book, you may realize that because college students represent small nonrandom samples, there are plenty of reasons to suspect that the distribution of grades would be nonnormal.)

Other misapplications of the normal distribution involve overlooking or not verifying the assumptions the normal distribution makes about the data. Such misuses not only have confounded businesses, but have played a role in important U.S. public policy debates during the past 50 years or so. In the end, remember that just because statisticians call it "normal" doesn't make it so for all cases.

# PROBLEMS FOR SECTION 6.2

## Learning the Basics

**6.1** Given a standardized normal distribution (with a mean of 0 and a standard deviation of 1, as in Table E.2), what is the probability that
a. $Z$ is less than 1.57?
b. $Z$ is greater than 1.84?
c. $Z$ is between 1.57 and 1.84?
d. $Z$ is less than 1.57 or greater than 1.84?

**6.2** Given a standardized normal distribution (with a mean of 0 and a standard deviation of 1, as in Table E.2), what is the probability that
a. $Z$ is between −1.57 and 1.84?
b. $Z$ is less than −1.57 or greater than 1.84?
c. What is the value of $Z$ if only 2.5% of all possible $Z$ values are larger?
d. Between what two values of $Z$ (symmetrically distributed around the mean) will 68.26% of all possible $Z$ values be contained?

**6.3** Given a standardized normal distribution (with a mean of 0 and a standard deviation of 1, as in Table E.2), what is the probability that
a. $Z$ is less than 1.08?
b. $Z$ is greater than −0.21?
c. $Z$ is less than −0.21 or greater than the mean?
d. $Z$ is less than −0.21 or greater than 1.08?

**6.4** Given a standardized normal distribution (with a mean of 0 and a standard deviation of 1, as in Table E.2), determine the following probabilities:

a. $P(Z > 1.08)$
b. $P(Z < -0.21)$
c. $P(-1.96 < Z < -0.21)$
d. What is the value of $Z$ if only 15.87% of all possible $Z$ values are larger?

**6.5** Given a normal distribution with $\mu = 100$ and $\sigma = 10$, what is the probability that
a. $X > 75$?
b. $X < 70$?
c. $X < 80$ or $X > 110$?
d. 80% of the values are between what two $X$ values (symmetrically distributed around the mean)?

**6.6** Given a normal distribution with $\mu = 50$ and $\sigma = 4$, what is the probability that
a. $X > 43$?
b. $X < 42$?
c. 5% of the values are less than what $X$ value?
d. 60% of the values are between what two $X$ values (symmetrically distributed around the mean)?

## Applying the Concepts

**6.7** In a recent year, about two-thirds of U.S. households purchased ground coffee. Consider the annual ground coffee expenditures for households purchasing ground coffee, assuming that these expenditures are approximately distributed as a normal random variable with a mean of $45.16 and a standard deviation of $10.00.
a. Find the probability that a household spent less than $25.00.

**b.** Find the probability that a household spent more than $50.00.

**c.** What proportion of the households spent between $30.00 and $40.00?

**d.** 99% of the households spent less than what amount?

✓SELF Test **6.8** Toby's Trucking Company determined that the distance traveled per truck per year is normally distributed, with a mean of 50.0 thousand miles and a standard deviation of 12.0 thousand miles.

**a.** What proportion of trucks can be expected to travel between 34.0 and 50.0 thousand miles in the year?

**b.** What percentage of trucks can be expected to travel either below 30.0 or above 60.0 thousand miles in the year?

**c.** How many miles will be traveled by at least 80% of the trucks?

**d.** What are your answers to (a) through (c) if the standard deviation is 10.0 thousand miles?

**6.9** The breaking strength of plastic bags used for packaging produce is normally distributed, with a mean of 5 pounds per square inch and a standard deviation of 1.5 pounds per square inch. What proportion of the bags have a breaking strength of

**a.** less than 3.17 pounds per square inch?

**b.** at least 3.6 pounds per square inch?

**c.** between 5 and 5.5 pounds per square inch?

**d.** 95% of the breaking strengths will be contained between what two values symmetrically distributed around the mean?

**6.10** A set of final examination grades in an introductory statistics course is normally distributed, with a mean of 73 and a standard deviation of 8.

**a.** What is the probability of getting a grade below 91 on this exam?

**b.** What is the probability that a student scored between 65 and 89?

**c.** The probability is 5% that a student taking the test scores higher than what grade?

**d.** If the professor grades on a curve (i.e., gives A's to the top 10% of the class, regardless of the score), are you better off with a grade of 81 on this exam or a grade of 68 on a different exam, where the mean is 62 and the standard deviation is 3? Show your answer statistically and explain.

**6.11** A statistical analysis of 1,000 long-distance telephone calls made from the headquarters of the Bricks and Clicks Computer Corporation indicates that the length of these calls is normally distributed, with $\mu = 240$ seconds and $\sigma = 40$ seconds.

**a.** What is the probability that a call lasted less than 180 seconds?

**b.** What is the probability that a call lasted between 180 and 300 seconds?

**c.** What is the probability that a call lasted between 110 and 180 seconds?

**d.** What is the length of a call if only 1% of all calls are shorter?

**6.12** The number of shares traded daily on the New York Stock Exchange (NYSE) is referred to as the *volume* of trading. During the first three months of 2006, daily volume ranged from 1.424 billion to 2.170 billion (NYSE Group, **www.nyse.com**, April 28, 2006). Assume that the number of shares traded on the NYSE is a normally distributed random variable, with a mean of 1.8 billion and a standard deviation of 0.15 billion. For a randomly selected day, what is the probability that the volume is

**a.** below 1.5 billion?

**b.** below 1.7 billion?

**c.** above 2.0 billion?

**d.** above 2.3 billion?

**6.13** Many manufacturing problems involve the matching of machine parts, such as shafts that fit into a valve hole. A particular design requires a shaft with a diameter of 22.000 mm, but shafts with diameters between 21.900 mm and 22.010 mm are acceptable. Suppose that the manufacturing process yields shafts with diameters normally distributed, with a mean of 22.002 mm and a standard deviation of 0.005 mm. For this process, what is

**a.** the proportion of shafts with a diameter between 21.90 mm and 22.00 mm?

**b.** the probability that a shaft is acceptable?

**c.** the diameter that will be exceeded by only 2% of the shafts?

**d.** What would be your answers in (a) through (c) if the standard deviation of the shaft diameters was 0.004 mm?

## 6.3    EVALUATING NORMALITY

As discussed in Section 6.2, many continuous variables used in business closely follow a normal distribution. This section presents two approaches for determining whether a set of data can be approximated by the normal distribution:

1. Compare the characteristics of the data with the theoretical properties of the normal distribution.
2. Construct a normal probability plot.

## Comparing Data Characteristics to Theoretical Properties

The normal distribution has several important theoretical properties:

- It is symmetrical; thus, the mean and median are equal.
- It is bell shaped; thus, the empirical rule applies.
- The interquartile range equals 1.33 standard deviations.
- The range is approximately equal to 6 standard deviations.

In actual practice, a continuous variable may have characteristics that approximate these theoretical properties. However, many continuous variables are neither normally distributed nor approximately normally distributed. For such variables, the descriptive characteristics of the data do not match well with the properties of a normal distribution. One approach to determining whether a data set follows a normal distribution is to compare the characteristics of the data with the corresponding properties from an underlying normal distribution, as follows:

- Construct charts and observe their appearance. For small- or moderate-sized data sets, construct a stem-and-leaf display or a boxplot. For large data sets, plot a histogram or polygon.
- Compute descriptive numerical measures and compare the characteristics of the data with the theoretical properties of the normal distribution. Compare the mean and median. Is the interquartile range approximately 1.33 times the standard deviation? Is the range approximately 6 times the standard deviation?
- Evaluate how the values in the data are distributed. Determine whether approximately two-thirds of the values lie between the mean and ±1 standard deviation. Determine whether approximately four-fifths of the values lie between the mean and ±1.28 standard deviations. Determine whether approximately 19 out of every 20 values lie between the mean and ±2 standard deviations.

Do the three-year returns discussed in Chapters 2 and 3 (see the **Mutual Funds** file) have the properties of the normal distribution? Figure 6.20 displays descriptive statistics for these data, and Figure 6.21 presents a boxplot.

**FIGURE 6.20**

Microsoft Excel descriptive statistics for the 2006 returns

*See Section E3.1 to create this. (Use Section M3.1 to create the Minitab equivalent.)*

|  | A | B |
|---|---|---|
| 1 | Return 2006 | |
| 2 | | |
| 3 | Mean | 12.5142 |
| 4 | Standard Error | 0.2136 |
| 5 | Median | 13.1000 |
| 6 | Mode | 16.6000 |
| 7 | Standard Deviation | 6.2916 |
| 8 | Sample Variance | 39.5840 |
| 9 | Kurtosis | 0.0200 |
| 10 | Skewness | -0.2982 |
| 11 | Range | 44.0000 |
| 12 | Minimum | -9.0000 |
| 13 | Maximum | 35.0000 |
| 14 | Sum | 10862.3000 |
| 15 | Count | 868.0000 |
| 16 | Largest(1) | 35.0000 |
| 17 | Smallest(1) | -9.0000 |

**FIGURE 6.21**

Minitab boxplot for the 2006 returns

*See Section M3.2 to create this. (Use Section P3.1 to create the PHStat2 equivalent.)*

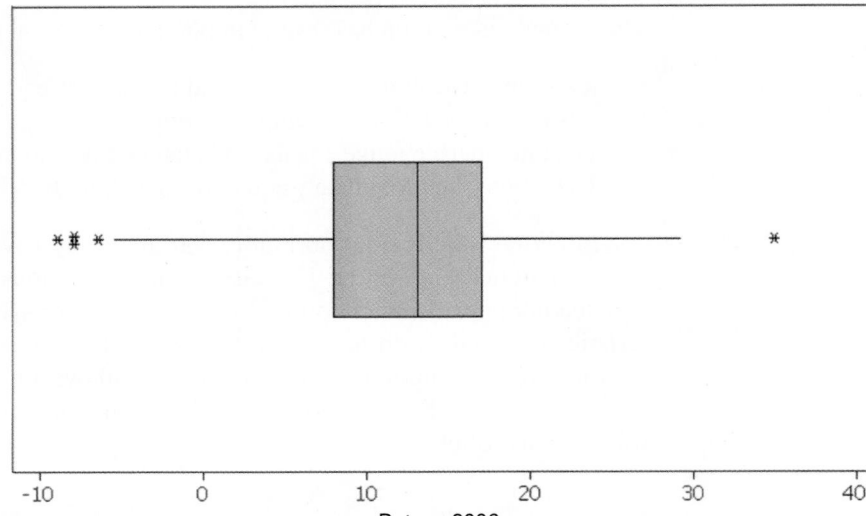

**Boxplot of 2006 Returns**

Return 2006

From Figures 6.20 and 6.21 and from an ordered array of the 2006 returns (not shown here), you can make the following statements:

1. The mean of 12.5142 is slightly lower than the median of 13.1. (In a normal distribution, the mean and median are equal.)
2. The boxplot appears symmetrical, with four lower outliers at −9.0, −8.0, −8.0, and −6.5 and one upper outlier at 35.0. (The normal distribution is symmetrical.)
3. The interquartile range of 9.2 is approximately 1.46 standard deviations. (In a normal distribution, the interquartile range is 1.33 standard deviations.)
4. The range of 44 is equal to 6.99 standard deviations. (In a normal distribution, the range is approximately six standard deviations.)
5. 72.2% of the returns are within ±1 standard deviation of the mean. (In a normal distribution, 68.26% of the values lie between the mean ±1 standard deviation.)
6. 87.0% of the returns are within ±1.28 standard deviations of the mean. (In a normal distribution, 80% of the values lie between the mean ±1.28 standard deviations.)

Based on these statements and the criteria given on page 235, the 2006 returns are slightly left-skewed and contain more values closer to the mean than expected. The range is higher than would be expected in a normal distribution, but this is mostly due to the single outlier at 35.0. You can conclude that the data characteristics of the 2006 returns do not greatly differ from the theoretical properties of a normal distribution.

## Constructing the Normal Probability Plot

A **normal probability plot** is a graphical approach for evaluating whether data are normally distributed. One common approach is called the **quantile-quantile plot**. In this method, you first transform each ordered value to a $Z$ value. For example, if you have a sample of $n = 19$, the $Z$ value for the smallest value corresponds to a cumulative area of $\dfrac{1}{n+1} = \dfrac{1}{19+1} = \dfrac{1}{20} = 0.05$.

The $Z$ value for a cumulative area of 0.05 (from Table E.2) is −1.65. Table 6.7 illustrates the entire set of $Z$ values for a sample of $n = 19$.

To construct the quantile-quantile plot, the $Z$ values are plotted on the $X$ axis, and the corresponding values of the variable are plotted on the $Y$ axis. If the data are normally distributed, the values will plot along an approximately straight line. (Minitab uses a slightly different approach that plots the original values on the $X$ axis and a theoretical percentage score based on

**TABLE 6.7**

Ordered Values and Corresponding Z Values for a Sample of n = 19

| Ordered Value | Z Value | Ordered Value | Z Value |
|---|---|---|---|
| 1 | −1.65 | 11 | 0.13 |
| 2 | −1.28 | 12 | 0.25 |
| 3 | −1.04 | 13 | 0.39 |
| 4 | −0.84 | 14 | 0.52 |
| 5 | −0.67 | 15 | 0.67 |
| 6 | −0.52 | 16 | 0.84 |
| 7 | −0.39 | 17 | 1.04 |
| 8 | −0.25 | 18 | 1.28 |
| 9 | −0.13 | 19 | 1.65 |
| 10 | 0.00 | | |

the normal distribution on the *Y* axis. Once again, if the data are normally distributed, the values will plot along an approximately straight line.)

Figure 6.22 illustrates the typical shape of normal probability plots for a left-skewed distribution (Panel A), a normal distribution (Panel B), and a right-skewed distribution (Panel C). If the data are left-skewed, the curve will rise more rapidly at first and then level off. If the data are normally distributed, the points will plot along an approximately straight line. If the data are right-skewed, the data will rise more slowly at first and then rise at a faster rate for higher values of the variable being plotted.

**FIGURE 6.22**

Normal probability plots for a left-skewed distribution, a normal distribution, and a right-skewed distribution

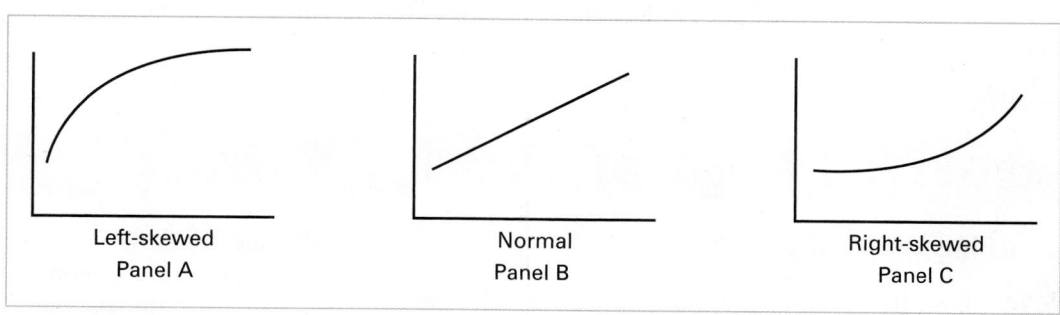

Left-skewed
Panel A

Normal
Panel B

Right-skewed
Panel C

Figure 6.23 shows a Microsoft Excel quantile-quantile normal probability plot and Figure 6.24 displays a Minitab normal probability plot for the 2006 returns.

**FIGURE 6.23**

Microsoft Excel normal probability plot for 2006 returns

*See Section P6.2 to create this.*

Normal Probability Plot of 2006 Returns

**FIGURE 6.24**

Minitab normal
probability plot
for 2006 returns

*See Section M6.2 to
create this.*

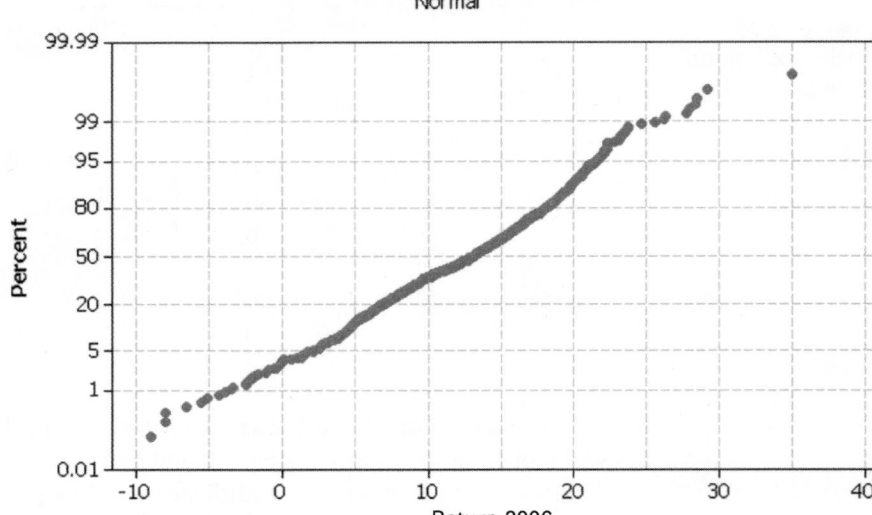

Figures 6.23 and 6.24 shows that the 2006 returns approximate a straight line with the exception of a few outliers at the lower and upper ends of the distribution. Thus, it is reasonable for you to conclude that the 2006 returns do not depart greatly from a normal distribution.

# PROBLEMS FOR SECTION 6.3

## Learning the Basics

**6.14** Show that for a sample of $n = 39$, the smallest and largest $Z$ values are $-1.96$ and $+1.96$, and the middle (i.e., 20th) $Z$ value is 0.00.

**6.15** For a sample of $n = 6$, list the six $Z$ values.

## Applying the Concepts

**SELF Test** **6.16** The data in the file **Chicken** contains the total fat, in grams per serving, for a sample of 20 chicken sandwiches from fast-food chains. The data are as follows:

7 8 4 5 16 20 20 24 19 30 23 30 25 19 29 29 30 30 40 56

Source: *Extracted from "Fast Food: Adding Health to the Menu,"* Consumer Reports, *September 2004, pp. 28–31.*

Decide whether the data appear to be approximately normally distributed by
**a.** comparing data characteristics to theoretical properties.
**b.** constructing a normal probability plot.

**6.17** As player salaries have increased, the cost of attending games has increased dramatically. The data in the file **BB2006** (extracted from K. Belson, "Oh Yeah, There's a

Ballgame Too," *The New York Times*, October 22, 2006, Business, pp. 1, 7–8) represent the cost of four tickets, two beers, four soft drinks, four hot dogs, two game programs, two baseball caps, and the parking fee for one car for each of the 30 major league teams. Decide whether the data appear to be approximately normally distributed by
**a.** comparing data characteristics to theoretical properties.
**b.** constructing a normal probability plot.

**6.18** The data in the file **Property Taxes** contain the property taxes per capita for the fifty states and the District of Columbia. Decide whether the data appear to be approximately normally distributed by
**a.** comparing data characteristics to theoretical properties.
**b.** constructing a normal probability plot.

**6.19** The data in the file **Spending** represent the per-capita spending, in thousands of dollars, for each state in 2004. Decide whether the data appear to be approximately normally distributed by
**a.** comparing data characteristics to theoretical properties.
**b.** constructing a normal probability plot.

**6.20** One operation of a mill is to cut pieces of steel into parts that will later be used as the frame for front seats in an automotive plant. The steel is cut with a diamond saw and requires the resulting parts to be within ±0.005 inch of the length specified by the automobile company. The data come from a sample of 100 steel parts and are stored in the file Steel. The measurement reported is the difference, in inches, between the actual length of the steel part, as measured by a laser measurement device, and the specified length of the steel part. Decide whether the data appear to be approximately normally distributed by

**a.** comparing data characteristics to theoretical properties.
**b.** constructing a normal probability plot.

**6.21** The data in the file Savings are the yields for a money market account, a one-year certificate of deposit (CD), and a five-year CD for 37 banks in south Florida, as of March 9, 2007 (extracted from **Bankrate.com**, March 9, 2007). For each of the three types of investments, decide whether the data appear to be approximately normally distributed by

**a.** comparing data characteristics to theoretical properties.
**b.** constructing a normal probability plot.

**6.22** The following data, stored in the file Utility, represent the electricity costs in dollars during July 2007 for a random sample of 50 two-bedroom apartments in a large city:

| | | | | | | | | | |
|---|---|---|---|---|---|---|---|---|---|
| 96 | 171 | 202 | 178 | 147 | 102 | 153 | 197 | 127 | 82 |
| 157 | 185 | 90 | 116 | 172 | 111 | 148 | 213 | 130 | 165 |
| 141 | 149 | 206 | 175 | 123 | 128 | 144 | 168 | 109 | 167 |
| 95 | 163 | 150 | 154 | 130 | 143 | 187 | 166 | 139 | 149 |
| 108 | 119 | 183 | 151 | 114 | 135 | 191 | 137 | 129 | 158 |

Decide whether the data appear to be approximately normally distributed by

**a.** comparing data characteristics to theoretical properties.
**b.** constructing a normal probability plot.

## 6.4    THE UNIFORM DISTRIBUTION

In the **uniform distribution**, a value has the same probability of occurrence anywhere in the range between the smallest value, $a$, and the largest value, $b$. Because of its shape, the uniform distribution is sometimes called the **rectangular distribution** (see Panel B of Figure 6.1 on page 218). Equation (6.4) defines the continuous probability density function for the uniform distribution.

---

Uniform Distribution

$$f(X) = \frac{1}{b-a} \text{ if } a \leq X \leq b \text{ and 0 elsewhere} \qquad (6.4)$$

where

$a$ = the minimum value of $X$

$b$ = the maximum value of $X$

---

Equation (6.5) defines the mean of the uniform distribution.

---

Mean of the Uniform Distribution

$$\mu = \frac{a+b}{2} \qquad (6.5)$$

Equation (6.6) defines the variance and standard deviation of the uniform distribution.

### Variance and Standard Deviation of the Uniform Distribution

$$\sigma^2 = \frac{(b-a)^2}{12} \tag{6.6a}$$

$$\sigma = \sqrt{\frac{(b-a)^2}{12}} \tag{6.6b}$$

One of the most common uses of the uniform distribution is in the selection of random numbers. When you use simple random sampling (see Section 7.1), you assume that each random number comes from a uniform distribution that has a minimum value of 0 and a maximum value of 1.

Figure 6.25 illustrates the uniform distribution with $a = 0$ and $b = 1$. The total area inside the rectangle is equal to the base (1.0) times the height (1.0). Thus, the resulting area of 1.0 satisfies the requirement that the area under any probability density function equals 1.0.

**FIGURE 6.25**

Probability density function for a uniform distribution with $a = 0$ and $b = 1$

In such a distribution, what is the probability of getting a random number between 0.10 and 0.30? The area between 0.10 and 0.30, depicted in Figure 6.26, is equal to the base (which is $0.30 - 0.10 = 0.20$) times the height (1.0). Therefore,

$$P(0.10 < X < 0.30) = (\text{Base})(\text{Height}) = (0.20)(1.0) = 0.20$$

**FIGURE 6.26**

Finding $P(0.10 < X < 0.30)$ for a uniform distribution with $a = 0$ and $b = 1$

From Equations (6.5) and (6.6), the mean and standard deviation of the uniform distribution for $a = 0$ and $b = 1$ are computed as follows:

$$\mu = \frac{a+b}{2}$$

$$= \frac{0+1}{2} = 0.5$$

and

$$\sigma^2 = \frac{(b-a)^2}{12}$$

$$= \frac{(1-0)^2}{12}$$

$$= \frac{1}{12} = 0.0833$$

$$\sigma = \sqrt{0.0833} = 0.2887$$

Thus, the mean is 0.5 and the standard deviation is 0.2887.

## PROBLEMS FOR SECTION 6.4

### Learning the Basics

**6.23** Suppose you sample one value from a uniform distribution with $a = 0$ and $b = 10$. What is the probability that the value will be
a. between 5 and 7?
b. between 2 and 3?
c. What is the mean?
d. What is the standard deviation?

### Applying the Concepts

**SELF Test** **6.24** The time between arrivals of customers at a bank during the noon-to-1 p.m. hour has a uniform distribution between 0 to 120 seconds. What is the probability that the time between the arrival of two customers will be
a. less than 20 seconds?
b. between 10 and 30 seconds?
c. more than 35 seconds?
d. What are the mean and standard deviation of the time between arrivals?

**6.25** A study of the time spent shopping in a supermarket for a market basket of 20 specific items showed an approximately uniform distribution between 20 minutes and 40 minutes. What is the probability that the shopping time will be
a. between 25 and 30 minutes?
b. less than 35 minutes?

c. What are the mean and standard deviation of the shopping time?

**6.26** How long does it take you to download a game for your iPod? According to Apple's technical support site, **www.apple.com/support/itunes**, downloading an iPod game using a broadband connection should take 3 to 6 minutes. Assume that the download times are uniformly distributed between 3 and 6 minutes. If you download a game, what is the probability that the download time will be
a. less than 3.3 minutes?
b. less than 4 minutes?
c. between 4 and 5 minutes?
d. What are the mean and standard deviation of the download times?

**6.27** The scheduled commuting time on the Long Island Rail Road from Glen Cove to New York City is 65 minutes. Suppose that the actual commuting time is uniformly distributed between 64 and 74 minutes. What is the probability that the commuting time will be
a. less than 70 minutes?
b. between 65 and 70 minutes?
c. greater than 65 minutes?
d. What are the mean and standard deviation of the commuting time?

## 6.5  THE EXPONENTIAL DISTRIBUTION

The **exponential distribution** is a continuous distribution that is right-skewed and ranges from zero to positive infinity (see Panel C of Figure 6.1 on page 218). The exponential distribution is widely used in waiting-line (i.e., queuing) theory to model the length of time between arrivals in processes such as customers at a bank's ATM, patients entering a hospital emergency room, and hits on a Web site.

The exponential distribution is defined by a single parameter, its mean, $\lambda$, the mean number of arrivals per unit of time. The value $1/\lambda$ is equal to the mean time between arrivals. For example, if the mean number of arrivals in a minute is $\lambda = 4$, then the mean time between arrivals is $1/\lambda = 0.25$ minutes, or 15 seconds. Equation (6.7) defines the probability that the length of time before the next arrival is less than $X$.

Exponential Distribution

$$P(\text{Arrival time} < X) = 1 - e^{-\lambda X} \qquad\qquad (6.7)$$

where

$e$ = the mathematical constant approximated by 2.71828

$\lambda$ = the mean number of arrivals per unit

$X$ = any value of the continuous variable where $0 < X < \infty$

To illustrate the exponential distribution, suppose that customers arrive at a bank's ATM at a rate of 20 per hour. If a customer has just arrived, what is the probability that the next customer will arrive within 6 minutes (i.e., 0.1 hour)? For this example, $\lambda = 20$ and $X = 0.1$. Using Equation (6.7),

$$P(\text{Arrival time} < 0.1) = 1 - e^{-20(0.1)}$$

$$= 1 - e^{-2}$$

$$= 1 - 0.1353 = 0.8647$$

Thus, the probability that a customer will arrive within 6 minutes is 0.8647, or 86.47%. You can also use Microsoft Excel or Minitab to compute this probability (see Figures 6.27 or 6.28). Note that Minitab uses the mean time between arrivals $(1/\lambda)$ as the mean in Figure 6.28.

**FIGURE 6.27**

Microsoft Excel worksheet for finding exponential probabilities (mean = $\lambda$)

*See Section E6.3 or P6.3 to create this.*

| | A | B | |
|---|---|---|---|
| 1 | **Exponential Probability** | | |
| 2 | | | |
| 3 | | **Data** | |
| 4 | Mean | 20 | |
| 5 | X Value | 0.1 | |
| 6 | | | |
| 7 | | **Results** | |
| 8 | P(<=X) | 0.8647 | =EXPONDIST(B5, B4, TRUE) |

**FIGURE 6.28**

Minitab results for finding exponential probabilities (mean = $1/\lambda$)

*See Section M6.3 to create this.*

```
Exponential with mean = 0.05

   x   P( X <= x )
  0.1     0.864665
```

**EXAMPLE 6.8**    COMPUTING EXPONENTIAL PROBABILITIES

In the ATM example, what is the probability that the next customer will arrive within 3 minutes (i.e., 0.05 hour)?

**SOLUTION**  For this example, $\lambda = 20$ and $X = 0.05$. Using Equation (6.7),

$$P(\text{Arrival time} < 0.05) = 1 - e^{-20(0.05)}$$

$$= 1 - e^{-1}$$

$$= 1 - 0.3679 = 0.6321$$

Thus, the probability that a customer will arrive within 3 minutes is 0.6321, or 63.21%.

## PROBLEMS FOR SECTION 6.5

### Learning the Basics

**6.28** Given an exponential distribution with $\lambda = 10$, what is the probability that the arrival time is
**a.** less than $X = 0.1$?
**b.** greater than $X = 0.1$?
**c.** between $X = 0.1$ and $X = 0.2$?
**d.** less than $X = 0.1$ or greater than $X = 0.2$?

**6.29** Given an exponential distribution with $\lambda = 30$, what is the probability that the arrival time is
**a.** less than $X = 0.1$?
**b.** greater than $X = 0.1$?
**c.** between $X = 0.1$ and $X = 0.2$?
**d.** less than $X = 0.1$ or greater than $X = 0.2$?

**6.30** Given an exponential distribution with $\lambda = 5$, what is the probability that the arrival time is
**a.** less than $X = 0.3$?
**b.** greater than $X = 0.3$?
**c.** between $X = 0.3$ and $X = 0.5$?
**d.** less than $X = 0.3$ or greater than $X = 0.5$?

### Applying the Concepts

**6.31** Autos arrive at a toll plaza located at the entrance to a bridge at the rate of 50 per minute during the 5:00–6:00 p.m. hour. If an auto has just arrived,
**a.** what is the probability that the next auto will arrive within 3 seconds (0.05 minute)?
**b.** what is the probability that the next auto will arrive within 1 second (0.0167 minute)?
**c.** What are your answers to (a) and (b) if the rate of arrival of autos is 60 per minute?
**d.** What are your answers to (a) and (b) if the rate of arrival of autos is 30 per minute?

**SELF** **6.32** Customers arrive at the drive-up window
**Test** of a fast-food restaurant at a rate of 2 per minute during the lunch hour.
**a.** What is the probability that the next customer will arrive within 1 minute?
**b.** What is the probability that the next customer will arrive within 5 minutes?
**c.** During the dinner time period, the arrival rate is 1 per minute. What are your answers to (a) and (b) for this period?

**6.33** Telephone calls arrive at the information desk of a large computer software company at a rate of 15 per hour.
**a.** What is the probability that the next call will arrive within 3 minutes (0.05 hour)?
**b.** What is the probability that the next call will arrive within 15 minutes (0.25 hour)?
**c.** Suppose the company has just introduced an updated version of one of its software programs, and telephone calls are now arriving at a rate of 25 per hour. Given this information, redo (a) and (b).

**6.34** An on-the-job injury occurs once every 10 days on average at an automobile plant. What is the probability that the next on-the-job injury will occur within
**a.** 10 days?
**b.** 5 days?
**c.** 1 day?

**6.35** The time between unplanned shutdowns of a power plant has an exponential distribution with a mean of 20 days. Find the probability that the time between two unplanned shutdowns is
**a.** less than 14 days.
**b.** more than 21 days.
**c.** less than 7 days.

**6.36** Golfers arrive at the starter's booth of a public golf course at a rate of 8 per hour during the Monday-to-Friday midweek period. If a golfer has just arrived,

**a.** what is the probability that the next golfer will arrive within 15 minutes (0.25 hour)?

**b.** what is the probability that the next golfer will arrive within 3 minutes (0.05 hour)?

**c.** The actual arrival rate on Fridays is 15 per hour. What are your answers to (a) and (b) for Fridays?

**6.37** TrafficWeb.org claims that it can deliver 10,000 hits to a Web site in the next 60 days for only $21.50 (**www.trafficweb.org**, July 16, 2007). If this amount of Web site traffic is experienced, then the time between hits has a mean of 8.64 minutes (or 0.116 per minute). Assume that your Web site does get 10,000 hits in the next 60 days and that the time between hits has an exponential distribution. What is the probability that the time between two hits is

**a.** less than 5 minutes?

**b.** less than 10 minutes?

**c.** more than 15 minutes?

**d.** Do you think it is reasonable to assume that the time between hits has an exponential distribution?

## 6.6  THE NORMAL APPROXIMATION TO THE BINOMIAL DISTRIBUTION

In Sections 6.2 and 6.3 you learned about the normal probability distribution. In this section, you will learn how to use the normal distribution to approximate the binomial distribution (see Section 5.3). Recall that the binomial distribution is a discrete distribution where the random variable $X$ is the number of events of interest occurring in a sample of $n$ trials. Calculating exact probabilities of $X$ using Equation (5.11) on page 191 becomes very tedious when $n$ is large, and thus, it is often useful to approximate the probability using the normal approximation introduced in this section.

### Need for a Correction for Continuity Adjustment

When using the normal distribution to approximate the binomial distribution, you can get more accurate approximations of the probabilities if you use a correction for continuity adjustment. There are two major reasons for using the correction. First, discrete random variables that follow the binomial distribution can take on only integer values, whereas a continuous random variable such as the normal can take on any values within a continuum or interval. Second, with a continuous distribution such as the normal, the probability of getting a specific value of a random variable is zero. However, when the normal distribution is used to approximate a discrete distribution, you can use a correction for continuity adjustment to get the approximate probability of a specific value of the binomial distribution.

Consider an experiment in which you toss a fair coin 10 times. Suppose you want to compute the probability of getting *exactly* 4 heads. Whereas a discrete random variable can have only an integer value (such as 4), a continuous random variable used to approximate it could take on any values within an interval around that specified value, as demonstrated on the accompanying scale:

The correction for continuity adjustment requires adding or subtracting 0.5 from the value or values of the discrete random variable $X$ as needed. To use the normal distribution to approximate the probability of getting *exactly* 4 heads (i.e., $X = 4$), you need to find the area under the normal curve from $X = 3.5$ to $X = 4.5$, the lower and upper boundaries of 4. To determine the approximate probability of getting *at least* 4 heads, you find the area under the normal curve greater than or equal to $X = 3.5$, since 3.5 is the lower boundary of 4. Similarly, to determine the approximate probability of getting *at most* 4 heads, you find the area under the normal curve equal to or less than $X = 4.5$, because 4.5 is the upper boundary of 4.

When using the normal distribution to approximate discrete probability distributions, wording is particularly important. To determine the approximate probability of getting *fewer* than 4 heads, you find the area under the normal curve less than or equal to $X = 3.5$. To determine the approximate probability of getting *more than* 4 heads, you find the area under the normal curve greater than or equal to $X = 4.5$. To determine the approximate probability of getting 4 *through* 7 heads, you find the area under the normal curve from $X = 3.5$ to $X = 7.5$.

## Approximating the Binomial Distribution

In Section 5.3 you learned that the binomial distribution is symmetrical (like the normal distribution) whenever $\pi = 0.5$. When $\pi \neq 0.5$, the binomial distribution is not symmetrical. However, the closer $\pi$ is to 0.5 and the larger the sample size $n$, the more symmetric the distribution becomes. On the other hand, the larger the sample size, the more tedious it is to compute the exact probabilities of a specific number of items of interest by using Equation (5.11) on page 191. Fortunately, whenever the sample size is large, you can use the normal distribution to approximate the exact probabilities of a specific number of items of interest.

As a general rule, you can use the normal distribution to approximate the binomial distribution whenever both $n\pi$ and $n(1 - \pi)$ are at least 5. From Section 5.3, you know that the mean of the binomial distribution is

$$\mu = n\pi$$

and the standard deviation of the binomial distribution is

$$\sigma = \sqrt{n\pi(1 - \pi)}$$

Substituting these results into the transformation formula [Equation (6.2) on page 221],

$$Z = \frac{X - \mu}{\sigma}$$

$$= \frac{X - n\pi}{\sqrt{n\pi(1 - \pi)}}$$

so that, for large enough $n$, the random variable $Z$ is approximately normally distributed. Hence, you find approximate probabilities corresponding to the values of the discrete random variable $X$, by using Equation (6.8).

---

Normal Approximation to the Binomial Distribution

$$Z = \frac{X_a - n\pi}{\sqrt{n\pi(1 - \pi)}} \qquad (6.8)$$

where

$\mu = n\pi$, mean of the binomial distribution

$\sigma = \sqrt{n\pi(1 - \pi)}$, standard deviation of the binomial distribution

$X_a$ = adjusted number of items of interest for the discrete random variable $X$, such that $X_a = X - 0.5$ or $X_a = X + 0.5$ as appropriate

**EXAMPLE 6.9**    USING THE NORMAL DISTRIBUTION TO APPROXIMATE THE BINOMIAL DISTRIBUTION

You select a random sample of $n = 1,600$ tires from an ongoing production process in which 8% of all such tires produced are defective. What is the probability that 150 or fewer tires will be defective?

**SOLUTION** Because both $n\pi = 1,600(0.08) = 128$ and $n(1 - \pi) = 1,600(0.92) = 1,472$ are greater than 5, you can use the normal distribution to approximate the binomial. Here $X_a$, the adjusted number of defective tires, is 150.5.

$$Z = \frac{X_a - n\pi}{\sqrt{n\pi(1 - \pi)}} = \frac{150.5 - 128}{\sqrt{(1,600)(0.08)(0.92)}} = \frac{22.5}{10.85} = +2.07$$

Using Table E.2, the area under the curve to the left of $Z = +2.07$ is 0.9808 (see Figure 6.29).

**FIGURE 6.29**

Approximating the binomial distribution

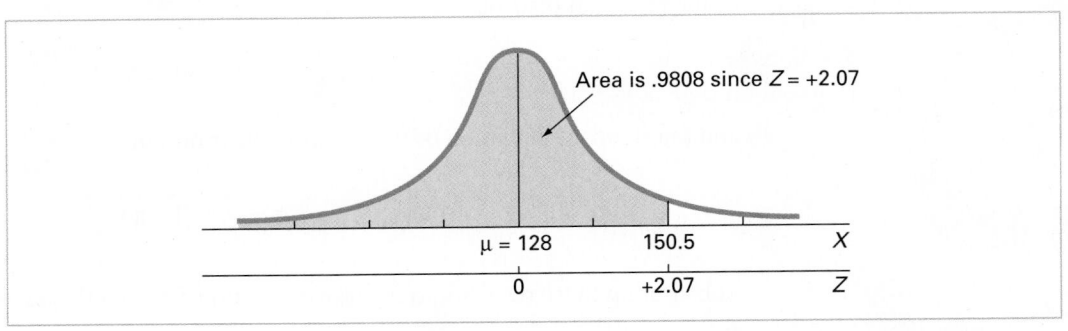

Area is .9808 since $Z = +2.07$

$\mu = 128$    150.5    $X$

0    +2.07    $Z$

Suppose that you want to approximate the probability of getting *exactly* 150 defective tires. The correction for continuity defines the integer value of interest to range from one-half unit below it to one-half unit above it. Therefore, you define the probability of getting 150 defective tires as the area (under the normal curve) between 149.5 and 150.5. Using Equation (6.8), you approximate the probability as follows:

$$Z = \frac{150.5 - 128}{\sqrt{(1,600)(0.08)(0.92)}} = \frac{22.5}{10.85} = +2.07$$

and

$$Z = \frac{149.5 - 128}{\sqrt{(1,600)(0.08)(0.92)}} = \frac{21.5}{10.85} = +1.98$$

From Table E.2, the area under the normal curve less than $X = 150.5$ ($Z = +2.07$) is 0.9808 and the area under the curve less than $X = 149.5$ ($Z = +1.98$) is 0.9761. Thus, the approximate probability of getting 150 defective tires is the difference in the two areas, 0.0047.

# PROBLEMS FOR SECTION 6.6

## Learning the Basics

**6.38** For $n = 100$ and $\pi = 0.20$, use the normal distribution to approximate the probability that
a. $X = 25$.
b. $X > 25$.
c. $X \le 25$.
d. $X < 25$.

**6.39** For $n = 100$ and $\pi = 0.40$, use the normal distribution to approximate the probability that
a. $X = 40$.
b. $X > 40$.
c. $X \le 40$.
d. $X < 40$.

## Applying the Concepts

**6.40** Consider an experiment in which you toss a fair coin 10 times and count the number of heads. Use Equation (5.11) on page 191, Table E.6, or Microsoft Excel, or Minitab to determine the probability of getting:
a. 4 heads.
b. at least 4 heads.
c. 4 through 7 heads.
d. Use the normal approximation to the binomial distribution to approximate the probabilities in (a) through (c).

**6.41** For short domestic flights, an airline has three different choices on its snack menu—pretzels, potato chips, and cookies. Based on past experience, the airline feels that each snack is equally likely to be chosen. If there are 150 passengers on a particular flight, what is the *approximate* probability that:
a. at least 60 will choose cookies for a snack?
b. exactly 60 will choose cookies for a snack?
c. less than 60 will choose cookies for a snack?
d. If the airline has 70 of each type of snack available on the flight, what is the likelihood that a passenger will not be able to get the snack that he or she desires?

**6.42** Stock options are usually awarded at the price of a company's shares on the date of the grant. A recent study (E. Awata, "Backdated Options May Snare Some Directors," *USA Today*, March 29, 2007, pp. 1B, 2B) found evidence that many outside directors received grants at the lowest price in a given month. Of 17,512 grants before the Sarbanes-Oxley Act tightened Security and Exchange Commission disclosure rules, 1,726 were at the lowest price in a given month. Assume that there is an average of 21 days in a month on which grants can be made. How likely do you think it is that these results or more extreme results could have occurred if the grant is equally likely to be given on any day of the month?

# SUMMARY

In this chapter, you used the normal distribution in the Using Statistics scenario to study the time to download a Web page. In addition, you studied the uniform distribution, the exponential distribution, the normal probability plot, and the normal approximation to the binomial distribution. In Chapter 7, the normal distribution is used in developing the subject of statistical inference.

# KEY EQUATIONS

**Normal Probability Density Function**

$$f(X) = \frac{1}{\sqrt{2\pi}\sigma} e^{-(1/2)[(X-\mu)/\sigma]^2} \qquad \textbf{(6.1)}$$

**Transformation Formula**

$$Z = \frac{X - \mu}{\sigma} \qquad \textbf{(6.2)}$$

**Finding an X Value Associated with Known Probability**

$$X = \mu + Z\sigma \qquad \textbf{(6.3)}$$

**Uniform Distribution**

$$f(X) = \frac{1}{b - a} \qquad \textbf{(6.4)}$$

**Mean of the Uniform Distribution**

$$\mu = \frac{a+b}{2} \qquad (6.5)$$

**Variance and Standard Deviation of the Uniform Distribution**

$$\sigma^2 = \frac{(b-a)^2}{12} \qquad (6.6a)$$

$$\sigma = \sqrt{\frac{(b-a)^2}{12}} \qquad (6.6b)$$

**Exponential Distribution**

$$P(\text{Arrival time} < X) = 1 - e^{-\lambda X} \qquad (6.7)$$

**Normal Approximation to the Binomial Distribution**

$$Z = \frac{X_a - n\pi}{\sqrt{n\pi(1-\pi)}} \qquad (6.8)$$

# KEY TERMS

continuous probability density function 218
cumulative standardized normal distribution 221
exponential distribution 241

normal distribution 219
normal probability density function 220
normal probability plot 236
quantile-quantile plot 236

rectangular distribution 239
standardized normal random variable 221
transformation formula 221
uniform distribution 239

# CHAPTER REVIEW PROBLEMS

## Checking Your Understanding

**6.43** Why is it that only one normal distribution table such as Table E.2 is needed to find any probability under the normal curve?

**6.44** How do you find the area between two values under the normal curve?

**6.45** How do you find the $X$ value that corresponds to a given percentile of the normal distribution?

**6.46** What are some of the distinguishing properties of a normal distribution?

**6.47** How does the shape of the normal distribution differ from those of the uniform and exponential distributions?

**6.48** How can you use the normal probability plot to evaluate whether a set of data is normally distributed?

**6.49** Under what circumstances can you use the exponential distribution?

**6.50** When can you use the normal distribution to approximate the binomial distribution?

## Applying the Concepts

**6.51** An industrial sewing machine uses ball bearings that are targeted to have a diameter of 0.75 inch. The lower and upper specification limits under which the ball bearings can operate are 0.74 inch and 0.76 inch, respectively. Past experience has indicated that the actual diameter of the ball bearings is approximately normally distributed, with a mean of 0.753 inch and a standard deviation of 0.004 inch. What is the probability that a ball bearing is
**a.** between the target and the actual mean?
**b.** between the lower specification limit and the target?
**c.** above the upper specification limit?
**d.** below the lower specification limit?
**e.** 93% of the diameters are greater than what value?

**6.52** The fill amount of soft drink bottles is normally distributed, with a mean of 2.0 liters and a standard deviation of 0.05 liter. If bottles contain less than 95% of the listed net content (1.90 liters, in this case), the manufacturer may be subject to penalty by the state office of consumer affairs. Bottles that have a net content above 2.10 liters may cause excess spillage upon opening. What proportion of the bottles will contain

**a.** between 1.90 and 2.0 liters?

**b.** between 1.90 and 2.10 liters?

**c.** below 1.90 liters or above 2.10 liters?

**d.** 99% of the bottles contain at least how much soft drink?

**e.** 99% of the bottles contain an amount that is between which two values (symmetrically distributed) around the mean?

**6.53** In an effort to reduce the number of bottles that contain less than 1.90 liters, the bottler in Problem 6.52 sets the filling machine so that the mean is 2.02 liters. Under these circumstances, what are your answers in (a) through (e)?

**6.54** An orange juice producer buys all his oranges from a large orange grove. The amount of juice squeezed from each of these oranges is approximately normally distributed, with a mean of 4.70 ounces and a standard deviation of 0.40 ounce.

**a.** What is the probability that a randomly selected orange will contain between 4.70 and 5.00 ounces of juice?

**b.** What is the probability that a randomly selected orange will contain between 5.00 and 5.50 ounces of juice?

**c.** 77% of the oranges will contain at least how many ounces of juice?

**d.** 80% of the oranges contain between what two values (in ounces of juice), symmetrically distributed around the population mean?

**6.55** Data concerning 71 of the best-selling domestic beers in the United States are located in the file `Domesticbeer`. The values for three variables are included: percentage alcohol, number of calories per 12 ounces, and number of carbohydrates (in grams) per 12 ounces. For each of the three variables, decide whether the data appear to be approximately normally distributed. Support your decision through the use of appropriate statistics and graphs.

Source: *Extracted from* **www.Beer100.com**, *May 4, 2007.*

**6.56** The evening manager of a restaurant was very concerned about the length of time some customers were waiting in line to be seated. She also had some concern about the seating times—that is, the length of time between when a customer is seated and the time he or she leaves the restaurant. Over the course of one week, 100 customers (no more than 1 per party) were randomly selected, and their waiting and seating times (in minutes) were recorded in the file `Wait`.

**a.** Think about your favorite restaurant. Do you think waiting times more closely resemble a uniform, exponential, or normal distribution?

**b.** Again, think about your favorite restaurant. Do you think seating times more closely resemble a uniform, exponential, or normal distribution?

**c.** Construct a histogram and a normal probability plot of the waiting times. Do you think these waiting times more closely resemble a uniform, exponential, or normal distribution?

**d.** Construct a histogram and a normal probability plot of the seating times. Do you think these seating times more closely resemble a uniform, exponential, or normal distribution?

**6.57** At the end of 2006, all the major stock market indexes had posted strong gains in the previous 12 months. The mean one-year return for stocks in the S&P 500, a group of 500 very large companies, was 13.62%. The mean one-year return for companies in the Russell 2000, a group of 2000 small companies, was 17%. Historically, the one-year returns are approximately normal, the standard deviation in the S&P 500 is approximately 20%, and the standard deviation in the Russell 2000 is approximately 35%.

**a.** What is the probability that a stock in the S&P 500 gained 25% or more in the last year? gained 50% or more?

**b.** What is the probability that a stock in the S&P 500 lost money in the last year? lost 25% or more? lost 50% or more?

**c.** Repeat (a) and (b) for a stock in the Russell 2000.

**d.** Write a short summary on your findings. Be sure to include a discussion of the risks associated with a large standard deviation.

**6.58** *The New York Times* reported (L. J. Flynn, "Tax Surfing," March 25, 2002, p. C10) that the mean time to download the home page for the Internal Revenue Service, **www.irs.gov**, is 0.8 second. Suppose that the download time is normally distributed with a standard deviation of 0.2 second. What is the probability that a download time is

**a.** less than 1 second?

**b.** between 0.5 and 1.5 seconds?

**c.** above 0.5 second?

**d.** 99% of the download times are above how many seconds?

**e.** 95% of the download times are between what two values, symmetrically distributed around the mean?

**6.59** The same article mentioned in Problem 6.58 also reported that the mean download time for the H&R Block Web site, **www.hrblock.com**, is 2.5 seconds. Suppose that the download time is normally distributed with a standard deviation of 0.5 second. What is the probability that a download time is

**a.** less than 1 second?

**b.** between 0.5 and 1.5 seconds?

**c.** above 0.5 second?

**d.** 99% of the download times are above how many seconds?

**e.** Compare the results for the IRS site computed in Problem 6.58 to those of the H&R Block site.

**6.60** When obtaining a mortgage, the borrower will pay closing costs to the lender. These costs vary from bank to bank, and from state to state. Bankrate.com conducted a survey in all fifty states to identify average closing costs on a $200,000 loan, assuming a 20-percent down payment and good credit. The file Closing includes the average rate for all fifty states and the District of Columbia for 2006, along with the state rank.

Source: *Extracted from "Closing Cost Survey,"* **www.bankrate.com**, *May 15, 2007.*

**a.** Is the distribution of state closing costs approximately distributed as a normal random variable?

**b.** The variable "RANK 2006" includes 51 numbers, 1, 2, 3, . . . , 51. What type of distribution does this column of numbers resemble? Construct a graphical display that supports your answer.

**6.61 (Class Project)** According to Burton G. Malkiel, the daily changes in the closing price of stock follow a *random walk*—that is, these daily events are independent of each other and move upward or downward in a random manner—and can be approximated by a normal distribution. To test this theory, use either a newspaper or the Internet to select one company traded on the NYSE, one company traded on the American Stock Exchange, and one company traded on the NASDAQ and then do the following:

1. Record the daily closing stock price of each of these companies for six consecutive weeks (so that you have 30 values per company).
2. Record the daily changes in the closing stock price of each of these companies for six consecutive weeks (so that you have 30 values per company).

For each of your six data sets, decide whether the data are approximately normally distributed by

**a.** examining the stem-and-leaf display, histogram or polygon, and boxplot.

**b.** comparing data characteristics to theoretical properties.

**c.** constructing a normal probability plot.

**d.** Discuss the results of (a) through (c). What can you say about your three stocks with respect to daily closing prices and daily changes in closing prices? Which, if any, of the data sets are approximately normally distributed?

*Note:* The random-walk theory pertains to the daily changes in the closing stock price, not the daily closing stock price.

## Team Projects

The data file Mutual Funds contains information regarding nine variables from a sample of 868 mutual funds. The variables are:

Category—Type of stocks comprising the mutual fund (small cap, mid cap, large cap)

Objective—Objective of stocks comprising the mutual fund (growth or value)

Assets—In millions of dollars

Fees—Sales charges (no or yes)

Expense ratio—Ratio of expenses to net assets, in percentage

Risk—Risk-of-loss factor of the mutual fund (low, average, high)

2006 return—Twelve-month return in 2006

Three-year return—Annualized return, 2004–2006

Five-year return—Annualized return, 2002–2006

**6.62** For the expense ratio, three-year return, and five-year return, decide whether the data are approximately normally distributed by

**a.** comparing data characteristics to theoretical properties.

**b.** constructing a normal probability plot.

## Student Survey Data Base

**6.63** Problem 1.27 on page 14 describes a survey of 50 undergraduate students (see the file Undergradsurvey). For these data, for each numerical variable, decide whether the data are approximately normally distributed by

**a.** comparing data characteristics to theoretical properties.

**b.** constructing a normal probability plot.

**6.64** Problem 1.27 on page 14 describes a survey of 50 undergraduate students (see the file Undergradsurvey).

**a.** Select a sample of 50 undergraduate students and conduct a similar survey for those students.

**b.** For the data collected in (a), repeat (a) and (b) of Problem 6.63.

**c.** Compare the results of (b) to those of Problem 6.63.

**6.65** Problem 1.28 on page 14 describes a survey of 40 MBA students (see the file Gradsurvey). For these data, for each numerical variable, decide whether the data are approximately normally distributed by

**a.** comparing data characteristics to theoretical properties.

**b.** constructing a normal probability plot.

**6.66** Problem 1.28 on page 14 describes a survey of 40 MBA students (see the file Gradsurvey).

**a.** Select a sample of 40 graduate students and conduct a similar survey for those students.

**b.** For the data collected in (a), repeat (a) and (b) of Problem 6.65.

**c.** Compare the results of (b) to those of Problem 6.65.

# MANAGING THE *SPRINGVILLE HERALD*

The production department of the newspaper has embarked on a quality improvement effort. Its first project relates to the blackness of the newspaper print. Each day, a determination needs to be made concerning how black the newspaper is printed. Blackness is measured on a standard scale in which the target value is 1.0. Data collected over the past year indicate that the blackness is normally distributed, with a mean of 1.005 and a standard deviation of 0.10. Each day, one spot on the first newspaper printed is chosen, and the blackness of the spot is measured. The blackness of the newspaper is considered acceptable if the blackness of a spot is between 0.95 and 1.05.

## EXERCISES

SH6.1 Assuming that the distribution has not changed from what it was in the past year, what is the probability that the blackness of the spot is

**a.** less than 1.0?
**b.** between 0.95 and 1.0?
**c.** between 1.0 and 1.05?
**d.** less than 0.95 or greater than 1.05?

SH6.2 The objective of the production team is to reduce the probability that the blackness is below 0.95 or above 1.05. Should the team focus on process improvement that lowers the mean to the target value of 1.0 or on process improvement that reduces the standard deviation to 0.075? Explain.

# WEB CASE

*Apply your knowledge about the normal distribution in this Web Case, which extends the Using Statistics scenario from this chapter.*

To satisfy concerns of potential advertisers, the management of OurCampus! has undertaken a research project to learn the amount of time it takes users to download a complex video features page. The marketing department has collected data and has made some claims based on the assertion that the data follow a normal distribution. These data and conclusions can be found in a report located on the internal Web page **www.prenhall.com/Springville/**

**Our_DownloadResearch.htm** (or in the file with the same name in the Student CD-ROM Web Case folder).

Read this marketing report and then answer the following:

1. Can the collected data be approximated by the normal distribution?

2. Review and evaluate the conclusions made by the OurCampus! marketing department. Which conclusions are correct? Which ones are incorrect?

3. If OurCampus! could improve the mean time by five minutes, how would the probabilities change?

# REFERENCES

1. Gunter, B., "Q-Q Plots," *Quality Progress* (February 1994), 81–86.
2. Levine, D. M., P. Ramsey, and R. Smidt, *Applied Statistics for Engineers and Scientists Using Microsoft Excel and Minitab* (Upper Saddle River, NJ: Prentice Hall, 2001).
3. *Microsoft Excel 2007* (Redmond, WA: Microsoft Corp., 2007).
4. Miller, J., "Earliest Known Uses of Some of the Words of Mathematics," **http://members.aol.com/jeff570/n.html**
5. *Minitab for Windows Version 15* (State College, PA: Minitab, Inc., 2006).
6. Pearl, R., "Karl Pearson, 1857–1936," *Journal of the American Statistical Association*, 31 (1936), 653–664.
7. Pearson, E. S., "Some Incidents in the Early History of Biometry and Statistics, 1890–94," *Biometrika*, 52 (1965), 3–18.
8. Walker, H., "The Contributions of Karl Pearson," *Journal of the American Statistical Association*, 53 (1958), 11–22.

# Appendix E6
## Using Microsoft Excel to Compute Probabilities from the Normal Distribution and Other Continuous Distributions

### E6.1 Computing Normal Probabilities

You compute normal probabilities by using either the **Normal** or **Normal Expanded** worksheets of the `Normal.xls` workbook. The **Normal** worksheet, shown in Figure 6.18 on page 232, contains the entries to solve the Example 6.5 and 6.6 problems on pages 227–228. Change the **Mean, Standard Deviation, X Value**, and/or **Cumulative Percentage** to solve similar problems. Use the **Normal Expanded** worksheet (part of which is shown in Figure E6.1) to compute all types of normal probabilities. In these worksheets, the STANDARDIZE function returns the Z value for a specific X value, mean, and standard deviation; the NORMDIST function returns the area or probability of less than a given X value for a specific mean and standard deviation; the NORMSINV function returns the Z value for a given probability of less than a given X, and the

NORMINV function returns the X value for a given probability, mean, and standard deviation.

### E6.2 Creating Normal Probability Plots

There are no Microsoft Excel features that directly create normal probability plots. Use PHStat2 (see Section P6.2) to create a normal probability plot in Excel.

### E6.3 Computing Exponential Probabilities

You compute exponential probabilities by making entries in the **Exponential** worksheet of the `Exponential.xls` workbook. This worksheet (see Figure 6.27 on page 242) uses the **EXPONDIST(X *value, mean*, True)** function to compute the exponential probability for the bank ATM problem of Section 6.5. To adapt this worksheet for other problems, change the **Mean** and **X Value** values in cells B4 and B5.

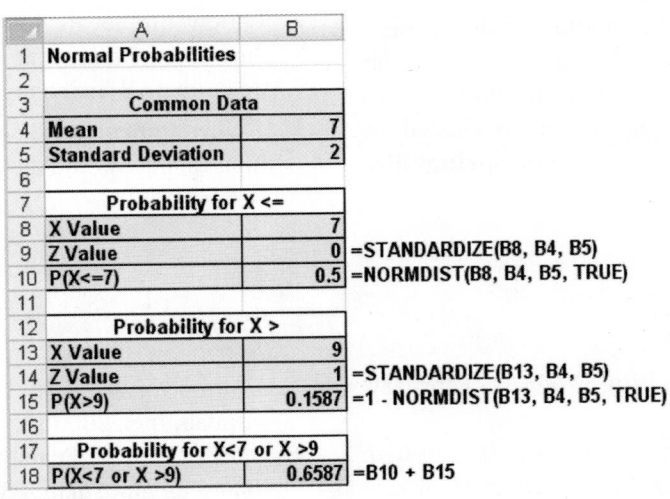

**FIGURE E6.1**

Normal Expanded worksheet (columns A and B)

# Appendix P6
## Using PHStat2 to Compute Probabilities from the Normal Distribution and Other Continuous Distributions

### P6.1 Computing Normal Probabilities

To compute normal probabilities, use **PHStat → Probability & Prob. Distributions → Normal**. The procedure creates a normal probabilities worksheet, similar to Figure 6.18 on page 232, that solves one or more types of normal probability problems based on the Input Options you select.

### P6.2 Creating Normal Probability Plots

To create a normal probability plot, use **PHStat2 → Probability & Prob. Distributions → Normal Probability Plot**. This procedure uses Excel charting features to create a normal probability plot from data from a custom worksheet that the procedure also creates.

The procedure creates a **Plot** worksheet on which the $Z$ values to be plotted are calculated using the NORMSINV function. The procedure then uses Excel charting features

to create a normal probability plot from the calculated $Z$ values and the data in the **Variable Cell Range**.

### P6.3 Computing Exponential Probabilities

To compute exponential probabilities, use **PHStat → Probability & Prob. Distributions → Exponential**. This procedure creates a worksheet similar to Figure 6.27 on page 242 using the mean per unit (*lambda*) and $X$ value that you specify.

# Appendix M6
## Using Minitab to Compute Probabilities from the Normal Distribution and Other Continuous Distributions

### M6.1 Computing Normal Probabilities

To illustrate computing normal probabilities, to find the probability that a download time is less than 9 seconds with $\mu = 7$ and $\sigma = 2$:

1. Open to a new, blank worksheet.
2. Enter **9** in the row 1 cell of column C1, leaving the unnumbered variable label cell at the top of the column empty.
3. Select **Calc → Probability Distributions → Normal**.

In the Normal Distribution dialog box (see Figure M6.1):

4. Click **Cumulative probability**.
5. Enter **7** in the **Mean** box.
6. Enter **2** in the **Standard deviation** box.
7. Click **Input column** and enter **C1** in its box.
8. Click **OK** (to create the results shown in the top portion of Figure 6.19 on page 232).

To find the $Z$ value corresponding to a cumulative area of 0.10:

1. Continue with the same worksheet and enter **.10** in the row 1 cell of column C2.
2. Select **Calc → Probability Distributions → Normal**.

In the Normal Distribution dialog box (see Figure M6.1):

3. Click **Inverse cumulative probability**.
4. Enter **7** in the **Mean** box
5. Enter **2** in the **Standard deviation** box.
6. Click **Input Column** and enter **C2** in its box.
7. Click **OK** (to create the results displayed in the bottom portion of Figure 6.19 on page 232).

### M6.2 Creating Normal Probability Plots

To create a normal probability plot for the 2006 returns of mutual funds:

1. Open the Mutual Funds.mtw worksheet.
2. Select **Graph → Probability Plot**.
3. In the Probability Plots dialog box gallery, click **Single** and then click **OK**.

In the Probability Plot - Single dialog box (see Figure M6.2):

4. Enter **'Return 2006'** in the **Graph variables** box.
5. Click **Distribution**.

**FIGURE M6.1**
Minitab Normal Distribution dialog box

**FIGURE M6.2**
Minitab Probability Plot - Single dialog box

6. In the Probability Plot - Distribution dialog box (see Figure M6.3), select **Normal** from the **Distribution** drop-down list and then click **OK** to return to the Probability Plot - Single dialog box.

7. Back in the Probability Plot - Single dialog box, click **OK** (to create the plot).

**FIGURE M6.3**

Minitab Probability Plot - Distribution

## M6.3 Computing Exponential Probabilities

To compute exponential probabilities for the Section 6.5 ATM customer-arrival example on page 242:

1. Open to a new, blank worksheet.

2. Enter **.1** in the row 1 cell of column C1, leaving the unnumbered variable label cell at the top of the column empty.

3. Select **Calc → Probability Distributions → Exponential**.

In the Exponential Distribution dialog box (see Figure M6.4):

4. Click **Cumulative probability**.

5. Enter **.05** in the **Scale** box. (Minitab defines Scale as the mean time *between* arrivals, $1/\lambda = 1/20 = 0.05$, not the mean number of arrivals, $\lambda = 20$.)

6. Click **Input column** and enter **C1** in its box.

7. Click **OK** (to compute the probability).

**FIGURE M6.4**

Minitab Exponential Distribution dialog box

# CHAPTER
# SEVEN

**USING STATISTICS @** Oxford Cereals

# LEARNING OBJECTIVES

## In this chapter, you learn:

- To distinguish between different sampling methods
- The concept of the sampling distribution
- To compute probabilities related to the sample mean and the sample proportion
- The importance of the Central Limit Theorem

# USING STATISTICS @ Oxford Cereals

Oxford Cereals fills thousands of boxes of cereal during an eight-hour shift. As the plant operations manager, you are responsible for monitoring the amount of cereal placed in each box. To be consistent with package labeling, boxes should contain a mean of 368 grams of cereal. Because of the speed of the process, the cereal weight varies from box to box, causing some boxes to be underfilled and others overfilled. If the process is not working properly, the mean weight in the boxes could vary too much from the label weight of 368 grams to be acceptable.

Because weighing every single box is too time-consuming, costly, and inefficient, you must take a sample of boxes. For each sample you select, you plan to weigh the individual boxes and calculate a sample mean. You need to determine the probability that such a sample mean could have been randomly selected from a population whose mean is 368 grams. Based on your analysis, you will have to decide whether to maintain, alter, or shut down the cereal-filling process.

In Chapter 6, you used the normal distribution to study the distribution of download times for the OurCampus! Web site. In this chapter, you need to make a decision about the cereal-filling process, based on the weights of a sample of cereal boxes packaged at Oxford Cereals. You will learn different methods of sampling and about sampling distributions and how to use them to solve business problems.

## 7.1 TYPES OF SAMPLING METHODS

In Section 1.3, a sample was defined as the portion of a population that has been selected for analysis. Rather than selecting every item in the population, statistical sampling procedures focus on collecting a small representative group of the larger population. The results of the sample are then used to estimate characteristics of the entire population. There are three main reasons for selecting a sample:

- Selecting a sample is less time-consuming than selecting every item in the population.
- Selecting a sample is less costly than selecting every item in the population.
- An analysis of a sample is less cumbersome and more practical than an analysis of the entire population.

The sampling process begins by defining the **frame**. The frame is a listing of items that make up the population. Frames are data sources such as population lists, directories, or maps. Samples are drawn from frames. Inaccurate or biased results can result if a frame excludes certain portions of the population. Using different frames to generate data can lead to dissimilar conclusions.

After you select a frame, you draw a sample from the frame. As illustrated in Figure 7.1, there are two kinds of samples: nonprobability samples and probability samples.

In a **nonprobability sample**, you select the items or individuals without knowing their probabilities of selection. Thus, the theory that has been developed for probability sampling cannot be applied to nonprobability samples. A common type of nonprobability sampling is **convenience sampling**. In convenience sampling, items selected are easy, inexpensive, or convenient to sample. For example, if you were sampling tires stacked in a warehouse, it would be much more convenient to sample tires that were at the top of a stack than tires that were at the bottom of a stack. In many cases, participants in the sample select themselves. For example, many

**FIGURE 7.1**

Types of samples

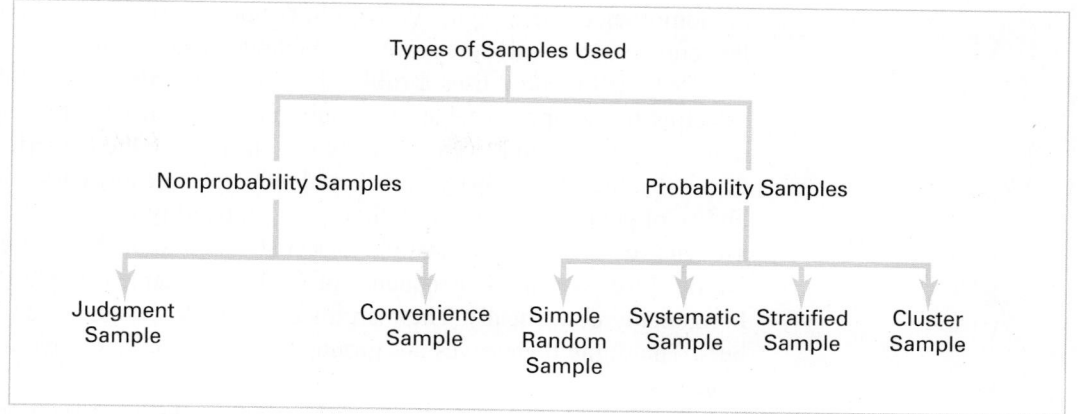

companies conduct surveys by giving visitors to their Web site the opportunity to complete survey forms and submit them electronically. The responses to these surveys can provide large amounts of data quickly and inexpensively, but the sample consists of self-selected Web users. For many studies, only a nonprobability sample such as a judgment sample is available. In a **judgment sample**, you get the opinions of preselected experts in the subject matter. Although the experts may be well informed, you cannot generalize their results to the general public.

Nonprobability samples can have certain advantages, such as convenience, speed, and low cost. However, their lack of accuracy due to selection bias and the fact that the results cannot be used for statistical inference more than offset these advantages.

In a **probability sample**, you select the items based on known probabilities. Whenever possible, you should use probability sampling methods. Probability samples allow you to make unbiased inferences about the population of interest. The four types of probability samples most commonly used are simple random, systematic, stratified, and cluster samples. These sampling methods vary in their cost, accuracy, and complexity.

## Simple Random Samples

In a **simple random sample**, every item from a frame has the same chance of selection as every other item. In addition, every sample of a fixed size has the same chance of selection as every other sample of that size. Simple random sampling is the most elementary random sampling technique. It forms the basis for the other random sampling techniques.

With simple random sampling, you use $n$ to represent the sample size and $N$ to represent the frame size. You number every item in the frame from 1 to $N$. The chance that you will select any particular member of the frame on the first selection is $1/N$.

You select samples with replacement or without replacement. **Sampling with replacement** means that after you select an item, you return it to the frame, where it has the same probability of being selected again. Imagine that you have a fishbowl containing $N$ business cards. On the first selection, you select the card for Judy Craven. You record pertinent information and replace the business card in the bowl. You then mix up the cards in the bowl and select the second card. On the second selection, Judy Craven has the same probability of being selected again, $1/N$. You repeat this process until you have selected the desired sample size, $n$. However, usually you do not want the same item to be selected again.

**Sampling without replacement** means that once you select an item, you cannot select it again. The chance that you will select any particular item in the frame—for example, the business card for Judy Craven—on the first draw is $1/N$. The chance that you will select any card not previously selected on the second draw is now 1 out of $N - 1$. This process continues until you have selected the desired sample of size $n$.

*See Sections P7.1 or M7.1 to create a random sample without replacement.*

Regardless of whether you have sampled with or without replacement, "fishbowl" methods of sample selection have a major drawback—the ability to thoroughly mix the cards and randomly select the sample. As a result, fishbowl methods are not very useful. You need to use less cumbersome and more scientific methods of selection.

One such method uses a **table of random numbers** (see Table E.1 in Appendix E) for selecting the sample. A table of random numbers consists of a series of digits listed in a randomly generated sequence (see reference 7). Because the numeric system uses 10 digits (0, 1, 2, . . . , 9), the chance that you will randomly generate any particular digit is equal to the probability of generating any other digit. This probability is 1 out of 10. Hence, if you generate a sequence of 800 digits, you would expect about 80 to be the digit 0, 80 to be the digit 1, and so on. Because every digit or sequence of digits in the table is random, the table can be read either horizontally or vertically. The margins of the table designate row numbers and column numbers. The digits themselves are grouped into sequences of five in order to make reading the table easier.

To use Table E.1 instead of a fishbowl for selecting the sample, you first need to assign code numbers to the individual items of the frame. Then you generate the random sample by reading the table of random numbers and selecting those individuals from the frame whose assigned code numbers match the digits found in the table. You can better understand the process of sample selection by examining Example 7.1.

**EXAMPLE 7.1**

SELECTING A SIMPLE RANDOM SAMPLE BY USING A TABLE OF RANDOM NUMBERS

A company wants to select a sample of 32 full-time workers from a population of 800 full-time employees in order to collect information on expenditures concerning a company-sponsored dental plan. How do you select a simple random sample?

**SOLUTION** The company decides to conduct an e-mail survey. Assuming that not everyone will respond to the survey, you need to send more than 32 surveys to get the necessary 32 responses. Assuming that 8 out of 10 full-time workers will respond to such a survey (i.e., a response rate of 80%), you decide to send 40 surveys. Because you want to send the 40 surveys to 40 different individuals, you should sample without replacement.

The frame consists of a listing of the names and e-mail addresses of all $N = 800$ full-time employees taken from the company personnel files. Thus, the frame is a complete listing of the population. To select the random sample of 40 employees from this frame, you use a table of random numbers. Because the frame size (800) is a three-digit number, each assigned code number must also be three digits so that every full-time worker has an equal chance of selection. You assign a code of 001 to the first full-time employee in the population listing, a code of 002 to the second full-time employee in the population listing, and so on, until a code of 800 is assigned to the $N$th full-time worker in the listing. Because $N = 800$ is the largest possible coded value, you discard all three-digit code sequences greater than 800 (i.e., 801 through 999 and 000).

To select the simple random sample, you choose an arbitrary starting point from the table of random numbers. One method you can use is to close your eyes and strike the table of random numbers with a pencil. Suppose you used this procedure and you selected row 06, column 05, of Table 7.1 (which is extracted from Table E.1) as the starting point. Although you can go in any direction, in this example you read the table from left to right, in sequences of three digits, without skipping.

The individual with code number 003 is the first full-time employee in the sample (row 06 and columns 05–07), the second individual has code number 364 (row 06 and columns 08–10), and the third individual has code number 884. Because the highest code for any employee is 800, you discard the number 884. Individuals with code numbers 720, 433, 463, 363, 109, 592, 470, and 705 are selected third through tenth, respectively.

You continue the selection process until you get the required sample size of 40 full-time employees. If any three-digit sequence repeats during the selection process, you discard the repeating sequence because you are sampling without replacement.

**TABLE 7.1**

Using a Table of Random Numbers

| | Row | 00000 12345 | 00001 67890 | 11111 12345 | 11112 67890 | 22222 12345 | 22223 67890 | 33333 12345 | 33334 67890 |
|---|---|---|---|---|---|---|---|---|---|
| | | | | | **Column** | | | | |
| | 01 | 49280 | 88924 | 35779 | 00283 | 81163 | 07275 | 89863 | 02348 |
| | 02 | 61870 | 41657 | 07468 | 08612 | 98083 | 97349 | 20775 | 45091 |
| | 03 | 43898 | 65923 | 25078 | 86129 | 78496 | 97653 | 91550 | 08078 |
| | 04 | 62993 | 93912 | 30454 | 84598 | 56095 | 20664 | 12872 | 64647 |
| | 05 | 33850 | 58555 | 51438 | 85507 | 71865 | 79488 | 76783 | 31708 |
| **Begin** | 06 | 97340 | 03364 | 88472 | 04334 | 63919 | 36394 | 11095 | 92470 |
| **selection** | 07 | 70543 | 29776 | 10087 | 10072 | 55980 | 64688 | 68239 | 20461 |
| **(row 06,** | 08 | 89382 | 93809 | 00796 | 95945 | 34101 | 81277 | 66090 | 88872 |
| **column 5)** | 09 | 37818 | 72142 | 67140 | 50785 | 22380 | 16703 | 53362 | 44940 |
| | 10 | 60430 | 22834 | 14130 | 96593 | 23298 | 56203 | 92671 | 15925 |
| | 11 | 82975 | 66158 | 84731 | 19436 | 55790 | 69229 | 28661 | 13675 |
| | 12 | 39087 | 71938 | 40355 | 54324 | 08401 | 26299 | 49420 | 59208 |
| | 13 | 55700 | 24586 | 93247 | 32596 | 11865 | 63397 | 44251 | 43189 |
| | 14 | 14756 | 23997 | 78643 | 75912 | 83832 | 32768 | 18928 | 57070 |
| | 15 | 32166 | 53251 | 70654 | 92827 | 63491 | 04233 | 33825 | 69662 |
| | 16 | 23236 | 73751 | 31888 | 81718 | 06546 | 83246 | 47651 | 04877 |
| | 17 | 45794 | 26926 | 15130 | 82455 | 78305 | 55058 | 52551 | 47182 |
| | 18 | 09893 | 20505 | 14225 | 68514 | 46427 | 56788 | 96297 | 78822 |
| | 19 | 54382 | 74598 | 91499 | 14523 | 68479 | 27686 | 46162 | 83554 |
| | 20 | 94750 | 89923 | 37089 | 20048 | 80336 | 94598 | 26940 | 36858 |
| | 21 | 70297 | 34135 | 53140 | 33340 | 42050 | 82341 | 44104 | 82949 |
| | 22 | 85157 | 47954 | 32979 | 26575 | 57600 | 40881 | 12250 | 73742 |
| | 23 | 11100 | 02340 | 12860 | 74697 | 96644 | 89439 | 28707 | 25815 |
| | 24 | 36871 | 50775 | 30592 | 57143 | 17381 | 68856 | 25853 | 35041 |
| | 25 | 23913 | 48357 | 63308 | 16090 | 51690 | 54607 | 72407 | 55538 |

Source: *Extracted from The Rand Corporation,* A Million Random Digits with 100,000 Normal Deviates *(Glencoe, IL: The Free Press, 1955) and displayed in Table E.1 in Appendix E.*

## Systematic Samples

In a **systematic sample**, you partition the $N$ items in the frame into $n$ groups of $k$ items, where

$$k = \frac{N}{n}$$

You round $k$ to the nearest integer. To select a systematic sample, you choose the first item to be selected at random from the first $k$ items in the frame. Then, you select the remaining $n - 1$ items by taking every $k$th item thereafter from the entire frame.

If the frame consists of a listing of prenumbered checks, sales receipts, or invoices, a systematic sample is faster and easier to take than a simple random sample. A systematic sample is also a convenient mechanism for collecting data from telephone books, class rosters, and consecutive items coming off an assembly line.

To take a systematic sample of $n = 40$ from the population of $N = 800$ full-time employees, you partition the frame of 800 into 40 groups, each of which contains 20 employees. You then select a random number from the first 20 individuals and include every twentieth individual after the first selection in the sample. For example, if the first random number you select is 008, your subsequent selections are 028, 048, 068, 088, 108, . . . , 768, and 788.

Although they are simpler to use, simple random sampling and systematic sampling are generally less efficient than other, more sophisticated, probability sampling methods. Even greater possibilities for selection bias and lack of representation of the population characteristics occur when using systematic samples than with simple random samples. If there is a pattern in the frame, you could have severe selection biases. To overcome the potential problem of disproportionate representation of specific groups in a sample, you can use either stratified sampling methods or cluster sampling methods.

## Stratified Samples

In a **stratified sample**, you first subdivide the $N$ items in the frame into separate subpopulations, or **strata**. A stratum is defined by some common characteristic, such as gender or year in school. You select a simple random sample within each of the strata and combine the results from the separate simple random samples. Stratified sampling is more efficient than either simple random sampling or systematic sampling because you are ensured of the representation of items across the entire population. The homogeneity of items within each stratum provides greater precision in the estimates of underlying population parameters.

---

**EXAMPLE 7.2**     SELECTING A STRATIFIED SAMPLE

A company wants to select a sample of 32 full-time workers from a population of 800 full-time employees in order to estimate expenditures from a company-sponsored dental plan. Of the full-time employees, 25% are managers and 75% are nonmanagerial workers. How do you select the stratified sample in order for the sample to represent the correct percentage of managers and nonmanagerial workers?

**SOLUTION** If you assume an 80% response rate, you need to send 40 surveys to get the necessary 32 responses. The frame consists of a listing of the names and e-mail addresses of all $N = 800$ full-time employees included in the company personnel files. Because 25% of the full-time employees are managers, you first separate the frame into two strata: a subpopulation listing of all 200 managerial-level personnel and a separate subpopulation listing of all 600 full-time nonmanagerial workers. Because the first stratum consists of a listing of 200 managers, you assign three-digit code numbers from 001 to 200. Because the second stratum contains a listing of 600 nonmanagerial workers, you assign three-digit code numbers from 001 to 600.

To collect a stratified sample proportional to the sizes of the strata, you select 25% of the overall sample from the first stratum and 75% of the overall sample from the second stratum. You take two separate simple random samples, each of which is based on a distinct random starting point from a table of random numbers (Table E.1). In the first sample, you select 10 managers from the listing of 200 in the first stratum, and in the second sample, you select 30 nonmanagerial workers from the listing of 600 in the second stratum. You then combine the results to reflect the composition of the entire company.

---

## Cluster Samples

In a **cluster sample**, you divide the $N$ items in the frame into several clusters so that each cluster is representative of the entire population. **Clusters** are naturally occurring designations, such as counties, election districts, city blocks, households, or sales territories. You then take a random sample of one or more clusters and study all items in each selected cluster. If clusters are large, a probability-based sample taken from a single cluster is all that is needed.

Cluster sampling is often more cost-effective than simple random sampling, particularly if the population is spread over a wide geographic region. However, cluster sampling often requires a larger sample size to produce results as precise as those from simple random sampling or stratified sampling. A detailed discussion of systematic sampling, stratified sampling, and cluster sampling procedures can be found in reference 1.

# PROBLEMS FOR SECTION 7.1

## Learning the Basics

**7.1** For a population containing $N = 902$ individuals, what code number would you assign for
a. the first person on the list?
b. the fortieth person on the list?
c. the last person on the list?

**7.2** For a population of $N = 902$, verify that by starting in row 05, column 1 of the table of random numbers (Table E.1), you need only six rows to select a sample of $n = 60$ *without* replacement.

**7.3** Given a population of $N = 93$, starting in row 29 of the table of random numbers (Table E.1), and reading across the row, select a sample of $n = 15$
a. *without* replacement.
b. *with* replacement.

## Applying the Concepts

**7.4** For a study that consists of personal interviews with participants (rather than mail or phone surveys), explain why simple random sampling might be less practical than some other sampling methods.

**7.5** You want to select a random sample of $n = 1$ from a population of three items (which are called $A$, $B$, and $C$). The rule for selecting the sample is: Flip a coin; if it is heads, pick item $A$; if it is tails, flip the coin again; this time, if it is heads, choose $B$; if it is tails, choose $C$. Explain why this is a probability sample but not a simple random sample.

**7.6** A population has four members (called $A$, $B$, $C$, and $D$). You would like to select a random sample of $n = 2$, which you decide to do in the following way: Flip a coin; if it is heads, the sample will be items $A$ and $B$; if it is tails, the sample will be items $C$ and $D$. Although this is a random sample, it is not a simple random sample. Explain why. (If you did Problem 7.5, compare the procedure described there with the procedure described in this problem.)

**7.7** The registrar of a college with a population of $N = 4,000$ full-time students is asked by the president to conduct a survey to measure satisfaction with the quality of life on campus. The following table contains a breakdown of the 4,000 registered full-time students, by gender and class designation:

| | Class Designation | | | | |
|---|---|---|---|---|---|
| Gender | Fr. | So. | Jr. | Sr. | Total |
| Female | 700 | 520 | 500 | 480 | 2,200 |
| Male | 560 | 460 | 400 | 380 | 1,800 |
| Total | 1,260 | 980 | 900 | 860 | 4,000 |

The registrar intends to take a probability sample of $n = 200$ students and project the results from the sample to the entire population of full-time students.
a. If the frame available from the registrar's files is an alphabetical listing of the names of all $N = 4,000$ registered full-time students, what type of sample could you take? Discuss.
b. What is the advantage of selecting a simple random sample in (a)?
c. What is the advantage of selecting a systematic sample in (a)?
d. If the frame available from the registrar's files is a listing of the names of all $N = 4,000$ registered full-time students compiled from eight separate alphabetical lists, based on the gender and class designation breakdowns shown in the class designation table, what type of sample should you take? Discuss.
e. Suppose that each of the $N = 4,000$ registered full-time students lived in one of the 10 campus dormitories. Each dormitory accommodates 400 students. It is college policy to fully integrate students by gender and class designation in each dormitory. If the registrar is able to compile a listing of all students by dormitory, explain how you could take a cluster sample.

**SELF Test** **7.8** Prenumbered sales invoices are kept in a sales journal. The invoices are numbered from 0001 to 5000.
a. Beginning in row 16, column 1, and proceeding horizontally in Table E.1, select a simple random sample of 50 invoice numbers.
b. Select a systematic sample of 50 invoice numbers. Use the random numbers in row 20, columns 5–7, as the starting point for your selection.
c. Are the invoices selected in (a) the same as those selected in (b)? Why or why not?

**7.9** Suppose that 5,000 sales invoices are separated into four strata. Stratum 1 contains 50 invoices, stratum 2 contains 500 invoices, stratum 3 contains 1,000 invoices, and stratum 4 contains 3,450 invoices. A sample of 500 sales invoices is needed.
a. What type of sampling should you do? Why?
b. Explain how you would carry out the sampling according to the method stated in (a).
c. Why is the sampling in (a) not simple random sampling?

## 7.2 EVALUATING SURVEY WORTHINESS

Surveys are used to collect data. Nearly every day, you read or hear about survey or opinion poll results in newspapers, on the Internet, or on radio or television. To identify surveys that lack objectivity or credibility, you must critically evaluate what you read and hear by examining the worthiness of the survey. First, you must evaluate the purpose of the survey, why it was conducted, and for whom it was conducted. A survey conducted to satisfy curiosity is mainly for entertainment. Its result is an end in itself rather than a means to an end.

The second step in evaluating the worthiness of a survey is to determine whether it was based on a probability or nonprobability sample (as discussed in Section 7.1). You need to remember that the only way to make valid statistical inferences from a sample to a population is through the use of a probability sample. Surveys that use nonprobability sampling methods are subject to serious, perhaps unintentional, biases that may make the results meaningless.

### Survey Error

Even when surveys use random probability sampling methods, they are subject to potential errors. There are four types of survey errors:

- Coverage error
- Nonresponse error
- Sampling error
- Measurement error

Well-designed surveys reduce or minimize these four types of errors, often at considerable cost.

***Coverage Error***   The key to proper sample selection is an adequate frame. Remember, a frame is an up-to-date list of all the items from which you will select the sample. **Coverage error** occurs if certain groups of items are excluded from this frame so that they have no chance of being selected in the sample. Coverage error results in a **selection bias**. If the frame is inadequate because certain groups of items in the population were not properly included, any random probability sample selected will provide an estimate of the characteristics of the frame, not the *actual* population.

***Nonresponse Error***   Not everyone is willing to respond to a survey. In fact, research has shown that individuals in the upper and lower economic classes tend to respond less frequently to surveys than do people in the middle class. **Nonresponse error** arises from the failure to collect data on all items in the sample and results in a **nonresponse bias**. Because you cannot always assume that persons who do not respond to surveys are similar to those who do, you need to follow up on the nonresponses after a specified period of time. You should make several attempts to convince such individuals to complete the survey. The follow-up responses are then compared to the initial responses in order to make valid inferences from the survey (reference 1). The mode of response you use affects the rate of response. The personal interview and the telephone interview usually produce a higher response rate than does the mail survey—but at a higher cost.

***Sampling Error***   A sample is selected because it is simpler, less costly, and more efficient. However, chance dictates which individuals or items will or will not be included in the sample. **Sampling error** reflects the variation, or "chance differences," from sample to sample, based on the probability of particular individuals or items being selected in the particular samples.

When you read about the results of surveys or polls in newspapers or magazines, there is often a statement regarding a margin of error, such as "the results of this poll are expected to be within ±4 percentage points of the actual value." This **margin of error** is the sampling error. You can reduce sampling error by taking larger sample sizes, although this also increases the cost of conducting the survey.

***Measurement Error***   In the practice of good survey research, you design a questionnaire with the intention of gathering meaningful information. But you have a dilemma here: Getting meaningful measurements is often easier said than done. Consider the following proverb:

A person with one watch always knows what time it is;
A person with two watches always searches to identify the correct one;
A person with ten watches is always reminded of the difficulty in measuring time.

Unfortunately, the process of measurement is often governed by what is convenient, not what is needed. The measurements you get are often only a proxy for the ones you really desire. Much attention has been given to measurement error that occurs because of a weakness in question wording (reference 2). A question should be clear, not ambiguous. Furthermore, in order to avoid *leading questions*, you need to present them in a neutral manner.

Three sources of **measurement error** are ambiguous wording of questions, the Hawthorne effect, and respondent error. As an example of ambiguous wording, in November 1993, the U.S. Department of Labor reported that the unemployment rate in the United States had been underestimated for more than a decade because of poor questionnaire wording in the Current Population Survey. In particular, the wording had led to a significant undercount of women in the labor force. Because unemployment rates are tied to benefit programs such as state unemployment compensation, survey researchers had to rectify the situation by adjusting the questionnaire wording.

The "Hawthorne effect" occurs when the respondent feels obligated to please the interviewer. Proper interviewer training can minimize the Hawthorne effect.

Respondent error occurs as a result of an overzealous or underzealous effort by the respondent. You can minimize this error in two ways: (1) by carefully scrutinizing the data and then recontacting those individuals whose responses seem unusual and (2) by establishing a program of recontacting a small number of randomly chosen individuals in order to determine the reliability of the responses.

## Ethical Issues

Ethical considerations arise with respect to the four types of potential errors that can occur when designing surveys: coverage error, nonresponse error, sampling error, and measurement error. Coverage error can result in selection bias and becomes an ethical issue if particular groups or individuals are *purposely* excluded from the frame so that the survey results are more favorable to the survey's sponsor. Nonresponse error can lead to nonresponse bias and becomes an ethical issue if the sponsor knowingly designs the survey so that particular groups or individuals are less likely than others to respond. Sampling error becomes an ethical issue if the findings are purposely presented without reference to sample size and margin of error so that the sponsor can promote a viewpoint that might otherwise be truly insignificant. Measurement error becomes an ethical issue in one of three ways: (1) a survey sponsor chooses leading questions that guide the responses in a particular direction; (2) an interviewer, through mannerisms and tone, purposely creates a Hawthorne effect or otherwise guides the responses in a particular direction; or (3) a respondent willfully provides false information.

Ethical issues also arise when the results of nonprobability samples are used to form conclusions about the entire population. When you use a nonprobability sampling method, you need to explain the sampling procedures and state that the results cannot be generalized beyond the sample.

# Probability Sampling vs. Web-Based Surveys

*From the Authors' Desktop*

In Sections 7.1 and 7.2, you learned that statistical inferences about populations can only be made by analyzing data collected from probability samples. This type of sampling has been the "gold standard" in survey research for more than fifty years. Companies using surveys based on probability sampling typically make a great effort (and spend large sums) to deal with coverage error, nonresponse error, sampling error, and measurement error.

A recent article (T. Crampton, "About Online Surveys, Traditional Pollsters Are Somewhat Disappointed," **www.nytimes.com/2007/05/31/business media**), reported that some survey companies are offering an Internet alternative to traditional surveys based on random sampling. YouGov, a British company, is planning to introduce Internet-based polling in the United States for the 2008 presidential election.

YouGov uses a large panel of respondents who answer questions online. These panelists supposedly come from a diverse group with special efforts made to include people who are less likely to use the Internet. In addition, panelists are paid to participate. This method of sampling (and the fact that respondents are paid and are not volunteers) makes Web-based sampling scientifically unacceptable to traditional pollsters.

Despite these concerns, YouGov has partnered with Polimetrix, an online company based in Palo Alto, California, to conduct surveys in the United States. The founder of Polimetrix, Professor Douglas Rivers of Stanford University, claims that the margin of error of Polimetrix polls is similar to telephone polls. YouGov's chief executive, Nadhim Zahawi, points out that modern technology, such as cell phones, has made old-fashioned polls more unreliable due to the increased difficulty of contacting people at home. In fact, a recent article (M. Thee, "Cellphones Challenge Poll Sampling," *The New York Times*, December 7, 2007, p. A27) indicated that cellphone-only households make up 16% of the households in the United States.

However, Leendert de Voogd, managing director of TSN Opinion in Brussels, believes that "Internet polling is like the Wild West, with no rules, no sheriff, and no reference points." He believes that only polling with probability sampling will deliver valid results. On the other hand, Professor Anthony King of the University of Essex does not believe that Internet polling fails to reflect a nation's population. According to Professor King, "There is no evidence to suggest that people who use the Internet are fundamentally different from those without it. One mad, awful lady living in a poor neighborhood without Internet does not differ much from her mad, awful friend next door who goes online."

Perhaps only time will tell who is right and perhaps we will know more after the 2008 U.S. presidential election.

## PROBLEMS FOR SECTION 7.2

### Applying the Concepts

**7.10** "A survey indicates that the vast majority of college students own their own personal computers." What information would you want to know before you accepted the results of this survey?

**7.11** A simple random sample of $n = 300$ full-time employees is selected from a company list containing the names of all $N = 5,000$ full-time employees in order to evaluate job satisfaction.
**a.** Give an example of possible coverage error.
**b.** Give an example of possible nonresponse error.
**c.** Give an example of possible sampling error.
**d.** Give an example of possible measurement error.

**7.12** Business professor Thomas Callarman traveled to China more than a dozen times from 2000 to 2005. He warns people about believing everything they read about surveys conducted in China and gives two specific reasons. Callarman stated, "First, things are changing so rapidly that what you hear today may not be true tomorrow. Second, the people who answer the surveys may tell you what they think you want to hear, rather than what they really believe" (T. E. Callarman, "Some Thoughts on China," *Decision Line*, March, 2006, pp. 1, 43–44).

**a.** List the four types (or categories) of survey error discussed in this section.
**b.** Which categories best describe the types of survey error discussed by Professor Callarman?

**7.13** The gourmet foods industry is expected to exceed $62 billion in sales by the year 2009. A survey conducted by Packaged Facts indicates that one-fifth of American adults consider themselves "gourmet consumers" ("Galloping Gourmet," *The Progressive Grocer*, January 1, 2006, pp. 80–81). What additional information would you want to know before you accepted the results of the survey?

**7.14** Only 10% of Americans rated their financial situation as "excellent," according to a Gallup Poll taken April 10–13, 2006. However, 41% rated their financial situation as "good," 37% said "only fair," and 12% "poor" (J. M. Jones, "Americans More Worried About Meeting Basic Financial Needs," *The Gallup Poll*, **galluppoll.com**, April 25, 2006). What additional information would you want to know before you accepted the results of the survey?

**7.15** In May of 2007, one of the nation's most respected cardiologists, Dr. Steven Nissen, reported his troubling analysis of the heavily prescribed diabetes drug Avandia. His analysis showed a 43% higher risk of heart attacks among patients taking Avandia, compared to other drugs used for the same condition. Furthermore, patients taking Avandia exhibited a 64% higher risk of cardiovascular death (S. Rubenstein, "What Diabetes Patients Need to Know," *The Wall Street Journal*, May 22, 2007, p. D2). What additional information would you want to know in order to make better-informed decisions regarding Avandia?

**7.16** A study investigating the effects of CEO succession on the stock performance of large publicly held corporations also investigated the demographics of the newly announced CEOs. The mean and standard deviation of the new CEO's age were 53.3 and 5.97, respectively. The mean and standard deviation of the number of years the new CEO had been with the firm were 20.1 and 12.6, respectively. 93.6% of the new CEOs held college degrees, 30.4% held MBAs, and 3.2% held doctorates (J. C. Rhim, J. V. Peluchette, and I. Song, "Stock Market Reactions and Firm Performance Surrounding CEO Succession: Antecedents of Succession and Successor Origin," *Mid-American Journal of Business*, Spring 2006, pp. 21–30). What additional information would you want to know before you accepted the results of this study?

## 7.3 SAMPLING DISTRIBUTIONS

In many applications, you want to make inferences that are based on statistics calculated from samples to estimate the values of population parameters. In the next two sections, you will learn about how the sample mean (a statistic) is used to estimate the population mean (a parameter) and how the sample proportion (a statistic) is used to estimate the population proportion (a parameter). Your main concern when making a statistical inference is drawing conclusions about a population, *not* about a sample. For example, a political pollster is interested in the sample results only as a way of estimating the actual proportion of the votes that each candidate will receive from the population of voters. Likewise, as plant operations manager for Oxford Cereals, you are only interested in using the sample mean weight calculated from a sample of cereal boxes for estimating the mean weight contained in a population of boxes.

In practice, you select a single random sample of a predetermined size from the population. Hypothetically, to use the sample statistic to estimate the population parameter, you could examine *every* possible sample of a given size that could occur. A **sampling distribution** is the distribution of the results if you actually selected all possible samples. The single result you obtain in practice is just one of the results in the sampling distribution.

## 7.4 SAMPLING DISTRIBUTION OF THE MEAN

In Chapter 3, several measures of central tendency, including the mean, median, and mode, were discussed. Undoubtedly, the mean is the most widely used measure of central tendency. The sample mean is often used to estimate the population mean. The **sampling distribution of the mean** is the distribution of all possible sample means if you select all possible samples of a given size.

### The Unbiased Property of the Sample Mean

The sample mean is **unbiased** because the mean of all the possible sample means (of a given sample size, $n$) is equal to the population mean, $\mu$. A simple example concerning a population of four administrative assistants demonstrates this property. Each assistant is asked to type the same page of a manuscript. Table 7.2 presents the number of errors. This population distribution is shown in Figure 7.2.

**TABLE 7.2**

Number of Errors Made by Each of Four Administrative Assistants

| Administrative Assistant | Number of Errors |
|---|---|
| Ann | $X_1 = 3$ |
| Bob | $X_2 = 2$ |
| Carla | $X_3 = 1$ |
| Dave | $X_4 = 4$ |

**FIGURE 7.2**

Number of errors made by a population of four administrative assistants

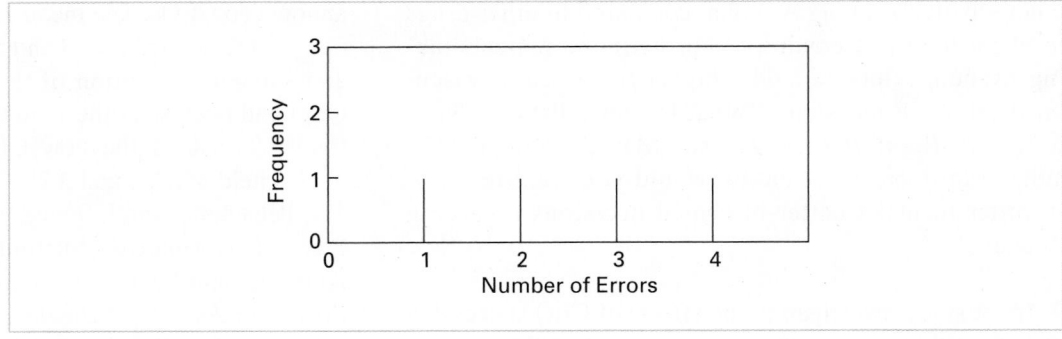

When you have the data from a population, you compute the mean by using Equation (7.1).

**Population Mean**

The population mean is the sum of the values in the population divided by the population size, $N$.

$$\mu = \frac{\sum_{i=1}^{N} X_i}{N} \qquad (7.1)$$

You compute the population standard deviation, $\sigma$, using Equation (7.2):

**Population Standard Deviation**

$$\sigma = \sqrt{\frac{\sum_{i=1}^{N}(X_i - \mu)^2}{N}} \qquad (7.2)$$

Thus, for the data of Table 7.1,

$$\mu = \frac{3 + 2 + 1 + 4}{4} = 2.5 \text{ errors}$$

and

$$\sigma = \sqrt{\frac{(3-2.5)^2 + (2-2.5)^2 + (1-2.5)^2 + (4-2.5)^2}{4}} = 1.12 \text{ errors}$$

If you select samples of two administrative assistants *with* replacement from this population, there are 16 possible samples ($N^n = 4^2 = 16$). Table 7.3 lists the 16 possible sample outcomes. If you average all 16 of these sample means, the mean of these values, $\mu_{\bar{X}}$, is equal to 2.5, which is also the mean of the population $\mu$.

Because the mean of the 16 sample means is equal to the population mean, the sample mean is an unbiased estimator of the population mean. Therefore, although you do not know how close the sample mean of any particular sample selected comes to the population mean,

**TABLE 7.3**

All 16 Samples of $n = 2$ Administrative Assistants from a Population of $N = 4$ Administrative Assistants When Sampling with Replacement

| Sample | Administrative Assistants | Sample Outcomes | Sample Means |
|--------|--------------------------|-----------------|--------------|
| 1 | Ann, Ann | 3, 3 | $\bar{X}_1 = 3$ |
| 2 | Ann, Bob | 3, 2 | $\bar{X}_2 = 2.5$ |
| 3 | Ann, Carla | 3, 1 | $\bar{X}_3 = 2$ |
| 4 | Ann, Dave | 3, 4 | $\bar{X}_4 = 3.5$ |
| 5 | Bob, Ann | 2, 3 | $\bar{X}_5 = 2.5$ |
| 6 | Bob, Bob | 2, 2 | $\bar{X}_6 = 2$ |
| 7 | Bob, Carla | 2, 1 | $\bar{X}_7 = 1.5$ |
| 8 | Bob, Dave | 2, 4 | $\bar{X}_8 = 3$ |
| 9 | Carla, Ann | 1, 3 | $\bar{X}_9 = 2$ |
| 10 | Carla, Bob | 1, 2 | $\bar{X}_{10} = 1.5$ |
| 11 | Carla, Carla | 1, 1 | $\bar{X}_{11} = 1$ |
| 12 | Carla, Dave | 1, 4 | $\bar{X}_{12} = 2.5$ |
| 13 | Dave, Ann | 4, 3 | $\bar{X}_{13} = 3.5$ |
| 14 | Dave, Bob | 4, 2 | $\bar{X}_{14} = 3$ |
| 15 | Dave, Carla | 4, 1 | $\bar{X}_{15} = 2.5$ |
| 16 | Dave, Dave | 4, 4 | $\bar{X}_{16} = 4$ |
| | | | $\mu_{\bar{X}} = 2.5$ |

you are at least assured that the mean of all the possible sample means that could have been selected is equal to the population mean.

## Standard Error of the Mean

Figure 7.3 illustrates the variation in the sample means when selecting all 16 possible samples. In this small example, although the sample means vary from sample to sample, depending on which two administrative assistants are selected, the sample means do not vary as much as the individual values in the population. That the sample means are less variable than the individual values in the population follows directly from the fact that each sample mean averages together all the values in the sample. A population consists of individual outcomes that can take on a wide range of values, from extremely small to extremely large. However, if a sample contains an extreme value, although this value will have an effect on the sample mean, the effect is reduced because the value is averaged with all the other values in the sample. As the sample size increases, the effect of a single extreme value becomes smaller because it is averaged with more values.

**FIGURE 7.3**

Sampling distribution of the mean, based on all possible samples containing two administrative assistants

*Source: Data are from Table 7.3*

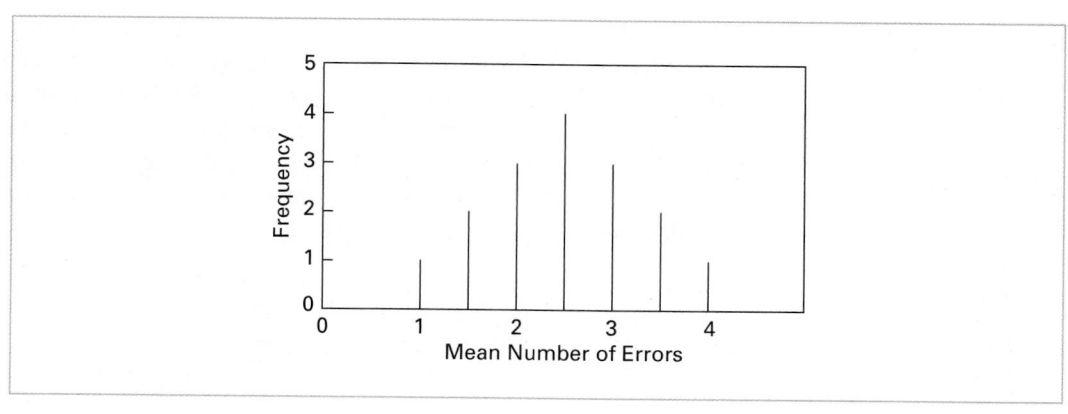

The value of the standard deviation of all possible sample means, called the **standard error of the mean**, expresses how the sample means vary from sample to sample. Equation (7.3) defines the standard error of the mean when sampling *with* replacement or *without* replacement from large or infinite populations.

---

**Standard Error of the Mean**

The standard error of the mean, $\sigma_{\bar{X}}$, is equal to the standard deviation in the population, $\sigma$, divided by the square root of the sample size, $n$.

$$\sigma_{\bar{X}} = \frac{\sigma}{\sqrt{n}} \qquad (7.3)$$

---

Therefore, as the sample size increases, the standard error of the mean decreases by a factor equal to the square root of the sample size.

You can also use Equation (7.3) as an approximation of the standard error of the mean when the sample is selected without replacement if the sample contains less than 5% of the entire population. Example 7.3 computes the standard error of the mean for such a situation. (See the section 7.6.pdf file on the Student CD-ROM that accompanies this book for the case in which more than 5% of the population is contained in a sample selected without replacement.)

**EXAMPLE 7.3**    COMPUTING THE STANDARD ERROR OF THE MEAN

Returning to the cereal-filling process described in the Using Statistics scenario on page 258, if you randomly select a sample of 25 boxes without replacement from the thousands of boxes filled during a shift, the sample contains far less than 5% of the population. Given that the standard deviation of the cereal-filling process is 15 grams, compute the standard error of the mean.

**SOLUTION**  Using Equation (7.3) with $n = 25$ and $\sigma = 15$, the standard error of the mean is

$$\sigma_{\bar{X}} = \frac{\sigma}{\sqrt{n}} = \frac{15}{\sqrt{25}} = \frac{15}{5} = 3$$

The variation in the sample means for samples of $n = 25$ is much less than the variation in the individual boxes of cereal (i.e., $\sigma_{\bar{X}} = 3$ while $\sigma = 15$).

## Sampling from Normally Distributed Populations

Now that the concept of a sampling distribution has been introduced and the standard error of the mean has been defined, what distribution will the sample mean, $\bar{X}$, follow? If you are sampling from a population that is normally distributed with mean, $\mu$, and standard deviation, $\sigma$, then regardless of the sample size, $n$, the sampling distribution of the mean is normally distributed, with mean, $\mu_{\bar{X}} = \mu$, and standard error of the mean, $\sigma_{\bar{X}} = \sigma/\sqrt{n}$.

In the simplest case, if you take samples of size $n = 1$, each possible sample mean is a single value from the population because

$$\bar{X} = \frac{\sum_{i=1}^{n} X_i}{n} = \frac{X_1}{1} = X_1$$

Therefore, if the population is normally distributed, with mean, $\mu$, and standard deviation, $\sigma$, the sampling distribution of $\bar{X}$ for samples of $n = 1$ must also follow the normal distribution, with mean $\mu_{\bar{X}} = \mu$ and standard error of the mean $\sigma_{\bar{X}} = \sigma/\sqrt{1} = \sigma$. In addition, as the sample size increases, the sampling distribution of the mean still follows a normal distribution, with $\mu_{\bar{X}} = \mu$, but the standard error of the mean decreases, so that a larger proportion of sample means are closer to the population mean. Figure 7.4 below illustrates this reduction in variability. Note that 500 samples of 1, 2, 4, 8, 16, and 32 were randomly selected from a normally distributed population. From the polygons in Figure 7.4, you can see that, although the sampling distribution of the mean is approximately[1] normal for each sample size, the sample means are distributed more tightly around the population mean as the sample size increases.

**FIGURE 7.4**

Sampling distributions of the mean from 500 samples of sizes $n = 1$, 2, 4, 8, 16, and 32 selected from a normal population

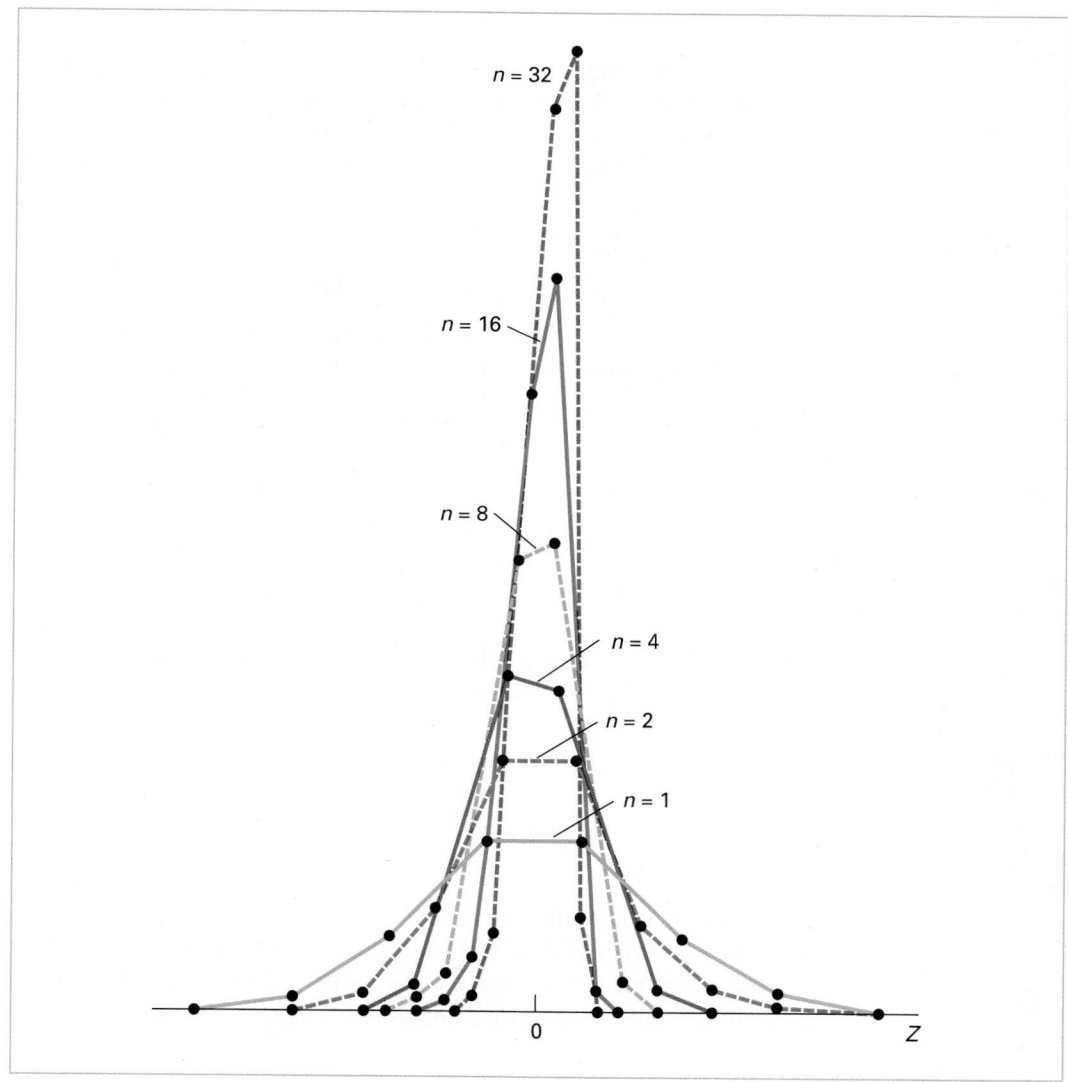

To further examine the concept of the sampling distribution of the mean, consider the Using Statistics scenario described on page 258. The packaging equipment that is filling 368-gram boxes of cereal is set so that the amount of cereal in a box is normally distributed, with a mean of 368 grams. From past experience, you know the population standard deviation for this filling process is 15 grams.

If you randomly select a sample of 25 boxes from the many thousands that are filled in a day and the mean weight is computed for this sample, what type of result could you expect? For example, do you think that the sample mean could be 368 grams? 200 grams? 365 grams?

The sample acts as a miniature representation of the population, so if the values in the population are normally distributed, the values in the sample should be approximately normally distributed. Thus, if the population mean is 368 grams, the sample mean has a good chance of being close to 368 grams.

How can you determine the probability that the sample of 25 boxes will have a mean below 365 grams? From the normal distribution (Section 6.2), you know that you can find the area below any value $X$ by converting to standardized $Z$ values:

$$Z = \frac{X - \mu}{\sigma}$$

In the examples in Section 6.2, you studied how any single value, $X$, differs from the population mean. Now, in this example, you want to study how a sample mean, $\bar{X}$ differs from the population mean. Substituting $\bar{X}$ for $X$, $\mu_{\bar{X}}$ for $\mu$, and $\sigma_{\bar{X}}$ for $\sigma$ in the equation above results in Equation (7.4).

Finding $Z$ for the Sampling Distribution of the Mean

The $Z$ value is equal to the difference between the sample mean, $\bar{X}$, and the population mean, $\mu$, divided by the standard error of the mean, $\sigma_{\bar{X}}$.

$$Z = \frac{\bar{X} - \mu_{\bar{X}}}{\sigma_{\bar{X}}} = \frac{\bar{X} - \mu}{\frac{\sigma}{\sqrt{n}}} \qquad (7.4)$$

To find the area below 365 grams, from Equation (7.4),

$$Z = \frac{\bar{X} - \mu_{\bar{X}}}{\sigma_{\bar{X}}} = \frac{365 - 368}{\frac{15}{\sqrt{25}}} = \frac{-3}{3} = -1.00$$

The area corresponding to $Z = -1.00$ in Table E.2 is 0.1587. Therefore, 15.87% of all the possible samples of 25 boxes have a sample mean below 365 grams.

The preceding statement is not the same as saying that a certain percentage of *individual* boxes will have less than 365 grams of cereal. You compute that percentage as follows:

$$Z = \frac{X - \mu}{\sigma} = \frac{365 - 368}{15} = \frac{-3}{15} = -0.20$$

The area corresponding to $Z = -0.20$ in Table E.2 is 0.4207. Therefore, 42.07% of the *individual* boxes are expected to contain less than 365 grams. Comparing these results, you see that many more *individual boxes* than *sample means* are below 365 grams. This result is explained by the fact that each sample consists of 25 different values, some small and some large. The averaging process dilutes the importance of any individual value, particularly when the sample size is large. Thus, the chance that the sample mean of 25 boxes is far away from the population mean is less than the chance that a *single* box is far away.

Examples 7.4 and 7.5 show how these results are affected by using different sample sizes.

---

**EXAMPLE 7.4**    THE EFFECT OF SAMPLE SIZE $n$ ON THE COMPUTATION OF $\sigma_{\bar{X}}$

How is the standard error of the mean affected by increasing the sample size from 25 to 100 boxes?

**SOLUTION**  If $n = 100$ boxes, then using Equation (7.3) on page 270:

$$\sigma_{\bar{X}} = \frac{\sigma}{\sqrt{n}} = \frac{15}{\sqrt{100}} = \frac{15}{10} = 1.5$$

The fourfold increase in the sample size from 25 to 100 reduces the standard error of the mean by half—from 3 grams to 1.5 grams. This demonstrates that taking a larger sample results in less variability in the sample means from sample to sample.

---

**EXAMPLE 7.5**    THE EFFECT OF SAMPLE SIZE $n$ ON THE CLUSTERING OF MEANS IN THE SAMPLING DISTRIBUTION

If you select a sample of 100 boxes, what is the probability that the sample mean is below 365 grams?

**SOLUTION**  Using Equation (7.4) on page 272,

$$Z = \frac{\bar{X} - \mu_{\bar{X}}}{\sigma_{\bar{X}}} = \frac{365 - 368}{\dfrac{15}{\sqrt{100}}} = \frac{-3}{1.5} = -2.00$$

From Table E.2, the area less than $Z = -2.00$ is 0.0228. Therefore, 2.28% of the samples of 100 boxes have means below 365 grams, as compared with 15.87% for samples of 25 boxes.

---

Sometimes you need to find the interval that contains a fixed proportion of the sample means. You need to determine a distance below and above the population mean containing a specific area of the normal curve. From Equation (7.4) on page 272,

$$Z = \frac{\bar{X} - \mu}{\dfrac{\sigma}{\sqrt{n}}}$$

Solving for $\bar{X}$ results in Equation (7.5).

Finding $\bar{X}$ for the Sampling Distribution of the Mean

$$\bar{X} = \mu + Z \frac{\sigma}{\sqrt{n}} \qquad \text{(7.5)}$$

Example 7.6 illustrates the use of Equation (7.5).

**EXAMPLE 7.6**    DETERMINING THE INTERVAL THAT INCLUDES A FIXED PROPORTION OF THE SAMPLE MEANS

In the cereal-fill example, find an interval symmetrically distributed around the population mean that will include 95% of the sample means based on samples of 25 boxes.

**SOLUTION** If 95% of the sample means are in the interval, then 5% are outside the interval. Divide the 5% into two equal parts of 2.5%. The value of $Z$ in Table E.2 corresponding to an area of 0.0250 in the lower tail of the normal curve is $-1.96$, and the value of $Z$ corresponding to a cumulative area of 0.975 (i.e., 0.025 in the upper tail of the normal curve) is $+1.96$. The lower value of $\bar{X}$ (called $\bar{X}_L$) and the upper value of $\bar{X}$ (called $\bar{X}_U$) are found by using Equation (7.5):

$$\bar{X}_L = 368 + (-1.96)\frac{15}{\sqrt{25}} = 368 - 5.88 = 362.12$$

$$\bar{X}_U = 368 + (1.96)\frac{15}{\sqrt{25}} = 368 + 5.88 = 373.88$$

Therefore, 95% of all sample means based on samples of 25 boxes are between 362.12 and 373.88 grams.

### Sampling from Non-Normally Distributed Populations— The Central Limit Theorem

Thus far in this section, only the sampling distribution of the mean for a normally distributed population has been considered. However, in many instances, either you know that the population is not normally distributed or it is unrealistic to assume that the population is normally distributed. An important theorem in statistics, the Central Limit Theorem, deals with this situation.

THE CENTRAL LIMIT THEOREM

The **Central Limit Theorem** states that as the sample size (i.e., the number of values in each sample) gets *large enough*, the sampling distribution of the mean is approximately normally distributed. This is true regardless of the shape of the distribution of the individual values in the population.

What sample size is large enough? A great deal of statistical research has gone into this issue. As a general rule, statisticians have found that for many population distributions, when the sample size is at least 30, the sampling distribution of the mean is approximately normal. However, you can apply the Central Limit Theorem for even smaller sample sizes if the population distribution is approximately bell shaped. In the uncommon case in which the distribution is extremely skewed or has more than one mode, you may need sample sizes larger than 30 to ensure normality.

Figure 7.5 illustrates the application of the Central Limit Theorem to different populations. The sampling distributions from three different continuous distributions (normal, uniform, and exponential) for varying sample sizes ($n = 2, 5, 30$) are displayed.

**FIGURE 7.5**

Sampling distribution of the mean for different populations for samples of $n = 2, 5,$ and 30

*See Section E7.2, P7.2, or M7.2 to create a simulated sampling distribution.*

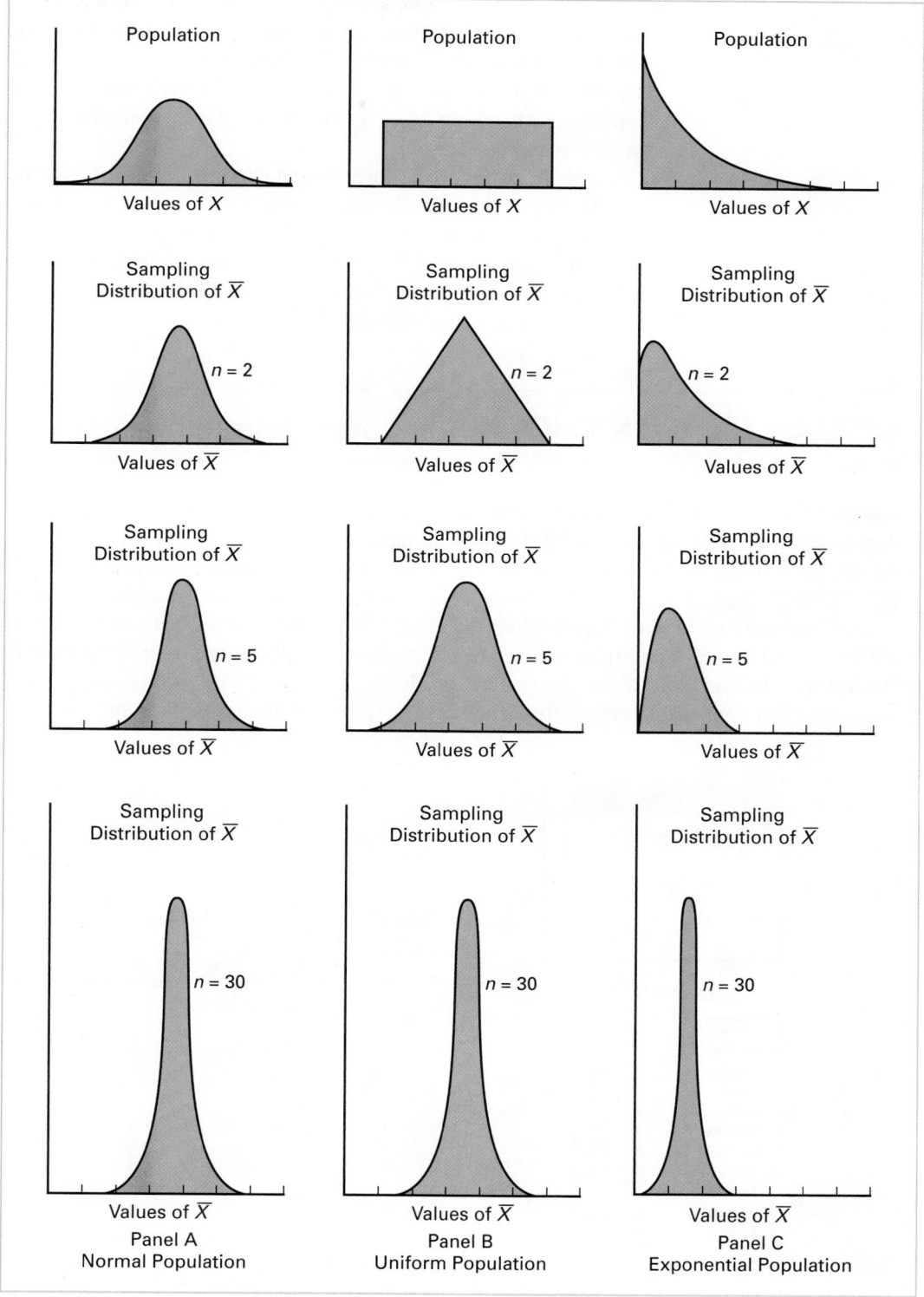

In each of the panels, because the sample mean has the property of being unbiased, the mean of any sampling distribution is always equal to the mean of the population.

Panel A of Figure 7.5 shows the sampling distribution of the mean selected from a normal population. As mentioned earlier in this section, when the population is normally distributed, the sampling distribution of the mean is normally distributed for any sample size. [You can measure the variability by using the standard error of the mean, Equation (7.3), on page 270.]

Panel B of Figure 7.5 depicts the sampling distribution from a population with a uniform (or rectangular) distribution (see Section 6.4). When samples of size $n = 2$ are selected, there is a peaking, or *central limiting*, effect already working. For $n = 5$, the sampling distribution is bell shaped and approximately normal. When $n = 30$, the sampling distribution looks very similar to a normal distribution. In general, the larger the sample size, the more closely the sampling distribution will follow a normal distribution. As with all cases, the mean of each sampling distribution is equal to the mean of the population, and the variability decreases as the sample size increases.

Panel C of Figure 7.5 presents an exponential distribution (see Section 6.5). This population is extremely right-skewed. When $n = 2$, the sampling distribution is still highly right-skewed but less so than the distribution of the population. For $n = 5$, the sampling distribution is slightly right-skewed. When $n = 30$, the sampling distribution looks approximately normal. Again, the mean of each sampling distribution is equal to the mean of the population, and the variability decreases as the sample size increases.

# VISUAL EXPLORATIONS: Exploring Sampling Distributions

Use the Visual Explorations **Two Dice Probability** procedure to observe the effects of simulated throws on the frequency distribution of the sum of the two dice. Open the Visual Explorations.xla add-in workbook and select **VisualExplorations → Two Dice Probability** (Excel 97-2003) or **Add-Ins → VisualExplorations → Two Dice Probability** (Excel 2007). The procedure produces a worksheet that contains an empty frequency distribution table and histogram and a floating control panel (see below).

Click the **Tally** button to tally a set of throws in the frequency distribution table and histogram. Optionally, use the spinner buttons to adjust the number of throws per tally (round). Click the **Help** button for more information about this simulation. Click **Finish** when you are done with this exploration.

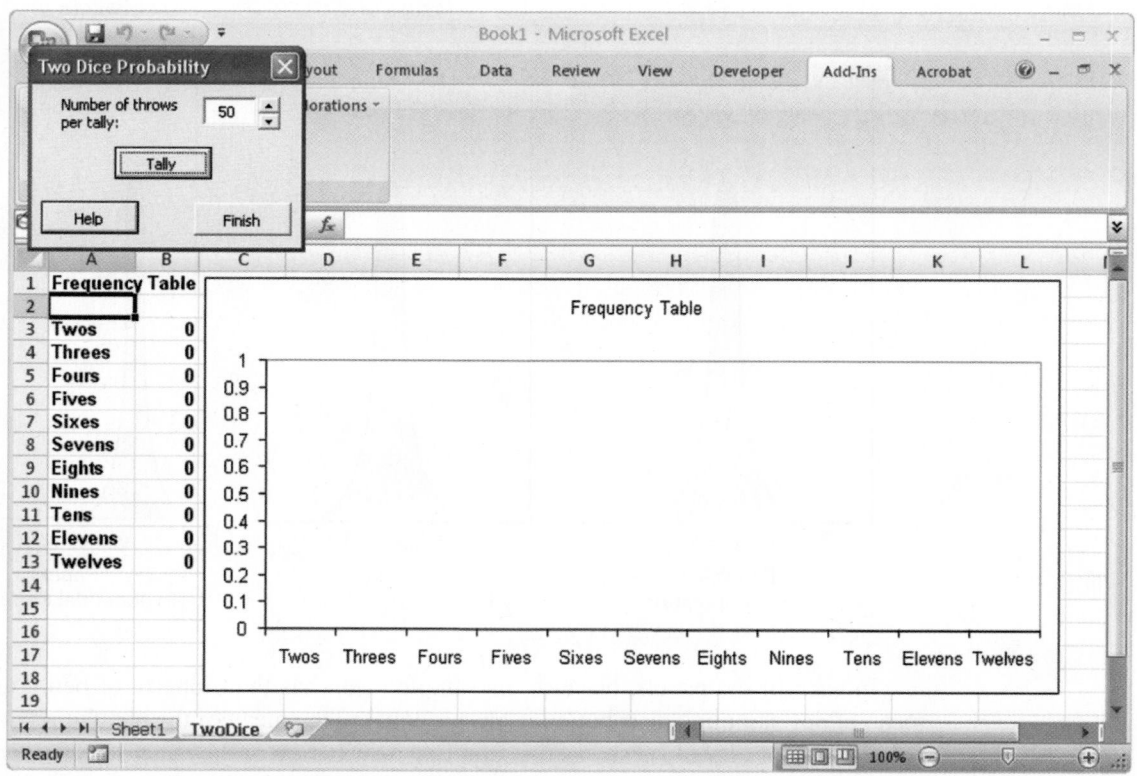

Using the results from the normal, uniform, and exponential distributions, you can reach the following conclusions regarding the Central Limit Theorem:

- For most population distributions, regardless of shape, the sampling distribution of the mean is approximately normally distributed if samples of at least size 30 are selected.
- If the population distribution is fairly symmetric, the sampling distribution of the mean is approximately normal for samples as small as size 5.
- If the population is normally distributed, the sampling distribution of the mean is normally distributed, regardless of the sample size.

The Central Limit Theorem is of crucial importance in using statistical inference to draw conclusions about a population. It allows you to make inferences about the population mean without having to know the specific shape of the population distribution.

# PROBLEMS FOR SECTION 7.4

## Learning the Basics

**7.17** Given a normal distribution with $\mu = 100$ and $\sigma = 10$, if you select a sample of $n = 25$, what is the probability that $\bar{X}$ is
a. less than 95?
b. between 95 and 97.5?
c. above 102.2?
d. There is a 65% chance that $\bar{X}$ is above what value?

**7.18** Given a normal distribution with $\mu = 50$ and $\sigma = 5$, if you select a sample of $n = 100$, what is the probability that $\bar{X}$ is
a. less than 47?
b. between 47 and 49.5?
c. above 51.1?
d. There is a 35% chance that $\bar{X}$ is above what value?

## Applying the Concepts

**7.19** For each of the following three populations, indicate what the sampling distribution for samples of 25 would consist of:
a. Travel expense vouchers for a university in an academic year
b. Absentee records (days absent per year) in 2007 for employees of a large manufacturing company
c. Yearly sales (in gallons) of unleaded gasoline at service stations located in a particular state

**7.20** The following data represent the number of days absent per year in a population of six employees of a small company:

1   3   6   7   9   10

a. Assuming that you sample without replacement, select all possible samples of $n = 2$ and construct the sampling distribution of the mean. Compute the mean of all the sample means and also compute the population mean. Are they equal? What is this property called?
b. Repeat (a) for all possible samples of $n = 3$.
c. Compare the shape of the sampling distribution of the mean in (a) and (b). Which sampling distribution has less variability? Why?
d. Assuming that you sample with replacement, repeat (a) through (c) and compare the results. Which sampling distributions have the least variability—those in (a) or (b)? Why?

**7.21** The diameter of a brand of Ping-Pong balls is approximately normally distributed, with a mean of 1.30 inches and a standard deviation of 0.04 inch. If you select a random sample of 16 Ping-Pong balls,
a. what is the sampling distribution of the mean?
b. what is the probability that the sample mean is less than 1.28 inches?
c. what is the probability that the sample mean is between 1.31 and 1.33 inches?
d. The probability is 60% that the sample mean will be between what two values, symmetrically distributed around the population mean?

**7.22** The U.S. Census Bureau announced that the median sales price of new houses sold in April 2007 was $229,100, whereas the mean sales price was $299,100 (**www.census. gov/newhomesales**, June 21, 2007). Assume that the standard deviation of the prices is $90,000.
a. If you select samples of $n = 2$, describe the shape of the sampling distribution of $\bar{X}$.
b. If you select samples of $n = 100$, describe the shape of the sampling distribution of $\bar{X}$.
c. If you select a random sample of $n = 100$, what is the probability that the sample mean will be less than $300,000?
d. If you select a random sample of $n = 100$, what is the probability that the sample mean will be between $275,000 and $290,000?

**7.23** Time spent using e-mail per session is normally distributed, with $\mu = 8$ minutes and $\sigma = 2$ minutes. If you select a random sample of 25 sessions,
a. what is the probability that the sample mean is between 7.8 and 8.2 minutes?
b. what is the probability that the sample mean is between 7.5 and 8 minutes?
c. If you select a random sample of 100 sessions, what is the probability that the sample mean is between 7.8 and 8.2 minutes?
d. Explain the difference in the results of (a) and (c).

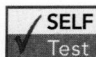 **7.24** The amount of time a bank teller spends with each customer has a population mean, $\mu$, of 3.10 minutes and standard deviation, $\sigma$, of 0.40 minute. If you select a random sample of 16 customers,
a. what is the probability that the mean time spent per customer is at least 3 minutes?
b. there is an 85% chance that the sample mean is less than how many minutes?
c. What assumption must you make in order to solve (a) and (b)?
d. If you select a random sample of 64 customers, there is an 85% chance that the sample mean is less than how many minutes?

**7.25** *The New York Times* reported (L. J. Flynn, "Tax Surfing," *The New York Times*, March 25, 2002, p. C10) that the mean time to download the home page for the Internal Revenue Service (IRS), **www.irs.gov**, was 0.8 second. Suppose that the download time was normally distributed, with a standard deviation of 0.2 second. If you select a random sample of 30 download times,
a. what is the probability that the sample mean is less than 0.75 second?
b. what is the probability that the sample mean is between 0.70 and 0.90 second?
c. the probability is 80% that the sample mean is between what two values, symmetrically distributed around the population mean?
d. the probability is 90% that the sample mean is less than what value?

**7.26** The article discussed in Problem 7.25 also reported that the mean download time for the H&R Block Web site, **www.hrblock.com**, was 2.5 seconds. Suppose that the download time for the H&R Block Web site was normally distributed, with a standard deviation of 0.5 second. If you select a random sample of 30 download times,
a. what is the probability that the sample mean is less than 2.75 seconds?
b. what is the probability that the sample mean is between 2.70 and 2.90 seconds?
c. the probability is 80% that the sample mean is between what two values symmetrically distributed around the population mean?
d. the probability is 90% that the sample mean is less than what value?

## 7.5   SAMPLING DISTRIBUTION OF THE PROPORTION

Consider a categorical variable that has only two categories, such as the customer prefers your brand or the customer prefers the competitor's brand. Of interest is the proportion of items belonging to one of the categories—for example, the proportion of customers that prefers your brand. The population proportion, represented by $\pi$, is the proportion of items in the entire population with the characteristic of interest. The sample proportion, represented by $p$, is the proportion of items in the sample with the characteristic of interest. The sample proportion, a statistic, is used to estimate the population proportion, a parameter. To calculate the sample proportion, you assign the two possible outcomes scores of 1 or 0 to represent the presence or absence of the characteristic. You then sum all the 1 and 0 scores and divide by $n$, the sample size. For example, if, in a sample of five customers, three preferred your brand and two did not, you have three 1s and two 0s. Summing the three 1s and two 0s and dividing by the sample size of 5 gives you a sample proportion of 0.60.

Sample Proportion

$$p = \frac{X}{n} = \frac{\text{Number of items having the characteristic of interest}}{\text{Sample size}} \quad \text{(7.6)}$$

The sample proportion, $p$, takes on values between 0 and 1. If all items have the characteristic, you assign each a score of 1, and $p$ is equal to 1. If half the items have the characteristic, you assign half a score of 1 and assign the other half a score of 0, and $p$ is equal to 0.5. If none of the items have the characteristic, you assign each a score of 0, and $p$ is equal to 0.

In Section 7.4, you learned that the sample mean, $\bar{X}$, is an unbiased estimator of the population mean, $\mu$. Similarly, the statistic $p$ is an unbiased estimator of the population proportion, $\pi$. By analogy to the sampling distribution of the mean whose standard error is $\sigma_{\bar{X}} = \dfrac{\sigma}{\sqrt{n}}$, the **standard error of the proportion**, $\sigma_p$, is given in Equation (7.7).

### Standard Error of the Proportion

$$\sigma_p = \sqrt{\frac{\pi(1-\pi)}{n}} \qquad (7.7)$$

The **sampling distribution of the proportion** follows the binomial distribution, as discussed in Section 5.3. However, you can use the normal distribution to approximate the binomial distribution when $n\pi$ and $n(1-\pi)$ are each at least 5 (see Section 6.6). In most cases in which inferences are made about the proportion, the sample size is substantial enough to meet the conditions for using the normal approximation (see reference 1). Therefore, in many instances, you can use the normal distribution to estimate the sampling distribution of the proportion.

Substituting $p$ for $\bar{X}$, $\pi$ for $\mu$, and $\sqrt{\dfrac{\pi(1-\pi)}{n}}$ for $\dfrac{\sigma}{\sqrt{n}}$ in Equation (7.4) on page 272 results in Equation (7.8).

### Finding Z for the Sampling Distribution of the Proportion

$$Z = \frac{p - \pi}{\sqrt{\dfrac{\pi(1-\pi)}{n}}} \qquad (7.8)$$

To illustrate the sampling distribution of the proportion, suppose that the manager of the local branch of a savings bank determines that 40% of all depositors have multiple accounts at the bank. If you select a random sample of 200 depositors, the probability that the sample proportion of depositors with multiple accounts is less than 0.30 is calculated as follows: Because $n\pi = 200(0.40) = 80 \geq 5$ and $n(1-\pi) = 200(0.60) = 120 \geq 5$, the sample size is large enough to assume that the sampling distribution of the proportion is approximately normally distributed. Using Equation (7.8),

$$Z = \frac{p - \pi}{\sqrt{\dfrac{\pi(1-\pi)}{n}}}$$

$$= \frac{0.30 - 0.40}{\sqrt{\dfrac{(0.40)(0.60)}{200}}} = \frac{-0.10}{\sqrt{\dfrac{0.24}{200}}} = \frac{-0.10}{0.0346}$$

$$= -2.89$$

Using Table E.2, the area under the normal curve less than $-2.89$ is 0.0019. Therefore, if the true proportion of items of interest in the population is 0.40, then only 0.19% of the samples of $n = 200$ would be expected to have sample proportions less than 0.30.

# PROBLEMS FOR SECTION 7.5

## Learning the Basics

**7.27** In a random sample of 64 people, 48 are classified as "successful."
a. Determine the sample proportion, $p$, of "successful" people.
b. If the population proportion is 0.70, determine the standard error of the proportion.

**7.28** A random sample of 50 households was selected for a telephone survey. The key question asked was, "Do you or any member of your household own a cellular telephone with a built-in camera?" Of the 50 respondents, 15 said yes and 35 said no.
a. Determine the sample proportion, $p$, of households with cellular telephones with built-in cameras.
b. If the population proportion is 0.40, determine the standard error of the proportion.

**7.29** The following data represent the responses ($Y$ for yes and $N$ for no) from a sample of 40 college students to the question "Do you currently own shares in any stocks?"

N N Y N N Y N Y N Y N N Y N Y Y N N N Y
N Y N N N N Y N N Y Y N N N Y N N Y N N

a. Determine the sample proportion, $p$, of college students who own shares of stock.
b. If the population proportion is 0.30, determine the standard error of the proportion.

## Applying the Concepts

**✓SELF** **7.30** A political pollster is conducting an analy-
**Test** sis of sample results in order to make predictions on election night. Assuming a two-candidate election, if a specific candidate receives at least 55% of the vote in the sample, then that candidate will be forecast as the winner of the election. If you select a random sample of 100 voters, what is the probability that a candidate will be forecast as the winner when
a. the true percentage of her vote is 50.1%?
b. the true percentage of her vote is 60%?
c. the true percentage of her vote is 49% (and she will actually lose the election)?
d. If the sample size is increased to 400, what are your answers to (a) through (c)? Discuss.

**7.31** You plan to conduct a marketing experiment in which students are to taste one of two different brands of soft drink. Their task is to correctly identify the brand tasted. You select a random sample of 200 students and assume that the students have no ability to distinguish between the two brands. (Hint: If an individual has no ability to distinguish between the two soft drinks, then each brand is equally likely to be selected.)
a. What is the probability that the sample will have between 50% and 60% of the identifications correct?
b. The probability is 90% that the sample percentage is contained within what symmetrical limits of the population percentage?
c. What is the probability that the sample percentage of correct identifications is greater than 65%?
d. Which is more likely to occur—more than 60% correct identifications in the sample of 200 or more than 55% correct identifications in a sample of 1,000? Explain.

**7.32** An online quiz available at **www.pewinternet. org/quiz** divides up people according to their usage of the computer. In a survey of 4,001 respondents, 8% were classified as productivity enhancers who are comfortable with technology and use the Internet for its practical value (M. Himowitz, "How to Tell What Kind of Tech User You Are," *Newsday*, May 27, 2007, p. F6). Suppose you select a sample of 400 students at your school, and the population proportion of productivity enhancers is 0.08.
a. What is the probability that in the sample, less than 10% of the students will be productivity enhancers?
b. What is the probability that in the sample, between 6% and 10% of the students will be productivity enhancers?
c. What is the probability that in the sample, more than 5% of the students will be productivity enhancers?
d. If a sample of 100 is taken, how does this change your answers to (a) through (c)?

**7.33** Companies often make flextime scheduling available to help recruit and keep women employees who have children at home. Other workers sometimes view these flextime schedules as unfair. An article in *USA Today* indicates that 25% of male employees state that they have to pick up the slack for moms working flextime schedules (D. Jones, "Poll Finds Resentment of Flextime," **usatoday.com**, May 11, 2007). Suppose you select a random sample of 100 male employees working for companies offering flextime.
a. What is the probability that 25% or fewer male employees will indicate that they have to pick up the slack for moms working flextime?

**b.** What is the probability that 20% or fewer will indicate that they have to pick up the slack for moms working flextime?

**c.** If a random sample of 500 is taken, how does this change your answers to (a) and (b)?

**7.34** According to Gallup's annual poll on personal finances, even though most U.S. workers reported living comfortably now, many expected a downturn in their lifestyle when they stop working. Approximately half said they have enough money to live comfortably now and expected to do so in the future (J. M. Jones, "Only Half of Non-Retirees Expect to be Comfortable in Retirement," *The Gallup Poll*, **galluppoll.com**, May 2, 2006). If you select a random sample of 200 U.S. workers,

**a.** what is the probability that the sample will have between 45% and 55% who say they have enough money to live comfortably now and expect to do so in the future?

**b.** the probability is 90% that the sample percentage will be contained within what symmetrical limits of the population percentage?

**c.** the probability is 95% that the sample percentage will be contained within what symmetrical limits of the population percentage?

**7.35** New research shows (J. O'Donnell, "Gen Y Sits on Top of Consumer Food Chain," *USA Today*, October 11, 2006, p. 3B) that members of generation Y (people born from 1982 to 2000) have a great say in household purchases. Specifically, 68% of Gen Y people have a say in computer purchases. Suppose you select a sample of 100 Gen Y respondents.

**a.** What is the probability that the sample percentage will be contained between 65% and 75%?

**b.** The probability is 90% that the sample percentage will be contained within what symmetrical limits of the population percentage?

**c.** The probability is 95% that the sample percentage will be contained within what symmetrical limits of the population percentage?

**d.** Suppose you selected a sample of 400 respondents. How does this change your answers in (a) through (c)?

**7.36** Yahoo HotJobs reported that 56% of full-time office workers believe that dressing-down can affect jobs, salaries,

or promotions (J. Yang and K. Carter, "Dress Can Affect Size of Paycheck," **usatoday.com**, May 9, 2007).

**a.** Suppose that you take a sample of 100 full-time workers. If the true population proportion of workers who believe that dressing-down can affect jobs, salaries, or promotions is 0.56, what is the probability that less than half in your sample hold that same belief?

**b.** Suppose that you take a sample of 500 full-time workers. If the true population proportion of workers who believe that dressing-down can affect jobs, salaries, or promotions is 0.56, what is the probability that less than half in your sample hold that same belief?

**c.** Discuss the effect of sample size on the sampling distribution of the proportion in general, and the effect on the probabilities in (a) and (b).

**7.37** The IRS discontinued random audits in 1988. Instead, the IRS conducts audits on returns deemed questionable by its Discriminant Function System (DFS), a complicated and highly secretive computerized analysis system. In an attempt to reduce the proportion of "no-change" audits (i.e., audits that uncover that no additional taxes are due), the IRS only audits returns that the DFS scores as highly questionable. The proportion of no-change audits has risen over the years and is currently approximately 0.25 (T. Herman, "Unhappy Returns: IRS Moves to Bring Back Random Audits," *The Wall Street Journal*, June 20, 2002, p. A1). Suppose that you select a random sample of 100 audits. What is the probability that the sample has

**a.** between 24% and 26% no-change audits?

**b.** between 20% and 30% no-change audits?

**c.** more than 30% no-change audits?

**7.38** Referring to Problem 7.37, the IRS announced that it planned to resume totally random audits in 2002. Suppose that you select a random sample of 200 totally random audits and that 90% of all the returns filed would result in no-change audits. What is the probability that the sample has

**a.** between 89% and 91% no-change audits?

**b.** between 85% and 95% no-change audits?

**c.** more than 95% no-change audits?

## 7.6 ● (CD-ROM TOPIC) SAMPLING FROM FINITE POPULATIONS

In this section, sampling without replacement from finite populations is considered. For further discussion, see section 7.6.pdf on the Student CD-ROM that accompanies this book.

# SUMMARY

In this chapter, you studied four common probability sampling methods—simple random, systematic, stratified, and cluster. You also studied the sampling distribution of the sample mean, the Central Limit Theorem, and the sampling distribution of the sample proportion. You learned that the sample mean is an unbiased estimator of the population mean, and the sample proportion is an unbiased estimator of the population proportion. By observing the mean weight in a sample of cereal boxes filled by Oxford Cereals, you were able to reach conclusions concerning the mean weight in the population of cereal boxes. In the next five chapters, the techniques of confidence intervals and tests of hypotheses commonly used for statistical inference are discussed.

# KEY EQUATIONS

**Population Mean**

$$\mu = \frac{\sum_{i=1}^{N} X_i}{N} \qquad (7.1)$$

**Population Standard Deviation**

$$\sigma = \sqrt{\frac{\sum_{i=1}^{N} (X_i - \mu)^2}{N}} \qquad (7.2)$$

**Standard Error of the Mean**

$$\sigma_{\bar{X}} = \frac{\sigma}{\sqrt{n}} \qquad (7.3)$$

**Finding Z for the Sampling Distribution of the Mean**

$$Z = \frac{\bar{X} - \mu_{\bar{X}}}{\sigma_{\bar{X}}} = \frac{\bar{X} - \mu}{\frac{\sigma}{\sqrt{n}}} \qquad (7.4)$$

**Finding $\bar{X}$ for the Sampling Distribution of the Mean**

$$\bar{X} = \mu + Z \frac{\sigma}{\sqrt{n}} \qquad (7.5)$$

**Sample Proportion**

$$p = \frac{X}{n} \qquad (7.6)$$

**Standard Error of the Proportion**

$$\sigma_p = \sqrt{\frac{\pi(1 - \pi)}{n}} \qquad (7.7)$$

**Finding Z for the Sampling Distribution of the Proportion**

$$Z = \frac{p - \pi}{\sqrt{\frac{\pi(1 - \pi)}{n}}} \qquad (7.8)$$

# KEY TERMS

Central Limit Theorem   274
cluster   262
cluster sample   262
convenience sampling   258
coverage error   264
frame   258
judgment sample   259
margin of error   265
measurement error   265
nonprobability sample   258

nonresponse bias   264
nonresponse error   264
probability sample   259
sampling distribution   267
sampling distribution of the
   mean   267
sampling distribution of the
   proportion   279
sampling error   264
sampling with replacement   259

sampling without replacement   259
selection bias   264
simple random sample   259
standard error of the mean   270
standard error of the proportion   279
strata   262
stratified sample   262
systematic sample   261
table of random numbers   260
unbiased   267

# CHAPTER REVIEW PROBLEMS

## Checking Your Understanding

**7.39** Why is the sample mean an unbiased estimator of the population mean?

**7.40** Why does the standard error of the mean decrease as the sample size, $n$, increases?

**7.41** Why does the sampling distribution of the mean follow a normal distribution for a large enough sample size, even though the population may not be normally distributed?

**7.42** What is the difference between a population and a sampling distribution?

**7.43** Under what circumstances does the sampling distribution of the proportion approximately follow the normal distribution?

**7.44** What is the difference between probability and non-probability sampling?

**7.45** What are some potential problems with using "fishbowl" methods to select a simple random sample?

**7.46** What is the difference between sampling *with* replacement versus *without* replacement?

**7.47** What is the difference between a simple random sample and a systematic sample?

**7.48** What is the difference between a simple random sample and a stratified sample?

**7.49** What is the difference between a stratified sample and a cluster sample?

## Applying the Concepts

**7.50** An industrial sewing machine uses ball bearings that are targeted to have a diameter of 0.75 inch. The lower and upper specification limits under which the ball bearing can operate are 0.74 inch (lower) and 0.76 inch (upper). Past experience has indicated that the actual diameter of the ball bearings is approximately normally distributed, with a mean of 0.753 inch and a standard deviation of 0.004 inch. If you select a random sample of 25 ball bearings, what is the probability that the sample mean is
a. between the target and the population mean of 0.753?
b. between the lower specification limit and the target?
c. greater than the upper specification limit?
d. less than the lower specification limit?
e. The probability is 93% that the sample mean diameter will be greater than what value?

**7.51** The fill amount of bottles of a soft drink is normally distributed, with a mean of 2.0 liters and a standard deviation of 0.05 liter. If you select a random sample of 25 bottles, what is the probability that the sample mean will be
a. between 1.99 and 2.0 liters?
b. below 1.98 liters?
c. greater than 2.01 liters?
d. The probability is 99% that the sample mean amount of soft drink will be at least how much?
e. The probability is 99% that the sample mean amount of soft drink will be between which two values (symmetrically distributed around the mean)?

**7.52** An orange juice producer buys all his oranges from a large orange grove that has one variety of orange. The amount of juice squeezed from these oranges is approximately normally distributed, with a mean of 4.70 ounces and a standard deviation of 0.40 ounce. Suppose that you select a sample of 25 oranges.
a. What is the probability that the sample mean amount of juice will be at least 4.60 ounces?
b. The probability is 70% that the sample mean amount of juice will be contained between what two values symmetrically distributed around the population mean?
c. The probability is 77% that the sample mean amount of juice will be greater than what value?

**7.53** In his management information systems textbook, Professor David Kroenke raises an interesting point: "If 98% of our market has Internet access, do we have a responsibility to provide non-Internet materials to that other 2%?" (D. M. Kroenke, *Using MIS*, Upper Saddle River, NJ: Prentice Hall, 2007, p. 29a). Suppose that 98% of the customers in your market have Internet access and you select a random sample of 500 customers. What is the probability that the sample has
a. greater than 99% with Internet access?
b. between 97% and 99% with Internet access?
c. less than 97% with Internet access?

**7.54** Mutual funds reported strong earnings in the fourth quarter of 2006. Especially strong growth occurred in mutual funds consisting of companies focusing on Latin America. This population of mutual funds earned a mean return of 22.5% in the fourth quarter (I. Salisbury, "Trying to Put 3.28 Billion to Work," *The Wall Street Journal*, January 4, 2007). Assume that the returns for the Latin America mutual funds were distributed as a normal random variable, with a mean of 22.5 and a standard deviation of 20. If you selected a random sample of 10 funds from this population, what is the probability that the sample would have a mean return
a. less than 0—that is, a loss?
b. between 0 and 20?
c. greater than 10?

**7.55** The same article as in Problem 7.54 reported that mutual funds focusing on Europe had a mean return of 12.2% during this time. Assume that the returns for the Europe mutual funds were distributed as a normal random variable, with a mean of 12.2 and a standard deviation of 12. If you select an individual fund from this population, what is the probability that it would have a return

**a.** less than 0—that is, a loss?

**b.** between 0 and 20?

**c.** greater than 10?

If you selected a random sample of 10 funds from this population, what is the probability that the sample would have a mean return

**d.** less than 0—that is, a loss?

**e.** between 0 and 20?

**f.** greater than 10?

**g.** Compare your results in parts (d) through (f) to (a) through (c).

**h.** Compare your results in parts (d) through (f) to Problem 7.54 (a) through (c).

**7.56** Telephone interviews have traditionally been the number one tool in political polling. Recently, many have argued that Internet polling is faster and less expensive and produces a higher response rate. Dr. Doug Usher, a leading authority on political polling, agrees that the telephone poll is still the gold standard in political polls due to its superior statistical reliability even though it is getting harder to reach people via the telephone with the growing use of caller ID and the fact that many younger people no longer have landlines (D. Usher, "The Internet's Unfulfilled Promise for Political Polling," **www.mysterypollster.com**, June 30, 2005). What concerns, if any, do you have on Internet polling?

**7.57** A survey sponsored by The American Dietetic Association and the agribusiness giant ConAgra found that 53% of office workers take 30 minutes or less for lunch each day. Approximately 37% take 30 to 60 minutes, and 10% take more than an hour ("Snapshots," **usatoday.com**, April 26, 2006).

**a.** What additional information would you want to know before you accepted the results of the survey?

**b.** Discuss the four types of survey errors in the context of this survey.

**c.** One of the types of survey errors discussed in part (b) should have been measurement error. Explain how the root cause of measurement error in this survey could be the Hawthorne effect.

**7.58** In a survey conducted by AOL and the Associated Press, less than 25% of adults use instant messaging (IM), and almost 75% of adults who use IM use e-mail more often than IM. The survey also showed that almost 50% of teens use IM, and almost 75% of teens who use IM use IM more often than e-mail (M. Levitt, "Bridging the Collaboration Age Gap with Unified Communications and Web 2.0," *KM World*, June 2007, p. 10).

**a.** What other information would you want to know before you used the results of this survey?

**b.** Suppose you work for AOL and wanted to investigate IM and e-mail usage by AOL users. Define the population, frame, and sampling method you would use.

**7.59** Connecticut shoppers spend more on women's clothing than do shoppers in any other state, according to a survey conducted by MapInfo. The mean spending per household in Connecticut was $975 annually ("Snapshots," **usatoday.com**, April 17, 2006).

**a.** What other information would you want to know before you accepted the results of this survey?

**b.** Suppose that you wished to conduct a similar survey for the geographic region you live in. Describe the population for your survey.

**c.** Explain how you could minimize the chance of coverage error in this type of survey.

**d.** Explain how you could minimize the chance of nonresponse error in this type of survey.

**e.** Explain how you could minimize the chance of sampling error in this type of survey.

**f.** Explain how you could minimize the chance of measurement error in this type of survey.

**7.60** Technology enables the rise of extreme workers who work more than 60 hours per week (S. Armour, "Hi, I'm Joan, and I'm a Workaholic," *USA Today*, May 23, 2007, pp. 1B, 2B). 90% of male extreme workers said that they work long hours because their jobs are stimulating or challenging or provide an adrenaline rush. However, 46% of male extreme workers said that working long hours undermined their relationship with their spouse or partner.

**a.** What other information would you want to know before you accepted the results of this study?

**b.** If you were to perform a similar study in the geographic area where you live, define a population, frame, and sampling method you could use.

**7.61 (Class Project)** The table of random numbers is an example of a uniform distribution because each digit is equally likely to occur. Starting in the row corresponding to the day of the month in which you were born, use the table of random numbers (Table E.1) to take one digit at a time.

Select five different samples each of $n = 2$, $n = 5$, and $n = 10$. Compute the sample mean of each sample. Develop a frequency distribution of the sample means for the results of the entire class, based on samples of sizes $n = 2$, $n = 5$, and $n = 10$.

What can be said about the shape of the sampling distribution for each of these sample sizes?

**7.62 (Class Project)** Toss a coin 10 times and record the number of heads. If each student performs this experiment five times, a frequency distribution of the number of heads can be developed from the results of the entire class. Does this distribution seem to approximate the normal distribution?

**7.63 (Class Project)** The number of cars waiting in line at a car wash is distributed as follows:

| Number of Cars | Probability |
|---|---|
| 0 | 0.25 |
| 1 | 0.40 |
| 2 | 0.20 |
| 3 | 0.10 |
| 4 | 0.04 |
| 5 | 0.01 |

You can use the table of random numbers (Table E.1) to select samples from this distribution by assigning numbers as follows:

1. Start in the row corresponding to the day of the month in which you were born.
2. Select a two-digit random number.
3. If you select a random number from 00 to 24, record a length of 0; if from 25 to 64, record a length of 1; if from 65 to 84, record a length of 2; if from 85 to 94, record a length of 3; if from 95 to 98, record a length of 4; if 99, record a length of 5.

Select samples of $n = 2$, $n = 5$, and $n = 10$. Compute the mean for each sample. For example, if a sample of size 2 results in the random numbers 18 and 46, these would correspond to lengths of 0 and 1, respectively, producing a sample mean of 0.5. If each student selects five different samples for each sample size, a frequency distribution of the sample means (for each sample size) can be developed from the results of the entire class. What conclusions can you reach concerning the sampling distribution of the mean as the sample size is increased?

**7.64 (Class Project)** Using Table E.1, simulate the selection of different-colored balls from a bowl as follows:

1. Start in the row corresponding to the day of the month in which you were born.
2. Select one-digit numbers.
3. If a random digit between 0 and 6 is selected, consider the ball white; if a random digit is a 7, 8, or 9, consider the ball red.

Select samples of $n = 10$, $n = 25$, and $n = 50$ digits. In each sample, count the number of white balls and compute the proportion of white balls in the sample. If each student in the class selects five different samples for each sample size, a frequency distribution of the proportion of white balls (for each sample size) can be developed from the results of the entire class. What conclusions can you reach about the sampling distribution of the proportion as the sample size is increased?

**7.65 (Class Project)** Suppose that step 3 of Problem 7.64 uses the following rule: "If a random digit between 0 and 8 is selected, consider the ball to be white; if a random digit of 9 is selected, consider the ball to be red." Compare and contrast the results in this problem and those in Problem 7.64.

# MANAGING THE *SPRINGVILLE HERALD*

Continuing its quality improvement effort first described in the Chapter 6 "Managing the *Springville Herald*" case, the production department of the newspaper has been monitoring the blackness of the newspaper print. As before, blackness is measured on a standard scale in which the target value is 1.0. Data collected over the past year indicate that the blackness is normally distributed, with a mean of 1.005 and a standard deviation of 0.10.

## EXERCISE

SH7.1 Each day, 25 spots on the first newspaper printed are chosen, and the blackness of the spots is measured.

Assuming that the distribution has not changed from what it was in the past year, what is the probability that the mean blackness of the spots is
a. less than 1.0?
b. between 0.95 and 1.0?
c. between 1.0 and 1.05?
d. less than 0.95 or greater than 1.05?
e. Suppose that the mean blackness of today's sample of 25 spots is 0.952. What conclusion can you make about the blackness of today's newspaper based on this result? Explain.

# WEB CASE

*Apply your knowledge about sampling distributions in this Web Case, which reconsiders the Oxford Cereals Using Statistics scenario.*

The advocacy group Consumers Concerned About Cereal Cheaters (CCACC) suspects that cereal companies, including Oxford Cereals, are cheating consumers by packaging cereals at less than labeled weights. Visit the organization's home page at **www.prenhall.com/Springville/ConsumersConcerned.htm** (or open the `ConsumersConcerned.htm` file in the Student CD-ROM Web Case folder), examine their claims and supporting data, and then answer the following:

1. Are the data collection procedures that the CCACC uses to form its conclusions flawed? What procedures could the group follow to make their analysis more rigorous?

2. Assume that the two samples of five cereal boxes (one sample for each of two cereal varieties) listed on the CCACC Web site were collected randomly by organization members. For each sample, do the following:

   a. Calculate the sample mean.

   b. Assume that the standard deviation of the process is 15 grams and a population mean is 368 grams. Calculate the percentage of all samples for each process that have a sample mean less than the value you calculated in (a).

   c. Again, assuming that the standard deviation is 15 grams, calculate the percentage of individual boxes of cereal that have a weight less than the value you calculated in (a).

3. What, if any, conclusions can you form by using your calculations about the filling processes of the two different cereals?

4. A representative from Oxford Cereals has asked that the CCACC take down its page discussing shortages in Oxford Cereals boxes. Is that request reasonable? Why or why not?

5. Can the techniques discussed in this chapter be used to prove cheating in the manner alleged by the CCACC? Why or why not?

# REFERENCES

1. Cochran, W. G., *Sampling Techniques*, 3rd ed. (New York: Wiley, 1977).

2. Gallup, G. H., *The Sophisticated Poll-Watcher's Guide* (Princeton, NJ: Princeton Opinion Press, 1972).

3. Goleman, D., "Pollsters Enlist Psychologists in Quest for Unbiased Results," *The New York Times*, September 7, 1993, pp. C1, C11.

4. Hahn, G., and W. Meeker, *Statistical Intervals, A Guide for Practioners* (New York: John Wiley and Sons, Inc., 1991).

5. *Microsoft Excel 2007* (Redmond, WA: Microsoft Corp., 2007).

6. *Minitab for Windows Version 15* (State College, PA: Minitab, Inc., 2006).

7. Rand Corporation, *A Million Random Digits with 100,000 Normal Deviates* (New York: The Free Press, 1955).

# Appendix E7
# Using Microsoft Excel for Sampling and Sampling Distributions

## E7.1 Creating Simple Random Samples Without Replacement

No Microsoft Excel features directly create simple random samples. Use PHStat2 Section P7.1 to create such samples.

## E7.2 Creating Simulated Sampling Distributions

You create simulated sampling distributions by first using the ToolPak Random Number Generation procedure to create a worksheet of multiple random samples and then adding formulas to that worksheet to compute the sample means and other appropriate measures.

To start, select **Tools → Data Analysis** and in the Data Analysis dialog box, click **Random Number Generation** and then click **OK**. In the Random Number Generation dialog box (shown at right), enter the number of samples as the **Number of Variables** and enter the sample size of each sample as the **Number of Random Numbers.** Select the type of distribution from the **Distribution** drop-down list and make entries in the Parameters area, the contents of which vary according to the distribution selected. (If you select the **Discrete** option, you will need to be opened to a

worksheet that contains a table of $X$ and $P(X)$ values and enter the range of the table as the **Value and Probability Input Range**.). To finish, click **New Worksheet Ply** and then **OK**.

# Appendix P7
## Using PHStat2 for Sampling and Sampling Distributions

### P7.1 Creating Simple Random Samples Without Replacement

To create a random sample without replacement use **PHStat → Sampling → Random Sample Generation**. In the Random Sample Generation dialog box (shown below), click **Select values from range** to have the procedure create the random sample for the values in the **Values Cell Range**. The created random sample appears on a new worksheet.

### P7.2 Creating Simulated Sampling Distributions

To create a simulated sampling distribution, use **PHStat → Sampling → Sampling Distributions Simulation**. This procedure creates a worksheet using the ToolPak

Random Number Generation procedure and the number of samples, sample size, and a type of distribution that you specify.

The procedure adds the sample means, the overall mean, and the standard error of the mean to the worksheet created by the ToolPak procedure. If you click **Histogram**, the procedure uses the ToolPak Histogram procedure to create a histogram of the simulation. (The histogram will contain a number of minor errors as discussed in Section E2.9.)

# Appendix M7
## Using Minitab for Sampling and Sampling Distributions

## M7.1 Creating Simple Random Samples Without Replacement

To create a random sample of size 40 from a frame of size 800 as in Example 7.1 on page 260,

1. Select **Calc → Make Patterned Data → Simple Set of Numbers**.

In the Simple Set of Numbers dialog box (see Figure M7.1):

2. Enter **C1** in the **Store patterned data in** box.
3. Enter **1** in the **From first value** box.
4. Enter **800** in the **To last value** box.
5. Click **OK**.

**FIGURE M7.1**

Minitab Simple Set of Numbers dialog box

With the worksheet containing the numbers in column C1:

6. Select **Calc → Random Data → Sample From Columns**.

In the Sample From Columns dialog box (see Figure M7.2):

7. Enter **40** in the **Number of rows to sample** box.
8. Enter **C1** in the **From columns** box.
9. Enter **C2** in the **Store samples in** box.
10. Click **OK**.

**FIGURE M7.2**

Minitab Sample From Columns dialog box

## M7.2 Creating Simulated Sampling Distributions

To develop a simulation of the sampling distribution of the mean from a uniformly distributed population with 100 samples of $n = 30$:

1. Select **Calc → Random Data → Uniform**.

In the Uniform Distribution dialog box (see Figure M7.3):

2. Enter **100** in the **Number of rows of data to generate** box.
3. Enter **C1–C30** in the **Store in column(s)** box.
4. Enter **0.0** in the **Lower endpoint** box
5. Enter **1.0** in the **Upper endpoint** box.
6. Click **OK**.

**FIGURE M7.3**

Minitab Uniform Distribution dialog box

One hundred rows of values are now entered in columns C1–C30. To calculate row statistics for each of the 100 samples:

1. Select **Calc → Row Statistics**.

In the Row Statistics dialog box (see Figure M7.4):

2. Click **Mean**.
3. Enter **C1–C30** in the **Input variables** box.
4. Enter **C31** in the **Store result in** box.
5. Click **OK**.

**FIGURE M7.4**

Minitab Row Statistics dialog box

The mean for each of the 100 samples is stored in column C31. To compute statistics for the set of 100 sample means:

1. Select **Stat → Basic Statistics → Display Descriptive Statistics**.
2. In the Display Descriptive Statistics dialog box, enter **C31** in the **Variables** box and then click **OK**.

To generate a histogram of the 100 sample means:

1. Select **Graph → Histogram** and do the following:

In the Histograms dialog box:

2. Select **Simple**.
3. Click **OK**.

In the Histogram - Simple dialog box:

4. Enter **C31** in the **Graph variables** box.
5. Click **OK**.

To create a simulation of the sampling distribution of the mean for a normal population:

1. Select **Calc → Random Data → Normal**.

In the Normal Distribution dialog box:

2. Enter **100** in the **Number of rows of data to generate** box.
3. Enter **C1–C30** in the **Store in column(s)** box.
4. Enter a value for μ in the **Mean** box.
5. Enter a value for σ in the **Standard deviation** box.
6. Click **OK**.

You can calculate row statistics (descriptive statistics for the set of 100 samples) and create a histogram by adapting the instructions given for a uniformly distributed population.

# CHAPTER
# EIGHT

## CONFIDENCE INTERVAL ESTIMATION

# LEARNING OBJECTIVES

## In this chapter, you learn:

- To construct and interpret confidence interval estimates for the mean and the proportion
- How to determine the sample size necessary to develop a confidence interval for the mean or proportion
  How to use confidence interval estimates in auditing

# USING STATISTICS @ Saxon Home Improvement

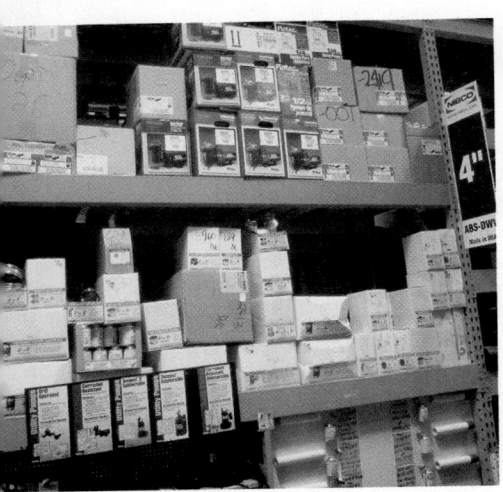

Saxon Home Improvement distributes home improvement supplies in the northeastern United States. As a company accountant, you are responsible for the accuracy of the integrated inventory management and sales information system. You could review the contents of each and every record to check the accuracy of this system, but such a detailed review would be time-consuming and costly. A better approach is to use statistical inference techniques to draw conclusions about the population of all records from a relatively small sample collected during an audit. At the end of each month, you could select a sample of the sales invoices to estimate the following:

- The mean dollar amount listed on the sales invoices for the month.
- The frequency of occurrence of errors that violate the internal control policy of the warehouse. Such errors include making a shipment when there is no authorized warehouse removal slip, failure to include the correct account number, and shipping the incorrect home improvement item.
- The total dollar amount listed on the sales invoices for the month.
- Any differences between the dollar amounts on the sales invoices and the amounts entered into the sales information system.

How accurate are the results from the samples and how do you use this information? Are the sample sizes large enough to give you the information you need?

In Section 7.4, you used the Central Limit Theorem and knowledge of the population distribution to determine the percentage of sample means that are within certain distances of the population mean. For instance, in the cereal-fill example used throughout Chapter 7 (see Example 7.6 on page 274), you can conclude that 95% of all sample means are between 362.12 and 373.88 grams. This is an example of *deductive* reasoning because the conclusion is based on taking something that is true in general (for the population) and applying it to something specific (the sample means).

To get the results that Saxon Home Improvement needs requires *inductive* reasoning. Inductive reasoning lets you use some specifics to make broader generalizations. You cannot guarantee that the broader generalizations are absolutely correct, but with a careful choosing of the specifics and a rigorous methodology, you can get useful conclusions. As a Saxon accountant, you need to use inferential statistics, the process of using sample results (the "some specifics") to *estimate* ("the making of the broader generalization") unknown population parameters such as a population mean or a population proportion. Note that statisticians use the word *estimate* in the same sense of the everyday usage, something you are reasonably certain about, but cannot flatly say is absolutely correct.

You estimate population parameters using either point estimates or interval estimates. A **point estimate** is the value of a single sample statistic. A **confidence interval estimate** is a range of numbers, called an interval, constructed around the point estimate. The confidence interval is constructed such that the probability that the population parameter is located somewhere within the interval is known.

Suppose you want to estimate the mean GPA of all the students at your university. The mean GPA for all the students is an unknown population mean, denoted by $\mu$. You select a sample of students and find that the sample mean is 2.80. The sample mean, $\bar{X} = 2.80$, is a point estimate of the population mean, $\mu$. How accurate is 2.80? To answer this question, you must construct a confidence interval estimate.

Recall that the sample mean, $\bar{X}$, is a point estimate of the population mean, μ. However, the sample mean varies from sample to sample because it depends on the items selected in the sample. By taking into account the known variability from sample to sample (see Section 7.4 on the sampling distribution of the mean), you can develop the interval estimate for the population mean. The interval constructed should have a specified confidence of correctly estimating the value of the population parameter, μ. In other words, there is a specified confidence that μ is somewhere in the range of numbers defined by the interval.

Suppose that after studying this chapter, you find that a 95% confidence interval for the mean GPA at your university is ($2.75 \leq \mu \leq 2.85$). You can interpret this interval estimate by stating that you are 95% confident that the mean GPA at your university is between 2.75 and 2.85. There is a 5% chance that the mean GPA is below 2.75 or above 2.85.

After learning about the confidence interval for the mean, you will learn how to develop an interval estimate for the population proportion. Then you will learn how large a sample to select when constructing confidence intervals and how to perform several important estimation procedures accountants use when performing audits.

# 8.1 CONFIDENCE INTERVAL ESTIMATION FOR THE MEAN (σ KNOWN)

In Section 7.4, you used the Central Limit Theorem and knowledge of the population distribution to determine the percentage of sample means that are within certain distances of the population mean. Suppose that in the cereal-fill example, you wished to estimate the population mean, using the information from a single sample. Thus, rather than taking $\mu \pm (1.96)(\sigma/\sqrt{n})$ to find the upper and lower limits around μ, as in Section 7.4, you substitute the sample mean, $\bar{X}$, for the unknown μ and use $\bar{X} \pm (1.96)(\sigma/\sqrt{n})$ as an interval to estimate the unknown μ. Although in practice you select a single sample of $n$ values and compute the mean, $\bar{X}$, in order to understand the full meaning of the interval estimate, you need to examine a hypothetical set of all possible samples of $n$ values.

Suppose that a sample of $n = 25$ boxes has a mean of 362.3 grams. The interval developed to estimate μ is $362.3 \pm (1.96)(15)/(\sqrt{25})$ or $362.3 \pm 5.88$. The estimate of μ is

$$356.42 \leq \mu \leq 368.18$$

Because the population mean, μ (equal to 368), is included within the interval, this sample results in a correct statement about μ (see Figure 8.1).

**FIGURE 8.1**

Confidence interval estimates for five different samples of $n = 25$ taken from a population where $\mu = 368$ and $\sigma = 15$

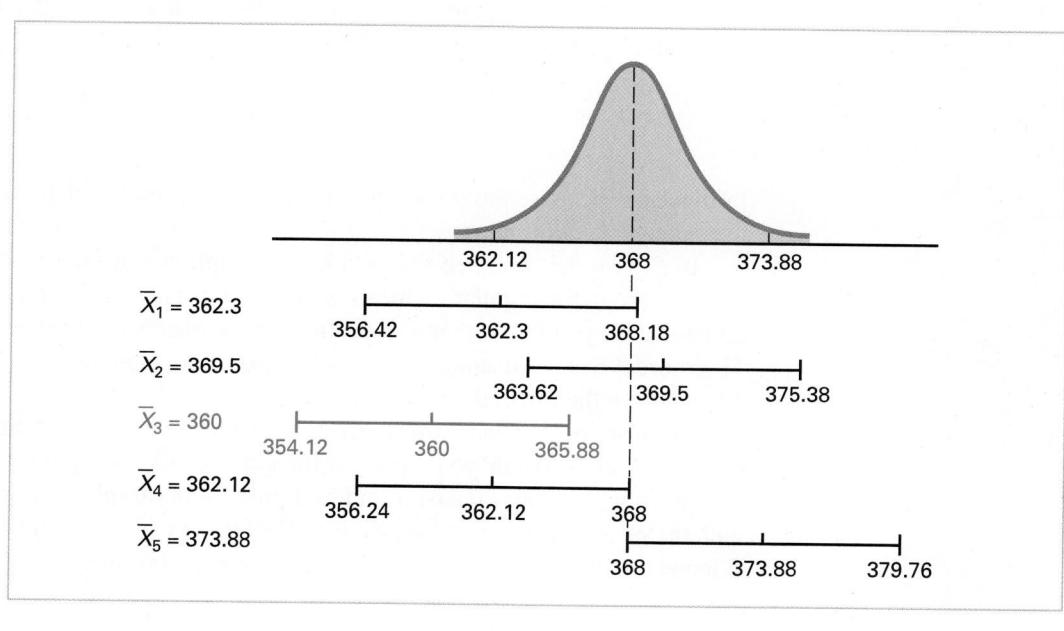

To continue this hypothetical example, suppose that for a different sample of $n = 25$ boxes, the mean is 369.5. The interval developed from this sample is

$$369.5 \pm (1.96)(15) / (\sqrt{25})$$

or $360 \pm 5.88$. The estimate is

$$363.62 \leq \mu \leq 375.38$$

Because the population mean, $\mu$ (equal to 368), is also included within this interval, this statement about $\mu$ is correct.

Now, before you begin to think that correct statements about $\mu$ are always made by developing a confidence interval estimate, suppose a third hypothetical sample of $n = 25$ boxes is selected and the sample mean is equal to 360 grams. The interval developed here is $360 \pm (1.96)(15) / (\sqrt{25})$, or $360 \pm 5.88$. In this case, the estimate of $\mu$ is

$$354.12 \leq \mu \leq 365.88$$

This estimate is *not* a correct statement because the population mean, $\mu$, is not included in the interval developed from this sample (see Figure 8.1). Thus, for some samples, the interval estimate of $\mu$ is correct, but for others it is incorrect. In practice, only one sample is selected, and because the population mean is unknown, you cannot determine whether the interval estimate is correct. To resolve this dilemma of sometimes having an interval that provides a correct estimate and sometimes having an interval that provides an incorrect estimate, you need to determine the proportion of samples producing intervals that result in correct statements about the population mean, $\mu$. To do this, consider two other hypothetical samples: the case in which $\bar{X} = 362.12$ grams and the case in which $\bar{X} = 373.88$ grams. If $\bar{X} = 362.12$, the interval is $362.12 \pm (1.96)(15) / (\sqrt{25})$, or $362.12 \pm 5.88$. This leads to the following interval:

$$356.24 \leq \mu \leq 368.00$$

Because the population mean of 368 is at the upper limit of the interval, the statement is a correct one (see Figure 8.1).

When $\bar{X} = 373.88$, the interval is $373.88 \pm (1.96)(15) / (\sqrt{25})$, or $373.88 \pm 5.88$. The interval estimate for the mean is

$$368.00 \leq \mu \leq 379.76$$

In this case, because the population mean of 368 is included at the lower limit of the interval, the statement is correct.

In Figure 8.1, you see that when the sample mean falls anywhere between 362.12 and 373.88 grams, the population mean is included *somewhere* within the interval. In Example 7.6 on page 274, you found that 95% of the sample means fall between 362.12 and 373.88 grams. Therefore, 95% of all samples of $n = 25$ boxes have sample means that include the population mean within the interval developed.

Because, in practice, you select only one sample of size $n$, and $\mu$ is unknown, you never know for sure whether your specific interval includes the population mean. However, if you take all possible samples of $n$ and compute their sample means, 95% of the intervals will include the population mean, and only 5% of them will not. In other words, you have 95% confidence that the population mean is somewhere in your interval.

Consider once again the first sample discussed in this section. A sample of $n = 25$ boxes had a sample mean of 362.3 grams. The interval constructed to estimate $\mu$ is:

$$362.3 \pm (1.96)(15)/(\sqrt{25})$$

$$362.3 \pm 5.88$$

$$356.42 \leq \mu \leq 368.18$$

The interval from 356.42 to 368.18 is referred to as a 95% confidence interval. The following box contains an interpretation of the interval that most business professionals will understand. (For a technical discussion of different ways to interpret confidence intervals, see Reference 3.)

"I am 95% confident that the mean amount of cereal in the population of boxes is somewhere between 356.42 and 368.18 grams."

To assist in your understanding of the meaning of the confidence interval, the following example concerns the order-filling process at a Web site. Filling orders consists of several steps including receiving an order, picking the parts of the order, checking the order, packing, and shipping the order. The data in the file **Order** consists of the time in minutes to fill orders for a population of 200 on a recent day. Although in practice, the population characteristics are rarely known, for this population of orders, the mean $\mu$ is known to be equal to 69.637 minutes and the standard deviation $\sigma$ is known to be equal to 10.411 minutes. To illustrate how the sample mean and sample standard deviation can vary from one sample to another, 20 different samples of $n = 10$ were selected from the population of 200 orders and the sample mean and sample standard deviation (and other statistics) were calculated for each sample using Minitab. Figure 8.2 shows these results.

**FIGURE 8.2**

Minitab sample statistics and 95% confidence intervals for 20 samples of $n = 10$ selected from the population of 200 orders

| Variable | Count | Mean | StDev | Minimum | Median | Maximum | Range | 95% CI |
|---|---|---|---|---|---|---|---|---|
| Sample 1 | 10 | 74.15 | 13.39 | 56.10 | 76.85 | 97.70 | 41.60 | (67.6973, 80.6027) |
| Sample 2 | 10 | 61.10 | 10.60 | 46.80 | 61.35 | 79.50 | 32.70 | (54.6473, 67.5527) |
| Sample 3 | 10 | 74.36 | 6.50 | 62.50 | 74.50 | 84.00 | 21.50 | (67.9073, 80.8127) |
| Sample 4 | 10 | 70.40 | 12.80 | 47.20 | 70.95 | 84.00 | 36.80 | (63.9473, 76.8527) |
| Sample 5 | 10 | 62.18 | 10.85 | 47.10 | 59.70 | 84.00 | 36.90 | (55.7273, 68.6327) |
| Sample 6 | 10 | 67.03 | 9.68 | 51.10 | 69.60 | 83.30 | 32.20 | (60.5773, 73.4827) |
| Sample 7 | 10 | 69.03 | 8.81 | 56.60 | 68.85 | 83.70 | 27.10 | (62.5773, 75.4827) |
| Sample 8 | 10 | 72.30 | 11.52 | 54.20 | 71.35 | 87.00 | 32.80 | (65.8473, 78.7527) |
| Sample 9 | 10 | 68.18 | 14.10 | 50.10 | 69.95 | 86.20 | 36.10 | (61.7273, 74.6327) |
| Sample 10 | 10 | 66.67 | 9.08 | 57.10 | 64.65 | 86.10 | 29.00 | (60.2173, 73.1227) |
| Sample 11 | 10 | 72.42 | 9.76 | 59.60 | 74.65 | 86.10 | 26.50 | (65.9673, 78.8727) |
| Sample 12 | 10 | 76.26 | 11.69 | 50.10 | 80.60 | 87.00 | 36.90 | (69.8073, 82.7127) |
| Sample 13 | 10 | 65.74 | 12.11 | 47.10 | 62.15 | 86.10 | 39.00 | (59.2873, 72.1927) |
| Sample 14 | 10 | 69.99 | 10.97 | 51.00 | 73.40 | 84.60 | 33.60 | (63.5373, 76.4427) |
| Sample 15 | 10 | 75.76 | 8.60 | 61.10 | 75.05 | 87.80 | 26.70 | (69.3073, 82.2127) |
| Sample 16 | 10 | 67.94 | 9.19 | 56.70 | 67.70 | 87.80 | 31.10 | (61.4873, 74.3927) |
| Sample 17 | 10 | 71.05 | 10.48 | 50.10 | 71.15 | 86.20 | 36.10 | (64.5973, 77.5027) |
| Sample 18 | 10 | 71.68 | 7.96 | 55.60 | 72.35 | 82.60 | 27.00 | (65.2273, 78.1327) |
| Sample 19 | 10 | 70.97 | 9.83 | 54.40 | 70.05 | 84.60 | 30.20 | (64.5173, 77.4227) |
| Sample 20 | 10 | 74.48 | 8.80 | 62.00 | 76.25 | 85.70 | 23.70 | (68.0273, 80.9327) |

From Figure 8.2, you can see the following:

1. The sample statistics differ from sample to sample. The sample means vary from 61.10 to 76.26 minutes, the sample standard deviations vary from 6.50 to 14.10 minutes, the sample medians vary from 59.70 to 76.85 minutes, and the sample ranges vary from 21.50 to 41.60 minutes.

2. Some of the sample means are greater than the population mean of 69.637 minutes, and some of the sample means are less than the population mean.

3. Some of the sample standard deviations are greater than the population standard deviation of 10.411 minutes, and some of the sample standard deviations are less than the population standard deviation.

4. The variation in the sample range from sample to sample is much more than the variation in the sample standard deviation.

The fact that sample statistics vary from sample to sample is called sampling error. Sampling error is the variation that occurs due to selecting a single sample from the population. The size of the sampling error is primarily based on the amount of variation in the population and on the sample size. Larger samples have less sampling error than small samples, but will cost more.

The last column of Figure 8.2 contains twenty 95% confidence interval estimates of the population mean order-filling time based on the results of those 20 samples of $n = 10$. Begin by examining the first sample selected. The sample mean is 74.15 minutes, and the interval estimate for the population mean is $67.6973 - 80.6027$ minutes. In a typical study, you would not know for sure whether this interval estimate is correct because you rarely know the value of the population mean. However, for this example *concerning the order-filling times*, the population mean is known to be 69.637 minutes. If you examine the interval $67.6973 - 80.6027$ minutes, you see that the population mean of 69.637 minutes is located *between* these lower and upper limits. Thus, the first sample provides a correct estimate of the population mean in the form of an interval estimate. Looking over the other 19 samples, you see that similar results occur for all the other samples *except* for samples 2, 5, and 12. For each of the intervals generated (other than samples 2, 5, and 12), the population mean of 69.637 minutes is located *somewhere* within the interval.

For sample 2, the sample mean is 61.10 minutes, and the interval is 54.6473 to 67.5527 minutes; for sample 5, the sample mean is 62.18, and the interval is between 55.7273 and 68.6327; whereas for sample 12, the sample mean is 76.26, and the interval is between 69.8073 and 82.7127 minutes. The population mean of 69.637 minutes is *not* located within any of these intervals, and any estimate of the population mean made using these intervals is incorrect.

In some situations, you might want a higher degree of confidence (such as 99%) of including the population mean within the interval. In other cases, you might accept less confidence (such as 90%) of correctly estimating the population mean. In general, the **level of confidence** is symbolized by $(1 - \alpha) \times 100\%$, where $\alpha$ is the proportion in the tails of the distribution that is outside the confidence interval. The proportion in the upper tail of the distribution is $\alpha/2$, and the proportion in the lower tail of the distribution is $\alpha/2$. You use Equation (8.1) to construct a $(1 - \alpha) \times 100\%$ confidence interval estimate of the mean with $\sigma$ known.

**Confidence Interval for the Mean ($\sigma$ Known)**

$$\bar{X} \pm Z_{\alpha/2} \frac{\sigma}{\sqrt{n}}$$

or

$$\bar{X} - Z_{\alpha/2} \frac{\sigma}{\sqrt{n}} \leq \mu \leq \bar{X} + Z_{\alpha/2} \frac{\sigma}{\sqrt{n}} \tag{8.1}$$

where $Z_{\alpha/2}$ is the value corresponding to an upper-tail probability of $\alpha/2$ from the standardized normal distribution (i.e., a cumulative area of $1 - \alpha/2$).

The value of $Z_{\alpha/2}$ needed for constructing a confidence interval is called the **critical value** for the distribution. 95% confidence corresponds to an $\alpha$ value of 0.05. The critical $Z$ value corresponding to a cumulative area of 0.975 is 1.96 because there is 0.025 in the upper tail of the distribution and the cumulative area less than $Z = 1.96$ is 0.975.

There is a different critical value for each level of confidence, $1 - \alpha$. A level of confidence of 95% leads to a $Z$ value of 1.96 (see Figure 8.3). 99% confidence corresponds to an $\alpha$ value of 0.01. The $Z$ value is approximately 2.58 because the upper-tail area is 0.005 and the cumulative area less than $Z = 2.58$ is 0.995 (see Figure 8.4).

**FIGURE 8.3**

Normal curve for determining the $Z$ value needed for 95% confidence

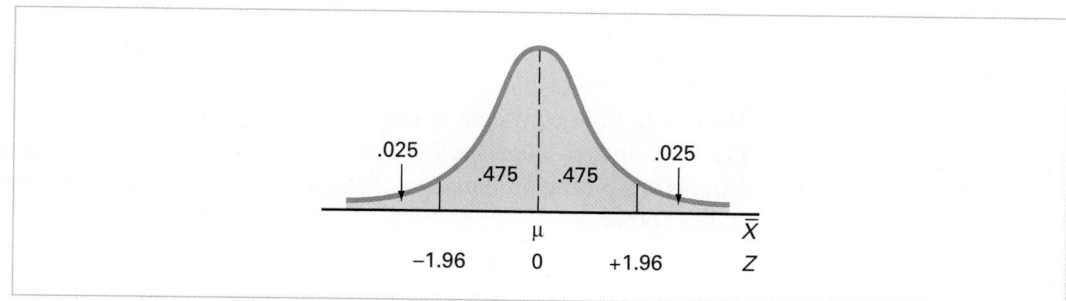

**FIGURE 8.4**

Normal curve for determining the $Z$ value needed for 99% confidence

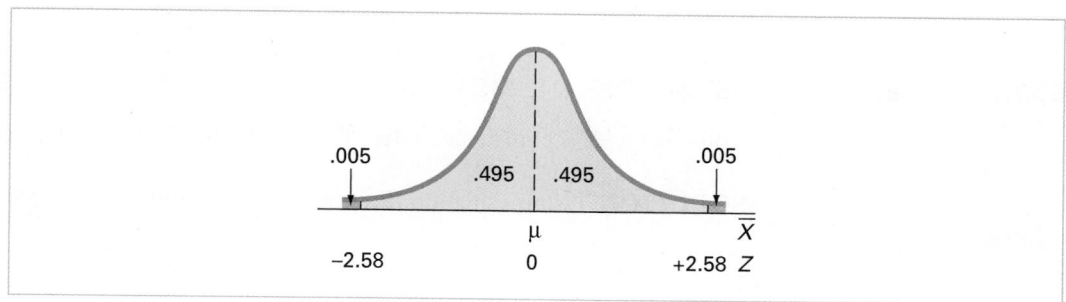

Now that various levels of confidence have been considered, why not make the confidence level as close to 100% as possible? Before doing so, you need to realize that any increase in the level of confidence is achieved only by widening (and making less precise) the confidence interval. There is no "free lunch" here. You would have more confidence that the population mean is within a broader range of values; however, this might make the interpretation of the confidence interval less useful. The trade-off between the width of the confidence interval and the level of confidence is discussed in greater depth in the context of determining the sample size in Section 8.4. Example 8.1 illustrates the application of the confidence interval estimate.

**EXAMPLE 8.1**   ESTIMATING THE MEAN PAPER LENGTH WITH 95% CONFIDENCE

A paper manufacturer has a production process that operates continuously throughout an entire production shift. The paper is expected to have a mean length of 11 inches, and the standard deviation of the length is 0.02 inch. At periodic intervals, a sample is selected to determine whether the mean paper length is still equal to 11 inches or whether something has gone wrong in the production process to change the length of the paper produced. You select a random sample of 100 sheets, and the mean paper length is 10.998 inches. Construct a 95% confidence interval estimate for the population mean paper length.

**SOLUTION**  Using Equation (8.1) on page 296, with $Z_{\alpha/2} = 1.96$ for 95% confidence,

$$\bar{X} \pm Z_{\alpha/2} \frac{\sigma}{\sqrt{n}} = 10.998 \pm (1.96) \frac{0.02}{\sqrt{100}}$$

$$= 10.998 \pm 0.00392$$

$$10.99408 \leq \mu \leq 11.00192$$

Thus, with 95% confidence, you conclude that the population mean is between 10.99408 and 11.00192 inches. Because the interval includes 11, the value indicating that the production process is working properly, you have no reason to believe that anything is wrong with the production process.

To see the effect of using a 99% confidence interval, examine Example 8.2.

**EXAMPLE 8.2**

ESTIMATING THE MEAN PAPER LENGTH WITH 99% CONFIDENCE

Construct a 99% confidence interval estimate for the population mean paper length.

**SOLUTION**  Using Equation (8.1) on page 296, with $Z_{\alpha/2} = 2.58$ for 99% confidence,

$$\bar{X} \pm Z_{\alpha/2} \frac{\sigma}{\sqrt{n}} = 10.998 \pm (2.58) \frac{0.02}{\sqrt{100}}$$

$$= 10.998 \pm 0.00516$$

$$10.99284 \leq \mu \leq 11.00316$$

Once again, because 11 is included within this wider interval, you have no reason to believe that anything is wrong with the production process.

As discussed in Section 7.4, the sampling distribution of the sample mean $\bar{X}$ is normally distributed if the population for your characteristic of interest $X$ is a normal distribution. And, if the population of $X$ is not a normal distribution, the Central Limit Theorem almost always ensures that $\bar{X}$ is normally distributed when $n$ is large. However, when dealing with a small sample size and a population of $X$ that is not a normal distribution, the sampling distribution of $\bar{X}$ is not normally distributed and therefore the confidence interval discussed in this section is inappropriate. In practice, however, as long as the sample size is large enough and the population is not very skewed, you can use the confidence interval defined in Equation (8.1) to estimate the population mean when $\sigma$ is known. To assess the assumption of normality, you can evaluate the shape of the sample data by using a histogram, stem-and-leaf display, boxplot, or normal probability plot.

# Can You Ever *Really* Know Sigma?

*From the Authors' Desktop*

Section 8.1 discusses the concept of the confidence interval estimate, how to develop it, and how to interpret it. The discussion limited itself to the case where the population standard deviation, sigma, is known. But, can you ever *really* know sigma? Probably not, but it is much easier to explain the confidence interval estimate using an example where the population standard deviation, sigma, is known. If sigma is known, then you can use the normal distribution, with which you are already famil-

iar from Chapters 6 and 7. In Section 8.2, you will learn how to construct confidence interval estimates when sigma is not known, and you will use the *t* distribution instead of the normal distribution.

In virtually all real-world business applications, you do not know the standard deviation of the population. If, for a particular case, you knew the population standard deviation, you would also already know (or could compute) the population mean. Why is that so? You could only know the population standard

deviation if you have access to all of the population data. And if you knew all of the population data, you could compute the population mean. There would be no need to employ the *inductive* reasoning of inferential statistics to estimate the population mean.

So why study the confidence interval estimate of the mean when sigma is known? Because it is a good way to understand the confidence interval concept—a very important concept to know when studying the rest of this book.

# PROBLEMS FOR SECTION 8.1

## Learning the Basics

**8.1** If $\bar{X} = 85$, $\sigma = 8$, and $n = 64$, construct a 95% confidence interval estimate of the population mean, $\mu$.

**8.2** If $\bar{X} = 125$, $\sigma = 24$, and $n = 36$, construct a 99% confidence interval estimate of the population mean, $\mu$.

**8.3** A market researcher collects a simple random sample of $n = 100$ customers from its population of two million customers. After analyzing the sample, she states that she has 95% confidence that the mean annual income of its two million customers is between $70,000 and $85,000. Explain the meaning of this statement.

**8.4** If you were to collect a set of data, either from an entire population or from a random sample taken from that population:
**a.** Which statistical measure would you compute first: the mean or the standard deviation? Explain.

**b.** What does your answer to (a) tell you about the "practicality" of using the confidence interval estimate formula given in Equation (8.1)?

**8.5** Consider the confidence interval estimate discussed in Problem 8.3. Suppose that the population mean annual income is $71,000. Is the confidence interval estimate stated in Problem 8.3 correct? Explain.

**8.6** You are working as an assistant to the dean of institutional research at your university. She wants to survey members of the alumni association who obtained their baccalaureate degrees 5 years ago to learn what their starting salaries were in their first full-time job after receiving their degrees. A sample of 100 alumni is to be randomly selected from the list of 2,500 graduates in that class. If her goal is to construct a 95% confidence interval estimate of the population mean starting salary, why is it unlikely that you will be able to use Equation (8.1) on page 296 for this purpose? Explain.

## 8.2  CONFIDENCE INTERVAL ESTIMATION FOR THE MEAN (σ UNKNOWN)

Just as the mean of the population, $\mu$, is usually unknown, you virtually never know the standard deviation of the population, $\sigma$. Therefore, you need to construct a confidence interval estimate of $\mu$, using the sample statistic $S$ as an estimate of the population parameter $\sigma$.

## Student's *t* Distribution

At the beginning of the twentieth century, William S. Gosset, a statistician for Guinness Breweries in Ireland (see reference 4), wanted to make inferences about the mean when σ was unknown. Because Guinness employees were not permitted to publish research work under their own names, Gosset adopted the pseudonym "Student." The distribution that he developed is known as **Student's *t* distribution** and is commonly referred to as the *t* distribution.

If the random variable *X* is normally distributed, then the following statistic has a *t* distribution with *n* − 1 **degrees of freedom**:

$$t = \frac{\bar{X} - \mu}{\dfrac{S}{\sqrt{n}}}$$

This expression has the same form as the *Z* statistic in Equation (7.4) on page 272, except that *S* is used to estimate the unknown σ.

## Properties of the *t* Distribution

The *t* distribution looks very similar to the standardized normal distribution. Both distributions are symmetrical and bell shaped with means and medians equal to zero. However, the *t* distribution has more area in the tails and less in the center than does the standardized normal distribution (see Figure 8.5). Because *S* is used to estimate the unknown σ, the values of *t* are more variable than those for *Z*.

**FIGURE 8.5**

Standardized normal distribution and *t* distribution for 5 degrees of freedom

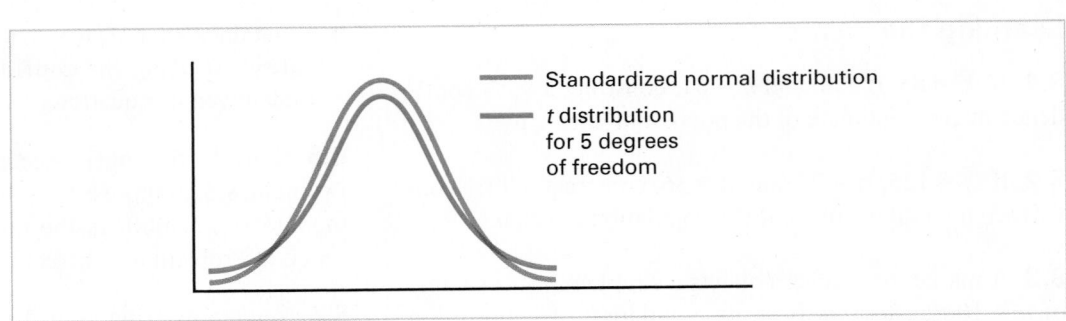

The degrees of freedom, *n* − 1, are directly related to the sample size, *n*. The concept of *degrees of freedom* is discussed further on pages 301 through 302. As the sample size and degrees of freedom increase, *S* becomes a better estimate of σ, and the *t* distribution gradually approaches the standardized normal distribution, until the two are virtually identical. With a sample size of about 120 or more, *S* estimates σ precisely enough so that there is little difference between the *t* and *Z* distributions.

As stated earlier, the *t* distribution assumes that the random variable *X* is normally distributed. In practice, however, when the sample size is large enough and the population is not very skewed, in most cases you can use the *t* distribution to estimate the population mean when σ is unknown. When dealing with a small sample size and a skewed population distribution, the confidence interval estimate may not provide a valid estimate of the population mean. To assess the assumption of normality, you can evaluate the shape of the sample data by using a histogram, stem-and-leaf display, boxplot, or normal probability plot. However, the usefulness of any of these graphs to evaluate normality is limited when you have a small sample size.

You find the critical values of *t* for the appropriate degrees of freedom from the table of the *t* distribution (see Table E.3). The columns of the table present the most commonly needed cumulative probabilities and corresponding upper-tail areas. The rows of the table represent the degrees of freedom. The critical $t$ values are found in the cells of the table. For example, with 99 degrees of freedom, if you want 95% confidence, you find the appropriate value of $t$, as shown in Table 8.1. The 95% confidence level means that 2.5% of the values (an area of 0.025) are in each tail of the distribution. Looking in the column for a cumulative probability of 0.975 and an upper-tail area of 0.025 in the row corresponding to 99 degrees of freedom gives you a critical value for $t$ of 1.9842 (see Figure 8.6). Because $t$ is a symmetrical distribution with a mean of 0, if the upper-tail value is +1.9842, the value for the lower-tail area (lower 0.025) is − 1.9842. A $t$ value of −1.9842 means that the probability that $t$ is less than −1.9842 is 0.025, or 2.5%.

Note that for a 95% confidence interval, you will always use a cumulative probability of 0.975 and an upper-tail area of 0.025. Similarly, for a 99% confidence interval, use 0.995 and 0.005, and for a 90% confidence interval use 0.95 and 0.05.

**TABLE 8.1**

Determining the Critical Value from the $t$ Table for an Area of 0.025 in Each Tail with 99 Degrees of Freedom

| | Cumulative Probabilities | | | | | |
|---|---|---|---|---|---|---|
| | .75 | .90 | .95 | .975 | .99 | .995 |
| | Upper Tail Areas | | | | | |
| Degrees of Freedom | .25 | .10 | .05 | .025 | .01 | .005 |
| 1 | 1.0000 | 3.0777 | 6.3138 | 12.7062 | 31.8207 | 63.6574 |
| 2 | 0.8165 | 1.8856 | 2.9200 | 4.3027 | 6.9646 | 9.9248 |
| 3 | 0.7649 | 1.6377 | 2.3534 | 3.1824 | 4.5407 | 5.8409 |
| 4 | 0.7407 | 1.5332 | 2.1318 | 2.7764 | 3.7469 | 4.6041 |
| 5 | 0.7267 | 1.4759 | 2.0150 | 2.5706 | 3.3649 | 4.0322 |
| . | . | . | . | . | . | . |
| . | . | . | . | . | . | . |
| . | . | . | . | . | . | . |
| 96 | 0.6771 | 1.2904 | 1.6609 | 1.9850 | 2.3658 | 2.6280 |
| 97 | 0.6770 | 1.2903 | 1.6607 | 1.9847 | 2.3654 | 2.6275 |
| 98 | 0.6770 | 1.2902 | 1.6606 | 1.9845 | 2.3650 | 2.6269 |
| 99 | 0.6770 | 1.2902 | 1.6604 | 1.9842 | 2.3646 | 2.6264 |
| 100 | 0.6770 | 1.2901 | 1.6602 | 1.9840 | 2.3642 | 2.6259 |

Source: *Extracted from Table E.3.*

**FIGURE 8.6**

$t$ distribution with 99 degrees of freedom

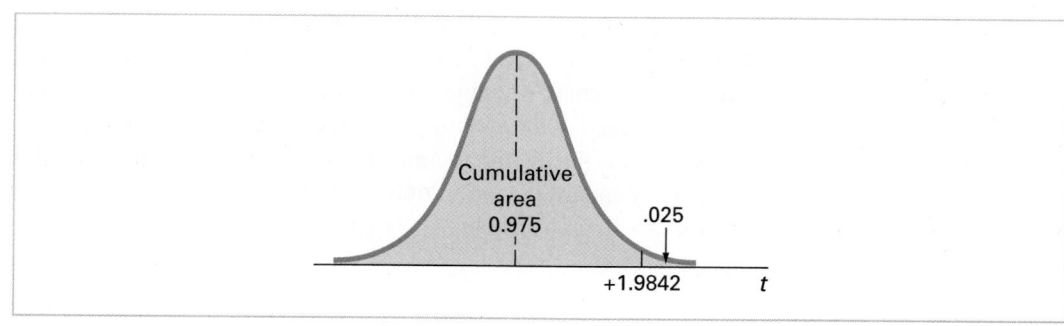

Cumulative area 0.975    .025    +1.9842    $t$

## The Concept of Degrees of Freedom

In Chapter 3, you learned that the numerator of the sample variance, $S^2$ [see Equation (3.6) on page 98], requires the computation of

$$\sum_{i=1}^{n}(X_i - \bar{X})^2$$

In order to compute $S^2$, you first need to know $\bar{X}$. Therefore, only $n-1$ of the sample values are free to vary. This means that you have $n-1$ degrees of freedom. For example, suppose a sample of five values has a mean of 20. How many values do you need to know before you can determine the remainder of the values? The fact that $n = 5$ and $\bar{X} = 20$ also tells you that

$$\sum_{i=1}^{n} X_i = 100$$

because

$$\frac{\sum_{i=1}^{n} X_i}{n} = \bar{X}$$

Thus, when you know four of the values, the fifth one is *not* free to vary because the sum must add to 100. For example, if four of the values are 18, 24, 19, and 16, the fifth value must be 23 so that the sum equals 100.

## The Confidence Interval Statement

Equation (8.2) defines the $(1-\alpha) \times 100\%$ confidence interval estimate for the mean with $\sigma$ unknown.

**Confidence Interval for the Mean ($\sigma$ Unknown)**

$$\bar{X} \pm t_{\alpha/2} \frac{S}{\sqrt{n}}$$

or

$$\bar{X} - t_{\alpha/2} \frac{S}{\sqrt{n}} \le \mu \le \bar{X} + t_{\alpha/2} \frac{S}{\sqrt{n}} \qquad \textbf{(8.2)}$$

where $t_{\alpha/2}$ is the critical value corresponding to an upper-tail probability of $\alpha/2$ from the $t$ distribution with $n-1$ degrees of freedom (i.e., a cumulative area of $1 - \alpha/2$).

To illustrate the application of the confidence interval estimate for the mean when the standard deviation, $\sigma$, is unknown, recall the Saxon Home Improvement Company Using Statistics scenario presented on page 292. You wanted to estimate the mean dollar amount listed on the sales invoices for the month. You select a sample of 100 sales invoices from the population of sales invoices during the month, and the sample mean of the 100 sales invoices is $110.27, with a sample standard deviation of $28.95. For 95% confidence, the critical value from the $t$ distribution (as shown in Table 8.1) is 1.9842. Using Equation (8.2),

$$\bar{X} \pm t_{\alpha/2} \frac{S}{\sqrt{n}}$$

$$= 110.27 \pm (1.9842)\frac{28.95}{\sqrt{100}}$$

$$= 110.27 \pm 5.74$$

$$\$104.53 \le \mu \le \$116.01$$

A Microsoft Excel worksheet for these data is presented in Figure 8.7.

**FIGURE 8.7**

Microsoft Excel worksheet to compute a confidence interval estimate for the mean sales invoice amount for the Saxon Home Improvement Company

*See Section E8.2 or P8.2 to create this. (Minitab users, see Section M8.2 to create the equivalent results.)*

|    | A | B | |
|----|---|---|---|
| 1 | **Estimate for the Mean Sales Invoice Amount** | | |
| 2 | | | |
| 3 | **Data** | | |
| 4 | **Sample Standard Deviation** | 28.95 | |
| 5 | **Sample Mean** | 110.27 | |
| 6 | **Sample Size** | 100 | |
| 7 | **Confidence Level** | 95% | |
| 8 | | | |
| 9 | Intermediate Calculations | | |
| 10 | Standard Error of the Mean | 2.8950 | =B4/SQRT(B6) |
| 11 | Degrees of Freedom | 99 | =B6 - 1 |
| 12 | *t* Value | 1.9842 | =TINV(1 - B7, B11) |
| 13 | Interval Half Width | 5.7443 | =B12 * B10 |
| 14 | | | |
| 15 | Confidence Interval | | |
| 16 | **Interval Lower Limit** | 104.53 | =B5 - B13 |
| 17 | **Interval Upper Limit** | 116.01 | =B5 + B13 |

Thus, with 95% confidence, you conclude that the mean amount of all the sales invoices is between \$104.53 and \$116.01. The 95% confidence level indicates that if you selected all possible samples of 100 (something that is never done in practice), 95% of the intervals developed would include the population mean somewhere within the interval. The validity of this confidence interval estimate depends on the assumption of normality for the distribution of the amount of the sales invoices. With a sample of 100, the normality assumption is not overly restrictive (see the Central Limit Theorem on page 274), and the use of the *t* distribution is likely appropriate. Example 8.3 further illustrates how you construct the confidence interval for a mean when the population standard deviation is unknown.

**EXAMPLE 8.3**

ESTIMATING THE MEAN FORCE REQUIRED TO BREAK ELECTRIC INSULATORS

A manufacturing company produces electric insulators. If the insulators break when in use, a short circuit is likely. To test the strength of the insulators, you carry out destructive testing to determine how much *force* is required to break the insulators. You measure force by observing how many pounds are applied to the insulator before it breaks. Table 8.2 lists 30 values from this experiment, which are located in the file **Force**. Construct a 95% confidence interval estimate for the population mean force required to break the insulator.

**TABLE 8.2**

Force (in Pounds) Required to Break the Insulator

| | | | | | | | | | |
|---|---|---|---|---|---|---|---|---|---|
| 1,870 | 1,728 | 1,656 | 1,610 | 1,634 | 1,784 | 1,522 | 1,696 | 1,592 | 1,662 |
| 1,866 | 1,764 | 1,734 | 1,662 | 1,734 | 1,774 | 1,550 | 1,756 | 1,762 | 1,866 |
| 1,820 | 1,744 | 1,788 | 1,688 | 1,810 | 1,752 | 1,680 | 1,810 | 1,652 | 1,736 |

**SOLUTION** Figure 8.8 shows that the sample mean is $\bar{X} = 1,723.4$ pounds and the sample standard deviation is $S = 89.55$ pounds. Using Equation (8.2) on page 302 to construct the confidence interval, you need to determine the critical value from the *t* table using the row for 29 degrees of freedom. For 95% confidence, you use the column corresponding to an upper-tail area of 0.025 and a cumulative probability of 0.975. From Table E.3, you see that $t_{\alpha/2} = 2.0452$. Thus, using $\bar{X} = 1{,}723$, $S = 89.55$, $n = 30$, and $t_{\alpha/2} = 2.0452$,

$$\bar{X} \pm t_{\alpha/2} \frac{S}{\sqrt{n}}$$

$$= 1{,}723.4 \pm (2.0452)\frac{89.55}{\sqrt{30}}$$

$$= 1{,}723.4 \pm 33.44$$

$$1{,}689.96 \leq \mu \leq 1{,}756.84$$

**FIGURE 8.8**

Minitab confidence interval estimate for the mean amount of force required to break electric insulators

*See Section M8.2 to create this. (Use Section E8.2 or P8.2 to create the Excel equivalent.)*

```
One-Sample T: Force

Variable   N    Mean   StDev   SE Mean        95% CI
Force      30   1723.4  89.6     16.3    (1690.0, 1756.8)
```

You conclude with 95% confidence that the mean breaking force required for the population of insulators is between 1,689.96 and 1,756.84 pounds. The validity of this confidence interval estimate depends on the assumption that the force required is normally distributed. Remember, however, that you can slightly relax this assumption for large sample sizes. Thus, with a sample of 30, you can use the $t$ distribution even if the amount of force required is only slightly left-skewed. From the normal probability plot displayed in Figure 8.9 or the boxplot displayed in Figure 8.10, the amount of force required appears only slightly left-skewed. Thus, the $t$ distribution is appropriate for these data.

**FIGURE 8.9**

Minitab normal probability plot for the amount of force required to break electric insulators

*See Section M6.2 to create this. (PHStat2 users, see Section P6.2 to create an equivalent chart.)*

**FIGURE 8.10**

Minitab boxplot for the amount of force required to break electric insulators

*See Section M3.4 to create this. (Microsoft Excel users, see Section E3.3 or P3.1 to create an equivalent chart.)*

The interpretation of the confidence interval when σ is unknown is the same as when σ is known. To illustrate the fact that the confidence interval for the mean varies more when σ is unknown, return to the example concerning the order-filling times discussed in Section 8.1 on page 295. Suppose that, in this case, you do not know the population standard deviation. Figure 8.11 shows the results for each of 20 samples of *n* = 10 orders.

**FIGURE 8.11**

Minitab confidence interval estimates of the mean for 20 samples of *n* = 10 selected from the population of 200 orders with σ unknown

*See Section M8.2 to create this. (Microsoft Excel users, see Section E8.2 or P8.2 to create equivalent results.)*

| Variable | N | Mean | StDev | SE Mean | 95% CI |
|----------|---|------|-------|---------|--------|
| Sample 1 | 10 | 71.64 | 7.58 | 2.40 | (66.22, 77.06) |
| Sample 2 | 10 | 67.22 | 10.95 | 3.46 | (59.39, 75.05) |
| Sample 3 | 10 | 67.97 | 14.83 | 4.69 | (57.36, 78.58) |
| Sample 4 | 10 | 73.90 | 10.59 | 3.35 | (66.33, 81.47) |
| Sample 5 | 10 | 67.11 | 11.12 | 3.52 | (59.15, 75.07) |
| Sample 6 | 10 | 68.12 | 10.83 | 3.43 | (60.37, 75.87) |
| Sample 7 | 10 | 65.80 | 10.85 | 3.43 | (58.03, 73.57) |
| Sample 8 | 10 | 77.58 | 11.04 | 3.49 | (69.68, 85.48) |
| Sample 9 | 10 | 66.69 | 11.45 | 3.62 | (58.50, 74.88) |
| Sample 10 | 10 | 62.55 | 8.58 | 2.71 | (56.41, 68.69) |
| Sample 11 | 10 | 71.12 | 12.82 | 4.05 | (61.95, 80.29) |
| Sample 12 | 10 | 70.55 | 10.52 | 3.33 | (63.02, 78.08) |
| Sample 13 | 10 | 65.51 | 8.16 | 2.58 | (59.67, 71.35) |
| Sample 14 | 10 | 64.90 | 7.55 | 2.39 | (59.50, 70.30) |
| Sample 15 | 10 | 66.22 | 11.21 | 3.54 | (58.20, 74.24) |
| Sample 16 | 10 | 70.43 | 10.21 | 3.23 | (63.12, 77.74) |
| Sample 17 | 10 | 72.04 | 6.25 | 1.98 | (67.57, 76.51) |
| Sample 18 | 10 | 73.91 | 11.29 | 3.57 | (65.83, 81.99) |
| Sample 19 | 10 | 71.49 | 9.76 | 3.09 | (64.51, 78.47) |
| Sample 20 | 10 | 70.15 | 10.84 | 3.43 | (62.39, 77.91) |

From Figure 8.11, observe that the standard deviation of the samples varies from 6.25 (sample 17) to 14.83 (sample 3). Thus, the width of the confidence interval developed varies from 8.94 in sample 17 to 21.22 in sample 3. Because you know that the population mean order time $\mu = 69.637$ minutes, you can see that the interval for sample 8 ($69.68 - 85.48$) and the interval for sample 10 ($56.41 - 68.69$) do not correctly estimate the population mean. All the other intervals correctly estimate the population mean. Once again, remember that in practice you select only one sample of a given size and you have no way of knowing for sure whether this one sample provides a confidence interval that includes the population mean.

## PROBLEMS FOR SECTION 8.2

### Learning the Basics

**8.7** If $\bar{X} = 75$, $S = 24$, and $n = 36$, and assuming that the population is normally distributed, construct a 95% confidence interval estimate of the population mean, $\mu$.

**8.8** Determine the critical value of $t$ in each of the following circumstances:
a. $1 - \alpha = 0.95$, $n = 10$
b. $1 - \alpha = 0.99$, $n = 10$
c. $1 - \alpha = 0.95$, $n = 32$
d. $1 - \alpha = 0.95$, $n = 65$
e. $1 - \alpha = 0.90$, $n = 16$

**8.9** Assuming that the population is normally distributed, construct a 95% confidence interval estimate for the population mean for each of the following samples:

Sample $A$: 1, 1, 1, 1, 8, 8, 8, 8

Sample $B$: 1, 2, 3, 4, 5, 6, 7, 8

Explain why these two samples produce different confidence intervals even though they have the same mean and range.

**8.10** Assuming that the population is normally distributed, construct a 95% confidence interval for the population mean, based on the following sample of size $n = 7$: 1, 2, 3, 4, 5, 6, and 20. Change the number 20 to 7 and recalculate the confidence interval. Using these results, describe the effect of an outlier (i.e., an extreme value) on the confidence interval.

### Applying the Concepts

**8.11** A stationery store wants to estimate the mean retail value of greeting cards that it has in its inventory. A random sample of 100 greeting cards indicates a mean value of $2.55 and a standard deviation of $0.44.
a. Assuming a normal distribution, construct a 95% confidence interval estimate of the mean value of all greeting cards in the store's inventory.
b. Suppose there were 2,500 greeting cards in the store's inventory. How are the results in (a) useful in assisting the store owner to estimate the total value of her inventory?

✓SELF Test **8.12** Southside Hospital in Bay Shore, New York, commonly conducts stress tests to study the heart muscle after a person has a heart attack. Members of the diagnostic imaging department conducted a quality improvement project to try to reduce the turnaround time for stress tests. Turnaround time is defined as the time from when the test is ordered to when the radiologist signs off on the test results. Initially, the mean turnaround time for a stress test was 68 hours. After incorporating changes into the stress-test process, the quality improvement team collected a sample of 50 turnaround times. In this sample, the mean turnaround time was 32 hours, with a standard deviation of 9 hours (extracted from E. Godin, D. Raven, C. Sweetapple, and F. R. Del Guidice, "Faster Test Results," *Quality Progress*, January 2004, 37(1), pp. 33–39).
a. Construct a 95% confidence interval estimate for the population mean turnaround time.
b. Interpret the interval constructed in (a).
c. Do you think the quality improvement project was a success?

**8.13** The U.S. Department of Transportation requires tire manufacturers to provide tire performance information on the sidewall of the tire to better inform prospective customers when making purchasing decisions. One very important measure of tire performance is the tread wear index, which indicates the tire's resistance to tread wear compared with a tire graded with a base of 100. This means that a tire with a grade of 200 should last twice as long, on average, as a tire graded with a base of 100. A consumer organization wants to estimate the actual tread wear index of a brand name of tires that claims "graded 200" on the sidewall of the tire. A random sample of $n = 18$ indicates a sample mean tread wear index of 195.3 and a sample standard deviation of 21.4.
a. Assuming that the population of tread wear indexes is normally distributed, construct a 95% confidence interval estimate of the population mean tread wear index for tires produced by this manufacturer under this brand name.
b. Do you think that the consumer organization should accuse the manufacturer of producing tires that do not meet the performance information provided on the sidewall of the tire? Explain.
c. Explain why an observed tread wear index of 210 for a particular tire is not unusual, even though it is outside the confidence interval developed in (a).

**8.14** The data in the file Movieprices contain the price for two tickets with online service charges, large popcorn, and two medium soft drinks at a sample of six theater chains:

$36.15  $31.00  $35.05  $40.25  $33.75  $43.00

Source: *Extracted from K. Kelly, "The Multiplex Under Siege," The Wall Street Journal, December 24–25, 2005, pp. P1, P5.*

a. Construct a 95% confidence interval estimate for the population mean price for two tickets with online service charges, large popcorn, and two medium soft drinks, assuming a normal distribution.
b. Interpret the interval constructed in (a).

**8.15** The data in the file `Sedans` represents the overall miles per gallon (MPG) of 2007 family sedans (4 cylinder).

| Model | MPG | Model | MPG |
|---|---|---|---|
| Volkswagen Passat | 24 | Mazda | 23 |
| Nissan Altima | 25 | Ford Fusion | 23 |
| Toyota Camry Hybrid | 34 | Mercury Milan | 23 |
| Honda Accord | 24 | Toyota Prius | 44 |
| Kia Optima | 23 | Chevrolet Malibu | 24 |
| Toyota Camry LE | 24 | Mitsubishi Galant | 23 |
| Subaru Legacy | 18 | Pontiac G6 | 22 |
| Hyundai Sonata | 23 | Chrysler Sebring | 23 |

Source: *Extracted from "Vehicle Ratings," Consumer Reports, April 2007, pp. 36–37.*

a. Construct a 95% confidence interval estimate for the population mean miles per gallon of 2007 family sedans (4 cylinder) assuming a normal distribution.
b. Interpret the interval constructed in (a).
c. Compare the results in (a) to those in Problem 8.16(a).

**8.16** The data in the file `SUV` represents the overall miles per gallon (MPG) of 2007 small SUVs.

| Model | MPG | Model | MPG |
|---|---|---|---|
| Toyota RAV4 6-cyl | 22 | Mazda Tribute | 18 |
| Hyundai Santa Fe | 18 | Mercury Mariner Luxury | 18 |
| Toyota RAV4 4-cyl | 23 | | |
| Subaru Forester Sports 2.5 XT | 20 | Nissan Xterra | 17 |
| | | Honda Element | 21 |
| Honda CR-V | 21 | Suzuki Grand Vitara | 18 |
| Subaru Forester Sports 2.5 X | 22 | Chevrolet Equinox | 18 |
| | | Pontiac Torrent | 18 |
| Mitsubishi Outlander | 19 | Jeep Compass | 22 |
| Hyundai Tucson | 18 | Saturn Vue | 19 |
| Kia Sportage | 18 | Saturn Vue Hybrid | 24 |
| Ford Escape Hybrid | 26 | Kia Sorento | 15 |
| Mercury Mariner Hybrid | 26 | Jeep Liberty | 15 |
| | | Toyota FJ Cruiser | 17 |
| Suzuki XL-7 | 17 | Dodge Nitro | 16 |
| Ford Escape | 18 | Jeep Wrangler | 15 |

Source: *Extracted from "Vehicle Ratings," Consumer Reports, April 2007, pp. 42–43.*

a. Construct a 95% confidence interval estimate for the population mean miles per gallon of 2007 small SUVs assuming a normal distribution.
b. Interpret the interval constructed in (a).
c. Compare the results in (a) to those in Problem 8.15(a).

**8.17** The data in the file `Chicken` represent the total fat, in grams per serving, for a sample of 20 chicken sandwiches from fast-food chains. The data are as follows:

| | | | | | | | | | |
|---|---|---|---|---|---|---|---|---|---|
| 7 | 8 | 4 | 5 | 16 | 20 | 20 | 24 | 19 | 30 |
| 23 | 30 | 25 | 19 | 29 | 29 | 30 | 30 | 40 | 56 |

Source: *Extracted from "Fast Food: Adding Health to the Menu," Consumer Reports, September 2004, pp. 28–31.*

a. Construct a 95% confidence interval for the population mean total fat, in grams per serving.
b. Interpret the interval constructed in (a).
c. What assumption must you make about the population distribution in order to construct the confidence interval estimate in (a)?
d. Do you think that the assumption needed in order to construct the confidence interval estimate in (a) is valid? Explain.

**8.18** One of the major measures of the quality of service provided by any organization is the speed with which it responds to customer complaints. A large family-held department store selling furniture and flooring, including carpet, had undergone a major expansion in the past several years. In particular, the flooring department had expanded from 2 installation crews to an installation supervisor, a measurer, and 15 installation crews. Last year, there were 50 complaints concerning carpet installation. The following data, also in the file `Furniture`, represent the number of days between the receipt of a complaint and the resolution of the complaint:

| | | | | | | | | | | | |
|---|---|---|---|---|---|---|---|---|---|---|---|
| 54 | 5 | 35 | 137 | 31 | 27 | 152 | 2 | 123 | 81 | 74 | 27 |
| 11 | 19 | 126 | 110 | 110 | 29 | 61 | 35 | 94 | 31 | 26 | 5 |
| 12 | 4 | 165 | 32 | 29 | 28 | 29 | 26 | 25 | 1 | 14 | 13 |
| 13 | 10 | 5 | 27 | 4 | 52 | 30 | 22 | 36 | 26 | 20 | 23 |
| 33 | 68 | | | | | | | | | | |

a. Construct a 95% confidence interval estimate of the population mean number of days between the receipt of a complaint and the resolution of the complaint.
b. What assumption must you make about the population distribution in order to construct the confidence interval estimate in (a)?
c. Do you think that the assumption needed in order to construct the confidence interval estimate in (a) is valid? Explain.
d. What effect might your conclusion in (c) have on the validity of the results in (a)?

**8.19** In New York State, savings banks are permitted to sell a form of life insurance called savings bank life insurance

(SBLI). The approval process consists of underwriting, which includes a review of the application, a medical information bureau check, possible requests for additional medical information and medical exams, and a policy compilation stage in which the policy pages are generated and sent to the bank for delivery. The ability to deliver approved policies to customers in a timely manner is critical to the profitability of this service to the bank. During a period of one month, a random sample of 27 approved policies was selected, and the total processing time, in days, was as shown below and stored in the file Insurance:

73 19 16 64 28 28 31 90 60 56 31 56 22 18
45 48 17 17 17 91 92 63 50 51 69 16 17

a. Construct a 95% confidence interval estimate of the population mean processing time.
b. What assumption must you make about the population distribution in order to construct the confidence interval estimate in (a)?
c. Do you think that the assumption needed in order to construct the confidence interval estimate in (a) is valid? Explain.

**8.20** The data in the file BatteryLife represent the battery life (in shots) for a sample of twelve three-pixel digital cameras:

300 180 85 170 380 460 260 35 380 120 110 240

Source: *Extracted from "Cameras: More Features in the Mix," Consumer Reports, July 2005, pp. 14–18.*

a. Construct a 95% confidence interval estimate for the population mean battery life (in shots).
b. What assumption do you need to make about the population of interest to construct the interval in (a)?
c. Given the data presented, do you think the assumption needed in (a) is valid? Explain.

**8.21** One operation of a mill is to cut pieces of steel into parts that are used later in the frame for front seats in an automobile. The steel is cut with a diamond saw and requires the resulting parts to be within ±0.005 inch of the length specified by the automobile company. The measurement reported from a sample of 100 steel parts (and stored in the file Steel) is the difference, in inches, between the actual length of the steel part, as measured by a laser measurement device, and the specified length of the steel part. For example, the first observation, −0.002, represents a steel part that is 0.002 inch shorter than the specified length.

a. Construct a 95% confidence interval estimate of the population mean difference between the actual length of the steel part and the specified length of the steel part.
b. What assumption must you make about the population distribution in order to construct the confidence interval estimate in (a)?
c. Do you think that the assumption needed in order to construct the confidence interval estimate in (a) is valid? Explain.
d. Compare the conclusions reached in (a) with those of Problem 2.25 on page 47.

## 8.3 CONFIDENCE INTERVAL ESTIMATION FOR THE PROPORTION

This section extends the concept of the confidence interval to categorical data. Here you are concerned with estimating the proportion of items in a population having a certain characteristic of interest. The unknown population proportion is represented by the Greek letter $\pi$. The point estimate for $\pi$ is the sample proportion, $p = X/n$, where $n$ is the sample size and $X$ is the number of items in the sample having the characteristic of interest. Equation (8.3) defines the confidence interval estimate for the population proportion.

Confidence Interval Estimate for the Proportion

$$p \pm Z_{\alpha/2} \sqrt{\frac{p(1-p)}{n}}$$

or

$$p - Z_{\alpha/2} \sqrt{\frac{p(1-p)}{n}} \leq \pi \leq p + Z_{\alpha/2} \sqrt{\frac{p(1-p)}{n}} \qquad (8.3)$$

where

$$p = \text{sample proportion} = \frac{X}{n} = \frac{\text{Number of items having the characteristic}}{\text{Sample size}}$$

$\pi = \text{population proportion}$

$Z_{\alpha/2} = \text{critical value from the standardized normal distribution}$

$n = \text{sample size}$

*Note:* To use this interval, the sample size $n$ must be large enough to ensure that both $X$ and $n - X$ are greater than 5.

You can use the confidence interval estimate of the proportion defined in Equation (8.3) to estimate the proportion of sales invoices that contain errors (see the Using Statistics scenario on page 292). Suppose that in a sample of 100 sales invoices, 10 contain errors. Thus, for these data, $p = X/n = 10/100 = 0.10$. Using Equation (8.3) and $Z_{\alpha/2} = 1.96$ for 95% confidence,

$$p \pm Z_{\alpha/2} \sqrt{\frac{p(1-p)}{n}}$$

$$= 0.10 \pm (1.96) \sqrt{\frac{(0.10)(0.90)}{100}}$$

$$= 0.10 \pm (1.96)(0.03)$$

$$= 0.10 \pm 0.0588$$

$$0.0412 \leq \pi \leq 0.1588$$

Therefore, you have 95% confidence that between 4.12% and 15.88% of all the sales invoices contain errors. Figure 8.12 shows a Microsoft Excel worksheet for these data and Figure 8.13 shows Minitab results.

**FIGURE 8.12**

Microsoft Excel worksheet to construct a confidence interval estimate for the proportion of sales invoices that contain errors

*See Section E8.3 or P8.3 to create this.*

| | A | B | |
|---|---|---|---|
| 1 | **Proportion of In-Error Sales Invoices** | | |
| 2 | | | |
| 3 | **Data** | | |
| 4 | Sample Size | 100 | |
| 5 | Number of Successes | 10 | |
| 6 | Confidence Level | 95% | |
| 7 | | | |
| 8 | **Intermediate Calculations** | | |
| 9 | Sample Proportion | 0.1 | =B5/B4 |
| 10 | Z Value | -1.9600 | =NORMSINV((1 - B6)/2) |
| 11 | Standard Error of the Proportion | 0.03 | =SQRT(B9 * (1 - B9)/B4) |
| 12 | Interval Half Width | 0.0588 | =ABS(B10 * B11) |
| 13 | | | |
| 14 | **Confidence Interval** | | |
| 15 | Interval Lower Limit | 0.0412 | =B9 - B12 |
| 16 | Interval Upper Limit | 0.1588 | =B9 + B12 |

**FIGURE 8.13**

Minitab confidence interval estimate for the proportion of sales invoices that contain errors

*See Section M8.3 to create this.*

```
Sample   X    N   Sample p         95% CI
1        10  100  0.100000  (0.041201, 0.158799)

Using the normal approximation.
```

Example 8.4 illustrates another application of a confidence interval estimate for the proportion.

**EXAMPLE 8.4**   ESTIMATING THE PROPORTION OF NONCONFORMING NEWSPAPERS PRINTED

The operations manager at a large newspaper wants to estimate the proportion of newspapers printed that have a nonconforming attribute, such as excessive ruboff, improper page setup, missing pages, or duplicate pages. A random sample of $n = 200$ newspapers is selected from all the newspapers printed during a single day. In this sample, 35 contain some type of nonconformance. Construct and interpret a 90% confidence interval for the proportion of newspapers printed during the day that have a nonconforming attribute.

**SOLUTION**   Using Equation (8.3),

$$p = \frac{X}{n} = \frac{35}{200} = 0.175, \text{ and with a 90\% level of confidence } Z_{\alpha/2} = 1.645$$

$$p \pm Z_{\alpha/2}\sqrt{\frac{p(1-p)}{n}}$$

$$= 0.175 \pm (1.645)\sqrt{\frac{(0.175)(0.825)}{200}}$$

$$= 0.175 \pm (1.645)(0.0269)$$

$$= 0.175 \pm 0.0442$$

$$0.1308 \le \pi \le 0.2192$$

You conclude with 90% confidence that between 13.08% and 21.92% of the newspapers printed on that day have some type of nonconformance.

Equation (8.3) contains a $Z$ statistic because you can use the normal distribution to approximate the binomial distribution when the sample size is sufficiently large. In Example 8.4, the confidence interval using $Z$ provides an excellent approximation for the population proportion because both $X$ and $n - X$ are greater than 5. However, if you do not have a sufficiently large sample size, you should use the binomial distribution rather than Equation (8.3) (see references 1, 2, and 7). The exact confidence intervals for various sample sizes and proportions of successes have been tabulated by Fisher and Yates (reference 2) and can be computed using Minitab.

## PROBLEMS FOR SECTION 8.3

### Learning the Basics

**8.22** If $n = 200$ and $X = 50$, construct a 95% confidence interval estimate of the population proportion.

**8.23** If $n = 400$ and $X = 25$, construct a 99% confidence interval estimate of the population proportion.

### Applying the Concepts

**SELF Test** **8.24** The telephone company wants to estimate the proportion of households that would purchase an additional telephone line if it were made available at a substantially reduced installation cost. A random sample of

500 households is selected. The results indicate that 135 of the households would purchase the additional telephone line at a reduced installation cost.

**a.** Construct a 99% confidence interval estimate of the population proportion of households that would purchase the additional telephone line.

**b.** How would the manager in charge of promotional programs concerning residential customers use the results in (a)?

**8.25** CareerBuilder.com surveyed 1,124 moms who were currently employed full-time. Of the women surveyed, 281 said that they were dissatisfied with their work-life balance, and 495 said that they would take a pay cut to spend more time with their kids (extracted from D. Jones, "Poll Finds Resentment of Flextime," **usatoday.com**, May 11, 2007).

**a.** Construct a 95% confidence interval estimate for the population proportion of moms employed full-time who are dissatisfied with their work-life balance.

**b.** Construct a 95% confidence interval estimate for the population proportion of moms employed full-time who would take a pay cut to spend more time with their kids.

**c.** Write a short summary of the information derived from (a) and (b).

**8.26** In a survey conducted for American Express, 27% of small business owners indicated that they never check in with the office when on vacation (extracted from "Snapshots," **usatoday.com**, April 18, 2006). The article did not disclose the sample size used in the study.

**a.** Suppose that the survey was based on 500 small business owners. Construct a 95% confidence interval estimate for the population proportion of small business owners who never check in with the office when on vacation.

**b.** Suppose that the survey was based on 1,000 small business owners. Construct a 95% confidence interval estimate for the population proportion of small business owners who never check in with the office when on vacation.

**c.** Discuss the effect of sample size on the confidence interval estimate.

**8.27** The start of the twenty-first century saw many corporate scandals and many individuals lost faith in business. In a 2007 poll conducted by the New York City-based Edelman Public Relations firm, 57% of respondents say they trust business to "do what is right." This percentage was the highest in the annual survey since 2001 (extracted from G. Colvin, "Business is Back!" *Fortune*, May 14, 2007, pp. 40–48).

**a.** Construct a 95% confidence interval estimate of the population proportion of individuals who trust business to "do what is right" assuming that the poll surveyed:
   1. 100 individuals.
   2. 200 individuals.
   3. 300 individuals.

**b.** Discuss the effect that sample size has on the width of confidence intervals.

**c.** Interpret the interval in (a).

**8.28** A survey of 705 workers (extracted from "Snapshots," *USA Today*, March 21, 2006, p. 1B) were asked how much they used the Internet at work. 423 said they used it within limits, and 183 said that they did not use the Internet at work.

**a.** Construct a 95% confidence interval estimate for the proportion of all workers who use the Internet within limits.

**b.** Construct a 95% confidence interval estimate for the proportion of all workers who did not use the Internet at work.

**8.29** When do Americans decide what to make for dinner? An online survey (extracted from N. Hellmich, "Americans Go for the Quick Fix for Dinner," *USA Today*, February 14, 2005, p. 1B) indicated that 74% of Americans decided either at the last minute or that day. Suppose that the survey was based on 500 respondents.

**a.** Construct a 95% confidence interval estimate for the proportion of Americans who decided what to make for dinner either at the last minute or that day.

**b.** Construct a 99% confidence interval for the proportion of Americans who decided what to make for dinner either at the last minute or that day.

**c.** Which interval is wider? Explain why this is true.

**8.30** In a survey of 894 respondents with salaries below $100,000 per year, 367 indicated that the primary reason for staying on their job was interesting job responsibilities (extracted from "Snapshots: What Is the Primary Reason for Staying on Your Job?" *USA Today*, October 5, 2005, p. 1B).

**a.** Construct a 95% confidence interval estimate for the proportion of all workers whose primary reason for staying on their job was interesting job responsibilities.

**b.** Interpret the interval constructed in (a).

**8.31** The utility of mobile devices raises new questions about the intrusion of work into personal life. In a recent survey by **CareerJournal.com** (extracted from P. Kitchen, "Can't Turn It Off," *Newsday*, October 20, 2006, pp. F4–F5), 158 of 473 employees responded that they typically took work with them on vacation and 85 responded that there are unwritten and unspoken expectations that they stay connected.

**a.** Construct a 95% confidence interval estimate for the population proportion of employees who typically take work with them on vacation.

**b.** Construct a 95% confidence interval estimate for the population proportion of employees who said that there are unwritten and unspoken expectations that they stay connected.

**c.** Interpret the intervals in (a) and (b).

**d.** Explain the difference in the results in (a) and (b).

## 8.4 DETERMINING SAMPLE SIZE

In each confidence interval developed so far in this chapter, the sample size was reported along with the results with little discussion of the width of the resulting confidence interval. In the business world, sample sizes are determined prior to data collection to ensure that the confidence interval is narrow enough to be useful in making decisions. Determining the proper sample size is a complicated procedure, subject to the constraints of budget, time, and the amount of acceptable sampling error. In the Saxon Home Improvement example, if you want to estimate the mean dollar amount of the sales invoices, you must determine in advance how large a sampling error to allow in estimating the population mean. You must also determine, in advance, the level of confidence (i.e., 90%, 95%, or 99%) to use in estimating the population parameter.

### Sample Size Determination for the Mean

To develop an equation for determining the appropriate sample size needed when constructing a confidence interval estimate of the mean, recall Equation (8.1) on page 296:

$$\bar{X} \pm Z_{\alpha/2} \frac{\sigma}{\sqrt{n}}$$

The amount added to or subtracted from $\bar{X}$ is equal to half the width of the interval. This quantity represents the amount of imprecision in the estimate that results from sampling error. The **sampling error**[1], $e$, is defined as

$$e = Z_{\alpha/2} \frac{\sigma}{\sqrt{n}}$$

[1] *In this context, some statisticians refer to e as the "margin of error."*

Solving for $n$ gives the sample size needed to construct the appropriate confidence interval estimate for the mean. "Appropriate" means that the resulting interval will have an acceptable amount of sampling error.

> ### Sample Size Determination for the Mean
>
> The sample size, $n$, is equal to the product of the $Z_{\alpha/2}$ value squared and the standard deviation, $\sigma$, squared, divided by the square of the sampling error, $e$,
>
> $$n = \frac{Z_{\alpha/2}^2 \sigma^2}{e^2} \qquad \text{(8.4)}$$

[2] *You use Z instead of t because, to determine the critical value of t, you need to know the sample size, but you do not know it yet. For most studies, the sample size needed is large enough that the standardized normal distribution is a good approximation of the t distribution.*

To determine the sample size, you must know three factors:

1. The desired confidence level, which determines the value of $Z_{\alpha/2}$, the critical value from the standardized normal distribution[2]
2. The acceptable sampling error, $e$
3. The standard deviation, $\sigma$

In some business-to-business relationships that require estimation of important parameters, legal contracts specify acceptable levels of sampling error and the confidence level required. For companies in the food or drug sectors, government regulations often specify sampling errors and confidence levels. In general, however, it is usually not easy to specify the two factors needed to determine the sample size. How can you determine the level of confidence and sampling error? Typically, these questions are answered only by the subject matter expert (i.e., the individual most familiar with the variables under study). Although 95% is the most common confidence level used, if more confidence is desired, then 99% might be more appropriate; if less confidence is deemed acceptable, then 90% might be used. For the sampling error, you should think not of how much sampling error you would like to have (you really do not want any error) but of how much you can tolerate when reaching conclusions from the confidence interval.

In addition to specifying the confidence level and the sampling error, you need an estimate of the standard deviation. Unfortunately, you rarely know the population standard deviation, $\sigma$. In some instances, you can estimate the standard deviation from past data. In other situations, you can make an educated guess by taking into account the range and distribution of the variable. For example, if you assume a normal distribution, the range is approximately equal to $6\sigma$ (i.e., $\pm 3\sigma$ around the mean) so that you estimate $\sigma$ as the range divided by 6. If you cannot estimate $\sigma$ in this way, you can conduct a small-scale study and estimate the standard deviation from the resulting data.

To explore how to determine the sample size needed for estimating the population mean, consider again the audit at Saxon Home Improvement. In Section 8.2, you selected a sample of 100 sales invoices and constructed a 95% confidence interval estimate of the population mean sales invoice amount. How was this sample size determined? Should you have selected a different sample size?

Suppose that, after consultation with company officials, you determine that a sampling error of no more than ±$5 is desired, along with 95% confidence. Past data indicate that the standard deviation of the sales amount is approximately $25. Thus, $e = \$5$, $\sigma = \$25$, and $Z_{\alpha/2} = 1.96$ (for 95% confidence). Using Equation (8.4),

$$n = \frac{Z_{\alpha/2}^2 \sigma^2}{e^2} = \frac{(1.96)^2 (25)^2}{(5)^2}$$

$$= 96.04$$

Because the general rule is to slightly oversatisfy the criteria by rounding the sample size up to the next whole integer, you should select a sample of size 97. Thus, the sample of size $n = 100$ used on page 302 is close to what is necessary to satisfy the needs of the company, based on the estimated standard deviation, desired confidence level, and sampling error. Because the calculated sample standard deviation is slightly higher than expected, $28.95 compared to $25.00, the confidence interval is slightly wider than desired. Figure 8.14 shows a Microsoft Excel worksheet to determine the sample size.

**FIGURE 8.14**

Microsoft Excel worksheet for determining sample size for estimating the mean sales invoice amount for the Saxon Home Improvement Company

*See Section E8.4 or P8.4 to create this.*

| | A | B | |
|---|---|---|---|
| 1 | **For Mean Sales Invoice Amount** | | |
| 2 | | | |
| 3 | **Data** | | |
| 4 | **Population Standard Deviation** | 25 | |
| 5 | **Sampling Error** | 5 | |
| 6 | **Confidence Level** | 95% | |
| 7 | | | |
| 8 | Intemediate Calculations | | |
| 9 | Z Value | -1.9600 | =NORMSINV((1 - B6)/2) |
| 10 | Calculated Sample Size | 96.0365 | =((B9 * B4)/B5)^2 |
| 11 | | | |
| 12 | Result | | |
| 13 | **Sample Size Needed** | 97 | =ROUNDUP(B10, 0) |

Example 8.5 illustrates another application of determining the sample size needed to develop a confidence interval estimate for the mean.

---

**EXAMPLE 8.5**

DETERMINING THE SAMPLE SIZE FOR THE MEAN

Returning to Example 8.3 on page 303, suppose you want to estimate the population mean force required to break the insulator to within ±25 pounds with 95% confidence. On the basis of a study taken the previous year, you believe that the standard deviation is 100 pounds. Find the sample size needed.

**SOLUTION** Using Equation (8.4) on page 312 and $e = 25$, $\sigma = 100$, and $Z_{\alpha/2} = 1.96$ for 95% confidence,

$$n = \frac{Z_{\alpha/2}^2 \sigma^2}{e^2} = \frac{(1.96)^2 (100)^2}{(25)^2}$$

$$= 61.47$$

Therefore, you should select a sample size of 62 insulators because the general rule for determining sample size is to always round up to the next integer value in order to slightly oversatisfy the criteria desired. An actual sampling error slightly larger than 25 will result if the sample standard deviation calculated in this sample of 62 is greater than 100 and slightly smaller if the sample standard deviation is less than 100.

---

## Sample Size Determination for the Proportion

So far in this section, you have learned how to determine the sample size needed for estimating the population mean. Now suppose that you want to determine the sample size necessary for estimating a population proportion.

To determine the sample size needed to estimate a population proportion, $\pi$, you use a method similar to the method for a population mean. Recall that in developing the sample size for a confidence interval for the mean, the sampling error is defined by

$$e = Z_{\alpha/2} \frac{\sigma}{\sqrt{n}}$$

When estimating a proportion, you replace $\sigma$ with $\sqrt{\pi(1-\pi)}$. Thus, the sampling error is

$$e = Z_{\alpha/2} \sqrt{\frac{\pi(1-\pi)}{n}}$$

Solving for $n$, you have the sample size necessary to develop a confidence interval estimate for a proportion.

Sample Size Determination for the Proportion

The sample size $n$ is equal to the product of $Z_{\alpha/2}$ squared, the population proportion, $\pi$, and 1 minus the population proportion, $\pi$, divided by the square of the sampling error, $e$,

$$n = \frac{Z_{\alpha/2}^2 \pi(1-\pi)}{e^2} \qquad \qquad \textbf{(8.5)}$$

To determine the sample size, you must know three factors:

1. The desired confidence level, which determines the value of $Z_{\alpha/2}$, the critical value from the standardized normal distribution
2. The acceptable sampling error (or margin of error), $e$
3. The population proportion, $\pi$

In practice, selecting these quantities requires some planning. Once you determine the desired level of confidence, you can find the appropriate $Z_{\alpha/2}$ value from the standardized normal distribution. The sampling error, $e$, indicates the amount of error that you are willing to tolerate in estimating the population proportion. The third quantity, $\pi$, is actually the population parameter that you want to estimate! Thus, how do you state a value for what you are taking a sample in order to determine?

Here you have two alternatives. In many situations, you may have past information or relevant experience that provide an educated estimate of $\pi$. Or, if you do not have past information or relevant experience, you can try to provide a value for $\pi$ that would never *underestimate* the sample size needed. Referring to Equation (8.5), you can see that the quantity $\pi(1 - \pi)$ appears in the numerator. Thus, you need to determine the value of $\pi$ that will make the quantity $\pi(1 - \pi)$ as large as possible. When $\pi = 0.5$, the product $\pi(1 - \pi)$ achieves its maximum value. To show this result, consider the following values of $\pi$, along with the accompanying products of $\pi (1 - \pi)$:

When $\pi = 0.9$, then $\pi(1 - \pi) = (0.9)(0.1) = 0.09$
When $\pi = 0.7$, then $\pi(1 - \pi) = (0.7)(0.3) = 0.21$
When $\pi = 0.5$, then $\pi(1 - \pi) = (0.5)(0.5) = 0.25$
When $\pi = 0.3$, then $\pi(1 - \pi) = (0.3)(0.7) = 0.21$
When $\pi = 0.1$, then $\pi(1 - \pi) = (0.1)(0.9) = 0.09$

Therefore, when you have no prior knowledge or estimate of the population proportion, $\pi$, you should use $\pi = 0.5$ for determining the sample size. Using $\pi = 0.5$ produces the largest possible sample size and results in the narrowest and most precise confidence interval. This increased precision comes at the cost of spending more time and money for an increased sample size. Also, note that if you use $\pi = 0.5$ instead of the actual sample proportion in developing the confidence interval, you will overestimate the sample size needed, because you will get a confidence interval narrower than originally intended.

Returning to the Saxon Home Improvement Using Statistics scenario, suppose that the auditing procedures require you to have 95% confidence in estimating the population proportion of sales invoices with errors to within ±0.07. The results from past months indicate that the largest proportion has been no more than 0.15. Thus, using Equation (8.5) on page 314 and $e = 0.07$, $\pi = 0.15$, and $Z_{\alpha/2} = 1.96$ for 95% confidence,

$$n = \frac{Z_{\alpha/2}^2 \pi(1 - \pi)}{e^2}$$

$$= \frac{(1.96)^2 (0.15)(0.85)}{(0.07)^2}$$

$$= 99.96$$

Because the general rule is to round the sample size up to the next whole integer to slightly oversatisfy the criteria, a sample size of 100 is needed. Thus, the sample size needed to satisfy the requirements of the company, based on the estimated proportion, desired confidence level, and sampling error, is equal to the sample size taken on page 309. The actual confidence interval is narrower than required because the sample proportion is 0.10, whereas 0.15 was used for $\pi$ in Equation (8.5). Figure 8.15 shows a Microsoft Excel worksheet for determining sample size.

**FIGURE 8.15**

Microsoft Excel worksheet for determining sample size for estimating the proportion of sales invoices with errors for the Saxon Home Improvement Company

*See Section E8.5 or P8.5 to create this.*

| | A | B | |
|---|---|---|---|
| 1 | For Proportion of In-Error Sales Invoices | | |
| 2 | | | |
| 3 | Data | | |
| 4 | Estimate of True Proportion | 0.15 | |
| 5 | Sampling Error | 0.07 | |
| 6 | Confidence Level | 95% | |
| 7 | | | |
| 8 | Intermediate Calculations | | |
| 9 | Z Value | -1.9600 | =NORMSINV((1 - B6)/2) |
| 10 | Calculated Sample Size | 99.9563 | =(B9^2 * B4 * (1 - B4))/B5^2 |
| 11 | | | |
| 12 | Result | | |
| 13 | Sample Size Needed | 100 | =ROUNDUP(B10, 0) |

Example 8.6 provides another application of determining the sample size for estimating the population proportion.

---

**EXAMPLE 8.6**

DETERMINING THE SAMPLE SIZE FOR THE POPULATION PROPORTION

You want to have 90% confidence of estimating the proportion of office workers who respond to e-mail within an hour to within ±0.05. Because you have not previously undertaken such a study, there is no information available from past data. Determine the sample size needed.

**SOLUTION** Because no information is available from past data, assume that $\pi = 0.50$. Using Equation (8.5) on page 314 and $e = 0.05$, $\pi = 0.50$, and $Z_{\alpha/2} = 1.645$ for 90% confidence,

$$n = \frac{Z_{\alpha/2}^2 \pi(1 - \pi)}{e^2}$$

$$= \frac{(1.645)^2(0.50)(0.50)}{(0.05)^2}$$

$$= 270.6$$

Therefore, you need a sample of 271 office workers to estimate the population proportion to within ±0.05 with 90% confidence.

---

# PROBLEMS FOR SECTION 8.4

## Learning the Basics

**8.32** If you want to be 95% confident of estimating the population mean to within a sampling error of ±5 and the standard deviation is assumed to be 15, what sample size is required?

**8.33** If you want to be 99% confident of estimating the population mean to within a sampling error of ±20 and the standard deviation is assumed to be 100, what sample size is required?

**8.34** If you want to be 99% confident of estimating the population proportion to within a sampling error of ±0.04, what sample size is needed?

**8.35** If you want to be 95% confident of estimating the population proportion to within a sampling error of ±0.02 and there is historical evidence that the population proportion is approximately 0.40, what sample size is needed?

## Applying the Concepts

**SELF** | ✓ Test  **8.36** A survey is planned to determine the mean annual family medical expenses of employees of a large company. The management of the company wishes to be 95% confident that the sample mean is correct to within ±$50 of the population mean annual family medical expenses. A previous study indicates that the standard deviation is approximately $400.

**a.** How large a sample size is necessary?

**b.** If management wants to be correct to within ±$25, how many employees need to be selected?

**8.37** If the manager of a paint supply store wants to estimate the mean amount of paint in a 1-gallon can to within ±0.004 gallon with 95% confidence and also assumes that the standard deviation is 0.02 gallon, what sample size is needed?

**8.38** If a quality control manager wants to estimate the mean life of lightbulbs to within ±20 hours with 95% confidence and also assumes that the population standard deviation is 100 hours, how many lightbulbs need to be selected?

**8.39** If the inspection division of a county weights and measures department wants to estimate the mean amount of soft-drink fill in 2-liter bottles to within ±0.01 liter with 95% confidence and also assumes that the standard deviation is 0.05 liter, what sample size is needed?

**8.40** A consumer group wants to estimate the mean electric bill for the month of July for single-family homes in a large city. Based on studies conducted in other cities, the standard deviation is assumed to be $25. The group wants to estimate the mean bill for July to within ±$5 with 99% confidence.

**a.** What sample size is needed?

**b.** If 95% confidence is desired, how many homes need to be selected?

**8.41** An advertising agency that serves a major radio station wants to estimate the mean amount of time that the station's audience spends listening to the radio daily. From past studies, the standard deviation is estimated as 45 minutes.

**a.** What sample size is needed if the agency wants to be 90% confident of being correct to within ±5 minutes?

**b.** If 99% confidence is desired, how many listeners need to be selected?

**8.42** A growing niche in the restaurant business is gourmet-casual breakfast, lunch, and brunch. Chains in this group include Le Peep, Good Egg, Eggs & I, First Watch, and Eggs Up Grill. The mean per-person check for First Watch is approximately $7, and the mean per-person check for Eggs Up Grill is $6.50 (extracted from J. Hayes, "Competition Heats Up as Breakfast Concepts Eye Growth," *Nation's Restaurant News*, April 24, 2006, pp. 8, 66).

**a.** Assuming a standard deviation of $2.00, what sample size is needed to estimate the mean per-person check for Good Egg to within ±$0.25 with 95% confidence?

**b.** Assuming a standard deviation of $2.50, what sample size is needed to estimate the mean per-person check for Good Egg to within ±$0.25 with 95% confidence?

**c.** Assuming a standard deviation of $3.00, what sample size is needed to estimate the mean per-person check for Good Egg to within ±$0.25 with 95% confidence?

**d.** Discuss the effect of variation on selecting the sample size needed.

**8.43** The U.S. Department of Transportation defines an airline flight as being "on time" if it lands less than 15 minutes after the scheduled time shown in the carrier's computerized reservation system. Cancelled and diverted flights are counted as late. A study of the 10 largest U.S. domestic airlines found Southwest Airlines to have the lowest proportion of late arrivals, at 0.1577 (extracted from N. Tsikriktsis and J. Heineke, "The Impact of Process Variation on Customer Dissatisfaction: Evidence from the U.S. Domestic Airline Industry," *Decision Sciences*, Winter 2004, 35(1), pp. 129–142). Suppose you were asked to perform a follow-up study for Southwest Airlines in order to update the estimated proportion of late arrivals. How many airline flights do you need to sample in order to estimate the population proportion to within an error of

**a.** ±0.06 with 95% confidence?

**b.** ±0.04 with 95% confidence?

**c.** ±0.02 with 95% confidence?

**8.44** In 2005, 34% of workers reported that their jobs were more difficult, with more stress, and 37% reported that they worry about retiring comfortably (extracted from S. Armour, "Money Worries Hinder Job Performance," *USA Today*, October 5, 2005, p. D1). Consider a follow-up study to be conducted in the near future.

**a.** What sample size is needed to estimate the population proportion of workers who reported that their jobs were more difficult, with more stress, to within ±0.02 with 95% confidence?

**b.** How many workers need to be sampled in order to estimate the population proportion of workers who worried about retiring comfortably to within ±0.02 with 95% confidence?

**c.** Compare the results of (a) and (b). Explain why these results differ.

**d.** If you were to design the follow-up study, would you use one sample and ask the respondents both questions, or would you select two separate samples? Explain the rationale behind your decision.

**8.45** What proportion of people hit snags with online transactions? According to a poll conducted by Harris Interactive, 89% hit snags with online transactions (extracted from "Snapshots: Top Online Transaction Trouble," *USA Today*, April 4, 2006, p. 1D).

**a.** To conduct a follow-up study that would provide 95% confidence that the point estimate is correct to within ±0.04 of the population proportion, how large a sample size is required?

**b.** To conduct a follow-up study that would provide 99% confidence that the point estimate is correct to within ±0.04 of the population proportion, how many people need to be sampled?

**c.** To conduct a follow-up study that would provide 95% confidence that the point estimate is correct to within ±0.02 of the population proportion, how large a sample size is required?

**d.** To conduct a follow-up study that would provide 99% confidence that the point estimate is correct to within ±0.02 of the population proportion, how many people need to be sampled?

**e.** Discuss the effects of changing the desired confidence level and the acceptable sampling error on sample size requirements.

**8.46** A poll of 1,286 young adult cellphone users was conducted in March 2006. These cellphone users, aged 18 to 29, were actively engaged in multiple uses of their cellphones. The data suggest that 707 took still pictures with their phones, 604 played games, and 360 used the Internet (extracted from "Poll: Cellphones Are Annoying but Invaluable," **usatoday.com**, April 3, 2006). Construct a 95% confidence interval estimate of the population proportion of young adults that used their cellphone to

**a.** take still pictures.

**b.** play games.

**c.** use the Internet.

**d.** You have been asked to update the results of this study. Determine the sample size necessary to estimate the population proportions in (a) through (c) to within ±0.02 with 95% confidence.

**8.47** A study of 658 CEOs conducted by the Conference Board reported that 250 stated that their company's greatest concern was sustained and steady top-line growth (extracted from "Snapshots: CEOs' Greatest Concerns," *USA Today*, May 8, 2006, p. 1D).

**a.** Construct a 95% confidence interval for the proportion of CEOs whose greatest concern was sustained and steady top-line growth.

**b.** Interpret the interval constructed in (a).

**c.** To conduct a follow-up study to estimate the population proportion of CEOs whose greatest concern was sustained and steady top-line growth to within ±0.01 with 95% confidence, how many CEOs would you survey?

**8.48** In 2007, oil companies posted huge profits and consumers paid record high prices at the gas pump. The president of Shell Oil stated that "we know for a fact that the favorability rating of oil companies today ranges from 10–15%" (extracted from D. J. Lynch, "Shell Oil Tries Different Path to Engage Public Opinion," **usatoday.com**, May 14, 2007).

**a.** If you conduct a follow-up study to estimate the population proportion of individuals who view oil companies favorably, would you use a $\pi$ of 0.10, 0.15, or 0.50 in the sample size formula? Discuss.

**b.** Using your answer to (a), find the sample size necessary to estimate the population proportion to within ±0.03 with 95% certainty.

**8.49** The Department of Commerce announced that the national rental vacancy rate during the first quarter of 2007 was 10.1%. The report noted that the proportion of rentals vacant was 0.101 with a 95% confidence interval and margin of error of 0.004 (extracted from R. R. Callis and L. B. Cavanaugh, "Census Bureau Reports on Residential Vacancies and Homeownership," *United States Department of Commerce News*, April 27, 2007, p.1).

**a.** Construct a 95% confidence interval estimate for the national rental vacancy rate.

**b.** Interpret the interval found in (a).

**c.** If the estimate reported was constructed using the methods in this section, what sample size was required?

## 8.5 APPLICATIONS OF CONFIDENCE INTERVAL ESTIMATION IN AUDITING

This chapter has focused on estimating either the population mean or the population proportion. In previous chapters, you have studied applications to different business scenarios. Auditing is one of the areas in business that makes widespread use of probability sampling methods in order to construct confidence interval estimates.

AUDITING

**Auditing** is the collection and evaluation of evidence about information relating to an economic entity, such as a sole business proprietor, a partnership, a corporation, or a government agency, in order to determine and report on how well the information corresponds to established criteria.

Auditors rarely examine a complete population of information. Instead, they rely on estimation techniques based on the probability sampling methods you have studied in this text. The following list contains some of the reasons sampling is advantageous compared to examining the entire population.

- Sampling is less time-consuming.
- Sampling is less costly.
- Sampling provides an objective way of estimating the sample size in advance.
- Sampling provides results that are objective and defensible. Because the sample size is based on demonstrable statistical principles, the audit is defensible before one's superiors and in a court of law.
- Sampling provides an estimate of the sampling error and therefore allows auditors to generalize their findings to the population with a known sampling error.
- Sampling is often more accurate for drawing conclusions about large populations than other methods. Examining every item in large populations is time-consuming and therefore often subject to more nonsampling error than statistical sampling.
- Sampling allows auditors to combine, and then evaluate collectively, samples collected by different individuals.

## Estimating the Population Total Amount

In auditing applications, you are often more interested in developing estimates of the population **total amount** than the population mean. Equation (8.6) shows how to estimate a population total amount.

---

**Estimating the Population Total Amount**

The point estimate for the population total is equal to the population size, $N$, times the sample mean.

$$\text{Total} = N\bar{X} \qquad\qquad (8.6)$$

---

Equation (8.7) defines the confidence interval estimate for the population total.

---

**Confidence Interval Estimate for the Total Amount**

$$N\bar{X} \pm N(t_{\alpha/2})\frac{S}{\sqrt{n}}\sqrt{\frac{N-n}{N-1}} \qquad\qquad (8.7)$$

where $t_{\alpha/2}$ is the critical value corresponding to an upper-tail probability of $\alpha/2$ from the $t$ distribution with $n-1$ degrees of freedom (i.e., a cumulative area of $1-\alpha/2$).

---

To demonstrate the application of the confidence interval estimate for the population total amount, return to the Saxon Home Improvement Using Statistics scenario on page 292. One of the auditing tasks is to estimate the total dollar amount of all sales invoices for the month. If there are 5,000 invoices for that month and $\bar{X} = \$110.27$, then using Equation (8.6),

$$N\bar{X} = (5{,}000)(\$110.27) = \$551{,}350$$

If $n = 100$ and $S = \$28.95$, then using Equation (8.7) with $t_{\alpha/2} = 1.9842$ for 95% confidence and 99 degrees of freedom,

$$N\bar{X} \pm N(t_{\alpha/2})\frac{S}{\sqrt{n}}\sqrt{\frac{N-n}{N-1}} = 551,350 \pm (5,000)(1.9842)\frac{28.95}{\sqrt{100}}\sqrt{\frac{5,000-100}{5,000-1}}$$

$$= 551,350 \pm 28,721.295(0.99005)$$

$$= 551,350 \pm 28,436$$

$$\$522,914 \le \text{Population total} \le \$579,786$$

Therefore, with 95% confidence, you estimate that the total amount of sales invoices is between $522,914 and $579,786. Figure 8.16 shows a Microsoft Excel worksheet for these data.

**FIGURE 8.16**

Microsoft Excel worksheet for the confidence interval estimate of the total amount of all invoices for the Saxon Home Improvement Company

*See Section E8.6 or P8.6 to create this.*

| | A | B | |
|---|---|---|---|
| 1 | **Total Amount of All Sales Invoices** | | |
| 2 | | | |
| 3 | **Data** | | |
| 4 | Population Size | 5000 | |
| 5 | Sample Mean | 110.27 | |
| 6 | Sample Size | 100 | |
| 7 | Sample Standard Deviation | 28.95 | |
| 8 | Confidence Level | 95% | |
| 9 | | | |
| 10 | **Intermediate Calculations** | | |
| 11 | Population Total | 551350.00 | =B4 * B5 |
| 12 | FPC Factor | 0.9900 | =SQRT((B4 - B6)/(B4 - 1)) |
| 13 | Standard Error of the Total | 14330.9521 | =(B4 * B7 * B12)/SQRT(B6) |
| 14 | Degrees of Freedom | 99 | =B6 - 1 |
| 15 | t Value | 1.9842 | =TINV(1 - B8, B14) |
| 16 | Interval Half Width | 28435.72 | =B15 * B13 |
| 17 | | | |
| 18 | **Confidence Interval** | | |
| 19 | Interval Lower Limit | 522914.28 | =B11 - B16 |
| 20 | Interval Upper Limit | 579785.72 | =B11 + B16 |

Example 8.7 further illustrates the population total.

**EXAMPLE 8.7**

DEVELOPING A CONFIDENCE INTERVAL ESTIMATE FOR THE POPULATION TOTAL

An auditor is faced with a population of 1,000 vouchers and wants to estimate the total value of the population of vouchers. A sample of 50 vouchers is selected, with the following results:

$$\text{Mean voucher amount } (\bar{X}) = \$1,076.39$$

$$\text{Standard deviation } (S) = \$273.62$$

Construct a 95% confidence interval estimate of the total amount for the population of vouchers.

**SOLUTION**  Using Equation (8.6) on page 319, the point estimate of the population total is

$$N\bar{X} = (1,000)(1,076.39) = \$1,076,390$$

From Equation (8.7) on page 319, a 95% confidence interval estimate of the population total amount is

$$(1,000)(1,076.39) \pm (1,000)(2.0096)\frac{273.62}{\sqrt{50}}\sqrt{\frac{1,000-50}{1,000-1}}$$

$$= 1,076,390 \pm 77,762.878(0.97517)$$

$$= 1,076,390 \pm 75,832$$

$$\$1,000,558 \le \text{Population total} \le \$1,152,222$$

Therefore, with 95% confidence, you estimate that the total amount of the vouchers is between $1,000,558 and $1,152,222.

## Difference Estimation

An auditor uses **difference estimation** when he or she believes that errors exist in a set of items and he or she wants to estimate the magnitude of the errors based only on a sample. The following steps are used in difference estimation:

1.  Determine the sample size required.
2.  Calculate the differences between the values reached during the audit and the original values recorded. The difference in value $i$, denoted $D_i$, is equal to 0 if the auditor finds that the original value is correct, is a positive value when the audited value is larger than the original value, and is negative when the audited value is smaller than the original value.
3.  Compute the mean difference in the sample, $\bar{D}$, by dividing the total difference by the sample size, as shown in Equation (8.8).

Mean Difference

$$\bar{D} = \frac{\sum\limits_{i=1}^{n} D_i}{n} \tag{8.8}$$

where $D_i$ = Audited value − Original value

4.  Compute the standard deviation of the differences, $S_D$, as shown in Equation (8.9). *Remember that any item that is not in error has a difference value of 0.*

Standard Deviation of the Difference

$$S_D = \sqrt{\frac{\sum\limits_{i=1}^{n}(D_i - \bar{D})^2}{n-1}} \tag{8.9}$$

**5.** Use Equation (8.10) to construct a confidence interval estimate of the total difference in the population.

---

Confidence Interval Estimate for the Total Difference

$$N\bar{D} \pm N(t_{\alpha/2}) \frac{S_D}{\sqrt{n}} \sqrt{\frac{N-n}{N-1}} \qquad (8.10)$$

where $t_{\alpha/2}$ is the critical value corresponding to an upper-tail probability of $\alpha/2$ from the $t$ distribution with $n-1$ degrees of freedom (i.e., a cumulative area of $1 - \alpha/2$).

---

The auditing procedures for Saxon Home Improvement require a 95% confidence interval estimate of the difference between the audited dollar amounts on the sales invoices and the amounts originally entered into the integrated inventory and sales information system. Suppose that in a sample of 100 sales invoices, you have 12 invoices in which the audited dollar amount on the sales invoice and the amount originally entered into the integrated inventory management and sales information system is different. These 12 differences (stored in the file Plumbinv ) are

$9.03  $7.47  $17.32  $8.30  $5.21  $10.80  $6.22  $5.63  $4.97  $7.43  $2.99  $4.63

The other 88 invoices are not in error. Their *differences* are each 0. Thus,

$$\bar{D} = \frac{\sum\limits_{i=1}^{n} D_i}{n} = \frac{90}{100} = 0.90$$

[3] In the numerator below, there are 100 differences. Each of the last 88 are equal to $(0 - 0.9)^2$.

and[3]

$$S_D = \sqrt{\frac{\sum\limits_{i=1}^{n}(D_i - \bar{D})^2}{n-1}}$$

$$= \sqrt{\frac{(9.03-0.9)^2 + (7.47-0.9)^2 + \cdots + (0-0.9)^2}{100-1}}$$

$$S_D = 2.752$$

Using Equation (8.10), construct the 95% confidence interval estimate for the total difference in the population of 5,000 sales invoices as follows:

$$(5,000)(0.90) \pm (5,000)(1.9842)\frac{2.752}{\sqrt{100}}\sqrt{\frac{5,000-100}{5,000-1}}$$

$$= 4,500 \pm 2,702.91$$

$$\$1,797.09 \le \text{Total difference} \le \$7,202.91$$

Thus, the auditor estimates with 95% confidence that the total difference between the sales invoices as determined during the audit and the amount originally entered into the accounting system is between $1,797.09 and $7,202.91. Figure 8.17 shows an Excel worksheet for these data.

**FIGURE 8.17**

Microsoft Excel worksheet for the total difference between the invoice amounts found during the audit and the amounts originally entered into the accounting system for the Saxon Home Improvement Company

*See Section E8.7 or P8.7 to create this.*

| | A | B | |
|---|---|---|---|
| 1 | **Total Difference In Actual and Entered** | | |
| 2 | | | |
| 3 | **Data** | | |
| 4 | **Population Size** | 5000 | |
| 5 | **Sample Size** | 100 | |
| 6 | **Confidence Level** | 95% | |
| 7 | | | |
| 8 | Intermediate Calculations | | |
| 9 | Sum of Differences | 90.0000 | =SUM(DifferencesData!A:A) |
| 10 | Average Difference in Sample | 0.9 | =B9/B5 |
| 11 | Total Difference | 4500 | =B4 * B10 |
| 12 | Standard Deviation of Differences | 2.7518 | =SQRT(E16) |
| 13 | FPC Factor | 0.9900 | =SQRT((B4 - B5)/(B4 - 1)) |
| 14 | Standard Error of the Total Diff. | 1362.2064 | =(B4 * B12 * B13)/SQRT(B5) |
| 15 | Degrees of Freedom | 99 | =B5 - 1 |
| 16 | *t* Value | 1.9842 | =TINV(1 - B6, B15) |
| 17 | Interval Half Width | 2702.9129 | =B16 * B14 |
| 18 | | | |
| 19 | **Confidence Interval** | | |
| 20 | **Interval Lower Limit** | 1797.09 | =B11 - B17 |
| 21 | **Interval Upper Limit** | 7202.91 | =B11 + B17 |

In the previous example, all 12 differences are positive because the audited amount on the sales invoice is more than the amount originally entered into the accounting system. In some circumstances, you could have negative errors. Example 8.8 illustrates such a situation.

**EXAMPLE 8.8**

DIFFERENCE ESTIMATION

Returning to Example 8.7 on page 320, suppose that 14 vouchers in the sample of 50 vouchers contain errors. The values of the 14 errors are listed below and stored in the file `Difftest`. Observe that two differences are negative:

$75.41    $38.97    $108.54    −$37.18    $62.75    $118.32    −$88.84

$127.74    $55.42    $39.03    $29.41    $47.99    $28.73    $84.05

Construct a 95% confidence interval estimate of the total difference in the population of 1,000 vouchers.

**SOLUTION** For these data,

$$\bar{D} = \frac{\sum_{i=1}^{n} D_i}{n} = \frac{690.34}{50} = 13.8068$$

and

$$S_D = \sqrt{\frac{\sum_{i=1}^{n}(D_i - \bar{D})^2}{n-1}}$$

$$= \sqrt{\frac{(75.41-13.8068)^2 + (38.97-13.8068)^2 + \cdots + (0-13.8068)^2}{50-1}}$$

$$= 37.427$$

Using Equation (8.10) on page 322, construct the confidence interval estimate for the total difference in the population as follows:

$$(1{,}000)(13.8068) \pm (1{,}000)(2.0096)\frac{37.427}{\sqrt{50}}\sqrt{\frac{1{,}000-50}{1{,}000-1}}$$

$$= 13{,}806.8 \pm 10{,}372.4$$

$$\$3{,}434.40 \le \text{Total difference} \le \$24{,}179.20$$

Therefore, with 95% confidence, you estimate that the total difference in the population of vouchers is between $3,434.40 and $24,179.20.

## One-Sided Confidence Interval Estimation of the Rate of Noncompliance with Internal Controls

Organizations use internal control mechanisms to ensure that individuals act in accordance with company guidelines. For example, Saxon Home Improvement requires that an authorized warehouse-removal slip be completed before goods are removed from the warehouse. During the monthly audit of the company, the auditing team is charged with the task of estimating the proportion of times goods were removed without proper authorization. This is referred to as the *rate of noncompliance with the internal control*. To estimate the rate of noncompliance, auditors take a random sample of sales invoices and determine how often merchandise was shipped without an authorized warehouse-removal slip. The auditors then compare their results with a previously established tolerable exception rate, which is the maximum allowable proportion of items in the population not in compliance. When estimating the rate of noncompliance, it is commonplace to use a **one-sided confidence interval**. That is, the auditors estimate an upper bound on the rate of noncompliance. Equation (8.11) defines a one-sided confidence interval for a proportion.

---

One-Sided Confidence Interval for a Proportion

$$\text{Upper bound} = p + Z_\alpha\sqrt{\frac{p(1-p)}{n}}\sqrt{\frac{N-n}{N-1}} \qquad \textbf{(8.11)}$$

where $Z_\alpha$ = the value corresponding to a cumulative area of $(1-\alpha)$ from the standardized normal distribution (i.e., a right-hand tail probability of $\alpha$).

---

If the tolerable exception rate is higher than the upper bound, the auditor concludes that the company is in compliance with the internal control. If the upper bound is higher than the tolerable exception rate, the auditor has failed to prove that the company is in compliance. The auditor may then request a larger sample.

Suppose that in the monthly audit, you select 400 sales invoices from a population of 10,000 invoices. In the sample of 400 sales invoices, 20 are in violation of the internal control. If the tolerable exception rate for this internal control is 6%, what should you conclude? Use a 95% level of confidence.

The one-sided confidence interval is computed using $p = 20/400 = 0.05$ and $Z_\alpha = 1.645$. Using Equation (8.11),

$$\text{Upper bound} = p + Z_\alpha\sqrt{\frac{p(1-p)}{n}}\sqrt{\frac{N-n}{N-1}} = 0.05 + 1.645\sqrt{\frac{0.05(1-0.05)}{400}}\sqrt{\frac{10{,}000-400}{10{,}000-1}}$$

$$= 0.05 + 1.645(0.0109)(0.98) = 0.05 + 0.0176 = 0.0676$$

One of the most common areas where ethical issues concerning confidence intervals occurs is in the publication of the results of political polls. Often, the results of the polls are highlighted on the front page of the newspaper, and the sampling error involved along with the methodology used is printed on the page where the article is continued, often in the middle of the newspaper. To ensure an ethical presentation of statistical results, the confidence levels, sample size, sampling error, and confidence limits should be made available for all surveys and other statistical studies.

## 8.7  ● (CD-ROM TOPIC) ESTIMATION AND SAMPLE SIZE DETERMINATION FOR FINITE POPULATIONS

In this section, confidence intervals are developed and the sample size is determined for situations in which sampling is done without replacement from a finite population. For further discussion, see section 8.7.pdf on the Student CD-ROM that accompanies this book.

# SUMMARY

This chapter discusses confidence intervals for estimating the characteristics of a population, along with how you can determine the necessary sample size. You learned how an accountant at Saxon Home Improvement can use the sample data from an audit to estimate important population parameters such as the total dollar amount on invoices and the proportion of shipments made without the proper authorization. Table 8.3 provides a list of topics covered in this chapter.

**TABLE 8.3**
Summary of Topics in Chapter 8

| Type of Analysis | Type of Data | |
| --- | --- | --- |
| | Numerical | Categorical |
| Confidence interval for a population parameter | Confidence interval estimate for the mean (Sections 8.1 and 8.2) | Confidence interval estimate for the proportion (Section 8.3) |
| | Confidence interval estimate for the total and the mean difference (Section 8.5) | One-sided confidence interval estimate for the proportion (Section 8.5) |

To determine what equation to use for a particular situation, you need to answer two questions:

• Are you developing a confidence interval or are you determining sample size?

• Do you have a numerical variable or do you have a categorical variable?

The next four chapters develop a hypothesis-testing approach to making decisions about population parameters.

# KEY EQUATIONS

**Confidence Interval for the Mean (σ Known)**

$$\bar{X} \pm Z_{\alpha/2} \frac{\sigma}{\sqrt{n}}$$

or

$$\bar{X} - Z_{\alpha/2} \frac{\sigma}{\sqrt{n}} \le \mu \le \bar{X} + Z_{\alpha/2} \frac{\sigma}{\sqrt{n}} \qquad \textbf{(8.1)}$$

**Confidence Interval for the Mean (σ Unknown)**

$$\bar{X} \pm t_{\alpha/2} \frac{S}{\sqrt{n}}$$

or

$$\bar{X} - t_{\alpha/2} \frac{S}{\sqrt{n}} \le \mu \le \bar{X} + t_{\alpha/2} \frac{S}{\sqrt{n}} \qquad \textbf{(8.2)}$$

**Confidence Interval Estimate for the Proportion**

$$p \pm Z_{\alpha/2} \sqrt{\frac{p(1-p)}{n}}$$

or

$$p - Z_{\alpha/2} \sqrt{\frac{p(1-p)}{n}} \leq \pi \leq p + Z_{\alpha/2} \sqrt{\frac{p(1-p)}{n}} \qquad (8.3)$$

**Sample Size Determination for the Mean**

$$n = \frac{Z_{\alpha/2}^2 \sigma^2}{e^2} \qquad (8.4)$$

**Sample Size Determination for the Proportion**

$$n = \frac{Z_{\alpha/2}^2 \pi(1-\pi)}{e^2} \qquad (8.5)$$

**Estimating the Population Total Amount**

$$\text{Total} = N\bar{X} \qquad (8.6)$$

**Confidence Interval Estimate for the Total Amount**

$$N\bar{X} \pm N(t_{\alpha/2}) \frac{S}{\sqrt{n}} \sqrt{\frac{N-n}{N-1}} \qquad (8.7)$$

**Mean Difference**

$$\bar{D} = \frac{\sum_{i=1}^{n} D_i}{n} \qquad (8.8)$$

**Standard Deviation of the Difference**

$$S_D = \sqrt{\frac{\sum_{i=1}^{n} (D_i - \bar{D})^2}{n-1}} \qquad (8.9)$$

**Confidence Interval Estimate for the Total Difference**

$$N\bar{D} \pm N(t_{\alpha/2}) \frac{S_D}{\sqrt{n}} \sqrt{\frac{N-n}{N-1}} \qquad (8.10)$$

**One-Sided Confidence Interval for a Proportion**

$$\text{Upper bound} = p + Z_{\alpha} \sqrt{\frac{p(1-p)}{n}} \sqrt{\frac{N-n}{N-1}} \qquad (8.11)$$

# KEY TERMS

| | | |
|---|---|---|
| auditing   318 | difference estimation   321 | point estimate   292 |
| confidence interval estimate   292 | level of confidence   296 | sampling error   312 |
| critical value   297 | margin of error   312 | Student's $t$ distribution   300 |
| degrees of freedom   300 | one-sided confidence interval   324 | total amount   319 |

# CHAPTER REVIEW PROBLEMS

## Checking Your Understanding

**8.60** Why can you never really have 100% confidence of correctly estimating the population characteristic of interest?

**8.61** When are you able to use the $t$ distribution to develop the confidence interval estimate for the mean?

**8.62** Why is it true that for a given sample size, $n$, an increase in confidence is achieved by widening (and making less precise) the confidence interval?

**8.63** Under what circumstances do you use a one-sided confidence interval instead of a two-sided confidence interval?

**8.64** When would you want to estimate the population total instead of the population mean?

**8.65** How does difference estimation differ from estimation of the mean?

## Applying the Concepts

**8.66** You work in the corporate office for a nationwide convenience store franchise that operates nearly 10,000 stores. The per-store daily customer count has been steady at 900 for some time (i.e., the mean number of customers in a store in one day is 900). To increase the customer count, the franchise is considering cutting coffee prices by approximately half. The 12-ounce size will now be $.59 instead of $.99, and the 16-ounce size will be $.69 instead of $1.19. Even with this reduction in price, the franchise will have a 40% gross margin on coffee. To test the new initiative, the franchise has reduced coffee prices in a sample of 34 stores, where customer counts have been running almost exactly at the national average of 900. After four weeks, the sample stores stabilize at a mean customer count of 974 and a standard deviation of 96. This increase seems like a substantial amount to you, but it also seems like a pretty small sample. Is there some way to get a feel for what the mean per-store count in all the stores will be if you cut coffee prices nationwide? Do you think reducing coffee prices is a good strategy for increasing the mean customer count?

**8.67** Companies are spending more time screening applicants than in the past. A study of 102 recruiters conducted by ExecuNet found that 77 did Internet research on candidates (extracted from P. Kitchen, "Don't Let Any 'Digital Dirt' Bury Your Job Prospects," *Newsday*, August 21, 2005, p. A59).
**a.** Construct a 95% confidence interval estimate of the population proportion of recruiters who do Internet research on candidates.
**b.** Based on (a), is it correct to conclude that more than 70% of recruiters do Internet research on candidates?
**c.** Suppose that the study uses a sample size of 400 recruiters and 302 did Internet research on candidates. Construct a 95% confidence interval estimate of the population proportion of recruiters who do Internet research on candidates.
**d.** Based on (c), is it correct to conclude that more than 70% of recruiters do Internet research on candidates?
**e.** Discuss the effect of sample size on your answers to (a) through (d).

**8.68** High-fructose corn syrup (HFCS) was created in the 1970s and is used today in a wide variety of foods and beverages. HFCS is cheaper than sugar and is about 75% sweeter than sucrose. Some researchers think that HFCS is linked to the growing obesity problem in the United States (extracted from P. Lempert, "War of the Sugars," *Progressive Grocer*, April 15, 2006, p. 20). The following consumer views are from a nationwide survey of 1,114 responses:

| Views on HFCS | Yes | No |
|---|---|---|
| Are you concerned about consuming HFCS? | 80% | 20% |
| Do you think HFCS should be banned in food sold to schools? | 88% | 12% |
| Do you think HFCS should be banned in all foods? | 56% | 44% |

Construct a 95% confidence interval estimate of the population proportion of people who
**a.** are concerned about consuming HFCS.
**b.** think HFCS should be banned in food sold to schools.
**c.** think HFCS should be banned in all foods.
**d.** You are in charge of a follow-up survey. Determine the sample size necessary to estimate the proportions in (a) through (c) to within $\pm 0.02$ with 95% confidence.

**8.69** Often, after a period of time, items that were considered luxuries become necessities. A survey by the Pew Research Center of 2,000 U.S. adults 18 and over (extracted from S. Jayson, "Luxuries of the Past Become Necessities," *USA Today*, December 15, 2006, p. 6A) found the following percentages that considered each of the following items as necessities
- Car—91%
- Home air conditioner—70%
- TV set—64%
- Car air-conditioning—59%
- Home computer—51%
- Cellphone—49%
- Cable or satellite TV—33%
- High-speed Internet—29%
- Flat-screen TV—5%
- IPod—3%

Construct a 95% confidence interval estimate for each of these questions. Based on these results, what conclusions can you reach about the items that Americans consider necessities?

**8.70** A market researcher for a consumer electronics company wants to study the television viewing habits of residents of a particular area. A random sample of 40 respondents is selected, and each respondent is instructed to keep a detailed record of all television viewing in a particular week. The results are as follows:
- Viewing time per week: $\bar{X} = 15.3$ hours, $S = 3.8$ hours.
- 27 respondents watch the evening news on at least 3 weeknights.

**a.** Construct a 95% confidence interval estimate for the mean amount of television watched per week in this city.
**b.** Construct a 95% confidence interval estimate for the population proportion who watch the evening news on at least 3 weeknights per week.

Suppose that the market researcher wants to take another survey in a different city. Answer these questions:
**c.** What sample size is required to be 95% confident of estimating the population mean to within $\pm 2$ hours and assumes that the population standard deviation is equal to 5 hours?
**d.** How many respondents need to be selected to be 95% confident of being within $\pm 0.035$ of the population pro-

portion who watch the evening news on at least 3 week-nights if no previous estimate is available?

e. Based on (c) and (d), how many respondents should the market researcher select if a single survey is being conducted?

**8.71** The real estate assessor for a county government wants to study various characteristics of single-family houses in the county. A random sample of 70 houses reveals the following:
- Heated area of the houses (in square feet): $\bar{X} = 1,759$, $S = 380$.
- 42 houses have central air-conditioning.

a. Construct a 99% confidence interval estimate of the population mean heated area of the houses.
b. Construct a 95% confidence interval estimate of the population proportion of houses that have central air-conditioning.

**8.72** The personnel director of a large corporation wishes to study absenteeism among clerical workers at the corporation's central office during the year. A random sample of 25 clerical workers reveals the following:
- Absenteeism: $\bar{X} = 9.7$ days, $S = 4.0$ days.
- 12 clerical workers were absent more than 10 days.

a. Construct a 95% confidence interval estimate of the mean number of absences for clerical workers during the year.
b. Construct a 95% confidence interval estimate of the population proportion of clerical workers absent more than 10 days during the year.

Suppose that the personnel director also wishes to take a survey in a branch office. Answer these questions:

c. What sample size is needed to have 95% confidence in estimating the population mean absenteeism to within ±1.5 days if the population standard deviation is estimated to be 4.5 days?
d. How many clerical workers need to be selected to have 90% confidence in estimating the population proportion to within ±0.075 if no previous estimate is available?
e. Based on (c) and (d), what sample size is needed if a single survey is being conducted?

**8.73** The market research director for Dotty's Department Store wants to study women's spending on cosmetics. A survey of the store's credit card holders is designed in order to estimate the proportion of women who purchase their cosmetics primarily from Dotty's Department Store and the mean yearly amount that women spend on cosmetics. A previous survey found that the standard deviation of the amount women spend on cosmetics in a year is approximately $18.

a. What sample size is needed to have 99% confidence of estimating the population mean to within ±$5?
b. How many of the store's credit card holders need to be selected to have 90% confidence of estimating the population proportion to within ±0.045?

c. Based on the results in (a) and (b), how many of the store's credit card holders should be sampled? Explain.

**8.74** The branch manager of a nationwide bookstore chain wants to study characteristics of her store's customers. She decides to focus on two variables: the amount of money spent by customers and whether the customers would consider purchasing educational DVDs relating to graduate preparation exams, such as the GMAT, GRE, or LSAT. The results from a sample of 70 customers are as follows:
- Amount spent: $\bar{X} = \$28.52$, $S = \$11.39$.
- 28 customers stated that they would consider purchasing the educational DVDs.

a. Construct a 95% confidence interval estimate of the population mean amount spent in the bookstore.
b. Construct a 90% confidence interval estimate of the population proportion of customers who would consider purchasing educational DVDs.

Assume that the branch manager of another store in the chain wants to conduct a similar survey in his store. Answer the following questions:

c. What sample size is needed to have 95% confidence of estimating the population mean amount spent in his store to within ±$2 if the standard deviation is assumed to be $10?
d. How many customers need to be selected to have 90% confidence of estimating the population proportion who would consider purchasing the educational DVDs to within ±0.04?
e. Based on your answers to (c) and (d), how large a sample should the manager take?

**8.75** The branch manager of an outlet (Store 1) of a nationwide chain of pet supply stores wants to study characteristics of her customers. In particular, she decides to focus on two variables: the amount of money spent by customers and whether the customers own only one dog, only one cat, or more than one dog and/or cat. The results from a sample of 70 customers are as follows:
- Amount of money spent: $\bar{X} = \$21.34$, $S = \$9.22$.
- 37 customers own only a dog.
- 26 customers own only a cat.
- 7 customers own more than one dog and/or cat.

a. Construct a 95% confidence interval estimate of the population mean amount spent in the pet supply store.
b. Construct a 90% confidence interval estimate of the population proportion of customers who own only a cat.

The branch manager of another outlet (Store 2) wishes to conduct a similar survey in his store. The manager does not have access to the information generated by the manager of Store 1. Answer the following questions:

c. What sample size is needed to have 95% confidence of estimating the population mean amount spent in his store to within ±$1.50 if the standard deviation is estimated to be $10?

**d.** How many customers need to be selected to have 90% confidence of estimating the population proportion of customers who own only a cat to within ±0.045?

**e.** Based on your answers to (c) and (d), how large a sample should the manager take?

**8.76** The owner of a restaurant that serves continental food wants to study characteristics of his customers. He decides to focus on two variables: the amount of money spent by customers and whether customers order dessert. The results from a sample of 60 customers are as follows:

*   Amount spent: $\bar{X} = \$38.54$, $S = \$7.26$.
*   18 customers purchased dessert.

**a.** Construct a 95% confidence interval estimate of the population mean amount spent per customer in the restaurant.

**b.** Construct a 90% confidence interval estimate of the population proportion of customers who purchase dessert.

The owner of a competing restaurant wants to conduct a similar survey in her restaurant. This owner does not have access to the information of the owner of the first restaurant. Answer the following questions:

**c.** What sample size is needed to have 95% confidence of estimating the population mean amount spent in her restaurant to within ±$1.50, assuming that the standard deviation is estimated to be $8?

**d.** How many customers need to be selected to have 90% confidence of estimating the population proportion of customers who purchase dessert to within ±0.04?

**e.** Based on your answers to (c) and (d), how large a sample should the owner take?

**8.77** The manufacturer of "Ice Melt" claims its product will melt snow and ice at temperatures as low as 0° Fahrenheit. A representative for a large chain of hardware stores is interested in testing this claim. The chain purchases a large shipment of 5-pound bags for distribution. The representative wants to know with 95% confidence, within ±0.05, what proportion of bags of Ice Melt perform the job as claimed by the manufacturer.

**a.** How many bags does the representative need to test? What assumption should be made concerning the population proportion? (This is called *destructive testing*; that is, the product being tested is destroyed by the test and is then unavailable to be sold.)

**b.** The representative tests 50 bags, and 42 of them do the job as claimed. Construct a 95% confidence interval estimate for the population proportion that will do the job as claimed.

**c.** How can the representative use the results of (b) to determine whether to sell the Ice Melt product?

**8.78** An auditor needs to estimate the percentage of times a company fails to follow an internal control procedure. A sample of 50 from a population of 1,000 items is selected, and in 7 instances, the internal control procedure was not followed.

**a.** Construct a 90% one-sided confidence interval estimate of the population proportion of items in which the internal control procedure was not followed.

**b.** If the tolerable exception rate is 0.15, what should the auditor conclude?

**8.79** An auditor for a government agency needs to evaluate payments for doctors' office visits paid by Medicare in a particular zip code during the month of June. A total of 25,056 visits occurred during June in this area. The auditor wants to estimate the total amount paid by Medicare to within ±$5 with 95% confidence. On the basis of past experience, she believes that the standard deviation is approximately $30.

**a.** What sample size should she select?

Using the sample size selected in (a), an audit is conducted with the following results.

Amount of Reimbursement

$\bar{X} = \$93.70$       $S = \$34.55$

In 12 of the office visits, an incorrect amount of reimbursement was provided. For the 12 office visits in which there was an incorrect reimbursement, the differences between the amount reimbursed and the amount that the auditor determined should have been reimbursed were as follows (and are stored in the file Medicare):

$17 $25 $14 –$10 $20 $40 $35 $30 $28 $22 $15 $5

**b.** Construct a 90% confidence interval estimate of the population proportion of reimbursements that contain errors.

**c.** Construct a 95% confidence interval estimate of the population mean reimbursement per office visit.

**d.** Construct a 95% confidence interval estimate of the population total amount of reimbursements for this geographic area in June.

**e.** Construct a 95% confidence interval estimate of the total difference between the amount reimbursed and the amount that the auditor determined should have been reimbursed.

**8.80** A home furnishings store that sells bedroom furniture is conducting an end-of-month inventory of the beds (mattress, bed spring, and frame) in stock. An auditor for the store wants to estimate the mean value of the beds in stock at that time. She wants to have 99% confidence that her estimate of the mean value is correct to within ±$100. On the basis of past experience, she estimates that the standard deviation of the value of a bed is $200.

**a.** How many beds should she select?

**b.** Using the sample size selected in (a), an audit was conducted, with the following results:

$\bar{X} = \$1,654.27$       $S = \$184.62$

Construct a 99% confidence interval estimate of the total value of the beds in stock at the end of the month if there were 258 beds in stock.

**8.81** A quality characteristic of interest for a tea-bag-filling process is the weight of the tea in the individual bags. In this example, the label weight on the package indicates that the mean amount is 5.5 grams of tea in a bag. If the bags are underfilled, two problems arise. First, customers may not be able to brew the tea to be as strong as they wish. Second, the company may be in violation of the truth-in-labeling laws. On the other hand, if the mean amount of tea in a bag exceeds the label weight, the company is giving away product. Getting an exact amount of tea in a bag is problematic because of variation in the temperature and humidity inside the factory, differences in the density of the tea, and the extremely fast filling operation of the machine (approximately 170 bags per minute). The following data (stored in the file Teabags ) are the weights, in grams, of a sample of 50 tea bags produced in one hour by a single machine:

5.65 5.44 5.42 5.40 5.53 5.34 5.54 5.45 5.52 5.41
5.57 5.40 5.53 5.54 5.55 5.62 5.56 5.46 5.44 5.51
5.47 5.40 5.47 5.61 5.53 5.32 5.67 5.29 5.49 5.55
5.77 5.57 5.42 5.58 5.58 5.50 5.32 5.50 5.53 5.58
5.61 5.45 5.44 5.25 5.56 5.63 5.50 5.57 5.67 5.36

**a.** Construct a 99% confidence interval estimate of the population mean weight of the tea bags.
**b.** Is the company meeting the requirement set forth on the label that the mean amount of tea in a bag is 5.5 grams?

**8.82** A manufacturing company produces steel housings for electrical equipment. The main component part of the housing is a steel trough that is made out of a 14-gauge steel coil. It is produced using a 250-ton progressive punch press with a wipe-down operation that puts two 90-degree forms in the flat steel to make the trough. The distance from one side of the form to the other is critical because of weatherproofing in outdoor applications. The widths (in inches) and stored in the file Trough from a sample of 49 troughs follows:

8.312 8.343 8.317 8.383 8.348 8.410 8.351 8.373 8.481 8.422
8.476 8.382 8.484 8.403 8.414 8.419 8.385 8.465 8.498 8.447
8.436 8.413 8.489 8.414 8.481 8.415 8.479 8.429 8.458 8.462
8.460 8.444 8.429 8.460 8.412 8.420 8.410 8.405 8.323 8.420
8.396 8.447 8.405 8.439 8.411 8.427 8.420 8.498 8.409

**a.** Construct a 95% confidence interval estimate of the mean width of the troughs.
**b.** Interpret the interval developed in (a).

**8.83** The manufacturer of Boston and Vermont asphalt shingles knows that product weight is a major factor in the customer's perception of quality. The last stage of the assembly line packages the shingles before they are placed on wooden pallets. Once a pallet is full (a pallet for most brands holds 16 squares of shingles), it is weighed, and the measurement is recorded. The file Pallet contains the weight (in pounds) from a sample of 368 pallets of Boston shingles and 330 pallets of Vermont shingles.

**a.** For the Boston shingles, construct a 95% confidence interval estimate of the mean weight.
**b.** For the Vermont shingles, construct a 95% confidence interval estimate of the mean weight.
**c.** Evaluate whether the assumption needed for (a) and (b) has been seriously violated.
**d.** Based on the results of (a) and (b), what conclusions can you reach concerning the mean weight of the Boston and Vermont shingles?

**8.84** The manufacturer of Boston and Vermont asphalt shingles provides its customers with a 20-year warranty on most of its products. To determine whether a shingle will last as long as the warranty period, accelerated-life testing is conducted at the manufacturing plant. Accelerated-life testing exposes the shingle to the stresses it would be subject to in a lifetime of normal use via a laboratory experiment that takes only a few minutes to conduct. In this test, a shingle is repeatedly scraped with a brush for a short period of time, and the shingle granules removed by the brushing are weighed (in grams). Shingles that experience low amounts of granule loss are expected to last longer in normal use than shingles that experience high amounts of granule loss. In this situation, a shingle should experience no more than 0.8 grams of granule loss if it is expected to last the length of the warranty period. The file Granule contains a sample of 170 measurements made on the company's Boston shingles and 140 measurements made on Vermont shingles.

**a.** For the Boston shingles, construct a 95% confidence interval estimate of the mean granule loss.
**b.** For the Vermont shingles, construct a 95% confidence interval estimate of the mean granule loss.
**c.** Evaluate whether the assumption needed for (a) and (b) has been seriously violated.
**d.** Based on the results of (a) and (b), what conclusions can you reach concerning the mean granule loss of the Boston and Vermont shingles?

## Report Writing Exercises

**8.85** Referring to the results in Problem 8.82 concerning the width of a steel trough, write a report that summarizes your conclusions.

## Team Project

**8.86** Refer to the team project on page 67. Construct all appropriate confidence interval estimates of the population characteristics of low-risk, average-risk, and high-risk mutual funds. Include these estimates in a report to the vice president for research at the financial investment service (The data are stored in the `Mutual Funds` file).

## Student Survey Database

**8.87** Problem 1.27 on page 14 describes a survey of 50 undergraduate students (see the file `Undergradsurvey`).
**a.** For these data, for each variable, construct a 95% confidence interval estimate of the population characteristic.
**b.** Write a report that summarizes your conclusions.

**8.88** Problem 1.27 on page 14 describes a survey of 50 undergraduate students (see the file `Undergradsurvey`).
**a.** Select a sample of 50 undergraduate students at your school and conduct a similar survey for those students.

**b.** For the data collected in (a), repeat (a) and (b) of Problem 8.87.
**c.** Compare the results of (b) to those of Problem 8.87.

**8.89** Problem 1.28 on page 14 describes a survey of 40 MBA students (see the file `Gradsurvey`).
**a.** For these data, for each variable, construct a 95% confidence interval estimate of the population characteristic.
**b.** Write a report that summarizes your conclusions.

**8.90** Problem 1.28 on page 14 describes a survey of 40 MBA students (see the file `Gradsurvey`).
**a.** Select a sample of 40 graduate students in your MBA program and conduct a similar survey for those students.
**b.** For the data collected in (a), repeat (a) and (b) of Problem 8.89.
**c.** Compare the results of (b) to those of Problem 8.89.

# MANAGING THE *SPRINGVILLE HERALD*

The marketing department has been considering ways to increase the number of new subscriptions and increase the rate of retention among customers who agreed to a trial subscription. Following the suggestion of Assistant Manager Lauren Adler, the department staff designed a survey to help determine various characteristics of readers of the newspaper who were not home-delivery subscribers. The survey consists of the following 10 questions:

1. Do you or a member of your household ever purchase the *Springville Herald*?
     (1) Yes     (2) No
   [If the respondent answers no, the interview is terminated.]
2. Do you receive the *Springville Herald* via home delivery?
     (1) Yes     (2) No
   [If no, skip to question 4.]
3. Do you receive the *Springville Herald*:
     (1) Monday–Saturday  (2) Sunday only  (3) Every day
   [If every day, skip to question 9.]
4. How often during the Monday–Saturday period do you purchase the *Springville Herald*?
     (1) Every day
     (2) Most days
     (3) Occasionally or never
5. How often do you purchase the *Springville Herald* on Sundays?
     (1) Every Sunday
     (2) 2–3 Sundays per month
     (3) No more than once a month

6. Where are you most likely to purchase the *Springville Herald*?
     (1) Convenience store
     (2) Newsstand/candy store
     (3) Vending machine
     (4) Supermarket
     (5) Other
7. Would you consider subscribing to the *Springville Herald* for a trial period if a discount were offered?
     (1) Yes     (2) No
   [If no, skip to question 9.]
8. The *Springville Herald* currently costs $0.50 Monday–Saturday and $1.50 on Sunday, for a total of $4.50 per week. How much would you be willing to pay per week to get home delivery for a 90-day trial period?
9. Do you read a daily newspaper other than the *Springville Herald*?
     (1) Yes     (2) No
10. As an incentive for long-term subscribers, the newspaper is considering the possibility of offering a card that would provide discounts at certain restaurants in the Springville area to all subscribers who pay in advance for six months of home delivery. Would you want to get such a card under the terms of this offer?
     (1) Yes     (2) No

The group agreed to use a random-digit dialing method to poll 500 local households by telephone. Using this approach, the last four digits of a telephone number are randomly selected to go with an area code and exchange (the first 6 digits of a 10-digit telephone number). Only those pairs of area codes and exchanges that were for the Springville city area were used for this survey.

Of the 500 households selected, 94 households either refused to participate, could not be contacted after repeated attempts, or represented telephone numbers that were not in service. The summary results are as follows:

| Households That Purchase the *Springville Herald* | Frequency |
|---|---|
| Yes | 352 |
| No | 54 |

| Households with Home Delivery | Frequency |
|---|---|
| Yes | 136 |
| No | 216 |

| Type of Home Delivery Subscription | Frequency |
|---|---|
| Monday–Saturday | 18 |
| Sunday only | 25 |
| 7 days a week | 93 |

| Purchase Behavior of Nonsubscribers for Monday–Saturday Editions | Frequency |
|---|---|
| Every day | 78 |
| Most days | 95 |
| Occasionally or never | 43 |

| Purchase Behavior of Nonsubscribers for Sunday Editions | Frequency |
|---|---|
| Every Sunday | 138 |
| 2–3 Sundays a month | 54 |
| No more than once a month | 24 |

| Nonsubscribers' Purchase Location | Frequency |
|---|---|
| Convenience store | 74 |
| Newsstand/candy store | 95 |
| Vending machine | 21 |
| Supermarket | 13 |
| Other locations | 13 |

| Would Consider Trial Subscription If Offered a Discount | Frequency |
|---|---|
| Yes | 46 |
| No | 170 |

**Rate ($) Willing to Pay per Week (data file SH8 ) for a 90-Day Home-Delivery Trial Subscription**

```
4.15 3.60 4.10 3.60 3.60 3.60 4.40 3.15 4.00 3.75 4.00
3.25 3.75 3.30 3.75 3.65 4.00 4.10 3.90 3.50 3.75 3.00
3.40 4.00 3.80 3.50 4.10 4.25 3.50 3.90 3.95 4.30 4.20
3.50 3.75 3.30 3.85 3.20 4.40 3.80 3.40 3.50 2.85 3.75
3.80 3.90
```

| Read a Daily Newspaper Other Than the *Springville Herald* | Frequency |
|---|---|
| Yes | 138 |
| No | 214 |

| Would Prepay Six Months to Receive a Restaurant Discount Card | Frequency |
|---|---|
| Yes | 66 |
| No | 286 |

## EXERCISES

SH8.1 Some members of the marketing department are concerned about the random-digit dialing method used to collect survey responses. Prepare a memorandum that examines the following issues:
 • The advantages and disadvantages of using the random-digit dialing method.
 • Possible alternative approaches for conducting the survey and their advantages and disadvantages.

SH8.2 Analyze the results of the survey of Springville households. Write a report that discusses the marketing implications of the survey results for the *Springville Herald*.

# WEB CASE

*Apply your knowledge about confidence interval estimation in this Web Case, which extends the OurCampus! Web Case from Chapter 6.*

Among its other features, the OurCampus! Web site allows customers to purchase OurCampus! LifeStyles merchandise online. To handle payment processing, the management of OurCampus! has contracted with the following firms:
 • PayAFriend (PAF): an online payment system with which customers and businesses such as OurCampus!

register in order to exchange payments in a secure and convenient manner without the need for a credit card.
 • Continental Banking Company (Conbanco): a processing services provider that allows OurCampus! customers to pay for merchandise using nationally recognized credit cards issued by a financial institution.

To reduce costs, the management is considering eliminating one of these two payment systems. However, Virginia Duffy of the sales department suspects that customers use the two forms of payment in unequal numbers and that customers display different buying behaviors when using the two forms of payment. Therefore, she would like to first determine:

**a.** the proportion of customers using PAF and the proportion of customers using a credit card to pay for their purchases.

**b.** the mean purchase amount when using PAF and the mean purchase amount when using a credit card.

Assist Ms. Duffy by preparing an appropriate analysis based on a random sample of 50 transactions that she has prepared and placed in an internal file on the OurCampus! Web site, **www.prenhall.com/Springville/OurCampus_ PymtSample.htm** or open **OurCampus_PymtSample. htm** from the Student CD-ROM Web Case folder. Summarize your findings and determine whether Ms. Duffy's conjectures about OurCampus! customer purchasing behaviors are correct. If you want the sampling error to be no more than $3 when estimating the mean purchase amount, is Ms. Duffy's sample large enough to perform a valid analysis?

# REFERENCES

1. Cochran, W. G., *Sampling Techniques*, 3rd ed. (New York: Wiley, 1977).

2. Fisher, R. A., and F. Yates, *Statistical Tables for Biological, Agricultural and Medical Research*, 5th ed. (Edinburgh: Oliver & Boyd, 1957).

3. Hahn, G., and W. Meeker, *Statistical Intervals, A Guide for Practioners*, (New York: John Wiley and Sons, Inc., 1991).

4. Kirk, R. E., ed., *Statistical Issues: A Reader for the Behavioral Sciences* (Belmont, CA: Wadsworth, 1972).

5. Larsen, R. L., and M. L. Marx, *An Introduction to Mathematical Statistics and Its Applications*, 4th ed. (Upper Saddle River, NJ: Prentice Hall, 2006).

6. *Microsoft Excel 2007* (Redmond, WA: Microsoft Corp., 2007).

7. *Minitab for Windows Version 15* (State College, PA: Minitab, Inc., 2006).

8. Snedecor, G. W., and W. G. Cochran, *Statistical Methods*, 7th ed. (Ames, IA: Iowa State University Press, 1980).

# Appendix E8
## Using Microsoft Excel for Confidence Interval Estimation

## E8.1 Computing the Confidence Interval Estimate for the Mean ($\sigma$ Known)

You compute the confidence interval estimate for the mean ($\sigma$ known) by making entries in the **CIE_SK** worksheet of the `CIE sigma known.xls` workbook. This worksheet uses the **NORMSINV($P < X$)** and **CONFIDENCE(1-*confidence level, population standard deviation, sample size*)** functions to compute the $Z$ value and interval half width for the Example 8.1 mean paper length problem on page 297. To adapt this worksheet to other problems, change the population standard deviation, sample mean, sample size, and confidence level values in the tinted cells B4 through B7, and enter a new title in cell A1.

## E8.2 Computing the Confidence Interval Estimate for the Mean ($\sigma$ Unknown)

You compute the confidence interval estimate for the mean ($\sigma$ unknown) by making entries in the **CIE_SU** worksheet of the `CIE sigma unknown.xls` workbook. The worksheet (see Figure 8.7 on page 303) uses the **TINV(1-*confidence level, degrees of freedom*)** function to determine the critical value from the $t$ distribution and compute the interval half width for the Section 8.2 Saxon Home Improvement Company example. To adapt this worksheet to other problems, change the sample statistics and confidence level values in the tinted cells B4 through B7, and enter a new title in cell A1.

## E8.3 Computing the Confidence Interval Estimate for the Proportion

You compute the confidence interval estimate for the proportion by making entries in the **CIE_P** worksheet of the `CIE Proportion.xls` workbook. The worksheet (see Figure 8.12 on page 309) uses the **NORMSINV(P < X)** function to determine the $Z$ value and uses the square root function to compute the standard error of the proportion for the Section 8.3 Saxon Home Improvement Company example. To adapt this worksheet to other problems, change the sample size, number of successes, and confidence level values in the tinted cells B4, B5, and B6, and enter a new title in cell A1.

## E8.4 Computing the Sample Size Needed for Estimating the Mean

You compute the sample size needed for estimating the mean by making entries in the **SampleSize_M** worksheet of the `Sample Size Mean.xls` workbook. The worksheet (see Figure 8.14 on page 313) uses the **NORMSINV(P < X)** function to compute the $Z$ value and uses the **ROUNDUP(value)** function to round up the sample size needed to the next higher integer for the Section 8.4 Saxon Home Improvement Company example. To adapt this worksheet to other problems, change the population standard deviation, sampling error, and confidence level values in the tinted cells B4, B5, and B6, and enter a new title in cell A1.

## E8.5 Computing the Sample Size Needed for Estimating the Proportion

You compute the sample size needed for estimating the proportion by making entries in the **SampleSize_P** worksheet of the `Sample Size Proportion.xls` workbook. The worksheet (see Figure 8.15 on page 316) uses the **ROUNDUP(value)** function to round up the sample size needed to the next higher integer for the Section 8.4 Saxon Home Improvement Company example. To adapt this worksheet to other problems, change the estimate of true proportion, sampling error, and confidence level values in the tinted cells B4 through B6, and enter a new title in cell A1.

## E8.6 Computing the Confidence Interval Estimate for the Population Total

You compute the confidence interval estimate for the population total by making entries in the **CIE_T** worksheet of the `CIE Total.xls` workbook. This worksheet (see Figure 8.16 on page 320) uses the **TINV(1-*confidence level, degrees of freedom*)** function to determine the critical value from the $t$ distribution and the interval half width for the Section 8.5 Saxon Home Improvement Company population total example. To adapt this worksheet to other problems, change the population size, sample mean, sample size, sample standard deviation, and confidence level values in the tinted cells B4 through B8, and enter a new title in cell A1.

## E8.7 Computing the Confidence Interval Estimate for the Total Difference

You compute the confidence interval estimate for the total difference by making entries in the **CIE_TD** worksheet of the `CIE Total Difference.xls` workbook. This worksheet (see Figure 8.17 on page 323) uses the **TINV(1-*confidence level, degrees of freedom*)** function to determine the critical value from the $t$ distribution and the interval half width for the Section 8.5 Saxon Home Improvement Company total difference example. The worksheet also contains a calculation area in cell range D9:E16 that counts and sums the differences computed in column B of a **DifferencesData** worksheet. (Neither cell range is shown in Figure 8.17. See the **CIE_TD Formulas** and the **DifferencesData Formulas** worksheets for more information about these ranges and the formulas they contain.)

To adapt this worksheet to other problems, change both the CIE_TD and DifferencesData worksheet. In the CIE_TD sheet, change the population size, sample mean, sample size, sample standard deviation, and confidence level values in the tinted cells B4 through B6, and enter a new title in cell A1. In the DiffererencesData worksheet, enter the differences in column A. Then adjust column B by either copying down the formula in cell B13 to all rows with difference data if you have more than 12 differences, or by deleting unnecessary column B formulas if you have less than 12 differences.

## E8.8 Computing Finite Correction Factors

The workbooks for confidence interval estimates of the mean and proportion and for computing the sample size needed for estimating the mean or proportion include **FPC** worksheets that calculate the finite population correction factor. Use these FPC worksheets if the sampling was done without replacement from a finite population (see Section 8.7).

# Appendix P8
## Using PHStat2 for Confidence Interval Estimation

## P8.1 Computing the Confidence Interval Estimate for the Mean (σ Known)

To compute the confidence interval estimate for the mean (σ known), use **PHStat → Confidence Intervals → Estimate for the Mean, sigma known**. This procedure creates a worksheet (similar to the **CIE_SK** worksheet of the **CIE sigma known.xls** workbook) using the population standard deviation, sample mean, sample size, and confidence level values that you specify. If you have unsummarized data, click **Sample Statistics Unknown** and the procedure will calculate the sample statistics for you.

## P8.2 Computing the Confidence Interval Estimate for the Mean (σ Unknown)

To compute the confidence interval estimate for the mean (σ unknown), use **PHStat → Confidence Intervals → Estimate for the Mean, sigma unknown**. This procedure

creates a worksheet similar to Figure 8.7 on page 303 using the sample statistics and a confidence level value that you specify. If you have unsummarized data, click **Sample Statistics Unknown** and the procedure will calculate the sample statistics for you.

## P8.3 Computing the Confidence Interval Estimate for the Proportion

To compute the confidence interval estimate for the proportion, use **PHStat → Confidence Intervals → Estimate for the Proportion**. This procedure creates a worksheet similar to Figure 8.12 on page 309 using the sample size, number of successes, and confidence level values that you specify. Click **Finite Population Correction** if the sampling is done without replacement from a finite population (see Section 8.7).

## P8.4 Computing the Sample Size Needed for Estimating the Mean

To compute the sample size needed for estimating the mean, use **PHStat → Sample Size → Determination for the Mean**. This procedure creates a worksheet similar to Figure 8.14 on page 313 using the population standard deviation, sampling error, and confidence level values that you specify. Click **Finite Population Correction** if the sampling is done without replacement from a finite population (see Section 8.7).

## P8.5 Computing the Sample Size Needed for Estimating the Proportion

To compute the sample size needed for estimating the proportion, use **PHStat → Sample Size → Determination for the Proportion**. This procedure creates a worksheet similar to Figure 8.15 on page 316 using the estimate of true proportion, sampling error, and confidence level values that you specify. Click **Finite Population Correction** if the

sampling is done without replacement from a finite population (see Section 8.7).

## P8.6 Computing the Confidence Interval Estimate for the Population Total Amount

To compute the confidence interval estimate for the population total, use **PHStat → Confidence Intervals → Estimate for the Population Total**. The procedure creates a worksheet similar to Figure 8.16 on page 320 using the population size, confidence level, sample mean, sample size, and sample standard deviation that you specify. If you have unsummarized data, click **Sample Statistics Unknown** and the procedure will calculate the sample statistics for you.

## P8.7 Computing the Confidence Interval Estimate for the Total Difference

To compute the confidence interval estimate for the total difference, use **PHStat → Confidence Intervals → Estimate for the Total Difference**. This procedure creates a worksheet similar to Figure 8.17 on page 323 using the sample size, population size, and confidence level values that you specify.

# Appendix M8
## Using Minitab for Confidence Interval Estimation

## M8.1 Computing the Confidence Interval Estimation for the Mean (σ Known)

To compute a confidence interval estimate for the mean when σ is known

1. Select **Stat → Basic Statistics → 1-Sample Z**.

In the 1-Sample Z (Test and Confidence Interval) dialog box

2. Click **Samples in columns**.
3. Enter the variable name in the **Samples in columns** box.
4. Enter the value for σ in the **Standard deviation** box.
5. Click **Options**.

In the 1-Sample Z - Options dialog box:

6. Enter the level of confidence in the **Confidence level** box.
7. Click **OK** (to return to the previous dialog box).
8. Back in the first dialog box, click **OK** (to compute the confidence interval estimate).

## M8.2 Computing the Confidence Interval Estimation for the Mean (σ Unknown)

To compute the confidence interval estimate for the population mean force required to break the insulators presented in Figure 8.8 on page 304:

1. Open the `Force.mtw` worksheet.
2. Select **Stat → Basic Statistics → 1-Sample t**.

In the 1-Sample t (Test and Confidence Interval) dialog box (see Figure M8.1):

3. Click **Samples in columns** and enter **Force** in its box. (For summarized data, click **Summarized data** and enter the sample size, sample mean, and sample standard deviation in their respective boxes.)
4. Click **Options**.

**FIGURE M8.1**

Minitab 1-Sample t (Test and Confidence Interval) dialog box

In the 1-Sample t - Options dialog box (see Figure M8.2):

5. Enter **95.0** in the **Confidence level** box.
6. Click **OK**.
7. Back in the first dialog box, click **OK**.

**FIGURE M8.2**

Minitab 1-Sample t - Options dialog box

## M8.3 Computing the Confidence Interval Estimation for the Proportion

To compute the confidence interval estimate for the population proportion for the Saxon Home Improvement Company problem of Section 8.3 on page 309:

1. Select **Stat → Basic Statistics → 1 Proportion**.

In the 1 Proportion (Test and Confidence Interval) dialog box (see Figure M8.3):

2. Click **Summarized data**.
3. Enter **10** in the **Number of events** box.
4. Enter **100** in the **Number of trials** box.
5. Click **Options**.

**FIGURE M8.3**

Minitab 1 Proportion (Test and Confidence Interval) dialog box

In the 1 Proportion-Options dialog box (see Figure M8.4):

6. Enter **95** in the **Confidence level** box.
7. Select **not equal** from the **Alternative** drop-down list.
8. Click **Use test and interval based on normal distribution**.
9. Click **OK**.
10. Back in the first dialog box, click **OK**.

**FIGURE M8.4**

Minitab 1 Proportion - Options dialog box

# CHAPTER NINE

# LEARNING OBJECTIVES

## In this chapter, you learn:

- The basic principles of hypothesis testing
- How to use hypothesis testing to test a mean or proportion
- The assumptions of each hypothesis-testing procedure, how to evaluate them, and the consequences if they are seriously violated
- How to avoid the pitfalls involved in hypothesis testing
- Ethical issues involved in hypothesis testing

# USING STATISTICS @ Oxford Cereals, Part II

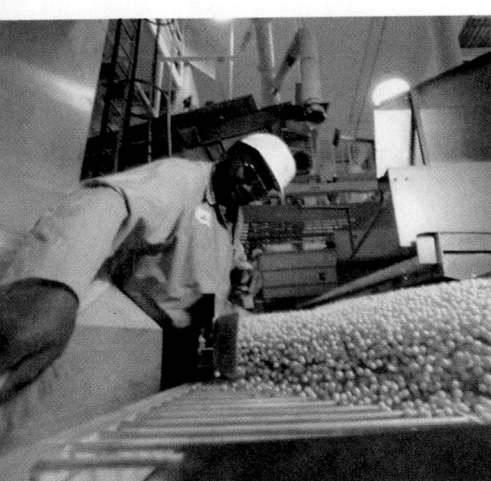

As in Chapter 7, you again find yourself as plant operations manager for Oxford Cereals. You are responsible for monitoring the amount in each cereal box filled. Company specifications require a mean weight of 368 grams per box. It is your responsibility to adjust the process when the mean fill weight in the population of boxes deviates from 368 grams. How can you rationally make the decision whether or not to adjust the process when it is impossible to weigh every single box as it is being filled? You begin by selecting and weighing a random sample of 25 cereal boxes. After computing a sample mean, how do you proceed?

In Chapter 7, you learned methods to determine whether a sample mean is consistent with a known population mean. In this Oxford Cereals scenario, you seek to use a sample mean to validate a claim about the population mean, a somewhat different problem. For this type of problem, you use an inferential method called **hypothesis testing**. Hypothesis testing requires that you state a claim unambiguously. In this scenario, the claim is that the population mean is 368 grams. You examine a sample statistic to see if it better supports the stated claim, called the *null hypothesis*, or the mutually exclusive alternative (for this scenario, that the population mean is not 368 grams).

In this chapter, you will learn several applications of hypothesis testing. You will learn how to make inferences about a population parameter by *analyzing differences* between the results observed, the sample statistic, and the results you would expect to get if an underlying hypothesis were actually true. For the Oxford Cereals scenario, hypothesis testing would allow you to infer one of the following:

- The mean weight of the cereal boxes in the sample is a value consistent with what you would expect if the mean of the entire population of cereal boxes is 368 grams.
- The population mean is not equal to 368 grams because the sample mean is significantly different from 368 grams.

## 9.1   FUNDAMENTALS OF HYPOTHESIS-TESTING METHODOLOGY

Hypothesis testing typically begins with some theory, claim, or assertion about a particular parameter of a population. For example, your initial hypothesis about the cereal example is that the process is working properly, so the mean fill is 368 grams, and no corrective action is needed.

### The Null and Alternative Hypotheses

The hypothesis that the population parameter is equal to the company specification is referred to as the null hypothesis. A **null hypothesis** is always one of status quo and is identified by the symbol $H_0$. Here the null hypothesis is that the filling process is working properly, and therefore the mean fill is the 368-gram specification provided by Oxford Cereals. This is stated as

$$H_0: \mu = 368$$

Even though information is available only from the sample, the null hypothesis is written in terms of the population. Remember, your focus is on the population of all cereal boxes. The sample statistic is used to make inferences about the entire filling process. One inference may be that the results observed from the sample data indicate that the null hypothesis is false. If the null hypothesis is considered false, something else must be true.

Whenever a null hypothesis is specified, an alternative hypothesis is also specified, and it must be true if the null hypothesis is false. The **alternative hypothesis**, $H_1$, is the opposite of the null hypothesis, $H_0$. This is stated in the cereal example as

$$H_1: \mu \neq 368$$

The alternative hypothesis represents the conclusion reached by rejecting the null hypothesis. The null hypothesis is rejected when there is sufficient evidence from the sample information that the null hypothesis is false. In the cereal example, if the weights of the sampled boxes are sufficiently above or below the expected 368-gram mean specified by Oxford Cereals, you reject the null hypothesis in favor of the alternative hypothesis that the mean fill is different from 368 grams. You stop production and take whatever action is necessary to correct the problem. If the null hypothesis is not rejected, you should continue to believe in the status quo, that the process is working correctly and therefore no corrective action is necessary. In this second circumstance, you have not proven that the process is working correctly. Rather, you have failed to prove that it is working incorrectly, and therefore you continue your belief (although unproven) in the null hypothesis.

In hypothesis testing, you reject the null hypothesis when the sample evidence suggests that it is far more likely that the alternative hypothesis is true. However, failure to reject the null hypothesis is not proof that it is true. You can never prove that the null hypothesis is correct because the decision is based only on the sample information, not on the entire population. Therefore, if you fail to reject the null hypothesis, you can only conclude that there is insufficient evidence to warrant its rejection. The following key points summarize the null and alternative hypotheses:

- The null hypothesis, $H_0$, represents the status quo or the current belief in a situation.
- The alternative hypothesis, $H_1$, is the opposite of the null hypothesis and represents a research claim or specific inference you would like to prove.
- If you reject the null hypothesis, you have statistical proof that the alternative hypothesis is correct.
- If you do not reject the null hypothesis, you have failed to prove the alternative hypothesis. The failure to prove the alternative hypothesis, however, does not mean that you have proven the null hypothesis.
- The null hypothesis, $H_0$, always refers to a specified value of the population parameter (such as $\mu$), not a sample statistic (such as $\bar{X}$).
- The statement of the null hypothesis always contains an equal sign regarding the specified value of the population parameter (e.g., $H_0: \mu = 368$ grams).
- The statement of the alternative hypothesis never contains an equal sign regarding the specified value of the population parameter (e.g., $H_1: \mu \neq 368$ grams).

---

**EXAMPLE 9.1**  THE NULL AND ALTERNATIVE HYPOTHESES

You are the manager of a fast-food restaurant. You want to determine whether the waiting time to place an order has changed in the past month from its previous population mean value of 4.5 minutes. State the null and alternative hypotheses.

**SOLUTION**  The null hypothesis is that the population mean has not changed from its previous value of 4.5 minutes. This is stated as

$$H_0: \mu = 4.5$$

The alternative hypothesis is the opposite of the null hypothesis. Because the null hypothesis is that the population mean is 4.5 minutes, the alternative hypothesis is that the population mean is not 4.5 minutes. This is stated as

$$H_1: \mu \neq 4.5$$

## The Critical Value of the Test Statistic

The logic of hypothesis testing involves determining how likely the null hypothesis is to be true by considering the information gathered in a sample. In the Oxford Cereal Company scenario, the null hypothesis is that the mean amount of cereal per box in the entire filling process is 368 grams (the population parameter specified by the company). You select a sample of boxes from the filling process, weigh each box, and compute the sample mean. This statistic is an estimate of the corresponding parameter (the population mean, $\mu$). Even if the null hypothesis is true, the statistic (the sample mean, $\bar{X}$) is likely to differ from the value of the parameter (the population mean, $\mu$) because of variation due to sampling. However, you expect the sample statistic to be close to the population parameter if the null hypothesis is true. If the sample statistic is close to the population parameter, you have insufficient evidence to reject the null hypothesis. For example, if the sample mean is 367.9, you conclude that the population mean has not changed (i.e., $\mu = 368$) because a sample mean of 367.9 is very close to the hypothesized value of 368. Intuitively, you think that it is likely that you could get a sample mean of 367.9 from a population whose mean is 368.

However, if there is a large difference between the value of the statistic and the hypothesized value of the population parameter, you conclude that the null hypothesis is false. For example, if the sample mean is 320, you conclude that the population mean is not 368 (i.e., $\mu \neq 368$), because the sample mean is very far from the hypothesized value of 368. In such a case, you conclude that it is very unlikely to get a sample mean of 320 if the population mean is really 368. Therefore, it is more logical to conclude that the population mean is not equal to 368. Here you reject the null hypothesis.

Unfortunately, the decision-making process is not always so clear-cut. Determining what is "very close" and what is "very different" is arbitrary without clear definitions. Hypothesis-testing methodology provides clear definitions for evaluating differences. Furthermore, it enables you to quantify the decision-making process by computing the probability of getting a given sample result if the null hypothesis is true. You calculate this probability by determining the sampling distribution for the sample statistic of interest (e.g., the sample mean) and then computing the particular **test statistic** based on the given sample result. Because the sampling distribution for the test statistic often follows a well-known statistical distribution, such as the standardized normal distribution or $t$ distribution, you can use these distributions to help determine whether the null hypothesis is true.

## Regions of Rejection and Nonrejection

The sampling distribution of the test statistic is divided into two regions, a **region of rejection** (sometimes called the critical region) and a **region of nonrejection** (see Figure 9.1). If the test statistic falls into the region of nonrejection, you do not reject the null hypothesis. In the Oxford Cereals scenario, you conclude that there is insufficient evidence that the population mean fill is different from 368 grams. If the test statistic falls into the rejection region, you reject the null hypothesis. In this case, you conclude that the population mean is not 368 grams.

The region of rejection consists of the values of the test statistic that are unlikely to occur if the null hypothesis is true. These values are much more likely to occur if the null hypothesis is false. Therefore, if a value of the test statistic falls into this *rejection region*, you reject the null hypothesis because that value is unlikely if the null hypothesis is true.

To make a decision concerning the null hypothesis, you first determine the **critical value** of the test statistic. The critical value divides the nonrejection region from the rejection region.

**FIGURE 9.1**

Regions of rejection and nonrejection in hypothesis testing

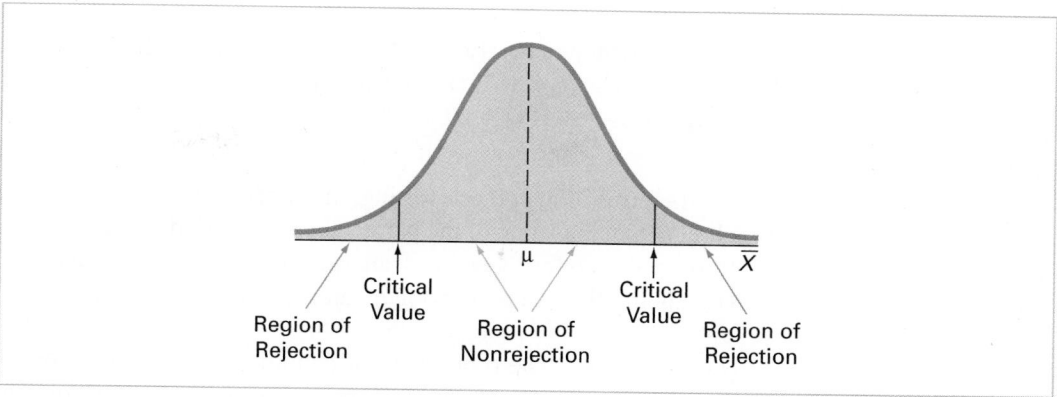

Determining this critical value depends on the size of the rejection region. The size of the rejection region is directly related to the risks involved in using only sample evidence to make decisions about a population parameter.

## Risks in Decision Making Using Hypothesis Testing

When using a sample statistic to make decisions about a population parameter, there is a risk that you will reach an incorrect conclusion. You can make two different types of errors when applying hypothesis testing, Type I and Type II errors.

> A **Type I error** occurs if you reject the null hypothesis, $H_0$, when it is true and should not be rejected. The probability of a Type I error occurring is $\alpha$.
>
> A **Type II error** occurs if you do not reject the null hypothesis, $H_0$, when it is false and should be rejected. The probability of a Type II error occurring is $\beta$.

In the Oxford Cereals scenario, you make a Type I error if you conclude that the population mean fill is *not* 368 when it *is* 368. This error causes you to adjust the filling process even though the process is working properly. Thus, a Type I error is a "false alarm". You make a Type II error if you conclude that the population mean fill *is* 368 when it is *not* 368. Here, you would allow the process to continue without adjustment even though adjustments are needed. Thus, a Type II error represents a "missed opportunity".

***The Level of Significance ($\alpha$)***    The probability of committing a Type I error, denoted by $\alpha$ (the lowercase Greek letter *alpha*), is referred to as the **level of significance** of the statistical test. Traditionally, you control the Type I error by deciding the risk level, $\alpha$, that you are willing to have of rejecting the null hypothesis when it is true. Because you specify the level of significance before the hypothesis test is performed, the risk of committing a Type I error, $\alpha$, is directly under your control. Traditionally, you select levels of 0.01, 0.05, or 0.10. The choice of a particular risk level for making a Type I error depends on the cost of making a Type I error. After you specify the value for $\alpha$, you can then determine the critical values that divide the rejection and nonrejection regions. You know the size of the rejection region because $\alpha$ is the probability of rejection when the null hypothesis is true. From this, you can then determine the critical value or values that divide the rejection and nonrejection regions.

***The Confidence Coefficient***    The complement of the probability of a Type I error, $(1 - \alpha)$, is called the confidence coefficient. When multiplied by 100%, the confidence coefficient yields the confidence level that was studied when constructing confidence intervals (see Section 8.1).

The **confidence coefficient**, $(1 - \alpha)$, is the probability that you will not reject the null hypothesis, $H_0$, when it is true and should not be rejected. The **confidence level** of a hypothesis test is $(1 - \alpha) \times 100\%$.

In terms of hypothesis testing, the confidence coefficient represents the probability of concluding that the value of the parameter as specified in the null hypothesis is plausible when it is true. In the Oxford Cereals scenario, the confidence coefficient measures the probability of concluding that the population mean fill is 368 grams when it is actually 368 grams.

***The $\beta$ Risk*** The probability of committing a Type II error is denoted by $\beta$ (the lowercase Greek letter *beta*). Unlike a Type I error, which you control by the selection of $\alpha$, the probability of making a Type II error depends on the difference between the hypothesized and actual values of the population parameter. Because large differences are easier to find than small ones, if the difference between the hypothesized and actual values of the population parameter is large, $\beta$ is small. For example, if the population mean is 330 grams, there is a small chance ($\beta$) that you will conclude that the mean has not changed from 368. However, if the difference between the hypothesized and actual values of the parameter is small, $\beta$ is large. For example, if the population mean is actually 367 grams, there is a large chance ($\beta$) that you will conclude that the mean is still 368 grams.

***The Power of a Test*** The complement of the probability of a Type II error, $(1 - \beta)$, is called the power of a statistical test.

The **power of a statistical test**, $(1 - \beta)$, is the probability that you will reject the null hypothesis when it is false and should be rejected.

In the Oxford Cereals scenario, the power of the test is the probability that you will correctly conclude that the mean fill amount is not 368 grams when it actually is not 368 grams. For a detailed discussion of the power of the test, see Section 9.5.

***Risks in Decision Making: A Delicate Balance*** Table 9.1 illustrates the results of the two possible decisions (do not reject $H_0$ or reject $H_0$) that you can make in any hypothesis test. You can make a correct decision or make one of two types of errors.

**TABLE 9.1**

Hypothesis Testing and Decision Making

| Statistical Decision | Actual Situation | |
| --- | --- | --- |
| | $H_0$ True | $H_0$ False |
| **Do not reject $H_0$** | Correct decision <br> Confidence $= (1 - \alpha)$ | Type II error <br> $P$ (Type II error) $= \beta$ |
| **Reject $H_0$** | Type I error <br> $P$ (Type I error) $= \alpha$ | Correct decision <br> Power $= (1 - \beta)$ |

One way to reduce the probability of making a Type II error is by increasing the sample size. Large samples generally permit you to detect even very small differences between the hypothesized values and the actual population parameters. For a given level of $\alpha$, increasing the sample size decreases $\beta$ and therefore increases the power of the test to detect that the null hypothesis, $H_0$, is false. However, there is always a limit to your resources, and this affects the decision as to how large a sample you can take. Thus, for a given sample size, you must consider the trade-offs between the two possible types of errors. Because you can directly control the risk of Type I error, you can reduce this risk by selecting a smaller value for $\alpha$. For example, if the negative consequences associated with making a Type I error are substantial, you could select $\alpha = 0.01$ instead of 0.05. However, when you decrease $\alpha$, you increase $\beta$, so reducing the risk of a Type I error results in an increased risk of a Type II error. However, if you wish to reduce $\beta$, you could select a larger value for $\alpha$. Therefore, if it is important to try to avoid a Type II error, you can select $\alpha$ of 0.05 or 0.10 instead of 0.01.

In the Oxford Cereals scenario, the risk of a Type I error involves concluding that the mean fill amount has changed from the hypothesized 368 grams when it actually has not changed. The risk of a Type II error involves concluding that the mean fill amount has not changed from the hypothesized 368 grams when it actually has changed. The choice of reasonable values for $\alpha$ and $\beta$ depends on the costs inherent in each type of error. For example, if it is very costly to change the cereal-fill process, you would want to be very confident that a change is needed before making any changes. In this case, the risk of a Type I error is more important, and you would choose a small $\alpha$. However, if you want to be very certain of detecting changes from a mean of 368 grams, the risk of a Type II error is more important, and you would choose a higher level of $\alpha$.

Now that you have been introduced to hypothesis testing, recall that in the Using Statistics scenario on page 342, Oxford Cereals wants to determine whether the cereal-fill process is working properly (i.e., whether the mean fill throughout the entire packaging process remains at the specified 368 grams, and no corrective action is needed). To evaluate the 368-gram requirement, you take a random sample of 25 boxes, weigh each box, and then evaluate the difference between the sample statistic and the hypothesized population parameter by comparing the mean weight (in grams) from the sample to the expected mean of 368 grams specified by the company. The null and alternative hypotheses are

$$H_0: \mu = 368$$

$$H_1: \mu \neq 368$$

When the standard deviation, $\sigma$, is known (which rarely occurs), you use the **Z test for the mean** if the population is normally distributed. If the population is not normally distributed, you can still use the $Z$ test if the sample size is large enough for the Central Limit Theorem to take effect (see Section 7.4). Equation (9.1) defines the Z-test statistic $Z_{STAT}$ for determining the difference between the sample mean, $\bar{X}$, and the population mean, $\mu$, when the standard deviation, $\sigma$, is known.

Z Test for the Mean ($\sigma$ Known)

$$Z_{STAT} = \frac{\bar{X} - \mu}{\frac{\sigma}{\sqrt{n}}} \qquad (9.1)$$

In Equation (9.1), the numerator measures the difference between the observed sample mean, $\bar{X}$, and the hypothesized mean, $\mu$. The denominator is the standard error of the mean, so $Z_{STAT}$ represents the difference between $\bar{X}$ and $\mu$ in standard error units.

## The Critical Value Approach to Hypothesis Testing

In the critical value approach to hypothesis testing, the observed value of the $Z_{STAT}$ test statistic, Equation (9.1), is compared to critical values. The critical values are expressed as standardized $Z$ values (i.e., in standard error units). For example, if you use a level of significance of 0.05, the size of the rejection region is 0.05. Because the rejection region is divided into the two tails of the distribution (this is called a **two-tail test**), you divide the 0.05 into two equal parts of 0.025 each. A rejection region of 0.025 in each tail of the normal distribution results in a cumulative area of 0.025 below the lower critical value and a cumulative area of 0.975 below the upper critical value (i.e., an area of 0.025 in the upper tail). According to the cumulative standardized normal distribution table (Table E.2), the critical values that divide the rejection and nonrejection regions are −1.96 and +1.96. Figure 9.2 illustrates that if the mean is actually 368 grams, as $H_0$ claims, the values of the $Z_{STAT}$ test statistic have a standardized normal distribution centered at $Z = 0$ (which corresponds to an $\bar{X}$ value of 368 grams). Values of $Z_{STAT}$ greater than +1.96 or less than −1.96 indicate that $\bar{X}$ is sufficiently different from the hypothesized $\mu = 368$ that it is unlikely that such an $\bar{X}$ value would occur if $H_0$ were true.

**FIGURE 9.2**

Testing a hypothesis about the mean (σ known) at the 0.05 level of significance

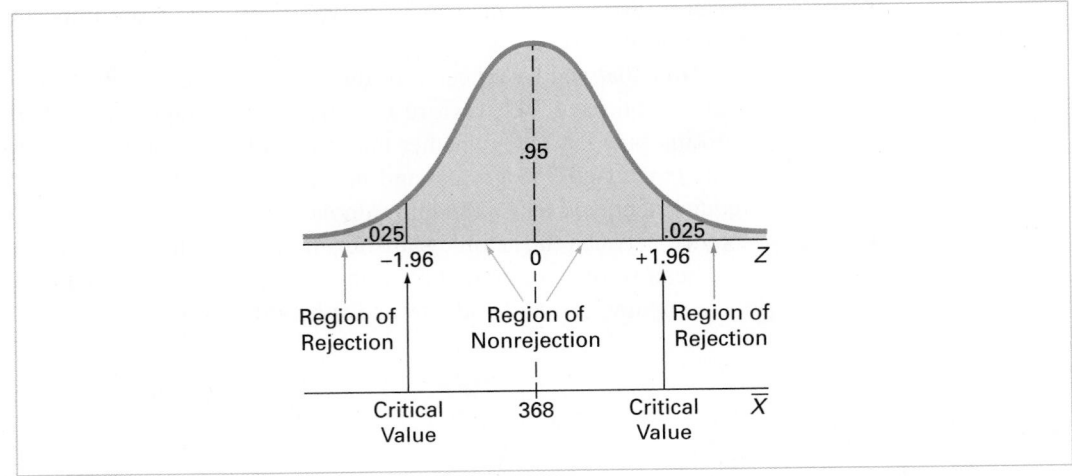

Therefore, the decision rule is

Reject $H_0$ if $Z_{STAT} > +1.96$

or if $Z_{STAT} < -1.96$;

otherwise, do not reject $H_0$.

Suppose that the sample of 25 cereal boxes indicates a sample mean, $\bar{X}$, of 372.5 grams, and the population standard deviation, σ, is 15 grams. Using Equation (9.1) on page 347,

$$Z_{STAT} = \frac{\bar{X} - \mu}{\dfrac{\sigma}{\sqrt{n}}} = \frac{372.5 - 368}{\dfrac{15}{\sqrt{25}}} = +1.50$$

Because $Z_{STAT} = +1.50$ is between −1.96 and +1.96, you do not reject $H_0$ (see Figure 9.3). You continue to believe that the mean fill amount is 368 grams. To take into account the possibility of a Type II error, you state the conclusion as "there is insufficient evidence that the mean fill is different from 368 grams."

**FIGURE 9.3**

Testing a hypothesis about the mean cereal weight (σ known) at the 0.05 level of significance

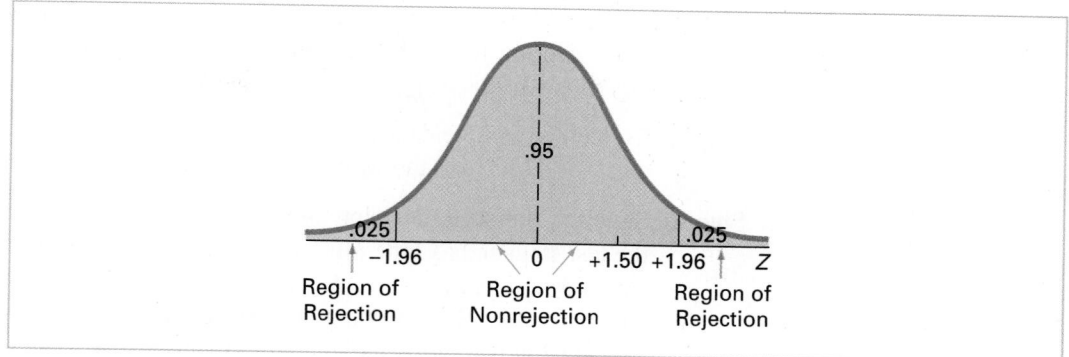

Exhibit 9.1 provides a summary of the critical value approach to hypothesis testing.

**EXHIBIT 9.1 THE SIX-STEP METHOD OF HYPOTHESIS TESTING**

1. State the null hypothesis, $H_0$, and the alternative hypothesis, $H_1$.
2. Choose the level of significance, $\alpha$, and the sample size, $n$. The level of significance is based on the relative importance of the risks of committing Type I and Type II errors in the problem.
3. Determine the appropriate test statistic and sampling distribution.
4. Determine the critical values that divide the rejection and nonrejection regions.
5. Collect the sample data and compute the value of the test statistic.
6. Make the statistical decision and state the managerial conclusion. If the test statistic falls into the nonrejection region, you do not reject the null hypothesis. If the test statistic falls into the rejection region, you reject the null hypothesis. The managerial conclusion is written in the context of the real-world problem.

**EXAMPLE 9.2**

APPLYING THE SIX-STEP METHOD OF HYPOTHESIS TESTING AT OXFORD CEREALS

State the six-step method of hypothesis testing at Oxford Cereals.

**SOLUTION**

**Step 1**  State the null and alternative hypotheses. The null hypothesis, $H_0$, is always stated as a mathematical expression using population parameters. In testing whether the mean fill is 368 grams, the null hypothesis states that $\mu$ equals 368. The alternative hypothesis, $H_1$, is also stated as a mathematical expression using population parameters. Therefore, the alternative hypothesis states that $\mu$ is not equal to 368 grams.

**Step 2**  Choose the level of significance and the sample size. You choose the level of significance, $\alpha$, according to the relative importance of the risks of committing Type I and Type II errors in the problem. The smaller the value of $\alpha$, the less risk there is of making a Type I error. In this example, making a Type I error means that you conclude that the population mean is not 368 grams when it is 368 grams. Thus, you will take corrective action on the filling process even though the process is working properly. Here, $\alpha = 0.05$ is selected. The sample size, $n$, is 25.

**Step 3**  Select the appropriate test statistic. Because $\sigma$ is known from information about the filling process, you use the normal distribution and the $Z_{STAT}$ test statistic.

**Step 4**  Determine the rejection region. Critical values for the appropriate test statistic are selected so that the rejection region contains a total area of $\alpha$ when $H_0$ is true and the nonrejection region contains a total area of $1 - \alpha$ when $H_0$ is true. Because $\alpha = 0.05$ in the cereal example, the critical values of the $Z_{STAT}$ test statistic are $-1.96$ and $+1.96$. The rejection region is therefore $Z_{STAT} < -1.96$ or $Z_{STAT} > +1.96$. The nonrejection region is $-1.96 < Z_{STAT} < +1.96$.

**Step 5**   Collect the sample data and compute the value of the test statistic. In the cereal example, $\bar{X} = 372.5$, and the value of the test statistic is $Z_{STAT} = +1.50$.

**Step 6**   State the statistical decision and the managerial conclusion. First, determine whether the test statistic has fallen into the rejection region or the nonrejection region. For the cereal example, $Z_{STAT} = +1.50$ is in the region of nonrejection because $-1.96 < Z_{STAT} = +1.50 < +1.96$. Because the test statistic falls into the nonrejection region, the statistical decision is to not reject the null hypothesis, $H_0$. The managerial conclusion is that insufficient evidence exists to prove that the mean fill is different from 368 grams. No corrective action on the filling process is needed.

---

**EXAMPLE 9.3**

TESTING AND REJECTING A NULL HYPOTHESIS

You are the manager of a fast-food restaurant. You want to determine whether the population mean waiting time to place an order has changed in the past month from its previous population mean value of 4.5 minutes. From past experience, you can assume that the population is normally distributed with a population standard deviation of 1.2 minutes. You select a sample of 25 orders during a one-hour period. The sample mean is 5.1 minutes. Use the six-step approach listed in Exhibit 9.1 on page 399 to determine whether there is evidence at the 0.05 level of significance that the population mean waiting time to place an order has changed in the past month from its previous population mean value of 4.5 minutes.

**SOLUTION**

**Step 1**   The null hypothesis is that the population mean has not changed from its previous value of 4.5 minutes:

$$H_0: \mu = 4.5$$

The alternative hypothesis is the opposite of the null hypothesis. Because the null hypothesis is that the population mean is 4.5 minutes, the alternative hypothesis is that the population mean is not 4.5 minutes:

$$H_1: \mu \neq 4.5$$

**Step 2**   You have selected a sample of $n = 25$. The level of significance is 0.05 (i.e., $\alpha = 0.05$).

**Step 3**   Because $\sigma$ is assumed known, you use the normal distribution and the $Z_{STAT}$ test statistic.

**Step 4**   Because $\alpha = 0.05$, the critical values of the $Z_{STAT}$ test statistic are $-1.96$ and $+1.96$. The rejection region is $Z_{STAT} < -1.96$ or $Z_{STAT} > +1.96$. The nonrejection region is $-1.96 < Z_{STAT} < +1.96$.

**Step 5**   You collect the sample data and compute $\bar{X} = 5.1$. Using Equation (9.1) on page 347, you compute the test statistic:

$$Z_{STAT} = \frac{\bar{X} - \mu}{\dfrac{\sigma}{\sqrt{n}}} = \frac{5.1 - 4.5}{\dfrac{1.2}{\sqrt{25}}} = 2.50$$

**Step 6**   Because $Z_{STAT} = 2.50 > 1.96$, you reject the null hypothesis. You conclude that there is evidence that the population mean waiting time to place an order has changed from its previous value of 4.5 minutes. The mean waiting time for customers is longer now than it was last month.

## The *p*-Value Approach to Hypothesis Testing

Most software packages, including Microsoft Excel and Minitab, compute the *p*-value when performing a test of hypothesis.

The ***p*-value** is the probability of getting a test statistic equal to or more extreme than the sample result, given that the null hypothesis, $H_0$, is true. The *p*-value is often referred to as the *observed level of significance*.

The decision rules for rejecting $H_0$ in the *p*-value approach are

- If the *p*-value is greater than or equal to α, do not reject the null hypothesis.
- If the *p*-value is less than α, reject the null hypothesis.

Many people confuse these rules, mistakenly believing that a high *p*-value is grounds for rejection. You can avoid this confusion by remembering the following mantra:

If the *p*-value is low, then $H_0$ must go.

To understand the *p*-value approach, consider the Oxford Cereals scenario. You tested whether the mean fill was equal to 368 grams. The test statistic resulted in a $Z_{STAT}$ value of +1.50, and you did not reject the null hypothesis because +1.50 was less than the upper critical value of +1.96 and more than the lower critical value of −1.96.

To use the *p*-value approach for the *two-tail test*, you find the probability of getting a test statistic $Z_{STAT}$ that is equal to or *more extreme than* 1.50 standard error units from the center of a standardized normal distribution. In other words, you need to compute the probability of a $Z_{STAT}$ value greater than +1.50, along with the probability of a $Z_{STAT}$ value less than −1.50. Table E.2 shows that the probability of a $Z_{STAT}$ value below −1.50 is 0.0668. The probability of a value below +1.50 is 0.9332, and the probability of a value above +1.50 is 1 − 0.9332 = 0.0668. Therefore, the *p*-value for this two-tail test is 0.0668 + 0.0668 = 0.1336 (see Figure 9.4). Thus, the probability of a test statistic equal to or more extreme than the sample result is 0.1336. Because 0.1336 is greater than α = 0.05, you do not reject the null hypothesis.

**FIGURE 9.4**

Finding a *p*-value for a two-tail test

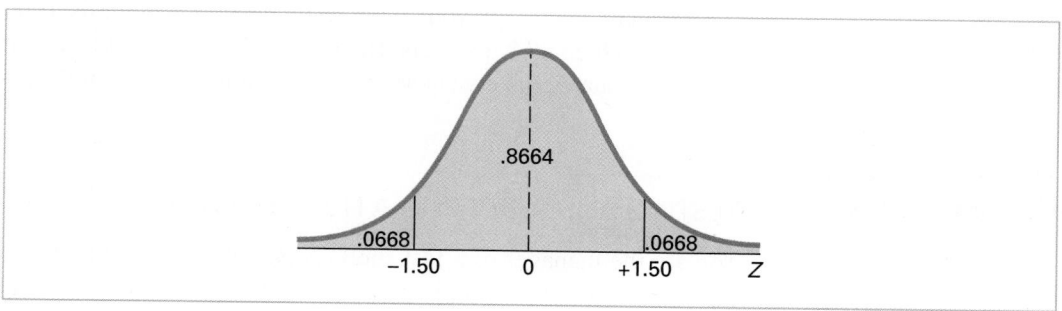

In this example, the observed sample mean is 372.5 grams, 4.5 grams above the hypothesized value, and the *p*-value is 0.1336. Thus, if the population mean is 368 grams, there is a 13.36% chance that the sample mean differs from 368 grams by more than 4.5 grams (i.e., is ≥ 372.5 grams or ≤ 363.5 grams). Therefore, even though 372.5 is above the hypothesized value of 368, a result as extreme as or more extreme than 372.5 is not highly unlikely when the population mean is 368.

Unless you are dealing with a test statistic that follows the normal distribution, you will only be able to approximate the *p*-value from the tables of the distribution. However, Microsoft Excel and Minitab routinely compute the *p*-values in each hypothesis-testing procedure. Once you understand the *p*-value approach, and assuming that you are using software such as Microsoft Excel or Minitab, you can just use the *p*-value approach instead of the critical value approach.

Figure 9.5 shows a Microsoft Excel worksheet for the cereal-filling example discussed in this section.

**FIGURE 9.5**

Microsoft Excel Z-test results for the cereal-fill example

*See Section E9.1 or P9.1 to create this. (Minitab users, see Section M9.1 to create the equivalent results.)*

| | A | B | |
|---|---|---|---|
| 1 | Cereal-Filling Process Hypothesis Test | | |
| 2 | | | |
| 3 | **Data** | | |
| 4 | Null Hypothesis          $\mu$= | 368 | |
| 5 | Level of Significance | 0.05 | |
| 6 | Population Standard Deviation | 15 | |
| 7 | Sample Size | 25 | |
| 8 | Sample Mean | 372.5 | |
| 9 | | | |
| 10 | Intermediate Calculations | | |
| 11 | Standard Error of the Mean | 3 | =B6/SQRT(B7) |
| 12 | Z Test Statistic | 1.5 | =(B8 - B4)/B11 |
| 13 | | | |
| 14 | **Two-Tail Test** | | |
| 15 | Lower Critical Value | -1.9600 | =NORMSINV(B5/2) |
| 16 | Upper Critical Value | 1.9600 | =NORMSINV(1 - B5/2) |
| 17 | *p*-Value | 0.1336 | =2 * (1 - NORMSDIST(ABS(B12))) |
| 18 | Do not reject the null hypothesis | | =IF(B17 < B5, "Reject the null hypothesis", "Do not reject the null hypothesis") |

Exhibit 9.2 provides a summary of the *p*-value approach for hypothesis testing.

**EXHIBIT 9.2  THE FIVE-STEP *p*-VALUE APPROACH TO HYPOTHESIS TESTING**

1. State the null hypothesis, $H_0$, and the alternative hypothesis, $H_1$.
2. Choose the level of significance, $\alpha$, and the sample size, *n*. The level of significance is based on the relative importance of the risks of committing Type I and Type II errors in the problem.
3. Determine the appropriate test statistic and the sampling distribution.
4. Collect the sample data, compute the value of the test statistic, and compute the *p*-value.
5. Make the statistical decision and state the managerial conclusion. If the *p*-value is greater than or equal to $\alpha$, you do not reject the null hypothesis. If the *p*-value is less than $\alpha$, you reject the null hypothesis. Remember the mantra: If the *p*-value is low, then $H_0$ must go. The managerial conclusion is written in the context of the real-world problem.

**EXAMPLE 9.4**

TESTING AND REJECTING A NULL HYPOTHESIS, USING THE *p*-VALUE APPROACH

You are the manager of a fast-food restaurant. You want to determine whether the population mean waiting time to place an order has changed in the past month from its previous value of 4.5 minutes. From past experience, you can assume that the population standard deviation is 1.2 minutes. You select a sample of 25 orders during a one-hour period. The sample mean is 5.1 minutes. Use the five-step *p*-value approach of Exhibit 9.2 to determine whether there is evidence that the population mean waiting time to place an order has changed in the past month from its previous population mean value of 4.5 minutes.

**SOLUTION**

**Step 1**  The null hypothesis is that the population mean has not changed from its previous value of 4.5 minutes:

$$H_0: \mu = 4.5$$

The alternative hypothesis is the opposite of the null hypothesis. Because the null hypothesis is that the population mean is 4.5 minutes, the alternative hypothesis is that the population mean is not 4.5 minutes:

$$H_1: \mu \neq 4.5$$

**Step 2**  You have selected a sample of $n = 25$. You choose a 0.05 level of significance (i.e., $\alpha = 0.05$).

**Step 3**  Select the appropriate test statistic. Because $\sigma$ is assumed known, you use the normal distribution and the $Z_{STAT}$ test statistic.

**Step 4**  You collect the data and compute $\bar{X} = 5.1$. Using Equation (9.1) on page 347, you compute the test statistic as follows:

$$Z_{STAT} = \frac{\bar{X} - \mu}{\dfrac{\sigma}{\sqrt{n}}} = \frac{5.1 - 4.5}{\dfrac{1.2}{\sqrt{25}}} = 2.50$$

To find the probability of getting a $Z_{STAT}$ test statistic that is equal to or more extreme than 2.50 standard error units from the center of a standardized normal distribution, you compute the probability of a $Z_{STAT}$ value greater than 2.50 along with the probability of a $Z_{STAT}$ value less than –2.50. From Table E.2, the probability of a $Z_{STAT}$ value below –2.50 is 0.0062. The probability of a value below +2.50 is 0.9938. Therefore, the probability of a value above +2.50 is 1 – 0.9938 = 0.0062. Thus, the $p$-value for this two-tail test is 0.0062 + 0.0062 = 0.0124.

**Step 5**  Because the $p$-value = 0.0124 < $\alpha$ = 0.05, you reject the null hypothesis. You conclude that there is evidence that the population mean waiting time to place an order has changed from its previous population mean value of 4.5 minutes. The mean waiting time for customers is longer now than it was last month.

## A Connection Between Confidence Interval Estimation and Hypothesis Testing

This chapter and Chapter 8 discuss the two major components of statistical inference: confidence interval estimation and hypothesis testing. Although they are based on the same set of concepts, they are used for different purposes. In Chapter 8, confidence intervals were used to estimate parameters. In this chapter, hypothesis testing is used for making decisions about specified values of population parameters. Hypothesis tests are used when trying to prove that a parameter is less than, more than, or not equal to a specified value. Proper interpretation of a confidence interval, however, can also indicate whether a parameter is less than, more than, or not equal to a specified value. For example, in this section, you tested whether the population mean fill amount was different from 368 grams by using Equation (9.1) on page 347:

$$Z_{STAT} = \frac{\bar{X} - \mu}{\dfrac{\sigma}{\sqrt{n}}}$$

Instead of testing the null hypothesis that $\mu = 368$ grams, you can reach the same conclusion by constructing a confidence interval estimate of $\mu$. If the hypothesized value of $\mu = 368$ is contained within the interval, you do not reject the null hypothesis because 368 would not be considered an unusual value. However, if the hypothesized value does not fall into the interval, you reject the null hypothesis because "$\mu = 368$ grams" is then considered an unusual value. Using Equation (8.1) on page 296 and the following data:

$$n = 25, \bar{X} = 372.5 \text{ grams}, \sigma = 15 \text{ grams}$$

for a confidence level of 95% (i.e., $\alpha = 0.05$),

$$\bar{X} \pm Z_{\alpha/2} \frac{\sigma}{\sqrt{n}}$$

$$372.5 \pm (1.96) \frac{15}{\sqrt{25}}$$

$$372.5 \pm 5.88$$

so that

$$366.62 \le \mu \le 378.38$$

Because the interval includes the hypothesized value of 368 grams, you do not reject the null hypothesis. There is insufficient evidence that the mean fill amount over the entire filling process is not 368 grams. You reached the same decision by using two-tail hypothesis testing.

## Can You Ever *Really* Know Sigma Part II?

*From the Authors' Desktop*

Section 9.1 discusses the fundamentals of hypothesis testing. Just as in Chapter 8 when confidence intervals were developed, using an example in which the population standard deviation $\sigma$ is known makes it much easier to explain the fundamentals of hypothesis testing. With a known population standard deviation, you can use the normal distribution and compute p-values from the tables of the normal distribution.

In virtually all situations, you do not know the standard deviation of the population. If you did, you would also know the population mean and therefore would not need to test a hypothesis about it. So, use this section to understand the fundamentals of hypothesis testing, but don't think that, in practice, you will ever know the population standard deviation $\sigma$.

## PROBLEMS FOR SECTION 9.1

### Learning the Basics

**9.1** For $H_0$: $\mu = 100$, $H_1$: $\mu \ne 100$, and for a sample of size $n$, why is $\beta$ larger if the actual value of $\mu$ is 90 than if the actual value of $\mu$ is 75?

**9.2** If you use a 0.05 level of significance in a (two-tail) hypothesis test, what will you decide if $Z_{STAT} = +2.21$?

**9.3** If you use a 0.10 level of significance in a (two-tail) hypothesis test, what is your decision rule for rejecting a null hypothesis that the population mean is 500 if you use the $Z$ test?

**9.4** If you use a 0.01 level of significance in a (two-tail) hypothesis test, what is your decision rule for rejecting $H_0$: $\mu = 12.5$ if you use the $Z$ test?

**9.5** What is your decision in Problem 9.4 if $Z_{STAT} = -2.61$?

**9.6** What is the *p*-value if, in a two-tail hypothesis test, $Z_{STAT} = +2.00$?

**9.7** In Problem 9.6, what is your statistical decision if you test the null hypothesis at the 0.10 level of significance?

**9.8** What is the *p*-value if, in a two-tail hypothesis test, $Z_{STAT} = -1.38$?

## Applying the Concepts

**9.9** In the U.S. legal system, a defendant is presumed innocent until proven guilty. Consider a null hypothesis, $H_0$, that the defendant is innocent, and an alternative hypothesis, $H_1$, that the defendant is guilty. A jury has two possible decisions: Convict the defendant (i.e., reject the null hypothesis) or do not convict the defendant (i.e., do not reject the null hypothesis). Explain the meaning of the risks of committing either a Type I or Type II error in this example.

**9.10** Suppose the defendant in Problem 9.9 is presumed guilty until proven innocent, as in some other judicial systems. How do the null and alternative hypotheses differ from those in Problem 9.9? What are the meanings of the risks of committing either a Type I or Type II error here?

**9.11** The U.S. Food and Drug Administration (FDA) is responsible for approving new drugs. Many consumer groups feel that the approval process is too easy and, therefore, too many drugs are approved that are later found to be unsafe. On the other hand, a number of industry lobbyists are pushing for a more lenient approval process so that pharmaceutical companies can get new drugs approved more easily and quickly (extracted from R. Sharpe, "FDA Tries to Find Right Balance on Drug Approvals," *The Wall Street Journal*, April 20, 1999, p. A24). Consider a null hypothesis that a new, unapproved drug is unsafe and an alternative hypothesis that a new, unapproved drug is safe.

**a.** Explain the risks of committing a Type I or Type II error.
**b.** Which type of error are the consumer groups trying to avoid? Explain.
**c.** Which type of error are the industry lobbyists trying to avoid? Explain.
**d.** How would it be possible to lower the chances of both Type I and Type II errors?

**√SELF Test** **9.12** As a result of complaints from both students and faculty about lateness, the registrar at a large university wants to adjust the scheduled class times to allow for adequate travel time between classes and is ready to undertake a study. Until now, the registrar has believed that there should be 20 minutes between scheduled classes. State the null hypothesis, $H_0$, and the alternative hypothesis, $H_1$.

**9.13** Do students at your school study more, less, or about the same as at other business schools? *Business Week* reported that at the top 50 business schools, students studied an average of 14.6 hours (extracted from "Cracking the Books," SPECIAL REPORT/Online Extra, **www.businessweek.com**, March 19, 2007). Set up a hypothesis test to try to prove that the mean number of hours studied at your school is different from the 14.6 hour benchmark reported by *Business Week*.
**a.** State the null and alternative hypotheses.
**b.** What is a Type I error for your test?
**c.** What is a Type II error for your test?

**9.14** The manager of a paint supply store wants to determine whether the amount of paint contained in 1-gallon cans purchased from a nationally known manufacturer actually averages 1 gallon. State the null and alternative hypotheses.

**9.15** The quality control manager at a lightbulb factory needs to determine whether the mean life of a large shipment of lightbulbs is equal to the specified value of 375 hours. State the null and alternative hypotheses.

## 9.2  *t* TEST OF HYPOTHESIS FOR THE MEAN (σ UNKNOWN)

In virtually all hypothesis-testing situations concerning the population mean, μ, you do not know the population standard deviation, σ. Instead, you use the sample standard deviation, *S*. If you assume that the population is normally distributed, then the sampling distribution of the mean follows a *t* distribution with $n - 1$ degrees of freedom and you use the ***t* test for the mean**. If the population is not normally distributed, you can still use the *t* test if the sample size is large enough for the Central Limit Theorem to take effect (see Section 7.4). Equation (9.2) defines the test statistic for determining the difference between the sample mean, $\bar{X}$, and the population mean, μ, when using the sample standard deviation, *S*.

### t Test of Hypothesis for the Mean (σ Unknown)

$$t_{STAT} = \frac{\bar{X} - \mu}{\dfrac{S}{\sqrt{n}}} \qquad (9.2)$$

where the $t_{STAT}$ test statistic follows a $t$ distribution having $n - 1$ degrees of freedom.

To illustrate the use of this $t$ test, return to the Using Statistics scenario concerning the Saxon Home Improvement Company on page 292. Over the past five years, the mean amount per sales invoice is $120. As an accountant for the company, you need to inform the finance department if this amount changes. In other words, the hypothesis test is used to try to prove that the mean amount per sales invoice is increasing or decreasing.

## The Critical Value Approach

To perform this two-tail hypothesis test, you use the six-step method listed in Exhibit 9.1 on page 349.

**Step 1**   $H_0$: $\mu = \$120$
$H_1$: $\mu \neq \$120$

The alternative hypothesis contains the statement you are trying to prove. If the null hypothesis is rejected, then there is statistical proof that the population mean amount per sales invoice is no longer $120. If the statistical conclusion is "do not reject $H_0$," then you will conclude that there is insufficient evidence to prove that the mean amount differs from the long-term mean of $120.

**Step 2**   You have selected a sample of $n = 12$. You decide to use $\alpha = 0.05$.

**Step 3**   Because σ is unknown, you use the $t$ distribution and the $t_{STAT}$ test statistic. You must assume that the population of sales invoices is normally distributed. This assumption is discussed on pages 358–360.

**Step 4**   For a given sample size, $n$, the test statistic $t_{STAT}$ follows a $t$ distribution with $n - 1$ degrees of freedom. The critical values of the $t$ distribution with $12 - 1 = 11$ degrees of freedom are found in Table E.3, as illustrated in Table 9.2 and Figure 9.6. The alternative hypothesis, $H_1$, $\mu \neq \$120$ is two-tail. Thus, the area in the rejection region of the $t$ distribution's left (lower) tail is 0.025, and the area in the rejection region of the $t$ distribution's right (upper) tail is also 0.025.

From the $t$ table as given in Table E.3, a portion of which is shown in Table 9.2, the critical values are ±2.2010. The decision rule is

Reject $H_0$ if $t_{STAT} < -t_{\alpha/2} = -2.2010$

or if $t_{STAT} > t_{\alpha/2} = +2.2010$;

otherwise, do not reject $H_0$.

**Step 5**   A random sample of 12 sales invoices is selected. The dollar amounts for the 12 invoices are given below (and in the file **Invoices**):

| | | | | | |
|---|---|---|---|---|---|
| 108.98 | 152.22 | 111.45 | 110.59 | 127.46 | 107.26 |
| 93.32 | 91.97 | 111.56 | 75.71 | 128.58 | 135.11 |

**TABLE 9.2**

Determining the Critical Value from the *t* Table for an Area of 0.025 in Each Tail with 11 Degrees of Freedom

| | Cumulative Probabilities | | | | | |
|---|---|---|---|---|---|---|
| | .75 | .90 | .95 | .975 | .99 | .995 |
| | Upper-Tail Areas | | | | | |
| **Degrees of Freedom** | .25 | .10 | .05 | .025 | .01 | .005 |
| 1 | 1.0000 | 3.0777 | 6.3138 | 12.7062 | 31.8207 | 63.6574 |
| 2 | 0.8165 | 1.8856 | 2.9200 | 4.3027 | 6.9646 | 9.9248 |
| 3 | 0.7649 | 1.6377 | 2.3534 | 3.1824 | 4.5407 | 5.8409 |
| 4 | 0.7407 | 1.5332 | 2.1318 | 2.7764 | 3.7469 | 4.6041 |
| 5 | 0.7267 | 1.4759 | 2.0150 | 2.5706 | 3.3649 | 4.0322 |
| 6 | 0.7176 | 1.4398 | 1.9432 | 2.4469 | 3.1427 | 3.7074 |
| 7 | 0.7111 | 1.4149 | 1.8946 | 2.3646 | 2.9980 | 3.4995 |
| 8 | 0.7064 | 1.3968 | 1.8595 | 2.3060 | 2.8965 | 3.3554 |
| 9 | 0.7027 | 1.3830 | 1.8331 | 2.2622 | 2.8214 | 3.2498 |
| 10 | 0.6998 | 1.3722 | 1.8125 | 2.2281 | 2.7638 | 3.1693 |
| 11 | 0.6974 | 1.3634 | 1.7959 | 2.2010 | 2.7181 | 3.1058 |

Source: *Extracted from Table E.3.*

**FIGURE 9.6**

Testing a hypothesis about the mean (σ unknown) at the 0.05 level of significance with 11 degrees of freedom

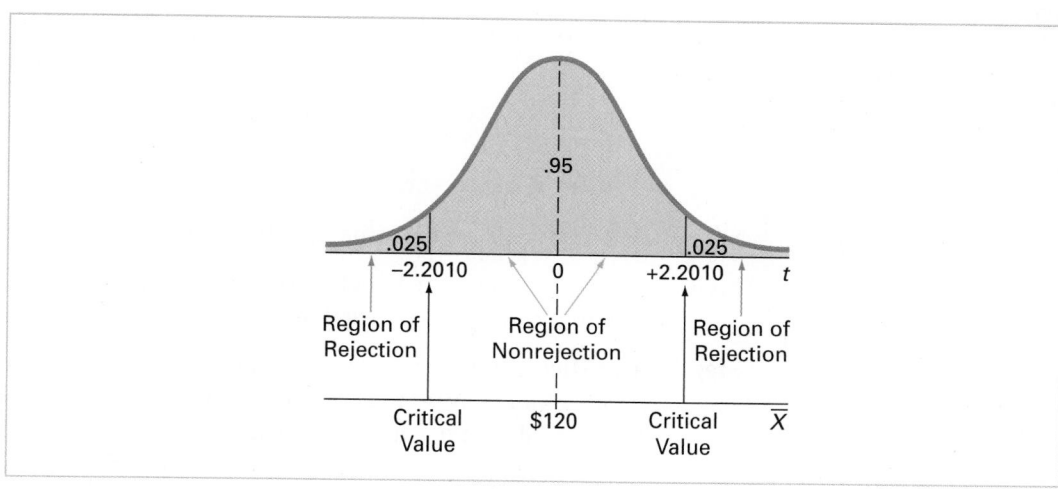

Using Equations (3.1) and (3.7) on pages 91 and 98, or Microsoft Excel or Minitab as shown in Figures 9.7 and 9.8,

$$\bar{X} = \frac{\displaystyle\sum_{i=1}^{n} X_i}{n} = \$112.85 \quad \text{and} \quad S = \sqrt{\frac{\displaystyle\sum_{i=1}^{n} (X_i - \bar{X}_i)^2}{n-1}} = \$20.80$$

From Equation (9.2) on page 356,

$$t_{STAT} = \frac{\bar{X} - \mu}{\dfrac{S}{\sqrt{n}}} = \frac{112.85 - 120}{\dfrac{20.80}{\sqrt{12}}} = -1.1908$$

**Step 6**  Because $-2.2010 < t_{STAT} = -1.1908 < 2.2010$, you do not reject $H_0$. You have insufficient evidence to conclude that the mean amount per sales invoice differs from \$120. You should inform the finance department that the audit suggests that the mean amount per invoice has not changed.

**FIGURE 9.7**

Microsoft Excel results for the *t* test of sales invoices

*See Section E9.2 or P9.2 to create this.*

| | A | B | |
|---|---|---|---|
| 1 | t Test for the Hypothesis of the Mean | | |
| 2 | | | |
| 3 | Data | | |
| 4 | Null Hypothesis  μ= | 120 | |
| 5 | Level of Significance | 0.05 | |
| 6 | Sample Size | 12 | |
| 7 | Sample Mean | 112.85 | |
| 8 | Sample Standard Deviation | 20.8 | |
| 9 | | | |
| 10 | Intermediate Calculations | | |
| 11 | Standard Error of the Mean | 6.0044 | =B8/SQRT(B6) |
| 12 | Degrees of Freedom | 11 | =B6 - 1 |
| 13 | t Test Statistic | -1.1908 | =(B7 - B4)/B11 |
| 14 | | | |
| 15 | Two-Tail Test | | |
| 16 | Lower Critical Value | -2.2010 | =-(TINV(B5, B12)) |
| 17 | Upper Critical Value | 2.2010 | =TINV(B5, B12) |
| 18 | p-Value | 0.2588 | =TDIST(ABS(B13), B12, 2) |
| 19 | Do not reject the null hypothesis | | =IF(B18 < B5, "Reject the null hypothesis", "Do not reject the null hypothesis") |

**FIGURE 9.8**

Minitab results for the *t* test of sales invoices

*See Section M9.2 to create this.*

```
Test of mu = 120 vs not = 120


Variable   N    Mean   StDev  SE Mean      95% CI         T      P
Amount    12  112.85   20.80    6.00  (99.64, 126.07)  -1.19  0.259
```

## The *p*-Value Approach

**Steps 1–3**  These steps are the same as in the critical value approach on page 356.

**Step 4**  From the Microsoft Excel worksheet of Figure 9.7 or from the Minitab results of Figure 9.8, $t_{STAT} = -1.19$ and the *p*-value = 0.259.

**Step 5**  The Microsoft Excel results in Figure 9.7 and the Minitab results in Figure 9.8 give the *p*-value for this two-tail test as 0.259. Because the *p*-value of 0.259 is greater than $\alpha = 0.05$, you do not reject $H_0$. The data provide insufficient evidence to conclude that the mean amount per sales invoice differs from \$120. You should inform the finance department that the audit suggests that the mean amount per invoice has not changed. The *p*-value indicates that if the null hypothesis is true, the probability that a sample of 12 invoices could have a sample mean that differs by \$7.15 or more from the stated \$120 is 0.259. In other words, if the mean amount per sales invoice is truly \$120, then there is a 25.9% chance of observing a sample mean below \$112.85 or above \$127.15.

In the preceding example, it is incorrect to state that there is a 25.9% chance that the null hypothesis is true. This misinterpretation of the *p*-value is sometimes used by those not properly trained in statistics. Remember that the *p*-value is a conditional probability, calculated by *assuming* that the null hypothesis is true. In general, it is proper to state the following:

> If the null hypothesis is true, there is a (*p*-value)*100% chance of observing a test statistic at least as contradictory to the null hypothesis as the sample result.

## Checking Assumptions

You use the *t* test when the population standard deviation, $\sigma$, is not known and is estimated using the sample standard deviation, *S*. To use the *t* test, you assume that the data represent a random sample from a population that is normally distributed. In practice, as long as the sample size is not very small and the population is not very skewed, the *t* distribution provides a good approximation to the sampling distribution of the mean when σ is unknown.

There are several ways to evaluate the normality assumption necessary for using the *t* test. You can observe how closely the sample statistics match the normal distribution's theoretical properties. You can also use a histogram, stem-and-leaf display, boxplot, or normal probability plot. For details on evaluating normality, see Section 6.3 on page 234.

Figure 9.9 presents descriptive statistics generated by Microsoft Excel. Figure 9.10 is a Microsoft Excel boxplot. Figure 9.11 on page 360 is a Microsoft Excel normal probability plot.

**FIGURE 9.9**

Microsoft Excel descriptive statistics for the sales invoice data

*See Section E3.1 to create this. (Minitab users, see Section M3.1 to create the equivalent results.)*

|   | A | B |
|---|---|---|
| 1 | *Invoice Amount* | |
| 2 | | |
| 3 | Mean | 112.8508 |
| 4 | Standard Error | 6.003863 |
| 5 | Median | 111.02 |
| 6 | Mode | #N/A |
| 7 | Standard Deviation | 20.79799 |
| 8 | Sample Variance | 432.5565 |
| 9 | Kurtosis | 0.172708 |
| 10 | Skewness | 0.133638 |
| 11 | Range | 76.51 |
| 12 | Minimum | 75.71 |
| 13 | Maximum | 152.22 |
| 14 | Sum | 1354.21 |
| 15 | Count | 12 |
| 16 | Largest(1) | 152.22 |
| 17 | Smallest(1) | 75.71 |

**FIGURE 9.10**

Microsoft Excel boxplot for the sales invoice data

*See Section E3.3 or P3.1 to create this. (Minitab users, see Section M3.2 to create the equivalent chart.)*

**Boxplot of Invoice Amount**

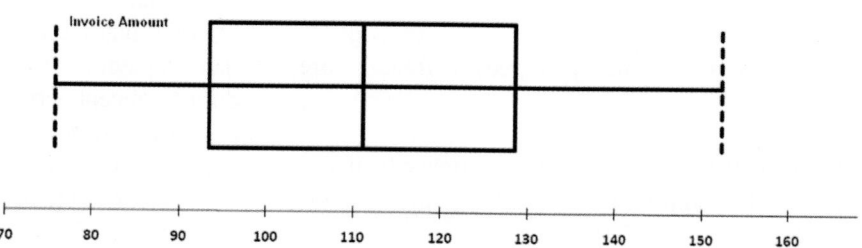

The mean is very close to the median and the points on the normal probability plot appear to be increasing approximately in a straight line. The boxplot appears approximately symmetrical. Thus, you can assume that the population of sales invoices is approximately normally distributed. The normality assumption is valid, and therefore the auditor's results are valid.

The *t* test is a **robust** test. It does not lose power if the shape of the population departs somewhat from a normal distribution, particularly when the sample size is large enough to enable the test statistic *t* to be influenced by the Central Limit Theorem (see Section 7.4).

**FIGURE 9.11**

Microsoft Excel normal probability plot for the sales invoice data

*See Section P6.2 to create this. (Minitab users, see Section M6.2 to create the equivalent chart.)*

However, you can reach erroneous conclusions and can lose statistical power if you use the *t* test incorrectly. If the sample size, *n*, is small (i.e., less than 30) and you cannot easily make the assumption that the underlying population is at least approximately normally distributed, then *nonparametric* testing procedures are more appropriate (see references 1 and 2).

## PROBLEMS FOR SECTION 9.2

### Learning the Basics

**9.16** If, in a sample of $n = 16$ selected from a normal population, $\bar{X} = 56$ and $S = 12$, what is the value of $t_{STAT}$ if you are testing the null hypothesis $H_0: \mu = 50$?

**9.17** In Problem 9.16, how many degrees of freedom are there in the *t* test?

**9.18** In Problems 9.16 and 9.17, what are the critical values of *t* if the level of significance, $\alpha$, is 0.05 and the alternative hypothesis, $H_1$, is $\mu \neq 50$?

**9.19** In Problems 9.16, 9.17, and 9.18, what is your statistical decision if the alternative hypothesis, $H_1$, is $\mu \neq 50$?

**9.20** If, in a sample of $n = 16$ selected from a left-skewed population, $\bar{X} = 65$ and $S = 21$, would you use the *t* test to test the null hypothesis $H_0: \mu = 60$? Discuss.

**9.21** If, in a sample of $n = 160$ selected from a left-skewed population, $\bar{X} = 65$ and $S = 21$, would you use the *t* test to test the null hypothesis $H_0: \mu = 60$? Discuss.

### Applying the Concepts

**9.22** Late payment of medical claims can add to the cost of health care. An article (M. Freudenheim, "The Check Is Not in the Mail," *The New York Times*, May 25, 2006, pp. C1, C6) reported that the mean time from the date of service to the date of payment for one insurance company was 41.4 days during a recent period. Suppose that a sample of 100 medical claims is selected during the latest time period. The sample mean time from the date of service to the date of payment was 39.6 days, and the sample standard deviation was 7.4 days.
a. Using the 0.05 level of significance, is there evidence that the population mean has changed from 41.4 days?
b. What is your answer in (a) if you use the 0.01 level of significance?
c. What is your answer in (a) if the sample mean is 38.2 days and the sample standard deviation is 10.7 days?
d. Because the sample size is 100, do you need to be concerned about the shape of the population distribution when conducting the *t*-test in (a)? Explain.

**9.23** An article (N. Hellmich, "'Supermarket Guru' Has a Simple Mantra," *USA Today*, June 19, 2002, p. 70)

claimed that the typical supermarket trip takes a mean of 22 minutes. Suppose that in an effort to test this claim, you select a sample of 50 shoppers at a local supermarket. The mean shopping time for the sample of 50 shoppers is 25.36 minutes, with a standard deviation of 7.24 minutes. Using the 0.10 level of significance, is there evidence that the mean shopping time at the local supermarket is different from the claimed value of 22 minutes?

**✓ SELF Test 9.24** You are the manager of a restaurant for a fast-food franchise. Last month, the mean waiting time at the drive-through window for branches in your geographical region, as measured from the time a customer places an order until the time the customer receives the order, was 3.7 minutes. You select a random sample of 64 orders. The sample mean waiting time is 3.57 minutes, with a sample standard deviation of 0.8 minute.

**a.** At the 0.05 level of significance, is there evidence that the population mean waiting time is different from 3.7 minutes?

**b.** Because the sample size is 64, do you need to be concerned about the shape of the population distribution when conducting the *t*-test in (a)? Explain.

**9.25** A manufacturer of chocolate candies uses machines to package candies as they move along a filling line. Although the packages are labeled as 8 ounces, the company wants the packages to contain a mean of 8.17 ounces so that virtually none of the packages contain less than 8 ounces. A sample of 50 packages is selected periodically, and the packaging process is stopped if there is evidence that the mean amount packaged is different from 8.17 ounces. Suppose that in a particular sample of 50 packages, the mean amount dispensed is 8.159 ounces, with a sample standard deviation of 0.051 ounce.

**a.** Is there evidence that the population mean amount is different from 8.17 ounces? (Use a 0.05 level of significance.)

**b.** Determine the *p*-value and interpret its meaning.

**9.26** The data in the file **MoviePrices** contain prices (in dollars) for two tickets, with online service charges, large popcorn, and two medium soft drinks at a sample of six theater chains:

    36.15   31.00   35.05   40.25   33.75   43.00

Source: *Extracted from K. Kelly, "The Multiplex Under Siege," The Wall Street Journal, December 24–25, 2005, pp. P1, P5.*

**a.** At the 0.05 level of significance, is there evidence that the mean price for two tickets, with online service charges, large popcorn, and two medium soft drinks, is different from $35?

**b.** Determine the *p*-value in (a) and interpret its meaning.

**c.** What assumption must you make about the population distribution in order to conduct the *t* test in (a) and (b)?

**d.** Because the sample size is 6, do you need to be concerned about the shape of the population distribution when conducting the *t* test in (a)? Explain.

**9.27** In New York State, savings banks are permitted to sell a form of life insurance called savings bank life insurance (SBLI). The approval process consists of underwriting, which includes a review of the application, a medical information bureau check, possible requests for additional medical information and medical exams, and a policy compilation stage in which the policy pages are generated and sent to the bank for delivery. The ability to deliver approved policies to customers in a timely manner is critical to the profitability of this service. During a period of one month, a random sample of 27 approved policies is selected, and the total processing time, in days, is recorded (as stored in the **Insurance** file):

| 73 | 19 | 16 | 64 | 28 | 28 | 31 | 90 | 60 | 56 | 31 | 56 | 22 | 18 |
|----|----|----|----|----|----|----|----|----|----|----|----|----|----|
| 45 | 48 | 17 | 17 | 17 | 91 | 92 | 63 | 50 | 51 | 69 | 16 | 17 | |

**a.** In the past, the mean processing time was 45 days. At the 0.05 level of significance, is there evidence that the mean processing time has changed from 45 days?

**b.** What assumption about the population distribution is needed in order to conduct the *t* test in (a)?

**c.** Use a boxplot or a normal probability plot to evaluate the assumption made in (b).

**d.** Do you think that the assumption needed in order to conduct the *t* test in (a) is valid? Explain.

**9.28** The following data (see the **Drink** file) represent the amount of soft-drink filled in a sample of 50 consecutive 2-liter bottles. The results, listed horizontally in the order of being filled, were:

| 2.109 | 2.086 | 2.066 | 2.075 | 2.065 | 2.057 | 2.052 | 2.044 | 2.036 | 2.038 |
|-------|-------|-------|-------|-------|-------|-------|-------|-------|-------|
| 2.031 | 2.029 | 2.025 | 2.029 | 2.023 | 2.020 | 2.015 | 2.014 | 2.013 | 2.014 |
| 2.012 | 2.012 | 2.012 | 2.010 | 2.005 | 2.003 | 1.999 | 1.996 | 1.997 | 1.992 |
| 1.994 | 1.986 | 1.984 | 1.981 | 1.973 | 1.975 | 1.971 | 1.969 | 1.966 | 1.967 |
| 1.963 | 1.957 | 1.951 | 1.951 | 1.947 | 1.941 | 1.941 | 1.938 | 1.908 | 1.894 |

**a.** At the 0.05 level of significance, is there evidence that the mean amount of soft drink filled is different from 2.0 liters?

**b.** Determine the *p*-value in (a) and interpret its meaning.

**c.** In (a), you assumed that the distribution of the amount of soft drink filled was normally distributed. Evaluate this assumption using a boxplot or a normal probability plot.

**d.** Do you think that the assumption needed in order to conduct the *t* test in (a) is valid? Explain.

**e.** Examine the values of the 50 bottles in their sequential order, as given in the problem. Is there a pattern to the results? If so, what impact might this pattern have on the validity of the results in (a)?

**9.29** One of the major measures of the quality of service provided by any organization is the speed with which it responds to customer complaints. A large family-held department store selling furniture and flooring, including carpet, had undergone a major expansion in the past several years. In particular, the flooring department had expanded from 2 installation crews to an installation supervisor, a measurer, and 15 installation crews. Last year there were 50 complaints concerning carpet installation. The following data (stored in the Furniture file) represent the number of days between the receipt of a complaint and the resolution of the complaint:

| 54 | 5 | 35 | 137 | 31 | 27 | 152 | 2 | 123 | 81 | 74 | 27 |
| 11 | 19 | 126 | 110 | 110 | 29 | 61 | 35 | 94 | 31 | 26 | 5 |
| 12 | 4 | 165 | 32 | 29 | 28 | 29 | 26 | 25 | 1 | 14 | 13 |
| 13 | 10 | 5 | 27 | 4 | 52 | 30 | 22 | 36 | 26 | 20 | 23 |
| 33 | 68 | | | | | | | | | | |

a. The installation supervisor claims that the mean number of days between the receipt of a complaint and the resolution of the complaint is 20 days. At the 0.05 level of significance, is there evidence that the claim is not true (i.e., that the mean number of days is different from 20)?
b. What assumption about the population distribution is needed in order to conduct the $t$ test in (a)?
c. Use a boxplot or a normal probability plot to evaluate the assumption made in (b).
d. Do you think that the assumption needed in order to conduct the $t$ test in (a) is valid? Explain.

**9.30** A manufacturing company produces steel housings for electrical equipment. The main component part of the housing is a steel trough that is made out of a 14-gauge steel coil. It is produced using a 250-ton progressive punch press with a wipe-down operation that puts two 90-degree forms in the flat steel to make the trough. The distance from one side of the form to the other is critical because of weatherproofing in outdoor applications. The company requires that the width of the trough be between 8.31 inches and 8.61 inches. The file Trough contains the widths of the troughs, in inches, for a sample of $n = 49$.

8.312 8.343 8.317 8.383 8.348 8.410 8.351 8.373 8.481 8.422
8.476 8.382 8.484 8.403 8.414 8.419 8.385 8.465 8.498 8.447
8.436 8.413 8.489 8.414 8.481 8.415 8.479 8.429 8.458 8.462
8.460 8.444 8.429 8.460 8.412 8.420 8.410 8.405 8.323 8.420
8.396 8.447 8.405 8.439 8.411 8.427 8.420 8.498 8.409

a. At the 0.05 level of significance, is there evidence that the mean width of the troughs is different from 8.46 inches?
b. What assumption about the population distribution is needed in order to conduct the $t$ test in (a)?
c. Evaluate the assumption made in (b).
d. Do you think that the assumption needed in order to conduct the $t$ test in (a) is valid? Explain.

**9.31** One operation of a steel mill is to cut pieces of steel into parts that are used in the frame for front seats in an automobile. The steel is cut with a diamond saw and requires the resulting parts to be within ±0.005 inch of the length specified by the automobile company. The data in the file Steel come from a sample of 100 steel parts. The measurement reported is the difference, in inches, between the actual length of the steel part, as measured by a laser measurement device, and the specified length of the steel part. For example, a value of –0.002 represents a steel part that is 0.002 inch shorter than the specified length.
a. At the 0.05 level of significance, is there evidence that the mean difference is not equal to 0.0 inches?
b. Construct a 95% confidence interval estimate of the population mean. Interpret this interval.
c. Compare the conclusions reached in (a) and (b).
d. Because $n = 100$, do you have to worry about the normality assumption needed for the $t$ test and $t$ interval?

**9.32** In Problem 3.67 on page 135, you were introduced to a tea-bag-filling operation. An important quality characteristic of interest for this process is the weight of the tea in the individual bags. The data in the file Teabags are provided in an ordered array of the weight, in grams, of a sample of 50 tea bags produced during an eight-hour shift.
a. Is there evidence that the mean amount of tea per bag is different from 5.5 grams (use $\alpha = 0.01$)?
b. Construct a 99% confidence interval estimate of the population mean amount of tea per bag. Interpret this interval.
c. Compare the conclusions reached in (a) and (b).

**9.33** Although many people think they can put a meal on the table in a short period of time, a recent article reported that they end up spending about 40 minutes doing so (extracted from N. Hellmich, "Americans Go for the Quick Fix for Dinner," *USA Today*, February 14, 2006). Suppose another study is conducted to test the validity of this statement. A sample of 25 people is selected, and the length of time to prepare and cook dinner (in minutes) is recorded, with the following results (stored in the file Dinner).

44.0 51.9 49.7 40.0 55.5 33.0 43.4 41.3 45.2 40.7 41.1 49.1 30.9
45.2 55.3 52.1 55.1 38.8 43.1 39.2 58.6 49.8 43.2 47.9 46.6

a. Is there evidence that the population mean time to prepare and cook dinner is different from 40 minutes? Use the $p$-value approach and a level of significance of 0.05.
b. What assumption about the population distribution is needed in order to conduct the $t$ test in (a)?
c. Make a list of the various ways you could evaluate the assumption noted in (b).
d. Evaluate the assumption noted in (b) and determine whether the $t$ test in (a) is valid.

## 9.3 ONE-TAIL TESTS

In Section 9.1, hypothesis testing was used to examine the question of whether the population mean amount of cereal filled is 368 grams. The alternative hypothesis ($H_1$: $\mu \neq 368$) contains two possibilities: Either the mean is less than 368 grams, or the mean is more than 368 grams. For this reason, the rejection region is divided into the two tails of the sampling distribution of the mean. In Section 9.2, once again a two-tail test was used to determine whether the mean amount per invoice had changed from $120.

In contrast to these two examples, many situations require an alternative hypothesis that focuses on a *particular direction*. For example, the population mean is *less than* a specified value. One such situation involves the service time at the drive-through window of a fast-food restaurant. The speed with which customers are served is of critical importance to the success of the service (see **www.qsrmagazine.com/reports/drive-thru_time_study**). In a recent study, McDonald's had a mean service time of 163.9 seconds, which was the fourth best in the industry. Suppose that McDonald's has embarked on a quality improvement effort to reduce the service time and has developed improvements to the service process at the drive-through. The new process will be tested in a sample of 25 stores. Because McDonald's would only want to institute the new process in all of its stores if it resulted in *decreased* drive-through time, the entire rejection region is located in the lower tail of the distribution.

### The Critical Value Approach

You wish to determine whether the new drive-through process has a mean that is less than 163.9 seconds. To perform this one-tail hypothesis test, you use the six-step method listed in Exhibit 9.1 on page 349.

**Step 1**

$$H_0: \mu \geq 163.9$$

$$H_1: \mu < 163.9$$

The alternative hypothesis contains the statement you are trying to prove. If the conclusion of the test is "reject $H_0$," there is statistical proof that the mean drive-through time is less than the drive-through time in the old process. This would be reason to change the drive-through process for the entire population of stores. If the conclusion of the test is "do not reject $H_0$," then there is insufficient evidence to prove that the mean drive-through time in the new process is significantly less than the drive-through time in the old process. If this occurs, there would be insufficient reason to institute the new drive-through process in the population of stores.

**Step 2**   You have selected a sample size of $n = 25$ stores. You decide to use $\alpha = 0.05$.

**Step 3**   Because $\sigma$ is unknown, you use the $t$ distribution and the $t_{STAT}$ test statistic. You must assume that the service time is normally distributed.

**Step 4**   The rejection region is entirely contained in the lower tail of the sampling distribution of the mean because you want to reject $H_0$ only when the sample mean is significantly less than 163.9 seconds. When the entire rejection region is contained in one tail of the sampling distribution of the test statistic, the test is called a **one-tail** or **directional test**. If the alternative hypothesis includes the *less than* sign, the critical value of $t$ is negative. As shown in Table 9.3 and Figure 9.12, because the entire rejection region is in the lower tail of the $t$ distribution and contains an area of 0.05, the critical value of the $t$ test statistic with $25 - 1 = 24$ degrees of freedom is $-1.7109$.

The decision rule is

$$\text{Reject } H_0 \text{ if } t_{STAT} < -1.7109;$$

$$\text{otherwise, do not reject } H_0.$$

**TABLE 9.3**

Determining the Critical Value from the *t* Table for an Area of 0.05 in the Lower Tail with 24 Degrees of Freedom

| | Cumulative Probabilities | | | | | |
|---|---|---|---|---|---|---|
| | .75 | .90 | .95 | .975 | .99 | .995 |
| | Upper-Tail Areas | | | | | |
| Degrees of Freedom | .25 | .10 | .05 | .025 | .01 | .005 |
| 1 | 1.0000 | 3.0777 | 6.3138 | 12.7062 | 31.8207 | 63.6574 |
| 2 | 0.8165 | 1.8856 | 2.9200 | 4.3027 | 6.9646 | 9.9248 |
| 3 | 0.7649 | 1.6377 | 2.3534 | 3.1824 | 4.5407 | 5.8409 |
| . | . | . | . | . | . | . |
| . | . | . | . | . | . | . |
| . | . | . | . | . | . | . |
| 23 | 0.6853 | 1.3195 | 1.7139 | 2.0687 | 2.4999 | 2.8073 |
| 24 | 0.6848 | 1.3178 | 1.7109 | 2.0639 | 2.4922 | 2.7969 |
| 25 | 0.6844 | 1.3163 | 1.7081 | 2.0595 | 2.4851 | 2.7874 |

Source: *Extracted from Table E.3.*

**FIGURE 9.12**

One-tail test of hypothesis for a mean (σ known) at the 0.05 level of significance

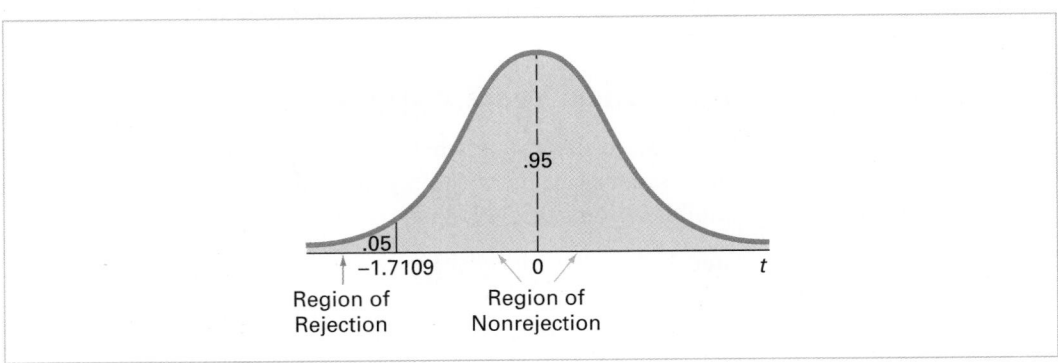

Region of Rejection    Region of Nonrejection

**Step 5**  You select a sample of 25 stores and find that the sample mean service time at the drive-through equals 152.7 seconds and the sample standard deviation equals 20 seconds. Using $n = 25$, $\bar{X} = 152.7$, $S = 20$, and Equation (9.2) on page 356,

$$t_{STAT} = \frac{\bar{X} - \mu}{\frac{S}{\sqrt{n}}} = \frac{152.7 - 163.9}{\frac{20}{\sqrt{25}}} = -2.80$$

**Step 6**  Because $t_{STAT} = -2.80 < -1.7109$, you reject the null hypothesis (see Figure 9.12). You conclude that the mean service time at the drive-through is below 163.9 seconds. There is sufficient evidence to change the drive-through process for the entire population of stores.

## The *p*-Value Approach

Use the five steps listed in Exhibit 9.2 on page 352 to illustrate the *t* test for the drive-through time study using the *p*-value approach.

**Steps 1–3**  These steps are the same as in the critical value approach on page 363.

**Step 4**  $t_{STAT} = -2.80$ (see step 5 of the critical value approach). Because the alternative hypothesis indicates a rejection region entirely in the *lower* tail of the sampling distribution, to compute the *p*-value you need to find the probability that the *t*-value will be *less than* the $t_{STAT}$ test statistic of −2.80. From Figure 9.13, the *p*-value is 0.0050.

**FIGURE 9.13**

Microsoft Excel *t* test results for the drive-through time study

*See Section E9.1 or P9.1 to create this. (Minitab users, see Section M9.1 to create the equivalent results.)*

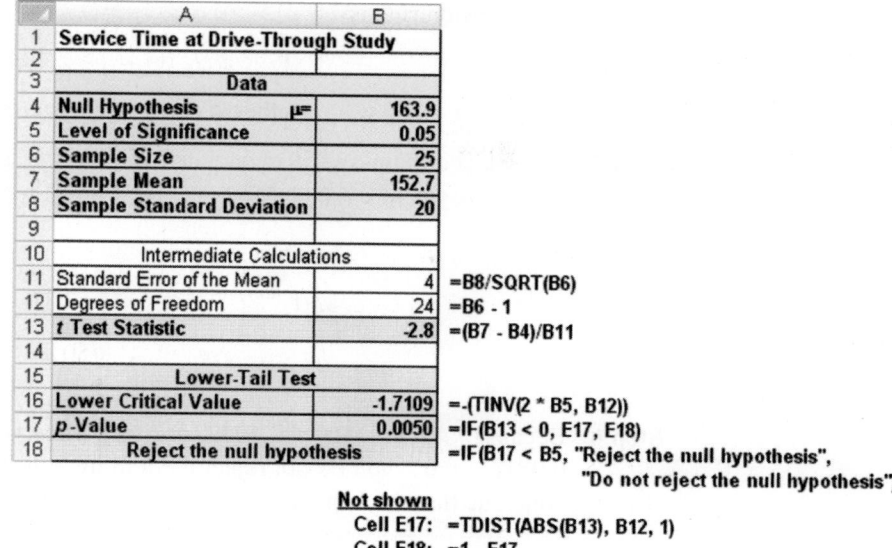

| | A | B | |
|---|---|---|---|
| 1 | Service Time at Drive-Through Study | | |
| 2 | | | |
| 3 | Data | | |
| 4 | Null Hypothesis μ= | 163.9 | |
| 5 | Level of Significance | 0.05 | |
| 6 | Sample Size | 25 | |
| 7 | Sample Mean | 152.7 | |
| 8 | Sample Standard Deviation | 20 | |
| 9 | | | |
| 10 | Intermediate Calculations | | |
| 11 | Standard Error of the Mean | 4 | =B8/SQRT(B6) |
| 12 | Degrees of Freedom | 24 | =B6 - 1 |
| 13 | *t* Test Statistic | -2.8 | =(B7 - B4)/B11 |
| 14 | | | |
| 15 | Lower-Tail Test | | |
| 16 | Lower Critical Value | -1.7109 | =-(TINV(2 * B5, B12)) |
| 17 | *p*-Value | 0.0050 | =IF(B13 < 0, E17, E18) |
| 18 | Reject the null hypothesis | | =IF(B17 < B5, "Reject the null hypothesis", "Do not reject the null hypothesis") |

Not shown
Cell E17:  =TDIST(ABS(B13), B12, 1)
Cell E18:  =1 - E17

**Step 5**   The *p*-value of 0.0050 is less than $\alpha = 0.05$ (see Figure 9.14). You reject $H_0$, and conclude that the mean service time at the drive-through is less than 163.9 seconds. There is sufficient evidence to change the drive-through process for the entire population of stores.

**FIGURE 9.14**

Determining the *p*-value for a one-tail test

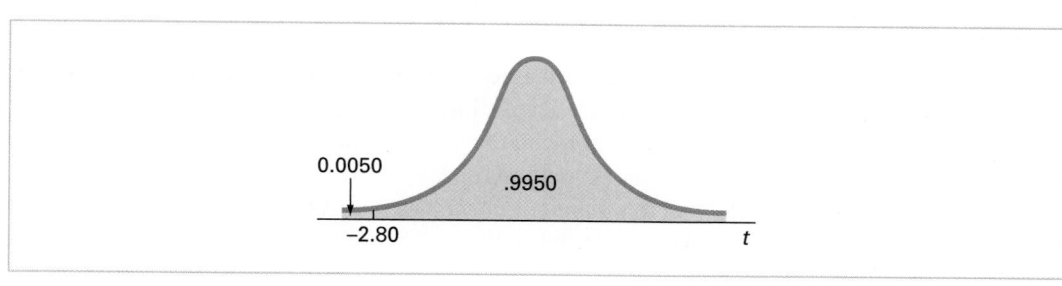

0.0050

.9950

−2.80        *t*

**EXAMPLE 9.5**

A ONE-TAIL TEST FOR THE MEAN

A company that manufactures chocolate bars is particularly concerned that the mean weight of a chocolate bar is not greater than 6.03 ounces. A sample of 50 chocolate bars is selected, and the sample mean is 6.034 ounces and the sample standard deviation is 0.02 ounces. Using the $\alpha = 0.01$ level of significance, is there evidence that the population mean weight of the chocolate bars is greater than 6.03 ounces?

**SOLUTION**   Using the critical value approach,

**Step 1**
$$H_0: \mu \le 6.03$$
$$H_1: \mu > 6.03$$

**Step 2**   You have selected a sample size of $n = 50$. You decide to use $\alpha = 0.01$.

**Step 3**   Because $\sigma$ is unknown, you use the *t* distribution and the $t_{STAT}$ test statistic.

**Step 4**   The rejection region is entirely contained in the upper tail of the sampling distribution of the mean because you want to reject $H_0$ only when the sample mean is significantly greater than 6.03 ounces. Because the entire rejection region is in the upper tail of the *t* distribution and contains an area of 0.01, the critical value of the *t* with $50 - 1 = 49$ degrees of freedom is 2.4049 (see Table E.3).

The decision rule is

$$\text{Reject } H_0 \text{ if } t_{STAT} > 2.4049;$$

otherwise, do not reject $H_0$.

**Step 5**   You select a sample of 50 chocolate bars, and the sample mean weight is 6.034 ounces. Using $n = 50$, $\bar{X} = 6.034$, $S = 0.02$, and Equation (9.2) on page 356,

$$t_{STAT} = \frac{\bar{X} - \mu}{\dfrac{S}{\sqrt{n}}} = \frac{6.034 - 6.03}{\dfrac{0.02}{\sqrt{50}}} = 1.414$$

**Step 6**   Because $t_{STAT} = 1.414 < 2.4049$, or using Microsoft Excel or Minitab, the $p$-value is $0.0818 > 0.01$, you do not reject the null hypothesis. There is insufficient evidence to conclude that the population mean weight is greater than 6.03 ounces.

To perform one-tail tests of hypotheses, you must properly formulate $H_0$ and $H_1$. A summary of the null and alternative hypotheses for one-tail tests is as follows:

- The null hypothesis, $H_0$, represents the status quo or the current belief in a situation.
- The alternative hypothesis, $H_1$, is the opposite of the null hypothesis and represents a research claim or specific inference you would like to prove.
- If you reject the null hypothesis, you have statistical proof that the alternative hypothesis is correct.
- If you do not reject the null hypothesis, then you have failed to prove the alternative hypothesis. The failure to prove the alternative hypothesis, however, does not mean that you have proven the null hypothesis.
- The null hypothesis always refers to a specified value of the *population parameter* (such as $\mu$), not to a *sample statistic* (such as $\bar{X}$).
- The statement of the null hypothesis *always* contains an equal sign regarding the specified value of the parameter (e.g., $H_0$: $\mu \geq 163.9$).
- The statement of the alternative hypothesis *never* contains an equal sign regarding the specified value of the parameter (e.g., $H_1$: $\mu < 163.9$).

# PROBLEMS FOR SECTION 9.3

## Learning the Basics

**9.34** In a one-tail hypothesis test where you reject $H_0$ only in the *upper* tail, what is the $p$-value if $Z_{STAT} = +2.00$?

**9.35** In Problem 9.34, what is your statistical decision if you test the null hypothesis at the 0.05 level of significance?

**9.36** In a one-tail hypothesis test where you reject $H_0$ only in the *lower* tail, what is the $p$-value if $Z_{STAT} = -1.38$?

**9.37** In Problem 9.36, what is your statistical decision if you test the null hypothesis at the 0.01 level of significance?

**9.38** In a one-tail hypothesis test where you reject $H_0$ only in the *lower* tail, what is the $p$-value if $Z_{STAT} = +1.38$?

**9.39** In Problem 9.38, what is the statistical decision if you test the null hypothesis at the 0.01 level of significance?

**9.40** In a one-tail hypothesis test where you reject $H_0$ only in the *upper* tail, what is the critical value of the $t$-test statistic with 10 degrees of freedom at the 0.01 level of significance?

**9.41** In Problem 9.40, what is your statistical decision if $t_{STAT} = +2.39$?

**9.42** In a one-tail hypothesis test where you reject $H_0$ only in the *lower* tail, what is the critical value of the $t_{STAT}$ test statistic with 20 degrees of freedom at the 0.01 level of significance?

**9.43** In Problem 9.42, what is your statistical decision if $t_{STAT} = -1.15$?

## Applying the Concepts

**9.44** ✓SELF Test The Glen Valley Steel Company manufactures steel bars. If the production process is working properly, it turns out steel bars that are normally distributed with mean length of *at least* 2.8 feet. Longer steel bars can be used or altered, but shorter bars must be scrapped. You select a sample of 25 bars, and the mean length is 2.73 feet and the sample standard deviation is 0.20 foot. Do you need to adjust the production equipment?

a. If you test the null hypothesis at the 0.05 level of significance, what decision do you make using the critical value approach to hypothesis testing?
b. If you test the null hypothesis at the 0.05 level of significance, what decision do you make using the *p*-value approach to hypothesis testing?
c. Interpret the meaning of the *p*-value in this problem.
d. Compare your conclusions in (a) and (b).

**9.45** You are the manager of a restaurant that delivers pizza to college dormitory rooms. You have just changed your delivery process in an effort to reduce the mean time between the order and completion of delivery from the current 25 minutes. A sample of 36 orders using the new delivery process yields a sample mean of 22.4 minutes and a sample standard deviation of 6 minutes.

a. Using the six-step critical value approach, at the 0.05 level of significance, is there evidence that the population mean delivery time has been reduced below the previous population mean value of 25 minutes?
b. At the 0.05 level of significance, use the five-step *p*-value approach.
c. Interpret the meaning of the *p*-value in (b).
d. Compare your conclusions in (a) and (b).

**9.46** Children in the United States account directly for $36 billion in sales annually. When their indirect influence over product decisions from stereos to vacations is considered, the total economic spending affected by children in the United States is $290 billion. It is estimated that by age 10, a child makes an average of more than five trips a week to a store (extracted from M. E. Goldberg, G. J. Gorn, L. A. Peracchio, and G. Bamossy, "Understanding Materialism Among Youth," *Journal of Consumer Psychology*, 2003, 13(3), pp. 278–288). Suppose that you want to prove that children in your city average more than five trips a week to a store. Let μ represent the population mean number of times children in your city make trips to a store.

a. State the null and alternative hypotheses.
b. Explain the meaning of the Type I and Type II errors in the context of this scenario.
c. Suppose that you carry out a similar study in the city in which you live. You take a sample of 100 children and find that the mean number of trips to the store is 5.47 and the sample standard deviation of the number of trips to the store is 1.6. At the 0.01 level of significance, is there evidence that the population mean number of trips to the store is greater than 5 per week?
d. Interpret the meaning of the *p*-value in (c).

**9.47** The waiting time to check out of a supermarket has had a population mean of 10.73 minutes. Recently, in an effort to reduce the waiting time, the supermarket has experimented with a system in which there is a single waiting line with multiple checkout servers. A sample of 100 customers was selected, and their mean waiting time to check out was 9.52 minutes with a sample standard deviation of 5.8 minutes.

a. At the 0.05 level of significance, using the critical value approach to hypothesis testing, is there evidence that the population mean waiting time to check out is less than 10.73 minutes?
b. At the 0.05 level of significance, using the *p*-value approach to hypothesis testing, is there evidence that the population mean waiting time to check out is less than 10.73 minutes?
c. Interpret the meaning of the *p*-value in this problem.
d. Compare your conclusions in (a) and (b).

## 9.4 *Z* TEST OF HYPOTHESIS FOR THE PROPORTION

In some situations, you want to test a hypothesis about the proportion of events of interest in the population, π, rather than testing the population mean. To begin, you select a random sample and compute the **sample proportion**, $p = X/n$. You then compare the value of this statistic to the hypothesized value of the parameter, π, in order to decide whether to reject the null hypothesis. If the number of events of interest ($X$) and the number of events that are not of interest ($n - X$) are each at least five, the sampling distribution of a proportion approximately follows a normal distribution. You use the **Z test for the proportion** given in Equation (9.3) to perform the hypothesis test for the difference between the sample proportion, $p$, and the hypothesized population proportion, $\pi$.

---

**Z Test for the Proportion**

$$Z_{STAT} = \frac{p - \pi}{\sqrt{\dfrac{\pi(1 - \pi)}{n}}}$$

(9.3)

where

$$p = \text{sample proportion} = \frac{X}{n} = \frac{\text{Number of events of interest in the sample}}{\text{Sample size}}$$

$\pi$ = hypothesized proportion of events of interest in the population

The $Z_{STAT}$ test statistic approximately follows a standardized normal distribution when $X$ and $(n - X)$ are each at least 5.

---

To illustrate the $Z$ test for a proportion, consider a survey that sought to determine whether customer service is better or worse at e-commerce sites than it is at physical stores (extracted from "Consumers Happier With E-Commerce," *USA Today Snapshots*, March 13, 2007, p. 1B). Of 1,100 respondents, 561 stated that customer service was better at e-commerce sites than at physical stores. For this survey, the null and alternative hypotheses are stated as follows:

$H_0$: $\pi = 0.50$ (i.e., half of all consumers believe that customer service is better at e-commerce sites than at physical stores)

$H_1$: $\pi \neq 0.50$ (i.e., either less than half or more than half of all consumers believe that customer service is better at e-commerce sites than at physical stores)

Alternatively, by multiplying the numerator and denominator by $n$, you can write the $Z_{STAT}$ test statistic in terms of the number of events of interest, $X$, as shown in Equation (9.4).

---

**Z Test for the Proportion in Terms of the Number of Events of Interest**

$$Z_{STAT} = \frac{X - n\pi}{\sqrt{n\pi(1 - \pi)}}$$

(9.4)

---

## The Critical Value Approach

Because you are interested in determining whether the population proportion of consumers who believe that customer service is better at e-commerce sites than at physical stores is 0.50, you use a two-tail test. If you select the $\alpha = 0.05$ level of significance, the rejection and nonrejection regions are set up as in Figure 9.15, and the decision rule is

Reject $H_0$ if $Z_{STAT} < -1.96$ or if $Z_{STAT} > +1.96$;

otherwise, do not reject $H_0$.

**FIGURE 9.15**

Two-tail test of hypothesis for the proportion at the 0.05 level of significance

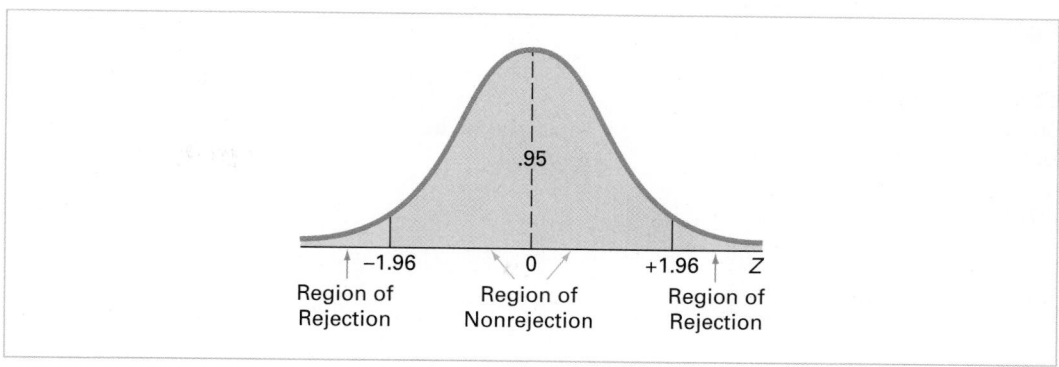

Because 561 of the 1,100 respondents stated that customer service was better at e-commerce sites than at physical stores,

$$p = \frac{561}{1,100} = 0.51$$

Using Equation (9.3),

$$Z_{STAT} = \frac{p - \pi}{\sqrt{\dfrac{\pi(1-\pi)}{n}}} = \frac{0.51 - 0.50}{\sqrt{\dfrac{0.50(1-0.50)}{1,100}}} = \frac{0.01}{0.0151} = 0.6633$$

or, using Equation (9.4),

$$Z_{STAT} = \frac{X - n\pi}{\sqrt{n\pi(1-\pi)}} = \frac{561 - (1,100)(0.50)}{\sqrt{1,100(0.50)(0.50)}} = \frac{11}{16.5831} = 0.6633$$

Because $-1.96 < Z_{STAT} = 0.6633 < 1.96$, you do not reject $H_0$. There is insufficient evidence that the population proportion of all consumers who believe that customer service is better at e-commerce sites than at physical stores is not 0.50. Figure 9.16 presents a Microsoft Excel worksheet and Figure 9.17 presents Minitab results for these data.

**FIGURE 9.16**

Microsoft Excel results for the survey of whether customer service is better or worse at e-commerce sites than it is at physical stores

*See Section E9.3 or P9.3 to create this.*

| | A | B | |
|---|---|---|---|
| 1 | **Z Test of Hypothesis for the Proportion** | | |
| 2 | | | |
| 3 | **Data** | | |
| 4 | **Null Hypothesis** p= | 0.5 | |
| 5 | **Level of Significance** | 0.05 | |
| 6 | **Number of Items of Interest** | 561 | |
| 7 | **Sample Size** | 1100 | |
| 8 | | | |
| 9 | **Intermediate Calculations** | | |
| 10 | Sample Proportion | 0.5100 | =B6/B7 |
| 11 | Standard Error | 0.0151 | =SQRT(B4*(1 - B4)/B7) |
| 12 | Z Test Statistic | 0.6633 | =(B10 - B4)/B11 |
| 13 | | | |
| 14 | **Two-Tail Test** | | |
| 15 | Lower Critical Value | -1.9600 | =NORMSINV(B5/2) |
| 16 | Upper Critical Value | 1.9600 | =NORMSINV(1 - B5/2) |
| 17 | p-Value | 0.5071 | =2 * (1 - NORMSDIST(ABS(B12))) |
| 18 | **Do not reject the null hypothesis** | | =IF(B17 < B5, "Reject the null hypothesis", "Do not reject the null hypothesis") |

**FIGURE 9.17**

Minitab results for the survey of whether customer service is better or worse at e-commerce sites than it is at physical stores

*See Section M9.3 to create this.*

```
Sample   X    N  Sample p        95% CI          Z-Value  P-Value
1       561 1100  0.510000  (0.480458, 0.539542)   0.66    0.507

Using the normal approximation.
```

## The *p*-Value Approach

As an alternative to the critical value approach, you can compute the *p*-value. For this two-tail test in which the rejection region is located in the lower tail and the upper tail, you need to find the area below a $Z$ value of $-0.66$ and above a $Z$ value of $+0.66$. Figures 9.16 and 9.17 report a *p*-value of 0.507. Because this value is greater than the selected level of significance ($\alpha = 0.05$), you do not reject the null hypothesis.

---

**EXAMPLE 9.6**   TESTING A HYPOTHESIS FOR A PROPORTION

A fast-food chain has developed a new process to ensure that orders at the drive-through are filled correctly. The previous process filled orders correctly 85% of the time. Based on a sample of 100 orders using the new process, 94 were filled correctly. At the 0.01 level of significance, can you conclude that the new process has increased the proportion of orders filled correctly?

**SOLUTION**  The null and alternative hypotheses are

$H_0$: $\pi \leq 0.85$ (i.e., the population proportion of orders filled correctly using the new process is less than or equal to 0.85)

$H_1$: $\pi > 0.85$ (i.e., the population proportion of orders filled correctly using the new process is greater than 0.85)

Using Equation (9.3) on page 368,

$$p = \frac{X}{n} = \frac{94}{100} = 0.94$$

$$Z_{STAT} = \frac{p - \pi}{\sqrt{\dfrac{\pi(1-\pi)}{n}}} = \frac{0.94 - 0.85}{\sqrt{\dfrac{0.85(1-0.85)}{100}}} = \frac{0.09}{0.0357} = 2.52$$

The *p*-value for $Z_{STAT} > 2.52$ is 0.0059.

Using the critical value approach, you reject $H_0$ if $Z_{STAT} > 2.33$. Using the *p*-value approach, you reject $H_0$ if the *p*-value $< 0.01$. Because $Z_{STAT} = 2.52 > 2.33$ or the *p*-value = $0.0059 < 0.01$, you reject $H_0$. You have evidence that the new process has increased the proportion of correct orders above 0.85.

# PROBLEMS FOR SECTION 9.4

## Learning the Basics

**9.48** If, in a random sample of 400 items, 88 are defective, what is the sample proportion of defective items?

**9.49** In Problem 9.48, if the null hypothesis is that 20% of the items in the population are defective, what is the value of $Z_{STAT}$?

**9.50** In Problems 9.48 and 9.49, suppose you are testing the null hypothesis $H_0$: $\pi = 0.20$ against the two-tail alternative hypothesis $H_1$: $\pi \neq 0.20$ and you choose the level of significance $\alpha = 0.05$. What is your statistical decision?

## Applying the Concepts

**9.51** Late payment of medical claims can add to the cost of health care. An article (M. Freudenheim, "The Check Is Not in the Mail," *The New York Times*, May 25, 2006, pp. C1, C6) reported that for one insurance company, 85.1% of the claims were paid in full when first submitted. Suppose that the insurance company developed a new payment system in an effort to increase this percentage. A sample of 200 claims processed under this system revealed that 180 of the claims were paid in full when first submitted.
**a.** At the 0.05 level of significance, is there evidence that the population proportion of claims processed under this new system is higher than the article reported for the previous system?
**b.** Compute the *p*-value and interpret its meaning.

**9.52** On Memorial Day weekend in 2007, gas prices in the United States reached an all-time high. An Ohio newspaper conducted a survey to see how its readers were reacting to the high prices. Of the 720 readers surveyed, 377 indicated that they planned to cut back on driving (extracted from "Gasoline Usage Poll," *The Oxford Press*, **www.oxfordpress.com**, May 24, 2007). Using a 0.05 level of significance and the 5-step *p*-value approach, can you prove that more than half of *The Oxford Press* readers planned to cut back on driving?

**9.53** A *Wall Street Journal* article suggested that age bias was a growing problem in the corporate world (extracted from C. Hymowitz, "Top Executives Chase Youthful Appearance, but Miss Real Issue," *The Wall Street Journal*, February 17, 2004, p. B1). In 2001, an estimated 78% of executives believed that age bias was a serious problem. In a 2004 study by ExecuNet, 82% of the executives surveyed considered age bias a serious problem. The sample size for the 2004 study was not disclosed. Suppose 50 executives were surveyed.

**a.** At the 0.05 level of significance, use the six-step critical value approach to hypothesis testing to try to prove that the 2004 proportion of executives who believed that age bias was a serious problem has increased.
**b.** Use the five-step *p*-value approach. Interpret the meaning of the *p*-value.
**c.** Suppose that the sample size used was 1,000. Redo (a) and (b).
**d.** Discuss the effect that sample size had on the outcome of this analysis and, in general, the effect that sample size plays in hypothesis testing.

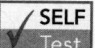 **9.54** A *Wall Street Journal* poll ("What's News Online," *The Wall Street Journal*, March 30, 2004, p. D7) asked respondents if they trusted energy-efficiency ratings on cars and appliances; 552 responded yes, and 531 responded no.
**a.** At the 0.05 level of significance, use the six-step critical value approach to hypothesis testing to try to prove that the percentage of people who trust energy-efficiency ratings differs from 50%.
**b.** Use the five-step *p*-value approach. Interpret the meaning of the *p*-value.

**9.55** One of the biggest issues facing e-retailers is the ability to reduce the proportion of customers who cancel their transactions after they have selected their products. It has been estimated that about half of prospective customers cancel their transactions after they have selected their products (extracted from B. Tedeschi, "E-Commerce, a Cure for Abandoned Shopping Carts: A Web Checkout System That Eliminates the Need for Multiple Screens," *The New York Times*, February 14, 2005, p. C3). Suppose that a company changed its Web site so that customers could use a single-page checkout process rather than multiple pages. A sample of 500 customers who had selected their products were provided with the new checkout system. Of these 500 customers, 210 cancelled their transactions after they had selected their products.
**a.** At the 0.01 level of significance, is there evidence that the population proportion of customers who select products and then cancel their transaction is less than 0.50 with the new system?
**b.** Suppose that a sample of *n* = 100 customers (instead of *n* = 500 customers) were provided with the new checkout system and that 42 of those customers cancelled their transactions after they had selected their products. At the 0.01 level of significance, is there evidence that the population proportion of customers who select

products and then cancel their transaction is less than 0.50 with the new system?

c. Compare the results of (a) and (b) and discuss the effect that sample size has on the outcome, and, in general, in hypothesis testing.

**9.56** A recent study by the Pew Internet and American Life Project (**pewinternet.org**) found that Americans had a complex and ambivalent attitude toward technology (extracted from M. Himowitz, "How to Tell What Kind of Tech User You Are," *Newsday*, May 27, 2007, p. F6). The study reported that 8% of the respondents were "Omnivores" who are gadget lovers, text messengers, and online gamers who often had

their own blogs, Web pages, video makers, and YouTube posters. You believe that the percentage of students at your school who are Omnivores is greater than 8% and you plan to carry out a study to prove that this is so.

a. State the null and alternative hypothesis.

You select a sample of 200 students at your school and find that 30 students can be classified as Omnivores.

b. Use either the six-step critical value hypothesis-testing approach or the five-step *p*-value approach to determine at the 0.05 level of significance whether there is evidence that the percentage of Omnivores at your school is greater than 8%.

## 9.5   THE POWER OF A TEST

Section 9.1 defined Type I and Type II errors and their associated risks. Recall that $\alpha$ represents the probability that you reject the null hypothesis when it is true and should not be rejected, and $\beta$ represents the probability that you do not reject the null hypothesis when it is false and should be rejected. The power of the test, $1 - \beta$, is the probability that you correctly reject a false null hypothesis. This probability depends on how different the actual population parameter is from the value being hypothesized (under $H_0$), the value of $\alpha$ used, and the sample size. If there is a large difference between the population parameter and the hypothesized value, the power of the test will be much greater than if the difference between the population parameter and the hypothesized value is small. Selecting a larger value of $\alpha$ makes it easier to reject $H_0$ and therefore increases the power of a test. Increasing the sample size increases the precision in the estimates and therefore increases the ability to detect differences in the parameters and increases the power of a test.

In this section, the power of a statistical test is illustrated using the Oxford Cereals scenario. The filling process is subject to periodic inspection from a representative of the consumer affairs office. The representative's job is to detect the possible "short weighting" of boxes (i.e., cereal boxes are being sold that, on average have less than the specified 368 grams). Thus, the representative is interested in determining whether there is evidence that the cereal boxes have a mean weight that is less than 368 grams. The null and alternative hypotheses are as follows:

$$H_0: \mu \geq 368 \text{ (filling process is working properly)}$$

$$H_1: \mu < 368 \text{ (filling process is not working properly)}$$

The representative is willing to accept the company's claim that the standard deviation $\sigma$ equals 15 grams. Therefore, you can use the $Z$ test. Using Equation (9.1) on page 347, with $\bar{X}_L$ (the lower critical $\bar{X}$ value) substituted for $\bar{X}$, you can find the value of $\bar{X}$ that enables you to reject the null hypothesis:

$$Z_\alpha = \frac{\bar{X}_L - \mu}{\dfrac{\sigma}{\sqrt{n}}}$$

$$Z_\alpha \frac{\sigma}{\sqrt{n}} = \bar{X}_L - \mu$$

$$\bar{X}_L = \mu + Z_\alpha \frac{\sigma}{\sqrt{n}}$$

Because you have a one-tail test with a level of significance of 0.05, the value of $Z_\alpha$ is equal to $-1.645$ (see Figure 9.18). The sample size $n = 25$. Therefore,

$$\bar{X}_L = 368 + (-1.645)\frac{(15)}{\sqrt{25}} = 368 - 4.935 = 363.065$$

The decision rule for this one-tail test is

$$\text{Reject } H_0 \text{ if } \bar{X} < 363.065;$$

$$\text{otherwise do not reject } H_0.$$

**FIGURE 9.18**

Determining the lower critical value for a one-tail $Z$ test for a population mean at the 0.05 level of significance

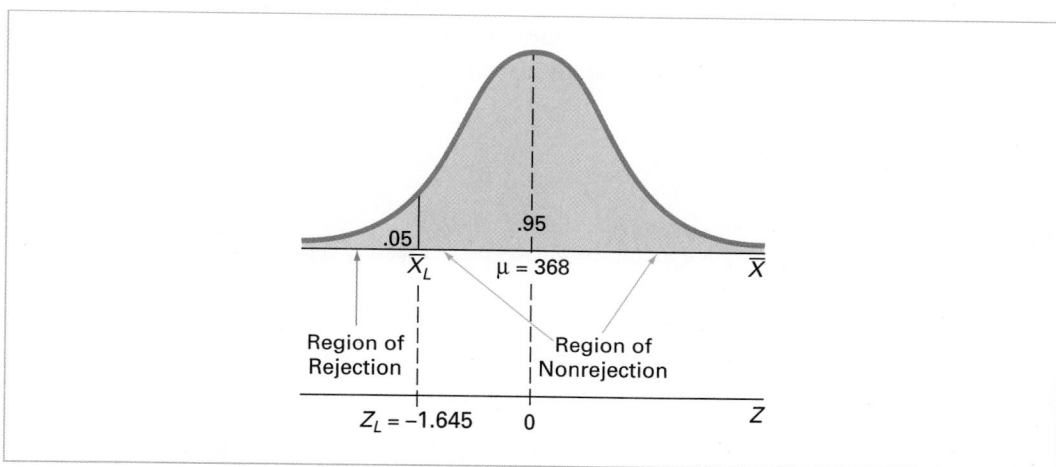

The decision rule states that if, in a random sample of 25 boxes, the sample mean is less than 363.065 grams, you reject the null hypothesis, and the representative concludes that the process is not working properly.

The power of the test measures the probability of concluding that the process is not working properly for differing values of the true population mean. What is the power of the test if the actual population mean is 360 grams? To determine the chance of rejecting the null hypothesis when the population mean is 360 grams, you need to determine the area under the normal curve below $\bar{X}_L = 363.065$ grams. Using Equation (9.1), with the population mean $\mu = 360$,

$$Z_{STAT} = \frac{\bar{X} - \mu}{\dfrac{\sigma}{\sqrt{n}}}$$

$$= \frac{363.065 - 360}{\dfrac{15}{\sqrt{25}}} = 1.02$$

From Table E.2, there is an 84.61% chance that the $Z$ value is less than $+1.02$. This is the power of the test when the population mean is 360 grams (see Figure 9.19 on page 374). The probability $(\beta)$ that you will not reject the null hypothesis $(\mu = 368)$ is $1 - 0.8461 = 0.1539$. Thus, the probability of committing a Type II error is 15.39%.

**FIGURE 9.19**

Determining the power of the test and the probability of a Type II error when $\mu = 360$ grams

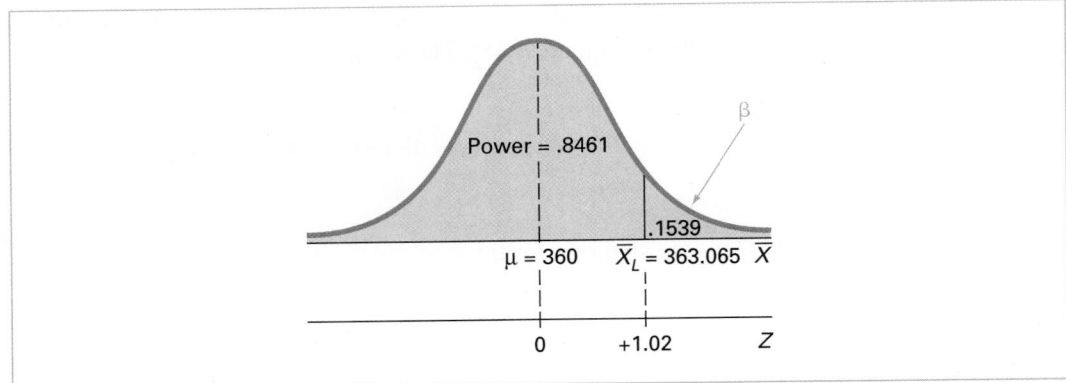

Now that you have determined the power of the test if the population mean were equal to 360, you can calculate the power for any other value of $\mu$. For example, what is the power of the test if the population mean is 352 grams? Assuming the same standard deviation, sample size, and level of significance, the decision rule is

$$\text{Reject } H_0 \text{ if } \overline{X} < 363.065;$$

$$\text{otherwise do not reject } H_0.$$

Once again, because you are testing a hypothesis for a mean, from Equation (9.1)

$$Z_{STAT} = \frac{\overline{X} - \mu}{\dfrac{\sigma}{\sqrt{n}}}$$

If the population mean shifts down to 352 grams (see Figure 9.20), then

$$Z_{STAT} = \frac{363.065 - 352}{\dfrac{15}{\sqrt{25}}} = 3.69$$

**FIGURE 9.20**

Determining the power of the test and the probability of a Type II error when $\mu = 352$ grams

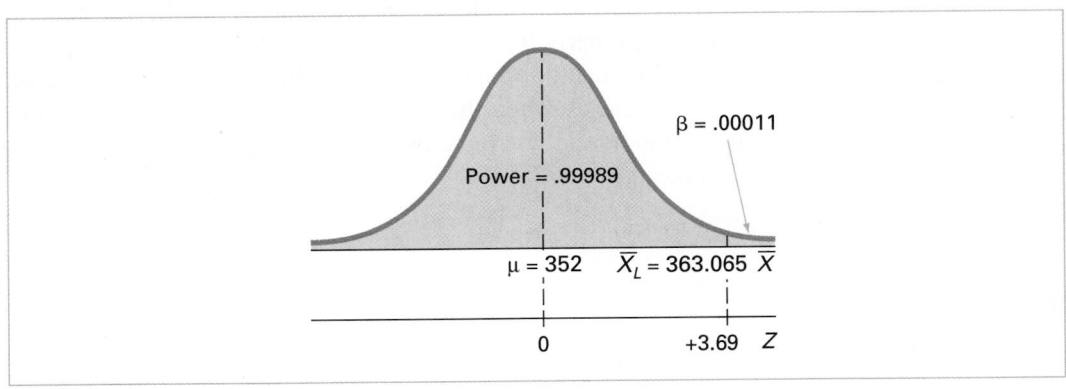

From Table E.2, there is a 99.989% chance that the $Z$ value is less than +3.69. This is the power of the test when the population mean is 352. The probability ($\beta$) that you will not reject the null hypothesis ($\mu = 368$) is $1 - 0.99989 = 0.00011$. Thus, the probability of committing a Type II error is only 0.011%.

In the preceding two examples the power of the test is high, and the chance of committing a Type II error is low. In the next example, you compute the power of the test when the population mean is equal to 367 grams—a value that is very close to the hypothesized mean of 368 grams.

Once again, from Equation (9.1),

$$Z_{STAT} = \frac{\overline{X} - \mu}{\dfrac{\sigma}{\sqrt{n}}}$$

If the population mean is equal to 367 grams (see Figure 9.21), then

$$Z_{STAT} = \frac{363.065 - 367}{\dfrac{15}{\sqrt{25}}} = -1.31$$

**FIGURE 9.21**

Determining the power of the test and the probability of a Type II error when $\mu = 367$ grams

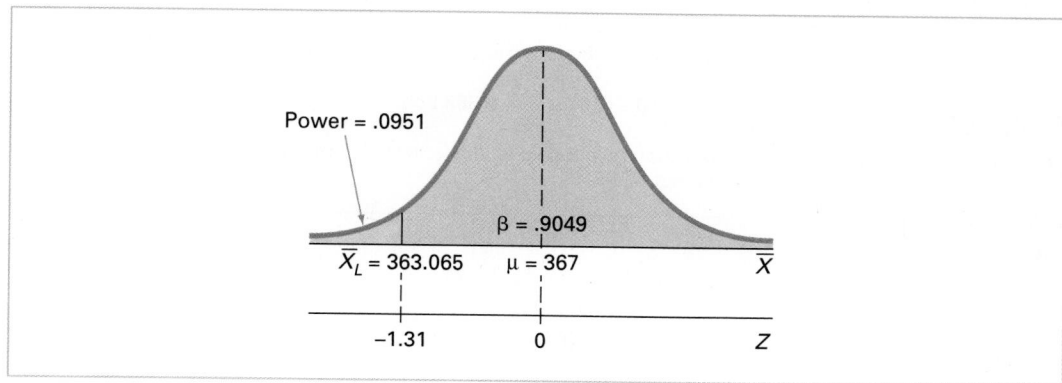

From Table E.2, the probability less than $Z = -1.31$ is 0.0951 (or 9.51%). Because the rejection region is in the lower tail of the distribution, the power of the test is 9.51% and the chance of making a Type II error is 90.49%.

Figure 9.22 illustrates the power of the test for various values of $\mu$ (including the three values examined). This graph is called a **power curve**.

**FIGURE 9.22**

Power curve of the cereal-box-filling process for $H_1$: $\mu < 368$ grams

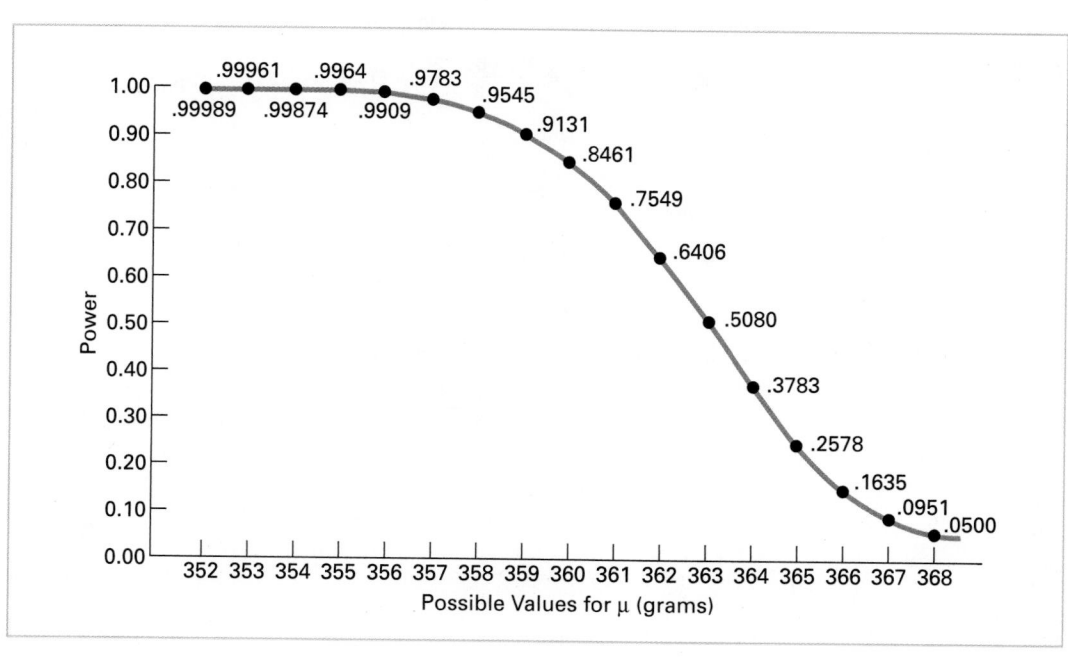

[1]For situations involving one-tail tests in which the actual mean is greater than the hypothesized mean, the converse would be true. The larger the actual mean compared with the hypothesized mean, the greater is the power. For two-tail tests, the greater the distance between the actual mean and the hypothesized mean, the greater the power of the test.

From Figure 9.22, you can see that the power of this one-tail test increases sharply (and approaches 100%) as the population mean takes on values farther below the hypothesized mean of 368 grams. Clearly, for this one-tail test, the smaller the actual mean $\mu$ the greater the power to detect this difference.[1] For values of $\mu$ close to 368 grams, the power is small because the test cannot effectively detect small differences between the actual population mean and the hypothesized value of 368 grams. When the population mean approaches 368 grams, the power of the test approaches $\alpha$, the level of significance (which is 0.05 in this example). Figure 9.23 summarizes the computations for the three cases combined.

**FIGURE 9.23**

Determining the power of the test for varying values of the population mean

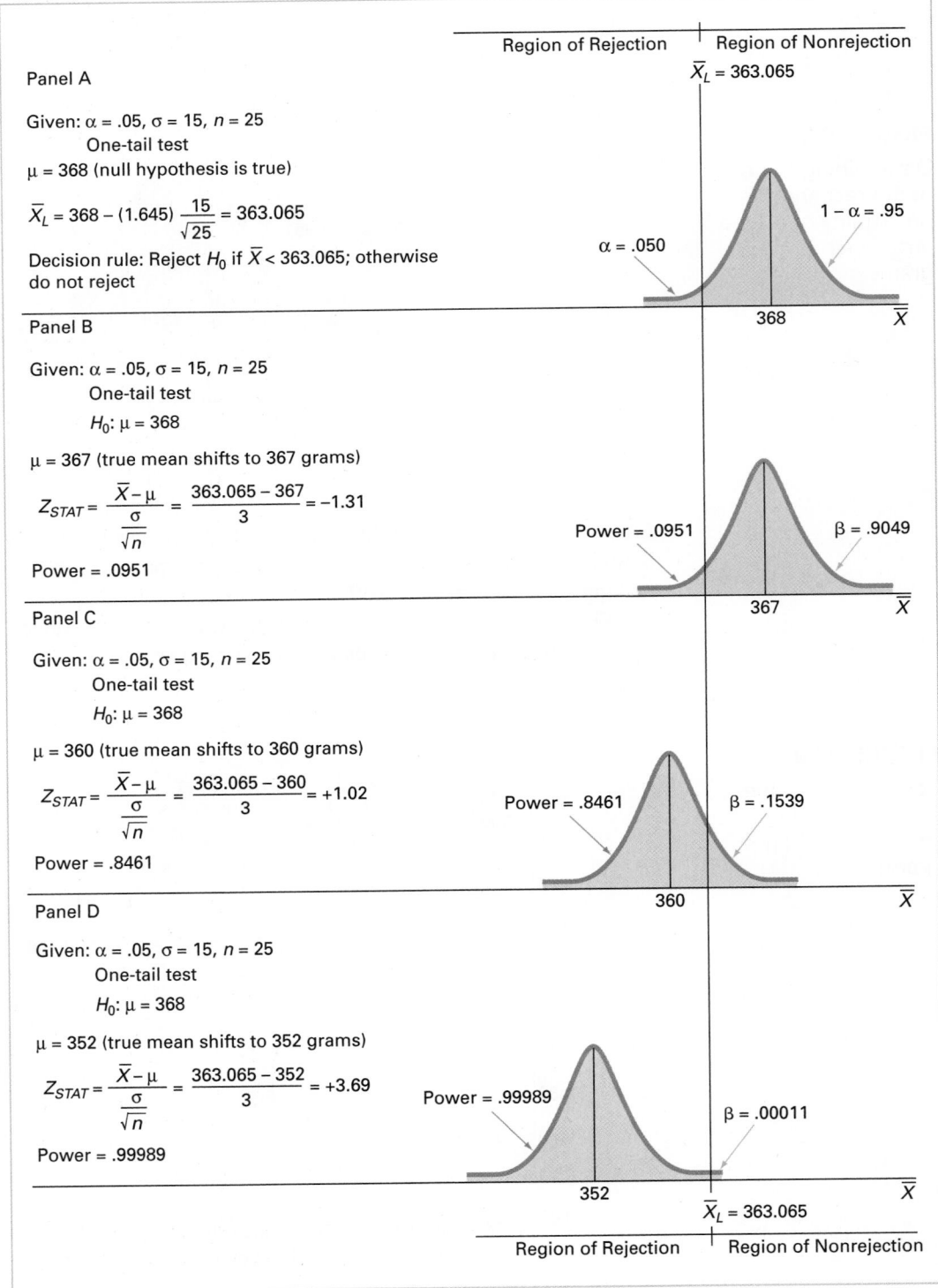

**Panel A**

Given: $\alpha = .05$, $\sigma = 15$, $n = 25$
One-tail test
$\mu = 368$ (null hypothesis is true)

$\overline{X}_L = 368 - (1.645)\dfrac{15}{\sqrt{25}} = 363.065$

Decision rule: Reject $H_0$ if $\overline{X} < 363.065$; otherwise do not reject

**Panel B**

Given: $\alpha = .05$, $\sigma = 15$, $n = 25$
One-tail test
$H_0$: $\mu = 368$

$\mu = 367$ (true mean shifts to 367 grams)

$Z_{STAT} = \dfrac{\overline{X} - \mu}{\dfrac{\sigma}{\sqrt{n}}} = \dfrac{363.065 - 367}{3} = -1.31$

Power = .0951

**Panel C**

Given: $\alpha = .05$, $\sigma = 15$, $n = 25$
One-tail test
$H_0$: $\mu = 368$

$\mu = 360$ (true mean shifts to 360 grams)

$Z_{STAT} = \dfrac{\overline{X} - \mu}{\dfrac{\sigma}{\sqrt{n}}} = \dfrac{363.065 - 360}{3} = +1.02$

Power = .8461

**Panel D**

Given: $\alpha = .05$, $\sigma = 15$, $n = 25$
One-tail test
$H_0$: $\mu = 368$

$\mu = 352$ (true mean shifts to 352 grams)

$Z_{STAT} = \dfrac{\overline{X} - \mu}{\dfrac{\sigma}{\sqrt{n}}} = \dfrac{363.065 - 352}{3} = +3.69$

Power = .99989

You can see the drastic changes in the power of the test for differing values of the actual population means by reviewing the different panels of Figure 9.23. From panels *A* and *B* you can see that when the population mean does not greatly differ from 368 grams, the chance of rejecting the null hypothesis is not large. However, once the population mean shifts substantially below the hypothesized 368 grams, the power of the test greatly increases, approaching its maximum value of 1 (or 100%).

In the above discussion, a one-tail test with $\alpha = 0.05$ and $n = 25$ was used. The type of statistical test (one-tail versus two-tail), the level of significance, and the sample size all affect the power. Three basic conclusions regarding the power of the test are summarized below:

1. A one-tail test is more powerful than a two-tail test.
2. An increase in the level of significance ($\alpha$) results in an increase in power. A decrease in $\alpha$ results in a decrease in power.
3. An increase in the sample size $n$ results in an increase in power. A decrease in the sample size $n$ results in a decrease in power.

# PROBLEMS FOR SECTION 9.5

## Applying the Concepts

**9.57** A coin-operated soft-drink machine is designed to discharge on average, at least 7 ounces of beverage per cup with a standard deviation of 0.2 ounce. The amount of beverage per cup is normally distributed. If you select a random sample of 16 cups and you are willing to have an $\alpha = 0.05$ risk of committing a Type I error, compute the power of the test and the probability of a Type II error ($\beta$) if the population mean amount dispensed is actually
a. 6.9 ounces per cup.
b. 6.8 ounces per cup.

**9.58** Refer to Problem 9.57. If you are willing to only have an $\alpha = 0.01$ risk of committing a Type I error, compute the power of the test and the probability of a Type II error ($\beta$) if the population mean amount dispensed is actually
a. 6.9 ounces per cup.
b. 6.8 ounces per cup.
c. Compare the results in (a) and (b) of this problem and in Problem 9.57. What conclusion can you reach?

**9.59** Refer to Problem 9.57. If you select a random sample of 25 cups and are willing to have an $\alpha = 0.05$ risk of committing a Type I error, compute the power of the test and the probability of a Type II error ($\beta$) if the population mean amount dispensed is actually
a. 6.9 ounces per cup.
b. 6.8 ounces per cup.
c. Compare the results in (a) and (b) of this problem and in Problem 9.57. What conclusion can you reach?

**9.60** A tire manufacturer produces tires that have a mean life of at least 25,000 miles when the production process is working properly. Based on past experience, the standard deviation of the tires is 3,500 miles and the tire life is normally distributed. The operations manager stops the production process if there is evidence that the population mean tire life is below 25,000 miles. If you select a random sample of 100 tires and you are willing to have an $\alpha = 0.05$ risk of committing a Type I error, compute the power of the test and the probability of a Type II error ($\beta$) if the population mean life is actually
a. 24,000 miles.
b. 24,900 miles.

**9.61** Refer to Problem 9.60. If you are willing to only have an $\alpha = 0.01$ risk of committing a Type I error, compute the power of the test and the probability of a Type II error ($\beta$) if the population mean life is actually
a. 24,000 miles.
b. 24,900 miles.
c. Compare the results in (a) and (b) of this problem and (a) and (b) in Problem 9.60. What conclusion can you reach?

**9.62** Refer to Problem 9.60. If you select a random sample of 25 tires and are willing to have an $\alpha = 0.05$ risk of committing a Type I error, compute the power of the test and the probability of a Type II error ($\beta$) if the population mean life is actually
a. 24,000 miles.
b. 24,900 miles.

**c.** Compare the results in (a) and (b) of this problem and (a) and (b) in Problem 9.60. What conclusion can you reach?

**9.63** Refer to Problem 9.60. If the operations manager stops the process when there is evidence that the population mean life is different from 25,000 miles (either less than or greater than) and a random sample of 100 tires is selected along with a level of significance of $\alpha = 0.05$, compute the power of the test and the probability of a Type II error ($\beta$) if the population mean life is actually

**a.** 24,000 miles.
**b.** 24,900 miles.
**c.** Compare the results in (a) and (b) of this problem and (a) and (b) in Problem 9.60. What conclusion can you reach?

## 9.6 POTENTIAL HYPOTHESIS-TESTING PITFALLS AND ETHICAL ISSUES

To this point, you have studied the fundamental concepts of hypothesis testing. You have used hypothesis testing to analyze differences between sample statistics and hypothesized population parameters in order to make business decisions concerning the underlying population characteristics. You have also learned how to evaluate the risks involved in making these decisions.

When planning to carry out a hypothesis test based on a survey, research study, or designed experiment, you must ask several questions to ensure that you use proper methodology. You need to raise and answer questions such as the following in the planning stage:

1. What is the goal of the survey, study, or experiment? How can you translate the goal into a null hypothesis and an alternative hypothesis?
2. Is the hypothesis test a two-tail test or one-tail test?
3. Can you select a random sample from the underlying population of interest?
4. What kinds of data will you collect in the sample? Are the variables numerical or categorical?
5. At what level of significance should you conduct the hypothesis test?
6. Is the intended sample size large enough to achieve the desired power of the test for the level of significance chosen?
7. What statistical test procedure should you use and why?
8. What conclusions and interpretations can you reach from the results of the hypothesis test?

Failing to consider these questions early in the planning process can lead to biased or incomplete results. Proper planning can help ensure that the statistical study will provide objective information needed to make good business decisions.

***Statistical Significance versus Practical Significance***   You need to make the distinction between the existence of a statistically significant result and its practical significance in the context within a field of application. Sometimes, due to a very large sample size, you may get a result that is statistically significant but has little practical significance. For example, suppose that prior to a national marketing campaign focusing on a series of expensive television commercials, you believe that the proportion of people who recognize your brand is 0.30. At the completion of the campaign, a survey of 20,000 people indicates that 6,168 recognized your brand. A one-tail test trying to prove that the proportion is now greater than 0.30 results in a *p*-value of 0.0047 and the correct statistical conclusion is that the proportion of consumers recognizing your brand name has now increased. Was the campaign successful? The result of the hypothesis test indicates a statistically significant increase in brand awareness, but is this increase practically important? The population proportion is now estimated at 6,168/20,000 = 0.3084, or 30.84%. This increase is less than 1% more than the hypothesized value of 30%. Did the large expenses associated with the marketing campaign produce a result with a meaningful increase in brand awareness? Because of the minimal real-world impact an increase of less than 1% has on the overall marketing strategy and the huge expenses associated with the marketing campaign, you should conclude that the campaign was not successful. On the other hand, if the campaign increased brand awareness by 20%, you could conclude that the campaign was successful.

**Ethical Issues**    You also need to distinguish between poor research methodology and unethical behavior. Ethical considerations arise when the hypothesis-testing process is manipulated. Some of the areas where ethical issues can arise include the use of human subjects in experiments, data collection method, the type of test (one-tail or two-tail test), the choice of the level of significance, data snooping, the cleansing and discarding of data, and the failure to report pertinent findings.

**Informed Consent from Human Respondents Being "Treated"**    Ethical considerations require that any individual who is to be subjected to some "treatment" in an experiment be made aware of the research endeavor and any potential behavioral or physical side effects. The person should also provide informed consent before participating.

**Data Collection Method—Randomization**    To eliminate the possibility of potential biases in the results, you must use proper data collection methods. To draw meaningful conclusions, the data must be the outcome of a random sample from a population or from an experiment in which a **randomization** process was used in which respondents are randomly assigned to groups. Potential respondents should not be permitted to self-select for a study, nor should they be purposely selected. Aside from the potential ethical issues that may arise, such a lack of randomization can result in serious coverage errors or selection biases that destroy the integrity of the study.

**Type of Test—Two-Tail or One-Tail Test**    If prior information is available that leads you to test the null hypothesis against a specifically directed alternative, then a one-tail test is more powerful than a two-tail test. However, if you are interested only in *differences* from the null hypothesis, not in the *direction* of the difference, the two-tail test is the appropriate procedure to use. For example, if previous research and statistical testing have already established the difference in a particular direction, or if an established scientific theory states that it is possible for results to occur in only one direction, then a one-tail test is appropriate. You should never change the direction of a test after the data are collected.

**Choice of Level of Significance, α**    In a well-designed study, you select the level of significance, α, before data collection occurs. You cannot alter the level of significance after the fact to achieve a specific result. You should always report the *p*-value, not just the conclusions of the hypothesis test.

**Data Snooping**    **Data snooping** involves performing a hypothesis test on a set of data, looking at the results, and only then specifying the level of significance or deciding whether to use a one-tail or two-tail test. This unethical approach is never permissible. You must make these decisions before the data are collected in order to achieve valid conclusions. In addition, you cannot arbitrarily change or discard extreme or unusual values in order to alter the results of the hypothesis tests.

**Cleansing and Discarding of Data**    In the data preparation stage of editing, coding, and transcribing, you have an opportunity to review the data for any extreme or unusual values. After reviewing the data, you should construct a stem-and-leaf display and/or a boxplot to determine whether there are possible outliers to double-check against the original data.

The process of data cleansing raises a major ethical question. Should you ever remove a value from a study? The answer is a qualified yes. If you can determine that a measurement is incomplete or grossly in error because of some equipment problem or unusual behavioral occurrence unrelated to the study, you can discard the value. Sometimes you have no choice—an individual may decide to quit a particular study he or she has been participating in before a final measurement can be made. In a well-designed experiment or study, you should decide, in advance, on all rules regarding the possible discarding of data.

***Reporting of Findings***   In conducting research, you should document both good and bad results. You should not just report the results of hypothesis tests that show statistical significance but omit those for which there is insufficient evidence in the findings. In instances in which there is insufficient evidence to reject $H_0$, you must make it clear that this does not prove that the null hypothesis is true. What the result does indicate is that with the sample size used, there is not enough information to *disprove* the null hypothesis.

***Summary***   To summarize, in discussing ethical issues concerning hypothesis testing, the key is *intent*. You must distinguish between poor data analysis and unethical practice. Unethical practice occurs when researchers *intentionally* create a selection bias in data collection, manipulate the treatment of human subjects without informed consent, use data snooping to select the type of test (two-tail or one-tail) and/or level of significance, discard values that do not support a stated hypothesis, or fail to report pertinent findings.

# SUMMARY

This chapter presented the foundation of hypothesis testing. You learned how to perform tests on the population mean and on the population proportion. You also learned how an operations manager of a production facility can use hypothesis testing to monitor and improve a cereal-fill process.

In deciding which test to use, you should ask the following question:

Does the test involve a numerical variable or a categorical variable? If the test involves a categorical variable, use the $Z$ test for the proportion. If the test involves a numerical variable, use the $t$ test for the mean.

Table 9.4 provides a list of topics covered in this chapter.

**TABLE 9.4**

Summary of Topics in Chapter 9

| Type of Analysis | Type of Data | |
| --- | --- | --- |
| | **Numerical** | **Categorical** |
| Hypothesis test concerning a single parameter | $t$ test of hypothesis for the mean (Section 9.2) | $Z$ test of hypothesis for the proportion (Section 9.4) |

# KEY EQUATIONS

**$Z$ Test for the Mean ($\sigma$ Known)**

$$Z_{STAT} = \frac{\bar{X} - \mu}{\dfrac{\sigma}{\sqrt{n}}} \qquad (9.1)$$

**$t$ Test for the Mean ($\sigma$ Unknown)**

$$t_{STAT} = \frac{\bar{X} - \mu}{\dfrac{S}{\sqrt{n}}} \qquad (9.2)$$

**Z Test for the Proportion**

$$Z_{STAT} = \frac{p - \pi}{\sqrt{\dfrac{\pi(1-\pi)}{n}}} \qquad (9.3)$$

**Z Test for the Proportion in Terms of the Number of Events of Interest**

$$Z_{STAT} = \frac{X - n\pi}{\sqrt{n\pi(1-\pi)}} \qquad (9.4)$$

# KEY TERMS

$\alpha$ (level of significance)   345
alternative hypothesis ($H_1$)   343
$\beta$ risk   346
confidence coefficient   346
confidence level   346
critical value   344
data snooping   379
directional test   363
hypothesis testing   342

level of significance ($\alpha$)   345
null hypothesis ($H_0$)   342
one-tail test   363
$p$-value   351
power curve   375
power of a statistical test   346
randomization   379
region of nonrejection   344
region of rejection   344

robust   359
sample proportion   367
$t$ test for the mean   355
test statistic   344
two-tail test   348
Type I error   345
Type II error   345
Z test for the mean   347
Z test for the proportion   367

# CHAPTER REVIEW PROBLEMS

## Checking Your Understanding

**9.64** What is the difference between a null hypothesis, $H_0$, and an alternative hypothesis, $H_1$?

**9.65** What is the difference between a Type I error and a Type II error?

**9.66** What is meant by the power of a test?

**9.67** What is the difference between a one-tail test and a two-tail test?

**9.68** What is meant by a $p$-value?

**9.69** How can a confidence interval estimate for the population mean provide conclusions to the corresponding two tail hypothesis test for the population mean?

**9.70** What is the six-step critical value approach to two-tail hypothesis testing?

**9.71** What is the five-step $p$-value approach to hypothesis testing?

**9.72** What are some of the ethical issues involved with performing a hypothesis test?

## Applying the Concepts

**9.73** An article in *Marketing News* (T. T. Semon, "Consider a Statistical Insignificance Test," *Marketing News*, February 1, 1999) argued that the level of significance used when comparing two products is often too low—that is, sometimes you should be using an $\alpha$ value greater than 0.05. Specifically, the article recounted testing the proportion of potential customers with a preference for product 1 over product 2. The null hypothesis was that the population proportion of potential customers preferring product 1 was 0.50, and the alternative hypothesis was that it was not equal to 0.50. The $p$-value for the test was 0.22. The article suggested that, in some cases, this should be enough evidence to reject the null hypothesis.

**a.** State the null and alternative hypotheses for this example in statistical terms.
**b.** Explain the risks associated with Type I and Type II errors in this case.
**c.** What would be the consequences if you rejected the null hypothesis for a $p$-value of 0.22?
**d.** Why do you think the article suggested raising the value of $\alpha$?
**e.** What would you do in this situation?
**f.** What is your answer in (e) if the $p$-value equals 0.12? What if it equals 0.06?

**9.74** La Quinta Motor Inns developed a computer model to help predict the profitability of sites that are being considered as locations for new hotels. If the computer model predicts large profits, La Quinta buys the proposed site and builds a new hotel. If the computer model predicts small or moderate profits, La Quinta chooses not to proceed with that site (extracted from S. E. Kimes and J. A. Fitzsimmons, "Selecting Profitable Hotel Sites at La Quinta Motor Inns," *Interfaces*, Vol. 20, March–April 1990, pp. 12–20). This decision-making procedure can be expressed in the hypothesis-testing framework. The null hypothesis is that the site is not a profitable location. The alternative hypothesis is that the site is a profitable location.

**a.** Explain the risks associated with committing a Type I error in this case.

**b.** Explain the risks associated with committing a Type II error in this case.

**c.** Which type of error do you think the executives at La Quinta Motor Inns are trying hard to avoid? Explain.

**d.** How do changes in the rejection criterion affect the probabilities of committing Type I and Type II errors?

**9.75** In 2006, Visa wanted to move away from its long-running television advertising theme of "Visa, it's everywhere you want to be." During the Winter Olympics, Visa featured Olympians in commercials with a broader message, including security, check cards, and payment technologies such as contactless processing. One of the first commercials featured snowboarder Lindsey Jacobellis being coached to calm down before a big race by imagining that her Visa Check Card got stolen. A key metric for the success of television advertisements is the proportion of viewers who "like the ads a lot." Harris Ad Research Service conducted a study of 903 adults who viewed the new Visa advertisement and reported that 54 indicated that they "like the ad a lot." According to Harris, the proportion of a typical television advertisement receiving the "like the ad a lot" score is 0.21 (extracted from T. Howard, "Visa to Change Strategies in Upcoming Ads," **usatoday.com**, January 23, 2006).

**a.** Use the six-step critical value approach to hypothesis testing and a 0.05 level of significance to try to prove that the new Visa ad is less successful than a typical television advertisement.

**b.** Use the five-step $p$-value approach to hypothesis testing and a 0.05 level of significance to try to prove that the new Visa ad is less successful than a typical television advertisement.

**c.** Compare the results of (a) and (b).

**9.76** The owner of a gasoline station wants to study gasoline purchasing habits by motorists at his station. He selects a random sample of 60 motorists during a certain week, with the following results:

- The amount purchased was $\bar{X} = 11.3$ gallons, $S = 3.1$ gallons.
- 11 motorists purchased premium-grade gasoline.

**a.** At the 0.05 level of significance, is there evidence that the population mean purchase was different from 10 gallons?

**b.** Determine the $p$-value in (a).

**c.** At the 0.05 level of significance, is there evidence that fewer than 20% of all the motorists at the station purchased premium-grade gasoline?

**d.** What is your answer to (a) if the sample mean equals 10.3 gallons?

**e.** What is your answer to (c) if 7 motorists purchased premium-grade gasoline?

**9.77** An auditor for a government agency is assigned the task of evaluating reimbursement for office visits to physicians paid by Medicare. The audit was conducted on a sample of 75 of the reimbursements, with the following results:
   In 12 of the office visits, an incorrect amount of reimbursement was provided.
   The amount of reimbursement was $\bar{X} = \$93.70$, $S = \$34.55$.

**a.** At the 0.05 level of significance, is there evidence that the population mean reimbursement was less than $100?

**b.** At the 0.05 level of significance, is there evidence that the proportion of incorrect reimbursements in the population was greater than 0.10?

**c.** Discuss the underlying assumptions of the test used in (a).

**d.** What is your answer to (a) if the sample mean equals $90?

**e.** What is your answer to (b) if 15 office visits had incorrect reimbursements?

**9.78** A bank branch located in a commercial district of a city has developed an improved process for serving customers during the noon-to-1:00 p.m. lunch period. The waiting time (defined as the time the customer enters the line until he or she reaches the teller window) of all customers during this hour is recorded over a period of 1 week. A random sample of 15 customers (see the data file **Bank1**) is selected, and the results are as follows:

| | | | | | | | |
|---|---|---|---|---|---|---|---|
| 4.21 | 5.55 | 3.02 | 5.13 | 4.77 | 2.34 | 3.54 | 3.20 |
| 4.50 | 6.10 | 0.38 | 5.12 | 6.46 | 6.19 | 3.79 | |

**a.** At the 0.05 level of significance, is there evidence that the population mean waiting time is less than 5 minutes?

**b.** What assumption about the population distribution is needed in order to conduct the $t$ test in (a)?

**c.** Use a boxplot or a normal probability plot to evaluate the assumption made in (b).

**d.** Do you think that the assumption needed in order to conduct the $t$ test in (a) is valid? Explain.

**e.** As a customer walks into the branch office during the lunch hour, she asks the branch manager how long she can expect to wait. The branch manager replies, "Almost certainly not longer than 5 minutes." On the basis of the results of (a), evaluate this statement.

**9.79** A manufacturing company produces electrical insulators. If the insulators break when in use, a short circuit is likely to occur. To test the strength of the insulators, destructive testing is carried out to determine how much *force* is required to break the insulators. Force is measured by observing the number of pounds of force applied to the insulator before it breaks. The following data (stored in the `Force` file) are from 30 insulators subject to this testing:

1,870 1,728 1,656 1,610 1,634 1,784 1,522 1,696 1,592 1,662

1,866 1,764 1,734 1,662 1,734 1,774 1,550 1,756 1,762 1,866

1,820 1,744 1,788 1,688 1,810 1,752 1,680 1,810 1,652 1,736

**a.** At the 0.05 level of significance, is there evidence that the population mean force is greater than 1,500 pounds?
**b.** What assumption about the population distribution is needed in order to conduct the *t* test in (a)?
**c.** Use a histogram, boxplot, or a normal probability plot to evaluate the assumption made in (b).
**d.** Do you think that the assumption needed in order to conduct the *t* test in (a) is valid? Explain.

**9.80** An important quality characteristic used by the manufacturer of Boston and Vermont asphalt shingles is the amount of moisture the shingles contain when they are packaged. Customers may feel that they have purchased a product lacking in quality if they find moisture and wet shingles inside the packaging. In some cases, excessive moisture can cause the granules attached to the shingle for texture and coloring purposes to fall off the shingle, resulting in appearance problems. To monitor the amount of moisture present, the company conducts moisture tests. A shingle is weighed and then dried. The shingle is then reweighed, and, based on the amount of moisture taken out of the product, the pounds of moisture per 100 square feet are calculated. The company would like to show that the mean moisture content is less than 0.35 pound per 100 square feet. The data file `Moisture` includes 36 measurements (in pounds per 100 square feet) for Boston shingles and 31 for Vermont shingles.

**a.** For the Boston shingles, is there evidence at the 0.05 level of significance that the population mean moisture content is less than 0.35 pound per 100 square feet?
**b.** Interpret the meaning of the *p*-value in (a).
**c.** For the Vermont shingles, is there evidence at the 0.05 level of significance that the population mean moisture content is less than 0.35 pound per 100 square feet?
**d.** Interpret the meaning of the *p*-value in (c).
**e.** What assumption about the population distribution is needed in order to conduct the *t* tests in (a) and (c)?
**f.** Use a histogram, boxplot, or a normal probability plot to evaluate the assumption made in (a) and (c).
**g.** Do you think that the assumption needed in order to conduct the *t* tests in (a) and (c) is valid? Explain.

**9.81** Studies conducted by the manufacturer of Boston and Vermont asphalt shingles have shown product weight

to be a major factor in the customer's perception of quality. Moreover, the weight represents the amount of raw materials being used and is therefore very important to the company from a cost standpoint. The last stage of the assembly line packages the shingles before the packages are placed on wooden pallets. Once a pallet is full (a pallet for most brands holds 16 squares of shingles), it is weighed, and the measurement is recorded. The data file `Pallet` contains the weight (in pounds) from a sample of 368 pallets of Boston shingles and 330 pallets of Vermont shingles.

**a.** For the Boston shingles, is there evidence that the population mean weight is different from 3,150 pounds?
**b.** Interpret the meaning of the *p*-value in (a).
**c.** For the Vermont shingles, is there evidence that the population mean weight is different from 3,700 pounds?
**d.** Interpret the meaning of the *p*-value in (c).
**e.** In (a) through (d), do you have to worry about the normality assumption? Explain.

**9.82** The manufacturer of Boston and Vermont asphalt shingles provides its customers with a 20-year warranty on most of its products. To determine whether a shingle will last as long as the warranty period, accelerated-life testing is conducted at the manufacturing plant. Accelerated-life testing exposes the shingle to the stresses it would be subject to in a lifetime of normal use in a laboratory setting via an experiment that takes only a few minutes to conduct. In this test, a shingle is repeatedly scraped with a brush for a short period of time, and the shingle granules removed by the brushing are weighed (in grams). Shingles that experience low amounts of granule loss are expected to last longer in normal use than shingles that experience high amounts of granule loss. The data file `Granule` contains a sample of 170 measurements made on the company's Boston shingles and 140 measurements made on Vermont shingles.

**a.** For the Boston shingles, is there evidence that the population mean granule loss is different from 0.50 gram?
**b.** Interpret the meaning of the *p*-value in (a).
**c.** For the Vermont shingles, is there evidence that the population mean granule loss is different from 0.50 gram?
**d.** Interpret the meaning of the *p*-value in (c).
**e.** In (a) through (d), do you have to worry about the normality assumption? Explain.

## Report Writing Exercises

**9.83** Referring to the results of Problems 9.80 through 9.82 concerning Boston and Vermont shingles, write a report that evaluates the moisture level, weight, and granule loss of the two types of shingles.

# MANAGING THE *SPRINGVILLE HERALD*

Continuing its monitoring of the blackness of the newspaper print, first described in the Chapter 6 Managing the *Springville Herald* case, the production department of the newspaper wants to ensure that the mean blackness of the print for all newspapers is at least 0.97 on a standard scale in which the target value is 1.0. A random sample of 50 newspapers was selected, and the blackness of one spot on each of the 50 newspapers measured (and stored in the **SH9** file).

```
0.854 1.023 1.005 1.030 1.219 0.977 1.044 0.778 1.122 1.114
1.091 1.086 1.141 0.931 0.723 0.934 1.060 1.047 0.800 0.889
1.012 0.695 0.869 0.734 1.131 0.993 0.762 0.814 1.108 0.805
1.223 1.024 0.884 0.799 0.870 0.898 0.621 0.818 1.113 1.286
1.052 0.678 1.162 0.808 1.012 0.859 0.951 1.112 1.003 0.972
```

Calculate the sample statistics and determine whether there is evidence that the population mean blackness is less than 0.97. Write a memo to management that summarizes your conclusions.

# WEB CASE

*Apply your knowledge about hypothesis testing in this Web Case, which continues the cereal-fill-packaging dispute Web Case from Chapter 7.*

In response to the negative statements made by the Consumers Concerned About Cereal Cheaters (CCACC) in the Chapter 7 Web Case, Oxford Cereals recently conducted an experiment concerning cereal packaging. The company claims that the results of the experiment refute the CCACC allegations that Oxford Cereals has been cheating consumers by packaging cereals at less than labeled weights. Review the Oxford Cereals' press release and supporting documents that describe the experiment at the company's Web site, **www.prenhall.com/Springville/**

**OC_FullUp.htm**, or open `OC_FullUp.htm` from the Student CD-ROM Web Case folder, and then answer the following:

1. Are the results of the experiment valid? Why or why not? If you were conducting the experiment, is there anything you would change?
2. Do the results support the claim that Oxford Cereals is not cheating its customers?
3. Is the claim of the Oxford Cereals CEO that many cereal boxes contain *more* than 368 grams surprising? Is it true?
4. Could there ever be a circumstance in which the results of the Oxford Cereals experiment *and* the CCACC's results are both correct? Explain.

# REFERENCES

1. Bradley, J. V., *Distribution-Free Statistical Tests* (Upper Saddle River, NJ: Prentice Hall, 1968).
2. Daniel, W., *Applied Nonparametric Statistics*, 2nd ed. (Boston: Houghton Mifflin, 1990).
3. *Microsoft Excel 2007* (Redmond, WA: Microsoft Corp., 2007).
4. *Minitab for Windows Version 15* (State College, PA: Minitab, Inc., 2006).

# Appendix E9
## Using Microsoft Excel for One-Sample Tests

### E9.1 Using the Z Test for the Mean (σ Known)

You perform the Z test for the mean (σ known) by making entries in either the **ZMean_TT** (see Figure 9.5 on page 352) or **ZMean_All** worksheets of the Z Mean.xls workbook. These worksheets use the **NORMSINV($P < X$)** function to determine the lower and upper critical values and use the **NORMSDIST(Z value)** function to compute the p-values from the Z value calculated in cell B12. The worksheets also use the **IF(comparison, what to do if comparison holds, what to do if comparison fails)** function to determine whether or not you should reject the null hypothesis. (Although shown as two lines in Figure 9.5, the function is entered as a single, continuous line.)

The **ZMean_TT** worksheet applies the two-tail Z test to the Example 9.2 cereal-filling process on page 349. The similar **ZMean_All** worksheet includes the two-tail test, the upper one-tail test, and the lower one-tail test on one worksheet. To adapt these worksheets to other problems, change the null hypothesis, level of significance, population standard deviation, sample size, and sample mean values, in the tinted cells B4 through B8, as is necessary.

### E9.2 Using the t Test for the Mean (σ Unknown)

You perform the t test for the mean (σ unknown) by making entries in either the **TMean_TT** (see Figure 9.7 on page 358) or **TMean_All** worksheets of the T Mean.xls workbook. These worksheets use the **TINV(1-confidence level, degrees of freedom)** function to determine the lower and upper critical values and use the **TDIST(ABS(t), degrees of freedom, tails)** function in which **ABS(t)** is the absolute value of the $t_{STAT}$ test statistic, and **tails** is either 1, for a one-tail test, or 2, for a two-tail test, to compute the p-values. The worksheets also use the IF function to determine whether or not you should reject the null hypothesis (see related material in Section P9.1).

The **TMean_TT** worksheet applies the two-tail t test to the Section 9.2 sales invoices example on page 356. The similar **TMean_All** worksheet includes the two-tail test, the upper one-tail test, and the lower one-tail test on one worksheet. To adapt these worksheets to other problems, change the null hypothesis, level of significance, sample size, sample mean, and sample standard deviation values, in the tinted cells B4 through B8, as is necessary.

### E9.3 Using the Z Test for the Proportion

You perform the Z test for the proportion by making entries in either the **ZProp_TT** (see Figure 9.16 on page 369) or **ZProp_All** worksheets of the Z Proportion.xls workbook. These worksheets use the **NORMSINV($P < X$)** function to determine the lower and upper critical values and use the **NORMSDIST(Z value)** function to compute the p-values. The worksheets also use the IF function to determine whether or not you should reject the null hypothesis (see related material in Section P9.1).

The **ZProp_TT** worksheet applies the two-tail Z test to the Section 9.4 example concerning customer satisfaction on pages 368–369. The **ZProp_All** worksheet includes the two-tail test, the upper one-tail test, and the lower one-tail test on one worksheet. To adapt these worksheets to other problems, enter the appropriate null hypothesis, level of significance, sample size, sample mean, and sample standard deviation values, in the tinted cells B4 through B8, as is necessary.

# Appendix P9
## Using PHStat2 for One-Sample Tests

### P9.1 Using the Z Test for the Mean (σ Known)

To perform the Z test for the mean (σ known), use **PHStat → One-Sample Tests → Z Test for the Mean, sigma known**. This procedure creates a worksheet similar to Figure 9.5 on page 352 using the test option you click and the null hypothesis, significance, population standard deviation, sample size, and sample mean values that you specify. If you have unsummarized data, click **Sample Statistics Unknown** and the procedure will calculate the sample statistics for you.

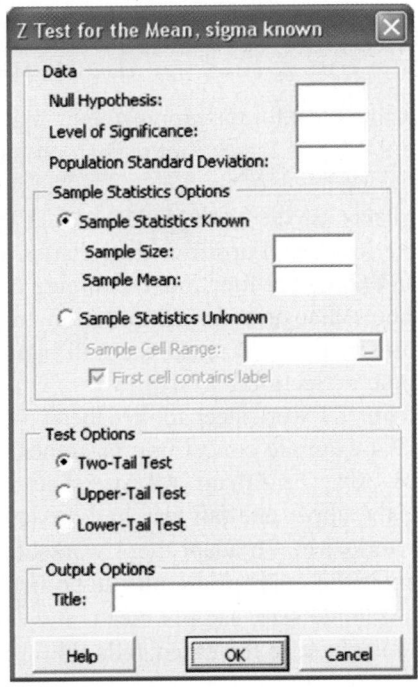

### P9.2 Using the t Test for the Mean (σ Unknown)

To perform the t test for the mean (σ unknown), use **PHStat → One-Sample Tests → t Test for the Mean, sigma unknown**. The procedure creates a worksheet similar to Figure 9.7 on page 358 using the test option you click and the null hypothesis, level of significance, sample size, sample mean, and sample standard deviation values you specify. If you have unsummarized data, click **Sample Statistics Unknown** and the procedure will calculate the sample statistics for you.

### P9.3 Using the Z Test for the Proportion

To perform the Z test for the proportion use **PHStat → One-Sample Tests → Z Test for the Proportion**. The procedure creates a worksheet similar to Figure 9.16 on page 369 using the test option you click and the null hypothesis, level of significance, number of events of interest, and sample size values that you specify.

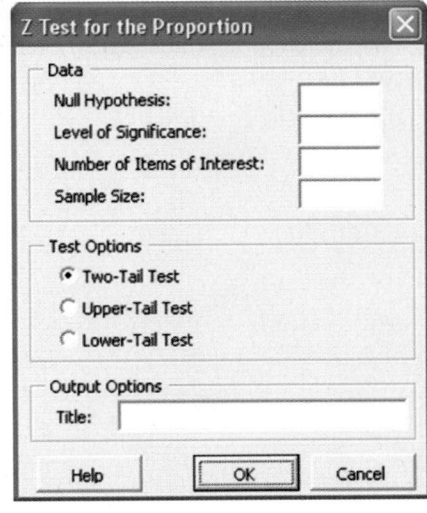

# Appendix M9
## Using Minitab for One-Sample Tests

### M9.1 Using the *Z* Test of Hypothesis for the Mean (σ Known)

To perform a test for the mean, return to the Oxford Cereals example discussed in Example 9.2 on pages 349–350.

1. Open a blank worksheet.
2. Select **Stat → Basic Statistics → 1-Sample Z**.

In the 1-Sample *Z* (Test and Confidence Interval) dialog box (see Figure M9.1):

3. Click **Summarized data**.
4. Enter **25** in the **Sample size** box.
5. Enter **372.5** in the **Mean** box.
6. Enter **15** in the **Standard deviation** box.
7. Click **Perform hypothesis test**.
8. Enter **368** in the **Hypothesized mean** box.
9. Click **Options**.

**FIGURE M9.1**

Minitab 1-Sample Z (Test and Confidence Interval) dialog box

In the 1-Sample *Z* - Options dialog box (see Figure M9.2):

10. Make sure that **95.0** is in the **Confidence level** box.
11. Select **not equal** from the **Alternative** drop-down list. (This selection performs a two-tail test. Select **less than** or **greater than** to perform a one-tail test.)
12. Click **OK** [to return to the 1-Sample *Z* (Test and Confidence Interval) dialog box].
13. Click **OK** (to perform the test).

**FIGURE M9.2**

Minitab 1-Sample Z - Options dialog box

### M9.2 Using the *t* Test of Hypothesis for the Mean (σ Unknown)

To illustrate the test of hypothesis for the mean when σ is unknown, return to the Saxon Home Improvement Company invoice example discussed in Section 9.2 on pages 356–358.

1. Open the **Invoices.mtw** worksheet.
2. Select **Stat → Basic Statistics → 1-Sample t**.

In the 1-Sample t (Test and Confidence Interval) dialog box (see Figure M9.3):

3. Click **Sample in columns**.
4. Enter **Amount** in the **Sample in columns** box.
5. Click **Perform hypothesis test**.
6. Enter **120** in the **Hypothesized mean** box.
7. Click **Options**.

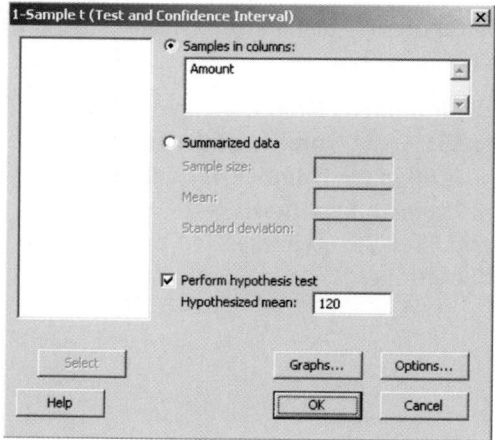

**FIGURE M9.3**

Minitab 1-Sample t (Test and Confidence Interval) dialog box

In the 1-Sample t - Options dialog box (see Figure M9.4)

8. Make sure that **95.0** is entered in the **Confidence level** box.
9. Select **not equal** from the **Alternative** drop-down list. (This selection performs a two-tail test. Select **less than** or **greater than** to perform a one-tail test.)
10. Click **OK** [to return to the 1-Sample t (Test and Confidence Interval) dialog box].
11. *Optional.* To create a boxplot, click **Graphs**. In the Minitab 1-Sample t - Graphs dialog box, click **Boxplot of data** and then click **OK** to return to the 1-Sample t dialog box.
12. Click **OK** (to perform the test).

**FIGURE M9.5**

Minitab 1-Proportion (Test and Confidence Interval) dialog box

In the 1 Proportion - Options dialog box (see Figure M9.6):

8. Make sure that **95.0** is entered in the **Confidence level** box.
9. Select **not equal** from the **Alternative** drop-down list. (This selection performs a two-tail test. Select **less than** or **greater than** to perform a one-tail test.)
10. Click **Use test and interval based on normal distribution**.
11. Click **OK** [to return to the 1 Proportion (Test and Confidence Interval) dialog box].
12. Click **OK** (to perform the test).

**FIGURE M9.4**

Minitab 1-Sample t - Options dialog box

## M9.3 Using the *Z* Test for the Proportion

To illustrate the *Z* test for the proportion, return to the Section 9.4 example examining whether customer service was better at e-commerce sites than at physical stores.

1. Select **Stat → Basic Statistics → 1 Proportion**.

In the 1 Proportion (Test and Confidence Interval) dialog box (see Figure M9.5):

2. Click **Summarized data**.
3. Enter **561** in the **Number of events** box.
4. Enter **1100** in the **Number of trials** box.
5. Click **Perform hypothesis test**.
6. Enter **0.50** in the **Hypothesized proportion** box.
7. Click **Options**.

**FIGURE M9.6**

1 Proportion - Options dialog box

# CHAPTER
## TEN

# LEARNING OBJECTIVES

In this chapter, you learn how to use hypothesis testing for comparing the difference between:

- The means of two independent populations
- The means of two related populations
- Two proportions
- The variances of two independent populations

# USING STATISTICS @ BLK Foods

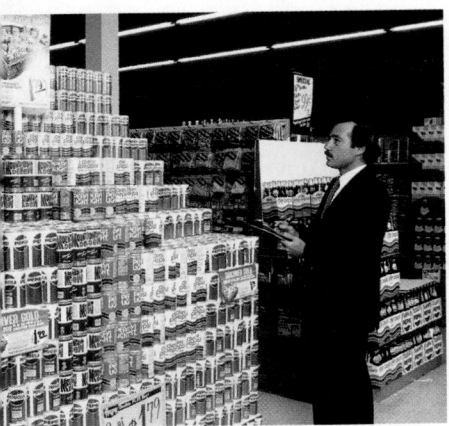

Does the type of display used in a supermarket affect the sales of products? As the regional sales manager for BLK Foods, you want to compare the sales volume of the BLK Cola when the product is placed in the normal shelf location to the sales volume when the product is featured in a special end-aisle display. To test the effectiveness of the end-aisle displays, you select 20 stores from the BLK supermarket chain that all experience similar storewide sales volumes. You then randomly assign 10 of the 20 stores to sample 1 and 10 to sample 2. The managers of the 10 stores in sample 1 place the BLK Cola in the normal shelf location alongside the other cola products. The 10 stores in sample 2 use the special end-aisle promotional display. At the end of one week, the sales of BLK Cola are recorded. How can you determine whether sales of BLK Cola using the end-aisle displays are the same as those when the cola is placed in the normal shelf location? How can you decide if the variability in BLK cola sales from store to store is the same for the two types of displays? How could you use the answers to these questions to improve sales of BLK Colas?

Hypothesis testing provides a *confirmatory* approach to data analysis. In Chapter 9, you learned a variety of commonly used hypothesis-testing procedures that relate to a single sample of data selected from a single population. In this chapter, you learn how to extend hypothesis testing to procedures that compare statistics from two samples of data selected from two populations. One such extension would be asking the question, "Are the mean weekly sales of BLK Cola when using the normal shelf location equal to the mean weekly sales of BLK Cola when placed in an end-aisle display?"

## 10.1   COMPARING THE MEANS OF TWO INDEPENDENT POPULATIONS

### Pooled-Variance *t* Test for the Difference Between Two Means

Suppose that you take a random sample of $n_1$ from the first population and a random sample of $n_2$ from the second population. The data collected in each sample are from a numerical variable. In the first population, the mean is represented by the symbol $\mu_1$ and the standard deviation is represented by the symbol $\sigma_1$. In the second population, the mean is represented by the symbol $\mu_2$ and the standard deviation is represented by the symbol $\sigma_2$.

In almost all cases, the variances of the two populations are not known. The only information you usually have are the sample means and the sample variances. If you assume that the samples are randomly and independently selected from populations that are normally distributed and that the population variances are equal (i.e., $\sigma_1^2 = \sigma_2^2$), you can use a **pooled-variance *t* test** to determine whether there is a significant difference between the means of the two populations. If the populations are not normally distributed, the pooled-variance *t* test is still appropriate if the sample sizes are large enough (typically $n_1$ and $n_2 \geq 30$; see the Central Limit Theorem in Section 7.4 on page 274).

To test the null hypothesis of no difference in the means of two independent populations:

$$H_0: \mu_1 = \mu_2 \text{ or } \mu_1 - \mu_2 = 0$$

against the alternative that the means are not the same

$$H_1: \mu_1 \neq \mu_2 \text{ or } \mu_1 - \mu_2 \neq 0$$

you use the pooled-variance $t$-test statistic $t_{STAT}$ shown in Equation (10.1). The pooled-variance $t$ test gets its name from the fact that the test statistic pools or combines the two sample variances $S_1^2$ and $S_2^2$ to compute $S_p^2$, the best estimate of the variance common to both populations under the assumption that the two population variances are equal.[1]

[1] *When the two sample sizes are equal (i.e., $n_1 = n_2$), the equation for the pooled variance can be simplified to*

$$S_p^2 = \frac{S_1^2 + S_2^2}{2}$$

### Pooled-Variance $t$ Test for the Difference Between Two Means

$$t_{STAT} = \frac{(\bar{X}_1 - \bar{X}_2) - (\mu_1 - \mu_2)}{\sqrt{S_p^2 \left( \frac{1}{n_1} + \frac{1}{n_2} \right)}} \qquad (10.1)$$

where

$$S_p^2 = \frac{(n_1 - 1)S_1^2 + (n_2 - 1)S_2^2}{(n_1 - 1) + (n_2 - 1)}$$

and

$S_p^2$ = pooled variance

$\bar{X}_1$ = mean of the sample taken from population 1

$S_1^2$ = variance of the sample taken from population 1

$n_1$ = size of the sample taken from population 1

$\bar{X}_2$ = mean of the sample taken from population 2

$S_2^2$ = variance of the sample taken from population 2

$n_2$ = size of the sample taken from population 2

The $t_{STAT}$ test statistic follows a $t$ distribution with $n_1 + n_2 - 2$ degrees of freedom.

For a given level of significance $\alpha$, in a two-tail test, you reject the null hypothesis if the computed $t_{STAT}$ test statistic is greater than the upper-tail critical value from the $t$ distribution or if the computed $t_{STAT}$ test statistic is less than the lower-tail critical value from the $t$ distribution. Figure 10.1 displays the regions of rejection.

In a one-tail test in which the rejection region is in the lower tail, you reject the null hypothesis if the computed $t_{STAT}$ test statistic is less than the lower-tail critical value from the $t$ distribution. In a one-tail test in which the rejection region is in the upper tail, you reject the null hypothesis if the computed $t_{STAT}$ test statistic is greater than the upper-tail critical value from the $t$ distribution.

**FIGURE 10.1**

Regions of rejection and nonrejection for the pooled-variance $t$ test for the difference between the means (two-tail test)

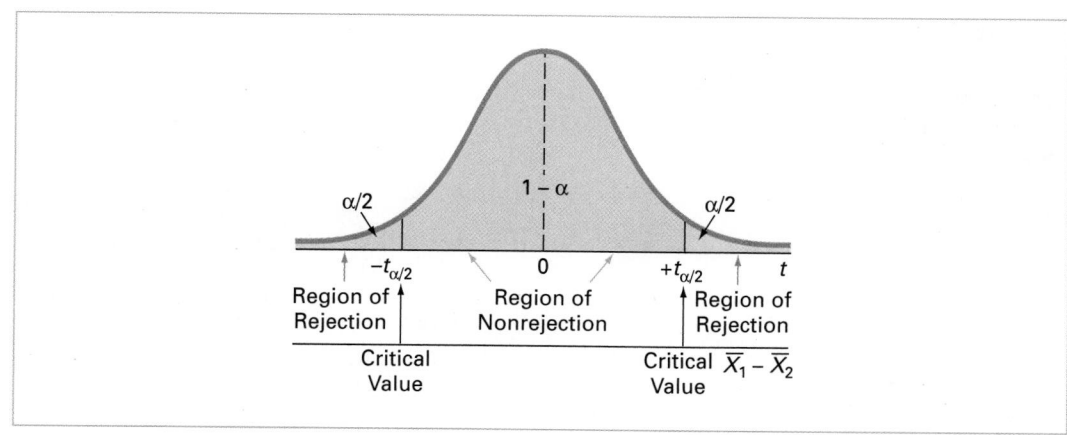

To demonstrate the use of the pooled-variance $t$ test, return to the Using Statistics scenario on page 390. You want to determine whether the mean weekly sales of BLK Cola are the same when using a normal shelf location and when using an end-aisle display. There are two populations of interest. The first population is the set of all possible weekly sales of BLK Cola *if* all the BLK supermarkets used the normal shelf location. The second population is the set of all possible weekly sales of BLK Cola *if* all the BLK supermarkets used the end-aisle displays. The first sample contains the weekly sales of BLK Cola from the 10 stores selected to use the normal shelf location, and the second sample contains the weekly sales of BLK Cola from the 10 stores selected to use the end-aisle display. Table 10.1 contains the cola sales (in number of cases) for the two samples (see the **Cola** file).

**TABLE 10.1**

Comparing BLK Cola Weekly Sales from Two Different Display Locations (in Number of Cases)

| Display Location | | | | | | | | | |
|---|---|---|---|---|---|---|---|---|---|
| **Normal** | | | | | **End-Aisle** | | | | |
| 22 | 34 | 52 | 62 | 30 | 52 | 71 | 76 | 54 | 67 |
| 40 | 64 | 84 | 56 | 59 | 83 | 66 | 90 | 77 | 84 |

The null and alternative hypotheses are

$$H_0: \mu_1 = \mu_2 \text{ or } \mu_1 - \mu_2 = 0$$

$$H_1: \mu_1 \neq \mu_2 \text{ or } \mu_1 - \mu_2 \neq 0$$

Assuming that the samples are from normal populations having equal variances, you can use the pooled-variance $t$ test. The $t_{STAT}$ test statistic follows a $t$ distribution with $10 + 10 - 2 = 18$ degrees of freedom. Using $\alpha = 0.05$ level of significance, you divide the rejection region into the two tails for this two-tail test (i.e., two equal parts of 0.025 each). Table E.3 shows that the critical values for this two-tail test are +2.1009 and −2.1009. As shown in Figure 10.2, the decision rule is:

$$\text{Reject } H_0 \text{ if } t_{STAT} > +2.1009$$

$$\text{or if } t_{STAT} < -2.1009;$$

$$\text{otherwise do not reject } H_0.$$

**FIGURE 10.2**

Two-tail test of hypothesis for the difference between the means at the 0.05 level of significance with 18 degrees of freedom

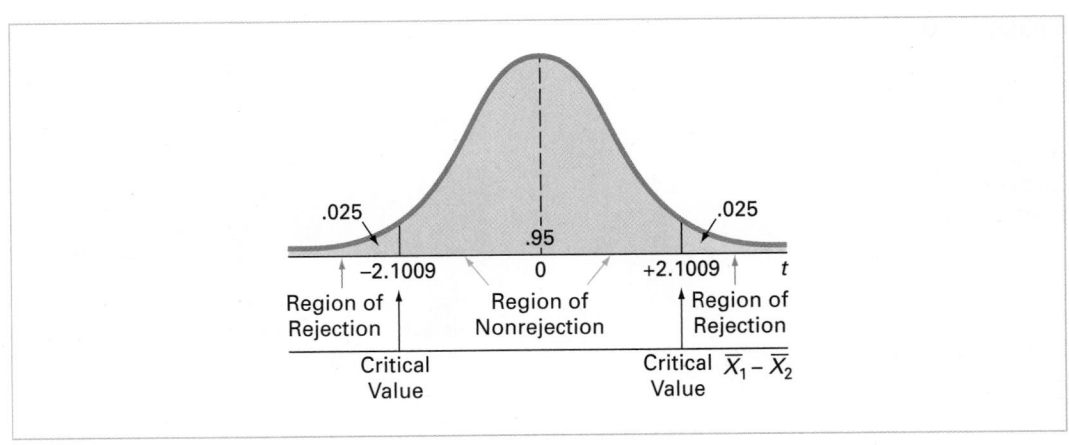

From Figures 10.3 or 10.4, the computed $t_{STAT}$ test statistic for this test is $-3.0446$ and the $p$-value is 0.0070.

**FIGURE 10.3**

Microsoft Excel *t*-test results for the two display locations

*See Section E10.2 to create this.*

| | A | B | C |
|---|---|---|---|
| 1 | t-Test: Two-Sample Assuming Equal Variances | | |
| 2 | | | |
| 3 | | *Normal* | *End-Aisle* |
| 4 | **Mean** | 50.3 | 72 |
| 5 | **Variance** | 350.6778 | 157.3333 |
| 6 | **Observations** | 10 | 10 |
| 7 | **Pooled Variance** | 254.0056 | |
| 8 | **Hypothesized Mean Difference** | 0 | |
| 9 | **df** | 18 | |
| 10 | **t Stat** | -3.0446 | |
| 11 | **P(T<=t) one-tail** | 0.0035 | |
| 12 | **t Critical one-tail** | 1.7341 | |
| 13 | **P(T<=t) two-tail** | 0.0070 | |
| 14 | **t Critical two-tail** | 2.1009 | |

**FIGURE 10.4**

Minitab *t*-test results for the two display locations

*See Section M10.2 to create this.*

```
Two-sample T for Sales_Normal vs Sales_EndAisle

                N   Mean   StDev   SE Mean
Sales_Normal    10   50.3   18.7     5.9
Sales_EndAisle  10   72.0   12.5     4.0


Difference = mu (Sales_Normal) - mu (Sales_EndAisle)
Estimate for difference:  -21.70
95% CI for difference:   (-36.67, -6.73)

T-Test of difference = 0 (vs not =): T-Value = -3.04  P-Value = 0.007  DF = 18
Both use Pooled StDev = 15.9376
```

Using Equation (10.1) on page 391 and the descriptive statistics provided in Figures 10.3 and 10.4,

$$t_{STAT} = \frac{(\bar{X}_1 - \bar{X}_2) - (\mu_1 - \mu_2)}{\sqrt{S_p^2 \left( \frac{1}{n_1} + \frac{1}{n_2} \right)}}$$

where

$$S_p^2 = \frac{(n_1 - 1)S_1^2 + (n_2 - 1)S_2^2}{(n_1 - 1) + (n_2 - 1)}$$

$$= \frac{9(350.6778) + 9(157.3333)}{9 + 9} = 254.0056$$

Therefore,

$$t_{STAT} = \frac{(50.3 - 72.0) - 0.0}{\sqrt{254.0056 \left( \frac{1}{10} + \frac{1}{10} \right)}} = \frac{-21.7}{\sqrt{50.801}} = -3.0446$$

You reject the null hypothesis because $t_{STAT} = -3.0446 < -2.1009$. The $p$-value (as computed from Microsoft Excel or Minitab) is 0.0070. In other words, the probability that $t_{STAT} > 3.0446$ or $t_{STAT} < -3.0446$ is equal to 0.0070. This $p$-value indicates that if the population means are equal, the probability of observing a difference this large or larger in the two sample means is only 0.0070. Because the $p$-value is less than $\alpha = 0.05$, there is sufficient evidence to reject the null hypothesis. You can conclude that the mean sales are different for the normal shelf location and the end-aisle location. Based on these results, the sales are lower for the normal location (i.e., higher for the end-aisle location). Example 10.1 provides another application of the pooled-variance $t$ test.

**EXAMPLE 10.1**

TESTING FOR THE DIFFERENCE IN THE MEAN DELIVERY TIMES

A local pizza restaurant and a local branch of a national chain are located across the street from a college campus. The local pizza restaurant advertises that they deliver to the dormitories faster than the national chain. In order to determine whether this advertisement is valid, you and some friends have decided to order 10 pizzas from the local pizza restaurant and 10 pizzas from the national chain, all at different times. The delivery times in minutes (see the `Pizzatime` file) are shown in Table 10.2:

**TABLE 10.2**

Delivery Times (in minutes) for Local Pizza Restaurant and National Pizza Chain

| Local | Chain | Local | Chain |
|-------|-------|-------|-------|
| 16.8 | 22.0 | 18.1 | 19.5 |
| 11.7 | 15.2 | 14.1 | 17.0 |
| 15.6 | 18.7 | 21.8 | 19.5 |
| 16.7 | 15.6 | 13.9 | 16.5 |
| 17.5 | 20.8 | 20.8 | 24.0 |

At the 0.05 level of significance, is there evidence that the mean delivery time for the local pizza restaurant is less than the mean delivery time for the national pizza chain?

**SOLUTION** Because you want to know whether the mean is *lower* for the local pizza restaurant than for the national pizza chain, you have a one-tail test with the following null and alternative hypotheses:

$H_0: \mu_1 \geq \mu_2$ (The mean delivery time for the local pizza restaurant is equal to or greater than the mean delivery time for the national pizza chain.)
$H_1: \mu_1 < \mu_2$ (The mean delivery time for the local pizza restaurant is less than the mean delivery time for the national pizza chain.)

Figure 10.5 displays Microsoft Excel results of the pooled $t$ test for these data.

**FIGURE 10.5**

Microsoft Excel results of the pooled $t$ test for the pizza delivery time data

*See Section E10.2 to create this. (Minitab users, see Section M10.2 to create equivalent results.)*

|  | A | B | C |
|---|---|---|---|
| 1 | t-Test: Two-Sample Assuming Equal Variances | | |
| 2 | | | |
| 3 | | Local | Chain |
| 4 | Mean | 16.7 | 18.88 |
| 5 | Variance | 9.5822 | 8.2151 |
| 6 | Observations | 10 | 10 |
| 7 | Pooled Variance | 8.8987 | |
| 8 | Hypothesized Mean Difference | 0 | |
| 9 | df | 18 | |
| 10 | t Stat | -1.6341 | |
| 11 | P(T<=t) one-tail | 0.0598 | |
| 12 | t Critical one-tail | 1.7341 | |
| 13 | P(T<=t) two-tail | 0.1196 | |
| 14 | t Critical two-tail | 2.1009 | |

Using Equation (10.1) on page 391,

$$t_{STAT} = \frac{(\bar{X}_1 - \bar{X}_2) - (\mu_1 - \mu_2)}{\sqrt{S_p^2 \left( \dfrac{1}{n_1} + \dfrac{1}{n_2} \right)}}$$

where

$$S_p^2 = \frac{(n_1 - 1)S_1^2 + (n_2 - 1)S_2^2}{(n_1 - 1) + (n_2 - 1)}$$

$$= \frac{9(9.5822) + 9(8.2151)}{9 + 9} = 8.8987$$

Therefore,

$$t_{STAT} = \frac{(16.7 - 18.88) - 0.0}{\sqrt{8.8987 \left( \dfrac{1}{10} + \dfrac{1}{10} \right)}} = \frac{-2.18}{\sqrt{1.7797}} = -1.6341$$

You do not reject the null hypothesis because tSTAT = -1.6341 > -1.7341. The p-value (as computed from Microsoft Excel) is 0.0598. This *p*-value indicates that the probability that $t_{STAT} < $ -1.6341 is equal to 0.0598. In other words, if the population means are equal, the probability that the sample mean delivery time for the local pizza restaurant is at least 2.18 minutes faster than the national chain is 0.0598. Because the p-value is greater than a = 0.05, there is insufficient evidence to reject the null hypothesis. Based on these results, there is insufficient evidence for the local pizza restaurant to make the advertising claim that they have a faster delivery time.

In testing for the difference between the means, you assume that the populations are normally distributed with equal variances. For situations in which the two populations have equal variances, the pooled-variance *t* test is **robust** (or not sensitive) to moderate departures from the assumption of normality, provided that the sample sizes are large. In such situations, you can use the pooled-variance *t* test without serious effects on its power. However, if you cannot assume that both populations are normally distributed, you have two choices. You can use a nonparametric procedure, such as the Wilcoxon rank sum test (covered in Section 12.6), that does not depend on the assumption of normality for the two populations, or you can use a normalizing transformation (see reference 6) on each of the outcomes and then use the pooled-variance *t* test.

To check the assumption of normality in each of the two populations, observe the boxplot of the sales for the two display locations in Figure 10.6 on page 396. For these two small samples, there appears to be only moderate departure from normality, so the assumption of normality needed for the *t* test is not seriously violated.

## Confidence Interval Estimate for the Difference Between Two Means

Instead of, or in addition to, testing for the difference in the means of two independent populations, you can use Equation (10.2) to develop a confidence interval estimate of the difference in the means.

**FIGURE 10.6**

Minitab boxplot for the sales for two display locations

*See Section M3.2 to create this. (PHStat2 users, see Section P3.4 to create an equivalent chart.)*

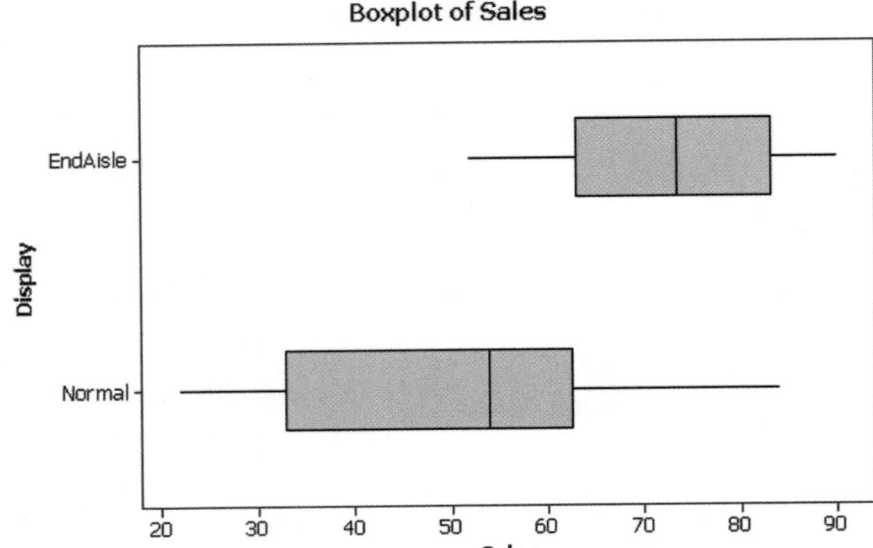

Boxplot of Sales

---

Confidence Interval Estimate of the Difference in the Means of Two Independent Populations

$$(\bar{X}_1 - \bar{X}_2) \pm t_{\alpha/2}\sqrt{S_p^2\left(\frac{1}{n_1} + \frac{1}{n_2}\right)} \qquad (10.2)$$

or

$$(\bar{X}_1 - \bar{X}_2) - t_{\alpha/2}\sqrt{S_p^2\left(\frac{1}{n_1} + \frac{1}{n_2}\right)} \le \mu_1 - \mu_2 \le (\bar{X}_1 - \bar{X}_2) + t_{\alpha/2}\sqrt{S_p^2\left(\frac{1}{n_1} + \frac{1}{n_2}\right)}$$

where $t_{\alpha/2}$ is the critical value of the $t$ distribution with $n_1 + n_2 - 2$ degrees of freedom for an area of $\alpha/2$ in the upper tail.

For the sample statistics pertaining to the two aisle locations reported in Figures 10.3 or 10.4 on page 393, using 95% confidence, and Equation (10.2),

$$\bar{X}_1 = 50.3, \ n_1 = 10, \ \bar{X}_2 = 72, \ n_2 = 10, \ S_p^2 = 254.0056, \text{ and with } 10 + 10 - 2$$

$$= 18 \text{ degrees of freedom}, \ t_{0.025} = 2.1009$$

$$(50.3 - 72) \pm (2.1009)\sqrt{254.0056\left(\frac{1}{10} + \frac{1}{10}\right)}$$

$$-21.7 \pm (2.1009)(7.1275)$$

$$-21.7 \pm 14.97$$

$$-36.67 \le \mu_1 - \mu_2 \le -6.73$$

Therefore, you are 95% confident that the difference in mean sales between the normal aisle location and the end-aisle location is between −36.67 cases of cola and −6.73 cases of cola. In other words, the end-aisle location sells, on average, 6.73 to 36.67 cases more than the normal aisle location. From a hypothesis-testing perspective, because the interval does not include zero, you reject the null hypothesis of no difference between the means of the two populations.

## Separate-Variance $t$ Test for the Difference Between Two Means

In testing for the difference between the means of two independent populations when the population variances are assumed to be equal, the sample variances are pooled together into a common estimate $S_p^2$. However, if you cannot make this assumption, then the pooled-variance $t$ test is inappropriate. In this case, you should use the **separate-variance $t$ test** developed by Satterthwaite (see reference 5). This test procedure includes the two separate sample variances in the computation of the $t$-test statistic. Equation (10.3) defines the test statistic for the separate-variance $t$ test.

### Separate-Variance $t$ Test for the Difference in Two Means

$$t_{STAT} = \frac{(\bar{X}_1 - \bar{X}_2) - (\mu_1 - \mu_2)}{\sqrt{\dfrac{S_1^2}{n_1} + \dfrac{S_2^2}{n_2}}} \qquad (10.3)$$

where

$\bar{X}_1$ = mean of the sample taken from population 1

$S_1^2$ = variance of the sample taken from population 1

$n_1$ = size of the sample taken from population 1

$\bar{X}_2$ = mean of the sample taken from population 2

$S_2^2$ = variance of the sample taken from population 2

$n_2$ = size of the sample taken from population 2

The separate-variance $t_{STAT}$ test statistic approximately follows a $t$ distribution with degrees of freedom $V$ equal to the integer portion of the following computation.

### Computing Degrees of Freedom in the Separate-Variance $t$ Test

$$V = \frac{\left( \dfrac{S_1^2}{n_1} + \dfrac{S_2^2}{n_2} \right)^2}{\dfrac{\left( \dfrac{S_1^2}{n_1} \right)^2}{n_1 - 1} + \dfrac{\left( \dfrac{S_2^2}{n_2} \right)^2}{n_2 - 1}} \qquad (10.4)$$

For a given level of significance $\alpha$, in a two-tail test you reject the null hypothesis if the computed $t_{STAT}$ test statistic is greater than the upper-tail critical value $t_{\alpha/2}$ from the $t$ distribution with $V$ degrees of freedom or if the computed $t_{STAT}$ test statistic is less than the lower-tail critical value $-t_{\alpha/2}$ from the $t$ distribution with $V$ degrees of freedom. Thus, the decision rule is

Reject $H_0$ if $t_{STAT} > t_{\alpha/2}$

or if $t_{STAT} < -t_{\alpha/2}$;

otherwise, do not reject $H_0$.

Return to the Using Statistics scenario on page 390 concerning the display location of BLK Cola. Using Equation (10.4), the separate-variance $t_{STAT}$ test statistic is approximated by a $t$ distribution with $V = 15$ degrees of freedom, the integer portion of the following computation.

$$V = \frac{\left(\dfrac{S_1^2}{n_1} + \dfrac{S_2^2}{n_2}\right)^2}{\dfrac{\left(\dfrac{S_1^2}{n_1}\right)^2}{n_1 - 1} + \dfrac{\left(\dfrac{S_2^2}{n_2}\right)^2}{n_2 - 1}}$$

$$= \frac{\left(\dfrac{350.6778}{10} + \dfrac{157.3333}{10}\right)^2}{\dfrac{\left(\dfrac{350.6778}{10}\right)^2}{9} + \dfrac{\left(\dfrac{157.3333}{10}\right)^2}{9}} = 15.72$$

Using $\alpha = 0.05$, the upper and lower critical values for this two-tail test found in Table E.3 are $+2.1315$ and $-2.1315$. As depicted in Figure 10.7, the decision rule is

$$\text{Reject } H_0 \text{ if } t_{STAT} > +2.1315$$

$$\text{or if } t_{STAT} < -2.1315;$$

$$\text{otherwise do not reject } H_0.$$

**FIGURE 10.7**

Two-tailed test of hypothesis for the difference between the means at the 0.05 level of significance with 15 degrees of freedom

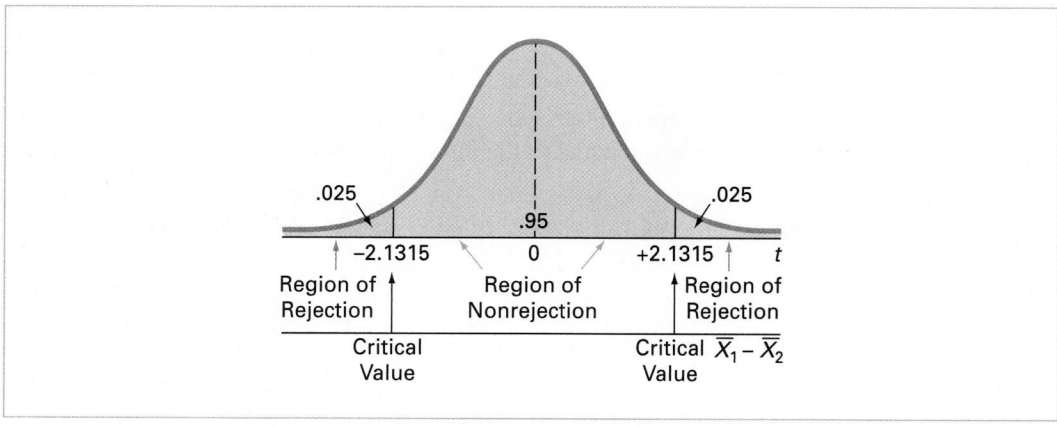

Using Equation (10.3) on page 397 and the descriptive statistics provided in Figures 10.3 and 10.4 on page 393,

$$t_{STAT} = \frac{(\bar{X}_1 - \bar{X}_2) - (\mu_1 - \mu_2)}{\sqrt{\dfrac{S_1^2}{n_1} + \dfrac{S_2^2}{n_2}}}$$

$$= \frac{50.3 - 72}{\sqrt{\left(\dfrac{350.6778}{10} + \dfrac{157.3333}{10}\right)}} = \frac{-21.7}{\sqrt{50.801}} = -3.04$$

Using a 0.05 level of significance, you reject the null hypothesis because $t_{STAT} = -3.04446 < -2.1315$.

Figure 10.8 illustrates Microsoft Excel results for this separate-variance $t$ test, and Figure 10.9 illustrates Minitab output. Note that Excel rounds the degrees of freedom while Minitab uses the integer portion.

**FIGURE 10.8**

Microsoft Excel results of the separate-variance $t$ test for the display location data

See Section E10.4 to create this.

| | A | B | C |
|---|---|---|---|
| 1 | t-Test: Two-Sample Assuming Unequal Variances | | |
| 2 | | | |
| 3 | | **Normal** | **End-Aisle** |
| 4 | Mean | 50.3 | 72 |
| 5 | Variance | 350.6778 | 157.3333 |
| 6 | Observations | 10 | 10 |
| 7 | Hypothesized Mean Difference | 0 | |
| 8 | df | 16 | |
| 9 | t Stat | -3.0446 | |
| 10 | P(T<=t) one-tail | 0.0039 | |
| 11 | t Critical one-tail | 1.7459 | |
| 12 | P(T<=t) two-tail | 0.0077 | |
| 13 | t Critical two-tail | 2.1199 | |

**FIGURE 10.9**

Minitab results of the separate-variance $t$ test for the display location data

See Section M10.2 to create this.

```
Two-sample T for Sales_Normal vs Sales_EndAisle

              N   Mean   StDev   SE Mean
Sales_Normal   10   50.3   18.7     5.9
Sales_EndAisle 10   72.0   12.5     4.0


Difference = mu (Sales_Normal) - mu (Sales_EndAisle)
Estimate for difference:  -21.70
95% CI for difference:  (-36.89, -6.51)
T-Test of difference = 0 (vs not =): T-Value = -3.04  P-Value = 0.008  DF = 15
```

# "This Call May Be Monitored . . ."

*From the Authors' Desktop*

If you have ever used a telephone to seek customer service, you've probably heard at least once a message that begins "this call may be monitored . . . " Most of the time the message explains the monitoring is for "quality assurance purposes," but do companies really monitor your calls to improve quality?

From one of our previous students, we've learned that a certain large financial corporation really does monitor calls for quality purposes. This student was asked to develop an improved training program for a call center that was hiring people to answer phone calls customers make about outstanding loans. For feedback and evaluation, she planned to randomly select phone calls received by each new employee and rate the employee on ten aspects of the call including did the employee maintain a pleasant tone with the customer?

*Who You Gonna Call?*

She presented her plan to her boss for approval, but her boss, remembering the words of a famous statistician, said, "In God we trust, all others must bring data." That is, her boss wanted proof that her new training program would improve customer service. Faced with such a request, who would you call? She called one of us. "Hey professor, you'll never believe why I called. I work for a large company and in the project I am currently working on, I have to put some of the statistics you taught us to work! Can you help?" The answer was "Yes" and together they formulated this test:

- Randomly assign the 60 most recent hires into two training programs. Half would go through the preexisting training program, and half would be trained using the new program.
- At the end of the first month, compare the mean score for the 30 employees in the new training program against the mean score for the 30 employees in the preexisting training program.

She listened as her professor explained, "What you are trying to prove is that the mean score from the new training program is higher than the mean score from the current program. You can make the null hypothesis that the means are equal, and see if you can reject it in favor of the alternative that the mean score from the new program is higher."

"Or, as you used to say, 'if the $p$-value is low, $H_0$ must go!'—yes, I do remember!" she replied. Her professor chuckled and said, "Yes, that's correct. And if you can reject $H_0$, you will have the proof to present to your boss." She thanked him for his help and got back to work with the newfound confidence that she would be able to successfully apply the $t$ test that compares the means of two independent populations.

In Figures 10.8 and 10.9 the test statistic $t_{STAT} = -3.0446$ and the $p$-value is $0.008 < 0.05$. Thus, the results for the separate-variance $t$ test are almost exactly the same as those of the pooled-variance $t$ test. The assumption of equality of population variances had no real effect on the results. Sometimes, however, the results from the pooled-variance and separate-variance $t$ tests conflict because the assumption of equal variances is violated. Therefore, it is important that you evaluate the assumptions and use those results as a guide in appropriately selecting a test procedure. In Section 10.4, the $F$ test is used to determine whether there is evidence of a difference in the two population variances. The results of that test can help you determine which of the $t$ tests—pooled-variance or separate-variance—is more appropriate.

# PROBLEMS FOR SECTION 10.1

## Learning the Basics

**10.1** If you have samples of $n_1 = 12$ and $n_2 = 15$, in performing the pooled-variance $t$ test, how many degrees of freedom do you have?

**10.2** Assume that you have a sample of $n_1 = 8$, with the sample mean $\bar{X}_1 = 42$, and a sample standard deviation of $S_1 = 4$, and you have an independent sample of $n_2 = 15$ from another population with a sample mean of $\bar{X}_2 = 34$ and the sample standard deviation $S_2 = 5$.
a. What is the value of the pooled-variance $t_{STAT}$ test statistic for testing $H_0: \mu_1 = \mu_2$?
b. In finding the critical value $t_{\alpha/2}$, how many degrees of freedom are there?
c. Using the level of significance $\alpha = 0.01$, what is the critical value for a one-tail test of the hypothesis $H_0: \mu_1 \leq \mu_2$ against the alternative $H_1: \mu_1 > \mu_2$?
d. What is your statistical decision?

**10.3** What assumptions about the two populations are necessary in Problem 10.2?

**10.4** Referring to Problem 10.2, construct a 95% confidence interval estimate of the population mean difference between $\mu_1$ and $\mu_2$.

**10.5** Referring to Problem 10.2, using the separate-variance $t$ test, how many degrees of freedom do you have?

**10.6** Referring to Problem 10.2, using the separate-variance $t$ test, at the 0.01 level of significance, is there evidence of a difference in the means of the two populations?

## Applying the Concepts

**10.7** The operations manager at a lightbulb factory wants to determine whether there is any difference in the mean life expectancy of bulbs manufactured on two different types of machines. A random sample of 25 lightbulbs from machine I indicates a sample mean of 375 hours and a sample standard deviation of 100 hours, and a similar sample of 25 from machine II indicates a sample mean of 362 hours and a sample standard deviation of 125 hours.
a. Using the 0.05 level of significance, and assuming that the population variances are equal, is there any evidence of a difference in the mean life of bulbs produced by the two types of machines?
b. Using the 0.05 level of significance, and assuming that the population variances are not equal, is there any evidence of a difference in the mean life of bulbs produced by the two types of machines?

**10.8** The purchasing director for an industrial parts factory is investigating the possibility of purchasing a new type of milling machine. She determines that the new machine will be purchased if there is evidence that the parts produced have a higher mean breaking strength than those from the old machine. A sample of 100 parts taken from the old machine indicates a sample mean of 65 kilograms and a sample standard deviation of 10 kilograms, and a similar sample of 100 from the new machine indicates a sample mean of 72 kilograms and a sample standard deviation of 9 kilograms.
a. Using the 0.01 level of significance, and assuming that the population variances are equal, is there evidence that the purchasing director should buy the new machine?
b. Using the 0.01 level of significance, and assuming that the population variances are not equal, is there evidence of a difference in the mean breaking strength of the two machines?

**10.9** Millions of dollars are spent each year on diet foods. Trends such as the low-fat diet or the low-carb Atkins diet have led to a host of new products. A study by Dr. Linda Stern of the Philadelphia Veterans Administration Hospital compared weight loss between obese patients on a low-fat diet and obese patients on a low-carb diet (extracted from R. Bazell, "Study Casts Doubt on Advantages of Atkins Diet," **msnbc.com**, May 17, 2004). Let $\mu_1$ represent the mean number of pounds obese patients on a low-fat diet lose in six months and $\mu_2$ represent the mean number of pounds obese patients on a low-carb diet lose in six months.

**a.** State the null and alternative hypotheses if you want to test whether the mean weight loss between the two diets is equal.

**b.** In the context of this study, what is the meaning of a Type I error?

**c.** In the context of this study, what is the meaning of a Type II error?

**d.** Suppose that a sample of 100 obese patients on a low-fat diet lost a mean of 7.6 pounds in six months, with a sample standard deviation of 3.2 pounds, whereas a sample of 100 obese patients on a low-carb diet lost a mean of 6.7 pounds in six months, with a sample standard deviation of 3.9 pounds. Assuming that the population variances are equal and using a 0.05 level of significance, is there evidence of a difference in the mean weight loss of obese patients between the low-fat and low-carb diets?

**10.10** When do children in the United States develop preferences for brand-name products? In a study reported in the *Journal of Consumer Psychology* (extracted from G. W. Achenreiner and D. R. John, "The Meaning of Brand Names to Children: A Developmental Investigation," *Journal of Consumer Psychology*, 2003, 13(3), pp. 205–219), marketers showed children identical pictures of athletic shoes. One picture was labeled Nike, and one was labeled K-Mart. The children were asked to evaluate the shoes based on their appearance, quality, price, prestige, favorableness, and preference for owning. A score from 2 (highest product evaluation possible) to −2 (lowest product evaluation possible) was recorded for each child. The following table reports the results of the study:

| Age by Brand | Sample Size | Sample Mean | Sample Standard Deviation |
|---|---|---|---|
| **Age 8** | | | |
| Nike | 27 | 0.89 | 0.98 |
| K-Mart | 22 | 0.86 | 1.07 |
| **Age 12** | | | |
| Nike | 39 | 0.88 | 1.01 |
| K-Mart | 41 | 0.09 | 1.08 |
| **Age 16** | | | |
| Nike | 35 | 0.41 | 0.81 |
| K-Mart | 33 | −0.29 | 0.92 |

**a.** Conduct a pooled-variance $t$ test for the difference between the two means for each of the three age groups. Use a level of significance of 0.05.

**b.** What assumptions are needed to conduct the tests in (a)?

**c.** Write a brief summary of your findings.

**10.11** Digital cameras have taken over the majority of the point-and-shoot camera market. One of the important

features of a camera is the battery life as measured by the number of shots taken until the battery needs to be recharged. The data in the file Digitalcameras contain the battery life of 31 subcompact cameras and 15 compact cameras (extracted from "Cameras," *Consumer Reports*, November 2006, pp. 20–21).

**a.** Assuming that the population variances from both types of digital cameras are equal, is there evidence of a difference in the mean battery life between the two types of digital cameras?

**b.** Determine the $p$-value in (a) and interpret its meaning.

**c.** Assuming that the population variances from both types of digital cameras are equal, construct and interpret a 95% confidence interval estimate of the difference between the population mean battery life of the two types of digital cameras.

✓ SELF Test **10.12** The Computer Anxiety Rating Scale (CARS) measures an individual's level of computer anxiety, on a scale from 20 (no anxiety) to 100 (highest level of anxiety). Researchers at Miami University administered CARS to 172 business students. One of the objectives of the study was to determine whether there is a difference in the level of computer anxiety experienced by female and male business students. They found the following:

| | Males | Females |
|---|---|---|
| $\bar{X}$ | 40.26 | 36.85 |
| $S$ | 13.35 | 9.42 |
| $n$ | 100 | 72 |

Source: *Extracted from T. Broome and D. Havelka, "Determinants of Computer Anxiety in Business Students,"* The Review of Business Information Systems, *Spring 2002, 6(2), pp. 9–16.*

**a.** At the 0.05 level of significance, is there evidence of a difference in the mean computer anxiety experienced by female and male business students?

**b.** Determine the $p$-value and interpret its meaning.

**c.** What assumptions do you have to make about the two populations in order to justify the use of the $t$ test?

**10.13** A company making plastic optical components for bar code scanners was studying inconsistencies in an optical measurement called tilt. The company knew that scanners work best when the tilt measurement is small. Two different types of locking mechanisms used in the mold produced the following results:

| | Taper Locks | Locking Pins |
|---|---|---|
| $\bar{X}$ | 1.262 | 0.561 |
| $S$ | 0.297 | 0.307 |
| $n$ | 20 | 20 |

Source: *Extracted from J. Duncan, "Ghosts in Your Process? Who Ya Gonna Call?"* Quality Progress, *May 2005, pp. 52–57.*

**a.** Assuming that the population variances are equal and the populations are normally distributed, at the 0.05 level of significance, is there evidence of a difference in the means between taper locks and locking pins?

**b.** Repeat (a), assuming that the population variances are not equal.

**c.** Compare the results of (a) and (b).

**10.14** A bank with a branch located in a commercial district of a city has developed an improved process for serving customers during the noon-to-1 p.m. lunch period. The waiting time (operationally defined as the time elapsed from when the customer enters the line until he or she reaches the teller window) needs to be shortened to increase customer satisfaction. A random sample of 15 customers is selected (and stored in the file Bank1), and the results (in minutes) are as follows:

| 4.21 | 5.55 | 3.02 | 5.13 | 4.77 | 2.34 | 3.54 | 3.20 |
|------|------|------|------|------|------|------|------|
| 4.50 | 6.10 | 0.38 | 5.12 | 6.46 | 6.19 | 3.79 | |

Suppose that another branch, located in a residential area, is also concerned with the noon-to-1 p.m. lunch period. A random sample of 15 customers is selected (and stored in the file Bank2), and the results are as follows:

| 9.66 | 5.90 | 8.02 | 5.79 | 8.73 | 3.82 | 8.01 | 8.35 |
|-------|------|------|------|------|------|------|------|
| 10.49 | 6.68 | 5.64 | 4.08 | 6.17 | 9.91 | 5.47 | |

**a.** Assuming that the population variances from both banks are equal, is there evidence of a difference in the mean waiting time between the two branches? (Use $\alpha = 0.05$.)

**b.** Determine the $p$-value in (a) and interpret its meaning.

**c.** In addition to equal variances, what other assumption is necessary in (a)?

**d.** Construct and interpret a 95% confidence interval estimate of the difference between the population means in the two branches.

**10.15** Repeat Problem 10.14(a), assuming that the population variances in the two branches are not equal. Compare the results with those of Problem 10.14(a).

**10.16** In intaglio printing, a design or figure is carved beneath the surface of hard metal or stone. Suppose that an experiment is designed to compare differences in mean surface hardness of steel plates used in intaglio printing (measured in indentation numbers), based on two different surface conditions—untreated and treated by lightly polishing with emery paper. In the experiment, 40 steel plates are randomly assigned—20 that are untreated, and 20 that are treated. The data are shown here and stored in the file Intaglio:

| Untreated | | Treated | |
|-----------|---------|---------|---------|
| 164.368 | 177.135 | 158.239 | 150.226 |
| 159.018 | 163.903 | 138.216 | 155.620 |
| 153.871 | 167.802 | 168.006 | 151.233 |
| 165.096 | 160.818 | 149.654 | 158.653 |
| 157.184 | 167.433 | 145.456 | 151.204 |
| 154.496 | 163.538 | 168.178 | 150.869 |
| 160.920 | 164.525 | 154.321 | 161.657 |
| 164.917 | 171.230 | 162.763 | 157.016 |
| 169.091 | 174.964 | 161.020 | 156.670 |
| 175.276 | 166.311 | 167.706 | 147.920 |

**a.** Assuming that the population variances from both conditions are equal, is there evidence of a difference in the mean surface hardness between untreated and treated steel plates? (Use $\alpha = 0.05$.)

**b.** Determine the $p$-value in (a) and interpret its meaning.

**c.** In addition to equal variances, what other assumption is necessary in (a)?

**d.** Construct and interpret a 95% confidence interval estimate of the difference between the population means from treated and untreated steel plates.

**10.17** Repeat Problem 10.16(a), assuming that the population variances from untreated and treated steel plates are not equal. Compare the results with those of Problem 10.16(a).

**10.18** The director of training for an electronic equipment manufacturer is interested in determining whether different training methods have an effect on the productivity of assembly-line employees. She randomly assigns 42 recently hired employees into two groups of 21. The first group receives a computer-assisted, individual-based training program, and the other receives a team-based training program. Upon completion of the training, the employees are evaluated on the time (in seconds) it takes to assemble a part. The results are in the data file Training.

**a.** Assuming that the variances in the populations of training methods are equal, is there evidence of a difference between the mean assembly times (in seconds) of employees trained in a computer-assisted, individual-based program and those trained in a team-based program? (Use a 0.05 level of significance.)

**b.** In addition to equal variances, what other assumption is necessary in (a)?

**c.** Repeat (a), assuming that the population variances are not equal.

**d.** Compare the results of (a) and (c).

**e.** Assuming normality and equal variances, construct and interpret a 95% confidence interval estimate of the difference between the population means of the two training methods.

**10.19** Nondestructive evaluation is a method that is used to describe the properties of components or materials without causing any permanent physical change to the units. It includes the determination of properties of materials and the classification of flaws by size, shape, type, and location. This method is most effective for detecting surface flaws and characterizing surface properties of electrically conductive materials. Recently, data were collected that classified each component as having a flaw or not based on manual inspection and operator judgment and also reported the size of the crack in the material. Do the components classified as unflawed have a smaller mean crack size than components classified as flawed? The results in terms of crack size

(in inches) are in the data file `Crack` (extracted from B. D. Olin and W. Q. Meeker, "Applications of Statistical Methods to Nondestructive Evaluation," *Technometrics*, 38, 1996, p. 101).

**a.** Assuming that the population variances are equal, is there evidence that the mean crack size is smaller for the unflawed specimens than for the flawed specimens? (Use $\alpha = 0.05$.)

**b.** Repeat (a), assuming that the population variances are not equal.

**c.** Compare the results of (a) and (b).

## 10.2  COMPARING THE MEANS OF TWO RELATED POPULATIONS

The hypothesis-testing procedures examined in Section 10.1 enable you to make comparisons and examine differences in the means of two *independent* populations. In this section, you will learn about a procedure for analyzing the difference between the means of two populations when you collect sample data from populations that are related—that is, when results of the first population are *not* independent of the results of the second population.

There are two situations that involve related data between populations. Either you take repeated measurements from the same set of items or individuals or you match items or individuals according to some characteristic. In either situation, you are interested in the *difference between the two related values* rather than the *individual values* themselves.

When you take **repeated measurements** on the same items or individuals, you assume that the same items or individuals will behave alike if treated alike. Your objective is to show that any differences between two measurements of the same items or individuals are due to different treatment conditions. For example, when performing a taste-testing experiment comparing two beverages, you can use each person in the sample as his or her own control so that you can have *repeated measurements* on the same individual.

The second situation that involves related data between populations is when you have **matched samples**. Here items or individuals are paired together according to some characteristic of interest. For example, in test marketing a product under two different advertising campaigns, a sample of test markets can be *matched* on the basis of the test market population size and/or demographic variables. By accounting for the differences in test market population size and/or demographic variables, you are better able to measure the effects of the two different advertising campaigns.

Regardless of whether you have matched samples or repeated measurements, the objective is to study the difference between two measurements by reducing the effect of the variability that is due to the items or individuals themselves. Table 10.3 on page 404 shows the differences in the individual values for two related populations. To read this table, let $X_{11}, X_{12}, \ldots, X_{1n}$ represent the $n$ values from a sample. And let $X_{21}, X_{22}, \ldots, X_{2n}$ represent either the corresponding $n$ matched values from a second sample or the corresponding $n$ repeated measurements from the initial sample. Then, $D_1, D_2, \ldots, D_n$ will represent the corresponding set of $n$ difference *scores* such that

$$D_1 = X_{11} - X_{21}, D_2 = X_{12} - X_{22}, \ldots, \text{ and } D_n = X_{1n} - X_{2n}.$$

To test for the mean difference between two related populations, you treat the difference scores, each $D_i$, as values from a single sample.

**TABLE 10.3**

Determining the
Difference Between
Two Related Samples

|  | Sample | | |
|---|---|---|---|
| **Value** | **1** | **2** | **Difference** |
| 1 | $X_{11}$ | $X_{21}$ | $D_1 = X_{11} - X_{21}$ |
| 2 | $X_{12}$ | $X_{22}$ | $D_2 = X_{12} - X_{22}$ |
| . | . | . | . |
| . | . | . | . |
| . | . | . | . |
| $i$ | $X_{1i}$ | $X_{2i}$ | $D_i = X_{1i} - X_{2i}$ |
| . | . | . | . |
| . | . | . | . |
| . | . | . | . |
| $n$ | $X_{1n}$ | $X_{2n}$ | $D_n = X_{1n} - X_{2n}$ |

## Paired $t$ Test

If you assume that the difference scores are randomly and independently selected from a population that is normally distributed, you can use the **paired $t$ test for the mean difference** in related populations to determine whether there is a significant population mean difference. Like the one-sample $t$ test developed in Section 9.2 [see Equation (9.2) on page 356], the $t$-test statistic developed here follows the $t$ distribution, with $n - 1$ degrees of freedom. Although you must assume that the population is normally distributed, as long as the sample size is not very small and the population is not highly skewed, you can use the paired $t$ test.

To test the null hypothesis that there is no difference in the means of two related populations:

$$H_0: \mu_D = 0 \text{ (where } \mu_D = \mu_1 - \mu_2)$$

against the alternative that the means are not the same:

$$H_1: \mu_D \neq 0$$

you compute the $t_{STAT}$ test statistic using Equation (10.5).

Paired $t$ Test for the Mean Difference

$$t_{STAT} = \frac{\bar{D} - \mu_D}{\frac{S_D}{\sqrt{n}}} \tag{10.5}$$

where

$$\mu_D = \text{hypothesized mean difference}$$

$$\bar{D} = \frac{\sum_{i=1}^{n} D_i}{n}$$

$$S_D = \sqrt{\frac{\sum_{i=1}^{n} (D_i - \bar{D})^2}{n - 1}}$$

The $t_{STAT}$ test statistic follows a $t$ distribution with $n - 1$ degrees of freedom.

For a two-tail test with a given level of significance, $\alpha$, you reject the null hypothesis if the computed $t_{STAT}$ test statistic is greater than the upper-tail critical value $t_{\alpha/2}$ from the $t$ distribution, or if the computed $t_{STAT}$ test statistic is less than the lower-tail critical value $-t_{\alpha/2}$ from the $t$ distribution. The decision rule is

$$\text{Reject } H_0 \text{ if } t_{STAT} > t_{\alpha/2}$$

$$\text{or if } t_{STAT} < -t_{\alpha/2};$$

$$\text{otherwise, do not reject } H_0.$$

The following example illustrates the use of the $t$ test for the mean difference. The Automobile Association of America (AAA) conducted a mileage test to compare the gasoline mileage from real-life driving done by AAA members and results of driving done according to government standards (extracted from J. Healey, "Fuel Economy Calculations to Be Altered," *USA Today*, January 11, 2006, p. 1B).

What is the best way to design an experiment to compare the gasoline mileage from real-life driving done by AAA members and results of driving done according to government standards? One approach is to take two independent samples and then use the hypothesis tests discussed in Section 10.1. In this approach, you would use one set of automobiles to test the real-life driving done by AAA members. Then you would use a second set of different automobiles to test the results of driving done according to government standards.

However, because the first set of automobiles to test the real-life driving done by AAA members may get lower or higher gasoline mileage than the second set of automobiles, this is not a good approach. A better approach is to use a repeated-measurements experiment. In this experiment, you use one set of automobiles. For each automobile, you conduct a test of real-life driving done by an AAA member and a test of driving done according to government standards. Measuring the two gasoline mileages for the same automobiles serves to reduce the variability in the gasoline mileages compared with what would occur if you used two independent sets of automobiles. This approach focuses on the differences between the real-life driving done by an AAA member and the driving done according to government standards.

Table 10.4 displays results (stored in the file ⬛AAAMileage⬛ ) from a sample of $n = 9$ automobiles from such an experiment.

**TABLE 10.4**

Repeated Measurements of Gasoline Mileage for Real-Life Driving by AAA Members and Driving Done According to Government Standards

| Model | Members | Government | Difference ($D_i$) |
|---|---|---|---|
| 2005 Ford F-150 | 14.3 | 16.8 | −2.5 |
| 2005 Chevrolet Silverado | 15.0 | 17.8 | −2.8 |
| 2002 Honda Accord LX | 27.8 | 26.2 | +1.6 |
| 2002 Honda Civic | 27.9 | 33.2 | −5.3 |
| 2004 Honda Civic Hybrid | 48.8 | 47.6 | +1.2 |
| 2002 Ford Explorer | 16.8 | 18.3 | −1.5 |
| 2005 Toyota Camry | 23.7 | 28.5 | −4.8 |
| 2003 Toyota Corolla | 32.8 | 33.1 | −0.3 |
| 2005 Toyota Prius | 37.3 | 44.0 | −6.7 |

You want to determine whether there is any difference in the mean gasoline mileage between the real-life driving done by an AAA member and the driving done according to government standards. In other words, is there evidence that the mean gasoline mileage is different between the two types of driving? Thus, the null and alternative hypotheses are

$H_0$: $\mu_D = 0$ (There is no difference in mean gasoline mileage between the real-life driving done by an AAA member and the driving done according to government standards.)

$H_1$: $\mu_D \neq 0$ (There is a difference in mean gasoline mileage between the real-life driving done by an AAA member and the driving done according to government standards.)

Choosing the level of significance of $\alpha = 0.05$ and assuming that the differences are normally distributed, you use the paired $t$ test [Equation (10.5)]. For a sample of $n = 9$ automobiles, there are $n - 1 = 8$ degrees of freedom. Using Table E.3, the decision rule is

$$\text{Reject } H_0 \text{ if } t_{STAT} > t_{0.025} = 2.3060;$$

$$\text{or if } t_{STAT} < -t_{0.025} = -2.3060;$$

$$\text{otherwise, do not reject } H_0.$$

For the $n = 9$ differences (see Table 10.4), the sample mean difference is

$$\bar{D} = \frac{\sum_{i=1}^{n} D_i}{n} = \frac{-21.1}{9} = -2.3444$$

and

$$S_D = \sqrt{\frac{\sum_{i=1}^{n} (D_i - \bar{D})^2}{n-1}} = 2.893575$$

From Equation (10.5) on page 404,

$$t_{STAT} = \frac{\bar{D} - \mu_D}{\frac{S_D}{\sqrt{n}}} = \frac{-2.3444 - 0}{\frac{2.893575}{\sqrt{9}}} = -2.4307$$

Because $t_{STAT} = -2.4307$ is less than $-2.3060$, you reject the null hypothesis, $H_0$ (see Figure 10.10). There is evidence of a difference in mean gasoline mileage between the real-life driving done by an AAA member and the driving done according to government standards. Real-life driving results in a lower mean gasoline mileage.

**FIGURE 10.10**

Two-tail paired $t$ test at the 0.05 level of significance with 8 degrees of freedom

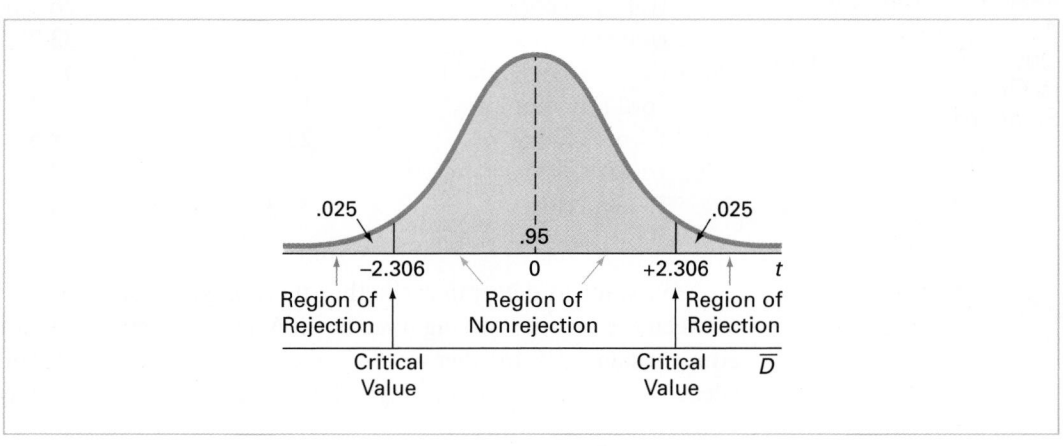

You can compute this test statistic along with the $p$-value by using Microsoft Excel or Minitab (see Figures 10.11 and 10.12). Because the $p$-value $= 0.0412 < \alpha = 0.05$, you reject $H_0$. The $p$-value indicates that if the two types of driving have the same population mean gasoline

**FIGURE 10.11**

Microsoft Excel results of paired *t* test for the car mileage data

*See Section E10.6 to create this worksheet.*

| | A | B | C |
|---|---|---|---|
| 1 | t-Test: Paired Two Sample for Means | | |
| 2 | | | |
| 3 | | *Members* | *Government* |
| 4 | Mean | 27.1556 | 29.5 |
| 5 | Variance | 129.5528 | 125.0025 |
| 6 | Observations | 9 | 9 |
| 7 | Pearson Correlation | 0.9673 | |
| 8 | Hypothesized Mean Difference | 0 | |
| 9 | df | 8 | |
| 10 | t Stat | -2.4307 | |
| 11 | P(T<=t) one-tail | 0.0206 | |
| 12 | t Critical one-tail | 1.8595 | |
| 13 | P(T<=t) two-tail | 0.0412 | |
| 14 | t Critical two-tail | 2.3060 | |

**FIGURE 10.12**

Minitab results of paired *t* test for the car mileage data

*See Section M10.3 to create this.*

```
Paired T-Test and CI: Owner, Government

Paired T for Owner - Government

              N    Mean   StDev   SE Mean
Owner         9   27.16   11.38     3.79
Government    9   29.50   11.18     3.73
Difference    9  -2.344   2.894     0.965


95% CI for mean difference: (-4.569, -0.120)
T-Test of mean difference = 0 (vs not = 0): T-Value = -2.43   P-Value = 0.041
```

mileage, the probability that one type of driving would have a sample mean that was 2.3444 miles per gallon less than the other type is 0.0412. Because this probability is less than α = 0.05, you conclude that the alternative hypothesis is true.

From Figure 10.13, observe that the boxplot shows approximate symmetry. Thus, the data do not greatly contradict the underlying assumption of normality. If a boxplot, histogram, or normal probability plot reveals that the assumption of underlying normality in the population is severely violated, then the *t* test is inappropriate. If this occurs, you can use either a *nonparametric* procedure that does not make the assumption of underlying normality (see Section 12.7) or make a data transformation (see reference 6), and then recheck the assumptions to determine whether you should use the *t* test.

**FIGURE 10.13**

Minitab results of boxplot for the car mileage data

*See Section M3.2 to create this. (PHStat2 users, see Section P3.1 to create an equivalent chart.)*

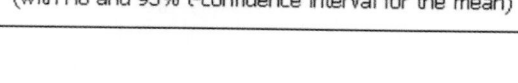

Boxplot of Differences
(with Ho and 95% t-confidence interval for the mean)

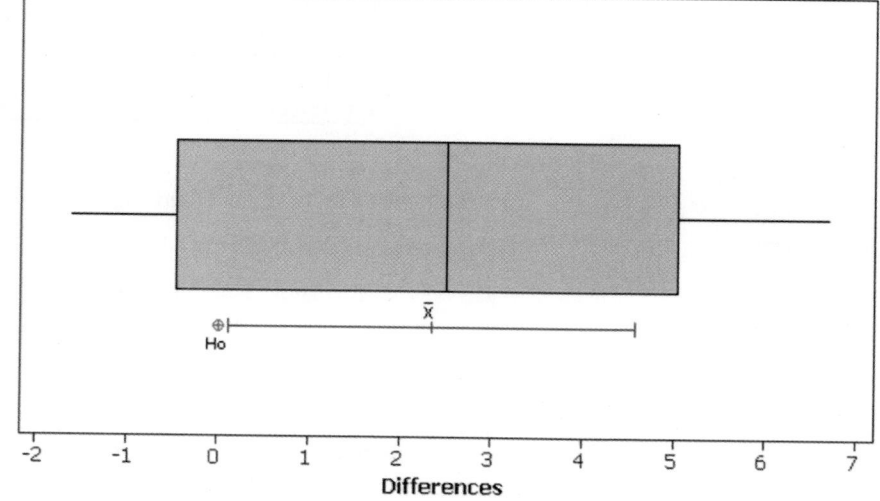

Differences

**EXAMPLE 10.2**

PAIRED $t$ TEST OF PIZZA DELIVERY TIMES

Recall from Example 10.1 on page 394 that a local pizza restaurant situated across the street from a college campus advertises that it delivers to the dormitories faster than the local branch of a national pizza chain. In order to determine whether this advertisement is valid, you and some friends have decided to order 10 pizzas from the local pizza restaurant and 10 pizzas from the national chain. In fact, each time you ordered a pizza from the local pizza restaurant, your friends ordered a pizza from the national pizza chain. Thus, you have matched samples. For each of the ten times pizzas were ordered, you have one measurement from the local pizza restaurant and one from the national chain. At the 0.05 level of significance, is the mean delivery time for the local pizza restaurant less than the mean delivery time for the national pizza chain?

**SOLUTION** Use the paired $t$ test to analyze the data in Table 10.5 (see the file `Pizzatime`). Figure 10.14 illustrates Microsoft Excel paired $t$-test results for the pizza delivery data and Figure 10.15 shows Minitab results.

**TABLE 10.5**

Delivery Times for Local Pizza Restaurant and National Pizza Chain

| Time | Local | Chain | Difference |
|------|-------|-------|------------|
| 1 | 16.8 | 22.0 | −5.2 |
| 2 | 11.7 | 15.2 | −3.5 |
| 3 | 15.6 | 18.7 | −3.1 |
| 4 | 16.7 | 15.6 | 1.1 |
| 5 | 17.5 | 20.8 | −3.3 |
| 6 | 18.1 | 19.5 | −1.4 |
| 7 | 14.1 | 17.0 | −2.9 |
| 8 | 21.8 | 19.5 | 2.3 |
| 9 | 13.9 | 16.5 | −2.6 |
| 10 | 20.8 | 24.0 | −3.2 |
| | | | −21.8 |

**FIGURE 10.14**

Microsoft Excel paired $t$-test results for the pizza delivery data

*See Section E10.6 to create this.*

| | A | B | C |
|---|---|---|---|
| 1 | t-Test: Paired Two Sample for Means | | |
| 2 | | | |
| 3 | | Local | Chain |
| 4 | Mean | 16.7 | 18.88 |
| 5 | Variance | 9.5822 | 8.2151 |
| 6 | Observations | 10 | 10 |
| 7 | Pearson Correlation | 0.7141 | |
| 8 | Hypothesized Mean Difference | 0 | |
| 9 | df | 9 | |
| 10 | t Stat | -3.0448 | |
| 11 | P(T<=t) one-tail | 0.0070 | |
| 12 | t Critical one-tail | 1.8331 | |
| 13 | P(T<=t) two-tail | 0.0139 | |
| 14 | t Critical two-tail | 2.2622 | |

**FIGURE 10.15**

Minitab paired $t$-test results for the pizza delivery data

*See Section M10.3 to create this.*

```
Paired T-Test and CI: Local, Chain

Paired T for Local - Chain

               N    Mean   StDev   SE Mean
Local         10  16.700   3.096    0.979
Chain         10  18.880   2.866    0.906
Difference    10  -2.180   2.264    0.716


95% upper bound for mean difference: -0.868
T-Test of mean difference = 0 (vs < 0): T-Value = -3.04  P-Value = 0.007
```

The null and alternative hypotheses are

$H_0: \mu_D \geq 0$ (Mean delivery time for the local pizza restaurant is greater than or equal to the mean delivery time for the national pizza chain.)
$H_1: \mu_D < 0$ (Mean delivery time for the local pizza restaurant is less than the mean delivery time for the national pizza chain.)

Choosing the level of significance $\alpha = 0.05$ and assuming that the differences are normally distributed, you use the paired $t$ test [Equation (10.5) on page 404]. For a sample of $n = 10$ delivery times, there are $n - 1 = 9$ degrees of freedom. Using Table E.3, the decision rule is

$$\text{Reject } H_0 \text{ if } t_{STAT} < -t_{0.05} = -1.8331;$$

$$\text{otherwise, do not reject } H_0.$$

For $n = 10$ differences (see Table 10.5), the sample mean difference is

$$\bar{D} = \frac{\sum\limits_{i=1}^{n} D_i}{n} = \frac{-21.8}{10} = -2.18$$

and the sample standard deviation of the difference is

$$S_D = \sqrt{\frac{\sum\limits_{i=1}^{n} (D_i - \bar{D})^2}{n-1}} = 2.2641$$

From Equation (10.5) on page 404,

$$t_{STAT} = \frac{\bar{D} - \mu_D}{\dfrac{S_D}{\sqrt{n}}} = \frac{-2.18 - 0}{\dfrac{2.2641}{\sqrt{10}}} = -3.0448$$

Because $t_{STAT} = -3.0448$ is less than $-1.8331$, you reject the null hypothesis $H_0$ (the $p$-value is $0.0070 < 0.05$). There is evidence that the mean delivery time is lower for the local pizza restaurant than for the national pizza chain.

This conclusion is different from the one you reached in Example 10.1 on page 394 when you used the pooled-variance $t$ test for these data. By pairing the delivery times, you are able to focus on the differences between the two pizza delivery services and not the variability created by ordering pizzas at different times of day. The paired $t$ test is a more powerful statistical procedure that is better able to detect the difference between the two pizza delivery services.

## Confidence Interval Estimate for the Mean Difference

Instead of, or in addition to, testing for the difference between the means of two related populations, you can use Equation (10.6) to construct a confidence interval estimate of the mean difference.

**Confidence Interval Estimate for the Mean Difference**

$$\bar{D} \pm t_{\alpha/2}\frac{S_D}{\sqrt{n}} \qquad\qquad (10.6)$$

or

$$\bar{D} - t_{\alpha/2}\frac{S_D}{\sqrt{n}} \leq \mu_D \leq \bar{D} + t_{\alpha/2}\frac{S_D}{\sqrt{n}}$$

where $t_{\alpha/2}$ is the critical value of the $t$ distribution with $n - 1$ degrees of freedom for an area of $\alpha/2$ in the upper tail.

Return to the example comparing gasoline mileage generated by real-life driving and by government standards. Using Equation (10.6), $\bar{D} = -2.3444$, $S_D = 2.8936$, $n = 9$, and $t_{\alpha/2} = 2.306$ (for 95% confidence and $n - 1 = 8$ degrees of freedom),

$$-2.3444 \pm (2.306)\frac{2.8936}{\sqrt{9}}$$

$$-2.3444 \pm 2.2242$$

$$-4.5686 \leq \mu_D \leq -0.1202$$

Thus, with 95% confidence, the mean difference in gasoline mileage between the real-life driving done by an AAA member and the driving done according to government standards is between −4.5686 and −0.1202 miles per gallon. Because the interval estimate contains only values less than zero, you can conclude that there is a difference in the population means. The mean miles per gallon for the real-life driving done by an AAA member is less than the mean miles per gallon for the driving done according to government standards.

# PROBLEMS FOR SECTION 10.2

## Learning the Basics

**10.20** An experimental design for a paired $t$ test has 20 pairs of identical twins. How many degrees of freedom are there in this $t$ test?

**10.21** An experiment requires a measurement before and after the presentation of a stimulus to each of 15 subjects. In the analysis of the data collected from this experiment, how many degrees of freedom are there in the test?

## Applying the Concepts

**✓SELF Test** **10.22** Nine experts rated two brands of Colombian coffee in a taste-testing experiment. A rating on a 7-point scale (1 = extremely unpleasing, 7 = extremely pleasing) is given for each of four character-

istics: taste, aroma, richness, and acidity. The following data (stored in the file **Coffee**) displays the summated ratings—accumulated over all four characteristics.

|  | BRAND | |
| --- | --- | --- |
| **EXPERT** | **A** | **B** |
| C.C. | 24 | 26 |
| S.E. | 27 | 27 |
| E.G. | 19 | 22 |
| B.L. | 24 | 27 |
| C.M. | 22 | 25 |
| C.N. | 26 | 27 |
| G.N. | 27 | 26 |
| R.M. | 25 | 27 |
| P.V. | 22 | 23 |

**a.** At the 0.05 level of significance, is there evidence of a difference in the mean summated ratings between the two brands?

**b.** What assumption is necessary about the population distribution in order to perform this test?

**c.** Determine the *p*-value in (a) and interpret its meaning.

**d.** Construct and interpret a 95% confidence interval estimate of the difference in the mean summated ratings between the two brands.

**10.23** In industrial settings, alternative methods often exist for measuring variables of interest. The data in the file Measurement (coded to maintain confidentiality) represent measurements in-line that were collected from an analyzer during the production process and from an analytical lab (extracted from M. Leitnaker, "Comparing Measurement Processes: In-line Versus Analytical Measurements," *Quality Engineering*, 13, 2000–2001, pp. 293–298).

**a.** At the 0.05 level of significance, is there evidence of a difference in the mean measurements in-line and from an analytical lab?

**b.** What assumption is necessary about the population distribution in order to perform this test?

**c.** Use a graphical method to evaluate the validity of the assumption in (a).

**d.** Construct and interpret a 95% confidence interval estimate of the difference in the mean measurements in-line and from an analytical lab.

**10.24** Can students save money by comparison shopping for textbooks at Amazon.com? To investigate this possibility, a random sample of 15 textbooks used during the Spring 2007 semester at Miami University was selected. The prices for these textbooks at both a local bookstore and through Amazon.com were recorded. The prices for the textbooks are given below (and are stored in the file Textbook):

| Book Name | Book Store | Amazon |
|---|---|---|
| *Principles of Microeconomics* | 120.00 | 101.22 |
| *Calculus: Early Transcendentals* | 137.50 | 115.33 |
| *Exploring Wine* | 65.00 | 37.05 |
| *Manual de Gramatica* | 82.75 | 71.36 |
| *Deviant Behavior* | 90.00 | 83.00 |
| *Modern Architecture Since 1900* | 39.95 | 26.37 |
| *Rise of Christianity* | 40.00 | 26.40 |
| *Commercial Banking* | 120.00 | 108.99 |
| *A Romance of a Republic* | 25.00 | 14.99 |
| *Chemistry in Context* | 133.75 | 102.30 |
| *Universal Principles of Design* | 40.00 | 26.40 |
| *In Mixed Company* | 79.50 | 68.76 |
| *International Marketing* | 154.75 | 126.15 |
| *Russia & Western Civilization* | 30.95 | 31.95 |
| *Enterprise Information Systems* | 155.75 | 126.97 |

**a.** At the 0.01 level of significance, is there evidence of a difference between the mean price of textbooks at the local bookstore and Amazon.com?

**b.** What assumption is necessary about the population distribution in order to perform this test?

**c.** Construct a 99% confidence interval estimate of the mean difference in price. Interpret the interval.

**d.** Compare the results of (a) and (c).

**10.25** A newspaper article discussed the opening of a Whole Foods Market in the Time-Warner building in New York City. The following data (stored in the file Wholefoods1) compared the prices of some kitchen staples at the new Whole Foods Market and at the Fairway supermarket located about 15 blocks from the Time-Warner building:

| Item | Whole Foods | Fairway |
|---|---|---|
| Half-gallon milk | 2.19 | 1.35 |
| Dozen eggs | 2.39 | 1.69 |
| Tropicana orange juice (64 oz.) | 2.00 | 2.49 |
| Head of Boston lettuce | 1.98 | 1.29 |
| Ground round, 1 lb. | 4.99 | 3.69 |
| Bumble Bee tuna, 6 oz. can | 1.79 | 1.33 |
| Granny Smith apples (1 lb.) | 1.69 | 1.49 |
| Box DeCecco linguini | 1.99 | 1.59 |
| Salmon steak, 1 lb. | 7.99 | 5.99 |
| Whole chicken, per pound | 2.19 | 1.49 |

Source: *Extracted from W. Grimes, "A Pleasure Palace Without the Guilt," The New York Times, February 18, 2004, pp. F1, F5.*

**a.** At the 0.01 level of significance, is there evidence that the mean price is higher at Whole Foods Market than at the Fairway supermarket?

**b.** Interpret the meaning of the *p*-value in (a).

**c.** What assumption is necessary about the population distribution in order to perform the test in (a)?

**10.26** Multiple myeloma, or blood plasma cancer, is characterized by increased blood vessel formulation (angiogenesis) in the bone marrow that is a predictive factor in survival. One treatment approach used for multiple myeloma is stem cell transplantation with the patient's own stem cells. The following data (stored in the file Myeloma) represent the bone marrow microvessel density for patients who had a complete response to the stem cell transplant (as measured by blood and urine tests). The measurements were taken immediately prior to the stem cell transplant and at the time the complete response was determined:

| Patient | Before | After |
|---------|--------|-------|
| 1 | 158 | 284 |
| 2 | 189 | 214 |
| 3 | 202 | 101 |
| 4 | 353 | 227 |
| 5 | 416 | 290 |
| 6 | 426 | 176 |
| 7 | 441 | 290 |

Source: *Extracted from S. V. Rajkumar, R. Fonseca, T. E. Witzig, M. A. Gertz, and P. R. Greipp, "Bone Marrow Angiogenesis in Patients Achieving Complete Response After Stem Cell Transplantation for Multiple Myeloma,"* Leukemia, *1999, 13, pp. 469–472.*

a. At the 0.05 level of significance, is there evidence that the mean bone marrow microvessel density is higher before the stem cell transplant than after the stem cell transplant?
b. Interpret the meaning of the *p*-value in (a).
c. Construct and interpret a 95% confidence interval estimate of the mean difference in bone marrow microvessel density before and after the stem cell transplant.
d. What assumption is necessary about the population distribution in order to perform the test in (a)?

**10.27** Over the past year, the vice president for human resources at a large medical center has run a series of three-month workshops aimed at increasing worker motivation and performance. To check the effectiveness of the workshops, she selected a random sample of 35 employees from the personnel files and recorded their most recent annual performance ratings, along with their ratings prior to attending the workshops. The data are stored in the file `Perform`. The Microsoft Excel results shown at right provide both descriptive and inferential information. State your findings and conclusions in a report to the vice president for human resources.

| | A | B |
|---|---|---|
| 1 | **Difference** | |
| 2 | | |
| 3 | Mean | -5.2571 |
| 4 | Standard Error | 1.9478 |
| 5 | Median | -5 |
| 6 | Mode | -10 |
| 7 | Standard Deviation | 11.5232 |
| 8 | Sample Variance | 132.7849 |
| 9 | Kurtosis | 1.1038 |
| 10 | Skewness | 0.1103 |
| 11 | Range | 61 |
| 12 | Minimum | -34 |
| 13 | Maximum | 27 |
| 14 | Sum | -184 |
| 15 | Count | 35 |
| 16 | Largest(1) | 27 |
| 17 | Smallest(1) | -34 |

| | A | B | C |
|---|---|---|---|
| 1 | t-Test: Paired Two Sample for Means | | |
| 2 | | | |
| 3 | | *Before* | *After* |
| 4 | Mean | 74.5429 | 79.8 |
| 5 | Variance | 80.9025 | 37.1647 |
| 6 | Observations | 35 | 35 |
| 7 | Pearson Correlation | -0.1342 | |
| 8 | Hypothesized Mean Difference | 0 | |
| 9 | df | 34 | |
| 10 | t Stat | -2.6990 | |
| 11 | P(T<=t) one-tail | 0.0054 | |
| 12 | t Critical one-tail | 1.6909 | |
| 13 | P(T<=t) two-tail | 0.0108 | |
| 14 | t Critical two-tail | 2.0322 | |

**10.28** The data in the file `Concrete1` represent the compressive strength, in thousands of pounds per square inch (psi), of 40 samples of concrete taken two and seven days after pouring.

Source: *Extracted from O. Carrillo-Gamboa and R. F. Gunst, "Measurement-Error-Model Collinearities,"* Technometrics, *34, 1992, pp. 454–464.*

a. At the 0.01 level of significance, is there evidence that the mean strength is lower at two days than at seven days?
b. What assumption is necessary about the population distribution in order to perform this test?
c. Find the *p*-value in (a) and interpret its meaning.

## 10.3    COMPARING TWO POPULATION PROPORTIONS

Often, you need to make comparisons and analyze differences between two population proportions. You can perform a test for the difference between two proportions selected from independent populations by using two different methods. This section presents a procedure whose test statistic, $Z_{STAT}$, is approximated by a standardized normal distribution. In Section 12.1, a procedure is developed whose test statistic, $\chi^2_{STAT}$, is approximated by a chi-square distribution. As you will see, the results from these two tests are equivalent.

## Z Test for the Difference Between Two Proportions

In evaluating differences between two population proportions, you can use a **Z test for the difference between two proportions**. The $Z_{STAT}$ test statistic is based on the difference between two sample proportions $(p_1 - p_2)$. This test statistic, given in Equation (10.7), approximately follows a standardized normal distribution for large enough sample sizes.

### Z Test for the Difference Between Two Proportions

$$Z_{STAT} = \frac{(p_1 - p_2) - (\pi_1 - \pi_2)}{\sqrt{\bar{p}(1 - \bar{p})\left(\dfrac{1}{n_1} + \dfrac{1}{n_2}\right)}} \tag{10.7}$$

with

$$\bar{p} = \frac{X_1 + X_2}{n_1 + n_2} \qquad p_1 = \frac{X_1}{n_1} \qquad p_2 = \frac{X_2}{n_2}$$

where

$p_1$ = proportion of items of interest in sample 1

$X_1$ = number of items of interest in sample 1

$n_1$ = sample size of sample 1

$\pi_1$ = proportion of items of interest in population 1

$p_2$ = proportion of items of interest in sample 2

$X_2$ = number of items of interest in sample 2

$n_2$ = sample size of sample 2

$\pi_2$ = proportion of items of interest in population 2

$\bar{p}$ = pooled estimate of the population proportion of items of interest

The $Z_{STAT}$ test statistic approximately follows a standardized normal distribution.

Under the null hypothesis, you assume that the two population proportions are equal ($\pi_1 = \pi_2$). Because the pooled estimate for the population proportion is based on the null hypothesis, you combine, or pool, the two sample proportions to compute an overall estimate of the common population proportion. This estimate is equal to the number of items of interest in the two samples combined ($X_1 + X_2$) divided by the total sample size from the two samples combined ($n_1 + n_2$).

As shown in the following table, you can use this Z test for the difference between population proportions to determine whether there is a difference in the proportion of items of interest in the two populations (two-tail test) or whether one population has a higher proportion of items of interest than the other population (one-tail test):

| Two-Tail Test | One-Tail Test | One-Tail Test |
|---|---|---|
| $H_0: \pi_1 = \pi_2$ | $H_0: \pi_1 \geq \pi_2$ | $H_0: \pi_1 \leq \pi_2$ |
| $H_1: \pi_1 \neq \pi_2$ | $H_1: \pi_1 < \pi_2$ | $H_1: \pi_1 > \pi_2$ |

where

$$\pi_1 = \text{proportion of items of interest in population 1}$$

$$\pi_2 = \text{proportion of items of interest in population 2}$$

To test the null hypothesis that there is no difference between the proportions of two independent populations:

$$H_0: \pi_1 = \pi_2$$

against the alternative that the two population proportions are not the same:

$$H_1: \pi_1 \neq \pi_2$$

use the $Z_{STAT}$ test statistic, given by Equation (10.7). For a given level of significance $\alpha$, reject the null hypothesis if the computed $Z_{STAT}$ test statistic is greater than the upper-tail critical value from the standardized normal distribution, or if the computed $Z_{STAT}$ test statistic is less than the lower-tail critical value from the standardized normal distribution.

To illustrate the use of the $Z$ test for the equality of two proportions, suppose that you are the manager of T.C. Resort Properties, a collection of five upscale resort hotels located on two tropical islands. On one of the islands, T.C. Resort Properties has two hotels, the Beachcomber and the Windsurfer. In tabulating the responses to the single question, "Are you likely to choose this hotel again?" 163 of 227 guests at the Beachcomber responded yes, and 154 of 262 guests at the Windsurfer responded yes. At the 0.05 level of significance, is there evidence of a significant difference in guest satisfaction (as measured by the likelihood to return to the hotel) between the two hotels?

The null and alternative hypotheses are

$$H_0: \pi_1 = \pi_2 \quad \text{or} \quad \pi_1 - \pi_2 = 0$$

$$H_1: \pi_1 \neq \pi_2 \quad \text{or} \quad \pi_1 - \pi_2 \neq 0$$

Using the 0.05 level of significance, the critical values are $-1.96$ and $+1.96$ (see Figure 10.16), and the decision rule is

$$\text{Reject } H_0 \text{ if } Z_{STAT} < -1.96$$

$$\text{or if } Z_{STAT} > +1.96;$$

$$\text{otherwise, do not reject } H_0.$$

**FIGURE 10.16**

Regions of rejection and nonrejection when testing a hypothesis for the difference between two proportions at the 0.05 level of significance

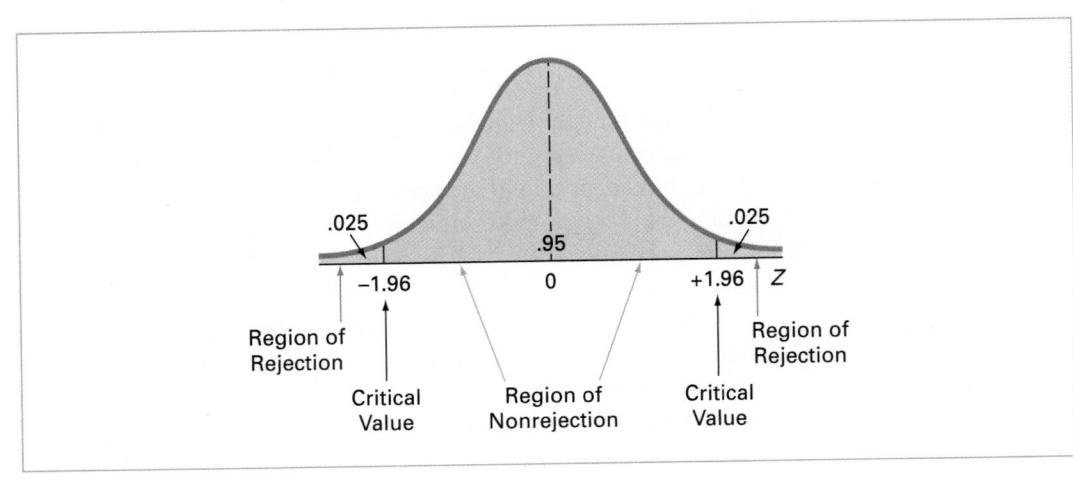

Using Equation (10.7) on page 413,

$$Z_{STAT} = \frac{(p_1 - p_2) - (\pi_1 - \pi_2)}{\sqrt{\bar{p}(1 - \bar{p})\left(\dfrac{1}{n_1} + \dfrac{1}{n_2}\right)}}$$

where

$$p_1 = \frac{X_1}{n_1} = \frac{163}{227} = 0.7181 \quad p_2 = \frac{X_2}{n_2} = \frac{154}{262} = 0.5878$$

and

$$\bar{p} = \frac{X_1 + X_2}{n_1 + n_2} = \frac{163 + 154}{227 + 262} = \frac{317}{489} = 0.6483$$

so that

$$Z_{STAT} = \frac{(0.7181 - 0.5878) - (0)}{\sqrt{0.6483(1 - 0.6483)\left(\dfrac{1}{227} + \dfrac{1}{262}\right)}}$$

$$= \frac{0.1303}{\sqrt{(0.228)(0.0082)}}$$

$$= \frac{0.1303}{\sqrt{0.00187}}$$

$$= \frac{0.1303}{0.0432} = +3.0088$$

Using the 0.05 level of significance, reject the null hypothesis because $Z_{STAT}$ = +3.0088 > +1.96. The p-value is 0.0026 (calculated from Table E.2 or from the Microsoft Excel results of Figure 10.17 or the Minitab results of Figure 10.18 on page 416), and indicates that if the null hypothesis is true, the probability that a $Z_{STAT}$ test statistic is less than −3.0088 is 0.0013, and, similarly, the probability that a $Z_{STAT}$ test statistic is greater than +3.0088 is 0.0013. Thus, for this two-tail test, the p-value is 0.0013 + 0.0013 = 0.0026. Because 0.0026 < $\alpha$ = 0.05, you reject the null hypothesis. There is evidence to conclude that the two hotels are significantly different with respect to guest satisfaction; a greater proportion of guests are willing to return to the Beachcomber than to the Windsurfer.

**EXAMPLE 10.3**

TESTING FOR THE DIFFERENCE IN TWO PROPORTIONS

Technology has led to the rise of extreme workers who are on the job 60 hours a week or more. One of the reasons cited by employees about why they worked long hours was that they loved their job because it is stimulating/challenging/provides an adrenaline rush (extracted from S. Armour, "Hi, I'm Joan and I'm a Workaholic," *USA Today*, May 23, 2007, pp. 1B, 2B). Suppose that the survey of 1,564 workaholics included 786 men and 778 women, and that 707 men and 638 women loved their job because it is stimulating/challenging/provides an

**FIGURE 10.17**

Microsoft Excel results for the Z test for the difference between two proportions for the hotel guest satisfaction problem

*See Section E10.7 or P10.4 to create this.*

| | A | B |
|---|---|---|
| 1 | Z Test for Differences in Two Proportions | |
| 2 | | |
| 3 | Data | |
| 4 | Hypothesized Difference | 0 |
| 5 | Level of Significance | 0.05 |
| 6 | Group 1 | |
| 7 | Number of Items of Interest | 163 |
| 8 | Sample Size | 227 |
| 9 | Group 2 | |
| 10 | Number of Items of Interest | 154 |
| 11 | Sample Size | 262 |
| 12 | | |
| 13 | Intermediate Calculations | |
| 14 | Group 1 Proportion | 0.7181 |
| 15 | Group 2 Proportion | 0.5878 |
| 16 | Difference in Two Proportions | 0.1303 |
| 17 | Average Proportion | 0.6483 |
| 18 | Z Test Statistic | 3.0088 |
| 19 | | |
| 20 | Two-Tail Test | |
| 21 | Lower Critical Value | -1.9600 |
| 22 | Upper Critical Value | 1.9600 |
| 23 | p-Value | 0.0026 |
| 24 | Reject the null hypothesis | |

Formulas (right of column B):
- Row 14: =B7/B8
- Row 15: =B10/B11
- Row 16: =B14 - B15
- Row 17: =(B7 + B10)/(B8 + B11)
- Row 18: =(B16 - B4)/SQRT(B17 * (1 - B17) * (1/B8 + 1/B11))
- Row 21: =NORMSINV(B5/2)
- Row 22: =NORMSINV(1 - B5/2)
- Row 23: =2 * (1 - NORMSDIST(ABS(B18)))
- Row 24: =IF(B23 < B5, "Reject the null hypothesis", "Do not reject the null hypothesis")

**FIGURE 10.18**

Minitab results for the Z test for the difference between two proportions for the hotel guest satisfaction problem

*See Section M10.4 to create this.*

```
Test and CI for Two Proportions

Sample   X    N    Sample p
1       163  227   0.718062
2       154  262   0.587786


Difference = p (1) - p (2)
Estimate for difference:  0.130275
95% CI for difference:  (0.0467379, 0.213813)
Test for difference = 0 (vs not = 0):  Z = 3.01  P-Value = 0.003
```

adrenaline rush. At the 0.05 level of significance, you would like to determine whether the proportion of workaholic men who love their job because it is stimulating/challenging/provides an adrenaline rush is greater than the proportion of women.

**SOLUTION** Because you want to know whether there is evidence that the proportion of workaholic men who love their job because it is stimulating/challenging/provides an adrenaline rush is *greater* than the proportion of women, you have a one-tail test. The null and alternative hypotheses are

$H_0$: $\pi_1 \leq \pi_2$ (Proportion of workaholic men who love their job because it is stimulating/challenging/provides an adrenaline rush is less than or equal to the proportion of women.)
$H_1$: $\pi_1 > \pi_2$ (Proportion of workaholic men who love their job because it is stimulating/challenging/provides an adrenaline rush is greater than the proportion of women.)

Using the 0.05 level of significance, for the one-tail test in the upper tail, the critical value is +1.645. The decision rule is

$$\text{Reject } H_0 \text{ if } Z_{STAT} > +1.645;$$

otherwise, do not reject $H_0$.

Using Equation (10.7) on page 413,

$$Z_{STAT} = \frac{(p_1 - p_2) - (\pi_1 - \pi_2)}{\sqrt{\bar{p}(1 - \bar{p})\left(\dfrac{1}{n_1} + \dfrac{1}{n_2}\right)}}$$

where

$$p_1 = \frac{X_1}{n_1} = \frac{707}{786} = 0.8995 \qquad p_2 = \frac{X_2}{n_2} = \frac{638}{778} = 0.8201$$

and

$$\bar{p} = \frac{X_1 + X_2}{n_1 + n_2} = \frac{707 + 638}{786 + 778} = \frac{1,345}{1,564} = 0.8600$$

so that

$$Z_{STAT} = \frac{(0.8995 - 0.8201) - (0)}{\sqrt{0.86(1 - 0.86)\left(\dfrac{1}{786} + \dfrac{1}{778}\right)}}$$

$$= \frac{0.0794}{\sqrt{(0.1204)(0.0025575)}}$$

$$= \frac{0.0794}{\sqrt{0.0003079}}$$

$$= \frac{0.0794}{0.017547} = +4.5266$$

Using the 0.05 level of significance, you reject the null hypothesis because $Z_{STAT} = +4.5266 >$ $+1.645$. The $p$-value is approximately 0.0000. Therefore, if the null hypothesis is true, the probability that a $Z_{STAT}$ test statistic is greater than $+4.526$ is approximately 0.0000 (which is less than $\alpha = 0.05$). You conclude that there is evidence that the proportion of workaholic men who love their job because it is stimulating/challenging/provides an adrenaline rush is greater than the proportion of women.

## Confidence Interval Estimate for the Difference Between Two Proportions

Instead of, or in addition to, testing for the difference between the proportions of two independent populations, you can construct a confidence interval estimate of the difference between the two proportions using Equation (10.8).

Confidence Interval Estimate for the Difference Between Two Proportions

$$(p_1 - p_2) \pm Z_{\alpha/2} \sqrt{\frac{p_1(1-p_1)}{n_1} + \frac{p_2(1-p_2)}{n_2}} \qquad \text{(10.8)}$$

or

$$(p_1 - p_2) - Z_{\alpha/2} \sqrt{\frac{p_1(1-p_1)}{n_1} + \frac{p_2(1-p_2)}{n_2}} \leq (\pi_1 - \pi_2)$$

$$\leq (p_1 - p_2) + Z_{\alpha/2} \sqrt{\frac{p_1(1-p_1)}{n_1} + \frac{p_2(1-p_2)}{n_2}}$$

To construct a 95% confidence interval estimate of the population difference between the proportion of guests who would return to the Beachcomber and who would return to the Windsurfer, you use the results on page 415 or from Figures 10.17 or 10.18 on page 416:

$$p_1 = \frac{X_1}{n_1} = \frac{163}{227} = 0.7181 \qquad p_2 = \frac{X_2}{n_2} = \frac{154}{262} = 0.5878$$

Using Equation (10.8),

$$(0.7181 - 0.5878) \pm (1.96)\sqrt{\frac{0.7181(1-0.7181)}{227} + \frac{0.5878(1-0.5878)}{262}}$$

$$0.1303 \pm (1.96)(0.0426)$$

$$0.1303 \pm 0.0835$$

$$0.0468 \leq (\pi_1 - \pi_2) \leq 0.2138$$

Thus, you have 95% confidence that the difference between the population proportion of guests who would return again to the Beachcomber and the Windsurfer is between 0.0468 and 0.2138. In percentages, the difference is between 4.68% and 21.38%. Guest satisfaction is higher at the Beachcomber than at the Windsurfer.

# PROBLEMS FOR SECTION 10.3

## Learning the Basics

**10.29** Let $n_1 = 100$, $X_1 = 50$, $n_2 = 100$, and $X_2 = 30$.
a. At the 0.05 level of significance, is there evidence of a significant difference between the two population proportions?
b. Construct a 95% confidence interval estimate of the difference between the two population proportions.

**10.30** Let $n_1 = 100$, $X_1 = 45$, $n_2 = 50$, and $X_2 = 25$.
a. At the 0.01 level of significance, is there evidence of a significant difference between the two population proportions?

b. Construct a 99% confidence interval estimate of the difference between the two population proportions.

## Applying the Concepts

**10.31** A sample of 500 shoppers was selected in a large metropolitan area to determine various information concerning consumer behavior. Among the questions asked was, "Do you enjoy shopping for clothing?" Of 240 males, 136 answered yes. Of 260 females, 224 answered yes.
a. Is there evidence of a significant difference between males and females in the proportion that enjoy shopping for clothing at the 0.01 level of significance?

**b.** Find the *p*-value in (a) and interpret its meaning.

**c.** Construct and interpret a 99% confidence interval estimate of the difference between the proportion of males and females who enjoy shopping for clothing.

**d.** What are your answers to (a) through (c) if 206 males enjoyed shopping for clothing?

**10.32** An article referencing a survey conducted by AP-LOL Learning Services claims that parents are more confident than teachers that their schools will meet the standards set by the No Child Left Behind Act. The survey asked parents (and teachers), "How confident are you that your child's school (the school where you work) will meet the standards by the deadline?" The responses to that question are given in the following table:

| | Parents | Teachers |
|---|---|---|
| **Very confident** | 401 | 162 |
| **Not very confident** | 684 | 648 |
| **Totals** | 1,085 | 810 |

Source: *Extracted from B. Feller, "Teachers More Likely Skeptics of No Child," The Cincinnati Enquirer, April 20, 2006, p. A4.*

**a.** Set up the null and alternative hypotheses needed to try to prove that the population proportion of parents that are very confident that their child's school will meet the standards by the deadline is greater than the population proportion of teachers that are very confident that the school where they work will meet standards by the deadline.

**b.** Conduct the hypothesis test defined in (a), using a 0.05 level of significance.

**c.** Does the result of your test in (b) make it appropriate for the article to claim that parents are more confident than teachers?

**10.33** The results of a study conducted as part of a yield-improvement effort at a semiconductor manufacturing facility provided defect data for a sample of 450 wafers. The following contingency table presents a summary of the responses to two questions: "Was a particle found on the die that produced the wafer?" and "Is the wafer good or bad?"

**QUALITY OF WAFER**

| PARTICLES | Good | Bad | Totals |
|---|---|---|---|
| **Yes** | 14 | 36 | 50 |
| **No** | 320 | 80 | 400 |
| **Totals** | 334 | 116 | 450 |

Source: *Extracted from S.W. Hall, "Analysis of Defectivity of Semiconductor Wafers by Contingency Table," Proceedings Institute of Environmental Sciences, Vol. 1, 1994, pp. 177–183.*

**a.** At the 0.05 level of significance, is there evidence of a significant difference between the proportion of good and bad wafers that have particles?

**b.** Determine the *p*-value in (a) and interpret its meaning.

**c.** Construct and interpret a 95% confidence interval estimate of the difference between the population proportion of good and bad wafers that contain particles.

**d.** What conclusions can you reach from this analysis?

**✓ SELF Test** **10.34** According to an Ipsos poll, the perception of unfairness in the U.S. tax code is spread fairly evenly across income groups, age groups, and education levels. In an April 2006 survey of 1,005 adults, Ipsos reported that almost 60% of all people said the code is unfair, whereas slightly more that 60% of those making more than $50,000 viewed the code as unfair (extracted from "People Cry Unfairness," *The Cincinnati Enquirer*, April 16, 2006, p. A8). Suppose that the following contingency table represents the specific breakdown of responses:

| | INCOME LEVEL | | |
|---|---|---|---|
| **U.S. TAX CODE** | **Less Than $50,000** | **More Than $50,000** | **Total** |
| **Fair** | 225 | 180 | 405 |
| **Unfair** | 280 | 320 | 600 |
| **Total** | 505 | 500 | 1,005 |

**a.** At the 0.05 level of significance, is there evidence of a difference in the proportion of adults who think the U.S. tax code is unfair between the two income groups?

**b.** Find the *p*-value in (a) and interpret its meaning.

**10.35** Are women more risk averse in the stock market? A sample of men and women were asked the following question: "If both the stock market and a stock you owned dropped 25% in three months, would you buy more shares while the price is low?" (extracted from "Snapshots: Women Are More Risk Adverse in the Stock Market," *USA Today*, September 25, 2006, p. 1C). Of 965 women, 338 said yes. Of 1,066 men, 554 said yes.

**a.** At the 0.05 level of significance, is there evidence that the proportion of women who would buy more shares while the price is low is less than the proportion of men?

**b.** Find the *p*-value in (a) and interpret its meaning.

**10.36** An experiment was conducted to study the choices made in mutual fund selection. Undergraduate and MBA students were presented with different S&P 500 index funds that were identical except for fees. Suppose 100 undergraduate students and 100 MBA students were selected. Partial results are shown in the following table:

| | STUDENT GROUP | |
|---|---|---|
| **FUND** | **Undergraduate** | **MBA** |
| **Highest-cost fund** | 27 | 18 |
| **Not-highest-cost fund** | 73 | 82 |

Source: *Extracted from J. Choi, D. Laibson, and B. Madrian, "Why Does the Law of One Practice Fail? An Experiment on Mutual Funds,"* **www.som.yale.edu/faculty/jjc83/fees.pdf.**

**a.** At the 0.05 level of significance, is there evidence of a difference between undergraduate and MBA students in the proportion who selected the highest-cost fund?

**b.** Find the *p*-value in (a) and interpret its meaning.

**10.37** Where people turn for news is different for various age groups (extracted from P. Johnson, "Young People Turn to the Web for News," *USA Today*, March 23, 2006, p. 9D). Suppose that a study conducted on this issue was based on 200 respondents who were between the ages of 36 and 50, and 200 respondents who were above age 50. Of the 200 respondents who were between the ages of 36 and 50, 82 got their news primarily from newspapers. Of the 200 respondents who were above age 50, 104 got their news primarily from newspapers.

**a.** Is there evidence of a significant difference in the proportion that get their news primarily from newspapers between those respondents 36 to 50 years old and those above 50 years old? (Use $\alpha = 0.05$.)

**b.** Determine the *p*-value in (a) and interpret its meaning.

**c.** Construct and interpret a 95% confidence interval estimate of the difference between the population proportion of respondents who get their news primarily from newspapers between those respondents 36 to 50 years old and those above 50 years old.

## 10.4 *F* TEST FOR THE DIFFERENCE BETWEEN TWO VARIANCES

Often you need to determine whether two independent populations have the same amount of variability. By testing variances, you can detect differences in the amount of variability. One important reason to test for the difference between the variances of two populations is to determine whether to use the pooled-variance *t* test (which assumes equal variances) or the separate-variance *t* test (which does not assume equal variances) while comparing two means.

The test for the difference between the variances of two independent populations is based on the ratio of the two sample variances. If you assume that each population is normally distributed, then the ratio $S_1^2/S_2^2$ follows the *F* distribution (see Table E.5). The critical values of the *F* distribution in Table E.5 depend on the degrees of freedom in the two samples. The degrees of freedom in the numerator of the ratio are for the first sample, and the degrees of freedom in the denominator are for the second sample. The first sample taken from the first population is defined as the sample that has the *larger* sample variance. The second sample taken from the second population is the sample with the *smaller* sample variance. Equation (10.9) defines the ***F*-test for the equality of two variances**.

F-Test Statistic for Testing the Equality of Two Variances

The $F_{STAT}$ test statistic is equal to the variance of sample 1 (the larger sample variance) divided by the variance of sample 2 (the smaller sample variance).

$$F_{STAT} = \frac{S_1^2}{S_2^2} \tag{10.9}$$

where

$S_1^2$ = variance of sample 1 (the larger sample variance)

$S_2^2$ = variance of sample 2 (the smaller sample variance)

$n_1$ = size of sample 1

$n_2$ = size of sample 2

$n_1 - 1$ = degrees of freedom from sample 1 (i.e., the numerator degrees of freedom)

$n_2 - 1$ = degrees of freedom from sample 2 (i.e., the denominator degrees of freedom)

The $F_{STAT}$ test statistic follows an *F* distribution with $n_1 - 1$ and $n_2 - 1$ degrees of freedom.

For a given level of significance, $\alpha$, to test the null hypothesis of equality of population variances:

$$H_0: \sigma_1^2 = \sigma_2^2$$

against the alternative hypothesis that the two population variances are not equal:

$$H_1: \sigma_1^2 \neq \sigma_2^2$$

because the $F_{STAT}$ test statistic is defined as the larger sample variance divided by the smaller sample variance, you reject the null hypothesis if the computed $F_{STAT}$ test statistic is greater than the upper-tail critical value, $F_{\alpha/2}$, from the *F* distribution with $n_1 - 1$ degrees of freedom in the numerator and $n_2 - 1$ degrees of freedom in the denominator. Thus, the decision rule is

$$\text{Reject } H_0 \text{ if } F_{STAT} > F_{\alpha/2};$$

otherwise, do not reject $H_0$.

To illustrate how to use the *F* test to determine whether the two variances are equal, return to the Using Statistics scenario on page 390 concerning the sales of BLK Cola in two different aisle locations. To determine whether to use the pooled-variance *t* test or the separate-variance *t* test in Section 10.1, you can test the equality of the two population variances. The null and alternative hypotheses are

$$H_0: \sigma_1^2 = \sigma_2^2$$
$$H_1: \sigma_1^2 \neq \sigma_2^2$$

Because you are defining sample 1 as having the larger sample variance, the rejection region in the upper tail of the *F* distribution contains $\alpha/2$. Using the level of significance $\alpha = 0.05$, the rejection region in the upper tail contains 0.025 of the distribution.

Because there are samples of 10 stores for each of the two display locations, there are $10 - 1 = 9$ degrees of freedom in the numerator (the sample with the larger variance) and also in the denominator (the sample with the smaller variance). $F_{\alpha/2}$, the upper-tail critical value of the *F* distribution, is found directly from Table E.5, a portion of which is presented in Table 10.6 on page 422. Because there are 9 degrees of freedom in the numerator and 9 degrees of freedom in the denominator, you find the upper-tail critical value, $F_{\alpha/2}$, by looking in the column labeled 9 and the row labeled 9. Thus, the upper-tail critical value of this *F* distribution is 4.03. Therefore the decision rule is

$$\text{Reject } H_0 \text{ if } F_{STAT} > F_{0.025} = 4.03;$$

otherwise, do not reject $H_0$.

Using Equation (10.9) on page 420 and the cola sales data (see Table 10.1 on page 392),

$$F_{STAT} = \frac{S_1^2}{S_2^2}$$

$$= \frac{350.6778}{157.3333} = 2.2289$$

**TABLE 10.6**

Finding the Upper-Tail Critical Value of $F$ with 9 and 9 Degrees of Freedom for Upper-Tail Area of 0.025

| | Cumulative Probabilities = 0.975 Upper-Tail Area = 0.025 Numerator $df_1$ | | | | | | |
|---|---|---|---|---|---|---|---|
| **Denominator $df_2$** | **1** | **2** | **3** | **...** | **7** | **8** | **9** |
| 1 | 647.80 | 799.50 | 864.20 | ... | 948.20 | 956.70 | 963.30 |
| 2 | 38.51 | 39.00 | 39.17 | ... | 39.36 | 39.37 | 39.39 |
| 3 | 17.44 | 16.04 | 15.44 | ... | 14.62 | 14.54 | 14.47 |
| . | . | . | . | | . | . | . |
| . | . | . | . | | . | . | . |
| . | . | . | . | | . | . | . |
| 7 | 8.07 | 6.54 | 5.89 | ... | 4.99 | 4.90 | 4.82 |
| 8 | 7.57 | 6.06 | 5.42 | ... | 4.53 | 4.43 | 4.36 |
| 9 | 7.21 | 5.71 | 5.08 | ... | 4.20 | 4.10 | 4.03 |

Source: *Extracted from Table E.5.*

Because $F_{STAT} = 2.2289 < 4.03$, you do not reject $H_0$. The $p$-value is 0.2482 for a two-tail test as shown in Figure 10.20 (twice the $p$-value for the one-tail test shown in the Microsoft Excel results in Figure 10.19). Because $0.2482 > 0.05$, you conclude that there is no significant difference in the variability of the sales of cola for the two display locations. Notice that in Figure 10.20, Minitab reports the $F$ statistic as 0.45, the reciprocal of 2.2289. This occurs because Minitab assigns samples in alphabetical order, so EndAisle is assigned to the numerator (sample 1) and Normal is assigned to the denominator (sample 2).

**FIGURE 10.19**

Microsoft Excel $F$ test results for the BLK Cola sales data

*See Section E10.9 or P10.5 to create this.*

| | A | B | C |
|---|---|---|---|
| 1 | F-Test Two-Sample for Variances | | |
| 2 | | | |
| 3 | | Normal | End-Aisle |
| 4 | Mean | 50.3 | 72 |
| 5 | Variance | 350.6778 | 157.3333 |
| 6 | Observations | 10 | 10 |
| 7 | df | 9 | 9 |
| 8 | F | 2.2289 | |
| 9 | P(F<=f) one-tail | 0.1241 | |
| 10 | F Critical one-tail | 3.1789 | |

**FIGURE 10.20**

Minitab $F$ test results for the BLK Cola sales data

*See Section M10.5 to create this.*

```
Display    N    Lower    StDev    Upper
EndAisle   10   8.2048   12.5433  25.2578
  Normal   10  12.2494   18.7264  37.7085


F-Test (Normal Distribution)
Test statistic = 0.45, p-value = 0.248
```

In testing for a difference between two variances using the $F$ test described in this section, you assume that each of the two populations is normally distributed. The $F$ test is very sensitive to the normality assumption. If boxplots or normal probability plots suggest even a mild departure from normality for either of the two populations, you should not use the $F$ test. If this happens, you should use the Levene test (see Section 11.1) or a nonparametric approach (see references 1 and 2).

In testing for the equality of variances as part of assessing the validity of the pooled-variance *t* test procedure, the *F* test is a two-tail test with $\alpha/2$ in the upper tail. However, when you are interested in examining the variability in situations other than the pooled-variance *t* test, the *F* test is often a one-tail test. Example 10.4 illustrates a one-tail test.

**EXAMPLE 10.4**   A ONE-TAIL TEST FOR THE DIFFERENCE BETWEEN TWO VARIANCES

Shipments of meat, meat by-products, and other ingredients are mixed together in several filling lines at a pet food canning factory. Operations managers suspect that, although the mean amount filled per can of pet food is usually the same, the variability of the cans filled in line *A* is greater than that of line *B*. The following data from a sample of eight-ounce cans is as follows:

|  | Line *A* | Line *B* |
|---|---|---|
| $\overline{X}$ | 8.005 | 7.997 |
| *S* | 0.012 | 0.005 |
| *n* | 11 | 16 |

At the 0.05 level of significance, is there evidence that the variance in line *A* is greater than the variance in line *B*? Assume that the population amounts filled are normally distributed.

**SOLUTION** The null and alternative hypotheses are

$$H_0: \sigma_A^2 \le \sigma_B^2$$

$$H_1: \sigma_A^2 > \sigma_B^2$$

The $F_{STAT}$ test statistic is given by Equation (10.9) on page 420:

$$F_{STAT} = \frac{S_1^2}{S_2^2}$$

You use Table E.5 to find the upper critical value of the *F* distribution. With $n_1 - 1 = 11 - 1 = 10$ degrees of freedom in the numerator, $n_2 - 1 = 16 - 1 = 15$ degrees of freedom in the denominator, and $\alpha = 0.05$, the upper critical value, $F_{0.05}$, is 2.54.

The decision rule is

$$\text{Reject } H_0 \text{ if } F_{STAT} > 2.54;$$

$$\text{otherwise, do not reject } H_0.$$

From Equation (10.9) on page 420,

$$F_{STAT} = \frac{S_1^2}{S_2^2}$$

$$= \frac{(0.012)^2}{(0.005)^2} = 5.76$$

Because $F_{STAT} = 5.76 > 2.54$, you reject $H_0$. Using a 0.05 level of significance, you conclude that there is evidence that the variance of line *A* is greater than the variance of line *B*. In other words, the amount of pet food in the cans filled by line *A* is more variable than the amount of pet food in cans filled by line *B*.

# PROBLEMS FOR SECTION 10.4

## Learning the Basics

**10.38** Determine the upper-tail critical values of $F$, in each of the following two-tail tests:
**a.** $\alpha = 0.10$, $n_1 = 16$, $n_2 = 21$
**b.** $\alpha = 0.05$, $n_1 = 16$, $n_2 = 21$
**c.** $\alpha = 0.01$, $n_1 = 16$, $n_2 = 21$

**10.39** Determine the upper-tail critical value of $F$ in each of the following one-tail tests:
**a.** $\alpha = 0.05$, $n_1 = 16$, $n_2 = 21$
**b.** $\alpha = 0.01$, $n_1 = 16$, $n_2 = 21$

**10.40** The following information is available for two samples drawn from independent normally distributed populations:

$$\text{Population A:} \quad n = 25 \quad S^2 = 16$$
$$\text{Population B:} \quad n = 25 \quad S^2 = 25$$

**a.** Which sample variance do you place in the numerator of $F_{STAT}$?
**b.** What is the value of $F_{STAT}$?

**10.41** The following information is available for two samples drawn from independent normally distributed populations:

$$\text{Population A:} \quad n = 25 \quad S^2 = 161.9$$
$$\text{Population B:} \quad n = 25 \quad S^2 = 133.7$$

What is the value of $F_{STAT}$ if you are testing the null hypothesis $H_0: \sigma_1^2 = \sigma_2^2$?

**10.42** In Problem 10.41, how many degrees of freedom are there in the numerator and denominator of the $F$ test?

**10.43** In Problems 10.41 and 10.42, what is the upper critical value for $F$ if the level of significance, $\alpha$, is 0.05 and the alternative hypothesis is $H_1: \sigma_1^2 \neq \sigma_2^2$?

**10.44** In Problems 10.41 through 10.43, what is your statistical decision?

**10.45** The following information is available for two samples selected from independent but very right-skewed populations:

$$\text{Population A:} \quad n = 16 \quad S^2 = 47.3$$
$$\text{Population B:} \quad n = 13 \quad S^2 = 36.4$$

Should you use the $F$ test to test the null hypothesis of equality of variances? Discuss.

**10.46** In Problem 10.45, assume that two samples are selected from independent normally distributed populations.
**a.** At the 0.05 level of significance, is there evidence of a difference between $\sigma_1^2$ and $\sigma_2^2$?

**b.** Suppose that you want to perform a one-tail test. At the 0.05 level of significance, what is the upper-tail critical value of $F$ to determine whether there is evidence that $\sigma_1^2 > \sigma_2^2$? What is your statistical decision?

## Applying the Concepts

**10.47** A professor in the accounting department of a business school claims that there is much more variability in the final exam scores of students taking the introductory accounting course who are not majoring in accounting than for students taking the course who are majoring in accounting. Random samples of 13 non-accounting majors and 10 accounting majors are taken from the professor's class roster in his large lecture, and the following results are computed based on the final exam scores:

$$\text{Non-Accounting:} \quad n = 13 \quad S^2 = 210.2$$
$$\text{Accounting:} \quad n = 10 \quad S^2 = 36.5$$

**a.** At the 0.05 level of significance, is there evidence to support the professor's claim?
**b.** Interpret the $p$-value.
**c.** What assumption do you need to make in (a) about the two populations in order to justify your use of the $F$ test?

**SELF Test** **10.48** The Computer Anxiety Rating Scale (CARS) measures an individual's level of computer anxiety, on a scale from 20 (no anxiety) to 100 (highest level of anxiety). Researchers at Miami University administered CARS to 172 business students. One of the objectives of the study was to determine whether there is a difference between the level of computer anxiety experienced by female students and male students. They found the following:

|   | Males | Females |
|---|---|---|
| $\overline{X}$ | 40.26 | 36.85 |
| $S$ | 13.35 | 9.42 |
| $n$ | 100 | 72 |

Source: *Extracted from T. Broome and D. Havelka, "Determinants of Computer Anxiety in Business Students,"* The Review of Business Information Systems, *Spring 2002, 6(2), pp. 9–16.*

**a.** At the 0.05 level of significance, is there evidence of a difference in the variability of the computer anxiety experienced by males and females?
**b.** Interpret the $p$-value.
**c.** What assumption do you need to make about the two populations in order to justify the use of the $F$ test?
**d.** Based on (a) and (b), which $t$ test defined in Section 10.1 should you use to test whether there is a significant difference in mean computer anxiety for female and male students?

**10.49** A bank with a branch located in a commercial district of a city has developed an improved process for serving customers during the noon-to-1 p.m. lunch period. The waiting time (defined as the time elapsed from when the customer enters the line until he or she reaches the teller window) needs to be shortened to increase customer satisfaction. A random sample of 15 customers is selected (and stored in the file Bank1), and the results (in minutes) are as follows:

4.21  5.55  3.02  5.13  4.77  2.34  3.54  3.20
4.50  6.10  0.38  5.12  6.46  6.19  3.79

Suppose that another branch, located in a residential area, is also concerned with the noon-to-1 p.m. lunch period. A random sample of 15 customers is selected (and stored in the file Bank2), and the results (in minutes) are as follows:

9.66  5.90  8.02  5.79  8.73  3.82  8.01  8.35
10.49  6.68  5.64  4.08  6.17  9.91  5.47

**a.** Is there evidence of a difference in the variability of the waiting time between the two branches? (Use $\alpha = 0.05$.)
**b.** Determine the $p$-value in (a) and interpret its meaning.
**c.** What assumption about the population distribution of the two banks is necessary in (a)? Is the assumption valid for these data?
**d.** Based on the results of (a), is it appropriate to use the pooled-variance $t$ test to compare the means of the two branches?

**10.50** Digital cameras have taken over the majority of the point-and-shoot camera market. One of the important features of a camera is the battery life as measured by the number of shots taken until the battery needs to be recharged. The data in the file Digitalcameras contains the battery life of 31 subcompact cameras and 15 compact cameras (extracted from "Cameras," *Consumer Reports*, November 2006, pp. 20–21)
**a.** Is there evidence of a difference in the variability of the battery life between the two types of digital cameras? (Use $\alpha = 0.05$.)

**b.** Determine the $p$-value in (a) and interpret its meaning.
**c.** What assumption about the population distribution of the two types of cameras is necessary in (a)? Is the assumption valid for these data?
**d.** Based on the results of (a), which $t$ test defined in Section 10.1 should you use to compare the mean battery life of the two types of cameras?

**10.51** The director of training for a company that manufactures electronic equipment is interested in determining whether different training methods have an effect on the productivity of assembly-line employees. She randomly assigns 21 of the 42 recently hired employees to a computer-assisted, individual-based training program. The other 21 are assigned to a team-based training program. Upon completion of the training, the employees are evaluated on the time (in seconds) it takes to assemble a part. The results are in the data file Training.
**a.** Using a 0.05 level of significance, is there evidence of a difference between the variances in assembly times (in seconds) of employees trained in a computer-assisted, individual-based program and those trained in a team-based program?
**b.** On the basis of the results in (a), which $t$ test defined in Section 10.1 should you use to compare the means of the two training programs? Discuss.

**10.52** Is there a difference in the variation of the yield of different types of investment between banks? The following data, from the file Bankyield, represent the nationwide highest yields for money market accounts and five-year CDs as of March 12, 2007:

| Money Market Accounts | Five-Year CD |
| --- | --- |
| 5.35  5.31  5.30  5.30  5.25 | 5.95  5.89  5.83  5.83  5.79 |

Source: *Extracted from Bankrate.com, March 12, 2007.*

At the 0.05 level of significance, is there evidence of a difference in the variance of the yield between money market accounts and five-year CDs? Assume that the population yields are normally distributed.

# SUMMARY

In this chapter, you were introduced to a variety of two-sample tests. For situations in which the samples are independent, you learned statistical test procedures for analyzing possible differences between means, variances, and proportions. In addition, you learned a test procedure that is frequently used when analyzing differences between the means of two related samples. Remember that you need to select the test that is most appropriate for a

given set of conditions and to critically investigate the validity of the assumptions underlying each of the hypothesis-testing procedures.

The roadmap in Figure 10.21 illustrates the steps needed in determining which two-sample test of hypothesis to use. The following are the questions you need to consider.

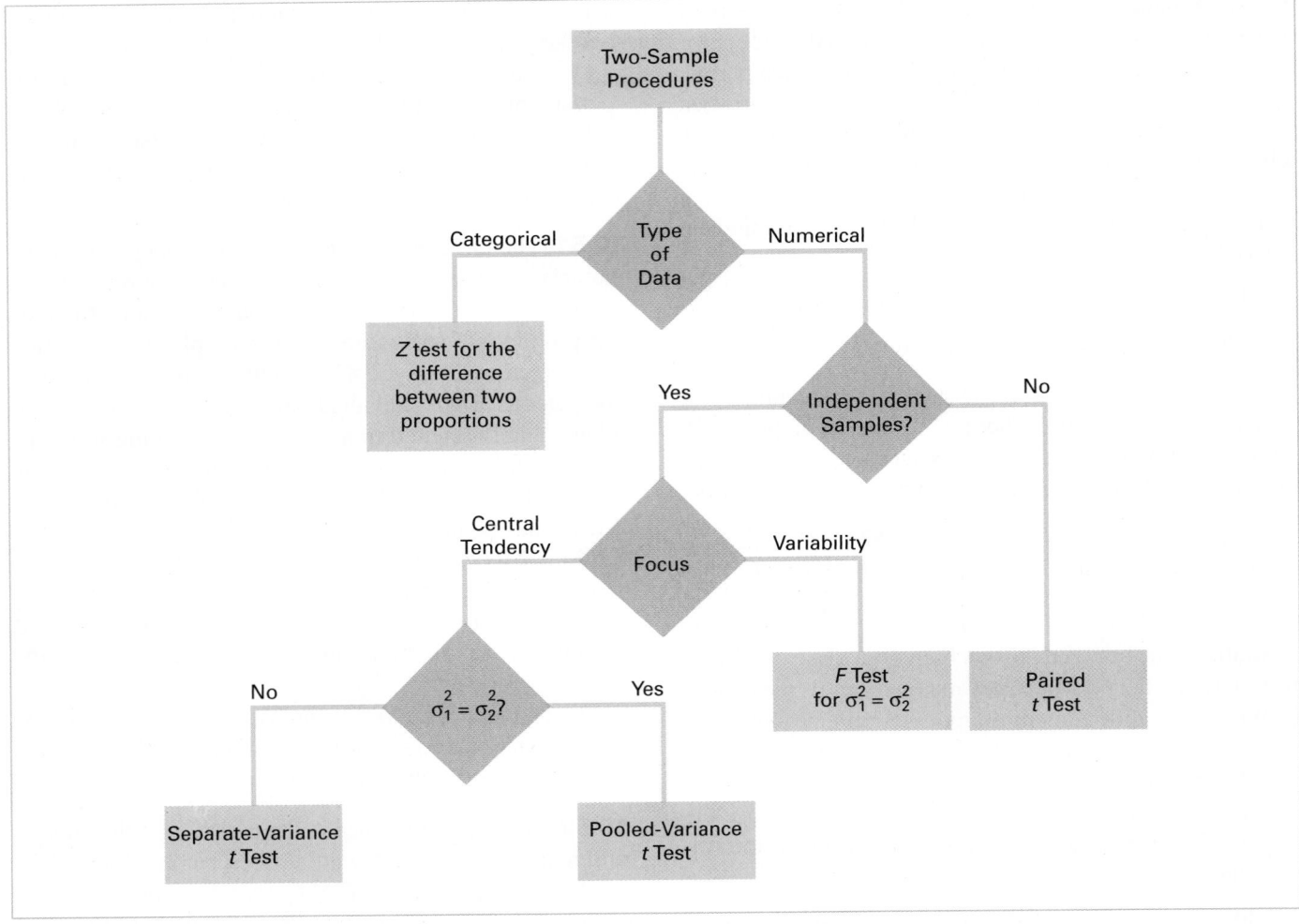

**FIGURE 10.21**   Roadmap for selecting a two-sample test of hypothesis

1. What type of data do you have? If you are dealing with categorical variables, use the $Z$ test for the difference between two proportions. (This test assumes independent samples.)
2. If you have a numerical variable, determine whether you have independent samples or related samples. If you have related samples, use the paired $t$ test.
3. If you have independent samples, is your focus on variability or central tendency? If the focus is variability, use the $F$ test.

4. If your focus is central tendency, determine whether you can assume that the variances of the two populations are equal. (This assumption can be tested using the $F$ test.)
5. If you can assume that the two populations have equal variances, use the pooled-variance $t$ test. If you cannot assume that the two populations have equal variances, use the separate-variance $t$ test.

Table 10.7 provides a list of topics covered in this chapter.

**TABLE 10.7**

Summary of Topics in Chapter 10

| Type of Analysis | Types of Data | |
| --- | --- | --- |
| | **Numerical** | **Categorical** |
| Comparing two populations | $t$ tests for the difference in the means of two independent populations (Section 10.1) | $Z$ test for the difference between two proportions (Section 10.3) |
| | Paired $t$ test (Section 10.2) | |
| | $F$ test for the difference between two variances (Section 10.4) | |

# KEY EQUATIONS

**Pooled-Variance *t* Test for the Difference Between Two Means**

$$t_{STAT} = \frac{(\bar{X}_1 - \bar{X}_2) - (\mu_1 - \mu_2)}{\sqrt{S_p^2 \left(\frac{1}{n_1} + \frac{1}{n_2}\right)}} \quad \text{(10.1)}$$

**Confidence Interval Estimate of the Difference in the Means of Two Independent Populations**

$$(\bar{X}_1 - \bar{X}_2) \pm t_{\alpha/2} \sqrt{S_p^2 \left(\frac{1}{n_1} + \frac{1}{n_2}\right)} \quad \text{(10.2)}$$

or

$$(\bar{X}_1 - \bar{X}_2) - t_{\alpha/2} \sqrt{S_p^2 \left(\frac{1}{n_1} + \frac{1}{n_2}\right)} \leq \mu_1 - \mu_2$$
$$\leq (\bar{X}_1 - \bar{X}_2) + t_{\alpha/2} \sqrt{S_p^2 \left(\frac{1}{n_1} + \frac{1}{n_2}\right)}$$

**Separate-Variance *t* Test for the Difference in Two Means**

$$t_{STAT} = \frac{(\bar{X}_1 - \bar{X}_2) - (\mu_1 - \mu_2)}{\sqrt{\frac{S_1^2}{n_1} + \frac{S_2^2}{n_2}}} \quad \text{(10.3)}$$

**Computing Degrees of Freedom in the Separate-Variance *t* Test**

$$V = \frac{\left(\frac{S_1^2}{n_1} + \frac{S_2^2}{n_2}\right)^2}{\frac{\left(\frac{S_1^2}{n_1}\right)^2}{n_1 - 1} + \frac{\left(\frac{S_2^2}{n_2}\right)^2}{n_2 - 1}} \quad \text{(10.4)}$$

**Paired *t* Test for the Mean Difference**

$$t_{STAT} = \frac{\bar{D} - \mu_D}{\frac{S_D}{\sqrt{n}}} \quad \text{(10.5)}$$

**Confidence Interval Estimate for the Mean Difference**

$$\bar{D} \pm t_{\alpha/2} \frac{S_D}{\sqrt{n}} \quad \text{(10.6)}$$

or

$$\bar{D} - t_{\alpha/2} \frac{S_D}{\sqrt{n}} \leq \mu_D \leq \bar{D} + t_{\alpha/2} \frac{S_D}{\sqrt{n}}$$

**Z Test for the Difference Between Two Proportions**

$$Z_{STAT} = \frac{(p_1 - p_2) - (\pi_1 - \pi_2)}{\sqrt{\bar{p}(1-\bar{p})\left(\frac{1}{n_1} + \frac{1}{n_2}\right)}} \quad \text{(10.7)}$$

**Confidence Interval Estimate for the Difference Between Two Proportions**

$$(p_1 - p_2) \pm Z_{\alpha/2} \sqrt{\frac{p_1(1-p_1)}{n_1} + \frac{p_2(1-p_2)}{n_2}} \quad \text{(10.8)}$$

or

$$(p_1 - p_2) - Z_{\alpha/2} \sqrt{\frac{p_1(1-p_1)}{n_1} + \frac{p_2(1-p_2)}{n_2}} \leq (\pi_1 - \pi_2)$$
$$\leq (p_1 - p_2) + Z_{\alpha/2} \sqrt{\frac{p_1(1-p_1)}{n_1} + \frac{p_2(1-p_2)}{n_2}}$$

**F Test for the Equality of Two Variances**

$$F_{STAT} = \frac{S_1^2}{S_2^2} \quad \text{(10.9)}$$

# KEY TERMS

*F* distribution    420
*F* test for the equality of two
    variances    420
matched samples    403

paired *t* test for the mean
    difference    404
pooled-variance *t* test    390
repeated measurements    403

robust    395
separate-variance *t* test    397
*Z* test for the difference between two
    proportions    413

# CHAPTER REVIEW PROBLEMS

## Checking Your Understanding

**10.53** What are some of the criteria used in the selection of a particular hypothesis-testing procedure?

**10.54** Under what conditions should you use the pooled-variance *t* test to examine possible differences in the means of two independent populations?

**10.55** Under what conditions should you use the *F* test to examine possible differences in the variances of two independent populations?

**10.56** What is the distinction between two independent populations and two related populations?

**10.57** What is the distinction between repeated measurements and matched items?

**10.58** Under what conditions should you use the paired *t* test for the mean difference?

**10.59** When you have two independent populations, explain the similarities and differences between the test of hypothesis for the difference between the means and the confidence interval estimate of the difference between the means.

## Applying the Concepts

**10.60** A study compared music compact disc prices for Internet-based retailers and traditional brick-and-mortar retailers [extracted from L. Zoonky and S. Gosain, "A Longitudinal Price Comparison for Music CDs in Electronic and Brick-and-Mortar Markets: Pricing Strategies in Emergent Electronic Commerce," *Journal of Business Strategies*, Spring 2002, 19(1), pp. 55–72]. Before collecting the data, the researchers carefully defined several research hypotheses, including:

1. The price dispersion on the Internet is lower than the price dispersion in the brick-and-mortar market.
2. Prices in electronic markets are lower than prices in physical markets.

**a.** Consider research hypothesis 1. Write the null and alternative hypotheses in terms of population parameters. Carefully define the population parameters used.

**b.** Define a Type I and Type II error for the hypotheses in (a).
**c.** What type of statistical test should you use?
**d.** What assumptions are needed to perform the test you selected?
**e.** Repeat (a) through (d) for research hypothesis 2.

**10.61** The pet-drug market is growing very rapidly. Before new pet drugs can be introduced into the marketplace, they must be approved by the U.S. Food and Drug Administration (FDA). In 1999, the Novartis company was trying to get Anafranil, a drug to reduce dog anxiety, approved. According to an article (E. Tanouye, "The Ow in Bowwow: With Growing Market in Pet Drugs, Makers Revamp Clinical Trials," *The Wall Street Journal*, April 13, 1999), Novartis had to find a way to translate a dog's anxiety symptoms into numbers that could be used to prove to the FDA that the drug had a statistically significant effect on the condition.

**a.** What is meant by the phrase *statistically significant effect*?
**b.** Consider an experiment in which dogs suffering from anxiety are divided into two groups. One group will be given Anafranil, and the other will be given a placebo (i.e., a drug without active ingredients). How can you translate a dog's anxiety symptoms into numbers? In other words, define a continuous variable, $X_1$, that measures the effectiveness of the drug Anafranil, and $X_2$, that measures the effectiveness of the placebo.
**c.** Building on your answer to part (b), define the null and alternative hypotheses for this study.

**10.62** In response to lawsuits filed against the tobacco industry, many companies, such as Philip Morris, are running television advertisements that are supposed to educate teenagers about the dangers of smoking. Are these tobacco industry antismoking campaigns successful? Are state-sponsored antismoking commercials more effective? An article (G. Fairclough, "Philip Morris's Antismoking Campaign Draws Fire," *The Wall Street Journal*, April 6, 1999, p. B1) discussed a study in California that compared commercials made by the state of California and commercials produced by

Philip Morris. Researchers showed the state ads and the Philip Morris ads to a group of California teenagers and measured the effectiveness of both. The researchers concluded that the state ads were more effective in relaying the dangers of smoking than the Philip Morris ads. The article suggests, however, that the study is not *statistically reliable* because the sample size was too small and because the study specifically selected participants who are considered more likely to start smoking than others.

a. How do you think the researchers measured effectiveness?

b. Define the null and alternative hypotheses for this study.

c. Explain the risks associated with Type I and Type II errors in this study.

d. What type of test is most appropriate in this situation?

e. What do you think is meant by the phrase *statistically reliable*?

**10.63** Do male and female students study the same amount per week? In 2007, 58 sophomore business students were surveyed at a large university, which has over 1000 sophomore business students each year. The file **Studytime** contains the gender and the number of hours spent studying in a typical week for the sampled students.

a. At the 0.05 level of significance, is there a difference in the variance of the study time for male students and female students?

b. Using the results of (a), which *t* test is appropriate to compare the mean study time for male and female students?

c. At the 0.05 level of significance, conduct the test selected in (b).

d. Write a short summary of your findings.

**10.64** Two professors wanted to study how students from their two universities compared in their capabilities of using Excel spreadsheets in undergraduate information systems courses (extracted from H. Howe and M. G. Simkin, "Factors Affecting the Ability to Detect Spreadsheet Errors," *Decision Sciences Journal of Innovative Education*, January 2006, pp. 101–122). A comparison of the student demographics was also performed. One school is a state university in the Western United States, and the other school is a state university in the Eastern United States. The following table contains information regarding the ages of the students:

| School | Sample Size | Mean Age | Standard Deviation |
|---|---|---|---|
| Western | 93 | 23.28 | 6.29 |
| Eastern | 135 | 21.16 | 1.32 |

a. Using a 0.01 level of significance, is there evidence of a difference between the variances in age of students at the Western school and at the Eastern school?

b. Discuss the practical implications of the test performed in (a). Address, specifically, the impact equal (or unequal) variances in age has on teaching an undergraduate information systems course.

c. To test for a difference in the mean age of students, is it most appropriate to use the pooled-variance *t* test or the separate-variance *t* test?

The following table contains information regarding the years of spreadsheet usage of the students:

| School | Sample Size | Mean Years | Standard Deviation |
|---|---|---|---|
| Western | 93 | 2.6 | 2.4 |
| Eastern | 135 | 4.0 | 2.1 |

d. Using a 0.01 level of significance, is there evidence of a difference between the variances in years of spreadsheet usage of students at the Western school and at the Eastern school?

e. Based on the results of (d), use the most appropriate test to determine, at the 0.01 level of significance, whether there is evidence of a difference in the mean years of spreadsheet usage of students at the Western school and at the Eastern school.

**10.65** The data file **Restaurants** contains the ratings for food, decor, service, and the price per person for a sample of 50 restaurants located in an urban area and 50 restaurants located in a suburban area. Completely analyze the differences between urban and suburban restaurants for the variables food rating, decor rating, service rating, and price per person, using $\alpha = 0.05$.

Source: *Extracted from* Zagat Survey 2006: New York City Restaurants *and* Zagat Survey 2005–2006: Long Island Restaurants.

**10.66** A computer information systems professor is interested in studying the amount of time it takes students enrolled in the introduction to computers course to write and run a program in Visual Basic. The professor hires you to analyze the following results (in minutes) from a random sample of nine students (the data are stored in the **VB** file):

10    13    9    15    12    13    11    13    12

a. At the 0.05 level of significance, is there evidence that the population mean amount is greater than 10 minutes? What will you tell the professor?

b. Suppose the computer professor, when checking her results, realizes that the fourth student needed 51 minutes rather than the recorded 15 minutes to write and run the Visual Basic program. At the 0.05 level of significance, reanalyze the question posed in (a), using the revised data. What will you tell the professor now?

c. The professor is perplexed by these paradoxical results and requests an explanation from you regarding the justification for the difference in your findings in (a) and (b). Discuss.

d. A few days later, the professor calls to tell you that the dilemma is completely resolved. The original number 15 (the fourth data value) was correct, and therefore your findings in (a) are being used in the article she is writing for a computer journal. Now she wants to hire you to compare the results from that group of introduction to computers students against those from a sample of 11 computer majors in order to determine whether there is evidence that computer majors can write a Visual Basic program in less time than introductory students. For the computer majors, the sample mean is 8.5 minutes, and the sample standard deviation is 2.0 minutes. At the 0.05 level of significance, completely analyze these data. What will you tell the professor?

e. A few days later, the professor calls again to tell you that a reviewer of her article wants her to include the *p*-value for the "correct" result in (a). In addition, the professor inquires about an unequal-variances problem, which the reviewer wants her to discuss in her article. In your own words, discuss the concept of *p*-value and also describe the unequal-variances problem. Then, determine the *p*-value in (a) and discuss whether the unequal-variances problem had any meaning in the professor's study.

**10.67** An article in *The New York Times* (A. Jennings, "What's Good for a Business Can be Hard on Friends," *The New York Times*, August 4, 2007, pp. C1–C2) reported that according to a poll, the mean number of cellphone calls per month was 290 for 18- to 24-year-olds and 194 for 45- to 54-year-olds, whereas the mean number of text messages per month was 290 for 18- to 24-year-olds and 57 for 45- to 54-year-olds. Suppose that the poll was based on a sample of 100 18- to 24-year-olds and 100 45- to 54-year-olds, and that the standard deviation of the number of cellphone calls per month was 100 for 18- to 24-year-olds and 90 for 45- to 54-year-olds, whereas the standard deviation of the number of text messages per month was 90 for 18- to 24-year-olds and 77 for 45- to 54-year-olds. Use a level of significance of 0.05.

a. Is there evidence of a difference in the variances of the number of cellphone calls per month for 18- to 24-year-olds and 45- to 54-year-olds?

b. Is there evidence of a difference in the mean number of cellphone calls per month for 18- to 24-year-olds and 45- to 54-year-olds?

c. Construct and interpret a 95% confidence interval estimate of the difference in the mean number of cellphone calls per month for 18- to 24-year-olds and 45- to 54-year-olds.

d. Is there evidence of a difference in the variances of the number of text messages per month for 18- to 24-year-olds and 45- to 54-year-olds?

e. Is there evidence of a difference in the mean number of text messages per month for 18- to 24-year-olds and 45- to 54-year-olds?

f. Construct and interpret a 95% confidence interval estimate of the difference in the mean number of text messages per month for 18- to 24-year-olds and 45- to 54-year-olds.

g. Based on the results of (a) through (f), what conclusions can you make concerning cellphone and text message usage between 18- to 24-year-olds and 45- to 54-year-olds?

**10.68** The lengths of life (in hours) of a sample of 40 100-watt lightbulbs produced by manufacturer A and a sample of 40 100-watt lightbulbs produced by manufacturer B are in the file `Bulbs`. Completely analyze the differences between the lengths of life of the bulbs produced by the two manufacturers (use $\alpha = 0.05$).

**10.69** A hotel manager is concerned with increasing the return rate for hotel guests. One aspect of first impressions by guests relates to the time it takes to deliver the guest's luggage to the room after check-in to the hotel. A random sample of 20 deliveries on a particular day were selected in Wing A of the hotel, and a random sample of 20 deliveries were selected in Wing B. The results are stored in the file `Luggage`. Analyze the data and determine whether there is a difference in the mean delivery time in the two wings of the hotel. (Use $\alpha = 0.05$.)

**10.70** A survey of 500 men and 500 women designed to study financial tensions between couples asked how likely they were to hide purchases, cash, or investments from their partners. The results were as follows:

| TYPE | LIKELY TO HIDE | |
|---|---|---|
| | **Men** | **Women** |
| **Auto-related** | 66 | 36 |
| **Cash** | 126 | 133 |
| **Clothes** | 62 | 116 |
| **Electronics** | 79 | 56 |
| **Entertainment** | 96 | 76 |
| **Food** | 74 | 94 |
| **Investments** | 76 | 52 |
| **Travel** | 53 | 39 |

Source: *Extracted from L. Wei, "Your Money Manager as Financial Therapist," The Wall Street Journal, November 5–6, 2005, p. B4.*

For *each type of purchase*, determine whether there is a difference between men and women at the 0.05 level of significance.

**10.71** As more Americans use cellphones, they question where it is okay to talk on cellphones. The following is a table of results, in percentages, for 2000 and 2006 (extracted from W. Koch, "Businesses Put a Lid on Chatterboxes," *USA Today*, February 7, 2006, p. 3A). Suppose the survey was based on 100 respondents in 2000 and 100 respondents in 2006.

| OKAY TO TALK ON A CELL PHONE IN A | YEAR | |
|---|---|---|
| | **2000** | **2006** |
| **Bathroom** | 39 | 38 |
| **Movie/theater** | 11 | 2 |
| **Car** | 76 | 63 |
| **Supermarket** | 60 | 66 |
| **Public transit** | 52 | 45 |
| **Restaurant** | 31 | 21 |

For *each type of location*, determine whether there is a difference between 2000 and 2006 in the proportion who think it is okay to talk on a cellphone. (Use the 0.05 level of significance.)

**10.72** Many companies are finding that customers are using various types of online content before purchasing products (extracted from K. Spors, "How Are We Doing?" *The Wall Street Journal*, November 13, 2006, p. R9). The following results are the percentages of adults and youths who use various sources of online content. Suppose the survey was based on 100 adults and 100 youths.

| TYPE OF ONLINE CONTENT | USE ONLINE CONTENT | |
|---|---|---|
| | **Adult** | **Youth** |
| **Customer product ratings/reviews** | 71 | 81 |
| **For sale listings with seller ratings** | 69 | 77 |
| **For sale listings without seller ratings** | 58 | 65 |
| **Online classified ads** | 57 | 66 |
| **Message-board posts** | 57 | 71 |
| **Web blogs** | 55 | 67 |
| **Dating site profiles/personals** | 49 | 59 |
| **Peer-generated and peer-reference information** | 49 | 68 |
| **Peer-posted event listings** | 46 | 71 |

For *each type of online content*, determine whether there is a difference between adults and youths in the proportion who use the type of online content at the 0.05 level of significance.

**10.73** The manufacturer of Boston and Vermont asphalt shingles knows that product weight is a major factor in the customer's perception of quality. Moreover, the weight represents the amount of raw materials being used and is therefore very important to the company from a cost standpoint. The last stage of the assembly line packages the shingles before they are placed on wooden pallets. Once a pallet is full (a pallet for most brands holds 16 squares of shingles), it is weighed, and the measurement is recorded. The data file Pallet contains the weight (in pounds) from a sample of 368 pallets of Boston shingles and 330 pallets of Vermont shingles. Completely analyze the differences in the weights of the Boston and Vermont shingles, using $\alpha = 0.05$.

**10.74** The manufacturer of Boston and Vermont asphalt shingles provides its customers with a 20-year warranty on most of its products. To determine whether a shingle will last as long as the warranty period, accelerated-life testing is conducted at the manufacturing plant. Accelerated-life testing exposes the shingle to the stresses it would be subject to in a lifetime of normal use in a laboratory setting via an experiment that takes only a few minutes to conduct. In this test, a shingle is repeatedly scraped with a brush for a short period of time, and the shingle granules removed by the brushing are weighed (in grams). Shingles that experience low amounts of granule loss are expected to last longer in normal use than shingles that experience high amounts of granule loss. In this situation, a shingle should experience no more than 0.8 grams of granule loss if it is expected to last the length of the warranty period. The data file Granule contains a sample of 170 measurements made on the company's Boston shingles and 140 measurements made on Vermont shingles. Completely analyze the differences in the granule loss of the Boston and Vermont shingles, using $\alpha = 0.05$.

## Report Writing Exercise

**10.75** Referring to the results of Problems 10.73 and 10.74 concerning the weight and granule loss of Boston and Vermont shingles, write a report that summarizes your conclusions.

## Team Project

The data file Mutual Funds contains information regarding nine variables from a sample of 868 mutual funds. The variables are

    Category—Type of stocks comprising the mutual fund (small cap, mid cap, or large cap)
    Objective—Objective of stocks comprising the mutual fund (growth or value)
    Assets—In millions of dollars
    Fees—Sales charges (no or yes)
    Expense ratio—Ratio of expenses to net assets, in percentage
    2006 return—Twelve-month return in 2006
    Three-year return—Annualized return, 2004–2006

Five-year return—Annualized return, 2002–2006

Risk—Risk-of-loss factor of the mutual fund (low, average, or high)

**10.76** Completely analyze the difference between mutual funds without fees and mutual funds with fees in terms of 2006 return, three-year return, five-year return, and expense ratio. Write a report summarizing your findings.

**10.77** Completely analyze the difference between mutual funds that have a growth objective and mutual funds that have a value objective in terms of 2006 return, three-year return, five-year return, and expense ratio. Write a report summarizing your findings.

## Student Survey Data Base

**10.78** Problem 1.27 on page 14 describes a survey of 50 undergraduate students (see the file Undergradsurvey). For these data,
a. at the 0.05 level of significance, is there evidence of a difference between males and females in grade point average, expected starting salary, salary expected in five years, age, and spending on textbooks and supplies?
b. at the 0.05 level of significance, is there evidence of a difference between those students who plan to go to graduate school and those who do not plan to go to grad-uate school in grade point average, expected starting salary, salary expected in five years, age, and spending on textbooks and supplies?

**10.79** Problem 1.27 on page 14 describes a survey of 50 undergraduate students (see the file Undergradsurvey).
a. Select a sample of 50 undergraduate students at your school and conduct a similar survey for them.
b. For the data collected in (a), repeat (a) and (b) of Problem 10.78.
c. Compare the results of (b) to those of Problem 10.78.

**10.80** Problem 1.28 on page 14 describes a survey of 40 MBA students (see the file Gradsurvey). For these data, at the 0.05 level of significance, is there evidence of a difference between males and females in age, undergraduate grade point average, graduate grade point average, GMAT score, expected salary upon graduation, salary expected in five years, and spending on textbooks and supplies?

**10.81** Problem 1.28 on page 14 describes a survey of 40 MBA students (see the file Gradsurvey).
a. Select a sample of 40 graduate students in your MBA program and conduct a similar survey for those students.
b. For the data collected in (a), repeat Problem 10.80.
c. Compare the results of (b) to those of Problem 10.80.

# MANAGING THE *SPRINGVILLE HERALD*

A marketing department team is charged with improving the telemarketing process in order to increase the number of home-delivery subscriptions sold. After several brainstorming sessions, it was clear that the longer a caller speaks to a respondent, the greater the chance that the caller will sell a home-delivery subscription. Therefore, the team decided to find ways to increase the length of the phone calls.

Initially, the team investigated the impact that the time of a call might have on the length of the call. Under current arrangements, calls were made in the evening hours, between 5:00 p.m. and 9:00 p.m., Monday through Friday. The team wanted to compare the length of calls made early in the evening (before 7:00 p.m.) with those made later in the evening (after 7:00 p.m.) to determine whether one of these time periods is more conducive to lengthier calls and, correspondingly, to increased subscription sales. The team selected a sample of 30 female callers who staff the telephone bank on Wednesday evenings and randomly assigned 15 of them to the "early" time period and 15 to the "later" time period. The callers knew that the team was observing their efforts that evening but didn't know which calls were monitored. The callers had been trained to make their telephone presentations in a structured manner. They were to read from a script, and

their greeting was personal but informal ("Hi, this is Leigh Richardson from the *Springville Herald*. May I speak to Stuart Knoll?").

Measurements were taken on the length of the call (defined as the difference, in seconds, between the time the person answered the phone and the time he or she hung up). The results (stored in the file SH10) are presented in Table SH10.1.

**TABLE SH10.1**

Length of Calls, in Seconds, Based on Time of Call—Early Versus Late in the Evening

| Time of Call | | Time of Call | |
|---|---|---|---|
| Early | Late | Early | Late |
| 41.3 | 37.1 | 40.6 | 40.7 |
| 37.5 | 38.9 | 33.3 | 38.0 |
| 39.3 | 42.2 | 39.6 | 43.6 |
| 37.4 | 45.7 | 35.7 | 43.8 |
| 33.6 | 42.4 | 31.3 | 34.9 |
| 38.5 | 39.0 | 36.8 | 35.7 |
| 32.6 | 40.9 | 36.3 | 47.4 |
| 37.3 | 40.5 | | |

difference, level of significance, and the sample statistics of the two samples in cells B4, B5, B7:B9, and B11:B13. If you do not want to include a confidence interval estimate in your worksheet (see Figure E10.2), select and delete the cell range D3:E16.

## E10.4 Using the Separate-Variance *t* test (unsummarized data)

For unsummarized data, you perform the separate-variance *t* test by using the ToolPak t-Test: Two-Sample Assuming Unequal Variances procedure. (There is no equivalent procedure for summarized data in Microsoft Excel.)

Open to the worksheet containing the unsummarized data for the two samples. Select **Tools → Data Analysis** (Excel 97–2003) or **Data → Data Analysis** (Excel 2007). Then select **t-Test: Two-Sample Assuming Unequal Variances** from the **Data Analysis** list and click **OK**. In the procedure's dialog box (shown below), enter the cell range of one sample as the **Variable 1 Range** and the cell range of the other sample as the **Variable 2 Range**. Enter the **Hypothesized Mean Difference**, click **Labels**, and click **OK**. Figure 10.8 on page 399 shows the results of applying this procedure to the Table 10.1 BLK Cola weekly sales data.

## E10.5 Using the Separate-Variance *t* test (summarized data)

For summarized data, you perform the separate-variance *t* test by making entries in the SVt worksheet of the `Separate-Variance T.xls` workbook. This worksheet (see Figure E10.3) uses the TINV and TDIST functions in ways similar to their use in the pooled-variance worksheet (see Section E10.3). IF functions in cells B32 and B37 select which one of two values computed in a calculations area (not shown in Figure E10.3) to use. IF functions in cells

A28, A33, and A38 determine which one of two phrases will be displayed in those cells.

The worksheet contains entries based on the Table 10.1 BLK Cola weekly sales data. To adapt this worksheet to other problems, change, as is necessary, the hypothesized difference, level of significance, and the sample statistics of the two samples in cells B4, B5, B7:B9, and B11:B13.

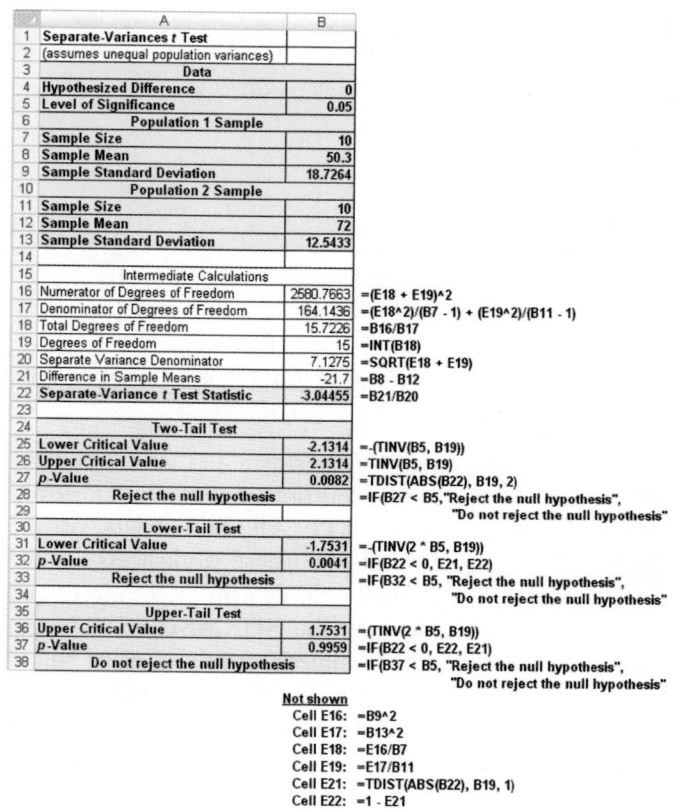

**FIGURE E10.3**

Separate-variance (SVt) worksheet

## E10.6 Using the Paired *t* Test (unsummarized data)

For unsummarized data, you perform the paired *t* test by using the ToolPak t-Test: Paired Two Sample for Mean procedure. (There is no equivalent procedure for summarized data in Microsoft Excel.)

Open to the worksheet containing the unsummarized data for the two samples. Select **Tools → Data Analysis** (Excel 97–2003) or **Data → Data Analysis** (Excel 2007). Then select **t-Test: Paired Two Sample for Means** from the **Data Analysis** list and click **OK**. In the procedure's dialog box (shown at the top of page 436), enter the cell range of one sample as the **Variable 1 Range** and the cell range of the other sample as the **Variable 2 Range**. Enter the

**Hypothesized Mean Difference**, click **Labels**, and click **OK**. Figure 10.11 on page 407 shows the results for the Table 10.4 car mileage data.

## E10.7 Using the *Z* Test for the Difference Between Two Proportions

For summarized data, you perform the *Z* test for the difference between two proportions by making entries in either the **ZTP_TT** or **ZTP_All** worksheets of the `Z Two Proportions.xls` workbook. These worksheets use the **NORMSINV(*P<X*)** function to determine the lower and upper critical values and use the **NORMSDIST(*Z value*)** function to compute the *p*-values from the *Z* value calculated in cell B12. IF functions in cell A24 and in A29 and A34 determine which one of two phrases will be displayed in those cells.

The **ZTP_TT** worksheet (see Figure 10.17 on page 416) applies the two-tail *Z* test to the Section 10.3 guest satisfaction example. The **ZTP_All** worksheet includes the two-tail test, the upper one-tail test, and the lower one-tail test on one worksheet and contains a confidence interval estimate of the difference between the two proportions. To adapt these worksheets to other problems, enter the hypothesized difference, level of significance, and the number of items of interest and sample size for each sample in cells B4, B5, B7, B8, B10, and B11, as is necessary.

## E10.8 Using the *F* Test for the Difference Between Two Variances (unsummarized data)

For unsummarized data, you use the *F* test for the difference between two variances by using the ToolPak F Test Two-Sample for Variances procedure.

Open to the worksheet containing the unsummarized data for the two samples. Select **Tools → Data Analysis** (Excel 97–2003) or **Data → Data Analysis** (Excel 2007). Then select **F Test Two-Sample for Variances** from the **Data Analysis** list and click **OK**. In the procedure's dialog box (shown below), enter the cell range of one sample as the **Variable 1 Range** and the cell range of the other sample as the **Variable 2 Range**. Click **Labels** and click **OK**. Results appear on a new worksheet. Figure 10.19 on page 422 shows results for the Table 10.1 BLK Cola weekly sales data.

## E10.9 Using the *F* Test for the Difference Between Two Variances (summarized data)

For summarized data, you perform the *F* test for the difference between two variances by making entries in the **F Two Variances** worksheet of the `F Two Variances.xls` workbook.

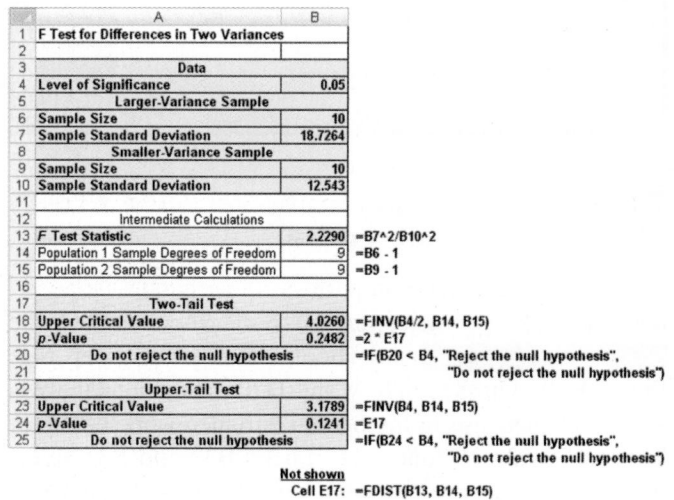

**FIGURE E10.4**
*F* Two Variances worksheet

The worksheet uses the **FINV(*upper-tailed* p-*value*, *numerator degrees of freedom, denominator degrees of freedom*)** function, in which ***upper-tailed* p-*value*** is the probability that $F$ will be greater than the value, to compute the upper and lower critical values and **FDIST(F-*test statistic, numerator degrees of freedom, denominator degrees of freedom*)** function to compute the *p*-values.

The worksheet (shown in Figure E10.4) applies the $F$ test to the Section 10.4 BLK Cola weekly sales example. Because sample 1 has been defined as the sample with the larger variance, a lower-tail test section is unnecessary in this worksheet.

To adapt this worksheet to other problems, change the level of significance and the sample statistics for the two population samples in the tinted cells B4, B6, B7, B9, and B10. Should you inadvertently enter the data of the sample with the largest standard deviation as the "smaller-variance sample," IF functions in cells A28 and A29 (not shown in Figure E10.4) will display messages asking you to review your entries.

# Appendix P10
## Using PHStat2 for Two-Sample Tests

## P10.1 Stacking and Unstacking Data

Specific PHStat2 or ToolPak procedures or Excel worksheets for analyses involving two or more samples will require that your data be arranged either as stacked or unstacked data.

To stack data, use **PHStat → Data Preparation → Stack Data.** This procedure places the data of the **Unstacked Data Cell Range** into a new worksheet containing two columns, one for the sample labels, the other for the data. The **Unstacked Data Cell Range** must be a contiguous multiple-column cell range in which each column contains the data of a sample.

To unstack data, use **PHStat → Data Preparation → Unstack Data**. This procedure places data into a new worksheet in which each column contains the data for one of the samples. The **Grouping Variable Cell Range** must be a single-column cell range containing the sample labels and the **Stacked Data Cell Range** must be a single-column cell range containing the data.

## P10.2 Using the Pooled-Variance *t* Test

To perform the pooled-variance *t* test, use **PHStat → Two-Sample Tests → Pooled-Variance t Test**. This procedure creates a worksheet similar to Figure E10.1 on page 434, based on the test option and the hypothesized difference, level of significance, and the sample statistics values that you specify. If you click **Confidence Interval Estimate**, the worksheet will also include a confidence interval estimate in columns D and E (shown in Figure E10.2 on page 434).

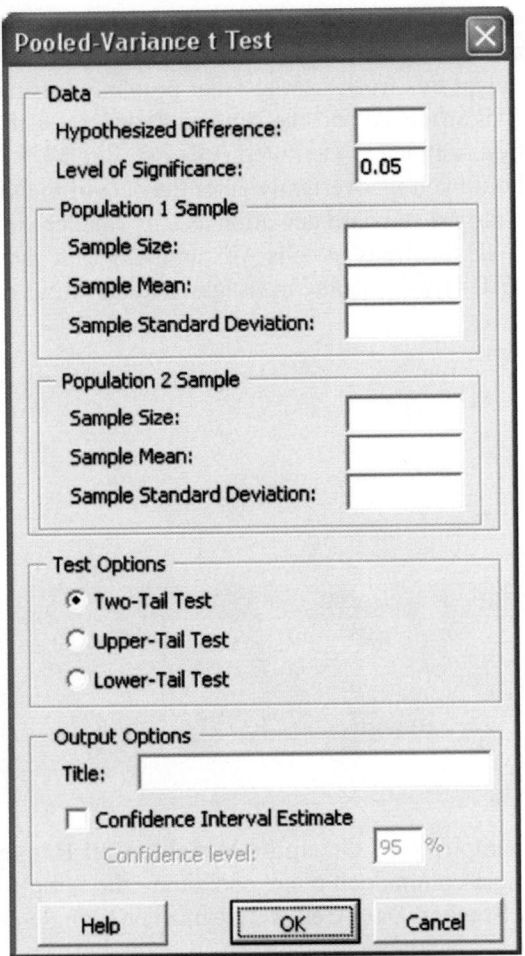

## P10.3 Using the Separate-Variance *t* Test

To perform the separate-variance *t* test, use **PHStat →
Two-Sample Tests → Separate-Variance t Test**. This procedure creates a worksheet similar to Figure E10.3 on page
435, based on the test option and the hypothesized difference, level of significance, and the sample statistics values
that you specify.

## P10.4 Using the *Z* Test for the Difference Between Two Proportions

To perform the *Z* test for the differences in two proportions, use **PHStat → Two-Sample Tests → Z Test for the Differences in Two Proportions**. This procedure creates a worksheet similar to Figure 10.17 on page 416, based on the test option and the null hypothesis, level of significance, number of items of interest, and sample size values that you specify.

## P10.5 Using the *F* Test for the Difference Between Two Variances

To perform the *F* test for the difference between two variances, use **PHStat → Two-Sample Tests → F Test for the Differences in Two Variances**. This procedure creates a worksheet similar to Figure E10.3 on page 435, based on the level of significance, sample statistics values, and the test option that you specify.

# Appendix M10
## Using Minitab for Two-Sample Tests

### M10.1 Stacking and Unstacking Data

Unsummarized data for two (or more) samples can be entered as **stacked** or **unstacked** worksheet data. As first mentioned in Section M2.1 on page 81, in a stacked arrangement, all the values for a variable appear in a single column next to a column that identifies the sample to which individual values belong. In an unstacked arrangement, the values for each sample appear in separate columns.

Although most Minitab procedures accept either stacked or unstacked data, you may discover situations when you need to change your data arrangement. To change stacked data into its unstacked equivalent, select **Data → Unstack Columns**. In the Unstack Columns dialog box enter the column that identifies the sample in the **Using subscripts in** box. Likewise, to stack unstacked data, select **Data → Stack → Columns** and enter the columns to be stacked in the **Stack the following columns** box. The `Cola.mtw` worksheet illustrates both the stacked and unstacked arrangement of the BLK Cola weekly sales data of Table 10.1 on page 392.

## M10.2 Using the *t* Test for the Difference Between Two Means

To illustrate the *t* test of the difference in two means:

1. Open the `Cola.mtw` worksheet.
2. Select **Stat → Basic Statistics → 2-Sample t**.

In the 2-Sample t (Test and Confidence Interval) dialog box (see Figure M10.1):

3. Click **Samples in one column** and enter **Sales** in the **Samples** box and **Display** in the **Subscripts** box. (If you had unstacked data, you would click **Samples in different columns** and enter the column names in the **First** and **Second** boxes.)
4. Click **Assume equal variances** to perform the pooled-variance *t* test. (To perform the separate-variance *t* test, leave this unchecked.)
5. Click **Options**.

**FIGURE M10.1**
2-Sample t (Test and Confidence Interval) dialog box

In the 2-Sample t - Options dialog box (see Figure M10.2):

6. Leave the **Confidence level** and **Test difference** values unchanged.

7. Select **not equal** from the **Alternative** drop-down list to perform the two-tail test. (To perform a one-tail test, select **less than** or **greater than**.)
8. Click **OK**.

**FIGURE M10.2**
2-Sample t - Options dialog box

9. Back in the 2-Sample t (Test and Confidence Interval) dialog box, click **Graphs**.
10. In the 2-Sample t - Graphs dialog box (not shown), click **Boxplots of data** and then click **OK**.
11. Back in the 2-Sample t (Test and Confidence Interval) dialog box, click **OK**.

To get the results in Figure 10.4 on page 393, you need to unstack the data.

1. Select **Data → Unstack Columns**.
2. Enter **Sales** in the **Unstack the data in** box.
3. Enter **Display** in the **Using subscripts in** box.
4. Click **After last column in use**.
5. Click **OK**.
6. Rename the **Sales_Normal** column as **Normal** and rename the **Sales_End_Aisle** column as **EndAisle**. (This will simplify entering their names.)

Then repeat the 11-step instructions, changing step 3 as follows: Click **Samples in different columns**. Enter **Normal** in the **First** box and enter **EndAisle** in the **Second** box.

## M10.3 Using the Paired *t* Test

To illustrate the paired *t* test,

1. Open the `AAAMileage.mtw` worksheet.
2. Select **Stat → Basic Statistics → Paired t**.

In the Paired *t* (Test and Confidence Interval) dialog box (see Figure M10.3):

**FIGURE M10.3**

Paired t (Test and Confidence Interval) dialog box

3. Click **Samples in columns**.
4. Enter **Owner** in the **First sample** box.
5. Enter **Government** in the **Second sample** box.
6. Click **Options**.

In the Paired t - Options dialog box (see Figure M10.4),

7. Leave the **Confidence level** and **Test mean** values unchanged.
8. Select **not equal** from the **Alternative** drop-down list to perform the two-tail test shown on page 407.
9. Click **OK**.
10. Back in the Paired t (Test and Confidence Interval) dialog box, click **Graphs**.

**FIGURE M10.4**

Paired t - Options dialog box

In the Paired t - Graphs dialog box (see Figure M10.5),

11. Click **Boxplot of differences**.
12. Click **OK**.
13. Back in the Paired t (Test and Confidence Interval) dialog box, click **OK**.

**FIGURE M10.5**

Paired t - Graphs dialog box

## M10.4 Using the *Z* Test for the Difference between Two Proportions

To illustrate the test for the difference between two proportions, using the example shown in Figure 10.18 on page 416,

1. Select **Stat → Basic Statistics → 2 Proportions**.

In the 2 Proportions (Test and Confidence Interval) dialog box (see Figure M10.6),

2. Click **Summarized data**.
3. In the **First** row, enter **163** in the **Events** box and **227** in the **Trials** box.
4. In the **Second** row, enter **154** in the **Events** box and **262** in the **Trials** box.
5. Click **Options**.

**FIGURE M10.6**

2 Proportions (Test and Confidence Interval) dialog box

In the 2 Proportions - Options dialog box (see Figure M10.7),

6. Leave the **Confidence level** and **Test difference** values unchanged.
7. Select **not equal** from the **Alternative** drop-down list to perform the two-tail test presented on page 415.
8. Click **Use pooled estimate of p for test**.
9. Click **OK**.
10. Back in the 2-Proportions (Test and Confidence Interval) dialog box click **OK**.

**FIGURE M10.7**

2 Proportions - Options dialog box

## M10.5 Using the *F* Test for the Difference Between Two Variances

To illustrate the *F* test of the difference in two variances as shown in Figure 10.20 on page 422,

1. Open the `Cola.mtw` worksheet.
2. Select **Stat → Basic Statistics → 2 Variances**.

In the 2 Variances dialog box (see Figure M10.8),

3. Click **Samples in one column**.
4. Enter **Sales** in the **Samples** box, and enter **Display** in the **Subscripts** box. (If you have unstacked data, click **Samples in different columns** and enter the names of the two columns in the **First** and **Second** boxes. If you have summarized data instead of the actual data, click **Summarized data** and enter the sample size and variance for each sample.)
5. Click **OK**.

**FIGURE M10.8**

2 Variances dialog box

# CHAPTER
# ELEVEN

## ANALYSIS OF VARIANCE

# LEARNING OBJECTIVES

## In this chapter, you learn:

- The basic concepts of experimental design
- How to use the one-way analysis of variance to test for differences among the means of several groups
- When and how to use a randomized block design
- How to use the two-way analysis of variance and interpret the interaction effect
- How to perform multiple comparisons in a one-way analysis of variance, a two-way analysis of variance, and a randomized block design

# USING STATISTICS @ Perfect Parachutes

You are the production manager at the Perfect Parachutes Company. Parachutes are woven in your factory using a synthetic fiber purchased from one of four different suppliers. Strength of these fibers is an important characteristic that ensures quality parachutes. You need to decide whether the synthetic fibers from each of your four suppliers result in parachutes of equal strength. Furthermore, your factory uses two types of looms to produce parachutes, the *Jetta* and the *Turk*. You need to establish that the parachutes woven on both types of looms are equally strong. You also want to know if any differences in the strength of the parachute that can be attributed to the four suppliers are dependent on the type of loom used. How would you go about finding this information?

In Chapter 10, you used hypothesis testing to reach conclusions about possible differences between two populations. As a manager at Perfect Parachutes, you need to design an experiment to test the strength of parachutes woven from the synthetic fibers from the *four* suppliers. That is, you need to evaluate differences among *more than two* populations. Populations are referred to as *groups* in this chapter.

This chapter begins by examining the *completely randomized design*, that has one *factor* (which supplier to use), with several groups (the four suppliers). The randomized block design, which is an extension of the paired *t* test of Section 10.2, is introduced next. The completely randomized design is then extended to the *factorial design*, in which more than one factor at a time is simultaneously studied in a single experiment. For example, an experiment incorporating the four suppliers and the two types of looms would help you determine which supplier and type of loom to use in order to manufacture the strongest parachutes. Throughout the chapter, emphasis is placed on the assumptions behind the use of the various testing procedures.

## 11.1 THE COMPLETELY RANDOMIZED DESIGN: ONE-WAY ANALYSIS OF VARIANCE

In many situations, you need to examine differences among more than two **groups**. The groups involved can be classified according to **levels** of a **factor** of interest. For example, a factor such as baking temperature may have several groups defined by *numerical levels* such as 300°, 350°, 400°, 450°, and a factor such as preferred supplier for a parachute manufacturer may have several groups defined by *categorical levels* such as Supplier 1, Supplier 2, Supplier 3, and Supplier 4. When there is only one factor, the experimental design is called a **completely randomized design**.

### F Test for Differences Among More Than Two Means

When you are analyzing a numerical variable and certain assumptions are met, you use the **analysis of variance (ANOVA)** to compare the means of the groups. The ANOVA procedure used for the completely randomized design is referred to as the **one-way ANOVA**, and it is an extension of the *t* test for the difference between two means discussed in Section 10.1. Although ANOVA is an acronym for *analysis of variance*, the term is misleading because the objective is to analyze differences among the group means, *not* the variances. However, by analyzing the variation among and within the groups, you can reach conclusions about possible differences in group means. In ANOVA, the total variation is subdivided into variation that is due to differences *among* the groups and variation that is due to differences *within* the groups (see Figure 11.1). **Within-group variation** measures random variation. **Among-group variation** is due to differences from group to group. The symbol $c$ is used to indicate the number of groups.

**FIGURE 11.1**

Partitioning the total variation in a completely randomized design

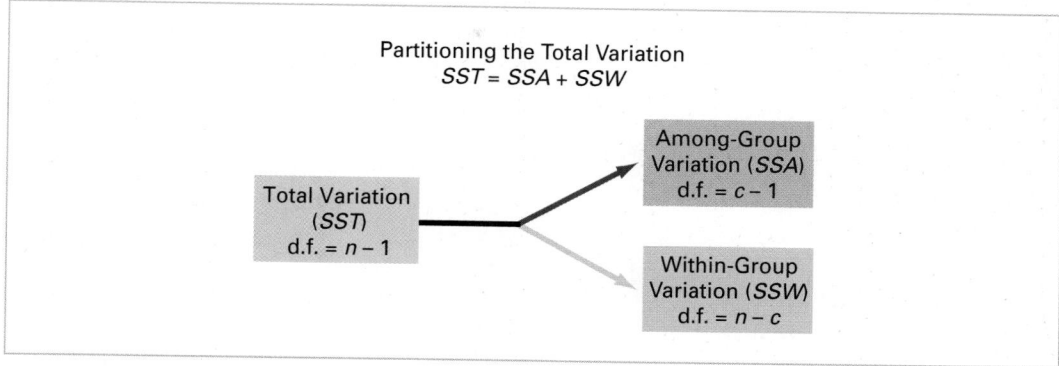

Partitioning the Total Variation
$SST = SSA + SSW$

Total Variation (SST)
d.f. $= n - 1$

Among-Group Variation (SSA)
d.f. $= c - 1$

Within-Group Variation (SSW)
d.f. $= n - c$

Assuming that the $c$ groups represent populations whose values are randomly and independently selected, follow a normal distribution, and have equal variances, the null hypothesis of no differences in the population means:

$$H_0: \mu_1 = \mu_2 = \cdots = \mu_c$$

is tested against the alternative that not all the $c$ population means are equal:

$$H_1: \text{Not all } \mu_j \text{ are equal (where } j = 1, 2, \ldots, c).$$

To perform an ANOVA test of equality of population means, you subdivide the total variation in the values into two parts—that which is due to variation among the groups and that which is due to variation within the groups. The **total variation** is represented by the **sum of squares total (SST)**. Because the population means of the $c$ groups are assumed to be equal under the null hypothesis, you compute the total variation among all the values by summing the squared differences between each individual value and the **grand mean, $\bar{\bar{X}}$**. The grand mean is the mean of all the values in all the groups combined. Equation (11.1) shows the computation of the total variation.

Total Variation in One-Way ANOVA

$$SST = \sum_{j=1}^{c} \sum_{i=1}^{n_j} (X_{ij} - \bar{\bar{X}})^2 \qquad (11.1)$$

where

$$\bar{\bar{X}} = \frac{\displaystyle\sum_{j=1}^{c} \sum_{i=1}^{n_j} X_{ij}}{n} = \text{Grand mean}$$

$X_{ij} = i$th value in group $j$

$n_j = $ number of values in group $j$

$n = $ total number of values in all groups combined
    (that is, $n = n_1 + n_2 + \cdots + n_c$)

$c = $ number of groups

You compute the among-group variation, usually called the **sum of squares among groups (SSA)**, by summing the squared differences between the sample mean of each group, $\bar{X}_j$, and the grand mean, $\bar{\bar{X}}$, weighted by the sample size, $n_j$, in each group. Equation (11.2) shows the computation of the among-group variation.

Among-Group Variation in One-Way ANOVA

$$SSA = \sum_{j=1}^{c} n_j (\bar{X}_j - \bar{\bar{X}})^2 \tag{11.2}$$

where

$c$ = number of groups

$n_j$ = number of values in group $j$

$\bar{X}_j$ = sample mean of group $j$

$\bar{\bar{X}}$ = grand mean

The within-group variation, usually called the **sum of squares within groups (SSW)**, measures the difference between each value and the mean of its own group and sums the squares of these differences over all groups. Equation (11.3) shows the computation of the within-group variation.

Within-Group Variation in One-Way ANOVA

$$SSW = \sum_{j=1}^{c} \sum_{i=1}^{n_j} (X_{ij} - \bar{X}_j)^2 \tag{11.3}$$

where

$X_{ij}$ = $i$th value in group $j$

$\bar{X}_j$ = sample mean of group $j$

Because you are comparing $c$ groups, there are $c - 1$ degrees of freedom associated with the sum of squares among groups. Because each of the $c$ groups contributes $n_j - 1$ degrees of freedom, there are $n - c$ degrees of freedom associated with the sum of squares within groups. In addition, there are $n - 1$ degrees of freedom associated with the sum of squares total because you are comparing each value, $X_{ij}$, to the grand mean, $\bar{\bar{X}}$, based on all $n$ values.

If you divide each of these sums of squares by its associated degrees of freedom, you have three variances or **mean square** terms—$MSA$ (mean square among), $MSW$ (mean square within), and $MST$ (mean square total).

Mean Squares in One-Way ANOVA

$$MSA = \frac{SSA}{c-1} \tag{11.4a}$$

$$MSW = \frac{SSW}{n-c} \tag{11.4b}$$

$$MST = \frac{SST}{n-1} \tag{11.4c}$$

Although you want to compare the means of the $c$ groups to determine whether a difference exists among them, the name ANOVA comes from the fact that you are comparing variances. If the null hypothesis is true and there are no differences in the $c$ group means, all three mean squares (or *variances*)—MSA, MSW, and MST—provide estimates of the overall variance in the data. Thus, to test the null hypothesis:

$$H_0: \mu_1 = \mu_2 = \cdots = \mu_c$$

against the alternative:

$$H_1: \text{Not all } \mu_j \text{ are equal (where } j = 1, 2, \ldots, c)$$

you compute the one-way ANOVA $F_{STAT}$ test statistic as the ratio of MSA to MSW, as in Equation (11.5).

One-Way ANOVA $F_{STAT}$ Test Statistic

$$F_{STAT} = \frac{MSA}{MSW}$$

(11.5)

The $F_{STAT}$ test statistic follows an **F distribution**, with $c - 1$ degrees of freedom in the numerator and $n - c$ degrees of freedom in the denominator. For a given level of significance, $\alpha$, you reject the null hypothesis if the $F_{STAT}$ test statistic computed in Equation (11.5), is greater than the upper-tail critical value, $F_\alpha$, from the F distribution having $c - 1$ degrees of freedom in the numerator and $n - c$ in the denominator (see Table E.5). Thus, as shown in Figure 11.2, the decision rule is

$$\text{Reject } H_0 \text{ if } F_{STAT} > F_\alpha;$$

otherwise, do not reject $H_0$.

**FIGURE 11.2**

Regions of rejection and nonrejection when using ANOVA

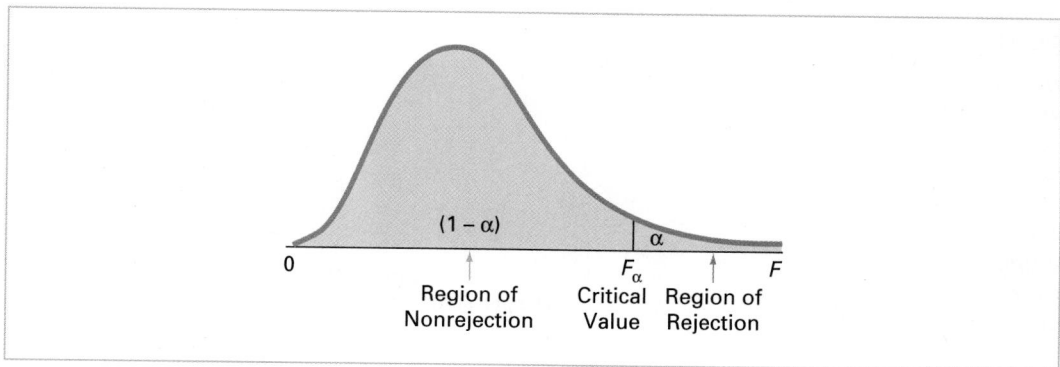

If the null hypothesis is true, the computed $F_{STAT}$ test statistic is expected to be approximately equal to 1 because both the numerator and denominator mean square terms are estimating the overall variance in the data. If $H_0$ is false (and there are differences in the group means), the computed $F_{STAT}$ test statistic is expected to be larger than 1 because the numerator, MSA, is estimating the differences among groups in addition to the overall variability in the values, whereas the denominator, MSW, is measuring only the overall variability. Thus, the ANOVA procedure provides an F test in which you reject the null hypothesis at a selected level of significance, $\alpha$, only if the computed $F_{STAT}$ test statistic is greater than $F_\alpha$, the upper-tail critical value of the F distribution having $c - 1$ and $n - c$ degrees of freedom, as illustrated in Figure 11.2.

The results of an analysis of variance are usually displayed in an **ANOVA summary table**, as shown in Table 11.1. The entries in this table include the sources of variation (i.e., among-groups, within-groups, and total), the degrees of freedom, the sums of squares, the mean squares (i.e., the variances), and the computed $F_{STAT}$ test statistic. In addition, Microsoft Excel and Minitab include the $p$-value (i.e., the probability of having an $F_{STAT}$ as large as or larger than the one computed, given that the null hypothesis is true) in the ANOVA summary table. The $p$-value allows you to make direct conclusions about the null hypothesis without referring to a table of critical values of the $F$ distribution. If the $p$-value is less than the chosen level of significance, $\alpha$, you reject the null hypothesis.

**TABLE 11.1**

Analysis-of-Variance Summary Table

| Source | Degrees of Freedom | Sum of Squares | Mean Square (Variance) | $F$ |
|--------|--------------------|----------------|------------------------|-----|
| Among groups | $c - 1$ | SSA | $MSA = \dfrac{SSA}{c-1}$ | $F_{STAT} = \dfrac{MSA}{MSW}$ |
| Within groups | $n - c$ | SSW | $MSW = \dfrac{SSW}{n-c}$ | |
| Total | $n - 1$ | SST | | |

To illustrate the one-way ANOVA $F$ test, return to the Using Statistics scenario concerning Perfect Parachutes (see page 444). An experiment was conducted to determine whether any significant differences exist in the strength of parachutes woven from synthetic fibers from the different suppliers. Five parachutes were woven for each group—Supplier 1, Supplier 2, Supplier 3, and Supplier 4. The strength of the parachutes is measured by placing them in a testing device that pulls on both ends of a parachute until it tears apart. The amount of force required to tear the parachute is measured on a tensile-strength scale, where the larger the value, the stronger the parachute. The results of this experiment (in terms of tensile strength) are contained in the Parachute file and are displayed in Figure 11.3, along with the sample mean and the sample standard deviation for each group.

**FIGURE 11.3**

Microsoft Excel worksheet of the tensile strength for parachutes woven with synthetic fibers from four different suppliers along with the sample mean and sample standard deviation

| | A | B | C | D | E |
|---|---|---|---|---|---|
| 1 | | Supplier 1 | Supplier 2 | Supplier 3 | Supplier 4 |
| 2 | | 18.5 | 26.3 | 20.6 | 25.4 |
| 3 | | 24.0 | 25.3 | 25.2 | 19.9 |
| 4 | | 17.2 | 24.0 | 20.8 | 22.6 |
| 5 | | 19.9 | 21.2 | 24.7 | 17.5 |
| 6 | | 18.0 | 24.5 | 22.9 | 20.4 |
| 7 | | | | | |
| 8 | Sample Mean | 19.52 | 24.26 | 22.84 | 21.16 |
| 9 | Sample Standard Deviation | 2.69 | 1.92 | 2.13 | 2.98 |

In Figure 11.3, observe that there are differences in the sample means for the four suppliers. For Supplier 1, the mean tensile strength is 19.52. For Supplier 2, the mean tensile strength is 24.26. For Supplier 3, the mean tensile strength is 22.84, and for Supplier 4, the mean tensile strength is 21.16. What you need to determine is whether these sample results are sufficiently different to conclude that the *population* means are not all equal.

In the scatter plot shown in Figure 11.4, you can visually inspect the data and see how the measurements of tensile strength distribute. You can also observe differences among the groups as well as within groups. If the sample sizes in each group were larger, you could develop stem-and-leaf displays, boxplots, and normal probability plots.

**FIGURE 11.4**

Microsoft Excel scatter plot of tensile strengths for four different suppliers

*See Section E2.13 or P2.9 to create this. (Minitab users, see Section M2.9 to create an equivalent chart.)*

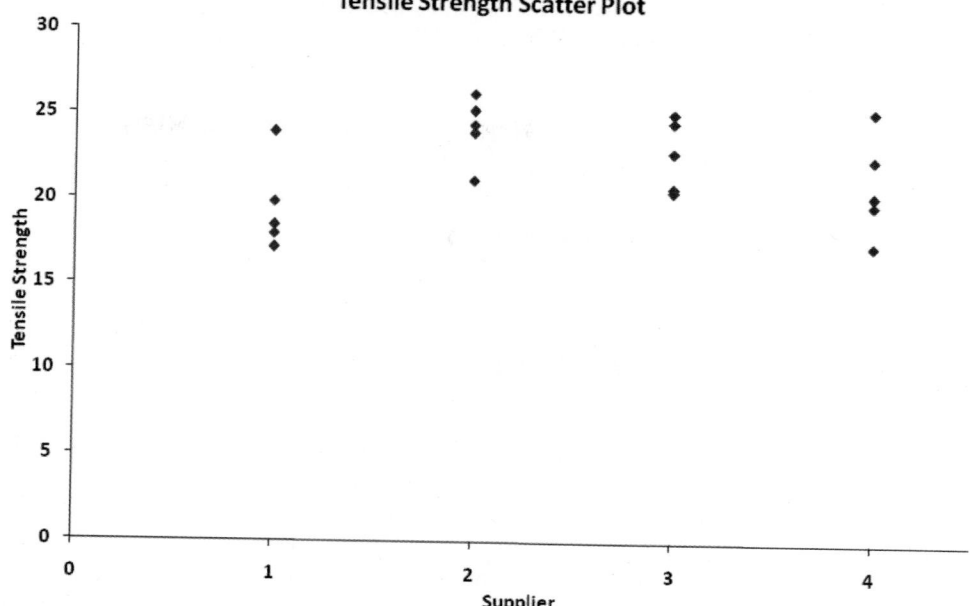

The null hypothesis states that there is no difference in mean tensile strength among the four suppliers:

$$H_0: \mu_1 = \mu_2 = \mu_3 = \mu_4$$

The alternative hypothesis states that at least one of the suppliers differs with respect to the mean tensile strength:

$$H_1: \text{Not all the means are equal.}$$

To construct the ANOVA summary table, you first compute the sample means in each group (see Figure 11.3 on page 448). Then you compute the grand mean by summing all 20 values and dividing by the total number of values:

$$\overline{\overline{X}} = \frac{\sum\limits_{j=1}^{c}\sum\limits_{i=1}^{n_j} X_{ij}}{n} = \frac{438.9}{20} = 21.945$$

Then, using Equations (11.1) through (11.3) on pages 445–446, you compute the sum of squares:

$$SSA = \sum_{j=1}^{c} n_j(\overline{X}_j - \overline{\overline{X}})^2 = (5)(19.52 - 21.945)^2 + (5)(24.26 - 21.945)^2$$

$$+ (5)(22.84 - 21.945)^2 + (5)(21.16 - 21.945)^2$$

$$= 63.2855$$

$$SSW = \sum_{j=1}^{c} \sum_{i=1}^{n_j} (X_{ij} - \bar{X}_j)^2$$

$$= (18.5 - 19.52)^2 + \cdots + (18 - 19.52)^2 + (26.3 - 24.26)^2 + \cdots + (24.5 - 24.26)^2$$
$$+ (20.6 - 22.84)^2 + \cdots + (22.9 - 22.84)^2 + (25.4 - 21.16)^2 + \cdots + (20.4 - 21.16)^2$$
$$= 97.5040$$

$$SST = \sum_{j=1}^{c} \sum_{i=1}^{n_j} (X_{ij} - \bar{\bar{X}})^2$$

$$= (18.5 - 21.945)^2 + (24 - 21.945)^2 + \cdots + (20.4 - 21.945)^2$$
$$= 160.7895$$

You compute the mean square terms by dividing the sum of squares by the corresponding degrees of freedom [see Equation (11.4) on page 446]. Because $c = 4$ and $n = 20$,

$$MSA = \frac{SSA}{c-1} = \frac{63.2855}{4-1} = 21.0952$$

$$MSW = \frac{SSW}{n-c} = \frac{97.5040}{20-4} = 6.0940$$

so that using Equation (11.5) on page 447,

$$F_{STAT} = \frac{MSA}{MSW} = \frac{21.0952}{6.0940} = 3.4616$$

For a selected level of significance, $\alpha$, you find the upper-tail critical value, $F_\alpha$, from the $F$ distribution using Table E.5. A portion of Table E.5 is presented in Table 11.2. In the parachute supplier example, there are 3 degrees of freedom in the numerator and 16 degrees of freedom in the denominator. $F_\alpha$, the upper-tail critical value at the 0.05 level of significance, is 3.24.

**TABLE 11.2**

Finding the Critical Value of $F$ with 3 and 16 Degrees of Freedom at the 0.05 Level of Significance

| | | | | Cumulative Probabilities = 0.95 Upper-Tail Area = 0.05 Numerator $df_1$ | | | | | |
| Denominator $df_2$ | 1 | 2 | [3] | 4 | 5 | 6 | 7 | 8 | 9 |
|---|---|---|---|---|---|---|---|---|---|
| . | . | . | | . | . | . | . | . | . |
| . | . | . | | . | . | . | . | . | . |
| . | . | . | | . | . | . | . | . | . |
| 11 | 4.84 | 3.98 | 3.59 | 3.36 | 3.20 | 3.09 | 3.01 | 2.95 | 2.90 |
| 12 | 4.75 | 3.89 | 3.49 | 3.26 | 3.11 | 3.00 | 2.91 | 2.85 | 2.80 |
| 13 | 4.67 | 3.81 | 3.41 | 3.18 | 3.03 | 2.92 | 2.83 | 2.77 | 2.71 |
| 14 | 4.60 | 3.74 | 3.34 | 3.11 | 2.96 | 2.85 | 2.76 | 2.70 | 2.65 |
| 15 | 4.54 | 3.68 | 3.29 | 3.06 | 2.90 | 2.79 | 2.71 | 2.64 | 2.59 |
| 16 | 4.49 | 3.63 | 3.24 | 3.01 | 2.85 | 2.74 | 2.66 | 2.59 | 2.54 |

Source: *Extracted from Table E.5.*

Because $F_{STAT} = 3.4616$ is greater than $F_\alpha = 3.24$, you reject the null hypothesis (see Figure 11.5). You conclude that there is a significant difference in the mean tensile strength among the four suppliers.

**FIGURE 11.5**

Regions of rejection and nonrejection for the one-way ANOVA at the 0.05 level of significance, with 3 and 16 degrees of freedom

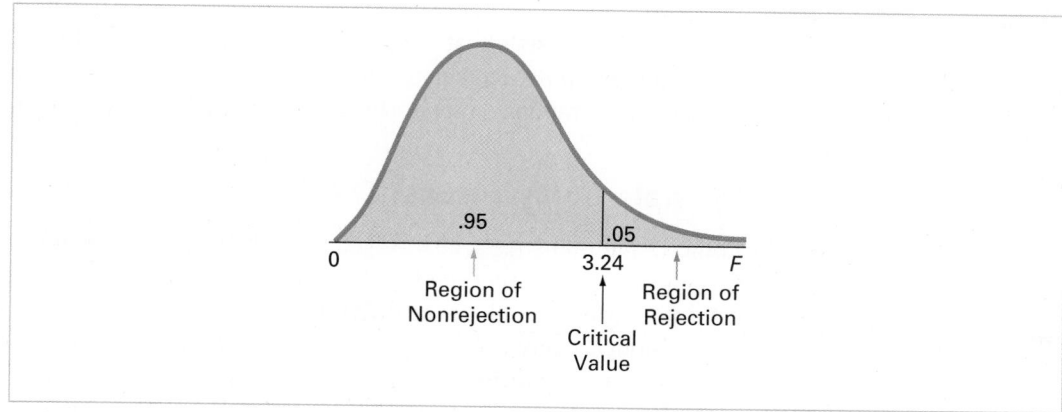

Figure 11.6 shows the Microsoft Excel ANOVA summary table and $p$-value. Figure 11.7 shows Minitab results.

**FIGURE 11.6**

Microsoft Excel ANOVA results for the parachute example

*See Section E11.1 to create this.*

| | A | B | C | D | E | F | G |
|---|---|---|---|---|---|---|---|
| 1 | **Anova: Single Factor** | | | | | | |
| 2 | | | | | | | |
| 3 | **SUMMARY** | | | | | | |
| 4 | *Groups* | *Count* | *Sum* | *Average* | *Variance* | | |
| 5 | Supplier 1 | 5 | 97.6 | 19.52 | 7.237 | | |
| 6 | Supplier 2 | 5 | 121.3 | 24.26 | 3.683 | | |
| 7 | Supplier 3 | 5 | 114.2 | 22.84 | 4.553 | | |
| 8 | Supplier 4 | 5 | 105.8 | 21.16 | 8.903 | | |
| 9 | | | | | | | |
| 10 | | | | | | | |
| 11 | **ANOVA** | | | | | | |
| 12 | *Source of Variation* | *SS* | *df* | *MS* | *F* | *P-value* | *F crit* |
| 13 | Between Groups | 63.2855 | 3 | 21.0952 | 3.4616 | 0.0414 | 3.2389 |
| 14 | Within Groups | 97.5040 | 16 | 6.094 | | | |
| 15 | | | | | | | |
| 16 | Total | 160.7895 | 19 | | | | |

**FIGURE 11.7**

Minitab ANOVA results for the parachute example

*See Section M11.1 to create this.*

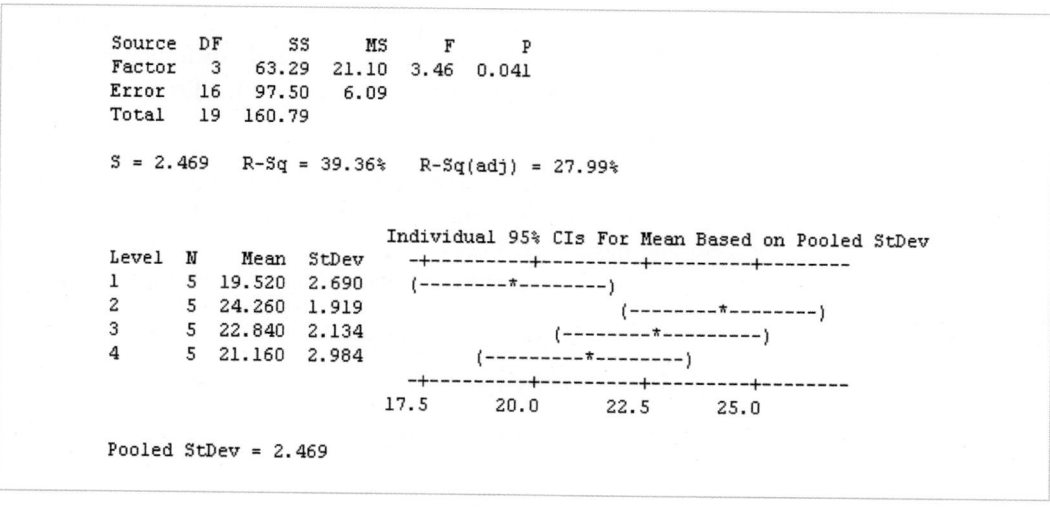

The $p$-value, or probability of getting a computed $F_{STAT}$ statistic of 3.4616 or larger when the null hypothesis is true, is 0.0414. Because this $p$-value is less than the specified $\alpha$ of 0.05, you reject the null hypothesis. The $p$-value of 0.0414 indicates that there is a 4.14% chance of observing differences this large or larger if the population means for the four suppliers are all equal. After performing the one-way ANOVA and finding a significant difference among the suppliers, you still do not know *which* suppliers differ. All that you know is that there is sufficient evidence to state that the population means are not all the same. In other words, at least one or more population means are significantly different. To determine which suppliers differ, you can use a multiple comparison procedure such as the Tukey-Kramer procedure.

## Multiple Comparisons: The Tukey-Kramer Procedure

In the Using Statistics scenario, you used the one-way ANOVA $F$ test to determine that there was a difference among the suppliers. The next step is to construct **multiple comparisons** to determine which suppliers are different.

Although many procedures are available (see references 5, 9, and 10), this text uses the **Tukey-Kramer multiple comparisons procedure for one-way ANOVA** to determine which of the $c$ means are significantly different. The Tukey-Kramer procedure enables you to simultaneously make comparisons between all pairs of groups. You use the following four steps to construct the comparisons.

1. Compute the absolute mean differences, $\left| \bar{X}_j - \bar{X}_{j'} \right|$ (where $j \neq j'$), among all $c(c-1)/2$ pairs of sample means.
2. Compute the **critical range** for the Tukey-Kramer procedure using Equation (11.6).

Critical Range for the Tukey-Kramer Procedure

$$\text{Critical range} = Q_\alpha \sqrt{\frac{MSW}{2}\left(\frac{1}{n_j} + \frac{1}{n_{j'}}\right)} \qquad \textbf{(11.6)}$$

where $Q_\alpha$ is the upper-tail critical value from a **Studentized range distribution** having $c$ degrees of freedom in the numerator and $n - c$ degrees of freedom in the denominator. (Values for the Studentized range distribution are found in Table E.10.)

If the sample sizes differ, you compute a critical range for each pairwise comparison of sample means.

3. Compare each of the $c(c-1)/2$ pairs of means against its corresponding critical range. You declare a specific pair significantly different if the absolute difference in the sample means $\left| \bar{X}_j - \bar{X}_{j'} \right|$ is greater than the critical range.
4. Interpret the results.

In the parachute example, there are four suppliers. Thus, there are $4(4-1)/2 = 6$ pairwise comparisons. To apply the Tukey-Kramer multiple comparison procedure, you first compute the absolute mean differences for all six pairwise comparisons. *Multiple comparison* refers to the fact that you are going to simultaneously make an inference about all six of these comparisons:

1. $\left| \bar{X}_1 - \bar{X}_2 \right| = \left| 19.52 - 24.26 \right| = 4.74$
2. $\left| \bar{X}_1 - \bar{X}_3 \right| = \left| 19.52 - 22.84 \right| = 3.32$
3. $\left| \bar{X}_1 - \bar{X}_4 \right| = \left| 19.52 - 21.16 \right| = 1.64$

4. $|\bar{X}_2 - \bar{X}_3| = |24.26 - 22.84| = 1.42$

5. $|\bar{X}_2 - \bar{X}_4| = |24.26 - 21.16| = 3.10$

6. $|\bar{X}_3 - \bar{X}_4| = |22.84 - 21.16| = 1.68$

You need to compute only one critical range because the sample sizes in the four groups are equal. From the ANOVA summary table (Figure 11.6 or 11.7 on page 451), $MSW = 6.094$ and $n_j = n_{j'} = 5$. From Table E.10, for $\alpha = 0.05$, $c = 4$, and $n - c = 20 - 4 = 16$, $Q_\alpha$, the upper-tail critical value of the test statistic, is 4.05 (see Table 11.3).

**TABLE 11.3**

Finding the Studentized Range $Q_\alpha$ Statistic for $\alpha = 0.05$, with 4 and 16 Degrees of Freedom

| | | | | | Cumulative Probabilities = 0.95 Upper-Tail Area = 0.05 Numerator $df_1$ | | | | |
| Denominator $df_2$ | 2 | 3 | 4 | 5 | 6 | 7 | 8 | 9 |
|---|---|---|---|---|---|---|---|---|
| . | . | . | | . | . | . | . | . |
| . | . | . | | . | . | . | . | . |
| . | . | . | | . | . | . | . | . |
| 11 | 3.11 | 3.82 | 4.26 | 4.57 | 4.82 | 5.03 | 5.20 | 5.35 |
| 12 | 3.08 | 3.77 | 4.20 | 4.51 | 4.75 | 4.95 | 5.12 | 5.27 |
| 13 | 3.06 | 3.73 | 4.15 | 4.45 | 4.69 | 4.88 | 5.05 | 5.19 |
| 14 | 3.03 | 3.70 | 4.11 | 4.41 | 4.64 | 4.83 | 4.99 | 5.13 |
| 15 | 3.01 | 3.67 | 4.08 | 4.37 | 4.60 | 4.78 | 4.94 | 5.08 |
| 16 | 3.00 | 3.65 | 4.05 | 4.33 | 4.56 | 4.74 | 4.90 | 5.03 |

Source: *Extracted from Table E.10.*

From Equation (11.6),

$$\text{Critical range} = 4.05\sqrt{\left(\frac{6.094}{2}\right)\left(\frac{1}{5} + \frac{1}{5}\right)} = 4.4712$$

Because $4.74 > 4.4712$, there is a significant difference between the means of Suppliers 1 and 2. All other pairwise differences are small enough that they may be due to chance. With 95% confidence, you can conclude that parachutes woven using fiber from Supplier 1 have a lower mean tensile strength than those from Supplier 2, but there are no statistically significant differences between Suppliers 1 and 3, Suppliers 1 and 4, Suppliers 2 and 3, Suppliers 2 and 4, and Suppliers 3 and 4. Note that by using $\alpha = 0.05$, you are able to make all six of the comparisons with an overall error rate of only 5%.

These results are shown in Figures 11.8 and 11.9 on page 454. Figure 11.8 follows the steps used on page 452 for evaluating the comparisons. Each mean is computed and the absolute differences are determined, the critical range is computed, and then each comparison is declared significant or not significant. In Figure 11.9, the comparisons are made using interval estimates. Each interval is computed. Any interval that does not include 0 is considered significant. Thus, in Figure 11.9, the only significant comparison is Supplier 1 versus Supplier 2 because its interval 0.269 to 9.211 does not include 0.

**FIGURE 11.8**

Microsoft Excel Tukey-Kramer procedure worksheet for the parachute example

*See Section E11.1 or P11.1 to create this.*

| | A | B | C | D | E | F | G | H | I |
|---|---|---|---|---|---|---|---|---|---|
| 1 | **Parachute Tensile-Strength Analysis** | | | | | | | | |
| 2 | | | | | | | | | |
| 3 | | **Sample** | **Sample** | | | **Absolute** | **Std. Error** | **Critical** | |
| 4 | **Group** | **Mean** | **Size** | | **Comparison** | **Difference** | **of Difference** | **Range** | **Results** |
| 5 | 1 | 19.52 | 5 | | **Group 1 to Group 2** | 4.74 | 1.10399275 | 4.4712 | **Means are different** |
| 6 | 2 | 24.26 | 5 | | **Group 1 to Group 3** | 3.32 | 1.10399275 | 4.4712 | **Means are not different** |
| 7 | 3 | 22.84 | 5 | | **Group 1 to Group 4** | 1.64 | 1.10399275 | 4.4712 | **Means are not different** |
| 8 | 4 | 21.16 | 5 | | **Group 2 to Group 3** | 1.42 | 1.10399275 | 4.4712 | **Means are not different** |
| 9 | | | | | **Group 2 to Group 4** | 3.1 | 1.10399275 | 4.4712 | **Means are not different** |
| 10 | Other Data | | | | **Group 3 to Group 4** | 1.68 | 1.10399275 | 4.4712 | **Means are not different** |
| 11 | Level of significance | 0.05 | | | | | | | |
| 12 | Numerator d.f. | 4 | | | | | | | |
| 13 | Denominator d.f. | 16 | | | | | | | |
| 14 | MSW | 6.094 | | | | | | | |
| 15 | Q Statistic | 4.05 | | | | | | | |

**FIGURE 11.9**

Minitab Tukey-Kramer results for the parachute example

*See Section M11.1 to create this.*

```
Tukey 95% Simultaneous Confidence Intervals
All Pairwise Comparisons
Individual confidence level = 98.87%

1 subtracted from:

     Lower   Center   Upper   -----+---------+---------+---------+----
2    0.269   4.740   9.211                      (-------*--------)
3   -1.151   3.320   7.791                 (--------*--------)
4   -2.831   1.640   6.111            (--------*--------)
                             -----+---------+---------+---------+----
                                -5.0      0.0       5.0      10.0

2 subtracted from:

     Lower   Center   Upper   -----+---------+---------+---------+----
3   -5.891  -1.420   3.051       (--------*--------)
4   -7.571  -3.100   1.371   (--------*--------)
                             -----+---------+---------+---------+----
                                -5.0      0.0       5.0      10.0

3 subtracted from:

     Lower   Center   Upper   -----+---------+---------+---------+----
4   -6.151  -1.680   2.791       (--------*--------)
```

## ANOVA Assumptions

In Chapters 9 and 10, you learned about the assumptions required in order to use each hypothesis-testing procedure and the consequences of departures from these assumptions. To use the one-way ANOVA $F$ test, you must also make certain assumptions about the populations. These assumptions are

- Randomness and independence
- Normality
- Homogeneity of variance

The first assumption, **randomness and independence**, is critically important. The validity of any experiment depends on random sampling and/or the randomization process. To avoid biases in the outcomes, you need to select random samples from the $c$ groups or randomly assign the items to the $c$ levels of the factor. Selecting a random sample, or randomly assigning the levels, ensures that a value from one group is independent of any other value in the experiment. Departures from this assumption can seriously affect inferences from the ANOVA. These problems are discussed more thoroughly in references 5 and 9.

The second assumption, **normality**, states that the sample values in each group are from a normally distributed population. Just as in the case of the $t$ test, the one-way ANOVA $F$ test is fairly robust against departures from the normal distribution. As long as the distributions are not extremely different from a normal distribution, the level of significance of the ANOVA $F$ test is usually not greatly affected, particularly for large samples. You can assess the normality of each of the $c$ samples by constructing a normal probability plot or a boxplot.

The third assumption, **homogeneity of variance**, states that the variances of the $c$ groups are equal (that is, $\sigma_1^2 = \sigma_2^2 = \cdots = \sigma_c^2$). If you have equal sample sizes in each group, inferences based on the $F$ distribution are not seriously affected by unequal variances. However, if you have unequal sample sizes, unequal variances can have a serious effect on inferences developed from the ANOVA procedure. Thus, when possible, you should have equal sample sizes in all groups. The Levene test for homogeneity of variance presented below is one method used to test whether the variances of the $c$ groups are equal.

When only the normality assumption is violated, the Kruskal-Wallis rank test, a nonparametric procedure discussed in Section 12.8, is appropriate. When only the homogeneity-of-variance assumption is violated, procedures similar to those used in the separate-variance $t$ test of Section 10.1 are available (see references 1 and 2). When both the normality and homogeneity-of-variance assumptions have been violated, you need to use an appropriate data transformation that both normalizes the data and reduces the differences in variances (see reference 10) or use a more general nonparametric procedure (see references 2 and 3).

## Levene Test for Homogeneity of Variance

Although the one-way ANOVA $F$ test is relatively robust with respect to the assumption of equal group variances, large differences in the group variances can seriously affect the level of significance and the power of the $F$ test. One procedure for testing the equality of the variances with high statistical power is the modified **Levene test** (see references 1, 4, 6, and 9). To test for the homogeneity of variance, you use the following null hypothesis:

$$H_0: \sigma_1^2 = \sigma_2^2 = \cdots = \sigma_c^2$$

against the alternative hypothesis:

$$H_1: \text{Not all } \sigma_j^2 \text{ are equal } (j = 1, 2, 3, \ldots, c).$$

To test the null hypothesis of equal variances, you first compute the absolute value of the difference between each value and the median of the group. Then you perform a one-way ANOVA on these *absolute differences*. Most statisticians suggest using a level of significance of $\alpha = 0.05$ when performing the ANOVA. To illustrate the modified Levene test, return to the Using Statistics scenario concerning the tensile strength of parachutes first presented on page 444. Table 11.4 summarizes the absolute differences from the median of each supplier.

**TABLE 11.4**

Absolute Differences from the Median Tensile Strength for Four Suppliers

| Supplier 1 (Median = 18.5) | Supplier 2 (Median = 24.5) | Supplier 3 (Median = 22.9) | Supplier 4 (Median = 20.4) |
|---|---|---|---|
| $\lvert 18.5 - 18.5 \rvert = 0.0$ | $\lvert 26.3 - 24.5 \rvert = 1.8$ | $\lvert 20.6 - 22.9 \rvert = 2.3$ | $\lvert 25.4 - 20.4 \rvert = 5.0$ |
| $\lvert 24.0 - 18.5 \rvert = 5.5$ | $\lvert 25.3 - 24.5 \rvert = 0.8$ | $\lvert 25.2 - 22.9 \rvert = 2.3$ | $\lvert 19.9 - 20.4 \rvert = 0.5$ |
| $\lvert 17.2 - 18.5 \rvert = 1.3$ | $\lvert 24.0 - 24.5 \rvert = 0.5$ | $\lvert 20.8 - 22.9 \rvert = 2.1$ | $\lvert 22.6 - 20.4 \rvert = 2.2$ |
| $\lvert 19.9 - 18.5 \rvert = 1.4$ | $\lvert 21.2 - 24.5 \rvert = 3.3$ | $\lvert 24.7 - 22.9 \rvert = 1.8$ | $\lvert 17.5 - 20.4 \rvert = 2.9$ |
| $\lvert 18.0 - 18.5 \rvert = 0.5$ | $\lvert 24.5 - 24.5 \rvert = 0.0$ | $\lvert 22.9 - 22.9 \rvert = 0.0$ | $\lvert 20.4 - 20.4 \rvert = 0.0$ |

Using the absolute differences given in Table 11.4, you perform a one-way ANOVA (see Figures 11.10 and 11.11).

| | A | B | C | D | E | F | G |
|---|---|---|---|---|---|---|---|
| 1 | Parachute Tensile-Strength Analysis | | | | | | |
| 2 | | | | | | | |
| 3 | SUMMARY | | | | | | |
| 4 | Groups | Count | Sum | Average | Variance | | |
| 5 | Supplier 1 | 5 | 8.7 | 1.74 | 4.753 | | |
| 6 | Supplier 2 | 5 | 6.4 | 1.28 | 1.707 | | |
| 7 | Supplier 3 | 5 | 8.5 | 1.7 | 0.945 | | |
| 8 | Supplier 4 | 5 | 10.6 | 2.12 | 4.007 | | |
| 9 | | | | | | | |
| 10 | | | | | | | |
| 11 | ANOVA | | | | | | |
| 12 | Source of Variation | SS | df | MS | F | P-value | F crit |
| 13 | Between Groups | 1.77 | 3 | 0.59 | 0.2068 | 0.8902 | 3.2389 |
| 14 | Within Groups | 45.648 | 16 | 2.853 | | | |
| 15 | | | | | | | |
| 16 | Total | 47.418 | 19 | | | | |

```
        Levene's Test (Any Continuous Distribution)
        Test statistic = 0.21, p-value = 0.890
```

From Figure 11.10 or 11.11, observe that $F_{STAT} = 0.2068$ (Excel labels this value "$F$" and Minitab calls it the "Test statistic.") Because $F_{STAT} = 0.2068 < 3.2389$ (or the $p$-value $= 0.8902 > 0.05$), you do not reject $H_0$. There is no evidence of a significant difference among the four variances. In other words, it is reasonable to assume that the materials from the four suppliers produce parachutes with an equal amount of variability. Therefore, the homogeneity-of-variance assumption for the ANOVA procedure is justified.

**EXAMPLE 11.1**    ANOVA OF THE SPEED OF DRIVE-THROUGH SERVICE AT FAST-FOOD CHAINS

For fast-food restaurants, the drive-through window is an increasing source of revenue. The chain that offers the fastest service is likely to attract additional customers. Each month QSR Magazine, **www.qsrmagazine.com**, publishes its results of drive-through service times (from menu board to departure) at fast-food chains. In a recent month, the mean time was 135.1 seconds for Wendy's, 156.2 seconds for Taco Bell, 163.9 seconds for McDonald's, 166 seconds for Burger King, and 173.2 seconds for KFC. Suppose the study was based on 20 customers for each fast-food chain and the ANOVA table given in Table 11.5 was developed.

**TABLE 11.5**

ANOVA Summary Table of Drive-Through Service Times at Fast-Food Chains

| Source | Degrees of Freedom | Sum of Squares | Mean Squares | F | p-Value |
|---|---|---|---|---|---|
| Among chains | 4 | 17,072.56 | 4,268.14 | 32.68 | 0.0000 |
| Within chains | 95 | 12,407.00 | 130.60 | | |

At the 0.05 level of significance, is there evidence of a difference in the mean drive-through service times of the five chains?

**SOLUTION**

$$H_0: \mu_1 = \mu_2 = \mu_3 = \mu_4 = \mu_5 \qquad \text{where } 1 = \text{Wendy's, } 2 = \text{Taco Bell, } 3 = \text{McDonald's,}$$
$$4 = \text{Burger King, } 5 = \text{KFC}$$
$$H_1: \text{Not all } \mu_j \text{ are equal} \qquad \text{where } j = 1, 2, 3, 4, 5$$

Decision rule: If $p$-value $< 0.05$, reject $H_0$. Because the $p$-value is virtually 0, which is less than $\alpha = 0.05$, reject $H_0$. You have sufficient evidence to conclude that the mean drive-through times of the five chains are not all equal.

To determine which of the means are significantly different from one another, use the Tukey-Kramer procedure [Equation (11.6) on page 452] to establish the critical range:

$$\text{Critical value of } Q \text{ with 5 and 95 degrees of freedom} \approx 3.92$$

$$\text{Critical range} = Q_\alpha \sqrt{\left(\frac{MSW}{2}\right)\left(\frac{1}{n_j} + \frac{1}{n_{j'}}\right)} = (3.92)\sqrt{\left(\frac{130.6}{2}\right)\left(\frac{1}{20} + \frac{1}{20}\right)}$$

$$= 10.02$$

Any observed difference greater than 10.02 is considered significant. The mean drive-through service times are different between Wendy's (mean of 135.1 seconds) and each of the other four chains. Also, the mean drive-through service time for Taco Bell is statistically different than KFC. Thus, with 95% confidence, you can conclude that the mean drive-through service time for Wendy's is faster than Taco Bell, McDonald's, Burger King, and KFC; Taco Bell is faster than KFC; and the other five differences between the mean drive-through service times are not statistically different.

# PROBLEMS FOR SECTION 11.1

## Learning the Basics

**11.1** An experiment has a single factor with five groups and seven values in each group.
a. How many degrees of freedom are there in determining the among-group variation?
b. How many degrees of freedom are there in determining the within-group variation?
c. How many degrees of freedom are there in determining the total variation?

**11.2** You are working with the same experiment as in Problem 11.1.
a. If $SSA = 60$ and $SST = 210$, what is $SSW$?
b. What is $MSA$?
c. What is $MSW$?
d. What is the value of $F_{STAT}$?

**11.3** You are working with the same experiment as in Problems 11.1 and 11.2.

a. Construct the ANOVA summary table and fill in all values in the table.
b. At the 0.05 level of significance, what is the upper-tail critical value from the $F$ distribution?
c. State the decision rule for testing the null hypothesis that all five groups have equal population means.
d. What is your statistical decision?

**11.4** Consider an experiment with three groups, with seven values in each.
a. How many degrees of freedom are there in determining the among-group variation?
b. How many degrees of freedom are there in determining the within-group variation?
c. How many degrees of freedom are there in determining the total variation?

**11.5** Consider an experiment with four groups, with eight values in each. For the ANOVA summary table at the top of page 458, fill in all the missing results:

| Source | Degrees of Freedom | Sum of Squares | Mean Square (Variance) | F |
|---|---|---|---|---|
| Among groups | $c - 1 = ?$ | $SSA = ?$ | $MSA = 80$ | $F_{STAT} = ?$ |
| Within groups | $n - c = ?$ | $SSW = 560$ | $MSW = ?$ | |
| Total | $n - 1 = ?$ | $SST = ?$ | | |

**11.6** You are working with the same experiment as in Problem 11.5.

a. At the 0.05 level of significance, state the decision rule for testing the null hypothesis that all four groups have equal population means.

b. What is your statistical decision?

c. At the 0.05 level of significance, what is the upper-tail critical value from the Studentized range distribution?

d. To perform the Tukey-Kramer procedure, what is the critical range?

## Applying the Concepts

**11.7** The Computer Anxiety Rating Scale (CARS) measures an individual's level of computer anxiety, on a scale from 20 (no anxiety) to 100 (highest level of anxiety). Researchers at Miami University administered CARS to 172 business students. One of the objectives of the study was to determine whether there are differences in the amount of computer anxiety experienced by students with different majors. They found the following:

| Source | Degrees of Freedom | Sum of Squares | Mean Squares | F |
|---|---|---|---|---|
| Among majors | 5 | 3,172 | | |
| Within majors | 166 | 21,246 | | |
| Total | 171 | 24,418 | | |

| Major | $n$ | Mean |
|---|---|---|
| Marketing | 19 | 44.37 |
| Management | 11 | 43.18 |
| Other | 14 | 42.21 |
| Finance | 45 | 41.80 |
| Accountancy | 36 | 37.56 |
| MIS | 47 | 32.21 |

Source: *Extracted from T. Broome and D. Havelka, "Determinants of Computer Anxiety in Business Students,"* The Review of Business Information Systems, *Spring 2002, 6(2), pp. 9–16.*

a. Complete the ANOVA summary table.

b. At the 0.05 level of significance, is there evidence of a difference in the mean computer anxiety experienced by different majors?

c. If the results in (b) indicate that it is appropriate, use the Tukey-Kramer procedure to determine which majors differ in mean computer anxiety. Discuss your findings.

**11.8** Periodically, *The Wall Street Journal* has conducted a stock-picking contest. The last one was conducted in March 2001. In this experiment, three different methods were used to select stocks that were expected to perform well during the next five months. Four Wall Street professionals, considered experts on picking stocks, each selected one stock. Four randomly chosen readers of the *Wall Street Journal* each selected one stock. Finally, four stocks were selected by flinging darts at a table containing a list of stocks. The returns of the selected stocks for March 20, 2001, to August 31, 2001 (in percentage return), are given in the following table and stored in the file `Contest2001`. Note that during this period, the Dow Jones Industrial Average gained 2.4% (extracted from G. Jasen, "In Picking Stocks, Dartboard Beats the Pros," *The Wall Street Journal*, September 27, 2001, pp. C1, C10).

| Experts | Readers | Darts |
|---|---|---|
| +39.5 | −31.0 | +39.0 |
| −1.1 | −20.7 | +31.9 |
| −4.5 | −45.0 | +14.1 |
| −8.0 | −73.3 | +5.4 |

a. Is there evidence of a significant difference in the mean return for the three categories? (Use $\alpha = 0.05$.)

b. If appropriate, determine which categories differ in mean return.

c. Comment on the validity of the inference implied by the title of the article, which suggests that the dartboard was better than the professionals.

d. Is there evidence of a significant difference in the variation in the returns for the three categories? (Use $\alpha = 0.05$.)

**11.9** A hospital conducted a study of the waiting time in its emergency room. The hospital has a main campus and three satellite locations. Management had a business objective of reducing waiting time for emergency room cases that did not require immediate attention. To study this, a random sample of 15 emergency room cases at each location were selected on a particular day, and the waiting time (measured from check-in to when the patient was called into the clinic area) was measured. The results are stored in the file `ERwaiting`.

a. At the 0.05 level of significance, is there evidence of a difference in the mean waiting times in the four locations?

b. If appropriate, determine which locations differ in mean waiting time.

c. At the 0.05 level of significance, is there evidence of a difference in the variation in waiting time among the four locations?

✓ **SELF Test** **11.10** Students in a business statistics course performed a completely randomized design to test the strength of four brands of trash bags. One-pound weights were placed into a bag, one at a time, until the bag broke. A total of 40 bags, 10 for each brand, were used. The data in the file `Trashbags` give the weight (in pounds) required to break the trash bags.

a. At the 0.05 level of significance, is there evidence of a difference in the mean strength of the four brands of trash bags?

b. If appropriate, determine which brands differ in mean strength.

c. At the 0.05 level of significance, is there evidence of a difference in the variation in strength among the four brands of trash bags?

d. Which brand(s) should you buy and which brand(s) should you avoid? Explain.

**11.11** The following data (stored in the file `CDyield`) represent the nationwide highest yield of different types of accounts (extracted from **Bankrate.com**, March 6, 2007):

| Money Market | Six-Month CD | One-Year CD | 2.5-Year CD | Five-Year CD |
|---|---|---|---|---|
| 5.21 | 5.50 | 5.41 | 5.35 | 5.35 |
| 5.19 | 5.44 | 5.40 | 5.25 | 5.30 |
| 5.20 | 5.40 | 5.40 | 5.20 | 5.25 |
| 5.16 | 5.40 | 5.40 | 5.20 | 5.25 |
| 5.12 | 5.39 | 5.39 | 5.15 | 5.22 |

a. At the 0.05 level of significance, is there evidence of a difference in the mean yields of the different accounts?

b. If appropriate, determine which accounts differ in mean yields.

c. At the 0.05 level of significance, is there evidence of a difference in the variation in yields among the different accounts?

d. What effect does your result in (c) have on the validity of the results in (a) and (b)?

**11.12** An advertising agency has been hired by a manufacturer of pens to develop an advertising campaign for the upcoming holiday season. To prepare for this project, the research director decides to initiate a study of the effect of advertising on product perception. An experiment is designed to compare five different advertisements. Advertisement *A* greatly undersells the pen's characteristics. Advertisement *B* slightly undersells the pen's characteristics. Advertisement *C* slightly oversells the pen's characteristics. Advertisement *D* greatly oversells the pen's characteristics. Advertisement *E* attempts to correctly state the pen's characteristics. A sample of 30 adult respondents, taken from a larger focus group, is randomly assigned to the five advertisements (so that there are six respondents to each). After reading the advertisement and developing a sense of "product expectation," all respondents unknowingly receive the same pen to evaluate. The respondents are permitted to test the pen and the plausibility of the advertising copy. The respondents are then asked to rate the pen from 1 to 7 (lowest to highest) on the product characteristic scales of appearance, durability, and writing performance. The *combined* scores of three ratings (appearance, durability, and writing performance) for the 30 respondents (stored in the file `Pen`) are as follows:

| A | B | C | D | E |
|---|---|---|---|---|
| 15 | 16 | 8 | 5 | 12 |
| 18 | 17 | 7 | 6 | 19 |
| 17 | 21 | 10 | 13 | 18 |
| 19 | 16 | 15 | 11 | 12 |
| 19 | 19 | 14 | 9 | 17 |
| 20 | 17 | 14 | 10 | 14 |

a. At the 0.05 level of significance, is there evidence of a difference in the mean rating of the five advertisements?

b. If appropriate, determine which advertisements differ in mean ratings.

c. At the 0.05 level of significance, is there evidence of a difference in the variation in ratings among the five advertisements?

d. Which advertisement(s) should you use and which advertisement(s) should you avoid? Explain.

**11.13** The retailing manager of a supermarket chain wants to determine whether product location has any effect on the sale of pet toys. Three different aisle locations are considered: front, middle, and rear. A random sample of 18 stores is selected, with 6 stores randomly assigned to each aisle location. The size of the display area and price of the product are constant for all stores. At the end of a one-month trial period, the sales volumes (in thousands of dollars) of the product in each store were as follows (and are stored in the file `Locate`).

| Aisle Location | | |
|---|---|---|
| **Front** | **Middle** | **Rear** |
| 8.6 | 3.2 | 4.6 |
| 7.2 | 2.4 | 6.0 |
| 5.4 | 2.0 | 4.0 |
| 6.2 | 1.4 | 2.8 |
| 5.0 | 1.8 | 2.2 |
| 4.0 | 1.6 | 2.8 |

**a.** At the 0.05 level of significance, is there evidence of a significant difference in mean sales among the various aisle locations?

**b.** If appropriate, which aisle locations appear to differ significantly in mean sales?

**c.** At the 0.05 level of significance, is there evidence of a significant difference in the variation in sales among the various aisle locations?

**d.** What should the retailing manager conclude? Fully describe the retailing manager's options with respect to aisle locations.

**11.14** A sporting goods manufacturing company wanted to compare the distance traveled by golf balls produced using each of four different designs. Ten balls were manufactured with each design and were brought to the local golf course for the club professional to test. The order in which the balls were hit with the same club from the first tee was randomized so that the pro did not know which type of ball was being hit. All 40 balls were hit in a short period of time, during which the environmental conditions were essentially the same. The results (distance traveled in yards) for the four designs were as follows (and are stored in the file Golfball):

| Design | | | |
|---|---|---|---|
| 1 | 2 | 3 | 4 |
| 206.32 | 217.08 | 226.77 | 230.55 |
| 207.94 | 221.43 | 224.79 | 227.95 |
| 206.19 | 218.04 | 229.75 | 231.84 |
| 204.45 | 224.13 | 228.51 | 224.87 |
| 209.65 | 211.82 | 221.44 | 229.49 |
| 203.81 | 213.90 | 223.85 | 231.10 |
| 206.75 | 221.28 | 223.97 | 221.53 |
| 205.68 | 229.43 | 234.30 | 235.45 |
| 204.49 | 213.54 | 219.50 | 228.35 |
| 210.86 | 214.51 | 233.00 | 225.09 |

**a.** At the 0.05 level of significance, is there evidence of a difference in the mean distances traveled by the golf balls with different designs?

**b.** If the results in (a) indicate that it is appropriate, use the Tukey-Kramer procedure to determine which designs differ in mean distances.

**c.** What assumptions are necessary in (a)?

**d.** At the 0.05 level of significance, is there evidence of a difference in the variation of the distances traveled by the golf balls with different designs?

**e.** What golf ball design should the manufacturing manager choose? Explain.

## 11.2   THE RANDOMIZED BLOCK DESIGN

In Section 11.1, you used the one-way ANOVA *F* test to evaluate differences among the means of more than two independent groups. In Section 10.2 you used the paired *t* test when you had repeated measurements or matched samples in order to evaluate the difference between the means of two groups. In this section, a method to analyze more than two groups using repeated measures or matched samples is developed. The heterogeneous sets of items or individuals that have been matched (or on whom repeated measurements have been taken) are called **blocks**. Experimental situations that use blocks are called **randomized block designs**.

Although groups and blocks are both used in a randomized block design, the focus of the analysis is on the differences among the different groups. As is the case in completely randomized designs, groups are often different levels pertaining to a factor of interest. The purpose of blocking is to remove as much variability as possible from the random error so that the differences among the groups are more evident. A randomized block design is often more efficient statistically than a completely randomized design and therefore produces more precise results (see references 9 and 10). For example, if the factor of interest is advertising medium, three groups could be subject to the following different levels: television, radio, and newspaper. Different cities could be used as blocks. The variability among the different cities is therefore removed from the random error in order to better detect differences among the three advertising mediums.

To compare a completely randomized design with a randomized block design, return to the Using Statistics scenario on page 444 concerning Perfect Parachutes. Suppose that a completely randomized design is used with 12 parachutes woven during a 24-hour period. Any variability among the shifts of workers becomes part of the random error, and therefore differences among the four suppliers might be hard to detect. To reduce the random error, a randomized block experiment is designed where three shifts of workers are used and four parachutes are woven during each shift (one parachute using fibers from Supplier 1, one parachute using fibers from Supplier 2, etc.). The three shifts are considered blocks, but the factor of interest is still the four suppliers. The advantage of the randomized block design is that the variability among the three shifts is removed from the random error. Therefore, this design should provide more precise results concerning differences among the four suppliers.

## Testing for Factor and Block Effects

Recall from Figure 11.1 on page 445 that, in the completely randomized design, the total variation (*SST*) is subdivided into variation due to differences *among* the *c* groups (*SSA*) and variation due to variation *within* the *c* groups (*SSW*). Within-group variation is considered random variation, and among-group variation is due to differences from group to group.

To remove the effects of the blocking from the random variation component in the randomized block design, the within-group variation (*SSW*) is subdivided into variation due to differences among the blocks (*SSBL*) and random variation (*SSE*). Therefore, as presented in Figure 11.12, in a randomized block design, the total variation is the sum of three components— among-group variation (*SSA*), among-block variation (*SSBL*), and random variation (*SSE*).

**FIGURE 11.12**

Partitioning the total variation in a randomized block design model

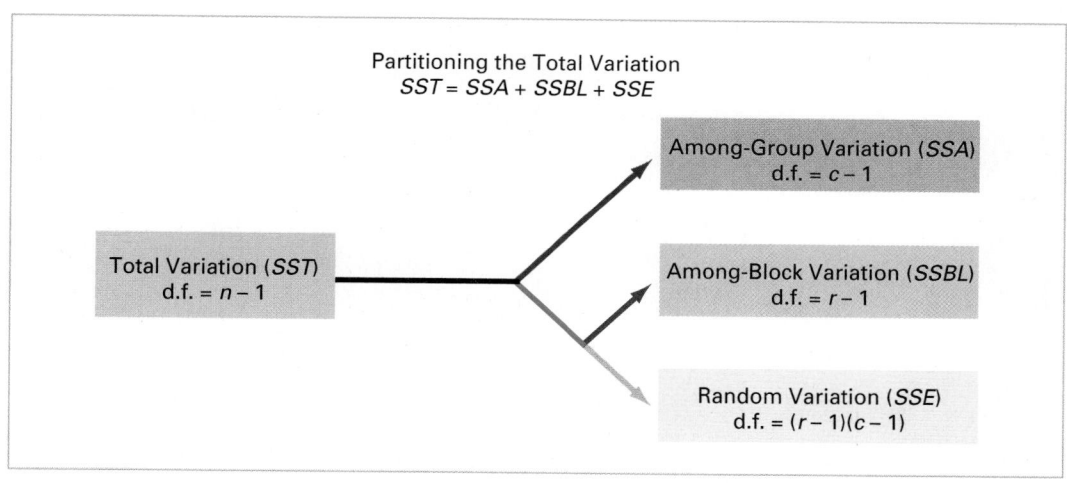

The following definitions are needed to develop the ANOVA procedure for the randomized block design:

$$r = \text{the number of blocks}$$

$$c = \text{the number of groups}$$

$$n = \text{the total number of values (where } n = rc)$$

$$X_{ij} = \text{the value of the } i\text{th block for the } j\text{th group}$$

$$\bar{X}_{i.} = \text{the mean of all the values in block } i$$

$$\bar{X}_{.j} = \text{the mean of all the values for group } j$$

$$\sum_{j=1}^{c}\sum_{i=1}^{r} X_{ij} = \text{the grand total}$$

The total variation, also called sum of squares total (*SST*), is a measure of the variation among all the values. You compute *SST* by summing the squared differences between each individual value and the grand mean $\bar{\bar{X}}$ that is based on all *n* values. Equation (11.7) shows the computation for total variation.

---

**Total Variation in the Randomized Block Design**

$$SST = \sum_{j=1}^{c} \sum_{i=1}^{r} (X_{ij} - \bar{\bar{X}})^2 \qquad \textbf{(11.7)}$$

where

$$\bar{\bar{X}} = \frac{\sum_{j=1}^{c} \sum_{i=1}^{r} X_{ij}}{rc} \quad \text{(i.e., the grand mean)}$$

---

You compute the among-group variation, also called the sum of squares among groups (*SSA*), by summing the squared differences between the sample mean of each group $\bar{X}_{.j}$ and the grand mean $\bar{\bar{X}}$, weighted by the number of blocks *r*. Equation (11.8) shows the computation for the among-group variation.

---

**Among-Group Variation in the Randomized Block Design**

$$SSA = r \sum_{j=1}^{c} (\bar{X}_{.j} - \bar{\bar{X}})^2 \qquad \textbf{(11.8)}$$

where

$$\bar{X}_{.j} = \frac{\sum_{i=1}^{r} X_{ij}}{r}$$

---

You compute the **among-block variation**, also called the **sum of squares among blocks (SSBL)**, by summing the squared differences between the mean of each block $\bar{X}_{i.}$ and the grand mean $\bar{\bar{X}}$, weighted by the number of groups *c*. Equation (11.9) shows the computation for the among-block variation.

---

**Among-Block Variation in the Randomized Block Design**

$$SSBL = c \sum_{i=1}^{r} (\bar{X}_{i.} - \bar{\bar{X}})^2 \qquad \textbf{(11.9)}$$

where

$$\bar{X}_{i.} = \frac{\sum_{j=1}^{c} X_{ij}}{c}$$

You compute the random variation, also called the **sum of squares error (SSE)**, by summing the squared differences among all the values after the effect of the groups and blocks have been accounted for. Equation (11.10) shows the computation for random variation.

Random Variation in the Randomized Block Design

$$SSE = \sum_{j=1}^{c} \sum_{i=1}^{r} (X_{ij} - \bar{X}_{.j} - \bar{X}_{i.} + \bar{\bar{X}})^2 \qquad \textbf{(11.10)}$$

Because you are comparing $c$ groups, there are $c - 1$ degrees of freedom associated with the sum of squares among groups ($SSA$). Similarly, because there are $r$ blocks, there are $r - 1$ degrees of freedom associated with the sum of squares among blocks ($SSBL$). Moreover, there are $n - 1$ degrees of freedom associated with the sum of squares total ($SST$) because you are comparing each value $X_{ij}$ to the grand mean $\bar{\bar{X}}$ based on all $n$ values. Therefore, because the degrees of freedom for each of the sources of variation must add to the degrees of freedom for the total variation, you compute the degrees of freedom for the sum of squares error ($SSE$) component by subtraction and algebraic manipulation. Thus, the degrees of freedom associated with the sum of squares error is $(r - 1)(c - 1)$.

If you divide each of the component sum of squares by its associated degrees of freedom, you have the three *variances* or mean square terms ($MSA$, $MSBL$, and $MSE$). Equations (11.11a–c) give the mean square terms needed for the ANOVA table.

The Mean Squares in the Randomized Block Design

$$MSA = \frac{SSA}{c - 1} \qquad \textbf{(11.11a)}$$

$$MSBL = \frac{SSBL}{r - 1} \qquad \textbf{(11.11b)}$$

$$MSE = \frac{SSE}{(r - 1)(c - 1)} \qquad \textbf{(11.11c)}$$

The first step in analyzing a randomized block design is to test for a factor effect, that is, to test for any differences among the $c$ group means. If the assumptions of the analysis of variance are valid, the null hypothesis of no differences in the $c$ group means:

$$H_0: \mu_{.1} = \mu_{.2} = \cdots = \mu_{.c}$$

is tested against the alternative that not all the $c$ group means are equal:

$$H_1: \text{Not all } \mu_{.j} \text{ are equal (where } j = 1, 2, \ldots, c)$$

by computing the $F_{STAT}$ test statistic given in Equation (11.12).

$F_{STAT}$ Test Statistic for Factor Effect

$$F_{STAT} = \frac{MSA}{MSE} \qquad \textbf{(11.12)}$$

The $F_{STAT}$ test statistic follows an $F$ distribution with $c - 1$ degrees of freedom for the $MSA$ term and $(r - 1)(c - 1)$ degrees of freedom for the $MSE$ term. For a given level of significance $\alpha$, you reject the null hypothesis if the computed $F_{STAT}$ test statistic is greater than the upper-tail critical value $F_\alpha$ from the $F$ distribution with $c - 1$ and $(r - 1)(c - 1)$ degrees of freedom (see Table E.5). The decision rule is:

$$\text{Reject } H_0 \text{ if } F_{STAT} > F_\alpha;$$
$$\text{otherwise do not reject } H_0.$$

To examine whether the randomized block design was advantageous to use, some statisticians suggest that you perform the $F$ test for block effects. The null hypothesis of no block effects:

$$H_0: \mu_{1.} = \mu_{2.} = \cdots = \mu_{r.}$$

is tested against the alternative:

$$H_1: \text{Not all } \mu_{i.} \text{ are equal (where } i = 1, 2, \ldots, r)$$

using the $F_{STAT}$ test statistic for block effect given in Equation (11.13).

---

$F_{STAT}$ **Test Statistic for Block Effect**

$$F_{STAT} = \frac{MSBL}{MSE} \tag{11.13}$$

---

You reject the null hypothesis at the $\alpha$ level of significance if the computed $F_{STAT}$ test statistic is greater than the upper-tail critical value $F_\alpha$ from the $F$ distribution with $r - 1$ and $(r - 1)(c - 1)$ degrees of freedom (see Table E.5). That is, the decision rule is:

$$\text{Reject } H_0 \text{ if } F_{STAT} > F_\alpha;$$
$$\text{otherwise do not reject } H_0.$$

The results of the analysis-of-variance procedure are usually displayed in an ANOVA summary table as shown in Table 11.6.

**TABLE 11.6**

Analysis-of-Variance Table for the Randomized Block Design

| Source | Degrees of Freedom | Sum of Squares | Mean Square (Variance) | F |
|---|---|---|---|---|
| Among blocks | $r - 1$ | $SSBL$ | $MSBL = \dfrac{SSBL}{r - 1}$ | $F_{STAT} = \dfrac{MSBL}{MSE}$ |
| Among groups | $c - 1$ | $SSA$ | $MSA = \dfrac{SSA}{c - 1}$ | $F_{STAT} = \dfrac{MSA}{MSE}$ |
| Error | $(r - 1)(c - 1)$ | $SSE$ | $MSE = \dfrac{SSE}{(r - 1)(c - 1)}$ | |
| Total | $rc - 1$ | $SST$ | | |

To illustrate the randomized block design, suppose that a fast-food chain wants to evaluate the service at four restaurants. The customer service director for the chain hires six evaluators with varied experiences in food-service evaluations to act as raters. To reduce the effect of the variability from rater-to-rater, you use a randomized block design with raters serving as the blocks. The four restaurants are the groups of interest.

The six raters evaluate the service at each of the four restaurants in a random order. A rating scale from 0 (low) to 100 (high) is used. Table 11.7 summarizes the results (stored in the file **FFChain**), along with the group totals, group means, block totals, block means, grand total, and grand mean.

**TABLE 11.7**

Ratings at Four Restaurants of a Fast-Food Chain

| Raters | A | B | C | D | Totals | Means |
|---|---|---|---|---|---|---|
| | | | Restaurants | | | |
| 1 | 70 | 61 | 82 | 74 | 287 | 71.75 |
| 2 | 77 | 75 | 88 | 76 | 316 | 79.00 |
| 3 | 76 | 67 | 90 | 80 | 313 | 78.25 |
| 4 | 80 | 63 | 96 | 76 | 315 | 78.75 |
| 5 | 84 | 66 | 92 | 84 | 326 | 81.50 |
| 6 | 78 | 68 | 98 | 86 | 330 | 82.50 |
| Totals | 465 | 400 | 546 | 476 | 1,887 | |
| Means | 77.50 | 66.67 | 91.00 | 79.33 | 78.625 | |

In addition, from Table 11.7,

$$r = 6 \quad c = 4 \quad n = rc = 24$$

and,

$$\overline{\overline{X}} = \frac{\sum_{j=1}^{c}\sum_{i=1}^{r} X_{ij}}{rc} = \frac{1,887}{24} = 78.625$$

Figures 11.13 and 11.14 present Microsoft Excel and Minitab results for this randomized block design.

**FIGURE 11.13**

Microsoft Excel randomized block design results for the fast-food chain study

*See Section E11.3 to create this.*

| | A | B | C | D | E | F | G |
|---|---|---|---|---|---|---|---|
| 1 | Anova: Two-Factor Without Replication | | | | | | |
| 2 | | | | | | | |
| 3 | SUMMARY | Count | Sum | Average | Variance | | |
| 4 | Rater 1 | 4 | 287 | 71.75 | 76.25 | | |
| 5 | Rater 2 | 4 | 316 | 79.00 | 36.67 | | |
| 6 | Rater 3 | 4 | 313 | 78.25 | 90.92 | | |
| 7 | Rater 4 | 4 | 315 | 78.75 | 184.92 | | |
| 8 | Rater 5 | 4 | 326 | 81.50 | 121.00 | | |
| 9 | Rater 6 | 4 | 330 | 82.50 | 161.00 | | |
| 10 | | | | | | | |
| 11 | Restaurant A | 6 | 465 | 77.50 | 21.50 | | |
| 12 | Restaurant B | 6 | 400 | 66.67 | 23.47 | | |
| 13 | Restaurant C | 6 | 546 | 91.00 | 33.20 | | |
| 14 | Restaurant D | 6 | 476 | 79.33 | 23.47 | | |
| 15 | | | | | | | |
| 16 | | | | | | | |
| 17 | ANOVA | | | | | | |
| 18 | Source of Variation | SS | df | MS | F | P-value | F crit |
| 19 | Rows | 283.375 | 5 | 56.675 | 3.782 | 0.020 | 2.901 |
| 20 | Columns | 1787.458333 | 3 | 595.819 | 39.758 | 0.000 | 3.287 |
| 21 | Error | 224.792 | 15 | 14.986 | | | |
| 22 | | | | | | | |
| 23 | Total | 2295.625 | 23 | | | | |

**FIGURE 11.14**

Minitab results for the fast-food chain study

*See Section M11.4 to create this.*

```
Source    DF       SS        MS       F      P
Raters     5   283.38    56.675    3.78  0.020
Restrat    3  1787.46   595.819   39.76  0.000
Error     15   224.79    14.986
Total     23  2295.63

S = 3.871   R-Sq = 90.21%   R-Sq(adj) = 84.99%
                Individual 95% CIs For Mean Based on Pooled StDev
Raters   Mean   -----+---------+---------+---------+----
1       71.75  (--------*-------)
2       79.00                   (-------*-------)
3       78.25               (--------*-------)
4       78.75               (--------*-------)
5       81.50                      (-------*-------)
6       82.50                        (-------*-------)
                -----+---------+---------+---------+----
                  70.0      75.0      80.0      85.0
                Individual 95% CIs For Mean Based on Pooled StDev
Restrat   Mean   -+---------+---------+---------+--------
A       77.5000                    (---*---)
B       66.6667   (---*----)
C       91.0000                              (---*---)
D       79.3333                  (---*---)
```

Using the 0.05 level of significance to test for differences among the restaurants, you reject the null hypothesis ($H_0$: $\mu_{.1} = \mu_{.2} = \mu_{.3} = \mu_{.4}$) if the computed $F_{STAT}$ test statistic is greater than 3.29, the upper-tail critical value from the $F$ distribution with 3 and 15 degrees of freedom in the numerator and denominator, respectively (see Figure 11.15). Because $F_{STAT} = 39.758 > F_\alpha = 3.29$, or because the $p$-value = 0.000 < 0.05, you reject $H_0$ and conclude that there is evidence of a difference in the mean ratings among the different restaurants. The extremely small $p$-value indicates that if the means from the four restaurants are equal, there is virtually no chance that you will get differences as large or larger among the sample means as observed in this study. Thus, there is little degree of belief in the null hypothesis. You conclude that the alternative hypothesis is correct, the mean ratings among the four restaurants are different.

**FIGURE 11.15**

Regions of rejection and nonrejection for the fast-food chain study at the 0.05 level of significance with 3 and 15 degrees of freedom

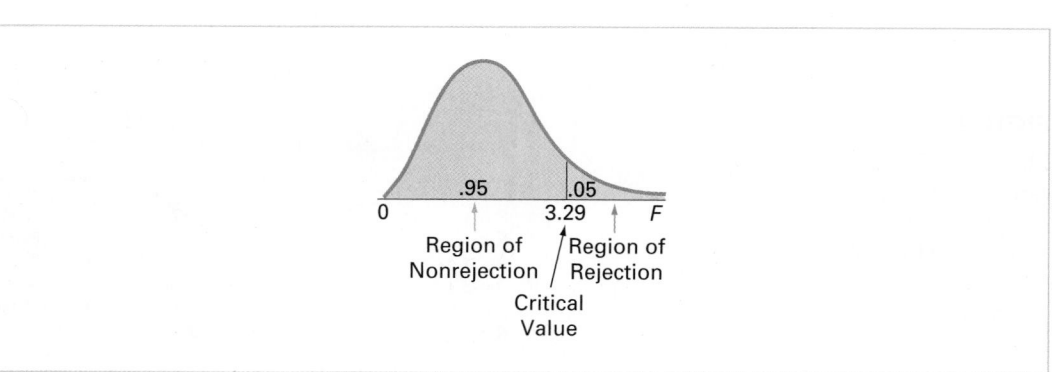

As a check on the effectiveness of blocking, you can test for a difference among the raters. The decision rule, using the 0.05 level of significance, is to reject the null hypothesis ($H_0$: $\mu_{1.} = \mu_{2.} = \cdots = \mu_{6.}$) if the computed $F_{STAT}$ test statistic is greater than 2.90, the upper-tail critical value from the $F$ distribution with 5 and 15 degrees of freedom (see Figure 11.16). Because $F_{STAT} = 3.782 > F_\alpha = 2.90$ or because the $p$-value = 0.02 < 0.05, you reject $H_0$ and conclude that there is evidence of a difference among the raters. Thus, you conclude that the blocking has been advantageous in reducing the random error.

**FIGURE 11.16**

Regions of rejection and nonrejection for the fast-food chain study at the 0.05 level of significance with 5 and 15 degrees of freedom

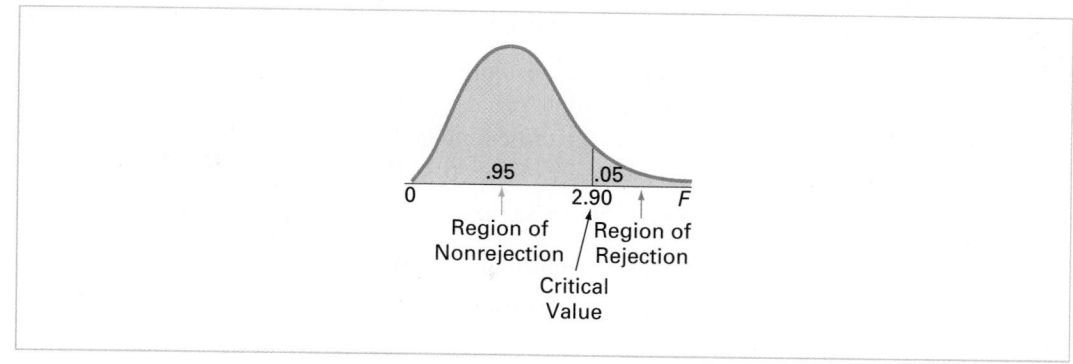

The assumptions of the one-way analysis of variance discussed on page 454 (randomness and independence, normality, and homogeneity of variance) also apply to the randomized block design. If the normality assumption is violated, you can use the Friedman rank test discussed in Section 12.9. In addition, you need to assume that there is no *interacting effect* between the groups and the blocks. In other words, you need to assume that any differences between the groups (the restaurants) are consistent across the entire set of blocks (the raters). The concept of *interaction* is discussed further in Section 11.3.

Did the blocking result in an increase in precision in comparing the different groups? To answer this question, use Equation (11.14) to calculate the **estimated relative efficiency (RE)** of the randomized block design as compared with the completely randomized design.

**Estimated Relative Efficiency**

$$RE = \frac{(r-1)MSBL + r(c-1)MSE}{(rc-1)MSE} \qquad \textbf{(11.14)}$$

Using Figure 11.13 or Figure 11.14,

$$RE = \frac{(5)(56.675) + (6)(3)(14.986)}{(23)(14.986)} = 1.60$$

This value for relative efficiency means that it would take 1.6 times as many observations in a one-way ANOVA design as compared to the randomized block design in order to have the same precision in comparing the restaurants.

## Multiple Comparisons: The Tukey Procedure

As in the case of the completely randomized design, once you reject the null hypothesis of no differences between the groups, you need to determine *which* groups are significantly different from the others. For the randomized block design, you can use a procedure developed by Tukey (see references 9 and 10). Equation (11.15) gives the critical range for the **Tukey multiple comparisons procedure for randomized block designs**.

**The Critical Range for the Randomized Block Design**

$$\text{Critical range} = Q_\alpha \sqrt{\frac{MSE}{r}} \qquad \textbf{(11.15)}$$

where $Q_\alpha$ is the upper-tail critical value from a Studentized range distribution having $c$ degrees of freedom in the numerator and $(r-1)(c-1)$ degrees of freedom in the denominator. Values for the Studentized range distribution are found in Table E.10.

To perform the multiple comparisons, you do the following:

1. Compute the absolute mean differences, $|\bar{X}_{.j} - \bar{X}_{.j'}|$, (where $j \neq j'$), among all $c(c-1)/2$ pairs of sample means.
2. Compute the critical range for the Tukey procedure using Equation (11.15).
3. Compare each of the $c(c-1)/2$ pairs against the critical range. If the absolute difference in a specific pair of sample means, say $|\bar{X}_{.j} - \bar{X}_{.j'}|$, is greater than the critical range, then group $j$ and group $j'$ are significantly different.
4. Interpret the results.

To apply the Tukey procedure, return to the fast-food chain study. Because there are four restaurants, there are $4(4-1)/2 = 6$ possible pairwise comparisons. From Figure 11.13 or Figure 11.14 on pages 465–466, the absolute mean differences are

1. $|\bar{X}_{.1} - \bar{X}_{.2}| = |77.50 - 66.67| = 10.83$
2. $|\bar{X}_{.1} - \bar{X}_{.3}| = |77.50 - 91.00| = 13.50$
3. $|\bar{X}_{.1} - \bar{X}_{.4}| = |77.50 - 79.33| = 1.83$
4. $|\bar{X}_{.2} - \bar{X}_{.3}| = |66.67 - 91.00| = 24.33$
5. $|\bar{X}_{.2} - \bar{X}_{.4}| = |66.67 - 79.33| = 12.66$
6. $|\bar{X}_{.3} - \bar{X}_{.4}| = |91.00 - 79.33| = 11.67$

Locate $MSE = 14.986$ and $r = 6$ in Figure 11.13 or Figure 11.14 on pages 465–466 to determine the critical range. From Table E.10 [for $\alpha = .05$, $c = 4$, and $(r-1)(c-1) = 15$], $Q_\alpha$, the upper-tail critical value of the test statistic with 4 and 15 degrees of freedom, is 4.08. Using Equation (11.15),

$$\text{Critical range} = 4.08 \sqrt{\frac{14.986}{6}} = 6.448$$

All pairwise comparisons except $|\bar{X}_{.1} - \bar{X}_{.4}|$ are greater than the critical range. Therefore, you conclude with 95% confidence that there is evidence of a significant difference in the mean rating between all pairs of restaurant branches except for branches $A$ and $D$. In addition, branch $C$ has the highest ratings (i.e., is most preferred) and branch $B$ has the lowest (i.e., is least preferred).

# PROBLEMS FOR SECTION 11.2

## Learning the Basics

**11.15** Given a randomized block experiment with five groups and seven blocks, answer the following.
a. How many degrees of freedom are there in determining the among-group variation?
b. How many degrees of freedom are there in determining the among-block variation?
c. How many degrees of freedom are there in determining the random variation?
d. How many degrees of freedom are there in determining the total variation?

**11.16** From Problem 11.15:
a. If $SSA = 60$, $SSBL = 75$, and $SST = 210$, what is $SSE$?
b. What are $MSA$, $MSBL$, and $MSE$?
c. What is the value of the $F_{STAT}$ test statistic for the factor effect?
d. What is the value of the $F_{STAT}$ test statistic for the block effect?

**11.17** From Problems 11.15 and 11.16:
a. Construct the ANOVA summary table and fill in all values in the body of the table.

**b.** At the 0.05 level of significance, is there evidence of a difference in the group means?

**c.** At the 0.05 level of significance, is there evidence of a difference due to blocks?

**11.18** From Problems 11.15, 11.16, and 11.17:

**a.** To perform the Tukey procedure, how many degrees of freedom are there in the numerator and how many degrees of freedom are there in the denominator of the Studentized range distribution?

**b.** At the 0.05 level of significance, what is the upper-tail critical value from the Studentized range distribution?

**c.** To perform the Tukey procedure, what is the critical range?

**11.19** Given a randomized block experiment with three groups and seven blocks:

**a.** How many degrees of freedom are there in determining the among-group variation?

**b.** How many degrees of freedom are there in determining the among-block variation?

**c.** How many degrees of freedom are there in determining the random variation?

**d.** How many degrees of freedom are there in determining the total variation?

**11.20** From Problem 11.19, if $SSA = 36$ and the randomized block $F_{STAT}$ statistic is 6.0:

**a.** What are $MSE$ and $SSE$?

**b.** What is $SSBL$ if the $F_{STAT}$ test statistic for block effect is 4.0?

**c.** What is $SST$?

**d.** At the 0.01 level of significance, is there evidence of an effect due to groups and is there evidence of an effect due to blocks?

**11.21** Given a randomized block experiment with four groups and eight blocks, from the ANOVA summary table below, fill in all the missing results.

| Source | Degrees of Freedom | Sum of Squares | Mean Square (Variance) | F |
|---|---|---|---|---|
| Among groups | $c - 1 = ?$ | $SSA = ?$ | $MSA = 80$ | $F_{STAT} = ?$ |
| Among blocks | $r - 1 = ?$ | $SSBL = 540$ | $MSBL = ?$ | $F_{STAT} = 5.0$ |
| Error | $(r-1)(c-1) = ?$ | $SSE = ?$ | $MSE = ?$ | |
| Total | $rc - 1 = ?$ | $SST = ?$ | | |

**11.22** From Problem 11.21:

**a.** At the 0.05 level of significance, is there evidence of a difference among the four group means?

**b.** At the 0.05 level of significance, is there evidence of an effect due to blocks?

## Applying the Concepts

**11.23** Nine experts rated four brands of Colombian coffee in a taste-testing experiment. A rating on a 7-point scale (1 = extremely unpleasing, 7 = extremely pleasing) is given for each of four characteristics: taste, aroma, richness, and acidity. The following data (stored in the file **Coffee**) displays the summated ratings—accumulated over all four characteristics.

| EXPERT | BRAND | | | |
|---|---|---|---|---|
| | **A** | **B** | **C** | **D** |
| C.C. | 24 | 26 | 25 | 22 |
| S.E. | 27 | 27 | 26 | 24 |
| E.G. | 19 | 22 | 20 | 16 |
| B.L. | 24 | 27 | 25 | 23 |
| C.M. | 22 | 25 | 22 | 21 |
| C.N. | 26 | 27 | 24 | 24 |
| G.N. | 27 | 26 | 22 | 23 |
| R.M. | 25 | 27 | 24 | 21 |
| P.V. | 22 | 23 | 20 | 19 |

At the 0.05 level of significance, completely analyze the data to determine whether there is evidence of a difference in the summated ratings of the four brands of Colombian coffee and, if so, which of the brands are rated highest (i.e., best). What can you conclude?

**11.24** Many U.S. citizens have turned to online pharmacies originating from Canada in an attempt to save money on their prescription drugs. The following table (see the file **RXdrugs**) contains 10 commonly purchased prescription drugs along with their prices (in U.S. dollars) from two online pharmacies in the United States and at Aptecha, the largest Canadian online pharmacy.

| Drug | U.S. #1 | U.S. #2 | Aptecha |
|---|---|---|---|
| Celebrex | 235.54 | 269.99 | 121.02 |
| Detrol LA | 157.99 | 190.99 | 55.30 |
| Flomax | 166.00 | 190.99 | 93.45 |
| Lipitor | 174.99 | 200.99 | 137.70 |
| Novaldex | 108.60 | 129.99 | 22.48 |
| Norvasc | 186.66 | 203.99 | 161.93 |
| Plavix | 107.99 | 106.99 | 64.53 |
| Prevacid | 117.39 | 134.99 | 59.83 |
| Prilosec | 115.99 | 126.99 | 57.75 |
| Zyrtec | 181.10 | 200.99 | 58.79 |

Source: *Extracted from P. Rosson, "Buying and Selling Prescription Drugs on the Internet: Canada–United States Trade,"* Journal of Electronic Commerce in Organizations, *2(4), Oct–Nov 2004, pp. 47–62.*

*(continued)*

**a.** At the 0.05 level of significance, determine if there is evidence of a difference in the mean prices of prescription drugs at the three online pharmacies.

**b.** If appropriate, use the Tukey procedure to determine which pharmacies' mean prices differ. Again, use a 0.05 level of significance.

**11.25** An article discussed the new Whole Foods Market in the Time-Warner building in New York City (W. Grimes, "A Pleasure Palace Without the Guilt," *The New York Times*, February 18, 2004, pp. F1, F5). The following data (stored in the file **Wholefoods2**) compared the price of some kitchen staples at the new Whole Foods Market, at the Gristede's supermarket, at the Fairway supermarket (both located about 15 blocks from the Time-Warner building), and at a Stop & Shop supermarket located in an outer borough of New York City.

| Item | Whole Foods | Gristede's | Fair-way | Stop & Shop |
|---|---|---|---|---|
| Half-gallon milk | 2.19 | 1.59 | 1.35 | 1.89 |
| Dozen eggs | 2.39 | 1.59 | 1.69 | 2.29 |
| Tropicana orange juice (64 oz.) | 2.00 | 2.99 | 2.49 | 2.00 |
| Head of Boston lettuce | 1.98 | 1.49 | 1.29 | 1.29 |
| Ground round 1 lb. | 4.99 | 3.99 | 3.69 | 3.59 |
| Bumble Bee tuna 6 oz. can | 1.79 | 0.79 | 1.33 | 1.50 |
| Granny Smith apples (1 lb.) | 1.69 | 1.99 | 1.49 | 0.99 |
| Box DeCecco linguini | 1.99 | 1.50 | 1.59 | 1.79 |
| Salmon steak 1 lb. | 7.99 | 4.99 | 5.99 | 5.99 |
| Whole chicken per pound | 2.19 | 1.19 | 1.49 | 1.49 |

Source: *Extracted from W. Grimes, "A Pleasure Palace Without the Guilt," The New York Times, February 18, 2004, pp. F1, F5.*

**a.** At the 0.05 level of significance, determine if there is evidence of a difference in the mean prices for these kitchen staples at the four supermarkets.

**b.** What assumptions are necessary to perform this test?

**c.** If appropriate, use the Tukey procedure to determine which supermarkets differ. (Use $\alpha = 0.05$.)

**d.** Do you think that there was a significant block effect in this experiment? Explain.

**SELF** **Test** **11.26** An article (J. Graham, "Prices Going Up, But It's Not Gas," *USA Today*, May 13, 2004, p. 1B) stated that the cost of a legitimate music download is increasing. The following data (stored in the file **Musiconline**) represent the prices of five albums at five digital music services.

| Album/Artist | Itunes | Wal-Mart | Music Now | Music Match | Napster |
|---|---|---|---|---|---|
| D12 World—D12 | 11.99 | 9.44 | 13.99 | 20.79 | 9.95 |
| Damita Jo—Janet Jackson | 13.99 | 9.44 | 13.99 | 12.49 | 13.95 |
| 30 #1 Hits—Elvis Presley | 9.99 | 27.28 | 13.99 | 9.99 | 9.95 |
| Feels Like Home—Norah Jones | 12.87 | 9.44 | 9.99 | 11.99 | 13.95 |
| Up—Shania Twain | 9.99 | 17.44 | 13.99 | 9.99 | 18.81 |

Source: *Extracted from J. Graham, "Prices Going Up, But It's Not Gas; It's Online Music," USA Today, May 13, 2004, p. 1B.*

**a.** At the 0.05 level of significance, determine if there is evidence of a difference in the mean prices for albums at the five digital music services.

**b.** What assumptions are necessary to perform this test?

**c.** If appropriate, use the Tukey procedure to determine which digital music services differ. (Use $\alpha = 0.05$.)

**d.** Do you think that there was a significant block effect in this experiment? Explain.

**11.27** Philips Semiconductors is a leading European manufacturer of integrated circuits. Integrated circuits are produced on silicon wafers, which are ground to target thickness early in the production process. The wafers are positioned in different locations on a grinder and kept in place through vacuum decompression. One of the goals of process improvement is to reduce the variability in the thickness of the wafers in different positions and in different batches. Data were collected from a sample of 30 batches. In each batch, the thickness of the wafers on positions 1 and 2 (outer circle), 18 and 19 (middle circle), and 28 (inner circle) was measured. The results are given in the **Circuits** file. At the 0.01 level of significance, completely analyze the data to determine whether there is evidence of a difference in the mean thickness of the wafers for the five positions and, if so, which of the positions are different. What can you conclude?

Source: *Extracted from K. C. B. Roes and R. J. M. M. Does, "Shewhart-type charts in nonstandard situations," Technometrics, 37, 1995, pp. 15–24.*

**11.28** The data in the **Concrete2** file represent the compressive strength in thousands of pounds per square inch of 40 samples of concrete taken 2, 7, and 28 days after pouring.

Source: *Extracted from O. Carrillo-Gamboa and R. F. Gunst, "Measurement-Error-Model Collinearities," Technometrics, 34, 1992, pp. 454–464.*

**a.** At the 0.05 level of significance, is there evidence of a difference in the mean compressive strength after 2, 7, and 28 days?

**b.** If appropriate, use the Tukey procedure to determine the days that differ in mean compressive strength. (Use $\alpha = 0.05$.)

**c.** Determine the relative efficiency of the randomized block design as compared with the completely randomized (one-way ANOVA) design.

**d.** Construct boxplots of the compressive strength for the different time periods.

**e.** Based on the results of (a), (b), and (d), is there a pattern in the compressive strength over the three time periods?

## 11.3    THE FACTORIAL DESIGN: TWO-WAY ANALYSIS OF VARIANCE

In Section 11.1, you learned about the completely randomized design and in Section 11.2 you studied the randomized block design. In this section, the single factor completely randomized design is extended to the **two-factor factorial design**, in which two factors are simultaneously evaluated. Each factor is evaluated at two or more levels. For example, in the Using Statistics scenario on page 444, Perfect Parachutes is interested in simultaneously evaluating four suppliers and two types of looms. Although the discussion here is limited to two factors, you can extend factorial designs to three or more factors (see references 4, 5, 6, 9, and 10).

Data from a two-factor factorial design are analyzed using **two-way ANOVA**. Because of the complexity of the calculations involved, you should use software such as Microsoft Excel or Minitab when conducting this analysis. However, for purposes of illustration and a better conceptual understanding of two-way ANOVA, the decomposition of the total variation is presented next. The following definitions are needed to develop the two-way ANOVA procedure:

$r$ = number of levels of factor $A$

$c$ = number of levels of factor $B$

$n'$ = number of values (replicates) for each cell (combination of a particular level of factor $A$ and a particular level of factor $B$)

$n$ = number of values in the entire experiment (where $n = rcn'$)

$X_{ijk}$ = value of the $k$th observation for level $i$ of factor $A$ and level $j$ of factor $B$

$$\overline{\overline{X}} = \frac{\displaystyle\sum_{i=1}^{r}\sum_{j=1}^{c}\sum_{k=1}^{n'} X_{ijk}}{rcn'} = \text{grand mean}$$

$$\overline{X}_{i..} = \frac{\displaystyle\sum_{j=1}^{c}\sum_{k=1}^{n'} X_{ijk}}{cn'} = \text{mean of the } i\text{th level of factor } A \text{ (where } i = 1, 2, \ldots, r)$$

$$\overline{X}_{.j.} = \frac{\displaystyle\sum_{i=1}^{r}\sum_{k=1}^{n'} X_{ijk}}{rn'} = \text{mean of the } j\text{th level of factor } B \text{ (where } j = 1, 2, \ldots, c)$$

$$\overline{X}_{ij.} = \frac{\displaystyle\sum_{k=1}^{n'} X_{ijk}}{n'} = \text{mean of cell } ij, \text{ the combination of the } i\text{th level of factor } A \text{ and the } j\text{th level of factor } B$$

This text deals only with situations in which there are an equal number of **replicates** (i.e., sample sizes $n'$) for each combination of the levels of factor $A$ with those of factor $B$. (See references 1 and 10 for a discussion of two-factor factorial designs with unequal sample sizes.)

## Testing for Factor and Interaction Effects

There is an **interaction** between factors $A$ and $B$ if the effect of factor $A$ is dependent on the level of factor $B$. Thus, when dividing the total variation into different sources of variation, you need to account for a possible interaction effect, as well as for factor $A$, factor $B$, and random error. To accomplish this, the total variation ($SST$) is subdivided into sum of squares due to factor $A$ (or $SSA$), sum of squares due to factor $B$ (or $SSB$), sum of squares due to the interaction effect of $A$ and $B$ (or $SSAB$), and sum of squares due to random variation (or $SSE$). This decomposition of the total variation ($SST$) is displayed in Figure 11.17.

**FIGURE 11.17**

Partitioning the total variation in a two-factor factorial design

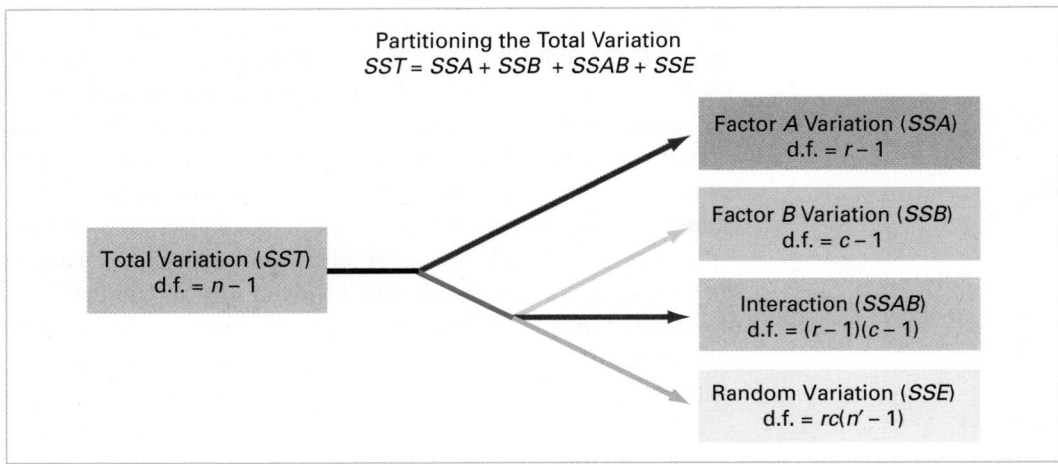

The sum of squares total ($SST$) represents the total variation among all the values around the grand mean. Equation (11.16) shows the computation for total variation.

**Total Variation in Two-Way ANOVA**

$$SST = \sum_{i=1}^{r}\sum_{j=1}^{c}\sum_{k=1}^{n'}(X_{ijk} - \bar{\bar{X}})^2 \qquad (11.16)$$

The **sum of squares due to factor $A$ ($SSA$)** represents the differences among the various levels of factor $A$ and the grand mean. Equation (11.17) shows the computation for factor $A$ variation.

**Factor A Variation**

$$SSA = cn'\sum_{i=1}^{r}(\bar{X}_{i..} - \bar{\bar{X}})^2 \qquad (11.17)$$

The **sum of squares due to factor $B$ ($SSB$)** represents the differences among the various levels of factor $B$ and the grand mean. Equation (11.18) shows the computation for factor $B$ variation.

**Factor B Variation**

$$SSB = rn'\sum_{j=1}^{c}(\bar{X}_{.j.} - \bar{\bar{X}})^2 \qquad (11.18)$$

The **sum of squares due to interaction (SSAB)** represents the interacting effect of specific combinations of factor $A$ and factor $B$. Equation (11.19) shows the computation for interaction variation.

Interaction Variation

$$SSAB = n' \sum_{i=1}^{r} \sum_{j=1}^{c} (\bar{X}_{ij.} - \bar{X}_{i..} - \bar{X}_{.j.} + \bar{\bar{X}})^2 \tag{11.19}$$

The **sum of squares error (SSE)** represents random variation, that is, the differences among the values within each cell and the corresponding cell mean. Equation (11.20) shows the computation for random variation.

Random Variation in Two-Way ANOVA

$$SSE = \sum_{i=1}^{r} \sum_{j=1}^{c} \sum_{k=1}^{n'} (X_{ijk} - \bar{X}_{ij.})^2 \tag{11.20}$$

Because there are $r$ levels of factor $A$, there are $r - 1$ degrees of freedom associated with $SSA$. Similarly, because there are $c$ levels of factor $B$, there are $c - 1$ degrees of freedom associated with $SSB$. Because there are $n'$ replicates in each of the $rc$ cells, there are $rc(n' - 1)$ degrees of freedom associated with the $SSE$ term. Carrying this further, there are $n - 1$ degrees of freedom associated with the sum of squares total ($SST$) because you are comparing each value, $X_{ijk}$, to the grand mean, $\bar{\bar{X}}$, based on all $n$ values. Therefore, because the degrees of freedom for each of the sources of variation must add to the degrees of freedom for the total variation ($SST$), you can calculate the degrees of freedom for the interaction component ($SSAB$) by subtraction. The degrees of freedom for interaction are $(r - 1)(c - 1)$.

If you divide each of the sum of squares by its associated degrees of freedom, you have the four variances or mean square terms (i.e., $MSA$, $MSB$, $MSAB$, and $MSE$). Equations (11.21a–d) give the mean square terms needed for the two-way ANOVA table.

Mean Squares in Two-Way ANOVA

$$MSA = \frac{SSA}{r - 1} \tag{11.21a}$$

$$MSB = \frac{SSB}{c - 1} \tag{11.21b}$$

$$MSAB = \frac{SSAB}{(r - 1)(c - 1)} \tag{11.21c}$$

$$MSE = \frac{SSE}{rc(n' - 1)} \tag{11.21d}$$

There are three different tests to perform in a two-way ANOVA:

1. To test the hypothesis of no difference due to factor $A$

$$H_0: \mu_{1..} = \mu_{2..} = \cdots = \mu_{r..}$$

against the alternative

$$H_1: \text{Not all } \mu_{i..} \text{ are equal}$$

you use the $F_{STAT}$ test statistic in Equation (11.22).

---

**F Test for Factor A Effect**

$$F_{STAT} = \frac{MSA}{MSE} \tag{11.22}$$

---

You reject the null hypothesis at the $\alpha$ level of significance if

$$F_{STAT} = \frac{MSA}{MSE} > F_\alpha$$

where $F_\alpha$ is the upper-tail critical value from an $F$ distribution with $r-1$ and $rc(n'-1)$ degrees of freedom.

**2.** To test the hypothesis of no difference due to factor $B$

$$H_0: \mu_{.1.} = \mu_{.2.} = \cdots = \mu_{.c.}$$

against the alternative

$$H_1: \text{Not all } \mu_{.j.} \text{ are equal}$$

you use the $F_{STAT}$ test statistic in Equation (11.23).

---

**F Test for Factor B Effect**

$$F_{STAT} = \frac{MSB}{MSE} \tag{11.23}$$

---

You reject the null hypothesis at the $\alpha$ level of significance if

$$F_{STAT} = \frac{MSB}{MSE} > F_\alpha$$

where $F_\alpha$ is the upper-tail critical value from an $F$ distribution with $c-1$ and $rc(n'-1)$ degrees of freedom.

**3.** To test the hypothesis of no interaction of factors $A$ and $B$

$$H_0: \text{The interaction of } A \text{ and } B \text{ is equal to zero}$$

against the alternative

$$H_1: \text{The interaction of } A \text{ and } B \text{ is not equal to zero}$$

you use the $F_{STAT}$ test statistic in Equation (11.24).

---

**F Test for Interaction Effect**

$$F_{STAT} = \frac{MSAB}{MSE} \tag{11.24}$$

You reject the null hypothesis at the $\alpha$ level of significance if

$$F_{STAT} = \frac{MSAB}{MSE} > F_{\alpha}$$

where $F_{\alpha}$ is the upper-tail critical value from an $F$ distribution with $(r-1)(c-1)$ and $rc(n'-1)$ degrees of freedom.

Table 11.8 presents the entire two-way ANOVA table.

**TABLE 11.8**

Analysis of Variance Table for the Two-Factor Factorial Design

| Source | Degrees of Freedom | Sum of Squares | Mean Square (Variance) | F |
|--------|--------------------|----------------|-------------------------|---|
| A | $r-1$ | SSA | $MSA = \dfrac{SSA}{r-1}$ | $F_{STAT} = \dfrac{MSA}{MSE}$ |
| B | $c-1$ | SSB | $MSB = \dfrac{SSB}{c-1}$ | $F_{STAT} = \dfrac{MSB}{MSE}$ |
| AB | $(r-1)(c-1)$ | SSAB | $MSAB = \dfrac{SSAB}{(r-1)(c-1)}$ | $F_{STAT} = \dfrac{MSAB}{MSE}$ |
| Error | $rc(n'-1)$ | SSE | $MSE = \dfrac{SSE}{rc(n'-1)}$ | |
| Total | $n-1$ | SST | | |

To examine a two-way ANOVA, return to the Using Statistics scenario on page 444. As production manager at Perfect Parachutes, you have decided not only to evaluate the different suppliers but also to determine whether parachutes woven on the Jetta looms are as strong as those woven on the Turk looms. In addition, you need to determine whether any differences among the four suppliers in the strength of the parachutes are dependent on the type of loom being used. Thus, you have decided to perform an experiment in which five different parachutes from each supplier are manufactured on each of the two different looms. The results are given in Table 11.9 and stored in the Parachute2 file.

**TABLE 11.9**

Tensile Strengths of Parachutes Woven by Two Types of Looms, Using Synthetic Fibers from Four Suppliers

| LOOM | SUPPLIER | | | |
|------|------|------|------|------|
| | 1 | 2 | 3 | 4 |
| **Jetta** | 20.6 | 22.6 | 27.7 | 21.5 |
| | 18.0 | 24.6 | 18.6 | 20.0 |
| | 19.0 | 19.6 | 20.8 | 21.1 |
| | 21.3 | 23.8 | 25.1 | 23.9 |
| | 13.2 | 27.1 | 17.7 | 16.0 |
| **Turk** | 18.5 | 26.3 | 20.6 | 25.4 |
| | 24.0 | 25.3 | 25.2 | 19.9 |
| | 17.2 | 24.0 | 20.8 | 22.6 |
| | 19.9 | 21.2 | 24.7 | 17.5 |
| | 18.0 | 24.5 | 22.9 | 20.4 |

Figure 11.18 presents Microsoft Excel results and Figure 11.19 illustrates Minitab results.

**FIGURE 11.18**

Microsoft Excel two-way ANOVA results for the parachute experiment

*See Section E11.4 to create this.*

| | A | B | C | D | E | F | G |
|---|---|---|---|---|---|---|---|
| 1 | **Anova: Two-Factor With Replication** | | | | | | |
| 2 | | | | | | | |
| 3 | **SUMMARY** | **Supplier 1** | **Supplier 2** | **Supplier 3** | **Supplier 4** | **Total** | |
| 4 | *Jetta* | | | | | | |
| 5 | Count | 5 | 5 | 5 | 5 | 20 | |
| 6 | Sum | 92.1 | 117.7 | 109.9 | 102.5 | 422.2 | |
| 7 | Average | 18.42 | 23.54 | 21.98 | 20.5 | 21.11 | |
| 8 | Variance | 10.202 | 7.568 | 18.397 | 8.355 | 13.1283 | |
| 9 | | | | | | | |
| 10 | *Turk* | | | | | | |
| 11 | Count | 5 | 5 | 5 | 5 | 20 | |
| 12 | Sum | 97.6 | 121.3 | 114.2 | 105.8 | 438.9 | |
| 13 | Average | 19.52 | 24.26 | 22.84 | 21.16 | 21.945 | |
| 14 | Variance | 7.237 | 3.683 | 4.553 | 8.903 | 8.4626 | |
| 15 | | | | | | | |
| 16 | *Total* | | | | | | |
| 17 | Count | 10 | 10 | 10 | 10 | | |
| 18 | Sum | 189.7 | 239 | 224.1 | 208.3 | | |
| 19 | Average | 18.97 | 23.9 | 22.41 | 20.83 | | |
| 20 | Variance | 8.0868 | 5.1444 | 10.4054 | 7.7912 | | |
| 21 | | | | | | | |
| 22 | | | | | | | |
| 23 | **ANOVA** | | | | | | |
| 24 | *Source of Variation* | *SS* | *df* | *MS* | *F* | *P-value* | *F crit* |
| 25 | Sample | 6.9723 | 1 | 6.9723 | 0.8096 | 0.3750 | 4.1491 |
| 26 | Columns | 134.3488 | 3 | 44.7829 | 5.1999 | 0.0049 | 2.9011 |
| 27 | Interaction | 0.2867 | 3 | 0.0956 | 0.0111 | 0.9984 | 2.9011 |
| 28 | Within | 275.5920 | 32 | 8.6123 | | | |
| 29 | | | | | | | |
| 30 | Total | 417.1998 | 39 | | | | |

**FIGURE 11.19**

Minitab two-way ANOVA results for the parachute experiment

*See Section M11.4 to create this.*

```
Source        DF      SS       MS      F      P
Loom           1    6.972   6.9722  0.81  0.375
Supplier       3  134.349  44.7829  5.20  0.005
Interaction    3    0.287   0.0956  0.01  0.998
Error         32  275.592   8.6123
Total         39  417.200

S = 2.935   R-Sq = 33.94%   R-Sq(adj) = 19.49%
                 Individual 95% CIs For Mean Based on
                 Pooled StDev
Loom      Mean   --+---------+---------+---------+-------
jetta   21.110   (------------*------------)
turk    21.945               (------------*-------------)
                 --+---------+---------+---------+-------
                 20.0       21.0      22.0      23.0


                 Individual 95% CIs For Mean Based on
                 Pooled StDev
Supplier  Mean   --+---------+---------+---------+-------
1        18.97   (-------*------)
2        23.90                       (-------*------)
3        22.41                  (-------*------)
4        20.83             (------*-------)
```

To interpret the results, you start by testing whether there is an interaction effect between factor $A$ (loom) and factor $B$ (supplier). If the interaction effect is significant, further analysis will focus on this interaction. If the interaction effect is not significant, you can focus on the

[1] Table E.5 does not provide
the upper-tail critical values
from the F distribution with
32 degrees of freedom in
the denominator. When the
desired degrees of freedom
are not provided in the
table, you can round to the
closest value that is given,
use the p-value approach or
use Microsoft Excel.

**main effects**—potential differences in looms (factor $A$) and potential differences in suppliers (factor $B$).

Using the 0.05 level of significance, to determine whether there is evidence of an interaction effect, you reject the null hypothesis of no interaction between loom and supplier if the computed $F_{STAT}$ statistic is greater than 2.92, the approximate upper-tail critical value from the $F$ distribution, with 3 and 32 degrees of freedom (see Figure 11.20).[1]

Because $F_{STAT} = 0.0111 < F_\alpha = 2.92$ or the $p$-value $= 0.9984 > 0.05$, you do not reject $H_0$. You conclude that there is insufficient evidence of an interaction effect between loom and supplier. You can now focus on the main effects.

**FIGURE 11.20**

Regions of rejection and nonrejection at the 0.05 level of significance, with 3 and 32 degrees of freedom

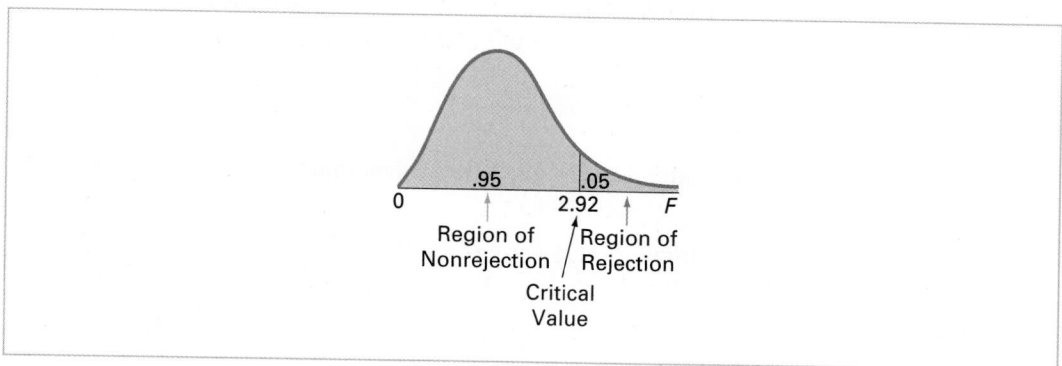

Using the 0.05 level of significance and testing for a difference between the two looms (factor $A$), you reject the null hypothesis if the computed $F_{STAT}$ test statistic is greater than 4.17, the (approximate) upper-tail critical value from the $F$ distribution with 1 and 32 degrees of freedom (see Figure 11.21). Because $F_{STAT} = 0.8096 < F_\alpha = 4.17$ or the $p$-value $= 0.3750 > 0.05$, you do not reject $H_0$. You conclude that there is insufficient evidence of a difference between the two looms in terms of the mean tensile strengths of the parachutes manufactured.

**FIGURE 11.21**

Regions of rejection and nonrejection at the 0.05 level of significance, with 1 and 32 degrees of freedom

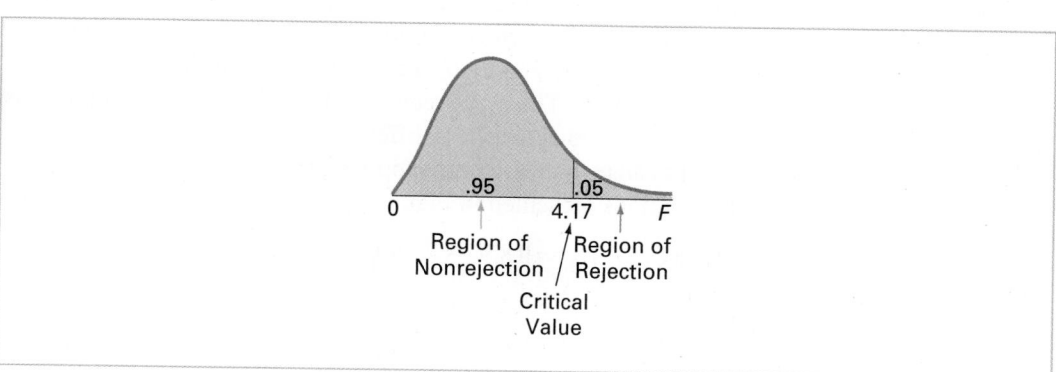

Using the 0.05 level of significance and testing for a difference among the suppliers (factor $B$), you reject the null hypothesis of no difference if the computed $F_{STAT}$ test statistic is greater than 2.92, the approximate upper-tail critical value from the $F$ distribution with 3 degrees of freedom in the numerator and 32 degrees of freedom in the denominator (see Figure 11.20). Because $F_{STAT} = 5.1999 > F_\alpha = 2.92$ or the $p$-value $= 0.0049 < 0.05$, reject $H_0$. You conclude that there is evidence of a difference among the suppliers in terms of the mean tensile strength of the parachutes.

## Multiple Comparisons: The Tukey Procedure

If one or both of the factor effects are significant, and there is no significant interaction effect, when there are more than two levels of a factor you can determine the particular levels that are significantly different by using the **Tukey multiple comparisons procedure for**

**two-way ANOVA** (see references 9 and 10). Equation (11.25) gives the critical range for factor $A$.

Critical Range for Factor $A$

$$\text{Critical range} = Q_\alpha \sqrt{\frac{MSE}{cn'}} \qquad (11.25)$$

where $Q_\alpha$ is the upper-tail critical value from a Studentized range distribution having $r$ and $rc(n' - 1)$ degrees of freedom. (Values for the Studentized range distribution are found in Table E.10.)

Equation (11.26) gives the critical range for factor $B$.

Critical Range for Factor $B$

$$\text{Critical range} = Q_\alpha \sqrt{\frac{MSE}{rn'}} \qquad (11.26)$$

where $Q_\alpha$ is the upper-tail critical value from a Studentized range distribution having $c$ and $rc(n' - 1)$ degrees of freedom. (Values for the Studentized range distribution are found in Table E.10.)

To use the Tukey procedure, return to the parachute manufacturing data of Table 11.9 on page 475. In Figures 11.18 or 11.19 on page 476 (the ANOVA summary table provided by Microsoft Excel and Minitab), the interaction effect is not significant. Using $\alpha = 0.05$, there is no evidence of a significant difference between the two looms (Jetta and Turk) that comprise factor $A$, but there is evidence of a significant difference among the four suppliers that comprise factor $B$. Thus, you can use the Tukey multiple comparisons procedure to determine which of the four suppliers differ.

Because there are four suppliers, there are $4(4 - 1)/2 = 6$ pairwise comparisons. Using the calculations presented in Figures 11.18 or 11.19, the absolute mean differences are as follows:

1. $\left| \bar{X}_{.1.} - \bar{X}_{.2.} \right| = \left| 18.97 - 23.90 \right| = 4.93$

2. $\left| \bar{X}_{.1.} - \bar{X}_{.3.} \right| = \left| 18.97 - 22.41 \right| = 3.44$

3. $\left| \bar{X}_{.1.} - \bar{X}_{.4.} \right| = \left| 18.97 - 20.83 \right| = 1.86$

4. $\left| \bar{X}_{.2.} - \bar{X}_{.3.} \right| = \left| 23.90 - 22.41 \right| = 1.49$

5. $\left| \bar{X}_{.2.} - \bar{X}_{.4.} \right| = \left| 23.90 - 20.83 \right| = 3.07$

6. $\left| \bar{X}_{.3.} - \bar{X}_{.4.} \right| = \left| 22.41 - 20.83 \right| = 1.58$

To determine the critical range, refer to Figures 11.18 or 11.19 to find $MSE = 8.612$, $r = 2$, $c = 4$, and $n' = 5$. From Table E.10 [for $\alpha = 0.05$, $c = 4$, and $rc(n' - 1) = 32$], $Q_\alpha$, the upper-tail critical value of the Studentized range distribution with 4 and 32 degrees of freedom, is approximated as 3.84. Using Equation (11.26),

$$\text{Critical range} = 3.84 \sqrt{\frac{8.6123}{10}} = 3.56$$

Because 4.93 > 3.56, only the means of Suppliers 1 and 2 are different. You can conclude that the mean tensile strength is lower for Supplier 1 than for Supplier 2, but there are no statistically significant differences between Suppliers 1 and 3, Suppliers 1 and 4, Suppliers 2 and 3, Suppliers 2 and 4, and Suppliers 3 and 4. Note that by using $\alpha = 0.05$, you are able to make all six comparisons with an overall error rate of only 5%.

## Interpreting Interaction Effects

You can get a better understanding of the interpretation of the interaction by plotting the cell means (i.e., the means of all possible factor-level combinations), as shown in Figure 11.22. Figure 11.18 on page 476 provides the cell means for the loom-supplier combinations. From the plot of the mean tensile strength for each combination of loom and supplier, observe that the two lines (representing the two looms) are roughly parallel. This indicates that the *difference* between the mean tensile strength of the two looms is virtually the same for the four suppliers. In other words, there is no *interaction* between these two factors, as was indicated by the *F* test.

**FIGURE 11.22**

Microsoft Excel cell means plot of tensile strength based on loom and supplier

*See Section E11.5 to create this. (Minitab users, see Section M11.5 to create an equivalent chart.)*

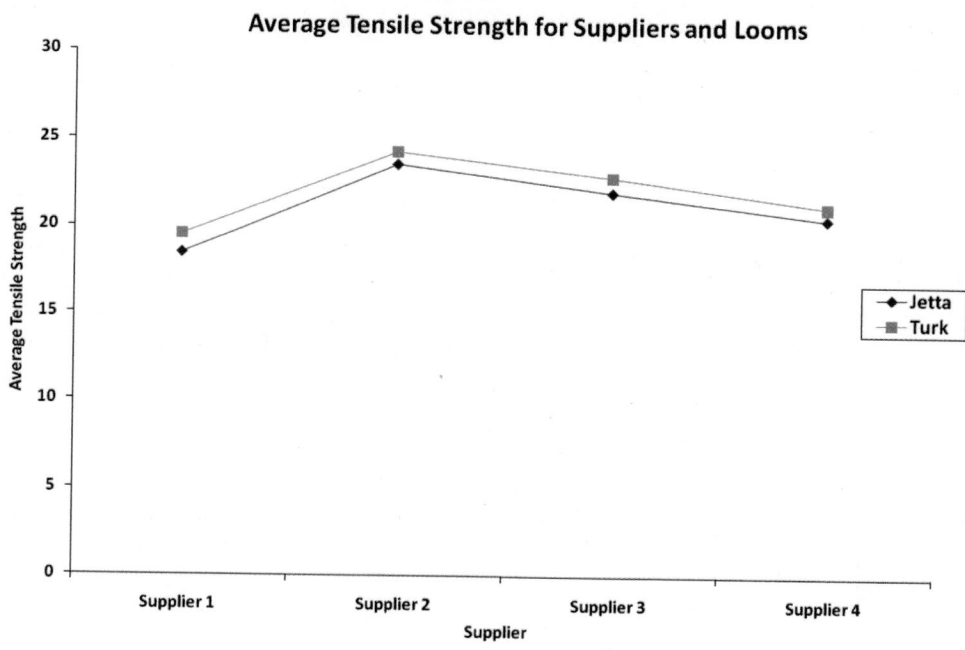

What is the interpretation if there is an interaction? In such a situation, some levels of factor *A* would respond better with certain levels of factor *B*. For example, with respect to tensile strength, suppose that some suppliers were better for the Jetta loom and other suppliers were better for the Turk loom. If this were true, the lines of Figure 11.22 would not be nearly as parallel, and the interaction effect might be statistically significant. In such a situation, the difference between the looms is no longer the same for all suppliers. Such an outcome would also complicate the interpretation of the *main effects* because differences in one factor (the loom) would not be consistent across the other factor (the supplier).

Example 11.2 illustrates a situation with a significant interaction effect.

**EXAMPLE 11.2**   INTERPRETING SIGNIFICANT INTERACTION EFFECTS

A nationwide company specializing in preparing students for college entrance exams, such as the SAT, ACT, and LSAT, decided to conduct an experiment to investigate ways to improve its ACT Preparatory Course. Two factors of interest to the company are the length of the course (a condensed 10-day period or regular 30-day period) and the type of course (traditional classroom or online distance learning). The company randomly assigned 10 clients to each of the four cells. Table 11.10 lists the students' scores on the ACT for this two-factor design. The data are stored in the file Act.

What are the effects of the type of course and the length of the course on ACT scores?

**TABLE 11.10**

ACT Scores for Different Types and Lengths of Courses

| | LENGTH OF COURSE | | | |
|---|---|---|---|---|
| **TYPE OF COURSE** | **Condensed** | | **Regular** | |
| **Traditional** | 26 | 18 | 34 | 28 |
| | 27 | 24 | 24 | 21 |
| | 25 | 19 | 35 | 23 |
| | 21 | 20 | 31 | 29 |
| | 21 | 18 | 28 | 26 |
| **Online** | 27 | 21 | 24 | 21 |
| | 29 | 32 | 16 | 19 |
| | 30 | 20 | 22 | 19 |
| | 24 | 28 | 20 | 24 |
| | 30 | 29 | 23 | 25 |

**SOLUTION** The interaction plot presented in Figure 11.23 illustrates a strong interaction between the type of course and the length of the course. The nonparallel lines indicate that the effect of condensing the course depends on whether the course is taught in the traditional classroom or via online distance learning. The online mean score is higher when the course is condensed to a 10-day period, whereas the traditional mean score is higher when the course takes place over the regular 30-day period.

**FIGURE 11.23**

Minitab interaction plot of ACT scores

*See Section M11.5 to create this. Excel users, see Section E11.5 to create an equivalent chart.*

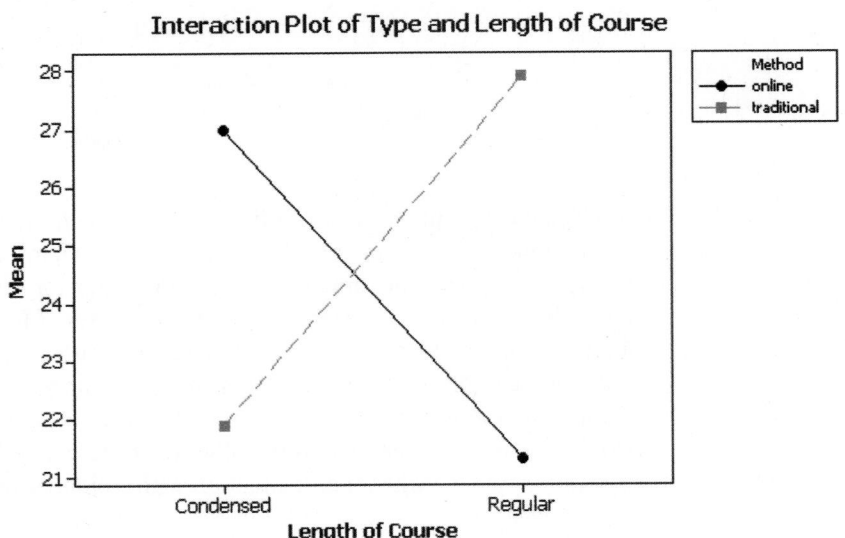

To verify the somewhat subjective analysis provided by interpreting the cell means plot, you begin by testing whether there is a statistically significant interaction between factor $A$ (length of course) and factor $B$ (type of course). Using a 0.05 level of significance, you reject the null hypothesis because $F_{STAT} = 25.69 > 4.1132$ or the $p$-value equals $0.000 < 0.05$ (see Figures 11.24 or 11.25). Thus, the hypothesis test confirms the interaction evident in the cell means plot. The existence of this significant interaction effect complicates the interpretation of the hypothesis tests concerning the two main effects. You cannot directly conclude that there is no effect with respect to length of course and type of course, even though both have $p$-values $> 0.05$.

**FIGURE 11.24**

Microsoft Excel two-way ANOVA results for ACT scores

*See Section E11.4 to create this.*

| | A | B | C | D | E | F | G |
|---|---|---|---|---|---|---|---|
| 1 | **Anova: Two-Factor With Replication** | | | | | | |
| 2 | | | | | | | |
| 3 | **SUMMARY** | **Condensed** | **Regular** | **Total** | | | |
| 4 | *Traditional* | | | | | | |
| 5 | Count | 10 | 10 | 20 | | | |
| 6 | Sum | 219 | 279 | 498 | | | |
| 7 | Average | 21.9 | 27.9 | 24.9 | | | |
| 8 | Variance | 11.2111 | 20.9889 | 24.7263 | | | |
| 9 | | | | | | | |
| 10 | *Online* | | | | | | |
| 11 | Count | 10 | 10 | 20 | | | |
| 12 | Sum | 270 | 213 | 483 | | | |
| 13 | Average | 27 | 21.3 | 24.15 | | | |
| 14 | Variance | 16.2222 | 8.0111 | 20.0289 | | | |
| 15 | | | | | | | |
| 16 | *Total* | | | | | | |
| 17 | Count | 20 | 20 | | | | |
| 18 | Sum | 489 | 492 | | | | |
| 19 | Average | 24.45 | 24.6 | | | | |
| 20 | Variance | 19.8395 | 25.2 | | | | |
| 21 | | | | | | | |
| 22 | | | | | | | |
| 23 | **ANOVA** | | | | | | |
| 24 | **Source of Variation** | **SS** | **df** | **MS** | **F** | **P-value** | **F crit** |
| 25 | Sample | 5.625 | 1 | 5.625 | 0.3987 | 0.5318 | 4.1132 |
| 26 | Columns | 0.225 | 1 | 0.225 | 0.0159 | 0.9002 | 4.1132 |
| 27 | Interaction | 342.225 | 1 | 342.225 | 24.2569 | 0.0000 | 4.1132 |
| 28 | Within | 507.900 | 36 | 14.108 | | | |
| 29 | | | | | | | |
| 30 | Total | 855.975 | 39 | | | | |

**FIGURE 11.25**

Minitab two-way ANOVA results for ACT scores

*See Section M11.4 to create this.*

```
Source            DF       SS        MS       F       P
Method             1    5.625     5.625    0.40    0.532
Length of Course   1    0.225     0.225    0.02    0.900
Interaction        1  342.225   342.225   24.26   0.000
Error             36  507.900    14.108
Total             39  855.975

S = 3.756    R-Sq = 40.66%    R-Sq(adj) = 35.72%


                       Individual 95% CIs For Mean Based on
                       Pooled StDev
Method        Mean     ---+---------+---------+---------+------
online        24.15    (-------------*-------------)
traditional   24.90          (-------------*-------------)
                       ---+---------+---------+---------+------
                       22.8      24.0      25.2      26.4


                       Individual 95% CIs For Mean Based on
Length of              Pooled StDev
Course        Mean     ---+---------+---------+---------+------
Condensed     24.45    (----------------*----------------)
Regular       24.60    (----------------*----------------)
```

Given that the interaction is significant, you can reanalyze the data with the two factors collapsed into four groups of a single factor rather than a two-way ANOVA with two levels of each of the two factors (see the `Act-Oneway` file). Group 1 is traditional condensed. Group 2 is traditional regular. Group 3 is online condensed. Group 4 is online regular. Figures 11.26 and 11.27 display Microsoft Excel and Minitab results.

**FIGURE 11.26**

Microsoft Excel one-way ANOVA results and Tukey-Kramer worksheet for the ACT scores

*See Section E11.1 to create this.*

| | A | B | C | D | E | F | G |
|---|---|---|---|---|---|---|---|
| 1 | Anova: Single Factor | | | | | | |
| 2 | | | | | | | |
| 3 | SUMMARY | | | | | | |
| 4 | *Groups* | *Count* | *Sum* | *Average* | *Variance* | | |
| 5 | Group 1 | 10 | 219 | 21.9 | 11.2111 | | |
| 6 | Group 2 | 10 | 279 | 27.9 | 20.9889 | | |
| 7 | Group 3 | 10 | 270 | 27 | 16.2222 | | |
| 8 | Group 4 | 10 | 213 | 21.3 | 8.0111 | | |
| 9 | | | | | | | |
| 10 | | | | | | | |
| 11 | ANOVA | | | | | | |
| 12 | *Source of Variation* | *SS* | *df* | *MS* | *F* | *P-value* | *F crit* |
| 13 | Between Groups | 348.075 | 3 | 116.025 | 8.2239 | 0.0003 | 2.8663 |
| 14 | Within Groups | 507.9 | 36 | 14.1083 | | | |
| 15 | | | | | | | |
| 16 | Total | 855.975 | 39 | | | | |

| | A | B | C | D | E | F | G | H | I |
|---|---|---|---|---|---|---|---|---|---|
| 1 | Tukey Kramer Multiple Comparisons | | | | | | | | |
| 2 | | | | | | | | | |
| 3 | | Sample | Sample | | | Absolute | Std. Error | Critical | |
| 4 | Group | Mean | Size | | Comparison | Difference | of Difference | Range | Results |
| 5 | 1 | 21.9 | 10 | | Group 1 to Group 2 | 6 | 1.18778505 | 4.5017 | Means are different |
| 6 | 2 | 27.9 | 10 | | Group 1 to Group 3 | 5.1 | 1.18778505 | 4.5017 | Means are different |
| 7 | 3 | 27 | 10 | | Group 1 to Group 4 | 0.6 | 1.18778505 | 4.5017 | Means are not different |
| 8 | 4 | 21.3 | 10 | | Group 2 to Group 3 | 0.9 | 1.18778505 | 4.5017 | Means are not different |
| 9 | | | | | Group 2 to Group 4 | 6.6 | 1.18778505 | 4.5017 | Means are different |
| 10 | Other Data | | | | Group 3 to Group 4 | 5.7 | 1.18778505 | 4.5017 | Means are different |
| 11 | Level of significance | 0.05 | | | | | | | |
| 12 | Numerator d.f. | 4 | | | | | | | |
| 13 | Denominator d.f. | 36 | | | | | | | |
| 14 | MSW | 14.10833 | | | | | | | |
| 15 | Q Statistic | 3.79 | | | | | | | |

**FIGURE 11.27**

Minitab one-way ANOVA results for the ACT scores

*See Section M11.1 to create this.*

```
Source   DF     SS      MS      F      P
Factor    3   348.1   116.0   8.22  0.000
Error    36   507.9    14.1
Total    39   856.0

S = 3.756    R-Sq = 40.66%    R-Sq(adj) = 35.72%


                              Individual 95% CIs For Mean Based on
                              Pooled StDev
Level      N    Mean   StDev  -------+---------+---------+---------+--
Group 1   10  21.900   3.348   (-------*-------)
Group 2   10  27.900   4.581                         (-------*-------)
Group 3   10  27.000   4.028                      (-------*-------)
Group 4   10  21.300   2.830  (-------*-------)
                              -------+---------+---------+---------+--
                                  21.0      24.0      27.0      30.0

Pooled StDev = 3.756
```

(continued)

**FIGURE 11.27**

(*continued*)

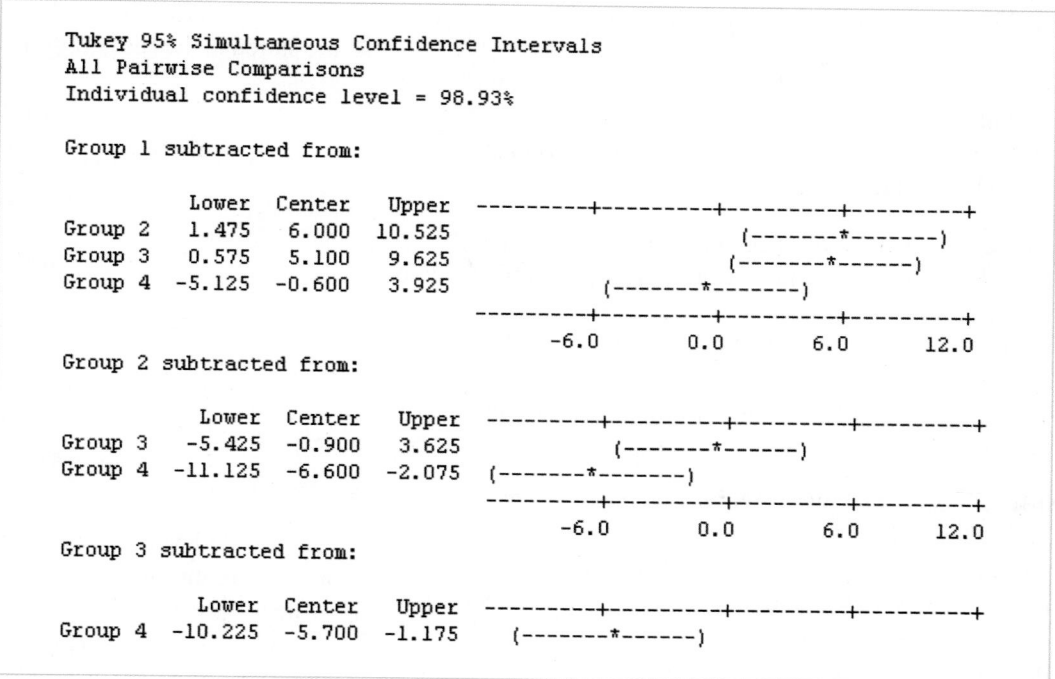

```
Tukey 95% Simultaneous Confidence Intervals
All Pairwise Comparisons
Individual confidence level = 98.93%

Group 1 subtracted from:

          Lower   Center   Upper   ---------+---------+---------+---------+
Group 2   1.475   6.000    10.525                    (-------*-------)
Group 3   0.575   5.100    9.625                    (-------*------)
Group 4  -5.125  -0.600    3.925          (-------*-------)
                                  ---------+---------+---------+---------+
                                        -6.0      0.0       6.0      12.0

Group 2 subtracted from:

           Lower    Center   Upper    ---------+---------+---------+---------+
Group 3   -5.425   -0.900    3.625             (-------*------)
Group 4  -11.125   -6.600   -2.075    (-------*-------)
                                      ---------+---------+---------+---------+
                                            -6.0      0.0       6.0      12.0

Group 3 subtracted from:

           Lower    Center   Upper    ---------+---------+---------+---------+
Group 4  -10.225   -5.700   -1.175       (-------*------)
```

From Figure 11.26 or 11.27, because $F_{STAT} = 8.2239 > 2.8663$ or $p$-value $= 0.000 < 0.05$, there is evidence of a significant difference in the four groups (traditional condensed, traditional regular, online condensed, and online regular). Traditional condensed is different from traditional regular and from online condensed. Traditional regular is also different from online regular, and online condensed is also different from online regular. Thus, whether condensing a course is a good idea depends on whether the course is a traditional class or an online distance learning course. To ensure the highest mean ACT scores, the company should use the traditional approach when offering courses over a 30-day period but use the online approach when offering the condensed courses over a 10-day period.

# PROBLEMS FOR SECTION 11.3

## Learning the Basics

**11.29** Consider a two-factor factorial design with three levels in factor $A$, three levels in factor $B$, and four replicates in each of the nine cells.

**a.** How many degrees of freedom are there in determining the factor $A$ variation and the factor $B$ variation?

**b.** How many degrees of freedom are there in determining the interaction variation?

**c.** How many degrees of freedom are there in determining the random variation?

**d.** How many degrees of freedom are there in determining the total variation?

**11.30** Assume that you are working with the results from Problem 11.29.

**a.** If $SSA = 120$, $SSB = 110$, $SSE = 270$, and $SST = 540$, what is $SSAB$?

**b.** What are $MSA$ and $MSB$?

**c.** What is $MSAB$?

**d.** What is $MSE$?

**11.31** Assume that you are working with the results of Problems 11.29 and 11.30.

**a.** What is the value of the $F_{STAT}$ test statistic for the interaction effect?

**b.** What is the value of the $F_{STAT}$ test statistic for the factor $A$ effect?

**c.** What is the value of the $F_{STAT}$ test statistic for the factor $B$ effect?

**d.** Form the ANOVA summary table and fill in all values in the body of the table.

**11.32** Given the results from Problems 11.29 through 11.31,

**a.** at the 0.05 level of significance, is there an effect due to factor $A$?

**b.** at the 0.05 level of significance, is there an effect due to factor $B$?

**c.** at the 0.05 level of significance, is there an interaction effect?

**11.33** Given a two-way ANOVA with two levels for factor $A$, five levels for factor $B$, and four replicates in each of the 10 cells, with $SSA = 18$, $SSB = 64$, $SSE = 60$, and $SST = 150$,

**a.** Form the ANOVA summary table and fill in all values in the body of the table.

**b.** At the 0.05 level of significance, is there an effect due to factor $A$?

**c.** At the 0.05 level of significance, is there an effect due to factor $B$?

**d.** At the 0.05 level of significance, is there an interaction effect?

**11.34** Given a two-factor factorial experiment and the ANOVA summary table that follows, fill in all the missing results:

| Source | Degrees of Freedom | Sum of Squares | Mean Square (Variance) | F |
|---|---|---|---|---|
| Factor $A$ | $r - 1 = 2$ | $SSA = ?$ | $MSA = 80$ | $F_{STAT} = ?$ |
| Factor $B$ | $c - 1 = ?$ | $SSB = 220$ | $MSB = ?$ | $F_{STAT} = 11.0$ |
| $AB$ interaction | $(r-1)(c-1) = 8$ | $SSAB = ?$ | $MSAB = 10$ | $F_{STAT} = ?$ |
| Error | $rc(n' - 1) = 30$ | $SSE = ?$ | $MSE = ?$ | |
| Total | $n - 1 = ?$ | $SST = ?$ | | |

**11.35** From the results of Problem 11.34,

**a.** At the 0.05 level of significance, is there an effect due to factor $A$?

**b.** At the 0.05 level of significance, is there an effect due to factor $B$?

**c.** At the 0.05 level of significance, is there an interaction effect?

## Applying the Concepts

**11.36** The effects of developer strength (factor $A$) and development time (factor $B$) on the density of photographic plate film were being studied. Two strengths and two development times were used, and four replicates in each of the four cells were evaluated. The results (with larger being best) are stored in the file **Photo** and shown in the following table:

| DEVELOPER STRENGTH | DEVELOPMENT TIME (MINUTES) | |
|---|---|---|
| | 10 | 14 |
| 1 | 0 | 1 |
| | 5 | 4 |
| | 2 | 3 |
| | 4 | 2 |
| 2 | 4 | 6 |
| | 7 | 7 |
| | 6 | 8 |
| | 5 | 7 |

At the 0.05 level of significance,

**a.** is there an interaction between developer strength and development time?

**b.** is there an effect due to developer strength?

**c.** is there an effect due to development time?

**d.** Plot the mean density for both developer strengths for both development times.

**e.** What can you conclude about the effect of developer strength and development time on density?

**11.37** A chef in a restaurant that specializes in pasta dishes was experiencing difficulty in getting brands of pasta to be *al dente*—that is, cooked enough so as not to feel starchy or hard but still feel firm when bitten into. She decided to conduct an experiment in which two brands of pasta, one American and one Italian, were cooked for either 4 or 8 minutes. The variable of interest was weight of the pasta because cooking the pasta enables it to absorb water. A pasta with a faster rate of water absorption may provide a shorter interval in which the pasta is *al dente*, thereby increasing the chance that it might be over-cooked. The experiment was conducted by using 150 grams of uncooked pasta. Each trial began by bringing a pot containing 6 quarts of cold, unsalted water to a moderate boil. The 150 grams of uncooked pasta was added and then weighed after a given period of time by lifting the pasta from the pot via a built-in strainer. The results (in terms of weight in grams) for two replicates of each type of pasta and cooking time are stored in the file **Pasta** and are as follows:

| TYPE OF PASTA | COOKING TIME (MINUTES) | |
|---|---|---|
| | 4 | 8 |
| **American** | 265 | 310 |
| | 270 | 320 |
| **Italian** | 250 | 300 |
| | 245 | 305 |

At the 0.05 level of significance,

a. is there an interaction between type of pasta and cooking time?

b. is there an effect due to type of pasta?

c. is there an effect due to cooking time?

d. Plot the mean weight for both types of pasta for both cooking times.

e. What conclusions can you reach concerning the importance of each of these two factors on the weight of the pasta?

**✓ SELF Test** **11.38** A student team in a business statistics course performed a factorial experiment to investigate the time required for pain-relief tablets to dissolve in a glass of water. The two factors of interest were brand name (Equate, Kroger, or Alka-Seltzer) and temperature of the water (hot or cold). The experiment consisted of four replicates for each of the six factor combinations. The following data (stored in the file **Pain-relief**) show the time a tablet took to dissolve (in seconds) for the 24 tablets used in the experiment:

| WATER | BRAND OF PAIN-RELIEF TABLET | | |
|-------|--------|--------|-------------|
|       | Equate | Kroger | Alka-Seltzer |
| **Cold** | 85.87 | 75.98 | 100.11 |
|       | 78.69 | 87.66 | 99.65 |
|       | 76.42 | 85.71 | 100.83 |
|       | 74.43 | 86.31 | 94.16 |
| **Hot** | 21.53 | 24.10 | 23.80 |
|       | 26.26 | 25.83 | 21.29 |
|       | 24.95 | 26.32 | 20.82 |
|       | 21.52 | 22.91 | 23.21 |

At the 0.05 level of significance,

a. Is there an interaction between brand of pain reliever and water temperature?

b. Is there an effect due to brand?

c. Is there an effect due to water temperature?

d. Plot the mean dissolving time for each brand for the two water temperatures.

e. Discuss the results of (a) through (d).

**11.39** Integrated circuits are manufactured on silicon wafers through a process that involves a series of steps. An experiment was carried out to study the effect of the cleansing and etching steps on the yield (coded to maintain confidentiality). The results (stored in the file **Yield**) are as follows:

| CLEANSING STEP | ETCHING STEP | |
|----------------|-----|----------|
|                | New | Standard |
| **New 1** | 38 | 34 |
|           | 34 | 19 |
|           | 38 | 28 |
| **New 2** | 29 | 20 |
|           | 35 | 35 |
|           | 34 | 37 |
| **Standard** | 31 | 29 |
|              | 23 | 32 |
|              | 38 | 30 |

Source: *Extracted from J. Ramirez and W. Taam, "An Autologistic Model for Integrated Circuit Manufacturing,"* Journal of Quality Technology, *2000, 32, pp. 254–262.*

At the 0.05 level of significance,

a. is there an interaction between the cleansing step and the etching step?

b. is there an effect due to the cleansing step?

c. is there an effect due to the etching step?

d. Plot the mean yield for each cleansing step for the two etching steps.

e. Discuss the results of (a) through (d).

**11.40** An experiment was conducted to study the distortion of drive gears in automobiles. Two factors were studied—the tooth size of the gear and the part positioning. The results (stored in the file **Gear**) are as follows:

| TOOTHSIZE | PART POSITIONING | |
|-----------|------|------|
|           | Low  | High |
| **Low** | 18.0 | 13.5 |
|         | 16.5 | 8.5 |
|         | 26.0 | 11.5 |
|         | 22.5 | 16.0 |
|         | 21.5 | −4.5 |
|         | 21.0 | 4.0 |
|         | 30.0 | 1.0 |
|         | 24.5 | 9.0 |
| **High** | 27.5 | 17.5 |
|          | 19.5 | 11.5 |
|          | 31.0 | 10.0 |
|          | 27.0 | 1.0 |
|          | 17.0 | 14.5 |
|          | 14.0 | 3.5 |
|          | 18.0 | 7.5 |
|          | 17.5 | 6.5 |

Source: *Extracted from D. R. Bingham and R. R. Sitter, "Design Issues in Fractional Factorial Split-Plot Experiments,"* Journal of Quality Technology, *33, 2001, pp. 2–15.*

At the 0.05 level of significance,

**a.** is there an interaction between the tooth size and the part positioning?

**b.** is there an effect due to tooth size?

**c.** is there an effect due to the part positioning?

**d.** Plot the mean yield for each tooth size for the two part positions.

**e.** Discuss the results of (a) through (d).

# Design of Experiments and Six Sigma

*From the Authors' Desktop*

When might you ever design an experiment and need to use the ANOVA methods you learned in this chapter? In the From the Authors' Desktop for Chapter 10 (see page 399), you learned about a prior student who graduated into a job in which she had to design an experiment to evaluate two training programs. If she had to evaluate three training programs, she would need to use the one-way ANOVA discussed in this chapter instead of the methods of Chapter 10.

Although the design of experiments was originally developed for the agricultural sector early in the twentieth century, design of experiments now show up commonly in the manufacturing and service sectors especially among the many companies that have adopted the Six Sigma quality improvement approach discussed in Chapter 18. This fact was reinforced recently when another prior student emailed one of us. She said "I never thought that I would ever need to know about design of experiments when I started working, but the company where I now work had me go through a Six Sigma training program in which I learned a great deal about ANOVA and factorial designs. At the end of the program, I took an exam and earned my Six Sigma Green Belt certification."

# SUMMARY

In this chapter, various statistical procedures were used to analyze the effect of one or two factors of interest. You learned how the production manager of the Perfect Parachutes Company could use these procedures to identify the best suppliers and loom types in order to increase the strength of the parachutes. The assumptions required for using these procedures were discussed in detail. Remember that you need to critically investigate the validity of the assumptions underlying the hypothesis-testing procedures. Table 11.11 summarizes the topics covered in this chapter.

**TABLE 11.11**

Summary of Topics in Chapter 11

| Type of Analysis | Type of Data Numerical |
|---|---|
| Comparing More than Two Groups | One-Way Analysis of Variance (Section 11.1) |
| | Randomized Block Design (Section 11.2) |
| | Two-Way Analysis of Variance (Section 11.3) |

# KEY EQUATIONS

**Total Variation in One-Way ANOVA**

$$SST = \sum_{j=1}^{c}\sum_{i=1}^{n_j}(X_{ij}-\bar{\bar{X}})^2 \qquad (11.1)$$

**Among-Group Variation in One-Way ANOVA**

$$SSA = \sum_{j=1}^{c}n_j(\bar{X}_j-\bar{\bar{X}})^2 \qquad (11.2)$$

**Within-Group Variation in One-Way ANOVA**

$$SSW = \sum_{j=1}^{c}\sum_{i=1}^{n_j}(X_{ij}-\bar{X}_j)^2 \qquad (11.3)$$

**Mean Squares in One-Way ANOVA**

$$MSA = \frac{SSA}{c-1} \qquad (11.4a)$$

$$MSW = \frac{SSW}{n-c} \qquad (11.4b)$$

$$MST = \frac{SST}{n-1} \qquad (11.4c)$$

**One-Way ANOVA $F_{STAT}$ Test Statistic**

$$F_{STAT} = \frac{MSA}{MSW} \qquad (11.5)$$

**Critical Range for the Tukey-Kramer Procedure**

$$\text{Critical range} = Q_\alpha\sqrt{\frac{MSW}{2}\left(\frac{1}{n_j}+\frac{1}{n_{j'}}\right)} \qquad (11.6)$$

**Total Variation in ihe Randomized Block Design**

$$SST = \sum_{j=1}^{c}\sum_{i=1}^{r}(X_{ij}-\bar{\bar{X}})^2 \qquad (11.7)$$

**Among-Group Variation in the Randomized Block Design**

$$SSA = r\sum_{j=1}^{c}(\bar{X}_{.j}-\bar{\bar{X}})^2 \qquad (11.8)$$

**Among-Block Variation in the Randomized Block Design**

$$SSBL = c\sum_{i=1}^{r}(\bar{X}_{i.}-\bar{\bar{X}})^2 \qquad (11.9)$$

**Random Variation in the Randomized Block Design**

$$SSE = \sum_{j=1}^{c}\sum_{i=1}^{r}(X_{ij}-\bar{X}_{.j}-\bar{X}_{i.}+\bar{\bar{X}})^2 \qquad (11.10)$$

**The Mean Squares in the Randomized Block Design**

$$MSA = \frac{SSA}{c-1} \qquad (11.11a)$$

$$MSBL = \frac{SSBL}{r-1} \qquad (11.11b)$$

$$MSE = \frac{SSE}{(r-1)(c-1)} \qquad (11.11c)$$

**$F_{STAT}$ Test Statistic for Factor Effect**

$$F_{STAT} = \frac{MSA}{MSE} \qquad (11.12)$$

**$F_{STAT}$ Test Statistic for Block Effect**

$$F_{STAT} = \frac{MSBL}{MSE} \qquad (11.13)$$

**Estimated Relative Efficiency**

$$RE = \frac{(r-1)MSBL+r(c-1)MSE}{(rc-1)MSE} \qquad (11.14)$$

**The Critical Range for the Randomized Block Design**

$$\text{Critical range} = Q_\alpha\sqrt{\frac{MSE}{r}} \qquad (11.15)$$

**Total Variation in Two-Way ANOVA**

$$SST = \sum_{i=1}^{r}\sum_{j=1}^{c}\sum_{k=1}^{n'}(X_{ijk} - \bar{\bar{X}})^2 \qquad \textbf{(11.16)}$$

**Factor $A$ Variation**

$$SSA = cn'\sum_{i=1}^{r}(\bar{X}_{i..} - \bar{\bar{X}})^2 \qquad \textbf{(11.17)}$$

**Factor $B$ Variation**

$$SSB = rn'\sum_{j=1}^{c}(\bar{X}_{.j.} - \bar{\bar{X}})^2 \qquad \textbf{(11.18)}$$

**Interaction Variation**

$$SSAB = n'\sum_{i=1}^{r}\sum_{j=1}^{c}(\bar{X}_{ij.} - \bar{X}_{i..} - \bar{X}_{.j.} + \bar{\bar{X}})^2 \qquad \textbf{(11.19)}$$

**Random Variation in Two-Way ANOVA**

$$SSE = \sum_{i=1}^{r}\sum_{j=1}^{c}\sum_{k=1}^{n'}(X_{ijk} - \bar{X}_{ij.})^2 \qquad \textbf{(11.20)}$$

**Mean Squares in Two-Way ANOVA**

$$MSA = \frac{SSA}{r-1} \qquad \textbf{(11.21a)}$$

$$MSB = \frac{SSB}{c-1} \qquad \textbf{(11.21b)}$$

$$MSAB = \frac{SSAB}{(r-1)(c-1)} \qquad \textbf{(11.21c)}$$

$$MSE = \frac{SSE}{rc(n'-1)} \qquad \textbf{(11.21d)}$$

**$F$ Test for Factor $A$ Effect**

$$F_{STAT} = \frac{MSA}{MSE} \qquad \textbf{(11.22)}$$

**$F$ Test for Factor $B$ Effect**

$$F_{STAT} = \frac{MSB}{MSE} \qquad \textbf{(11.23)}$$

**$F$ Test for Interaction Effect**

$$F_{STAT} = \frac{MSAB}{MSE} \qquad \textbf{(11.24)}$$

**Critical Range for Factor $A$**

$$\text{Critical range} = Q_\alpha\sqrt{\frac{MSE}{cn'}} \qquad \textbf{(11.25)}$$

**Critical Range for Factor $B$**

$$\text{Critical range} = Q_\alpha\sqrt{\frac{MSE}{rn'}} \qquad \textbf{(11.26)}$$

# KEY TERMS

among-block variation 462
among-group variation 445
analysis of variance (ANOVA) 444
ANOVA summary table 448
blocks 460
completely randomized design 444
critical range 452
estimated relative efficiency
(RE) 467
$F$ distribution 447
factor 444
grand mean, $\bar{\bar{X}}$ 445
groups 444
homogeneity of variance 455
interaction 472
levels 444
Levene test 455

main effects 477
mean square 446
multiple comparisons 452
normality 455
one-way ANOVA 444
randomized block designs 460
randomness and independence 454
replicates 471
Studentized range distribution 452
sum of squares among blocks
(SSBL) 462
sum of squares among groups
(SSA) 446
sum of squares due to factor $A$
(SSA) 472
sum of squares due to factor $B$
(SSB) 472

sum of squares due to interaction
(SSAB) 473
sum of squares error (SSE) 463, 473
sum of squares total (SST) 445
sum of squares within groups
(SSW) 446
total variation 445
Tukey multiple comparisons procedure
for randomized block designs 467
Tukey multiple comparisons procedure
for two-way ANOVA 477
Tukey-Kramer multiple comparisons
procedure for one-way
ANOVA 452
two-factor factorial design 471
two-way ANOVA 471
within-group variation 445

# CHAPTER REVIEW PROBLEMS

## Checking Your Understanding

**11.41** In a one-way ANOVA, what is the difference between the among-groups variance $MSA$ and the within-groups variance $MSW$?

**11.42** What is the difference between the randomized block design and the completely randomized design?

**11.43** What are the distinguishing features of the completely randomized design, randomized block design, and two-factor factorial designs?

**11.44** What are the assumptions of ANOVA?

**11.45** Under what conditions should you select the one-way ANOVA $F$ test to examine possible differences among the means of $c$ independent populations?

**11.46** When and how should you use multiple comparison procedures for evaluating pairwise combinations of the group means?

**11.47** What is the difference between the randomized block design and the two-factor factorial design?

**11.48** What is the difference between the one-way ANOVA $F$ test and the Levene test?

**11.49** Under what conditions should you use the two-way ANOVA $F$ test to examine possible differences among the means of each factor in a factorial design?

**11.50** What is meant by the concept of interaction in a two-factor factorial design?

**11.51** How can you determine whether there is an interaction in the two-factor factorial design?

## Applying the Concepts

**11.52** The operations manager for an appliance manufacturer wants to determine the optimal length of time for the washing cycle of a household clothes washer. An experiment is designed to measure the effect of detergent brand and washing cycle time on the amount of dirt removed from standard household laundry loads. Four brands of detergent (*A, B, C, D*) and four levels of washing cycle (18, 20, 22, and 24 minutes) are specifically selected for analysis. In order to run the experiment, 32 standard household laundry loads (having equal weight and dirt) are randomly assigned, 2 each, to the 16 detergent-washing cycle time combinations. The results, in pounds of dirt removed (stored in the Laundry file), are as follows:

| DETERGENT BRAND | WASHING CYCLE TIME (IN MINUTES) | | | |
| --- | --- | --- | --- | --- |
| | **18** | **20** | **22** | **24** |
| **A** | 0.11 | 0.13 | 0.17 | 0.17 |
| | 0.09 | 0.13 | 0.19 | 0.18 |
| **B** | 0.12 | 0.14 | 0.17 | 0.19 |
| | 0.10 | 0.15 | 0.18 | 0.17 |
| **C** | 0.08 | 0.16 | 0.18 | 0.20 |
| | 0.09 | 0.13 | 0.17 | 0.16 |
| **D** | 0.11 | 0.12 | 0.16 | 0.15 |
| | 0.13 | 0.13 | 0.17 | 0.17 |

At the 0.05 level of significance,

**a.** is there an interaction between detergent brand and washing cycle time?

**b.** is there an effect due to detergent brand?

**c.** is there an effect due to washing cycle time?

**d.** Plot the mean amount of dirt removed (in pounds) for each detergent brand for each washing cycle time.

**e.** If appropriate, use the Tukey procedure to determine differences between detergent brands and between washing cycle times.

**f.** What washing cycle time should be used for this type of household clothes washer?

**g.** Repeat the analysis, using washing cycle time as the only factor. Compare your results to those of (c), (e), and (f).

**11.53** The quality control director for a clothing manufacturer wants to study the effect of operators and machines on the breaking strength (in pounds) of wool serge material. A batch of the material is cut into square-yard pieces, and these are randomly assigned, 3 each, to all 12 combinations of 4 operators and 3 machines chosen specifically for the experiment. The results (stored in the file Breakstw) are as follows:

| OPERATOR | MACHINE | | |
| --- | --- | --- | --- |
| | **I** | **II** | **III** |
| **A** | 115 | 111 | 109 |
| | 115 | 108 | 110 |
| | 119 | 114 | 107 |

*(continued)*

| | MACHINE | | |
| OPERATOR | I | II | III |
|---|---|---|---|
| B | 117 | 105 | 110 |
| | 114 | 102 | 113 |
| | 114 | 106 | 114 |
| C | 109 | 100 | 103 |
| | 110 | 103 | 102 |
| | 106 | 101 | 105 |
| D | 112 | 105 | 108 |
| | 115 | 107 | 111 |
| | 111 | 107 | 110 |

At the 0.05 level of significance,
a. is there an interaction between operator and machine?
b. is there an effect due to operator?
c. is there an effect due to machine?
d. Plot the mean breaking strength for each operator for each machine.
e. If appropriate, use the Tukey procedure to examine differences among operators and among machines.
f. What can you conclude about the effects of operators and machines on breaking strength? Explain.
g. Repeat the analysis, using machines as the only factor. Compare your results to those of (c), (e), and (f).

**11.54** An operations manager wants to examine the effect of air-jet pressure (in psi) on the breaking strength of yarn. Three different levels of air-jet pressure are to be considered: 30 psi, 40 psi, and 50 psi. A random sample of 18 homogeneous filling yarns are selected from the same batch, and the yarns are randomly assigned, 6 each, to the 3 levels of air-jet pressure. The breaking strength scores are in the file Yarn.
a. Is there evidence of a significant difference in the variances of the breaking strengths for the three air-jet pressures? (Use $\alpha = 0.05$).
b. At the 0.05 level of significance, is there evidence of a difference among mean breaking strengths for the three air-jet pressures?
c. If appropriate, use the Tukey-Kramer procedure to determine which air-jet pressures significantly differ with respect to mean breaking strength. (Use $\alpha = 0.05$.)
d. What should the operations manager conclude?

**11.55** Suppose that, when setting up his experiment in Problem 11.54, the operations manager had access to only six samples of yarn from the batch but was able to divide each yarn sample into three parts and randomly assign them, one each, to the three air-jet pressure levels. Thus, instead of the one-factor completely randomized

design model in Problem 11.54, he used a randomized block design with the six yarn samples being the blocks and one yarn part each assigned to the three air-jet pressure levels. The breaking-strength scores are in the data file Yarn.
a. At the 0.05 level of significance, is there evidence of a difference in the mean breaking strengths for the three air-jet pressures?
b. If appropriate, use the Tukey procedure to determine the air-jet pressures that differ in mean breaking strength. (Use $\alpha = 0.05$.)
c. At the 0.05 level of significance, is there evidence of a blocking effect?
d. Determine the relative efficiency of the randomized block design as compared with the completely randomized design.
e. Compare your result in (a) with your result in Problem 11.54(b). Given your results in Problem 11.55(c) and (d), what do you think happened? What can you conclude about the "impact of blocking" when the blocks themselves are not really different from each other?

**11.56** Suppose that, when setting up his experiment in Problem 11.54, the operations manager is able to study the effect of side-to-side aspect in addition to air-jet pressure. Thus, instead of the one-factor completely randomized design in Problem 11.54, he used a two-factor factorial design, with the first factor, side-to-side aspects, having two levels (nozzle and opposite) and the second factor, air-jet pressure, having three levels (30 psi, 40 psi, and 50 psi). A sample of 18 yarns is randomly assigned, 3 to each of the 6 side-to-side aspect and pressure level combinations. The breaking-strength scores are as follows (and are in the file Yarn):

| | AIR-JET PRESSURE | | |
| SIDE-TO-SIDE ASPECT | 30 psi | 40 psi | 50 psi |
|---|---|---|---|
| **Nozzle** | 25.5 | 24.8 | 23.2 |
| | 24.9 | 23.7 | 23.7 |
| | 26.1 | 24.4 | 22.7 |
| **Opposite** | 24.7 | 23.6 | 22.6 |
| | 24.2 | 23.3 | 22.8 |
| | 23.6 | 21.4 | 24.9 |

At the 0.05 level of significance,
a. is there an interaction between side-to-side aspect and air-jet pressure?
b. is there an effect due to side-to-side aspect?
c. is there an effect due to air-jet pressure?
d. Plot the mean yarn breaking strength for the two levels of side-to-side aspect for each level of air-jet pressure.
e. If appropriate, use the Tukey procedure to study differences among the air-jet pressures.

**f.** On the basis of the results of (a) through (e), what conclusions can you reach concerning yarn breaking strength? Discuss.

**g.** Compare your results in (a) through (f) with those from the completely randomized design in Problem 11.54. Discuss fully.

**11.57** A hotel wanted to develop a new system for delivering room service breakfasts. In the current system, an order form is left on the bed in each room. If the customer wishes to receive a room service breakfast, he or she places the order form on the doorknob before 11 p.m. The current system requires customers to select a 15-minute interval for desired delivery time (6:30–6:45 a.m., 6:45–7:00 a.m., etc.). The new system is designed to allow the customer to request a specific delivery time. The hotel wants to measure the difference between the actual delivery time and the requested delivery time of room service orders for breakfast. (A negative time means that the order was delivered before the requested time. A positive time means that the order was delivered after the requested time.) The factors included were the menu choice (American or Continental) and the desired time period in which the order was to be delivered (Early Time Period [6:30–8:00 a.m.] or Late Time Period [8:00–9:30 a.m.]). Ten orders for each combination of menu choice and desired time period were studied on a particular day. The data (stored in the file Breakfast) are as follows:

|                    | DESIRED TIME | |
| TYPE OF BREAKFAST | Early Time Period | Late Time Period |
| --- | --- | --- |
| **Continental** | 1.2 | −2.5 |
|  | 2.1 | 3.0 |
|  | 3.3 | −0.2 |
|  | 4.4 | 1.2 |
|  | 3.4 | 1.2 |
|  | 5.3 | 0.7 |
|  | 2.2 | −1.3 |
|  | 1.0 | 0.2 |
|  | 5.4 | −0.5 |
|  | 1.4 | 3.8 |
| **American** | 4.4 | 6.0 |
|  | 1.1 | 2.3 |
|  | 4.8 | 4.2 |
|  | 7.1 | 3.8 |
|  | 6.7 | 5.5 |
|  | 5.6 | 1.8 |
|  | 9.5 | 5.1 |
|  | 4.1 | 4.2 |
|  | 7.9 | 4.9 |
|  | 9.4 | 4.0 |

At the 0.05 level of significance,

**a.** is there an interaction between type of breakfast and desired time?

**b.** is there an effect due to type of breakfast?

**c.** is there an effect due to desired time?

**d.** Plot the mean delivery time difference for the two desired times for both types of breakfast.

**e.** On the basis of the results of (a) through (d), what conclusions can you reach concerning delivery time difference? Discuss.

**11.58** Refer to the room service experiment in Problem 11.57. Now suppose that the results are as shown below (and stored in the file Breakfast2). Repeat (a) through (e), using these data and compare the results to those of (a) through (e) of Problem 11.57.

|                    | DESIRED TIME | |
| TYPE OF BREAKFAST | Early | Late |
| --- | --- | --- |
| **Continental** | 1.2 | −0.5 |
|  | 2.1 | 5.0 |
|  | 3.3 | 1.8 |
|  | 4.4 | 3.2 |
|  | 3.4 | 3.2 |
|  | 5.3 | 2.7 |
|  | 2.2 | 0.7 |
|  | 1.0 | 2.2 |
|  | 5.4 | 1.5 |
|  | 1.4 | 5.8 |
| **American** | 4.4 | 6.0 |
|  | 1.1 | 2.3 |
|  | 4.8 | 4.2 |
|  | 7.1 | 3.8 |
|  | 6.7 | 5.5 |
|  | 5.6 | 1.8 |
|  | 9.5 | 5.1 |
|  | 4.1 | 4.2 |
|  | 7.9 | 4.9 |
|  | 9.4 | 4.0 |

**11.59** Modern software applications require rapid data access capabilities. An experiment was conducted to test the effect of data file size on the ability to access the files (as measured by read time, in milliseconds). Three different levels of data file size were considered: small—50,000 characters; medium—75,000 characters; or large—100,000 characters. A sample of eight files of each size was evaluated. The access read times, in milliseconds, are in the data file Access.

**a.** Is there evidence of a significant difference in the variance of the access read times for the three file sizes? (Use $\alpha = 0.05$.)

**b.** At the 0.05 level of significance, is there evidence of a difference among mean access read times for the three file sizes?

**c.** If appropriate, use the Tukey-Kramer multiple comparisons procedure to determine which file sizes significantly differ with respect to mean access read time. (Use $\alpha = 0.05$.)

**d.** What conclusions can you reach?

**11.60** Suppose, when designing the experiment in Problem 11.59, that the effect of the input/output buffer size was studied in addition to the effect of the data file size. Thus, instead of the one-factor completely randomized design given in Problem 11.59, the experiment used a two-factor factorial design, with the first factor, buffer size, having two levels (20 kilobytes and 40 kilobytes) and the second factor, data file size, having three levels (small, medium, and large). That is, there are two factors under consideration: buffer size and data file size. A sample of four programs (replicates) were evaluated for each buffer size and data file size combination. The access read times, in milliseconds, are in the data file **Access**.

At the 0.05 level of significance,

**a.** is there an interaction between buffer size and data file size?

**b.** is there an effect due to buffer size?

**c.** is there an effect due to data file size?

**d.** Plot the mean access read times (in milliseconds) for the two buffer size levels for each of the three data file size levels. Describe the interaction and discuss why you can or cannot interpret the main effects in (b) and (c).

**e.** On the basis of the results of (a) through (d), what conclusions can you reach concerning access read times? Discuss.

**f.** Compare and contrast your results in (a) through (e) with those from the completely randomized design in Problem 11.59. Discuss fully.

**11.61** A student team in a business statistics course conducted an experiment to test the download times of the three different types of computers (Mac, iMac, and Dell) available at the university library. The students randomly selected one computer of each type. The students went to the Microsoft game Web site and clicked on the download link for the NBA game. The time (in seconds) between clicking on the link and the completion of the download was recorded. After each download, the file was deleted, and the trash folder was emptied. A total of 30 downloads were completed, in random order. Completely analyze the data shown in the following table and stored in the file **Computers**.

| COMPUTER | | |
|---|---|---|
| **Mac** | **iMac** | **Dell** |
| 156 | 160 | 236 |
| 166 | 165 | 238 |
| 148 | 184 | 257 |
| 160 | 192 | 242 |
| 139 | 197 | 282 |
| 151 | 172 | 253 |
| 158 | 189 | 270 |
| 167 | 179 | 256 |
| 142 | 200 | 267 |
| 219 | 193 | 259 |

**11.62** In a second experiment performed by the team in Problem 11.61, the browser (Netscape Communicator or Internet Explorer) was added as a second factor. In this experiment, only two of the types of computers were used (MAC and Dell). Eight downloads from each of the four factor combinations were completed. Completely analyze the data shown in the following table and stored in the file **Computers2**.

| | COMPUTER | |
|---|---|---|
| **BROWSER** | **Mac** | **Dell** |
| **Netscape Communicator** | 142 | 284 |
| | 132 | 304 |
| | 125 | 273 |
| | 136 | 340 |
| | 127 | 326 |
| | 138 | 301 |
| | 147 | 291 |
| | 143 | 285 |
| **Internet Explorer** | 198 | 285 |
| | 210 | 292 |
| | 199 | 305 |
| | 202 | 325 |
| | 196 | 297 |
| | 213 | 301 |
| | 207 | 285 |
| | 201 | 290 |

**11.63** A recent wine tasting was held by the J. S. Wine Club in which eight wines were rated by club members. Information concerning the country of origin and the price were not known to the club members until after the tasting took place. The wines rated (and the prices paid for them) were

1. French white $10.59
2. Italian white $8.50
3. Italian red $8.50
4. French burgundy (red) $10.69

5. French burgundy (red) $11.75
6. California Beaujolais (red) $10.50
7. French white $9.75
8. California white $13.59

The summated ratings over several characteristics for the 12 club members are in the data file **Wine**.

**a.** At the 0.01 level of significance, is there evidence of a difference in the mean rating scores among the wines?

**b.** What assumptions are necessary in order to do (a) of this problem? Comment on the validity of these assumptions.

**c.** If appropriate, use the Tukey procedure to determine the wines that differ in mean rating. (Use $\alpha = 0.01$.)

**d.** Based upon your results in (c), do you think that country of origin, the type of wine, or the price has had an effect on the ratings?

**e.** Determine the relative efficiency of the randomized block design as compared with the completely randomized design.

**11.64** Ignore the blocking variable in Problem 11.63.

**a.** "Erroneously" reanalyze the data as a one-factor completely randomized design where the one factor (brands of wines) has eight levels and each level contains a sample of 12 independent values.

**b.** Compare the *SSBL* and *SSE* terms in Problem 11.63(a) to the *SSW* term in (a). Discuss.

**c.** Using the results in Problem 11.63(a) and this problem, describe the issues that can arise when analyzing data if the wrong procedures are applied.

## Team Project

The data file **Mutual Funds** contains information regarding nine variables from a sample of 868 mutual funds. The variables are

Category—Type of stocks comprising the mutual fund (small cap, mid cap, or large cap)
Objective—Objective of stocks comprising the mutual fund (growth or value)
Assets—In millions of dollars
Fees—Sales charges (no or yes)
Expense ratio—Ratio of expenses to net assets in percentage
2006 return—Twelve-month return in 2006
Three-year return—Annualized return, 2004–2006
Five-year return—Annualized return, 2004–2006
Risk—Risk-of-loss factor of the mutual fund (low, average, or high)

**11.65** Completely analyze the difference between small cap, mid cap, and large cap mutual funds in terms of 2006 return, three-year return, five-year return, and expense ratio. Write a report summarizing your findings.

**11.66** Completely analyze the difference between low-risk, average-risk, and high-risk mutual funds in terms of

2006 return, three-year return, five-year return, and expense ratio. Write a report summarizing your findings.

## Student Survey Database

**11.67** Problem 1.27 on page 14 describes a survey of 50 undergraduate students (see the file **Undergradsurvey**). For these data,

**a.** at the 0.05 level of significance, is there evidence of a difference based on academic major in grade point index, expected starting salary, salary expected in five years, age, and spending on textbooks and supplies?

**b.** at the 0.05 level of significance, is there evidence of a difference based on graduate school intention in grade point index, expected starting salary, salary expected in five years, age, and spending on textbooks and supplies?

**c.** at the 0.05 level of significance, is there evidence of a difference based on employment status in grade point index, expected starting salary, salary expected in five years, age, and spending on textbooks and supplies?

**11.68** Problem 1.27 on page 14 describes a survey of 50 undergraduate students (see the file **Undergradsurvey**).

**a.** Select a sample of 50 undergraduate students at your school and conduct a similar survey for those students.

**b.** For the data collected in (a), repeat (a) through (c) of Problem 11.67.

**c.** Compare the results of (b) to those of Problem 11.67.

**11.69** Problem 1.28 on page 14 describes a survey of 40 MBA students (see the file **Gradsurvey**). For these data, at the 0.05 level of significance,

**a.** is there evidence of a difference, based on undergraduate major, in age, undergraduate grade point index, graduate grade point index, GMAT score, expected salary upon graduation, salary expected in five years, and spending on textbooks and supplies?

**b.** is there evidence of a difference, based on graduate major, in age, undergraduate grade point index, graduate grade point index, GMAT score, expected salary upon graduation, salary expected in five years, and spending on textbooks and supplies?

**c.** is there evidence of a difference, based on employment status, in age, undergraduate grade point index, graduate grade point index, GMAT score, expected salary upon graduation, salary expected in five years, and spending on textbooks and supplies?

**11.70** Problem 1.28 on page 14 describes a survey of 40 MBA students (see the file **Gradsurvey**).

**a.** Select a sample of 40 graduate students in your MBA program and conduct a similar survey for those students.

**b.** For the data collected in (a), repeat (a) through (c) of Problem 11.69.

**c.** Compare the results of (b) to those of Problem 11.69.

# MANAGING THE *SPRINGVILLE HERALD*

## Phase 1

In studying the home delivery solicitation process, the marketing department team determined that the so-called "later" calls made between 7:00 p.m. and 9:00 p.m. were significantly more conducive to lengthier calls than those made earlier in the evening (between 5:00 p.m. and 7:00 p.m.).

Knowing that the 7:00 p.m. to 9:00 p.m. time period is superior, the team sought to investigate the effect of the type of presentation on the length of the call. A group of 24 female callers was randomly assigned, 8 each, to one of three presentation plans—structured, semistructured, and unstructured—and trained to make the telephone presentation. All calls were made between 7:00 p.m. and 9:00 p.m., the later time period, and the callers were to provide an introductory greeting that was personal but informal ("Hi, this is Leigh Richardson from the *Springville Herald*. May I speak to Stuart Knoll?"). The callers knew that the team was observing their efforts that evening but didn't know which particular calls were monitored. Measurements were taken on the length of call (defined as the difference, in seconds, between the time the person answers the phone and the time he or she hangs up). Table SH11.1 presents the results (which are stored in the file SH11-1 ).

### TABLE SH11.1

Length of Calls (in Seconds) Based on Presentation Plan

| PRESENTATION PLAN | | |
|---|---|---|
| **Structured** | **Semistructured** | **Unstructured** |
| 38.8 | 41.8 | 32.9 |
| 42.1 | 36.4 | 36.1 |
| 45.2 | 39.1 | 39.2 |
| 34.8 | 28.7 | 29.3 |
| 48.3 | 36.4 | 41.9 |
| 37.8 | 36.1 | 31.7 |
| 41.1 | 35.8 | 35.2 |
| 43.6 | 33.7 | 38.1 |

### EXERCISE

SH11.1 Analyze these data and write a report to the team that indicates your findings. Be sure to include your recommendations based on your findings. Also, include an appendix in which you discuss the reason you selected a particular statistical test to compare the three independent groups of callers.

DO NOT CONTINUE UNTIL THE PHASE 1 EXERCISE HAS BEEN COMPLETED.

## Phase 2

In analyzing the data of Table SH11.1, the marketing department team observed that the structured presentation plan resulted in a significantly longer call than either the semistructured or unstructured plans. The team decided to tentatively recommend that all solicitations be completely structured calls made later in the evening, from 7:00 p.m. to 9:00 p.m. The team also decided to study the effect of two additional factors on the length of call:

- Gender of the caller: male versus female.
- Type of greeting: personal but formal (for example, "Hello, my name is Leigh Richardson from the *Springville Herald*. May I speak to Mr. Knoll?"), personal but informal (for example, "Hi, this is Leigh Richardson from the *Springville Herald*. May I speak to Stuart Knoll?"), or impersonal (for example, "I represent the *Springville Herald* . . . ").

The team acknowledged that in its previous studies, it had controlled for these variables. Only female callers were selected to participate in the studies, and they were trained to use a personal but informal greeting style. However, the team wondered if this choice of gender and greeting type was, in fact, best.

The team designed a study in which a total of 30 callers, 15 males and 15 females, were chosen to participate. The callers were randomly assigned to one of the three greeting-style training groups so that there were five callers in each of the six combinations of the two factors, gender and greeting style (personal but formal—PF; personal but informal—PI; and impersonal). The callers knew that the team was observing their efforts that evening but didn't know which particular calls were monitored.

### TABLE SH11.2

Length of Calls (in Seconds), Based on Gender and Type of Greeting

| GENDER | GREETING | | |
|---|---|---|---|
| | **PF** | **PI** | **Impersonal** |
| **Male** | 45.6 | 41.7 | 35.3 |
| | 49.0 | 42.8 | 37.7 |
| | 41.8 | 40.0 | 41.0 |
| | 35.6 | 39.6 | 28.7 |
| | 43.4 | 36.0 | 31.8 |
| **Female** | 44.1 | 37.9 | 43.3 |
| | 40.8 | 41.1 | 40.0 |
| | 46.9 | 35.8 | 43.1 |
| | 51.8 | 45.3 | 39.6 |
| | 48.5 | 40.2 | 33.2 |

Measurements were taken on the length of call (defined as the difference, in seconds, between the time the person answers and the time he or she hangs up the phone). Table SH11.2 summarizes the results (which are stored in the file SH11-2).

## EXERCISES

SH11.2 Completely analyze these data and write a report to the team that indicates the importance of each of the two factors and/or the interaction between them on the length of the call. Include recommendations for future experiments to perform.

SH11.3 Do you believe the length of the telephone call is the most appropriate outcome to study? What other variables should be investigated next? Discuss.

# WEB CASE

*Apply your knowledge about ANOVA in this Web Case, which continues the cereal-fill packaging dispute Web Case from Chapters 7, 9, and 10.*

After reviewing CCACC's latest posting (see Web Case for Chapter 10), Oxford Cereals is complaining that CCACC is guilty of using selective data. Visit Oxford Cereals' response page at **www.prenhall.com/Springville/OC_DataSelective.htm**, or open the OC_DataSelective.htm file from the Student CD-ROM Web Case folder and then answer the following:

1. Does Oxford Cereals have a legitimate argument? Why or why not?
2. Assuming that the samples Oxford Cereals has posted were randomly selected, perform the appropriate analysis to resolve the ongoing weight dispute.
3. What conclusions can you reach from your results? If you were called as an expert witness, would you support the claims of the CCACC or the claims of Oxford Cereals? Explain.

# REFERENCES

1. Berenson, M. L., D. M. Levine, and M. Goldstein, *Intermediate Statistical Methods and Applications: A Computer Package Approach* (Upper Saddle River, NJ: Prentice Hall, 1983).
2. Conover, W. J., *Practical Nonparametric Statistics*, 3rd ed. (New York: Wiley, 2000).
3. Daniel, W. W., *Applied Nonparametric Statistics*, 2nd ed. (Boston: PWS Kent, 1990).
4. Gitlow, H. S., and D. M. Levine, *Six Sigma for Green Belts and Champions: Foundations, DMAIC, Tools, Cases, and Certification* (Upper Saddle River, NJ: Financial Times/Prentice Hall, 2005).
5. Hicks, C. R., and K. V. Turner, *Fundamental Concepts in the Design of Experiments*, 5th ed. (New York: Oxford University Press, 1999).
6. Levine, D. M., *Statistics for Six Sigma Green Belts* (Upper Saddle River, NJ: Financial Times/Prentice Hall, 2006).
7. *Microsoft Excel 2007* (Redmond, WA: Microsoft Corp., 2007).
8. *Minitab for Windows Version 15* (State College, PA: Minitab, Inc., 2006).
9. Montgomery, D. M., *Design and Analysis of Experiments*, 6th ed. (New York: Wiley, 2005).
10. Neter, J., M. H. Kutner, C. Nachtsheim, and W. Wasserman, *Applied Linear Statistical Models*, 5th ed. (New York: McGraw-Hill-Irwin, 2005).

# Appendix E11
## Using Microsoft Excel for Analysis of Variance

### E11.1 Using One-Way ANOVA with Multiple Comparisons

You perform a one-way ANOVA with multiple comparisons by first using the ToolPak Anova: Single Factor procedure and then making entries in a worksheet in the **Tukey-Kramer.xls** workbook.

Open to the worksheet containing unstacked data for the three or more independent groups. Select **Tools → Data Analysis** (Excel 97–2003) or **Data → Data Analysis** (Excel 2007). Then select **Anova: Single Factor** from the **Data Analysis** list and click **OK**. In the procedure's dialog box (shown below), enter the cell range of the data as the **Input Range**, click **Columns** (if necessary), click **Labels in first row**, and click **OK**. Results appear on a new worksheet. Record the sample size and sample mean of each group (found in the Count and Average columns, respectively). Also record the *MSW* value, found in the cell that is the intersection of the **MS** column and **Within Groups** row, and the denominator degrees of freedom, found in the cell that is the intersection of the **df** column and **Within Groups** row.

Next, open the **Tukey-Kramer.xls** workbook and select the worksheet for your number of groups. If you have three groups, select the **TukeyKramer3** worksheet. If you have four groups, select the **TukeyKramer4** worksheet. (There are also worksheets for five, six, and seven groups.) Enter the sample size, sample mean, *MSW* value, and the denominator degrees of freedom you recorded earlier. Then look up the Studentized Range *Q* statistic from Table E.10 on page 933 for the level of significance of 0.05

and the numerator and denominator degrees of freedom values displayed in the worksheet.

To learn about the formulas used in the worksheets, open to the **TukeyKramer4Formulas** worksheet that displays the formulas that are used to compute the results shown in Figure 11.8 on page 454.

### E11.2 Using the Levene Test

You perform the Levene test by using the instructions of Section E11.1 with data from an Excel worksheet. Open to the worksheet that contains your unstacked multiple group data. The procedure must contain groups with equal sample sizes.

Add a row of formulas that use the **MEDIAN(*cell range*)** function to compute the median for each group. Then add a new set of columns that compute the absolute differences of each measurement and its corresponding median. Use the worksheets of the **Absolute Differences.xls** workbook as guides for creating these formulas. Once you create your new columns, follow the instructions of Section E11.1, using the cell range of the set of new absolute difference columns as the **Input Range** cell range. For example, if you were using the **Model** worksheet of the Absolute Differences workbook, you would enter **F1:I6** as the **Input Range**.

### E11.3 Using Randomized Block Designs

You perform an ANOVA for a randomized block design by using the ToolPak Anova: Two-Factor Without Replication procedure.

Open to a worksheet that contains block data in rows, starting with row 2, and group data in columns, starting with column B. Column A, starting with cell A2, should contain label values for the blocks and row 1, starting with cell B1, should contain label values for the groups. Use the **Data** worksheet of the **FFChain.xls** workbook as a guide for this design.

Select **Tools → Data Analysis** (Excel 97–2003) or **Data → Data Analysis** (Excel 2007). Then select **Anova: Two-Factor Without Replication**. In the procedure's dialog box (shown at the top of page 497), enter the cell range of the data (including all labels) as the **Input Range** and click **OK**. Results appear on a new worksheet.

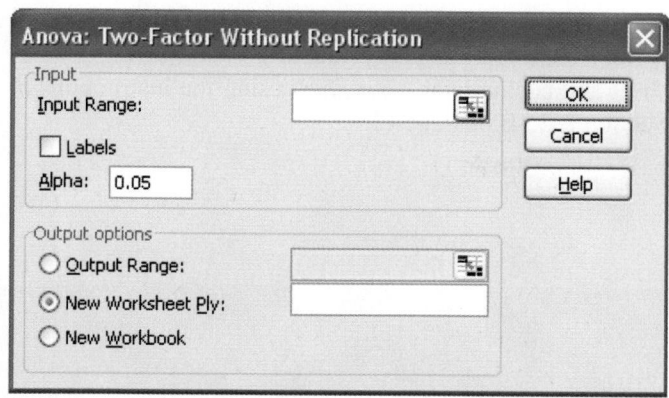

## E11.4 Using Two-Factor Factorial Designs

You perform a two-way ANOVA for a two-factor factorial design by using the ToolPak Anova: Two-Factor With Replication procedure.

Open to a worksheet that contains Factor A data in rows, starting with row 2, and Factor B data in columns, starting with column B. Column A, starting with cell A2, should contain label values for Factor A and row 1, starting with cell B1, should contain label values for Factor B. Use the **Data** worksheet of the `Parachute2.xls` workbook as a guide for this design.

Select **Tools → Data Analysis** (Excel 97–2003) or **Data → Data Analysis** (Excel 2007). Then select **Anova: Two-Factor With Replication**. In the procedure's dialog box (shown below), enter the cell range of the data (including all labels) as the **Input Range** and the **Rows per sample** (**5**, if you were using the **Data** worksheet of `Parachute2.xls`), and then click **OK**. Results appear on a new worksheet.

## E11.5 Creating Interaction Plots

You create interaction plots by first copying results found in the worksheet created by the ToolPak Anova: Two-Factor With Replication procedure and then by using Excel charting features to create the plot.

Begin with the instructions of Section E11.4 to create the necessary ANOVA results worksheet. Copy the SUMMARY row and the Average rows for factor A to a new worksheet, excluding the Total column. For example, if you were using the ANOVA results for the ACT scores shown in Figure 11.24 on page 481, copy cell range A3:C3 to row 1 of the new worksheet, copy cell range A7:C7 to row 2 of the new worksheet, and copy cell range A13:C13 to row 3 of the new worksheet.

In the new worksheet, change the **Average** labels in column A to distinctive labels and delete the label SUMMARY from cell A1. If you were copying data from the Figure 11.24 worksheet, your new worksheet would look similar to Figure E11.1, in which the labels **Traditional** and **Online** have replaced the Average labels in column A.

|   | A | B | C |
|---|---|---|---|
| 1 |   | Condensed | Regular |
| 2 | Traditional | 21.9 | 27.9 |
| 3 | Online | 27 | 21.3 |

**FIGURE E11.1** Example worksheet based on Figure 11.24 worksheet

To create the actual interaction plot continue with either Section E11.5A or Section E11.5B depending on which Excel version you use.

## E11.5A Creating Interaction Plots (Excel 97–2003)

Open to the new worksheet created in Section E11.5. Select **Insert → Chart** (to begin the Chart Wizard) and make the following entries in the Wizard Step dialog boxes:

**Wizard Step 1**   Click **Line** from the **Standard Types Chart Type** box and select the first Chart sub-type in the second row, identified as **Line with markers displayed at each value**.

**Wizard Step 2**   Enter the cell range of the data in your new worksheet in the **Data range** box and click the **Rows** option. (You would enter A1:C3 as the **Data range** if you were using the worksheet shown in Figure E11.1 above.)

**Wizard Step 3**   Click the **Titles** tab. Enter a title as the **Chart title** and enter appropriate values for the **Category (X) axis** and **Value (Y) axis** titles. Click the **Legend** tab and click **Show legend**. Click, in turn, the **Axes, Gridlines, Data Labels**, and **Data Table** tabs and use the formatting settings that are given in Section E2.3A on page 72.

### E11.5B Creating Interaction Plots (Excel 2007)

Open to the new worksheet created in Section E11.5. Select the cell range of the data in your new worksheet (A1:C3, if using the Figure E11.1 worksheet on page 497). Then select **Insert → Line** and click the **Line with Markers** gallery choice. Finish by relocating your chart to a chart sheet and customizing your chart using the instructions in Section E.2.3B on page 73.

# Appendix P11
## Using PHStat2 for Analysis of Variance

### P11.1 Using One-Way ANOVA with Multiple Comparisons

To perform a one-way ANOVA with multiple comparisons, use **PHStat → Multiple-Sample Tests → One-Way ANOVA**. This procedure uses the ToolPak Anova: Single Factor procedure to create a worksheet of ANOVA results and then creates a Tukey-Kramer worksheet similar to the ones described in Section E11.1 based on the unstacked data found in the **Group Data Cell Range**.

To complete the analysis, you will need to look up the Studentized Range $Q$ statistic from Table E.10 on page 933 for the level of significance ($\alpha$) equal to 0.05 and the numerator and denominator degrees of freedom displayed in the worksheet.

### P11.2 Using the Levene Test

To perform the Levene test, use **PHStat → Multiple-Sample Tests → Levene Test**. This procedure runs the ToolPak Anova: Single Factor procedure using a worksheet of absolute differences from the median that the procedure creates using the unstacked data from the **Sample Data Cell Range** that you specify. The procedure must contain groups with equal sample sizes in each group.

# Appendix M11
## Using Minitab for Analysis of Variance

## M11.1 Using One-Way ANOVA with Multiple Comparisons

To illustrate the one-way ANOVA:

1. Open the Parachute.mtw worksheet. (This worksheet contains unstacked data, with the data from each group in a separate column.)
2. Select **Stat → ANOVA → One-Way (Unstacked)**.

In the One-Way Analysis of Variance dialog box (see Figure M11.1):

3. Enter **Supplier1-Supplier4** in the **Responses (in separate columns)** box.
4. Click **Comparisons**.

**FIGURE M11.1** Minitab One-Way Analysis of Variance dialog box

In the One-Way Multiple Comparisons dialog box (see Figure M11.2):

5. Click **Tukey's, family error rate** and enter **5** in its box. (A family error rate of 5 produces confidence intervals with an overall confidence level of 95%.)
6. Click **OK**.
7. Back in the original dialog box, click **Graphs**.

8. In the One-Way Analysis of Variance - Graphs dialog box (not shown), click **Boxplots of data** and then click **OK**.
9. Back in the original dialog box, click **OK**.

**FIGURE M11.2** Minitab One-Way Multiple Comparisons dialog box

For stacked data, replace steps 2 and 3 with these instructions:

2. Select **Stat → ANOVA → Oneway**.

In the One-Way Analysis of Variance dialog box (not shown):

3. Enter the column containing the response variable (Strength for the Parachute.mtw worksheet) in the **Response** box and enter the column in containing the factor (Supplier for the Parachute.mtw worksheet) in the **Factor** box.

## M11.2 Creating Main Effects Plots

To illustrate creating a main effects plot:

1. Open the ParachuteStacked.mtw worksheet. This worksheet contains the data of Parachute.mtw in stacked order.
2. Select **Stat → ANOVA → Main Effects Plot**.

In the Main Effects Plot dialog box (see Figure M11.3):

3. Enter **Strength** in the **Responses** box.
4. Enter **Suppliers** in the **Factors** box.
5. Click **OK**.

**FIGURE M11.3** Minitab Main Effects Plot dialog box

## M11.3 Using the Levene Test

To illustrate the Levene test:

1. Open the ParachuteStacked.mtw worksheet.
2. Select **Stat → ANOVA → Test for Equal Variances**.

In the Test for Equal Variances dialog box (see Figure M11.4):

3. Enter **Strength** in the **Response** box
4. Enter **Suppliers** in the **Factor** box.
5. Enter **95.0** in the **Confidence level** box.
6. Click **OK**.

**FIGURE M11.4** Minitab Test for Equal Variances dialog box

## M11.4 Using Randomized Block and Two-Factor Designs

To illustrate the two-factor design:

1. Open the Parachute2.mtw worksheet.
2. Select **Stat → ANOVA → Two-Way**.

In the Two-Way Analysis of Variance dialog box (see Figure M11.5):

3. Enter **Strength** in the **Response** box.
4. Enter **Loom** in the **Row factor** box.
5. Enter **Supplier** in the **Column factor** box.
6. Click **Display means** for both the row and column factors.
7. Enter **95.0** in the **Confidence level** box.
8. Click **OK**.

**FIGURE M11.5** Minitab Two-Way Analysis of Variance dialog box

To illustrate the randomized block design:

1. Open the FFchain.mtw worksheet.
2. Select **Stat → ANOVA → Two-Way**.

In the Two-Way Analysis of Variance dialog box:

3. Enter **Rating** in the **Response** box.
4. Enter **Raters** in the **Row factor** box.
5. Enter **Restrat** in the **Column factor** box.
6. Click **Display means** for both the row and column factors.
7. Click **Fit Additive Model**.
8. Enter **95.0** in the **Confidence level** box.
9. Click **OK**.

## M11.5 Creating Interaction Plots

To illustrate creating an interaction plot:

1. Open the `Parachute2.mtw` worksheet.
2. Select **Stat → ANOVA → Interactions Plot**.

In the Interactions Plot dialog box (see Figure M11.6):

3. Enter **Strength** in the **Responses** box.
4. Enter **Loom** and **Supplier** in the **Factors** box.
5. Click **OK**.

**FIGURE M11.6** Minitab Interactions Plot dialog box

# CHAPTER TWELVE

## CHI-SQUARE TESTS AND NONPARAMETRIC TESTS

**USING STATISTICS @** T.C. Resort Properties

## LEARNING OBJECTIVES

### In this chapter, you learn:

- How and when to use the chi-square test for contingency tables
- How to use the Marascuilo procedure for determining pairwise differences when evaluating more than two proportions
- How and when to use the McNemar test
- How to use the chi-square test for a variance or standard deviation
- How and when to use nonparametric tests

# USING STATISTICS @ T.C. Resort Properties

You are the manager of T.C. Resort Properties, a collection of five upscale hotels located on two tropical islands. Guests who are satisfied with the quality of services during their stay are more likely to return on a future vacation and to recommend the hotel to friends and relatives. To assess the quality of services being provided by your hotels, guests are encouraged to complete a satisfaction survey when they check out. You need to analyze the data from these surveys to determine the overall satisfaction with the services provided, the likelihood that the guests will return to the hotel, and the reasons some guests indicate that they will not return. For example, on one island, T.C. Resort Properties operates the Beachcomber and Windsurfer hotels. Is the perceived quality at the Beachcomber Hotel the same as at the Windsurfer Hotel? If a difference is present, how can you use this information to improve the overall quality of service at T.C. Resort Properties? Furthermore, if guests indicate that they are not planning to return, what are the most common reasons given for this decision? Are the reasons given unique to a certain hotel or common to all hotels operated by T.C. Resort Properties?

In the preceding three chapters, you used hypothesis-testing procedures to analyze both numerical and categorical data. Chapter 9 presented some one-sample tests, and Chapter 10 developed several two-sample tests. Chapter 11 discussed the analysis of variance (ANOVA) that you use to study one or two factors of interest. This chapter extends hypothesis testing to analyze differences between population proportions based on two or more samples, as well as the hypothesis of *independence* in the joint responses to two categorical variables. The chapter concludes with nonparametric tests as alternatives to several hypothesis tests considered in Chapters 10 and 11.

## 12.1 CHI-SQUARE TEST FOR THE DIFFERENCE BETWEEN TWO PROPORTIONS (INDEPENDENT SAMPLES)

In Section 10.3, you studied the $Z$ test for the difference between two proportions. In this section, the data are examined from a different perspective. The hypothesis-testing procedure uses a test statistic that is approximated by a chi-square ($\chi^2$) distribution. The results of this $\chi^2$ test are equivalent to those of the $Z$ test described in Section 10.3.

If you are interested in comparing the counts of categorical responses between two independent groups, you can develop a two-way **contingency table** (see Section 2.4) to display the frequency of occurrence of items of interest and items not of interest for each group. In Chapter 4, contingency tables were used to define and study probability.

To illustrate the contingency table, return to the Using Statistics scenario concerning T.C. Resort Properties. On one of the islands, T.C. Resort Properties has two hotels (the Beachcomber and the Windsurfer). In tabulating the responses to the single question "Are you likely to choose this hotel again?" 163 of 227 guests at the Beachcomber responded yes, and 154 of 262 guests at the Windsurfer responded yes. At the 0.05 level of significance, is there evidence of a significant difference in guest satisfaction (as measured by likelihood to return to the hotel) between the two hotels?

The contingency table displayed in Table 12.1 has two rows and two columns and is called a **2 × 2 contingency table**. The cells in the table indicate the frequency for each row and column combination.

**TABLE 12.1**

Layout of a 2 × 2 Contingency Table

| ROW VARIABLE | COLUMN VARIABLE (GROUP) | | |
| --- | --- | --- | --- |
| | 1 | 2 | Totals |
| Items of interest | $X_1$ | $X_2$ | $X$ |
| Items not of interest | $n_1 - X_1$ | $n_2 - X_2$ | $n - X$ |
| Totals | $n_1$ | $n_2$ | $n$ |

where

$$X_1 = \text{number of items of interest in group 1}$$

$$X_2 = \text{number of items of interest in group 2}$$

$$n_1 - X_1 = \text{number of items that are not of interest in group 1}$$

$$n_2 - X_2 = \text{number of items that are not of interest in group 2}$$

$$X = X_1 + X_2, \text{ the total number of items of interest}$$

$$n - X = (n_1 - X_1) + (n_2 - X_2), \text{ the total number of items that are not of interest}$$

$$n_1 = \text{sample size in group 1}$$

$$n_2 = \text{sample size in group 2}$$

$$n = n_1 + n_2 = \text{total sample size}$$

Table 12.2 contains the contingency table for the hotel guest satisfaction study. The contingency table has two rows, indicating whether the guests would return to the hotel or would not return to the hotel, and two columns, one for each hotel. The cells in the table indicate the frequency of each row and column combination. The row totals indicate the number of guests who would return to the hotel and those who would not return to the hotel. The column totals are the sample sizes for each hotel location.

**TABLE 12.2**

2 × 2 Contingency Table for the Hotel Guest Satisfaction Survey

| CHOOSE HOTEL AGAIN? | HOTEL | | |
| --- | --- | --- | --- |
| | Beachcomber | Windsurfer | Total |
| Yes | 163 | 154 | 317 |
| No | 64 | 108 | 172 |
| Total | 227 | 262 | 489 |

To test whether the population proportion of guests who would return to the Beachcomber, $\pi_1$, is equal to the population proportion of guests who would return to the Windsurfer, $\pi_2$, you can use the $\chi^2$ **test for the difference between two proportions**. To test the null hypothesis that there is no difference between the two population proportions:

$$H_0: \pi_1 = \pi_2$$

against the alternative that the two population proportions are not the same:

$$H_1: \pi_1 \neq \pi_2$$

you use the $\chi^2_{STAT}$ test statistic, shown in Equation (12.1).

## $\chi^2$ Test for the Difference Between Two Proportions

The $\chi^2_{STAT}$ test statistic is equal to the squared difference between the observed and expected frequencies, divided by the expected frequency in each cell of the table, summed over all cells of the table.

$$\chi^2_{STAT} = \sum_{all\ cells} \frac{(f_o - f_e)^2}{f_e} \qquad \text{(12.1)}$$

where

$f_o$ = **observed frequency** in a particular cell of a contingency table

$f_e$ = **expected frequency** in a particular cell if the null hypothesis is true

The $\chi^2_{STAT}$ test statistic approximately follows a chi-square distribution with 1 degree of freedom.[1]

[1] In general, in a contingency table, the degrees of freedom are equal to the (number of rows – 1) times the (number of columns – 1).

To compute the expected frequency, $f_e$, in any cell, you need to understand that if the null hypothesis is true, the proportion of items of interest in the two populations will be equal. Then the sample proportions you compute from each of the two groups would differ from each other only by chance. Each would provide an estimate of the common population parameter, $\pi$. A statistic that combines these two separate estimates together into one overall estimate of the population parameter provides more information than either of the two separate estimates could provide by itself. This statistic, given by the symbol $\bar{p}$, represents the estimated overall proportion of items of interest for the two groups combined (i.e., the total number of items of interest divided by the total sample size). The complement of $\bar{p}$, $1 - \bar{p}$, represents the estimated overall proportion of items that are not of interest in the two groups. Using the notation presented in Table 12.1 on page 505, Equation (12.2) defines $\bar{p}$.

### Computing the Estimated Overall Proportion for 2 Groups

$$\bar{p} = \frac{X_1 + X_2}{n_1 + n_2} = \frac{X}{n} \qquad \text{(12.2)}$$

To compute the expected frequency, $f_e$, for each cell pertaining to items of interest (i.e., the cells in the first row in the contingency table), you multiply the sample size (or column total) for a group by $\bar{p}$. To compute the expected frequency, $f_e$, for each cell pertaining to items that are not of interest (i.e., the cells in the second row in the contingency table), you multiply the sample size (or column total) for a group by $1 - \bar{p}$.

The $\chi^2_{STAT}$ test statistic shown in Equation (12.1) approximately follows a **chi-square ($\chi^2$) distribution** (see Table E.4) with 1 degree of freedom. Using a level of significance $\alpha$, you reject the null hypothesis if the computed $\chi^2_{STAT}$ test statistic is greater than $\chi^2_\alpha$, the upper-tail critical value from the $\chi^2$ distribution having 1 degree of freedom. Thus, the decision rule is

Reject $H_0$ if $\chi^2_{STAT} > \chi^2_\alpha$;

otherwise do not reject $H_0$.

Figure 12.1 illustrates the decision rule.

**FIGURE 12.1**

Regions of rejection and nonrejection when using the chi-square test for the difference between two proportions, with level of significance α

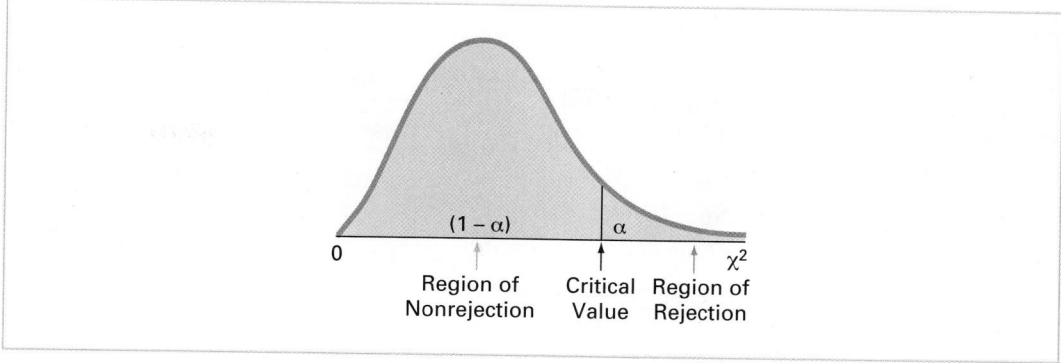

If the null hypothesis is true, the computed $\chi^2_{STAT}$ test statistic should be close to zero because the squared difference between what is actually observed in each cell, $f_o$, and what is theoretically expected, $f_e$, should be very small. If $H_0$ is false, then there are differences in the population proportions and the computed $\chi^2_{STAT}$ test statistic is expected to be large. However, what is a large difference in a cell is relative. The same actual difference between $f_o$ and $f_e$ from a cell with a small number of expected frequencies contributes more to the $\chi^2_{STAT}$ test statistic than a cell with a large number of expected frequencies.

To illustrate the use of the chi-square test for the difference between two proportions, return to the Using Statistics scenario concerning T.C. Resort Properties and the corresponding contingency table displayed in Table 12.2 on page 505. The null hypothesis ($H_0: \pi_1 = \pi_2$) states that there is no difference between the proportion of guests who are likely to choose either of these hotels again. To begin,

$$\bar{p} = \frac{X_1 + X_2}{n_1 + n_2} = \frac{163 + 154}{227 + 262} = \frac{317}{489} = 0.6483$$

$\bar{p}$ is the estimate of the common parameter $\pi$, the population proportion of guests who are likely to choose either of these hotels again if the null hypothesis is true. The estimated proportion of guests who are *not* likely to choose these hotels again is the complement of $\bar{p}$, $1 - 0.6483 = 0.3517$. Multiplying these two proportions by the sample size for the Beachcomber Hotel gives the number of guests expected to choose the Beachcomber again and the number not expected to choose this hotel again. In a similar manner, multiplying the two proportions by the Windsurfer Hotel's sample size yields the corresponding expected frequencies for that group.

**EXAMPLE 12.1**

COMPUTING THE EXPECTED FREQUENCIES

Compute the expected frequencies for each of the four cells of Table 12.2 on page 505.

**SOLUTION**

Yes—Beachcomber: $\bar{p} = 0.6483$ and $n_1 = 227$, so $f_e = 147.16$

Yes—Windsurfer: $\bar{p} = 0.6483$ and $n_2 = 262$, so $f_e = 169.84$

No—Beachcomber: $1 - \bar{p} = 0.3517$ and $n_1 = 227$, so $f_e = 79.84$

No—Windsurfer: $1 - \bar{p} = 0.3517$ and $n_2 = 262$, so $f_e = 92.16$

Table 12.3 presents these expected frequencies next to the corresponding observed frequencies.

**TABLE 12.3**

Comparing the Observed ($f_o$) and Expected ($f_e$) Frequencies

| CHOOSE HOTEL AGAIN? | HOTEL | | | | |
| --- | --- | --- | --- | --- | --- |
| | BEACHCOMBER | | WINDSURFER | | |
| | Observed | Expected | Observed | Expected | Total |
| Yes | 163 | 147.16 | 154 | 169.84 | 317 |
| No | 64 | 79.84 | 108 | 92.16 | 172 |
| Total | 227 | 227.00 | 262 | 262.00 | 489 |

To test the null hypothesis that the population proportions are equal:

$$H_0: \pi_1 = \pi_2$$

against the alternative that the population proportions are not equal:

$$H_1: \pi_1 \neq \pi_2$$

you use the observed and expected frequencies from Table 12.3 to compute the $\chi^2_{STAT}$ test statistic given by Equation (12.1) on page 506. Table 12.4 presents the calculations.

**TABLE 12.4**

Computing the $\chi^2_{STAT}$ Test Statistic for the Hotel Guest Satisfaction Survey

| $f_o$ | $f_e$ | $(f_o - f_e)$ | $(f_o - f_e)^2$ | $(f_o - f_e)^2 / f_e$ |
| --- | --- | --- | --- | --- |
| 163 | 147.16 | 15.84 | 250.91 | 1.71 |
| 154 | 169.84 | −15.84 | 250.91 | 1.48 |
| 64 | 79.84 | −15.84 | 250.91 | 3.14 |
| 108 | 92.16 | 15.84 | 250.91 | 2.72 |
| | | | | 9.05 |

The chi-square ($\chi^2$) distribution is a right-skewed distribution whose shape depends solely on the number of degrees of freedom. You find the critical value for the $\chi^2$ test from Table E.4, a portion of which is presented as Table 12.5.

**TABLE 12.5**

Finding the Critical Value from the Chi-Square Distribution with 1 Degree of Freedom, Using the 0.05 Level of Significance

| | Cumulative Probabilities | | | | | | |
| --- | --- | --- | --- | --- | --- | --- | --- |
| | .005 | .01 | ... | .95 | .975 | .99 | .995 |
| | Upper-Tail Area | | | | | | |
| Degrees of Freedom | .995 | .99 | ... | .05 | .025 | .01 | .005 |
| 1 | | | ... | 3.841 | 5.024 | 6.635 | 7.879 |
| 2 | 0.010 | 0.020 | ... | 5.991 | 7.378 | 9.210 | 10.597 |
| 3 | 0.072 | 0.115 | ... | 7.815 | 9.348 | 11.345 | 12.838 |
| 4 | 0.207 | 0.297 | ... | 9.488 | 11.143 | 13.277 | 14.860 |
| 5 | 0.412 | 0.554 | ... | 11.071 | 12.833 | 15.086 | 16.750 |

The values in Table 12.5 refer to selected upper-tail areas of the $\chi^2$ distribution. A 2 × 2 contingency table has $(2 - 1)(2 - 1) = 1$ degree of freedom. Using $\alpha = 0.05$, with 1 degree of freedom, the critical value of $\chi^2$ from Table 12.5 is 3.841. You reject $H_0$ if the computed $\chi^2_{STAT}$ test statistic is greater than 3.841 (see Figure 12.2). Because $\chi^2_{STAT} = 9.05 > 3.841$, you reject $H_0$. You conclude that the proportion of guests who would return to the Beachcomber is different from the proportion of guests who would return to the Windsurfer.

Figure 12.3 represents a Microsoft Excel worksheet for the guest satisfaction contingency table (Table 12.2 on page 505) and Figure 12.4 illustrates Minitab results.

**FIGURE 12.2**

Regions of rejection and nonrejection when finding the $\chi^2$ critical value with 1 degree of freedom, at the 0.05 level of significance

**FIGURE 12.3**

Microsoft Excel worksheet for the hotel guest satisfaction data

*See Section E12.1 or P12.1 to create this.*

|   | A | B | C | D |
|---|---|---|---|---|
| 1 | **Guest Satisfaction Analysis** | | | |
| 2 | | | | |
| 3 | **Observed Frequencies** | | | |
| 4 | | **Hotel** | | |
| 5 | **Choose Again?** | **Beachcomber** | **Windsurfer** | **Total** |
| 6 | Yes | 163 | 154 | 317 =SUM(B6:C6) |
| 7 | No | 64 | 108 | 172 =SUM(B7:C7) |
| 8 | Total | 227 | 262 | 489 =SUM(B8:C8) |
| 9 | | | | |
| 10 | Expected Frequencies | | | |
| 11 | | Hotel | | |
| 12 | Choose Again? | Beachcomber | Windsurfer | Total |
| 13 | Yes | 147.1554 | 169.8446 | 317 =SUM(B13:C13) |
| 14 | No | 79.8446 | 92.1554 | 172 =SUM(B14:C14) |
| 15 | Total | 227 | 262 | 489 =SUM(B15:C15) |
| 16 | | | | |
| 17 | **Data** | | | |
| 18 | Level of Significance | 0.05 | | |
| 19 | Number of Rows | 2 | | |
| 20 | Number of Columns | 2 | | |
| 21 | Degrees of Freedom | 1 | | |
| 22 | | | | |
| 23 | **Results** | | | |
| 24 | Critical Value | 3.8415 | =CHIINV(B18, B21) | |
| 25 | Chi-Square Test Statistic | 9.0526 | =SUM(F13:G14) | |
| 26 | *p*-Value | 0.0026 | =CHIDIST(B25, B21) | |
| 27 | Reject the null hypothesis | | =IF(B26 < B18, "Reject the null hypothesis", | |
| 28 | | | "Do not reject the null hypothesis") | |
| 29 | **Expected frequency assumption** | | | |
| 30 | **is met.** | | =IF(OR(B13 < 5, C13 < 5, B14 < 5, C14 < 5), | |
|   | | | "   is violated.", "   is met.") | |

**FIGURE 12.4**

Minitab results for the hotel guest satisfaction data

*See Section M12.2 to create this.*

```
Expected counts are printed below observed counts
Chi-Square contributions are printed below expected counts

          Beachcomber  Windsurfer  Total
    1           163         154      317
             147.16      169.84
              1.706       1.478

    2            64         108      172
              79.84       92.16
              3.144       2.724

 Total          227         262      489

Chi-Sq = 9.053, DF = 1, P-Value = 0.003
```

These results include the expected frequencies, $\chi^2_{STAT}$, degrees of freedom, and p-value. The computed $\chi^2_{STAT}$ test statistic is 9.0526, which is greater than the critical value of 3.8415 (or the p-value = 0.0026 < 0.05), so you reject the null hypothesis that there is no difference in guest satisfaction between the two hotels. The p-value of 0.0026 is the probability of observing sample proportions as different as or more different than the actual difference (0.718 − 0.588 = 0.13 observed in the sample data), if the population proportions for the Beachcomber and Windsurfer hotels are equal. Thus, there is strong evidence to conclude that the two hotels are significantly different with respect to guest satisfaction, as measured by whether the guest is likely to return to the hotel again. An examination of Table 12.3 on page 508 indicates that a greater proportion of guests are likely to return to the Beachcomber than to the Windsurfer.

For the $\chi^2$ test to give accurate results for a 2 × 2 table, you must assume that each expected frequency is at least 5. If this assumption is not satisfied, you can use alternative procedures such as Fisher's exact test (see references 1, 2, and 4).

In the hotel guest satisfaction survey, both the Z test based on the standardized normal distribution (see Section 10.3) and the $\chi^2$ test based on the chi-square distribution provide the same conclusion. You can explain this result by the interrelationship between the standardized normal distribution and a chi-square distribution with 1 degree of freedom. For such situations, the $\chi^2_{STAT}$ test statistic is the square of the $Z_{STAT}$ test statistic. For instance, in the guest satisfaction study, the computed $Z_{STAT}$ test statistic is +3.0088 and the computed $\chi^2_{STAT}$ test statistic is 9.0526. Except for rounding error, this latter value is the square of +3.0088 [i.e., $(+3.0088)^2 \cong 9.0526$]. Also, if you compare the critical values of the test statistics from the two distributions, at the 0.05 level of significance, the $\chi^2$ value of 3.841 with one degree of freedom is the square of the Z value of ±1.96. Furthermore, the p-values for both tests are equal. Therefore, when testing the null hypothesis of equality of proportions:

$$H_0: \pi_1 = \pi_2$$

against the alternative that the population proportions are not equal:

$$H_1: \pi_1 \neq \pi_2$$

the Z test and the $\chi^2$ test are equivalent. However, if you are interested in determining whether there is evidence of a *directional* difference, such as $\pi_1 > \pi_2$, you must use the Z test, with the entire rejection region located in one tail of the standardized normal distribution. In Section 12.2, the $\chi^2$ test is extended to make comparisons and evaluate differences between the proportions among more than two groups. However, you cannot use the Z test if there are more than two groups.

# PROBLEMS FOR SECTION 12.1

## Learning the Basics

**12.1** Determine the critical value of $\chi^2$ with 1 degree of freedom in each of the following circumstances:
a. $\alpha = 0.01$
b. $\alpha = 0.025$
c. $\alpha = 0.05$

**12.2** Determine the critical value of $\chi^2$ with 1 degree of freedom in each of the following circumstances:
a. $\alpha = 0.05$
b. $\alpha = 0.025$
c. $\alpha = 0.01$

**12.3** Use the following contingency table:

|       | A  | B  | Total |
|-------|----|----|-------|
| 1     | 20 | 30 | 50    |
| 2     | 30 | 45 | 75    |
| Total | 50 | 75 | 125   |

a. Find the expected frequency for each cell.
b. Compare the observed and expected frequencies for each cell.
c. Compute $\chi^2_{STAT}$. Is it significant at $\alpha = 0.05$?

**12.4** Use the following contingency table:

|        | A  | B  | Total |
|--------|----|----|-------|
| 1      | 20 | 30 | 50    |
| 2      | 30 | 20 | 50    |
| Total  | 50 | 50 | 100   |

a. Find the expected frequency for each cell.
b. Compute $\chi^2_{STAT}$. Is it significant at $\alpha = 0.05$?

## Applying the Concepts

**12.5** A sample of 500 shoppers was selected in a large metropolitan area to determine various information concerning consumer behavior. Among the questions asked was, "Do you enjoy shopping for clothing?" The results are summarized in the following contingency table:

| ENJOY SHOPPING | GENDER | | |
|----------------|--------|--------|-------|
| FOR CLOTHING   | Male   | Female | Total |
| Yes            | 136    | 224    | 360   |
| No             | 104    | 36     | 140   |
| Total          | 240    | 260    | 500   |

a. Is there evidence of a significant difference between the proportion of males and females who enjoy shopping for clothing at the 0.01 level of significance?
b. Determine the *p*-value in (a) and interpret its meaning.
c. What are your answers to (a) and (b) if 206 males enjoyed shopping for clothing and 34 did not?
d. Compare the results of (a) through (c) to those of Problem 10.31(a) through (c) on page 418.

**12.6** An article referencing a survey conducted by AP-LOL Learning Services claims that parents are more confident than teachers that their schools will meet the standards set by the No Child Left Behind Act. The survey asked parents (and teachers), "How confident are you that your child's school (the school where you work) will meet the standards by the deadline?" The responses to that question are given in the following table:

|                     | Parents | Teachers |
|---------------------|---------|----------|
| Very confident      | 401     | 162      |
| Not very confident  | 684     | 648      |
| Total               | 1,085   | 810      |

Source: *Extracted from B. Feller, "Teachers More Likely Skeptics of No Child," The Cincinnati Enquirer, April 20, 2006, p. A4.*

a. Is there evidence of a significant difference between the proportion of parents and teachers who are confident that schools will meet the standards set by No Child Left Behind at the 0.05 level of significance?
b. Determine the *p*-value in (a) and interpret its meaning.
c. Why shouldn't you compare the results in (a) to those of Problem 10.32 part (b) on p. 419?

**12.7** Some people enjoy the *anticipation* of an upcoming product or event and prefer to pay in advance and delay the actual consumption/delivery date. In other cases, people do not want a delay. An article in the *Journal of Marketing Research* reported on an experiment where 50 individuals were told that they had just purchased a ticket to a concert and 50 were told that they had just purchased a personal digital assistant (PDA). The participants were then asked to indicate their preferences for attending the concert or receiving the PDA. Did they prefer tonight or tomorrow, or would they prefer to wait two to four weeks? The individuals were told to ignore their schedule restraints in order to better measure their willingness to delay the consumption/delivery of their purchase. The following table gives partial results of the study.

|                      | Concert | PDA |
|----------------------|---------|-----|
| Tonight or Tomorrow  | 28      | 47  |
| Two to Four Weeks    | 22      | 3   |
| Total                | 50      | 50  |

Source: *Adapted from O. Amir and D. Ariely, "Decisions by Rules: The Case of Unwillingness to Pay for Beneficial Delays,"* Journal of Marketing Research, *February 2007, Vol. XLIV, pp. 142–152.*

a. What proportion of the participants would prefer delaying the date of the concert?
b. What proportion of the participants would prefer delaying receipt of a new PDA?
c. Using the 0.05 level of significance, is there evidence of a significance difference in the proportion willing to delay the date of the concert and the proportion willing to delay receipt of a new PDA?

**SELF Test** **12.8** According to an Ipsos poll, the perception of unfairness in the U.S. tax code is spread fairly evenly across income groups, age groups, and education levels. In an April 2006 survey of 1,005 adults, Ipsos reported that almost 60% of all people said the code is unfair, whereas slightly more that 60% of those making more than $50,000 viewed the code as unfair (extracted from "People Cry Unfairness," *The Cincinnati Enquirer*, April 16, 2006, p. A8). Suppose that the following contingency table represents the specific breakdown of responses:

| | INCOME LEVEL | | |
| U.S. TAX CODE | Less Than $50,000 | More Than $50,000 | Total |
| --- | --- | --- | --- |
| Fair | 225 | 180 | 405 |
| Unfair | 280 | 320 | 600 |
| Total | 505 | 500 | 1,005 |

**a.** At the 0.05 level of significance, is there evidence of a difference in the proportion of adults who think the U.S. tax code is unfair between the two income groups?

**b.** Determine the *p*-value in (a) and interpret its meaning.

**c.** Compare the results of (a) and (b) to those of Problem 10.34 on page 419.

**12.9** Where people turn to for news is different for various age groups. Suppose that a study conducted on this issue (extracted from P. Johnson, "Young People Turn to the Web for News," *USA Today*, March 23, 2006, p. 9D) was based on 200 respondents who were between the ages of 36 and 50 and 200 respondents who were above age 50. Of the 200 respondents who were between the ages of 36 and 50, 82 got their news primarily from newspapers. Of the 200 respondents who were above age 50, 104 got their news primarily from newspapers.

**a.** Construct a 2 × 2 contingency table.

**b.** Is there evidence of a significant difference in the proportion who get their news primarily from newspapers between those 36 to 50 years old and those above 50 years old? (Use $\alpha = 0.05$.)

**c.** Determine the *p*-value in (a) and interpret its meaning.

**d.** Compare the results of (b) and (c) to those of Problem 10.37 on page 480.

**12.10** An experiment was conducted to study the choices made in mutual fund selection. Undergraduate and MBA students were presented with different S&P 500 index funds that were identical except for fees. Suppose 100 undergraduate students and 100 MBA students were selected. Partial results are shown as follows:

| | STUDENT GROUP | |
| FUND | Undergraduate | MBA |
| --- | --- | --- |
| Highest-cost fund | 27 | 18 |
| Not highest-cost fund | 73 | 82 |

Source: *Extracted from J. Choi, D. Laibson, and B. Madrian, "Why Does the Law of One Practice Fail? An Experiment on Mutual Funds," www.som.yale.edu/faculty/jjc83/fees.pdf.*

**a.** At the 0.05 level of significance, is there evidence of a difference between undergraduate and MBA students in the proportion who selected the highest-cost fund?

**b.** Determine the *p*-value in (a) and interpret its meaning.

**c.** Compare the results of (a) and (b) to those of Problem 10.36 on page 419.

## 12.2  CHI-SQUARE TEST FOR DIFFERENCES AMONG MORE THAN TWO PROPORTIONS

In this section, the $\chi^2$ test is extended to compare more than two independent populations. The letter $c$ is used to represent the number of independent populations under consideration. Thus, the contingency table now has two rows and $c$ columns. To test the null hypothesis that there are no differences among the $c$ population proportions:

$$H_0: \pi_1 = \pi_2 = \cdots = \pi_c$$

against the alternative that not all the $c$ population proportions are equal:

$$H_1: \text{Not all } \pi_j \text{ are equal (where } j = 1, 2, \ldots, c)$$

you use Equation (12.1) on page 506:

$$\chi^2_{STAT} = \sum_{all\ cells} \frac{(f_o - f_e)^2}{f_e}$$

where

$f_o$ = observed frequency in a particular cell of a 2 × c contingency table

$f_e$ = expected frequency in a particular cell if the null hypothesis is true

If the null hypothesis is true and the proportions are equal across all $c$ populations, the $c$ sample proportions should differ only by chance. In such a situation, a statistic that combines these $c$ separate estimates into one overall estimate of the population proportion, $\pi$, provides more information than any one of the $c$ separate estimates alone. To expand on Equation (12.2) on page 506, the statistic $\bar{p}$ in Equation (12.3) represents the estimated overall proportion for all $c$ groups combined.

### Computing the Estimated Overall Proportion for c Groups

$$\bar{p} = \frac{X_1 + X_2 + \cdots + X_c}{n_1 + n_2 + \cdots + n_c} = \frac{X}{n} \qquad (12.3)$$

To compute the expected frequency, $f_e$, for each cell in the first row in the contingency table, multiply each sample size (or column total) by $\bar{p}$. To compute the expected frequency, $f_e$, for each cell in the second row in the contingency table, multiply each sample size (or column total) by $(1 - \bar{p})$. The test statistic shown in Equation (12.1) on page 506 approximately follows a chi-square distribution, with degrees of freedom equal to the number of rows in the contingency table minus 1, times the number of columns in the table minus 1. For a **2 × c contingency table**, there are $c - 1$ degrees of freedom:

$$\text{Degrees of freedom} = (2 - 1)(c - 1) = c - 1$$

Using the level of significance $\alpha$, you reject the null hypothesis if the computed $\chi^2_{STAT}$ test statistic is greater than $\chi^2_\alpha$, the upper-tail critical value from a chi-square distribution with $c - 1$ degrees of freedom. Therefore, the decision rule is

$$\text{Reject } H_0 \text{ if } \chi^2_{STAT} > \chi^2_\alpha;$$

otherwise do not reject $H_0$.

**FIGURE 12.5**

Regions of rejection and nonrejection when testing for differences among c proportions using the $\chi^2$ test

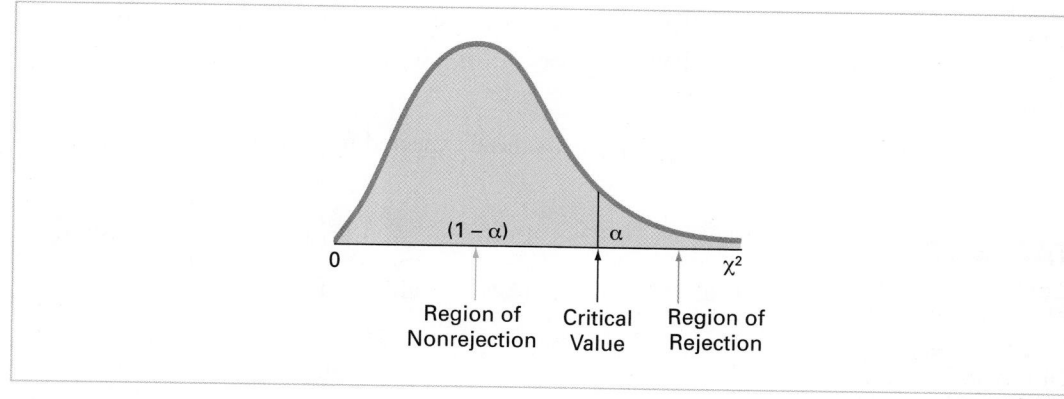

Figure 12.5 illustrates the decision rule.

To illustrate the $\chi^2$ test for equality of proportions when there are more than two groups, return to the Using Statistics scenario on page 504 concerning T.C. Resort Properties. A similar survey was recently conducted on a different island on which T.C. Resort Properties has three different hotels. Table 12.6 presents the responses to a question concerning whether guests would be likely to choose this hotel again.

**TABLE 12.6**

2 × 3 Contingency Table for Guest Satisfaction Survey

| | HOTEL | | | |
|---|---|---|---|---|
| **CHOOSE HOTEL AGAIN?** | **Golden Palm** | **Palm Royale** | **Palm Princess** | **Total** |
| **Yes** | 128 | 199 | 186 | 513 |
| **No** | 88 | 33 | 66 | 187 |
| **Total** | 216 | 232 | 252 | 700 |

Because the null hypothesis states that there are no differences among the three hotels in the proportion of guests who would likely return again, you use Equation (12.3) to calculate an estimate of $\pi$, the population proportion of guests who would likely return again:

$$\bar{p} = \frac{X_1 + X_2 + \cdots + X_c}{n_1 + n_2 + \cdots + n_c} = \frac{X}{n}$$

$$= \frac{(128 + 199 + 186)}{(216 + 232 + 252)} = \frac{513}{700}$$

$$= 0.733$$

The estimated overall proportion of guests who would *not* be likely to return again is the complement, $(1 - \bar{p})$, or 0.267. Multiplying these two proportions by the sample size taken at each hotel yields the expected number of guests who would and would not likely return.

**EXAMPLE 12.2**

COMPUTING THE EXPECTED FREQUENCIES

Compute the expected frequencies for each of the six cells in Table 12.6.

**SOLUTION**

Yes—Golden Palm: $\bar{p} = 0.733$ and $n_1 = 216$, so $f_e = 158.30$
Yes—Palm Royale: $\bar{p} = 0.733$ and $n_2 = 232$, so $f_e = 170.02$
Yes—Palm Princess: $\bar{p} = 0.733$ and $n_3 = 252$, so $f_e = 184.68$
No—Golden Palm: $1 - \bar{p} = 0.267$ and $n_1 = 216$, so $f_e = 57.70$
No—Palm Royale: $1 - \bar{p} = 0.267$ and $n_2 = 232$, so $f_e = 61.98$
No—Palm Princess: $1 - \bar{p} = 0.267$ and $n_3 = 252$, so $f_e = 67.32$

Table 12.7 presents these expected frequencies.

**TABLE 12.7**

Contingency Table of Expected Frequencies from a Guest Satisfaction Survey of Three Hotels

| | HOTEL | | | |
|---|---|---|---|---|
| **CHOOSE HOTEL AGAIN?** | **Golden Palm** | **Palm Royale** | **Palm Princess** | **Total** |
| **Yes** | 158.30 | 170.02 | 184.68 | 513 |
| **No** | 57.70 | 61.98 | 67.32 | 187 |
| **Total** | 216.00 | 232.00 | 252.00 | 700 |

To test the null hypothesis that the proportions are equal:

$$H_0: \pi_1 = \pi_2 = \pi_3$$

against the alternative that not all three proportions are equal:

$$H_1: \text{Not all } \pi_j \text{ are equal (where } j = 1, 2, 3).$$

You use the observed frequencies from Table 12.6 on page 514 and the expected frequencies from Table 12.7 to compute the $\chi^2_{STAT}$ test statistic (given by Equation (12.1) on page 506. Table 12.8 presents the calculations.

**TABLE 12.8**

Computing the $\chi^2_{STAT}$ Test Statistic for the Guest Satisfaction Survey of Three Hotels

| $f_o$ | $f_e$ | $(f_o - f_e)$ | $(f_o - f_e)^2$ | $(f_o - f_e)^2/f_e$ |
|---|---|---|---|---|
| 128 | 158.30 | −30.30 | 918.09 | 5.80 |
| 199 | 170.02 | 28.98 | 839.84 | 4.94 |
| 186 | 184.68 | 1.32 | 1.74 | 0.01 |
| 88 | 57.70 | 30.30 | 918.09 | 15.91 |
| 33 | 61.98 | −28.98 | 839.84 | 13.55 |
| 66 | 67.32 | −1.32 | 1.74 | 0.02 |
| | | | | 40.23 |

You use Table E.4 to find the critical value of the $\chi^2$ test statistic. In the guest satisfaction survey, because three hotels are evaluated, there are $(2 - 1)(3 - 1) = 2$ degrees of freedom. Using $\alpha = 0.05$, the $\chi^2$ critical value with 2 degrees of freedom is 5.991. Because the computed $\chi^2_{STAT}$ test statistic is 40.23 which is greater than this critical value, you reject the null hypothesis (see Figure 12.6). Microsoft Excel and Minitab (see Figures 12.7 and 12.8 on page 516) also report the $p$-value. Likewise, because the $p$-value is approximately 0.0000, which is less than $\alpha = 0.05$, you reject the null hypothesis. Further, this $p$-value indicates that there is virtually no chance to see differences this large or larger among the three sample proportions, if the population proportions for the three hotels are equal. Thus, there is sufficient evidence to conclude that the hotel properties are different with respect to the proportion of guests who are likely to return.

**FIGURE 12.6**

Regions of rejection and nonrejection when testing for differences in three proportions at the 0.05 level of significance, with 2 degrees of freedom

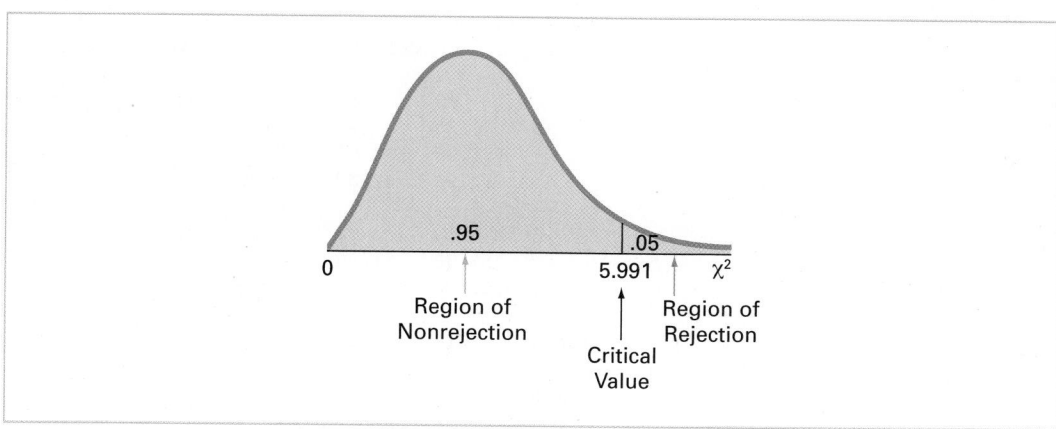

For the $\chi^2$ test to give accurate results when dealing with $2 \times c$ contingency tables, all expected frequencies must be large. There is much debate among statisticians about the definition of *large*. Some statisticians (see reference 6) have found that the test gives accurate results as long as all expected frequencies are at least 0.5. Other statisticians, more conservative in their approach, require that no more than 20% of the cells contain expected frequencies less than 5 and no cells have expected frequencies less than 1 (see reference 3). A reasonable compromise between these points of view is to make sure that each expected frequency is at least 1. To ensure that the expected frequencies are sufficiently large to conduct the $\chi^2$ test accurately, you may need to collapse two or more low-expected-frequency categories into one category in

**FIGURE 12.7**

Microsoft Excel worksheet for the guest satisfaction data of Table 12.6

*See Section E12.2 or P12.2 to create this.*

| | A | B | C | D | E |
|---|---|---|---|---|---|
| 1 | Guest Satisfaction (3-Hotels) Analysis | | | | |
| 2 | | | | | |
| 3 | Observed Frequencies | | | | |
| 4 | | Hotel | | | |
| 5 | Choose Again? | Golden Palm | Palm Royale | Palm Princess | Total |
| 6 | Yes | 128 | 199 | 186 | 513 |
| 7 | No | 88 | 33 | 66 | 187 |
| 8 | Total | 216 | 232 | 252 | 700 |
| 9 | | | | | |
| 10 | Expected Frequencies | | | | |
| 11 | | Hotel | | | |
| 12 | Choose Again? | Golden Palm | Palm Royale | Palm Princess | Total |
| 13 | Yes | 158.2971 | 170.0229 | 184.68 | 513 |
| 14 | No | 57.7029 | 61.9771 | 67.32 | 187 |
| 15 | Total | 216 | 232 | 252 | 700 |
| 16 | | | | | |
| 17 | Data | | | | |
| 18 | Level of Significance | 0.05 | | | |
| 19 | Number of Rows | 2 | | | |
| 20 | Number of Columns | 3 | | | |
| 21 | Degrees of Freedom | 2 | =(B19 - 1) * (B20 - 1) | | |
| 22 | | | | | |
| 23 | Results | | | | |
| 24 | Critical Value | 5.9915 | =CHIINV(B18, B21) | | |
| 25 | Chi-Square Test Statistic | 40.2284 | =SUM(G13:I14) | | |
| 26 | p-Value | 0.0000 | =CHIDIST(B25, B21) | | |
| 27 | Reject the null hypothesis | | =IF(B26 < B18, "Reject the null hypothesis", "Do not reject the null hypothesis") | | |
| 28 | | | | | |
| 29 | Expected frequency assumption | | =IF(OR(B13 < 1, C13 < 1, D13 < 1, B14 < 1, C14 < 1, D14 < 1), | | |
| 30 | is met. | | " is violated.", " is met.") | | |

**FIGURE 12.8**

Minitab results for the guest satisfaction data of Table 12.6

*See Section M12.2 to create this.*

```
Chi-Square Test: C3, C4, C5

Expected counts are printed below observed counts
Chi-Square contributions are printed below expected counts

             C3       C4       C5   Total
   1        128      199      186     513
         158.30   170.02   184.68
          5.799    4.939    0.009

   2         88       33       66     187
          57.70    61.98    67.32
         15.908   13.548    0.026

Total      216      232      252     700

Chi-Sq = 40.228, DF = 2, P-Value = 0.000
```

the contingency table before performing the test. If combining categories is undesirable, alternative procedures are available (see references 1, 2, and 8).

## The Marascuilo Procedure

Rejecting the null hypothesis in a $\chi^2$ test of equality of proportions in a $2 \times c$ table only allows you to reach the conclusion that not all $c$ population proportions are equal. But *which* of the proportions differ? Because the result of the $\chi^2$ test for equality of proportions does not specifically answer this question, you need to use a multiple comparisons procedure such as the Marascuilo procedure.

The **Marascuilo procedure** enables you to make comparisons between all pairs of groups. First, you compute the sample proportions. Then, you use Equation (12.4) to compute the critical ranges for the Marascuilo procedure. You need to compute a different critical range for each pairwise comparison of sample proportions.

---

**Critical Range for the Marascuilo Procedure**

$$\text{Critical range} = \sqrt{\chi_\alpha^2} \sqrt{\frac{p_j(1-p_j)}{n_j} + \frac{p_{j'}(1-p_{j'})}{n_{j'}}} \qquad \textbf{(12.4)}$$

---

In the final step, you compare each of the $c(c-1)/2$ pairs of sample proportions against its corresponding critical range. You declare a specific pair significantly different if the absolute difference in the sample proportions $|p_j - p_{j'}|$ is greater than its critical range.

To apply the Marascuilo procedure, return to the guest satisfaction survey. Using the $\chi^2$ test, you concluded that there was evidence of a significant difference among the population proportions. From Table 12.6 on page 514, the three sample proportions are

$$p_1 = \frac{X_1}{n_1} = \frac{128}{216} = 0.593$$

$$p_2 = \frac{X_2}{n_2} = \frac{199}{232} = 0.858$$

$$p_3 = \frac{X_3}{n_3} = \frac{186}{252} = 0.738$$

Next, you compute the absolute differences in sample proportions and their corresponding critical ranges. Because there are three hotels, there are $(3)(3-1)/2 = 3$ pairwise comparisons. Using Table E.4 and an overall level of significance of 0.05, the upper-tail critical value for a chi-square distribution having $(c-1) = 2$ degrees of freedom is 5.991. Thus,

$$\sqrt{\chi_\alpha^2} = \sqrt{5.991} = 2.448$$

| **Absolute Difference in Proportions** | **Critical Range** |
|---|---|
| $\lvert p_j - p_{j'} \rvert$ | $2.448\sqrt{\dfrac{p_j(1-p_j)}{n_j} + \dfrac{p_{j'}(1-p_{j'})}{n_{j'}}}$ |
| $\lvert p_1 - p_2 \rvert = \lvert 0.593 - 0.858 \rvert = 0.265$ | $2.448\sqrt{\dfrac{(0.593)(0.407)}{216} + \dfrac{(0.858)(0.142)}{232}} = 0.0992$ |
| $\lvert p_1 - p_3 \rvert = \lvert 0.593 - 0.738 \rvert = 0.145$ | $2.448\sqrt{\dfrac{(0.593)(0.407)}{216} + \dfrac{(0.738)(0.262)}{252}} = 0.1063$ |
| $\lvert p_2 - p_3 \rvert = \lvert 0.858 - 0.738 \rvert = 0.120$ | $2.448\sqrt{\dfrac{(0.858)(0.142)}{232} + \dfrac{(0.738)(0.262)}{252}} = 0.0880$ |

These computations are shown in Figure 12.9.

**FIGURE 12.9**

Microsoft Excel
Marascuilo procedure
worksheet

*See Section E12.2 or P12.2
to create this or for more
information about the
formulas this worksheet
uses.*

| | A | B | C | D |
|---|---|---|---|---|
| 1 | **Marascuilo Procedure** | | | |
| 2 | **Guest Satisfaction (3-Hotels) Analysis** | | | |
| 3 | Level of Significance | 0.05 | | |
| 4 | Square Root of Critical Value | 2.4477 | | |
| 5 | | | | |
| 6 | Sample Proportions | | | |
| 7 | Group 1 | 0.5926 | | |
| 8 | Group 2 | 0.8578 | | |
| 9 | Group 3 | 0.7381 | | |
| 10 | | | | |
| 11 | MARASCUILO TABLE | | | |
| 12 | **Proportions** | **Absolute Differences** | **Critical Range** | |
| 13 | \| Group 1 - Group 2 \| | 0.2652 | 0.0992 | Significant |
| 14 | \| Group 1 - Group 3 \| | 0.1455 | 0.1063 | Significant |
| 15 | | | | |
| 16 | \| Group 2 - Group 3 \| | 0.1197 | 0.0880 | Significant |

The final step is to compare the absolute differences to the critical ranges. If the absolute difference is greater than its critical range, the proportions are significantly different. With 95% confidence, you can conclude that guest satisfaction is higher at the Palm Royale ($p_2 = 0.858$) than at either the Golden Palm ($p_1 = 0.593$) or the Palm Princess ($p_3 = 0.738$) and that guest satisfaction is also higher at the Palm Princess than at the Golden Palm. These results clearly suggest that you investigate possible reasons for these differences. In particular, you should try to determine why satisfaction is significantly lower at the Golden Palm than at the other two hotels.

# PROBLEMS FOR SECTION 12.2

## Learning the Basics

**12.11** Consider a contingency table with two rows and five columns.
**a.** Find the degrees of freedom.
**b.** Find the critical value for $\alpha = 0.05$.
**c.** Find the critical value for $\alpha = 0.01$.

**12.12** Use the following contingency table:

| | A | B | C | Total |
|---|---|---|---|---|
| **1** | 10 | 30 | 50 | 90 |
| **2** | 40 | 45 | 50 | 135 |
| **Total** | 50 | 75 | 100 | 225 |

**a.** Compute the expected frequencies for each cell.
**b.** Compute $\chi^2_{STAT}$. Is it significant at $\alpha = 0.05$?
**c.** If appropriate, use the Marascuilo procedure and $\alpha = 0.05$ to determine which groups are different.

**12.13** Use the following contingency table:

| | A | B | C | Total |
|---|---|---|---|---|
| **1** | 20 | 30 | 25 | 75 |
| **2** | 30 | 20 | 25 | 75 |
| **Total** | 50 | 50 | 50 | 150 |

**a.** Compute the expected frequencies for each cell.
**b.** Compute $\chi^2_{STAT}$. Is it significant at $\alpha = 0.05$?
**c.** If appropriate, use the Marascuilo procedure and $\alpha = 0.05$ to determine which groups are different.

## Applying the Concepts

**12.14** A survey was conducted in five countries. The percentages of respondents who said that they eat out once a week or more are as follows:

| | |
|---|---|
| Germany | 10% |
| France | 12% |
| United Kingdom | 28% |
| Greece | 39% |
| United States | 57% |

Source: *Adapted from M. Kissel, "Americans Are Keen on Cocooning," The Wall Street Journal, July 22, 2003, p. D3.*

Suppose that the survey was based on 1,000 respondents in each country.
**a.** At the 0.05 level of significance, determine whether there is a significant difference in the proportion of people who eat out at least once a week in the various countries.
**b.** Find the *p*-value in (a) and interpret its meaning.

**c.** If appropriate, use the Marascuilo procedure and $\alpha = 0.05$ to determine which countries are different. Discuss your results.

**12.15** The health-care industry and consumer advocacy groups are at odds over the sharing of a patient's medical records without the patient's consent. The health-care industry believes that no consent should be necessary to openly share data among doctors, hospitals, pharmacies, and insurance companies.

Suppose a study is conducted in which 600 patients are randomly assigned, 200 each, to three "organizational groupings"—insurance companies, pharmacies, and medical researchers. Each patient is given material to read about the advantages and disadvantages concerning the sharing of medical records within the assigned "organizational grouping." Each patient is then asked "would you object to the sharing of your medical records with. . ." and the results are recorded in the cross-classification table below.

| OBJECT TO SHARING INFORMATION | ORGANIZATIONAL GROUPING | | |
|---|---|---|---|
| | Insurance | Pharmacies | Research |
| Yes | 40 | 80 | 90 |
| No | 160 | 120 | 110 |

**a.** Is there evidence of a difference in objection to sharing information among the organizational groupings? (Use $\alpha = 0.05$.)

**b.** Compute the $p$-value and interpret its meaning.

**c.** If appropriate, use the Marascuilo procedure and $\alpha = 0.05$ to determine which groups are different.

✓ SELF Test **12.16** More shoppers do the majority of their grocery shopping on Saturday than any other day of the week. However, is there a difference in the various age groups in the proportion of people who do the majority of their grocery shopping on Saturday? A study showed the results for the different age groups (extracted from "Major Shopping by Day," *Progressive Grocer Annual Report*, April 30, 2002). The data were reported as percentages, and no sample sizes were given:

| MAJOR SHOPPING DAY | AGE | | |
|---|---|---|---|
| | Under 35 | 35–54 | Over 54 |
| Saturday | 24% | 28% | 12% |
| A day other than Saturday | 76% | 72% | 88% |

Assume that 200 shoppers for each age category were surveyed.

**a.** Is there evidence of a significant difference among the age groups with respect to major grocery shopping day? (Use $\alpha = 0.05$.)

**b.** Determine the $p$-value in (a) and interpret its meaning.

**c.** If appropriate, use the Marascuilo procedure and $\alpha = 0.05$ to determine which age groups are different. Discuss your results.

**d.** Discuss the managerial implications of (a) and (c). How can grocery stores use this information to improve marketing and sales? Be specific.

**12.17** Repeat (a) through (b) of Problem 12.16, assuming that only 50 shoppers for each age category were surveyed. Discuss the implications of sample size on the $\chi^2$ test for differences among more than two populations.

**12.18** More and more people are finding that they need to delay retirement for financial reasons (extracted from T. Luhby, "When Retirement Is a Luxury You Can't Afford," *Newsday*, September 30, 2006, pp. B4, B5, B8). A study reported that 52% of men age 62–64 were still working, 41% of women age 62–64 were still working, 31% men age 65–69 were still working, and 23% of women age 65–69 were still working. Suppose that the study was based on a sample size of 100 in each group.

**a.** Is there evidence of a significant difference among the groups with respect to the proportion who are still working? (Use $\alpha = 0.05$.)

**b.** Determine the $p$-value in (a) and interpret its meaning.

**c.** If appropriate, use the Marascuilo procedure and $\alpha = 0.05$ to determine which age groups are different. Discuss your results.

**12.19** More and more people are paying with plastic (extracted from *USA Today Snapshots*, March 6, 2007, p. 1B). A study taken in 1995 reported that 18% of the respondents paid for a specific type of purchase with plastic, whereas a similar study in 2005 indicated that 25% paid for a specific type of purchase with plastic. (No sample sizes were reported for either study.) Suppose that a new survey taken in 2007 indicated that 31% paid for a specific type of purchase with plastic. Suppose that all three studies used a sample size of 500.

**a.** Is there evidence of a significant difference between the years in the proportion of respondents who paid for a specific type of purchase with plastic? (Use $\alpha = 0.05$.)

**b.** Determine the $p$-value in (a) and interpret its meaning.

**c.** If appropriate, use the Marascuilo procedure and $\alpha = 0.05$ to determine which years are different. Discuss your results.

## 12.3    CHI-SQUARE TEST OF INDEPENDENCE

In Sections 12.1 and 12.2, you used the $\chi^2$ test to evaluate potential differences among population proportions. For a contingency table that has $r$ rows and $c$ columns, you can generalize the $\chi^2$ test as a *test of independence* for two categorical variables.

For a test of independence, the null and alternative hypotheses follow:

$H_0$: The two categorical variables are independent (i.e., there is no relationship between them).
$H_1$: The two categorical variables are dependent (i.e., there is a relationship between them).

Once again, you use Equation (12.1) on page 506 to compute the test statistic:

$$\chi^2_{STAT} = \sum_{all\ \text{cells}} \frac{(f_o - f_e)^2}{f_e}$$

You reject the null hypothesis at the $\alpha$ level of significance if the computed value of the $\chi^2_{STAT}$ test statistic is greater than $\chi^2_\alpha$, the upper-tail critical value from a chi-square distribution with $(r - 1)(c - 1)$ degrees of freedom (see Figure 12.10). Thus, the decision rule is

Reject $H_0$ if $\chi^2_{STAT} > \chi^2_\alpha$;

otherwise do not reject $H_0$.

**FIGURE 12.10**

Regions of rejection and nonrejection when testing for independence in an $r \times c$ contingency table, using the $\chi^2$ test

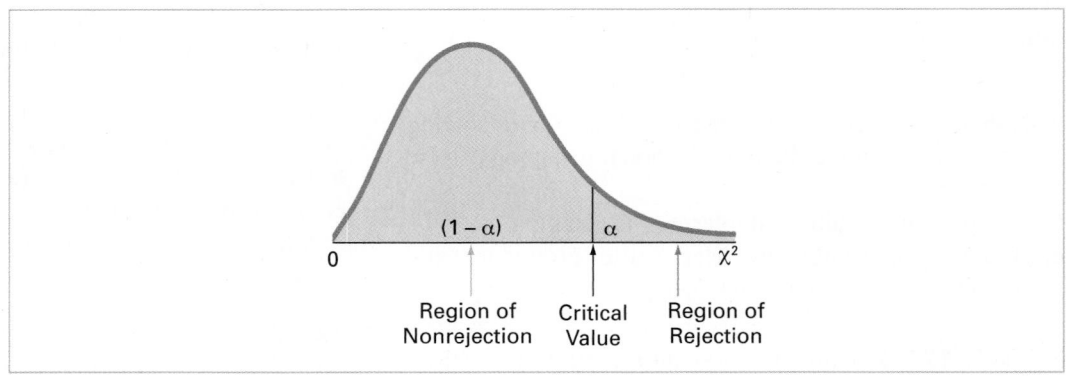

The $\chi^2$ **test of independence** is similar to the $\chi^2$ test for equality of proportions. The test statistics and the decision rules are the same, but the stated hypotheses and conclusions are different. For example, in the guest satisfaction survey of Sections 12.1 and 12.2, there is evidence of a significant difference between the hotels with respect to the proportion of guests who would return. From a different viewpoint, you could conclude that there is a significant relationship between the hotels and the likelihood that a guest would return. Nevertheless, there is a fundamental difference between the two types of tests. The major difference is in how the samples are selected.

In a test for equality of proportions, there is one factor of interest, with two or more levels. These levels represent samples drawn from independent populations. The categorical responses in each sample group or level are classified into two categories, such as *item of interest* and *not an item of interest*. The objective is to make comparisons and evaluate differences between the proportions of *the items of interest* among the various levels. However, in a test for independence, there are two factors of interest, each of which has two or more levels. You select one sample and tally the joint responses to the two categorical variables into the cells of a contingency table.

To illustrate the $\chi^2$ test for independence, suppose that, in the survey on hotel guest satisfaction, a second question was asked of all respondents who indicated that they were not likely to return. These guests were asked to indicate the primary reason for their response. Table 12.9 presents the resulting 4 × 3 contingency table.

**TABLE 12.9**

Contingency Table of Primary Reason for Not Returning and Hotel

| PRIMARY REASON FOR NOT RETURNING | HOTEL | | | |
| --- | --- | --- | --- | --- |
| | **Golden Palm** | **Palm Royale** | **Palm Princess** | **Total** |
| **Price** | 23 | 7 | 37 | 67 |
| **Location** | 39 | 13 | 8 | 60 |
| **Room accommodation** | 13 | 5 | 13 | 31 |
| **Other** | 13 | 8 | 8 | 29 |
| **Total** | 88 | 33 | 66 | 187 |

In Table 12.9, observe that of the primary reasons for not planning to return to the hotel, 67 were due to price, 60 were due to location, 31 were due to room accommodation, and 29 were due to other reasons. As in Table 12.6 on page 514, there were 88 guests in the Golden Palm, 33 guests in the Palm Royale, and 66 guests in the Palm Princess who were not planning to return. The observed frequencies in the cells of the 4 × 3 contingency table represent the joint tallies of the sampled guests with respect to primary reason for not returning and the hotel.

The null and alternative hypotheses are:

$H_0$: There is no relationship between the primary reason for not returning and the hotel.
$H_1$: There is a relationship between the primary reason for not returning and the hotel.

To test this null hypothesis of independence against the alternative that there is a relationship between the two categorical variables, you use Equation (12.1) on page 506 to compute the test statistic:

$$\chi^2_{STAT} = \sum_{all\ cells} \frac{(f_o - f_e)^2}{f_e}$$

where

$f_o$ = observed frequency in a particular cell of the $r \times c$ contingency table

$f_e$ = expected frequency in a particular cell if the null hypothesis of independence were true

To compute the expected frequency, $f_e$, in any cell, you use the multiplication rule for independent events discussed on page 159 [see Equation (4.7)]. For example, under the null hypothesis of independence, the probability of responses expected in the upper-left-corner cell representing primary reason of price for the Golden Palm is the product of the two separate probabilities: $P(Price)$ and $P(Golden\ Palm)$. Here, the proportion of reasons that are due to price, $P(Price)$, is $67/187 = 0.3583$, and the proportion of all responses from the Golden Palm, $P(Golden\ Palm)$, is $88/187 = 0.4706$. If the null hypothesis is true, then the primary reason for not returning and the hotel are independent:

$$P(Price\ and\ Golden\ Palm) = P(Price) \times P(Golden\ Palm)$$

$$= (0.3583) \times (0.4706)$$

$$= 0.1686$$

The expected frequency is the product of the overall sample size, $n$, and this probability, $187 \times 0.1686 = 31.53$. The $f_e$ values for the remaining cells are calculated in a similar manner (see Table 12.10).

Equation (12.5) presents a simpler way to compute the expected frequency.

**Computing the Expected Frequency**

The expected frequency in a cell is the product of its row total and column total, divided by the overall sample size.

$$f_e = \frac{\text{Row total} \times \text{Column total}}{n} \qquad (12.5)$$

where

row total = sum of all the frequencies in the row

column total = sum of all the frequencies in the column

$n$ = overall sample size

For example, using Equation (12.5) for the upper-left-corner cell (price for the Golden Palm),

$$f_e = \frac{\text{Row total} \times \text{Column total}}{n} = \frac{(67)(88)}{187} = 31.53$$

and for the lower-right-corner cell (other reason for the Palm Princess),

$$f_e = \frac{\text{Row total} \times \text{Column total}}{n} = \frac{(29)(66)}{187} = 10.24$$

Table 12.10 lists the entire set of $f_e$ values.

**TABLE 12.10**

Contingency Table of Expected Frequencies of Primary Reason for Not Returning with Hotel

| PRIMARY REASON FOR NOT RETURNING | HOTEL | | | |
|---|---|---|---|---|
| | Golden Palm | Palm Royale | Palm Princess | Total |
| Price | 31.53 | 11.82 | 23.65 | 67 |
| Location | 28.24 | 10.59 | 21.18 | 60 |
| Room accommodation | 14.59 | 5.47 | 10.94 | 31 |
| Other | 13.65 | 5.12 | 10.24 | 29 |
| Total | 88.00 | 33.00 | 66.00 | 187 |

To perform the test of independence, you use the $\chi^2_{STAT}$ test statistic shown in Equation (12.1) on page 506. Here, the $\chi^2_{STAT}$ test statistic approximately follows a chi-square distribution, with degrees of freedom equal to the number of rows in the contingency table minus 1, times the number of columns in the table minus 1:

$$\text{Degrees of freedom} = (r-1)(c-1)$$
$$= (4-1)(3-1) = 6$$

Table 12.11 illustrates the computations for the $\chi^2_{STAT}$ test statistic.

**TABLE 12.11**

Computing the $\chi^2_{STAT}$ Test Statistic for the Test of Independence

| Cell | $f_o$ | $f_e$ | $(f_o - f_e)$ | $(f_o - f_e)^2$ | $(f_o - f_e)^2/f_e$ |
|------|-------|-------|---------------|-----------------|---------------------|
| Price/Golden Palm | 23 | 31.53 | −8.53 | 72.76 | 2.31 |
| Price/Palm Royale | 7 | 11.82 | −4.82 | 23.23 | 1.97 |
| Price/Palm Princess | 37 | 23.65 | 13.35 | 178.22 | 7.54 |
| Location/Golden Palm | 39 | 28.24 | 10.76 | 115.78 | 4.10 |
| Location/Palm Royale | 13 | 10.59 | 2.41 | 5.81 | 0.55 |
| Location/Palm Princess | 8 | 21.18 | −13.18 | 173.71 | 8.20 |
| Room/Golden Palm | 13 | 14.59 | −1.59 | 2.53 | 0.17 |
| Room/Palm Royale | 5 | 5.47 | −0.47 | 0.22 | 0.04 |
| Room/Palm Princess | 13 | 10.94 | 2.06 | 4.24 | 0.39 |
| Other/Golden Palm | 13 | 13.65 | −0.65 | 0.42 | 0.03 |
| Other/Palm Royale | 8 | 5.12 | 2.88 | 8.29 | 1.62 |
| Other/Palm Princess | 8 | 10.24 | −2.24 | 5.02 | 0.49 |
| | | | | | 27.41 |

Using the level of significance $\alpha = 0.05$, the upper-tail critical value from the chi-square distribution with 6 degrees of freedom is 12.592 (see Table E.4). Because $\chi^2_{STAT} = 27.41 > 12.592$, you reject the null hypothesis of independence (see Figure 12.11).

**FIGURE 12.11**

Regions of rejection and nonrejection when testing for independence in the hotel guest satisfaction survey example at the 0.05 level of significance, with 6 degrees of freedom

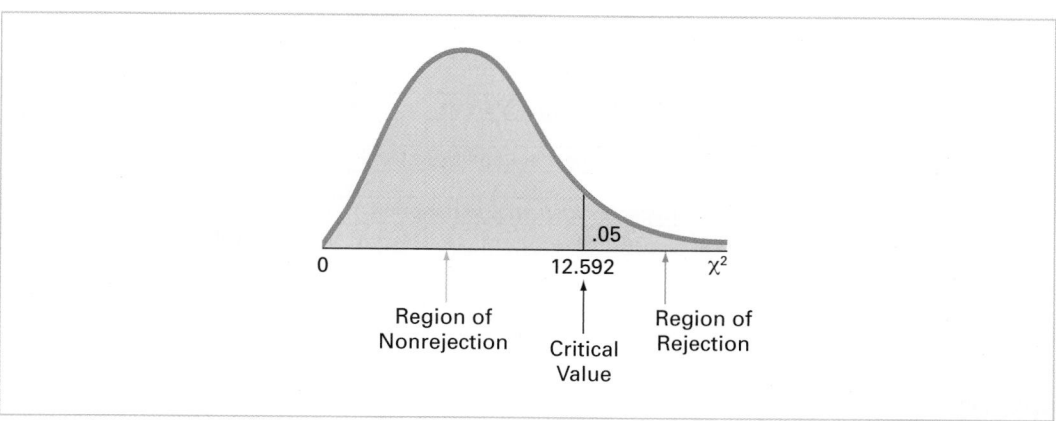

You can use the Microsoft Excel worksheet in Figure 12.12 or the Minitab results of Figure 12.13 on page 524 to conduct the test of independence using the $p$-value approach. Because the $p$-value = 0.0001 < 0.05, you reject the null hypothesis of independence. The $p$-value indicates that there is virtually no chance of having a relationship this large or larger between hotels and primary reasons for not returning in a sample, if the primary reasons for not returning are independent of the specific hotels in the entire population. Thus, there is strong evidence of a relationship between primary reason for not returning and the hotel.

Examination of the observed and expected frequencies (see Table 12.11) reveals that price is underrepresented as a reason for not returning to the Golden Palm (i.e., $f_o = 23$ and $f_e = 31.53$) but is overrepresented at the Palm Princess. Guests are more satisfied with the price at the Golden Palm compared to the Palm Princess. Location is overrepresented as a reason for not returning to the Golden Palm but greatly underrepresented at the Palm Princess. Thus, guests are much more satisfied with the location of the Palm Princess than that of the Golden Palm.

To ensure accurate results, all expected frequencies need to be large in order to use the $\chi^2$ test when dealing with $r \times c$ contingency tables. As in the case of $2 \times c$ contingency tables on pages 512–516, all expected frequencies should be at least 1. For cases in which one or more expected frequencies are less than 1, you can use the test after collapsing two or more low-frequency rows into one row (or collapsing two or more low-frequency columns into one column). Merging of rows or columns usually results in expected frequencies sufficiently large to conduct the $\chi^2$ test accurately.

**FIGURE 12.12**

Microsoft Excel worksheet for the 4 × 3 contingency table for primary reason for not returning and hotel

*See Section E12.3 or P12.3 to create this.*

| | A | B | C | D | E |
|---|---|---|---|---|---|
| 1 | **Cross-Classification Hotel Analysis** | | | | |
| 2 | | | | | |
| 3 | | **Observed Frequencies** | | | |
| 4 | | | **Hotel** | | |
| 5 | **Reason for Not Returning** | **Golden Palm** | **Palm Royale** | **Palm Princess** | **Total** |
| 6 | **Price** | 23 | 7 | 37 | 67 |
| 7 | **Location** | 39 | 13 | 8 | 60 |
| 8 | **Room accommodation** | 13 | 5 | 13 | 31 |
| 9 | **Other** | 13 | 8 | 8 | 29 |
| 10 | **Total** | 88 | 33 | 66 | 187 |
| 11 | | | | | |
| 12 | | Expected Frequencies | | | |
| 13 | | | Hotel | | |
| 14 | Reason for Not Returning | Golden Palm | Palm Royale | Palm Princess | Total |
| 15 | Price | 31.5294 | 11.8235 | 23.6471 | 67 |
| 16 | Location | 28.2353 | 10.5882 | 21.1765 | 60 |
| 17 | Room accommodation | 14.5882 | 5.4706 | 10.9412 | 31 |
| 18 | Other | 13.6471 | 5.1176 | 10.2353 | 29 |
| 19 | Total | 88 | 33 | 66 | 187 |
| 20 | | | | | |
| 21 | **Data** | | | | |
| 22 | **Level of Significance** | 0.05 | | | |
| 23 | Number of Rows | 4 | | | |
| 24 | Number of Columns | 3 | | | |
| 25 | Degrees of Freedom | 6 | =(B23 - 1) * (B24 - 1) | | |
| 26 | | | | | |
| 27 | **Results** | | | | |
| 28 | **Critical Value** | 12.5916 | =CHIINV(B22, B25) | | |
| 29 | **Chi-Square Test Statistic** | 27.4104 | =SUM(G15:I18) | | |
| 30 | **p-Value** | 0.0001 | =CHIDIST(B29, B25) | | |
| 31 | **Reject the null hypothesis** | | =IF(B30 < B22, "Reject the null hypothesis", | | |
| 32 | | | "Do not reject the null hypothesis") | | |
| 33 | ***Expected frequency assumption*** | | =IF(OR(B15 < 1, C15 < 1, D15 < 1, B16 < 1, C16 < 1 ,D16 < 1, | | |
| 34 | ***is met.*** | | B17 < 1, C17 < 1, D17 < 1, B18 < 1, C18 < 1, D18 < 1) | | |

"       is violated.","       is met.")

**FIGURE 12.13**

Minitab results for the 4 × 3 contingency table for primary reason for not returning and hotel

*See Section M12.2 to create this.*

```
Expected counts are printed below observed counts
Chi-Square contributions are printed below expected counts

         C6     C7     C8   Total
   1     23      7     37     67
       31.53  11.82  23.65
       2.307  1.968  7.540

   2     39     13      8     60
       28.24  10.59  21.18
       4.104  0.549  8.199

   3     13      5     13     31
       14.59   5.47  10.94
       0.173  0.040  0.387

   4     13      8      8     29
       13.65   5.12  10.24
       0.031  1.623  0.488

Total    88     33     66    187

Chi-Sq = 27.410, DF = 6, P-Value = 0.000
```

# PROBLEMS FOR SECTION 12.3

## Learning the Basics

**12.20** If a contingency table has three rows and four columns, how many degrees of freedom are there for the $\chi^2$ test for independence?

**12.21** When performing a $\chi^2$ test for independence in a contingency table with $r$ rows and $c$ columns, determine the upper-tail critical value of the test statistic in each of the following circumstances:
**a.** $\alpha = 0.05$, $r = 4$ rows, $c = 5$ columns
**b.** $\alpha = 0.01$, $r = 4$ rows, $c = 5$ columns
**c.** $\alpha = 0.01$, $r = 4$ rows, $c = 6$ columns
**d.** $\alpha = 0.01$, $r = 3$ rows, $c = 6$ columns
**e.** $\alpha = 0.01$, $r = 6$ rows, $c = 3$ columns

## Applying the Concepts

**12.22** The Committee of 200 is an international not-for-profit association comprised of preeminent business-women who collectively control over $100 billion annually in revenue. According to the association's Web site, **www.c200.org**, the purpose of the Committee of 200 "is to meet the needs of our membership in areas of business synergies, leadership advancement, education, mentoring, and recognition. Additionally, as an agent of change, we want to improve opportunities for women business leaders, be a source for governmental representation, and a source for research on issues relevant to women in business." The association sponsored a survey where MBAs from top business schools were asked if executives were paid too much. The responses (in percentages, but without sample sizes) are in the following table and were published in "Snapshots: Are Execs Paid Too Much?" *USA Today*, **www.usatoday.com**, January 15, 2007.

|       | Yes | No  | Neutral |
|-------|-----|-----|---------|
| Women | 61% | 11% | 28%     |
| Men   | 49% | 27% | 24%     |

**a.** Do you think executives are paid too much?
**b.** Suppose that the survey was based on 100 males and 100 females. Using the 0.01 level of significance, perform a hypothesis test to see if you can prove that men and women feel differently about executive pay.
**c.** Suppose that the survey was based on 200 males and 200 females. Using the 0.01 level of significance, perform a hypothesis test to see if you can prove that men and women feel differently about executive pay.
**d.** Discuss the importance of sample size on reporting survey results.

**12.23** *USA Today* reported on preferred types of office communication by different age groups ("Talking Face to Face vs. Group Meetings," *USA Today*, October 13, 2003, p. A1). Suppose the results were based on a survey of 500 respondents in each age group. The results are cross-classified in the following table:

|                | TYPE OF COMMUNICATION PREFERRED | | | | |
|----------------|---------------|-----------------------------------|---------|-------|-------|
| AGE GROUP      | Group Meetings | Face-to-Face Meetings with Individuals | E-mails | Other | Total |
| Generation Y   | 180           | 260                               | 50      | 10    | 500   |
| Generation X   | 210           | 190                               | 65      | 35    | 500   |
| Boomer         | 205           | 195                               | 65      | 35    | 500   |
| Mature         | 200           | 195                               | 50      | 55    | 500   |
| Total          | 795           | 840                               | 230     | 135   | 2,000 |

Source: *Extracted from "Talking Face to Face vs. Group Meetings,"* USA Today, *October 13, 2003, p. A1.*

At the 0.05 level of significance, is there evidence of a relationship between age group and type of communication preferred?

**SELF Test** **12.24** A large corporation is interested in determining whether a relationship exists between the commuting time of its employees and the level of stress-related problems observed on the job. A study of 116 assembly-line workers reveals the following:

| COMMUTING TIME | STRESS LEVEL | | | |
|----------------|------|----------|-----|-------|
|                | High | Moderate | Low | Total |
| Under 15 min.  | 9    | 5        | 18  | 32    |
| 15–45 min.     | 17   | 8        | 28  | 53    |
| Over 45 min.   | 18   | 6        | 7   | 31    |
| Total          | 44   | 19       | 53  | 116   |

**a.** At the 0.01 level of significance, is there evidence of a significant relationship between commuting time and stress level?
**b.** What is your answer to (a) if you use the 0.05 level of significance?

**12.25** Where people turn to for news is different for various age groups. A study indicated where different age groups primarily get their news:

| MEDIA | AGE GROUP | | |
|---|---|---|---|
| | Under 36 | 36–50 | 50+ |
| Local TV | 107 | 119 | 133 |
| National TV | 73 | 102 | 127 |
| Radio | 75 | 97 | 109 |
| Local newspaper | 52 | 79 | 107 |
| Internet | 95 | 83 | 76 |

At the 0.05 level of significance, is there evidence of a significant relationship between the age group and where people primarily get their news? If so, explain the relationship.

**12.26** *USA Today* reported on when the decision of what to have for dinner is made. Suppose the results were based on a survey of 1,000 respondents and considered whether the household included any children under 18 years old. The results were cross-classified in the following table:

| WHEN DECISION MADE | TYPE OF HOUSEHOLD | | |
|---|---|---|---|
| | One Adult/ No Children | Two or More Adults/ Children | Two or More Adults/ No Children |
| Just before eating | 162 | 54 | 154 |
| In the afternoon | 73 | 38 | 69 |
| In the morning | 59 | 58 | 53 |
| A few days before | 21 | 64 | 45 |
| The night before | 15 | 50 | 45 |
| Always eat the same thing on this night | 2 | 16 | 2 |
| Not sure | 7 | 6 | 7 |

Source: *Extracted from "What's for Dinner,"* USA Today, *January 10, 2000.*

At the 0.05 level of significance, is there evidence of a significant relationship between when the decision is made of what to have for dinner and the type of household?

## 12.4  McNEMAR TEST FOR THE DIFFERENCE BETWEEN TWO PROPORTIONS (RELATED SAMPLES)

In Section 10.3, you used the $Z$ test, and in Section 12.1, you used the chi-square test to test for the difference between two proportions. These tests require that the samples are independent from one another. However, sometimes when you are testing differences between two proportions, the data are from repeated measurements or matched samples, and therefore the samples are related. Such situations arise often in marketing when you want to determine whether there has been a change in attitude, perception, or behavior from one time period to another. To test whether there is evidence of a difference between the proportions of two related samples, you can use the **McNemar test**.

Table 12.12 presents the 2 × 2 table needed for the McNemar test.

**TABLE 12.12**

2 × 2 Contingency Table for the McNemar Test

| CONDITION (GROUP) 1 | CONDITION (GROUP) 2 | | |
|---|---|---|---|
| | Yes | No | Totals |
| Yes | $A$ | $B$ | $A + B$ |
| No | $C$ | $D$ | $C + D$ |
| Totals | $A + C$ | $B + D$ | $n$ |

where

$A$ = number of respondents who answer yes to condition 1 and yes to condition 2

$B$ = number of respondents who answer yes to condition 1 and no to condition 2

$C$ = number of respondents who answer no to condition 1 and yes to condition 2

$D$ = number of respondents who answer no to condition 1 and no to condition 2

$n$ = number of respondents in the sample

The sample proportions are

$$p_1 = \frac{A + B}{n} = \text{proportion of respondents in the sample who answer yes to condition 1}$$

$$p_2 = \frac{A + C}{n} = \text{proportion of respondents in the sample who answer yes to condition 2}$$

The population proportions are

$\pi_1$ = proportion in the population who would answer yes to condition 1

$\pi_2$ = proportion in the population who would answer yes to condition 2

When testing differences between the proportions, you can perform a two-tail test or a one-tail test. In both cases, you use a test statistic that approximately follows the normal distribution. Equation (12.6) presents the McNemar test statistic used to test $H_0: \pi_1 = \pi_2$.

**McNemar Test**

$$Z_{STAT} = \frac{B - C}{\sqrt{B + C}} \tag{12.6}$$

where the $Z_{STAT}$ test statistic is approximately normally distributed.

To illustrate the McNemar test, suppose that a consumer panel of $n = 600$ participants is selected for a marketing study and the panel members are initially asked to state their preferences for two competing cellphone providers, Sprint and Verizon. Initially, 282 panelists say they prefer Sprint and 318 say they prefer Verizon. After exposing the entire panel to an intensive marketing campaign strategy for Verizon, the same 600 panelists are again asked to state their preferences, with the following results: Of the 282 panelists who previously preferred Sprint, 246 maintain their brand loyalty, but 36 switch to Verizon. Of the 318 panelists who initially preferred Verizon, 306 remain brand loyal, but 12 switch to Sprint. Table 12.13 displays the results.

**TABLE 12.13**

Brand Loyalty for Cellphone Providers

| | AFTER MARKETING CAMPAIGN | | |
|---|---|---|---|
| **BEFORE MARKETING CAMPAIGN** | **Sprint** | **Verizon** | **Total** |
| **Sprint** | 246 | 36 | 282 |
| **Verizon** | 12 | 306 | 318 |
| **Total** | 258 | 342 | 600 |

You use the McNemar test for these data because you have repeated measurements from the same set of panelists. Each panelist gave a response about whether he or she preferred Sprint or Verizon before exposure to the intensive marketing campaign and then again after exposure to the campaign.

To determine whether the intensive marketing campaign was effective, you want to investigate whether there is a difference between the population proportion who favor Sprint before the campaign, $\pi_1$, versus the proportion who favor Sprint after the campaign, $\pi_2$. The null and alternative hypotheses are

$$H_0: \pi_1 = \pi_2$$
$$H_1: \pi_1 \neq \pi_2$$

Using a 0.05 level of significance, the critical values are $-1.96$ and $+1.96$ (see Figure 12.14), and the decision rule is

Reject $H_0$ if $Z_{STAT} < -1.96$ or if $Z_{STAT} > +1.96$;

otherwise, do not reject $H_0$.

**FIGURE 12.14**

Two-tail McNemar test at the 0.05 level of significance

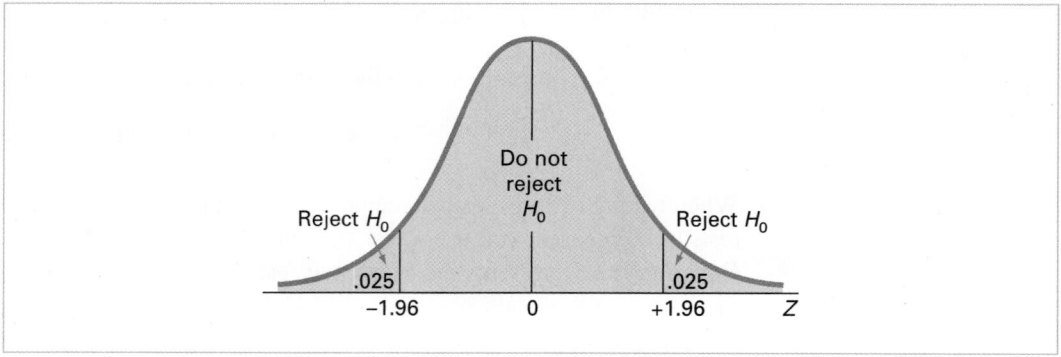

For the data in Table 12.13,

$$A = 246 \quad B = 36 \quad C = 12 \quad D = 306$$

so that

$$p_1 = \frac{A+B}{n} = \frac{246+36}{600} = \frac{282}{600} = 0.47 \quad \text{and} \quad p_2 = \frac{A+C}{n} = \frac{246+12}{600} = \frac{258}{600} = 0.43$$

Using Equation (12.6),

$$X = \frac{B-C}{\sqrt{B+C}} = \frac{36-12}{\sqrt{36+12}} = \frac{24}{\sqrt{48}} = 3.4641$$

Because $Z_{STAT} = 3.4641 > 1.96$, you reject $H_0$. Using the p-value approach (see Figure 12.15), the p-value is 0.0005. Because $0.0005 < 0.05$, you reject $H_0$. You can conclude that the population proportion who prefer Sprint before the intensive marketing campaign is different from the population proportion who prefer Sprint after exposure to the intensive Verizon marketing campaign. In fact, from Figure 12.15, observe that more panelists actually preferred Verizon over Sprint after exposure to the intensive marketing campaign.

**FIGURE 12.15**

Microsoft Excel McNemar test worksheet for brand loyalty of cellphone providers

*See Section E12.4 or P12.4 to create this.*

| | A | B | C | D |
|---|---|---|---|---|
| 1 | McNemar Test | | | |
| 2 | | | | |
| 3 | Observed Frequencies | | | |
| 4 | | Column variable | | |
| 5 | Row variable | Sprint | Verizon | Total |
| 6 | Sprint | 246 | 36 | 282 |
| 7 | Verizon | 12 | 306 | 318 |
| 8 | Total | 258 | 342 | 600 |
| 9 | | | | |
| 10 | Data | | | |
| 11 | Level of Significance | 0.05 | | |
| 12 | | | | |
| 13 | Intermediate Calculations | | | |
| 14 | Numerator | 24 | =C6 - B7 | |
| 15 | Denominator | 6.9282 | =SQRT(C6 + B7) | |
| 16 | Z Test Statistic | 3.4641 | =B14/B15 | |
| 17 | | | | |
| 18 | Two-Tail Test | | | |
| 19 | Lower Critical Value | -1.9600 | =NORMSINV(B11/2) | |
| 20 | Upper Critical Value | 1.9600 | =NORMSINV(1 - B11/2) | |
| 21 | p-Value | 0.0005 | =2 * (1 - NORMSDIST(ABS(B16))) | |
| 22 | Reject the null hypothesis | | =IF(B21 < B11, "Reject the null hypothesis", "Do not reject the null hypothesis") | |

## PROBLEMS FOR SECTION 12.4

### Learning the Basics

**12.27** Given the following table for two related samples:

| GROUP 1 | GROUP 2 | | |
|---------|-----|-----|-------|
|         | Yes | No  | Total |
| Yes     | 46  | 25  | 71    |
| No      | 16  | 59  | 75    |
| Total   | 62  | 84  | 146   |

a. Compute the McNemar test statistic.
b. At the 0.05 level of significance, is there evidence of a difference between group 1 and group 2?

### Applying the Concepts

**12.28** A market researcher wanted to determine whether the proportion of coffee drinkers who preferred Brand $A$ increased as the result of an advertising campaign. A random sample of 200 coffee drinkers was selected. The results indicating preference for Brand $A$ or Brand $B$ prior to the beginning of the advertising campaign and after its completion are shown in the following table:

| PREFERENCE PRIOR TO ADVERTISING CAMPAIGN | PREFERENCE AFTER COMPLETION OF ADVERTISING CAMPAIGN | | |
|---------|---------|---------|-------|
|         | Brand $A$ | Brand $B$ | Total |
| Brand $A$ | 101   | 9       | 110   |
| Brand $B$ | 22    | 68      | 90    |
| Total     | 123   | 77      | 200   |

a. At the 0.05 level of significance, is there evidence that the proportion of coffee drinkers who prefer Brand $A$ is lower at the beginning of the advertising campaign than at the end of the advertising campaign?
b. Compute the $p$-value in (a) and interpret its meaning.

**12.29** Two candidates for governor participated in a televised debate. A political pollster recorded the preferences of 500 registered voters in a random sample prior to and after the debate:

| PREFERENCE PRIOR TO DEBATE | PREFERENCE AFTER DEBATE | | |
|---------|------------|------------|-------|
|         | Candidate $A$ | Candidate $B$ | Total |
| Candidate $A$ | 269  | 21         | 290   |
| Candidate $B$ | 36   | 174        | 210   |
| Total         | 305  | 195        | 500   |

a. At the 0.01 level of significance, is there evidence of a difference in the proportion of voters who favor Candidate $A$ prior to and after the debate?
b. Compute the $p$-value in (a) and interpret its meaning.

**12.30** A taste-testing experiment compared two brands of Chilean merlot wines. After the initial comparison, 60 preferred Brand $A$, and 40 preferred Brand $B$. The 100 respondents were then exposed to a very professional and powerful advertisement promoting Brand $A$. The 100 respondents were then asked to taste the two wines again and declare which brand they preferred. The results are shown in the following table.

| PREFERENCE PRIOR TO ADVERTISING | PREFERENCE AFTER COMPLETION OF ADVERTISING | | |
|---------|---------|---------|-------|
|         | Brand $A$ | Brand $B$ | Total |
| Brand $A$ | 55    | 5       | 60    |
| Brand $B$ | 15    | 25      | 40    |
| Total     | 70    | 30      | 100   |

a. At the 0.05 level of significance, is there evidence that the proportion who prefer Brand $A$ is lower before the advertising than after the advertising?
b. Compute the $p$-value in (a) and interpret its meaning.

**12.31** The CEO of a large metropolitan health care facility would like to assess the effects of recent implementation of Six Sigma management on customer satisfaction. A random sample of 100 patients is selected from a list of patients who were at the facility the past week and also a year ago:

| SATISFIED LAST YEAR | SATISFIED NOW | | |
|---------|-----|-----|-------|
|         | Yes | No  | Total |
| Yes     | 67  | 5   | 72    |
| No      | 20  | 8   | 28    |
| Total   | 87  | 13  | 100   |

a. At the 0.05 level of significance, is there evidence that satisfaction was lower last year, prior to introduction of Six Sigma management?
b. Compute the $p$-value in (a) and interpret its meaning.

**12.32** The personnel director of a large department store wants to reduce absenteeism among sales associates. She decides to institute an incentive plan that provides financial rewards for sales associates who are absent fewer than five days in a given calendar year. A sample of 100 sales associates selected at the end of the second year reveals the following:

|  | YEAR 2 | | |
|---|---|---|---|
| YEAR 1 | <5 Days Absent | ≥5 Days Absent | Total |
| <5 Days Absent | 32 | 4 | 36 |
| ≥5 Days Absent | 25 | 39 | 64 |
| Total | 57 | 43 | 100 |

**a.** At the 0.05 level of significance, is there evidence that the proportion of employees absent fewer than 5 days was lower in year 1 than in year 2?

**b.** Compute the *p*-value in (a) and interpret its meaning.

## 12.5 CHI-SQUARE TEST FOR THE VARIANCE OR STANDARD DEVIATION

When analyzing numerical data, sometimes you need to draw conclusions about the population variance or standard deviation. For example, recall that in the cereal-filling process described in Section 9.1, you assumed the population standard deviation σ was equal to 15 grams. To see if the variability of the process has changed, you need to test whether the standard deviation has changed from the previously specified level of 15 grams.

Assuming that the data are normally distributed, you use the $\chi^2$ **test for the variance or standard deviation** defined in Equation (12.7) to test whether or not the population variance or standard deviation is equal to a specified value.

$\chi^2$ Test Statistic for the Variance or Standard Deviation

$$\chi^2_{STAT} = \frac{(n-1)S^2}{\sigma^2}$$ (12.7)

where

$n$ = sample size

$S^2$ = sample variance

$\sigma^2$ = hypothesized population variance

The $\chi^2_{STAT}$ test statistic follows a chi-square distribution with $n - 1$ degrees of freedom.

To apply the test of hypothesis, return to the cereal-filling example. You are interested in determining whether the standard deviation has changed from the previously specified level of 15 grams. Thus, you use a two-tail test with the following null and alternative hypotheses:

$$H_0: \sigma^2 = 225 \text{ (i.e., } \sigma = 15 \text{ grams)}$$

$$H_0: \sigma^2 \neq 225 \text{ (i.e., } \sigma \neq 15 \text{ grams)}$$

If you select a sample of 25 cereal boxes, you reject the null hypothesis if the computed $\chi^2_{STAT}$ test statistic falls into either the lower or upper tail of a chi-square distribution with $25 - 1 = 24$ degrees of freedom as shown in Figure 12.16. From Equation (12.7), observe that the $\chi^2_{STAT}$ test statistic falls into the lower tail of the chi-square distribution if the sample standard deviation (*S*) is sufficiently smaller than the hypothesized σ of 15 grams, and it falls into the upper tail if *S* is sufficiently larger than 15 grams. From Table 12.14 (extracted from Table

E.4), if you select a level of significance of 0.05, the lower $(\chi^2_{\alpha/2})$ and upper $(\chi^2_{1-\alpha/2})$ critical values are 12.401 and 39.364, respectively. Therefore, the decision rule is:

$$\text{Reject } H_0 \text{ if } \chi^2_{STAT} < \chi^2_{\alpha/2} = 12.401 \text{ or if } \chi^2_{STAT} > \chi^2_{1-\alpha/2} = 39.364;$$

$$\text{otherwise, do not reject } H_0.$$

**FIGURE 12.16**

Determining the lower and upper critical values of a chi-square distribution with 24 degrees of freedom corresponding to a 0.05 level of significance for a two-tail test of hypothesis about a population variance or standard deviation

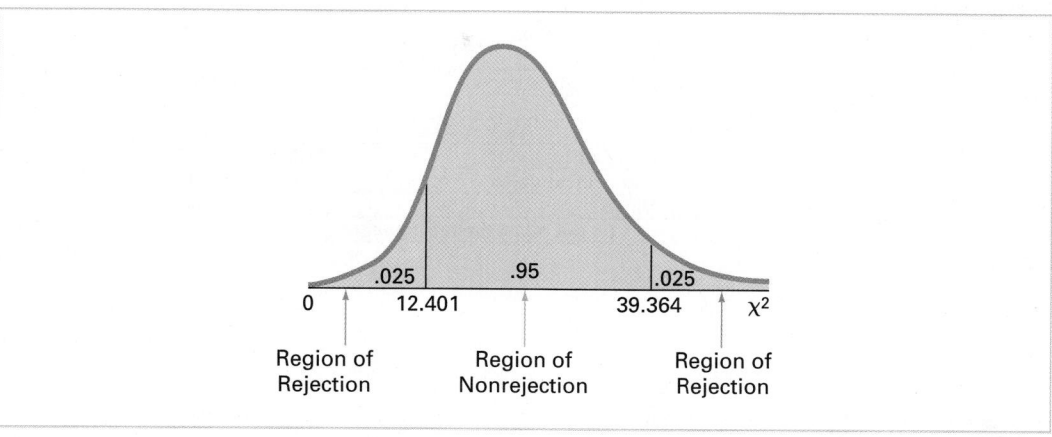

**TABLE 12.14**

Finding the Critical Values Corresponding to a 0.05 Level of Significance for a Two-Tail Test from the Chi-Square Distribution with 24 Degrees of Freedom

| | Cumulative Area | | | | | | | |
|---|---|---|---|---|---|---|---|---|
| | .005 | .01 | .025 | .05 | .10 | .90 | .95 | .975 |
| | Upper-Tail Areas | | | | | | | |
| **Degrees of Freedom** | .995 | .99 | .975 | .95 | .90 | .10 | .05 | .025 |
| 1 | ... | ... | 0.001 | 0.004 | 0.016 | 2.706 | 3.841 | 5.024 |
| 2 | 0.010 | 0.020 | 0.051 | 0.103 | 0.211 | 4.605 | 5.991 | 7.378 |
| 3 | 0.072 | 0.115 | 0.216 | 0.352 | 0.584 | 6.251 | 7.815 | 9.348 |
| . | . | . | . | . | . | . | . | . |
| . | . | . | . | . | . | . | . | . |
| . | . | . | . | . | . | . | . | . |
| 23 | 9.260 | 10.196 | 11.689 | 13.091 | 14.848 | 32.007 | 35.172 | 38.076 |
| 24 | 9.886 | 10.856 | 12.401 | 13.848 | 15.659 | 33.196 | 36.415 | 39.364 |
| 25 | 10.520 | 11.524 | 13.120 | 14.611 | 16.473 | 34.382 | 37.652 | 40.646 |

Source: *Extracted from Table E.4.*

Suppose that in the sample of 25 cereal boxes, the standard deviation $S$ is 17.7 grams. Using Equation (12.7)

$$\chi^2_{STAT} = \frac{(n-1)S^2}{\sigma^2} = \frac{(25-1)(17.7)^2}{(15)^2} = 33.42$$

Because $\chi^2_{0.025} = 12.401 < \chi^2_{STAT} = 33.42 < \chi^2_{0.975} = 39.364$, or because the *p*-value = 0.0956 > 0.05 (see Figure 12.17 on page 532), you do not reject $H_0$. You conclude that there is insufficient evidence that the population standard deviation is different from 15 grams.

In testing a hypothesis about a population variance or standard deviation, you assume that the values in the population are normally distributed. Unfortunately, the $\chi^2_{STAT}$ test statistic discussed in this section is very sensitive to departures from this assumption (i.e., it is not a robust test). Thus, if the population is not normally distributed, particularly for small sample sizes, the accuracy of the test can be seriously affected (see reference 11).

**FIGURE 12.17**

Microsoft Excel worksheet for testing the variance in the cereal-filling process

*See Section E12.5 or P12.5 to create this.*

| | A | B | |
|---|---|---|---|
| 1 | **Cereal-Filling Analysis** | | |
| 2 | | | |
| 3 | **Data** | | |
| 4 | **Null Hypothesis**                    σ^2= | 225 | |
| 5 | **Level of Significance** | 0.05 | |
| 6 | **Sample Size** | 25 | |
| 7 | **Sample Standard Deviation** | 17.7 | |
| 8 | | | |
| 9 | Intermediate Calculations | | |
| 10 | Degrees of Freedom | 24 | =B6 - 1 |
| 11 | Half Area | 0.025 | =B5/2 |
| 12 | Chi-Square Statistic | 33.4176 | =B10 * B7^2/B4 |
| 13 | | | |
| 14 | **Two-Tail Test** | | |
| 15 | Lower Critical Value | 12.4012 | =CHIINV(1 - B11, B10) |
| 16 | Upper Critical Value | 39.3641 | =CHIINV(B11, B10) |
| 17 | *p*-Value | 0.0956 | =IF(B12 - B15 < 0, 1 - CHIDIST(B12, B10), CHIDIST(B12, B10)) |
| 18 | Do not reject the null hypothesis | | =IF(B17 < B5/2, "Reject the null hypothesis", "Do not reject the null hypothesis") |

# PROBLEMS FOR SECTION 12.5

## Learning the Basics

**12.33** Determine the lower- and upper-tail critical values of $\chi^2$ for each of the following two-tail tests:
a. $\alpha = 0.01$, $n = 26$
b. $\alpha = 0.05$, $n = 17$
c. $\alpha = 0.10$, $n = 14$

**12.34** Determine the lower- and upper-tail critical values of $\chi^2$ for each of the following two-tail tests:
a. $\alpha = 0.01$, $n = 24$
b. $\alpha = 0.05$, $n = 20$
c. $\alpha = 0.10$, $n = 16$

**12.35** In a sample of $n = 25$ selected from an underlying normal population, $S = 150$. What is the value of $\chi^2_{STAT}$ if you are testing the null hypothesis $H_0$: $\sigma = 100$?

**12.36** In a sample of $n = 16$ selected from an underlying normal population, $S = 10$. What is the value of $\chi^2_{STAT}$ if you are testing the null hypothesis $H_0$: $\sigma = 12$?

**12.37** In Problem 12.36, how many degrees of freedom are there in the hypothesis test?

**12.38** In Problems 12.36 and 12.37, what are the critical values from Table E.4 if the level of significance $\alpha = 0.05$ and $H_1$ is as follows:
a. $\sigma \neq 12$?
b. $\sigma < 12$?

**12.39** In Problems 12.36, 12.37, and 12.38, what is your statistical decision if $H_1$ is
a. $\sigma \neq 12$?
b. $\sigma < 12$?

**12.40** If, in a sample of size $n = 16$ selected from a very left-skewed population, the sample standard deviation is $S = 24$, would you use the hypothesis test given in Equation (12.7) to test $H_0$: $\sigma = 20$? Discuss.

## Applying the Concepts

**12.41** A manufacturer of candy must monitor the temperature at which the candies are baked. Too much variation will cause inconsistency in the taste of the candy. Past records show that the standard deviation of the temperature has been 1.2°F. A random sample of 30 batches of candy is selected and the sample standard deviation of the temperature is 2.1°F.
a. At the 0.05 level of significance, is there evidence that the population standard deviation has increased above 1.2°F?
b. What assumption do you need to make in order to perform this test?
c. Compute the *p*-value in (a) and interpret its meaning.

**12.42** A market researcher for an automobile dealer intends to conduct a nationwide survey concerning car repairs. Among the questions included in the survey is the following: "What was the cost of all repairs performed on your car last year?" In order to determine the sample size necessary, he needs to provide an estimate of the standard deviation. Using his past experience and judgment, he estimates that the standard deviation of the amount of repairs is $200. Suppose that a small scale study of 25 auto owners selected at random indicates a sample standard deviation of $237.52.
a. At the 0.05 level of significance, is there evidence that the population standard deviation is different from $200?
b. What assumption do you need to make in order to perform this test?
c. Compute the *p*-value in part (a) and interpret its meaning.

**12.43** The marketing manager of a branch office of a local telephone operating company wants to study characteristics of residential customers served by her office. In particular, she wants to estimate the mean monthly cost of calls within the local calling region. In order to determine the sample size necessary, she needs an estimate of the standard deviation. On the basis of her past experience and judgment, she estimates that the standard deviation is equal to $12. Suppose that a small scale study of 15 residential customers indicates a sample standard deviation of $9.25.

**a.** At the 0.10 level of significance, is there evidence that the population standard deviation is different from $12?

**b.** What assumption do you need to make in order to perform this test?

**c.** Compute the $p$-value in part (a) and interpret its meaning.

**12.44** A manufacturer of doorknobs has a production process that is designed to provide a doorknob with a target diameter of 2.5 inches. In the past, the standard deviation of the diameter has been 0.035 inch. In an effort to reduce the variation in the process, various studies have resulted in a redesigned process. A sample of 25 doorknobs produced under the new process indicates a sample standard deviation of 0.025 inch.

**a.** At the 0.05 level of significance, is there evidence that the population standard deviation is less than 0.035 inch in the new process?

**b.** What assumption do you need to make in order to perform this test?

**c.** Compute the $p$-value in part (a) and interpret its meaning.

**12.45** The population standard deviation of the weight of raisins packaged per box is specified as 0.25 ounce. The operations manager selects a sample of 30 raisin packages filled during the last 24 hours. Their weights are in the file Raisins.

**a.** At the 0.05 level of significance, is there evidence that the population standard deviation differs from 0.25 ounce?

**b.** What assumption do you need to make in order to perform this test?

**c.** Compute the $p$-value in part (a) and interpret its meaning.

**12.46** A manufacturer claims that the standard deviation in capacity of a certain type of battery the company produces is 2.5 ampere-hours. An independent consumer protection agency wishes to test the credibility of the manufacturer's claim and measures the capacity of a random sample of 20 batteries from a recently produced batch. The results are in the file Amphrs.

**a.** At the 0.05 level of significance, is there evidence that the population standard deviation in battery capacity is greater than 2.5 ampere-hours?

**b.** What assumption do you need to make in order to perform this test?

**c.** Compute the $p$-value in part (a) and interpret its meaning.

## 12.6 WILCOXON RANK SUM TEST: NONPARAMETRIC ANALYSIS FOR TWO INDEPENDENT POPULATIONS

"A nonparametric procedure is a statistical procedure that has (certain) desirable properties that hold under relatively mild assumptions regarding the underlying population(s) from which the data are obtained."
—Myles Hollander and Douglas A. Wolfe (reference 5, p. 1)

In Section 10.1, you used the $t$ test for the difference between the means of two independent populations. If sample sizes are small and you cannot assume that the data in each sample are from normally distributed populations, you have two choices:

- Use the Wilcoxon rank sum test that does not depend on the assumption of normality for the two populations.
- Use the pooled-variance $t$ test, following some *normalizing transformation* on the data (see reference 12).

This section introduces the **Wilcoxon rank sum test** for testing whether there is a difference between two *medians*. The $t$ test in Section 10.1 examined the difference between two *means*, but because both the mean and median are measures of central tendency, the tests are similar. The Wilcoxon rank sum test is almost as powerful as the pooled-variance and separate-variance $t$ tests under conditions appropriate to these tests and is likely to be more powerful when the assumptions of those $t$ tests are not met. In addition, you can use the Wilcoxon rank sum test when you have only ordinal data, as often happens when dealing with studies in consumer behavior and marketing research.

To perform the Wilcoxon rank sum test, you replace the values in the two samples of size $n_1$ and $n_2$ with their combined ranks (unless the data contained the ranks initially). You begin by defining $n = n_1 + n_2$ as the total sample size. Next, you assign the ranks so that rank 1 is given to the smallest of the $n$ combined values, rank 2 is given to the second smallest, and so on, until rank $n$ is given to the largest. If several values are tied, you assign each the average of the ranks that otherwise would have been assigned had there been no ties.

For convenience, whenever the two sample sizes are unequal, $n_1$ represents the smaller sample and $n_2$ the larger sample. The Wilcoxon rank sum test statistic, $T_1$, is defined as the sum of the ranks assigned to the $n_1$ values in the smaller sample. (For equal-sized samples, either sample may be selected for determining $T_1$.) For any integer value $n$, the sum of the first $n$ consecutive integers is $n(n + 1)/2$. Therefore, the test statistic $T_1$ plus $T_2$, the sum of the ranks assigned to the $n_2$ items in the second sample, must equal $n(n + 1)/2$. You can use Equation (12.8) to check the accuracy of your rankings.

### Checking the Rankings

$$T_1 + T_2 = \frac{n(n + 1)}{2} \qquad (12.8)$$

When both samples $n_1$ and $n_2$ are $\leq 10$, you use Table E.8 to find the critical values of the test statistic $T_1$. For a two-tail test, you reject the null hypothesis (see Panel A of Figure 12.18) if the computed value of $T_1$ equals or is greater than the upper critical value, or if $T_1$ is less than or equal to the lower critical value. For one-tail tests having the alternative hypothesis $H_1: M_1 < M_2$ [i.e., the median of population 1 $(M_1)$ is less than the median of population 2 $(M_2)$] you reject the null hypothesis if the observed value of $T_1$ is less than or equal to the lower critical value (see Panel B of Figure 12.18). For one-tail tests having the alternative hypothesis $H_1: M_1 > M_2$, you reject the null hypothesis if the observed value of $T_1$ equals or is greater than the upper critical value (see Panel C of Figure 12.18).

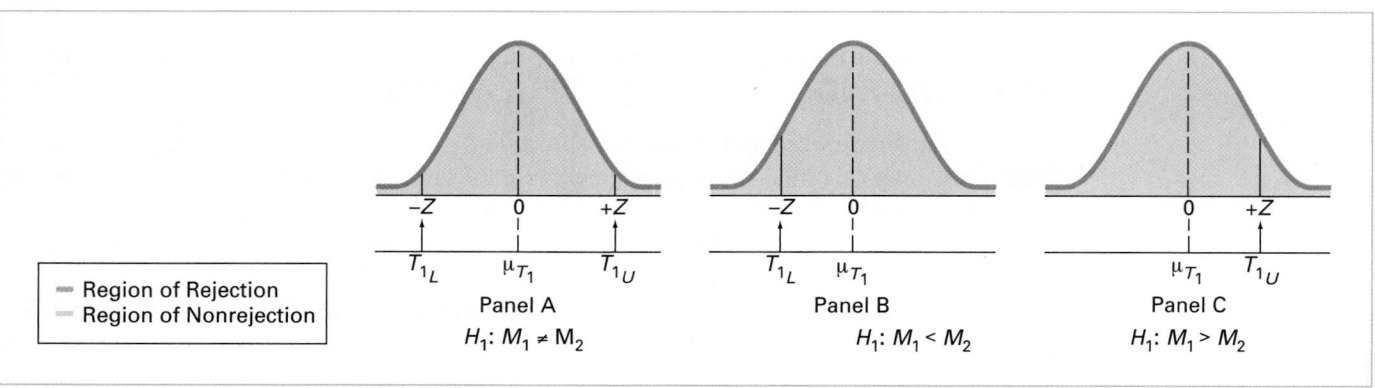

**FIGURE 12.18** Regions of rejection and nonrejection using the Wilcoxon rank sum test

For large sample sizes, the test statistic $T_1$ is approximately normally distributed, with the mean, $\mu_{T_1}$, equal to

$$\mu_{T_1} = \frac{n_1(n + 1)}{2}$$

and the standard deviation, $\sigma_{T_1}$, equal to

$$\sigma_{T_1} = \sqrt{\frac{n_1 n_2 (n + 1)}{12}}$$

Therefore, Equation (12.9) defines the standardized $Z_{STAT}$ test statistic.

Large Sample Wilcoxon Rank Sum Test

$$Z_{STAT} = \frac{T_1 - \frac{n_1(n+1)}{2}}{\sqrt{\frac{n_1 n_2 (n+1)}{12}}} \qquad (12.9)$$

where the $Z_{STAT}$ test statistic approximately follows a standardized normal distribution.

[2]To test for differences in the median sales between the two locations, you must assume that the distributions of sales in both populations are identical except for differences in location (i.e., the medians).

You use Equation (12.9) for testing the null hypothesis when the sample sizes are outside the range of Table E.8. Based on $\alpha$, the level of significance selected, you reject the null hypothesis if the $Z_{STAT}$ test statistic falls in the rejection region.

To study an application of the Wilcoxon rank sum test, return to the Using Statistics scenario of Chapter 10 concerning sales of BLK Cola for the two locations: normal shelf display and end-aisle location (see page 390). If you do not think that the populations are normally distributed, you can use the Wilcoxon rank sum test for evaluating possible differences in the median sales for the two display locations.[2] The data (stored in the file Cola) and the combined ranks are shown in Table 12.15.

**TABLE 12.15**

Forming the Combined Rankings

| Sales | | | |
|---|---|---|---|
| **Normal Display** $(n_1 = 10)$ | **Combined Ranking** | **End-Aisle Display** $(n_2 = 10)$ | **Combined Ranking** |
| 22 | 1.0 | 52 | 5.5 |
| 34 | 3.0 | 71 | 14.0 |
| 52 | 5.5 | 76 | 15.0 |
| 62 | 10.0 | 54 | 7.0 |
| 30 | 2.0 | 67 | 13.0 |
| 40 | 4.0 | 83 | 17.0 |
| 64 | 11.0 | 66 | 12.0 |
| 84 | 18.5 | 90 | 20.0 |
| 56 | 8.0 | 77 | 16.0 |
| 59 | 9.0 | 84 | 18.5 |

Source: *Data are taken from Table 10.1 on page 392.*

Because you have not specified in advance which aisle location is likely to have a higher median, you use a two-tail test with the following null and alternative hypotheses:

$$H_0: M_1 = M_2 \text{ (the median sales are equal)}$$

$$H_1: M_1 \neq M_2 \text{ (the median sales are not equal)}$$

Now you need to compute $T_1$, the sum of the ranks assigned to the *smaller* sample. When the sample sizes are equal, as in this example, you can identify either sample as the group from which to compute $T_1$. Choosing the normal display as the first sample,

$$T_1 = 1 + 3 + 5.5 + 10 + 2 + 4 + 11 + 18.5 + 8 + 9 = 72$$

As a check on the ranking procedure, you compute $T_2$ from

$$T_2 = 5.5 + 14 + 15 + 7 + 13 + 17 + 12 + 20 + 16 + 18.5 = 138$$

and then use Equation (12.8) on page 534 to show that the sum of the first $n = 20$ integers in the combined ranking is equal to $T_1 + T_2$:

$$T_1 + T_2 = \frac{n(n+1)}{2}$$

$$72 + 138 = \frac{20(21)}{2} = 210$$

$$210 = 210$$

Next, you use Table E.8 to determine the lower- and upper-tail critical values for the test statistic $T_1$. From Table 12.16, a portion of Table E.8, observe that for a level of significance of 0.05, the critical values are 78 and 132. The decision rule is

Reject $H_0$ if $T_1 \leq 78$ or if $T_1 \geq 132$;

otherwise, do not reject $H_0$.

**TABLE 12.16**

Finding the Lower- and Upper-Tail Critical Values for the Wilcoxon Rank Sum Test Statistic, $T_1$, Where $n_1 = 10$, $n_2 = 10$, and $\alpha = 0.05$

| $n_2$ | One-Tail $\alpha$ | Two-Tail | 4 | 5 | 6 | 7 | 8 | 9 | 10 |
|-------|------|------|---|---|---|---|---|---|----|
| | | | | | (Lower, Upper) | | | | |
| | .05 | .10 | 16,40 | 24,51 | 33,63 | 43,76 | 54,90 | 66,105 | |
| 9 | .025 | .05 | 14,42 | 22,53 | 31,65 | 40,79 | 51,93 | 62,109 | |
| | .01 | .02 | 13,43 | 20,55 | 28,68 | 37,82 | 47,97 | 59,112 | |
| | .005 | .01 | 11,45 | 18,57 | 26,70 | 35,84 | 45,99 | 56,115 | |
| | .05 | .10 | 17,43 | 26,54 | 35,67 | 45,81 | 56,96 | 69,111 | 82,128 |
| 10 | .025 | .05 | 15,45 | 23,57 | 32,70 | 42,84 | 53,99 | 65,115 | 78,132 |
| | .01 | .02 | 13,47 | 21,59 | 29,73 | 39,87 | 49,103 | 61,119 | 74,136 |
| | .005 | .01 | 12,48 | 19,61 | 27,75 | 37,89 | 47,105 | 58,122 | 71,139 |

Source: *Extracted from Table E.8.*

Because the test statistic $T_1 = 72 < 78$, you reject $H_0$. There is evidence of a significant difference in the median sales for the two displays. Because the sum of the ranks is higher for the end-aisle display, you conclude that median sales are higher for the end-aisle display. From the Microsoft Excel worksheet in Figure 12.19, observe that the $p$-value is 0.0126, which is less than $\alpha = 0.05$. The $p$-value indicates that if the medians of the two populations are equal, the chance of finding a difference at least this large in the samples is only 0.0126.

Figure 12.20 displays Minitab results for the *Mann-Whitney test*, which is numerically equivalent to the Wilcoxon rank sum test (see references 1, 2, and 11). In Figure 12.20, ETA1 and ETA2 refer to the hypothesized population medians $M_1$ and $M_2$. Also, the test statistic $W = 72$ is the sum of the ranks for the normal display. The $p$-value for this two-tail hypothesis test is 0.0139, adjusted for ties in the rankings. Although you should use these adjusted $p$-values in making statistical decisions, a discussion of such adjustments is beyond the scope of this text (see references 1 and 2).

**FIGURE 12.19**

Microsoft Excel Wilcoxon rank sum test worksheet for the BLK Cola sales example

*See Section E12.6 or P12.6 to create this. Also see Section E12.7 for related material.*

| | A | B | |
|---|---|---|---|
| 1 | **Display Location Analysis** | | |
| 2 | | | |
| 3 | **Data** | | |
| 4 | **Level of Significance** | 0.05 | |
| 5 | | | |
| 6 | **Population 1 Sample** | | |
| 7 | **Sample Size** | 10 | |
| 8 | **Sum of Ranks** | 72 | |
| 9 | **Population 2 Sample** | | |
| 10 | **Sample Size** | 10 | |
| 11 | **Sum of Ranks** | 138 | |
| 12 | | | |
| 13 | Intermediate Calculations | | |
| 14 | Total Sample Size n | 20 | =B7 + B10 |
| 15 | $T1$ Test Statistic | 72 | =IF(B7 <= B10, B8, B11) |
| 16 | $T1$ Mean | 105 | =IF(B7 <= B10, B7 * (B14 + 1)/2, B10 * (B14 + 1)/2) |
| 17 | Standard Error of $T1$ | 13.2288 | =SQRT(B7 * B10 * (B14 + 1)/12) |
| 18 | **Z Test Statistic** | -2.4946 | =(B15 - B16)/B17 |
| 19 | | | |
| 20 | **Two-Tail Test** | | |
| 21 | **Lower Critical Value** | -1.9600 | =NORMSINV(B4/2) |
| 22 | **Upper Critical Value** | 1.9600 | =NORMSINV(1 - B4/2) |
| 23 | **p-Value** | 0.0126 | =2 * (1 - NORMSDIST(ABS(B18))) |
| 24 | **Reject the null hypothesis** | | =IF(B23 < B4, "Reject the null hypothesis", "Do not reject the null hypothesis") |

**FIGURE 12.20**

Minitab Wilcoxon rank sum test results for the BLK Cola sales example

*See Section M12.3 to create this.*

```
Mann-Whitney Test and CI: Normal, EndAisle

            N   Median
Normal     10    54.00
EndAisle   10    73.50


Point estimate for ETA1-ETA2 is -21.50
95.5 Percent CI for ETA1-ETA2 is (-37.01,-6.00)
W = 72.0
Test of ETA1 = ETA2 vs ETA1 not = ETA2 is significant at 0.0140
The test is significant at 0.0139 (adjusted for ties)
```

Table E.8 shows the lower and upper critical values of the Wilcoxon rank sum test statistic, $T_1$, but only for situations in which both $n_1$ and $n_2$ are less than or equal to 10. If either one or both of the sample sizes are greater than 10, you *must* use the large-sample $Z$ approximation formula [Equation (12.9) on page 535]. However, you can also use this approximation formula for small sample sizes. To demonstrate the large-sample $Z$ approximation formula, consider the BLK Cola sales data. Using Equation (12.9),

$$Z_{STAT} = \frac{T_1 - \dfrac{n_1(n+1)}{2}}{\sqrt{\dfrac{n_1 n_2 (n+1)}{12}}}$$

$$= \frac{72 - \dfrac{(10)(21)}{2}}{\sqrt{\dfrac{(10)(10)(21)}{12}}}$$

$$= \frac{72 - 105}{13.2288} = -2.4946$$

Because $Z_{STAT} = -2.4946 < -1.96$, the critical value of $Z$ at the 0.05 level of significance, you reject $H_0$.

# PROBLEMS FOR SECTION 12.6

## Learning the Basics

**12.47** Using Table E.8, determine the lower- and upper-tail critical values for the Wilcoxon rank sum test statistic, $T_1$, in each of the following two-tail tests:
**a.** $\alpha = 0.10$, $n_1 = 6$, $n_2 = 8$
**b.** $\alpha = 0.05$, $n_1 = 6$, $n_2 = 8$
**c.** $\alpha = 0.01$, $n_1 = 6$, $n_2 = 8$
**d.** Given your results in (a) through (c), what do you conclude regarding the width of the region of nonrejection as the selected level of significance $\alpha$ gets smaller?

**12.48** Using Table E.8, determine the lower-tail critical value for the Wilcoxon rank sum test statistic, $T_1$, in each of the following one-tail tests:
**a.** $\alpha = 0.05$, $n_1 = 6$, $n_2 = 8$
**b.** $\alpha = 0.025$, $n_1 = 6$, $n_2 = 8$
**c.** $\alpha = 0.01$, $n_1 = 6$, $n_2 = 8$
**d.** $\alpha = 0.005$, $n_1 = 6$, $n_2 = 8$

**12.49** The following information is available for two samples selected from independent populations:

Sample 1: $n_1 = 7$   Assigned ranks: 4 1 8 2 5 10 11

Sample 2: $n_2 = 9$   Assigned ranks: 7 16 12 9 3 14 13 6 15

What is the value of $T_1$ if you are testing the null hypothesis $H_0: M_1 = M_2$?

**12.50** In Problem 12.49, what are the lower- and upper-tail critical values for the test statistic $T_1$ from Table E.8 if you use a 0.05 level of significance and the alternative hypothesis is $H_1: M_1 \neq M_2$?

**12.51** In Problems 12.49 and 12.50, what is your statistical decision?

**12.52** The following information is available for two samples selected from independent and similarly shaped right-skewed populations:

Sample 1: $n_1 = 5$   1.1 2.3 2.9 3.6 14.7

Sample 2: $n_2 = 6$   2.8 4.4 4.4 5.2 6.0 18.5

**a.** Replace the observed values with the corresponding ranks (where 1 = smallest value; $n = n_1 + n_2 = 11$ = largest value) in the combined samples.
**b.** What is the value of the test statistic $T_1$?
**c.** Compute the value of $T_2$, the sum of the ranks in the larger sample.
**d.** To check the accuracy of your rankings, use Equation (12.8) on page 534 to demonstrate that

$$T_1 + T_2 = \frac{n(n+1)}{2}$$

**12.53** From Problem 12.52, at the 0.05 level of significance, determine the lower-tail critical value for the Wilcoxon rank sum test statistic, $T_1$, if you want to test the null hypothesis, $H_0: M_1 \geq M_2$, against the one-tail alternative, $H_1: M_1 < M_2$.

**12.54** In Problems 12.52 and 12.53, what is your statistical decision?

## Applying the Concepts

**12.55** A vice president for marketing recruits 20 college graduates for management training. The 20 individuals are randomly assigned, 10 each, to one of two groups. A "traditional" method of training ($T$) is used in one group, and an "experimental" method ($E$) is used in the other. After the graduates spend six months on the job, the vice president ranks them on the basis of their performance, from 1 (worst) to 20 (best), with the following results (stored in the file Testrank):

| $T$ | 1 | 2 | 3 | 5 | 9 | 10 | 12 | 13 | 14 | 15 |
|---|---|---|---|---|---|---|---|---|---|---|
| $E$ | 4 | 6 | 7 | 8 | 11 | 16 | 17 | 18 | 19 | 20 |

Is there evidence of a difference in the median performance between the two methods? (Use $\alpha = 0.05$.)

**12.56** Wine experts Gaiter and Brecher use a six-category scale when rating wines: Yech, OK, Good, Very Good, Delicious, and Delicious! (extracted from D. Gaiter and J. Brecher, "A Good U.S. Cabernet Is Hard to Find," *The Wall Street Journal*, May 19, 2006, p. W7). Suppose Gaiter and Brecher tested a random sample of eight inexpensive California Cabernets and a random sample of eight inexpensive Washington Cabernets. *Inexpensive* is defined as a suggested retail value in the United States of under $20. The data, stored in the Cabernet file are as follows:
California—Good, Delicious, Yech, OK, OK, Very Good, Yech, OK
Washington—Very Good, OK, Delicious!, Very Good, Delicious, Good, Delicious, Delicious!
**a.** Are the data collected by rating wines using this scale nominal, ordinal, interval, or ratio?
**b.** Why is the two-sample $t$ test defined in Section 10.1 inappropriate to test the mean rating of California Cabernets versus Washington Cabernets?
**c.** Is there evidence of a significance difference in the median rating of California Cabernets and Washington Cabernets? (Use $\alpha = 0.05$.)

**12.57** In intaglio printing, a design or figure is carved beneath the surface of hard metal or stone. Suppose that an experiment is designed to compare differences in surface hardness of steel plates used in intaglio printing (measured in indentation numbers), based on two different surface conditions—untreated and treated by lightly polishing with emery paper. In the experiment, 40 steel plates are randomly assigned—20 that are untreated and 20 that are treated. The data are shown in the following table and are stored in the file Intaglio:

| Untreated | | Treated | |
|---|---|---|---|
| 164.368 | 177.135 | 158.239 | 150.226 |
| 159.018 | 163.903 | 138.216 | 155.620 |
| 153.871 | 167.802 | 168.006 | 151.233 |
| 165.096 | 160.818 | 149.654 | 158.653 |
| 157.184 | 167.433 | 145.456 | 151.204 |
| 154.496 | 163.538 | 168.178 | 150.869 |
| 160.920 | 164.525 | 154.321 | 161.657 |
| 164.917 | 171.230 | 162.763 | 157.016 |
| 169.091 | 174.964 | 161.020 | 156.670 |
| 175.276 | 166.311 | 167.706 | 147.920 |

a. Is there evidence of a difference in the median surface hardness between untreated and treated steel plates? (Use $\alpha = 0.05$.)
b. What assumptions must you make in (a)?
c. Compare the results of (a) with those of Problem 10.16(a) on page 402.

**SELF Test** **12.58** The management of a hotel was concerned with increasing the return rate for hotel guests. One aspect of first impressions by guests relates to the time it takes to deliver a guest's luggage to the room after check-in to the hotel. A random sample of 20 deliveries on a particular day were selected in Wing *A* of the hotel, and a random sample of 20 deliveries were selected in Wing *B*. The results are stored in the file Luggage.
a. Is there evidence of a difference in the median delivery time in the two wings of the hotel? (Use $\alpha = 0.05$.)
b. Compare the results of (a) with those of Problem 10.69 on page 430.

**12.59** The director of training for an electronic equipment manufacturer wants to determine whether different training methods have an effect on the productivity of assembly-line employees. She randomly assigns 42 recently hired employees to two groups of 21. The first group receives a computer-assisted, individual-based training program, and the other group receives a team-based training program. Upon completion of the training, the employees are evaluated on the time (in seconds) it takes to assemble a part. The results are in the data file Training.
a. Using a 0.05 level of significance, is there evidence of a difference in the median assembly times (in seconds) between employees trained in a computer-assisted,

individual-based program and those trained in a team-based program?
b. What assumptions must you make in order to do (a) of this problem?
c. Compare the results of Problem 10.18(a) on page 402 with the results of (a) in this problem. Discuss.

**12.60** Nondestructive evaluation is used to measure the properties of components or materials without causing any permanent physical change to the components or materials. It includes the determination of properties of materials and the classification of flaws by size, shape, type, and location. Nondestructive evaluation is very effective for detecting surface flaws and characterizing surface properties of electrically conductive materials. Recently, data were collected that classified each component as having a flaw or not, based on manual inspection and operator judgment, and also reported the size of the crack in the material. Do the components classified as unflawed have a smaller median crack size than components classified as flawed? The results in terms of crack size (in inches) are in the data file Crack (extracted from B. D. Olin and W. Q. Meeker, "Applications of Statistical Methods to Nondestructive Evaluation," *Technometrics*, 38, 1996, p. 101).

**Unflawed**

0.003 0.004 0.012 0.014 0.021 0.023 0.024 0.030 0.034

0.041 0.041 0.042 0.043 0.045 0.057 0.063 0.074 0.076

**Flawed**

0.022 0.026 0.026 0.030 0.031 0.034 0.042 0.043 0.044

0.046 0.046 0.052 0.055 0.058 0.060 0.060 0.070 0.071

0.073 0.073 0.078 0.079 0.079 0.083 0.090 0.095 0.095

0.096 0.100 0.102 0.103 0.105 0.114 0.119 0.120 0.130

0.160 0.306 0.328 0.440

a. Using a 0.05 level of significance, is there evidence that the median crack size is less for unflawed components than for flawed components?
b. What assumptions must you make in (a)?
c. Compare the results of Problem 10.19(a) on page 403 with the results of (a) in this problem. Discuss.

**12.61** A bank with a branch located in a commercial district of a city has developed an improved process for serving customers during the noon-to-1 p.m. lunch period. The waiting time (defined as the time elapsed from when the customer enters the line until he or she reaches the teller window) needs to be shortened to increase customer satisfaction. A random sample of 15 customers is selected (and stored in the file [Bank1]), and the results (in minutes) are as follows:

$$4.21 \quad 5.55 \quad 3.02 \quad 5.13 \quad 4.77 \quad 2.34 \quad 3.54 \quad 3.20$$
$$4.50 \quad 6.10 \quad 0.38 \quad 5.12 \quad 6.46 \quad 6.19 \quad 3.79$$

Another branch, located in a residential area, is also concerned with the noon-to-1 p.m. lunch period. A random sample of 15 customers is selected (and stored in the file [Bank2]), and the results (in minutes) are as follows:

$$9.66 \quad 5.90 \quad 8.02 \quad 5.79 \quad 8.73 \quad 3.82 \quad 8.01 \quad 8.35$$
$$10.49 \quad 6.68 \quad 5.64 \quad 4.08 \quad 6.17 \quad 9.91 \quad 5.47$$

**a.** Is there evidence of a difference in the median waiting time between the two branches? (Use $\alpha = 0.05$.)
**b.** What assumptions must you make in (a)?
**c.** Compare the results of Problem 10.14(a) on page 402 with the results of (a) in this problem. Discuss.

**12.62** Digital cameras have taken over the majority of the point-and-shoot camera market. One of the important features of a camera is the battery life as measured by the number of shots taken until the battery needs to be recharged. The data in the file [Digitalcameras] contains the battery life of 31 subcompact cameras and 15 compact cameras (extracted from "Cameras," *Consumer Reports*, November 2006, pp. 20–21).
**a.** Is there evidence of a difference in the median battery life between subcompact cameras and compact cameras? (Use $\alpha = 0.05$.)
**b.** What assumptions must you make in (a)?
**c.** Compare the results of Problem 10.11(a) on page 401 with the results of (a) in this problem. Discuss.

## 12.7 WILCOXON SIGNED RANKS TEST: NONPARAMETRIC ANALYSIS FOR TWO RELATED POPULATIONS

In Section 10.2, you used the paired $t$ test to compare the means of two populations when you had repeated measures or matched samples. The paired $t$ test assumes that the data are measured on an interval or a ratio scale and are normally distributed. If you cannot make these assumptions, you can use the nonparametric **Wilcoxon signed ranks test** to test for the median difference. The Wilcoxon signed ranks test requires that the differences are approximately symmetric and that the data are measured on an ordinal, interval, or ratio scale. When the assumptions for the Wilcoxon signed ranks test are met, but the assumptions of the $t$ test are violated, the Wilcoxon signed ranks test is usually more powerful in detecting a difference in the two populations. Even under conditions appropriate to the paired $t$ test, the Wilcoxon signed ranks test is almost as powerful.

The Wilcoxon signed ranks test uses the test statistic $W$. Exhibit 12.1 lists the steps required to compute $W$.

---

**EXHIBIT 12.1: STEPS IN COMPUTING THE WILCOXON SIGNED RANKS TEST STATISTIC $W$**

1. For each item in a sample of $n$ items, compute a difference score $D_i$ between the two paired values.
2. Neglect the "+" and "–" signs and list the set of $n$ absolute differences $|D_i|$.
3. Omit from further analysis any absolute difference score of zero, thereby yielding a set of $n'$ nonzero absolute difference scores, where $n' \leq n$. After you remove values with absolute difference scores of zero, $n'$ becomes the actual sample size.
4. Assign ranks $R_i$ from 1 to $n'$ to each of the $|D_i|$ such that the smallest absolute difference score gets rank 1 and the largest gets rank $n'$. If two or more $|D_i|$ are equal, assign each of them the mean of the ranks they would have been assigned individually had ties in the data not occurred.
5. Reassign the symbol "+" or "–" to each of the $n'$ ranks $R_i$, depending on whether $D_i$ was originally positive or negative.
6. Compute the Wilcoxon test statistic $W$ as the sum of the positive ranks [see Equation (12.10)].

**Wilcoxon Signed Ranks Test**
The Wilcoxon test statistic $W$ is computed as the sum of the positive ranks.

$$W = \sum_{i=1}^{n'} R_i^{(+)} \qquad\qquad \textbf{(12.10)}$$

The null and alternative hypotheses for the Wilcoxon signed rank test are:

| Two-Tail Test | One-Tail Test | One-Tail Test |
|---|---|---|
| $H_0: M_D = 0$ | $H_0: M_D \geq 0$ | $H_0: M_D \leq 0$ |
| $H_1: M_D \neq 0$ | $H_1: M_D < 0$ | $H_1: M_D > 0$ |

Because the sum of the first $n'$ integers $(1, 2, \ldots, n')$ equals $n'(n' + 1)/2$, the Wilcoxon test statistic $W$ ranges from a minimum of 0 (where all the difference scores are negative) to a maximum of $n'(n' + 1)/2$ (where all the difference scores are positive). If the null hypothesis is true, the test statistic $W$ is expected to be close to its mean $\mu_W = n'(n' + 1)/4$. If the null hypothesis is false, the value of the test statistic is expected to be close to one of the extremes.

You use Table E.9 to find the critical values of the test statistic $W$ for both one- and two-tail tests for samples of $n' \leq 20$. For a two-tail test, you reject the null hypothesis (panel A of Figure 12.21) if the computed $W$ test statistic equals or is greater than the upper critical value or is equal to or less than the lower critical value. For a one-tail test in the lower tail, you reject the null hypothesis if the computed $W$ test statistic is less than or equal to the lower critical value (panel B of Figure 12.21). For a one-tail test in the upper tail, the decision rule is to reject the null hypothesis if the computed $W$ test statistic equals or is greater than the upper critical value (panel C of Figure 12.21).

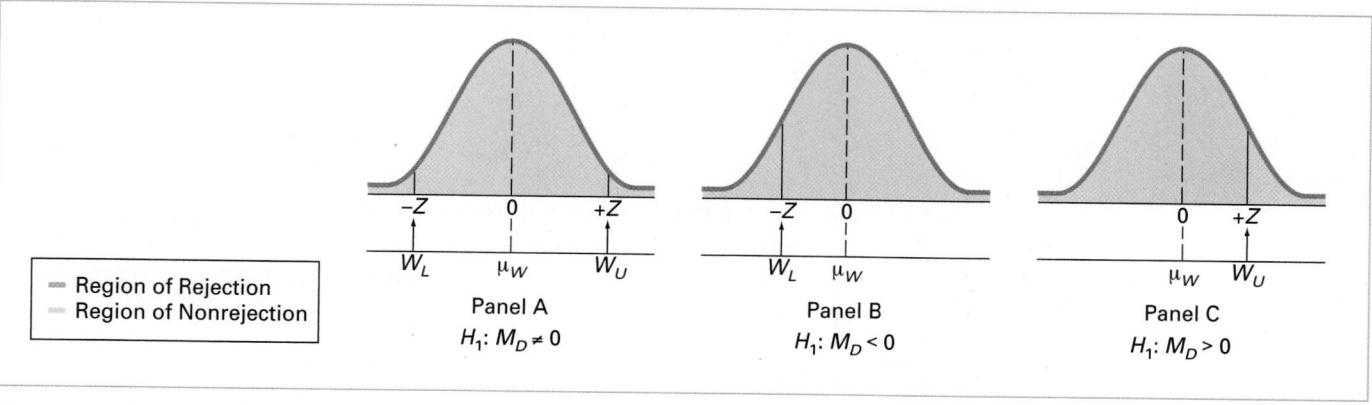

**FIGURE 12.21** Regions of rejection and nonrejection using the Wilcoxon signed ranks test

For samples of $n' > 20$, the test statistic $W$ is approximately normally distributed with mean $\mu_W$ and standard deviation $\sigma_W$. The mean of the test statistic $W$ is

$$\mu_W = \frac{n'(n' + 1)}{4}$$

and the standard deviation of the test statistic $W$ is

$$\sigma_W = \sqrt{\frac{n'(n' + 1)(2n' + 1)}{24}}$$

Therefore, Equation (12.11) defines the $Z_{STAT}$ test statistic.

---

**Large-Sample Wilcoxon Signed Ranks Test**

$$Z_{STAT} = \frac{W - \dfrac{n'(n'+1)}{4}}{\sqrt{\dfrac{n'(n'+1)(2n'+1)}{24}}}$$ (12.11)

---

You use this large-sample approximation formula when sample sizes are outside the range of Table E.9. You reject the null hypothesis if the computed $Z_{STAT}$ test statistic falls in the rejection region. The region of rejection used depends on the level of significance and whether the test is one-tail or two-tail (see Figure 12.21).

To demonstrate how to use the Wilcoxon signed ranks test, return to the example concerning gasoline mileage discussed on page 405. If you cannot assume that the differences are taken from normally distributed populations, you can use the Wilcoxon signed ranks test to determine whether there is a difference in median gasoline mileage between the real-life driving done by an AAA member and the driving done according to government standards.

The null and alternative hypotheses for this two-tail test are:

$$H_0: M_D = 0$$

$$H_1: M_D \neq 0$$

To perform the test, follow the six steps listed in Exhibit 12.1 on page 540. First, compute a set of difference scores $D_i$ between each of the $n$ paired values:

$$D_i = X_{1i} - X_{2i}$$

where

$$i = 1, 2, \ldots, n$$

In this example, you compute a set of $n$ difference scores using $D_i = X_{member} - X_{govt}$. If there is no difference in the gasoline mileage between the two measurement standards, the difference scores will cluster near zero (i.e., $\bar{D} \cong 0$) and you will not reject $H_0$. The remaining steps of the six-step procedure are developed in Table 12.17.

**TABLE 12.17**

Setting Up the Wilcoxon Signed Ranks Test for the Median Difference

| Model | Members | Government | $D_i = X_{1i} - X_{2i}$ | $|D_i|$ | $R_i$ | Sign of $D_i$ |
|---|---|---|---|---|---|---|
| **2005 Ford F-150** | 14.3 | 16.8 | −2.5 | 2.5 | 5.0 | − |
| **2005 Chevrolet Silverado** | 15.0 | 17.8 | −2.8 | 2.8 | 6.0 | − |
| **2002 Honda Accord LX** | 27.8 | 26.2 | +1.6 | 1.6 | 4.0 | + |
| **2002 Honda Civic** | 27.9 | 33.2 | −5.3 | 5.3 | 8.0 | − |
| **2004 Honda Civic Hybrid** | 48.8 | 47.6 | +1.2 | 1.2 | 2.0 | + |
| **2002 Ford Explorer** | 16.8 | 18.3 | −1.5 | 1.5 | 3.0 | − |
| **2005 Toyota Camry** | 23.7 | 28.5 | −4.8 | 4.8 | 7.0 | − |
| **2003 Toyota Corolla** | 32.8 | 33.1 | −0.3 | 0.3 | 1.0 | − |
| **2005 Toyota Prius** | 37.3 | 44.0 | −6.7 | 6.7 | 9.0 | − |

Two of the nine difference scores have a positive sign. You now compute the test statistic $W$ as the sum of the positive ranks:

$$W = \sum_{i=1}^{n'} R_i^{(+)} = 4 + 2 = 6$$

Because $n = 9 \le 20$, use Table E.9 to determine the upper-tail critical value. Using $\alpha = 0.05$ for this two-tail test, the lower-tail critical value is 5 and the upper-tail critical value is 40 (see Table 12.18, which is a portion of Table E.9).

**TABLE 12.18**

Finding the Upper-Tail Critical Value for the Wilcoxon Signed Ranks Test Statistic $W$ Where $n = 9$ and $\alpha = 0.05$

| One-Tail: | $\alpha = 0.05$ | $\alpha = 0.025$ | $\alpha = 0.01$ | $\alpha = 0.005$ |
|---|---|---|---|---|
| Two-Tail: | $\alpha = 0.10$ | $\alpha = 0.05$ | $\alpha = 0.02$ | $\alpha = 0.010$ |
| $n$ | | (Lower, Upper) | | |
| 5 | 0,15 | — | — | — |
| 6 | 2,19 | 0,21 | — | — |
| 7 | 3,25 | 2,26 | 0,28 | — |
| 8 | 5,31 | 3,33 | 1,35 | 0,36 |
| 9 | 8,37 | 5,40 | 3,42 | 1,44 |
| 10 | 10,45 | 8,47 | 5,50 | 3,52 |

Source: *Extracted from Table E.9.*

Because $5 < W = 6 < 40$, do not reject the null hypothesis. There is no significant evidence that there is a difference in the median gasoline mileage between the real-life driving done by an AAA member and the driving done according to government standards. From the Minitab results in Figure 12.22, the $p$-value is 0.058, which is greater than 0.05. Therefore, you can conclude that there is no difference in the median gasoline mileage between the real-life driving done by an AAA member and the driving done according to government standards.

**FIGURE 12.22**

Minitab Wilcoxon signed ranks test results for the gasoline mileage example

*See Section M12.4 to create this.*

```
Wilcoxon Signed Rank Test: Difference

Test of median = 0.000000 versus median not = 0.000000

                      N for   Wilcoxon            Estimated
                 N    Test    Statistic      P      Median
Difference       9     9          6.0    0.058     -2.500
```

Interestingly, these results are different from those of Section 10.2. When you used the paired $t$ test, you rejected the null hypothesis of no difference in the mean gasoline mileage between the real-life driving done by an AAA member and the driving done according to government standards with a $p$-value $= 0.0412$. Because the Wilcoxon signed ranks test does not assume normality in the differences, given the inconsistency of the results, you should not conclude that the differences are significant unless you are convinced that they follow a normal distribution (something that would be very difficult to evaluate with a sample of only nine differences).

Table E.9 provides critical values only for situations involving small samples (where $n' \le 20$). If the sample size $n'$ is greater than 20, you must use the large-sample $Z$ approximation formula [Equation (12.11) on page 542]. For small samples, you can use either Table E.9 or the $Z$ approximation approach.

To demonstrate the large-sample $Z$ approximation approach, even for samples as small as nine, consider again the gasoline mileage data. Using Equation (12.11):

$$Z_{STAT} = \frac{W - \dfrac{n'(n'+1)}{4}}{\sqrt{\dfrac{n'(n'+1)(2n'+1)}{24}}}$$

$$= \frac{6 - \dfrac{(9)(10)}{4}}{\sqrt{\dfrac{(9)(10)(19)}{24}}}$$

$$= \frac{6 - 22.5}{8.44} = -1.955$$

The decision rule is

Reject $H_0$ if $Z_{STAT} > +1.96$ or if $Z_{STAT} < -1.96$;

otherwise do not reject $H_0$.

Because $-1.96 < Z_{STAT} = -1.955 < +1.96$, do not reject $H_0$. The $p$-value is slightly more than 0.05. Because the $p$-value is greater than $\alpha = 0.05$, you do not reject the null hypothesis. Thus, without having to assume that the original population of difference scores are normally distributed, you can conclude that there is no difference in median gasoline mileage between the real-life driving done by an AAA member and the driving done according to government standards.

The Wilcoxon signed ranks test makes fewer and less stringent assumptions than does the paired $t$ test. The assumptions are:

- The data are a random sample of $n$ independent difference scores. The difference scores are the result of repeated measures or matched pairs.
- The underlying variable is continuous.
- The data are measured on an ordinal, interval, or ratio scale.
- The distribution of the population of difference scores is approximately symmetric.

# PROBLEMS FOR SECTION 12.7

## Learning the Basics

**12.63** Using Table E.9, determine the lower- and upper-tail critical values for the Wilcoxon signed ranks test statistic $W$ in each of the following two-tail tests:
**a.** $\alpha = 0.10$, $n' = 11$
**b.** $\alpha = 0.05$, $n' = 11$
**c.** $\alpha = 0.02$, $n' = 11$
**d.** $\alpha = 0.01$, $n' = 11$

**12.64** Using Table E.9, determine the upper-tail critical value for the Wilcoxon signed ranks test statistic $W$ in each of the following one-tail tests:
**a.** $\alpha = 0.05$, $n' = 11$
**b.** $\alpha = 0.025$, $n' = 11$

**c.** $\alpha = 0.01$, $n' = 11$
**d.** $\alpha = 0.005$, $n' = 11$

**12.65** Using Table E.9, determine the lower-tail critical value for the Wilcoxon signed ranks test statistic $W$ in each of the following one-tail tests:
**a.** $\alpha = 0.05$, $n' = 11$
**b.** $\alpha = 0.025$, $n' = 11$
**c.** $\alpha = 0.01$, $n' = 11$
**d.** $\alpha = 0.005$, $n' = 11$

**12.66** Consider the following $n = 12$ difference scores from two related samples:

Difference scores ($D_i$): +3.2, +1.7, +4.5, 0.0, +11.1, −0.8, +2.3, −2.0, 0.0, +14.8, +5.6, +1.7

What is the value of the test statistic $W$ if you are testing $H_0: M_D = 0$?

**12.67** In Problem 12.66, what are the lower- and upper-tail critical values for the test statistic $W$ from Table E.9 if the level of significance $\alpha$ is 0.05 and the alternative hypothesis is $H_1: M_D \neq 0$?

**12.68** In Problems 12.66 and 12.67, what is your statistical decision?

**12.69** Consider the following $n' = 12$ signed ranks $(R_i)$ computed from the difference scores $(D_i)$ from two related samples:

> Signed ranks $(R_i)$: +5, +6.5, +4, +11, –8, +2.5, –2.5, +1, +12, +6.5, +10, +9

What is the value of the test statistic $W$ if you are testing $H_0: M_D \leq 0$?

**12.70** For Problem 12.69, at a level of significance of 0.05, determine the upper-tail critical value for the Wilcoxon signed ranks test statistic $W$ if you want to test $H_0: M_D \leq 0$ against $H_1: M_D > 0$.

**12.71** For Problems 12.69 and 12.70, what is your statistical decision?

## Applying the Concepts

**12.72** Nine experts rated two brands of Colombian coffee in a taste-testing experiment. A rating on a 7-point scale (1 = extremely unpleasing, 7 = extremely pleasing) is given for each of four characteristics: taste, aroma, richness, and acidity. The following data (stored in the file Coffee) displays the summated ratings—accumulated over all four characteristics.

| | BRAND | |
|---|---|---|
| EXPERT | A | B |
| C.C. | 24 | 26 |
| S.E. | 27 | 27 |
| E.G. | 19 | 22 |
| B.L. | 24 | 27 |
| C.M. | 22 | 25 |
| C.N. | 26 | 27 |
| G.N. | 27 | 26 |
| R.M. | 25 | 27 |
| P.V. | 22 | 23 |

**a.** At the 0.05 level of significance, is there evidence of a difference in the median summated rating between brand $A$ and brand $B$?
**b.** Compare the results of (a) with those of Problem 10.22 on page 410.

**12.73** An article discussed the new Whole Foods Market in the Time-Warner building in New York City (W. Grimes, "A

Pleasure Palace Without the Guilt," *The New York Times*, February 18, 2004, pp. F1, F5). The following data (in the file Wholefoods1) compared the price of some kitchen staples at the new Whole Foods Market and at the Fairway supermarket located about 15 blocks from the Time-Warner building.

| Item | Whole Foods | Fairway |
|---|---|---|
| Half-gallon milk | 2.19 | 1.35 |
| Dozen eggs | 2.39 | 1.69 |
| Tropicana orange juice (64 oz.) | 2.00 | 2.49 |
| Head of Boston lettuce | 1.98 | 1.29 |
| Ground round 1 lb. | 4.99 | 3.69 |
| Bumble Bee tuna 6 oz. can | 1.79 | 1.33 |
| Granny Smith apples (1 lb.) | 1.69 | 1.49 |
| Box DeCecco linguini | 1.99 | 1.59 |
| Salmon steak 1 lb. | 7.99 | 5.99 |
| Whole chicken per pound | 2.19 | 1.49 |

Source: *Extracted from W. Grimes, "A Pleasure Palace Without the Guilt," The New York Times, February 18, 2004, pp. F1, F5.*

**a.** At the 0.01 level of significance, is there evidence that the median price is higher at Whole Foods Market than at the Fairway supermarket?
**b.** Compare the results of (a) with those of Problem 10.25 on page 411.

**12.74** In industrial settings, alternative methods often exist for measuring variables of interest. The data in the file Measurement (coded to maintain confidentiality) represent measurements in-line (collected from an analyzer during the production process) and from an analytical lab (extracted from M. Leitnaker, "Comparing Measurement Processes: In-Line versus Analytical Measurements," *Quality Engineering*, 13, 2000–2001, pp. 293–298).

**a.** At the 0.05 level of significance, is there evidence of a difference in the median measurements in-line and from an analytical lab?
**b.** Compare the results of (a) with those of Problem 10.23 on page 411.

**12.75** Can students save money by comparison shopping at Amazon.com? To investigate this possibility, a random sample of 15 textbooks used during a recent semester at Miami University was selected. The prices for these textbooks at both a local bookstore and through Amazon.com were recorded. The prices for the textbooks, including all relevant taxes and shipping, are in the file Textbook.

**a.** At the 0.01 level of significance, is there evidence of a difference in the median price of textbooks between the local bookstore and Amazon.com?
**b.** Compare the results of (a) with those of Problem 10.24 on page 411.

**12.76** Over the past year the vice president for human resources at a large medical center conducted a series of three-month workshops aimed at increasing worker motivation and performance. As a check on the effectiveness of the workshops, she selected a random sample of 35 employees from the personnel files and recorded their most recent annual performance ratings along with the ratings attained prior to attending the workshops. The data are stored in the Perform file.

**a.** At the 0.05 level of significance, is there evidence of a difference in the median performance ratings?

**b.** Compare the results of (a) with those of Problem 10.27 on page 412.

**12.77** The data in the file Concrete1 represent the compressive strength in thousands of pounds per square inch (psi) of 40 samples of concrete taken two and seven days after pouring.

Source: *Extracted from O. Carrillo-Gamboa and R. F. Gunst, "Measurement-Error-Model Collinearities,"* Technometrics, *34, 1992, pp. 454–464.*

**a.** At the 0.01 level of significance, is there evidence that the median strength is less at two days than at seven days?

**b.** Compare the results of (a) with those of Problem 10.28 on page 412.

## 12.8  KRUSKAL-WALLIS RANK TEST: NONPARAMETRIC ANALYSIS FOR THE ONE-WAY ANOVA

If the normality assumption of the one-way ANOVA $F$ test is not met, you can use the Kruskal-Wallis rank test. The Kruskal-Wallis rank test for differences among $c$ medians (where $c > 2$) is an extension of the Wilcoxon rank sum test for two independent populations, discussed in Section 12.6. Thus, the Kruskal-Wallis test has the same power relative to the one-way ANOVA $F$ test that the Wilcoxon rank sum test has relative to the $t$ test.

You use the **Kruskal-Wallis rank test** to test whether $c$ independent groups have equal medians. The null hypothesis is

$$H_0: M_1 = M_2 = \cdots = M_c$$

and the alternative hypothesis is

$$H_1: \text{Not all } M_j \text{ are equal (where } j = 1, 2, \ldots, c).$$

To use the Kruskal-Wallis rank test, you first replace the values in the $c$ samples with their combined ranks (if necessary). Rank 1 is given to the smallest of the combined values and rank $n$ to the largest of the combined values (where $n = n_1 + n_2 + \cdots + n_c$). If any values are tied, you assign them the mean of the ranks they would have otherwise been assigned if ties had not been present in the data.

The Kruskal-Wallis test is an alternative to the one-way ANOVA $F$ test. Instead of comparing each of the $c$ group means, $\bar{X}_j$, against the grand mean, $\bar{\bar{X}}$, the Kruskal-Wallis test compares the mean rank in each of the $c$ groups against the overall mean rank, based on all $n$ combined values. Equation (12.12) defines the Kruskal-Wallis test statistic, $H$.

Kruskal-Wallis Rank Test for Differences Among $c$ Medians

$$H = \left[ \frac{12}{n(n+1)} \sum_{j=1}^{c} \frac{T_j^2}{n_j} \right] - 3(n+1) \tag{12.12}$$

where

$n$ = total number of values over the combined samples

$n_j$ = number of values in the $j$th sample ($j = 1, 2, \ldots, c$)

$T_j$ = sum of the ranks assigned to the $j$th sample

$T_j^2$ = square of the sum of the ranks assigned to the $j$th sample

$c$ = number of groups

If there is a significant difference among the $c$ groups, the mean rank differs considerably from group to group. In the process of squaring these differences, the test statistic $H$ becomes large. If there are no differences present, the test statistic $H$ is small because the mean of the ranks assigned in each group should be very similar from group to group.

As the sample sizes in each group get large (i.e., greater than 5), you can approximate the test statistic, $H$, by the chi-square distribution with $c - 1$ degrees of freedom. Thus, you reject the null hypothesis if the computed value of $H$ is greater than the $\chi_\alpha^2$ upper-tail critical value (see Figure 12.23). Therefore, the decision rule is

$$\text{Reject } H_0 \text{ if } H > \chi_\alpha^2;$$

$$\text{otherwise do not reject } H_0.$$

**FIGURE 12.23**

Determining the rejection region for the Kruskal-Wallis test

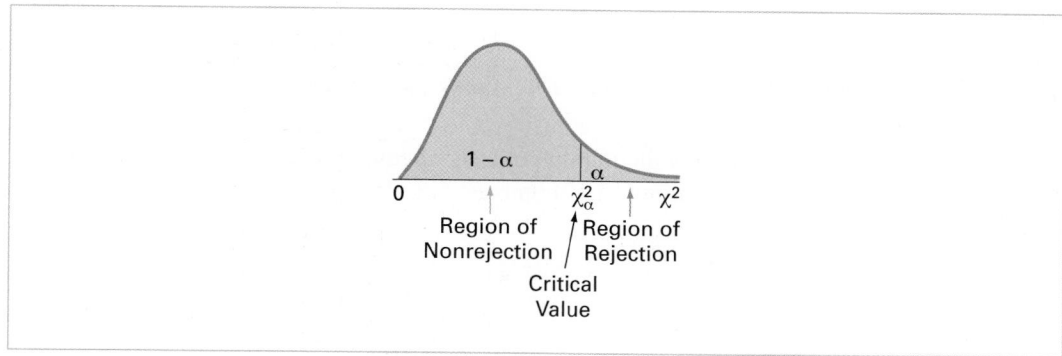

To illustrate the Kruskal-Wallis rank test for differences among $c$ medians, return to the Using Statistics scenario from Chapter 11 on page 444, concerning the strength of parachutes. If you cannot assume that the tensile strength is normally distributed in all $c$ groups, you can use the Kruskal-Wallis rank test.

The null hypothesis is that the median tensile strengths of parachutes for the four suppliers are equal. The alternative hypothesis is that at least one of the suppliers differs from the others.

$$H_0: M_1 = M_2 = M_3 = M_4$$

$$H_1: \text{Not all } M_j \text{ are equal (where } j = 1, 2, 3, 4).$$

Table 12.19 presents the data (stored in the file Parachute ), along with the corresponding ranks.

**TABLE 12.19**

Tensile Strength and Ranks of Parachutes Woven from Synthetic Fibers from Four Suppliers

| | | | | | | Supplier | | |
|---|---|---|---|---|---|---|---|---|
| **1** | | **2** | | **3** | | **4** | |
| Amount | Rank | Amount | Rank | Amount | Rank | Amount | Rank |
| 18.5 | 4 | 26.3 | 20 | 20.6 | 8 | 25.4 | 19 |
| 24.0 | 13.5 | 25.3 | 18 | 25.2 | 17 | 19.9 | 5.5 |
| 17.2 | 1 | 24.0 | 13.5 | 20.8 | 9 | 22.6 | 11 |
| 19.9 | 5.5 | 21.2 | 10 | 24.7 | 16 | 17.5 | 2 |
| 18.0 | 3 | 24.5 | 15 | 22.9 | 12 | 20.4 | 7 |

In converting the 20 tensile strengths to ranks, observe in Table 12.19 that the third parachute for Supplier 1 has the lowest tensile strength, 17.2. It is given a rank of 1. The fourth value for Supplier 1 and the second value for Supplier 4 each have a value of 19.9. Because they are tied for ranks 5 and 6, they are assigned the rank 5.5. Finally, the first value for Supplier 2 is the largest value, 26.3, and is assigned a rank of 20.

After all the ranks are assigned, you compute the sum of the ranks for each group:

$$\text{Rank sums:} \quad T_1 = 27 \quad T_2 = 76.5 \quad T_3 = 62 \quad T_4 = 44.5$$

As a check on the rankings, recall from Equation (12.8) on page 534 that for any integer $n$, the sum of the first $n$ consecutive integers is $\dfrac{n(n+1)}{2}$. Therefore

$$T_1 + T_2 + T_3 + T_4 = \frac{n(n+1)}{2}$$

$$27 + 76.5 + 62 + 44.5 = \frac{(20)(21)}{2}$$

$$210 = 210$$

To test the null hypothesis of equal population medians, you calculate the test statistic $H$ using Equation (12.12) on page 546:

$$H = \left[ \frac{12}{n(n+1)} \sum_{j=1}^{c} \frac{T_j^2}{n_j} \right] - 3(n+1)$$

$$= \left\{ \frac{12}{(20)(21)} \left[ \frac{(27)^2}{5} + \frac{(76.5)^2}{5} + \frac{(62)^2}{5} + \frac{(44.5)^2}{5} \right] \right\} - 3(21)$$

$$= \left( \frac{12}{420} \right) (2,481.1) - 63 = 7.8886$$

The statistic $H$ approximately follows a chi-square distribution with $c - 1$ degrees of freedom. Using a 0.05 level of significance, $\chi_\alpha^2$, the upper-tail critical value of the chi-square distribution with $c - 1 = 3$ degrees of freedom is 7.815 (see Table 12.20). Because the computed value of the test statistic $H = 7.8886$ is greater than the critical value, you reject the null hypothesis and conclude that not all the suppliers are the same with respect to median tensile strength. The same conclusion is reached by using the $p$-value approach. In Figures 12.24 and 12.25, observe that the $p$-value $= 0.0484 < 0.05$.

**TABLE 12.20**

Finding $\chi_\alpha^2$, the Upper-Tail Critical Value for the Kruskal-Wallis Rank Test, at the 0.05 Level of Significance with 3 Degrees of Freedom

| | Cumulative Area | | | | | | | | | |
|---|---|---|---|---|---|---|---|---|---|---|
| | .005 | .01 | .025 | .05 | .10 | .25 | .75 | .90 | .95 | .975 |
| | Upper-Tail Area | | | | | | | | | |
| Degrees of Freedom | .995 | .99 | .975 | .95 | .90 | .75 | .25 | .10 | .05 | .025 |
| 1 | – | – | 0.001 | 0.004 | 0.016 | 0.102 | 1.323 | 2.706 | 3.841 | 5.024 |
| 2 | 0.010 | 0.020 | 0.051 | 0.103 | 0.211 | 0.575 | 2.773 | 4.605 | 5.991 | 7.378 |
| 3 | 0.072 | 0.115 | 0.216 | 0.352 | 0.584 | 1.213 | 4.108 | 6.251 | 7.815 | 9.348 |
| 4 | 0.207 | 0.297 | 0.484 | 0.711 | 1.064 | 1.923 | 5.385 | 7.779 | 9.488 | 11.143 |
| 5 | 0.412 | 0.554 | 0.831 | 1.145 | 1.610 | 2.675 | 6.626 | 9.236 | 11.071 | 12.833 |

Source: *Extracted from Table E.4.*

**FIGURE 12.24**

Microsoft Excel
worksheet for the
Kruskal-Wallis rank test
for differences among
the four medians in the
parachute example

*See Section E12.8 or P12.7
to create this.*

| | A | B | C | D | E | F | G |
|---|---|---|---|---|---|---|---|
| 1 | **Tensile-Strength Analysis** | | | | | | |
| 2 | | | | | | | |
| 3 | **Data** | | | | | | |
| 4 | **Level of Significance** | 0.05 | | | | | |
| 5 | | | | Group | Sample Size | Sum of Ranks | Mean Ranks |
| 6 | Intermediate Calculations | | | 1 | 5 | 27 | 5.4 |
| 7 | Sum of Squared Ranks/Sample Size | 2481.1 | | 2 | 5 | 76.5 | 15.3 |
| 8 | Sum of Sample Sizes | 20 | | 3 | 5 | 62 | 12.4 |
| 9 | Number of Groups | 4 | | 4 | 5 | 44.5 | 8.9 |
| 10 | | | | | | | |
| 11 | **Test Result** | | | | | | |
| 12 | **H Test Statistic** | 7.8886 | | =(12/(B8 * (B8 + 1))) * B7 - (3 * (B8 + 1)) | | | |
| 13 | **Critical Value** | 7.8147 | | =CHIINV(B4, B9 - 1) | | | |
| 14 | **p-Value** | 0.0484 | | =CHIDIST(B12, B9 - 1) | | | |
| 15 | **Reject the null hypothesis** | | | =IF(B14 < B4, "Reject the null hypothesis", "Do not reject the null hypothesis") | | | |

**Also**
Cell B7: =(G6 * F6) + (G7 * F7) + (G8 * F8) + (G9 * F9)
Cell B8: =SUM(E6:E9)

**FIGURE 12.25**

Minitab results for the
Kruskal-Wallis rank test
for differences among
the four medians in the
parachute example

*See Section M12.5 to create
this.*

**Kruskal-Wallis Test: Strength versus Suppliers**

Kruskal-Wallis Test on Strength

| Suppliers | N | Median | Ave Rank | Z |
|---|---|---|---|---|
| 1 | 5 | 18.50 | 5.4 | -2.23 |
| 2 | 5 | 24.50 | 15.3 | 2.09 |
| 3 | 5 | 22.90 | 12.4 | 0.83 |
| 4 | 5 | 20.40 | 8.9 | -0.70 |
| Overall | 20 | | 10.5 | |

H = 7.89   DF = 3   P = 0.048
H = 7.90   DF = 3   P = 0.048   (adjusted for ties)

You reject the null hypothesis and conclude that there is evidence of a significant difference among the suppliers with respect to the median tensile strength. At this point, you could simultaneously compare all pairs of suppliers to determine which ones differ (see reference 2).

The following assumptions are needed to use the Kruskal-Wallis rank test:

- The $c$ samples are randomly and independently selected from their respective populations.
- The underlying variable is continuous.
- The data provide at least a set of ranks, both within and among the $c$ samples.
- The $c$ populations have the same variability.
- The $c$ populations have the same shape.

The Kruskal-Wallis procedure makes less stringent assumptions than does the $F$ test. If you ignore the last two assumptions (variability and shape), you can still use the Kruskal-Wallis rank test to determine whether at least one of the populations differs from the other populations in some characteristic—such as central tendency, variation, or shape.

To use the $F$ test, you must assume that the $c$ samples are from normal populations that have equal variances. When the more stringent assumptions of the $F$ test hold, you should use the $F$ test instead of the Kruskal-Wallis test because it has slightly more power to detect significant differences among groups. However, if the assumptions of the $F$ test do not hold, you should use the Kruskal-Wallis test.

## Satisfying Customers with Nonparametrics

*From the Authors' Desktop*

Many organizations use customer satisfaction surveys as part of their quality improvement program. In customer satisfaction surveys, customers are asked to indicate their satisfaction with various aspects of the product purchased or the service received on a scale that usually has between 5 and 10 points. Each response represents a value on an ordinal scale, because although you can assume that a rating of 10 is better than a rating of 5, you cannot assume that a rating of 10 is twice a rating of 5. Also, with such restrictions on the data, the ratings often do not cluster near the middle and form a normal distribution. This makes nonparametric methods, such as those covered in Sections 12.6 through 12.9 particularly appropriate for analyzing customer satisfaction surveys.

Recently, an article by Sheldon Goldstein appeared in *Quality Progress* (see reference 4) that used the Kruskal-Wallis test to analyze the customer satisfaction surveys conducted for an entire year by a company that sold commercial plumbing products and services to businesses. The focus of the analysis was to determine whether there were differences in the rating of nine attributes. These attributes were:

1. Courtesy
2. Convenience of scheduling service
3. On-time arrival for service requested
4. Meeting customer expectations
5. Neatness and cleanliness
6. Answers to questions during service
7. Competitive pricing
8. Quality of the products
9. Overall value

Separate analyses were conducted for first-time customers and repeat customers and for those who completed the survey initially and those who completed the survey after they had been contacted again. The results of the analyses using the Kruskal-Wallis test showed that for first-time customers who responded initially, there were differences in the satisfaction ratings of the attributes with price standing out from the other attributes. However, for first-time customers who did not respond initially, there was insufficient evidence of any difference in the ratings of the attributes. Using these results, management can conduct further analyses to find the reason why the median satisfaction with price was lower than the satisfaction rating for the other eight attributes for new customers.

## PROBLEMS FOR SECTION 12.8

### Learning the Basics

**12.78** What is the upper-tail critical value from the chi-square distribution if you use the Kruskal-Wallis rank test for comparing the medians in six populations at the 0.01 level of significance?

**12.79** Using the results of Problem 12.78,
**a.** State the decision rule for testing the null hypothesis that all six groups have equal population medians.
**b.** What is your statistical decision if the computed value of the test statistic $H$ is 13.77?

### Applying the Concepts

**12.80** The retailing manager of a supermarket chain wants to determine whether product location has any effect on the sale of pet toys. Three different aisle locations are considered: front, middle, and rear. A random sample of 18 stores is selected, with 6 stores randomly assigned to each aisle location. The size of the display area and price of the product are constant for all stores. At the end of a one-month trial period, the sales volumes (in thousands of

dollars) of the product in each store were as follows (and are stored in the file **Locate** ).

| Aisle Location | | |
|---|---|---|
| **Front** | **Middle** | **Rear** |
| 8.6 | 3.2 | 4.6 |
| 7.2 | 2.4 | 6.0 |
| 5.4 | 2.0 | 4.0 |
| 6.2 | 1.4 | 2.8 |
| 5.0 | 1.8 | 2.2 |
| 4.0 | 1.6 | 2.8 |

**a.** Is there evidence of a significant difference in the median sales for the three locations? (Use $\alpha = 0.05$.)
**b.** Compare the results of (a) with those of Problem 11.13(a) on page 459.
**c.** Which test is more appropriate for these data, the Kruskal-Wallis rank test or the one-way ANOVA $F$ test? Explain.

**12.81** Periodically, *The Wall Street Journal* has conducted a stock-picking contest. The last one was conducted in March

2001. In this experiment, three different methods were used to select stocks that were expected to perform well during the next five months. Four Wall Street professionals, considered experts on picking stocks, each selected one stock. Four randomly chosen readers of *The Wall Street Journal* each selected one stock. Finally, four stocks were selected by flinging darts at a table containing a list of stocks. The returns of the selected stocks for March 20, 2001, to August 31, 2001 (in percentage return), are given in the following table and stored in the file `Contest2001`. Note that during this period, the Dow Jones Industrial Average gained 2.4% (extracted from G. Jasen, "In Picking Stocks, Dartboard Beats the Pros," *The Wall Street Journal*, September 27, 2001, pp. C1, C10).

| Experts | Readers | Darts |
|---------|---------|-------|
| +39.5 | −31.0 | +39.0 |
| −1.1 | −20.7 | +31.9 |
| −4.5 | −45.0 | +14.1 |
| −8.0 | −73.3 | +5.4 |

**a.** Is there evidence of a significant difference in the median return for the three categories? (Use $\alpha = 0.05$.)

**b.** Compare the results of (a) with those of Problem 11.8(a) on page 458.

**c.** Which test is more appropriate for these data, the Kruskal-Wallis rank test or the one-way ANOVA $F$ test? Explain.

**12.82** A hospital conducted a study of the waiting time in its emergency room. The hospital has a main campus, along with three satellite locations. Management had a business objective of reducing waiting time for emergency room cases that did not require immediate attention. To study this, a random sample of 15 emergency room cases at each location were selected on a particular day, and the waiting time (recorded from check-in to when the patient was called into the clinic area) was measured. The results are stored in the file `ERwaiting`.

**a.** At the 0.05 level of significance, is there evidence of a difference in the median waiting times in the four locations?

**b.** Compare the results of (a) with those of Problem 11.9(a) on page 458.

**12.83** The following data (stored in the file `CDyield`) represent the nationwide highest yield of different types of accounts (extracted from **Bankrate.com**, March 6, 2007):

| Money Market | Six-Month CD | One-Year CD | 2.5-Year CD | Five-Year CD |
|--------------|--------------|-------------|-------------|--------------|
| 5.21 | 5.50 | 5.41 | 5.35 | 5.35 |
| 5.19 | 5.44 | 5.40 | 5.25 | 5.30 |
| 5.20 | 5.40 | 5.40 | 5.20 | 5.25 |
| 5.16 | 5.40 | 5.40 | 5.20 | 5.25 |
| 5.12 | 5.39 | 5.39 | 5.15 | 5.22 |

**a.** At the 0.05 level of significance, is there evidence of a difference in the median yields of the different accounts?

**b.** Compare the results of (a) with those of Problem 11.11(a) on page 459.

**12.84** An advertising agency has been hired by a manufacturer of pens to develop an advertising campaign for the upcoming holiday season. To prepare for this project, the research director decides to initiate a study of the effect of advertising on product perception. An experiment is designed to compare five different advertisements. Advertisement *A* greatly undersells the pen's characteristics. Advertisement *B* slightly undersells the pen's characteristics. Advertisement *C* slightly oversells the pen's characteristics. Advertisement *D* greatly oversells the pen's characteristics. Advertisement *E* attempts to correctly state the pen's characteristics. A sample of 30 adult respondents, taken from a larger focus group, is randomly assigned to the five advertisements (so that there are six respondents to each). After reading the advertisement and developing a sense of product expectation, all respondents unknowingly receive the same pen to evaluate. The respondents are permitted to test the pen and the plausibility of the advertising copy. The respondents are then asked to rate the pen from 1 to 7 on the product characteristic scales of appearance, durability, and writing performance. The *combined* scores of three ratings (appearance, durability, and writing performance) for the 30 respondents (stored in the file `Pen`) are as follows:

| A | B | C | D | E |
|---|---|---|---|---|
| 15 | 16 | 8 | 5 | 12 |
| 18 | 17 | 7 | 6 | 19 |
| 17 | 21 | 10 | 13 | 18 |
| 19 | 16 | 15 | 11 | 12 |
| 19 | 19 | 14 | 9 | 17 |
| 20 | 17 | 14 | 10 | 14 |

**a.** At the 0.05 level of significance, is there evidence of a difference in the median ratings of the five advertisements?

**b.** Compare the results of (a) with those of Problem 11.12(a) on page 459.

**c.** Which test is more appropriate for these data, the Kruskal-Wallis rank test or the one-way ANOVA $F$ test? Explain.

**12.85** A sporting goods manufacturing company wanted to compare the distance traveled by golf balls produced using each of four different designs. Ten balls were manufactured with each design and were brought to the local golf course for the club professional to test. The order in which the balls were hit with the same club from the first tee was randomized so that the pro did not know which type of ball was being hit. All 40 balls were hit in a short period of time, during which the environmental conditions were essentially the same. The results (distance traveled in yards) for the four designs are stored in the file Golfball:

a. At the 0.05 level of significance, is there evidence of a difference in the median distances traveled by the golf balls with different designs?

b. Compare the results of (a) with those of Problem 11.14(a) on page 460.

**12.86** Students in a business statistics course performed an experiment to test the strength of four brands of trash

bags. One-pound weights were placed into a bag, one at a time, until the bag broke. A total of 40 bags were used (10 for each brand). The data file Trashbags gives the weight (in pounds) required to break the trash bags.

a. At the 0.05 level of significance, is there evidence of a difference in the median strength of the four brands of trash bags?

b. Compare the results in (a) to those in Problem 11.10(a) on page 459.

## 12.9 FRIEDMAN RANK TEST: NONPARAMETRIC ANALYSIS FOR THE RANDOMIZED BLOCK DESIGN

When analyzing a randomized block design, sometimes the data consist of only the ranks within each block. Other times, you cannot assume that the data from each of the $c$ groups are from normally distributed populations. In these situations, you can use the **Friedman rank test**.

You use the Friedman rank test to determine whether $c$ groups have been selected from populations having equal medians. That is, you test

$$H_0: M_{.1} = M_{.2} = \cdots = M_{.c}$$

against the alternative

$$H_1: \text{Not all } M_j \text{ are equal (where } j = 1, 2, \ldots, c).$$

To conduct the test, you replace the data values in each of the $r$ independent blocks with the corresponding ranks, so that you assign rank 1 to the smallest value in the block and rank $c$ to the largest. If any values in a block are tied, you assign them the mean of the ranks that they would otherwise have been assigned. Thus, $R_{ij}$ is the rank (from 1 to $c$) associated with the $j$th group in the $i$th block.

Equation (12.13) defines the test statistic for the Friedman rank test.

Friedman Rank Test for Differences Among $c$ Medians

$$F_R = \frac{12}{rc(c+1)} \sum_{j=1}^{c} R_{.j}^2 - 3r(c+1) \qquad (12.13)$$

where

$R_{.j}^2$ = the square of the total of the ranks for group $j$ ($j = 1, 2, \ldots, c$)

$r$ = the number of blocks

$c$ = the number of groups

As the number of blocks in the experiment gets large (greater than 5), you can approximate the test statistic $F_R$ by the chi-square distribution with $c - 1$ degrees of freedom. Thus, for any selected level of significance $\alpha$, you reject the null hypothesis if the computed value of $F_R$ is greater than $\chi_\alpha^2$, the upper-tail critical value for the chi-square distribution having $c - 1$ degrees of freedom as shown in Figure 12.26. That is,

$$\text{Reject } H_0 \text{ if } F_R > \chi_\alpha^2;$$

$$\text{otherwise, do not reject } H_0.$$

The critical values from the chi-square distribution are given in Table E.4.

**FIGURE 12.26**

Determining the rejection region for the Friedman test

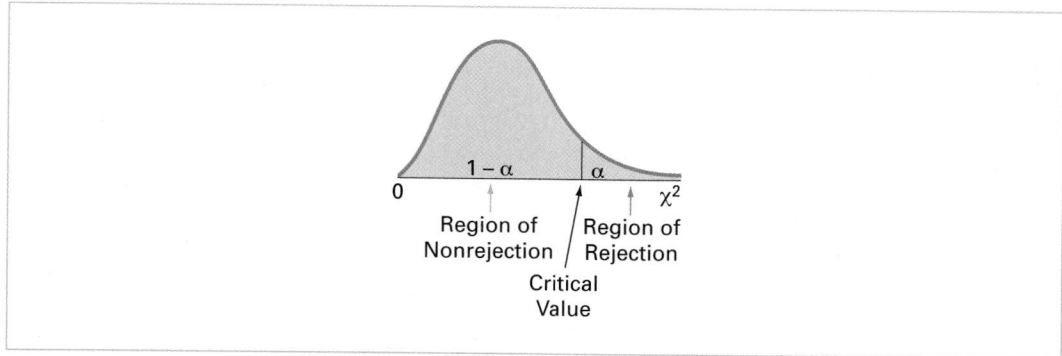

To illustrate the Friedman rank test, return to the fast-food chain study from page 465 in which six raters (blocks) evaluated four restaurants (groups). The results of the experiment are displayed in Table 12.21 along with some summary computations. If you cannot make the assumption that the service ratings are normally distributed for each restaurant, the Friedman rank test is more appropriate than the $F$ test.

The null hypothesis is that the median service ratings for the four restaurants are equal. The alternative hypothesis is that at least one of the restaurants differs from at least one of the others.

$$H_0: M_{.1} = M_{.2} = M_{.3} = M_{.4}$$

$$H_1: \text{Not all the medians are equal.}$$

Table 12.21 provides the 24 service ratings from Table 11.7 (see the FFChain file) along with the ranks assigned within each block.

**TABLE 12.21**

Converting Data to Ranks Within Blocks

| Blocks of Raters | Restaurants | | | | | | | |
|---|---|---|---|---|---|---|---|---|
| | A | | B | | C | | D | |
| | Rating | Rank | Rating | Rank | Rating | Rank | Rating | Rank |
| 1 | 70 | 2.0 | 61 | 1.0 | 82 | 4.0 | 74 | 3.0 |
| 2 | 77 | 3.0 | 75 | 1.0 | 88 | 4.0 | 76 | 2.0 |
| 3 | 76 | 2.0 | 67 | 1.0 | 90 | 4.0 | 80 | 3.0 |
| 4 | 80 | 3.0 | 63 | 1.0 | 96 | 4.0 | 76 | 2.0 |
| 5 | 84 | 2.5 | 66 | 1.0 | 92 | 4.0 | 84 | 2.5 |
| 6 | 78 | 2.0 | 68 | 1.0 | 98 | 4.0 | 86 | 3.0 |
| Rank total | | 14.5 | | 6.0 | | 24.0 | | 15.5 |

From Table 12.21, you compute the following rank totals for each group:

$$\text{Rank Totals:} \quad R_{.1} = 14.5 \quad R_{.2} = 6.0 \quad R_{.3} = 24.0 \quad R_{.4} = 15.5$$

Equation (12.14) provides a check on the rankings.

**Checking the Rankings in the Friedman Test**

$$R_{.1} + R_{.2} + R_{.3} + R_{.4} = \frac{rc(c+1)}{2} \tag{12.14}$$

For the data in Table 12.21,

$$14.5 + 6 + 24 + 15.5 = \frac{(6)(4)(5)}{2}$$

$$60 = 60$$

Using Equation (12.13),

$$F_R = \frac{12}{rc(c+1)} \sum_{j=1}^{c} R_{.j}^2 - 3r(c+1)$$

$$= \left\{ \frac{12}{(6)(4)(5)} [14.5^2 + 6.0^2 + 24.0^2 + 15.5^2] \right\} - (3)(6)(5)$$

$$= \left( \frac{12}{120} \right) (1,062.5) - 90 = 16.25$$

Because $F_R = 16.25 > 7.815$, the upper-tail critical value $\chi_\alpha^2$ of the chi-square distribution with $c - 1 = 3$ degrees of freedom (see Table E.4), you reject the null hypothesis at the $\alpha = 0.05$ level. You conclude that there are significant differences (as perceived by the raters) in the median service rating at the four restaurants. Using the Minitab results of Figure 12.27, because the $p$-value $= 0.001 < 0.05$, you reject the null hypothesis. As a follow-up to the Friedman rank test, you can use a *post hoc* multiple comparison procedure developed by Nemenyi (see reference 8).

**FIGURE 12.27**

Minitab results of Friedman rank test for differences among the four medians in the fast-food chain study

*See Section M12.6 to create this.*

```
Friedman Test: Rating versus Restrat blocked by Raters

S =  16.25   DF = 3   P = 0.001
S =  16.53   DF = 3   P = 0.001 (adjusted for ties)

                        Est    Sum of
Restrat   N   Median    Ranks
A         6    76.88     14.5
B         6    66.50      6.0
C         6    90.38     24.0
D         6    79.25     15.5

Grand median = 78.25
```

The Minitab results include the sample size, the estimated median rating, and the rank total (Sum of Ranks) for each restaurant along with the Friedman test statistic $S$ (which is equivalent to the statistic $F_R$), the degrees of freedom ($df$), and the p-value. If there are ties in the rankings, as is the case here, Minitab provides an adjustment to the test statistic $S$ along with an adjusted p-value. This adjustment has a minimal impact on these results.

The following assumptions are needed to use the Friedman rank test:

- The $r$ blocks are independent so that the values in one block have no influence on the values in any other block.
- The underlying variable is continuous.
- The data constitute at least an ordinal scale of measurement within each of the $r$ blocks.
- There is no interaction between the $r$ blocks and the $c$ treatment levels.
- The $c$ populations have the same variability.
- The $c$ populations have the same shape.

The Friedman procedure makes less stringent assumptions than does the randomized block $F$ test. If you ignore the last two assumptions (variability and shape), you could still use the Friedman rank test to test whether at least one of the populations differs from the other populations in some characteristic—either central tendency, variation, or shape.

On the other hand, the randomized block $F$ test requires that the level of measurement is an interval or ratio scale and that the $c$ samples are from underlying normal populations having equal variances. Both the randomized block $F$ test and the Friedman test assume that there is no interaction between the treatments and the blocks.

When the more stringent assumptions of the randomized block $F$ test hold, you should select it over the Friedman test because it has more power to detect significant differences among the groups. However, if the assumptions of the randomized block $F$ test are inappropriate, you should use the Friedman rank test.

# PROBLEMS FOR SECTION 12.9

## Learning the Basics

**12.87** What is the upper-tail critical value $\chi_\alpha^2$ when testing for the equality of the medians in six populations using $\alpha = 0.10$?

**12.88** For Problem 12.87:
a. State the decision rule for testing the null hypothesis that all six groups have equal population medians.
b. What is your statistical decision if $F_R = 11.56$?

## Applying the Concepts

**12.89** Nine experts rated four brands of Colombian coffee in a taste-testing experiment (see the Coffee file). A rating on a 7-point scale (1 = extremely unpleasing, 7 = extremely pleasing) is given for each of the following four characteristics: taste, aroma, richness, and acidity. The following table displays the summated ratings—accumulated over all four characteristics.

|  | | BRAND | | |
|---|---|---|---|---|
| EXPERT | A | B | C | D |
| C.C. | 24 | 26 | 25 | 22 |
| S.E. | 27 | 27 | 26 | 24 |
| E.G. | 19 | 22 | 20 | 16 |
| B.L. | 24 | 27 | 25 | 23 |
| C.M. | 22 | 25 | 22 | 21 |
| C.N. | 26 | 27 | 24 | 24 |
| G.N. | 27 | 26 | 22 | 23 |
| R.M. | 25 | 27 | 24 | 21 |
| P.V. | 22 | 23 | 20 | 19 |

a. At the 0.05 level of significance, is there evidence of a difference in the median summated ratings of the four brands of Colombian coffee?
b. Are there any differences in the results of (a) from those of Problem 11.23 on page 469? Discuss.

**12.90** An article (J. Graham, "Prices Going Up, But It's Not Gas; It's Online Music," *USA Today*, May 13, 2004, p. 1B) stated that the cost of a legitimate music download is increasing. The following data (stored in the file Musiconline) represent the prices of five albums at five digital music services:

| Album/Artist | Itunes | Wal-Mart | Music Now | Music Match | Napster |
|---|---|---|---|---|---|
| D12 World—D12 | 11.99 | 9.44 | 13.99 | 20.79 | 9.95 |
| Damita Jo—Janet Jackson | 13.99 | 9.44 | 13.99 | 12.49 | 13.95 |
| 30 #1 Hits—Elvis Presley | 9.99 | 27.28 | 13.99 | 9.99 | 9.95 |
| Feels Like Home—Norah Jones | 12.87 | 9.44 | 9.99 | 11.99 | 13.95 |
| Up—Shania Twain | 9.99 | 17.44 | 13.99 | 9.99 | 18.81 |

Source: *Extracted from J. Graham, "Prices Going Up, But It's Not Gas; It's Online Music," USA Today, May 13, 2004, p. 1B.*

a. Using a 0.05 level of significance, is there evidence of a difference in the median prices at the digital music services?

b. Are there any differences in the results of (a) from those of Problem 11.26 on page 470? Discuss.

**12.91** An article discussed the new Whole Foods Market in the Time-Warner building in New York City. The data in the file Wholefoods2 compared the price of some kitchen staples at the new Whole Foods Market, at the Gristede's supermarket, at the Fairway supermarket (both located about 15 blocks from the Time-Warner building), and at a Stop & Shop supermarket located in one of the outer boroughs of New York City.

| Item | Whole Foods | Gristede's | Fairway | Stop & Shop |
|---|---|---|---|---|
| Half-gallon milk | 2.19 | 1.59 | 1.35 | 1.89 |
| Dozen eggs | 2.39 | 1.59 | 1.69 | 2.29 |
| Tropicana orange juice (64 oz.) | 2.00 | 2.99 | 2.49 | 2.00 |
| Head of Boston lettuce | 1.98 | 1.49 | 1.29 | 1.29 |
| Ground round 1 lb. | 4.99 | 3.99 | 3.69 | 3.59 |
| Bumble Bee tuna 6 oz. can | 1.79 | 0.79 | 1.33 | 1.50 |
| Granny Smith apples (1 lb.) | 1.69 | 1.99 | 1.49 | 0.99 |

| Item | Whole Foods | Gristede's | Fairway | Stop & Shop |
|---|---|---|---|---|
| Box DeCecco linguini | 1.99 | 1.50 | 1.59 | 1.79 |
| Salmon steak 1 lb. | 7.99 | 4.99 | 5.99 | 5.99 |
| Whole chicken per pound | 2.19 | 1.19 | 1.49 | 1.49 |

Source: *Extracted from W. Grimes, "A Pleasure Palace Without the Guilt," The New York Times, February 18, 2004, pp. F1, F5.*

a. At the 0.05 level of significance, use the Friedman rank test to determine if there is evidence of a difference in the median prices for these kitchen staples at the four stores?

b. Are there any differences in the results of (a) from those of Problem 11.25 on page 470? Discuss.

**12.92** Philips Semiconductors is a leading European manufacturer of integrated circuits. Integrated circuits are produced on silicon wafers, which are ground to target thickness early in the production process. The wafers are positioned in various locations on a grinder and kept in place through vacuum decompression. One of the goals of process improvement is to reduce the variability in the thickness of the wafers in different positions and in different batches. Data were collected from a sample of 30 batches. In each batch, the thickness of the wafers on positions 1 and 2 (outer circle), 18 and 19 (middle circle), and 28 (inner circle) was measured. The results are given in the Circuits file.

Source: *Extracted from K. C. B. Roes and R. J. M. M. Does, "Shewhart-Type Charts in Nonstandard Situations," Technometrics, 37, 1995, pp. 15–24.*

a. At the 0.05 level of significance, is there evidence of a difference in the median thickness of the wafers for the five positions?

b. Are there any differences in the results of (a) from those of Problem 11.27 on page 470? Discuss.

c. Which test is more appropriate for these data, the Friedman rank test or the randomized block *F* test? Explain.

**12.93** The data in the Concrete2 file represent the compressive strength in thousands of pounds per square inch of 40 samples of concrete taken 2, 7, and 28 days after pouring.

Source: *O. Carrillo-Gamboa and R. F. Gunst, "Measurement-Error-Model Collinearities," Technometrics, 34, 1992, pp. 454–464.*

a. At the 0.05 level of significance, is there evidence of a difference in the median compressive strength after 2, 7, and 28 days?

b. Are there any differences in the results of (a) from those of Problem 11.28 on page 470? Discuss.

c. Which test is more appropriate for these data, the Friedman rank test or the randomized block *F* test? Explain.

*(continued)*

## 12.10 ● (CD-ROM TOPIC) CHI-SQUARE GOODNESS OF FIT TESTS

Chi-square goodness of fit tests are used to determine whether a set of data matches a specific probability distribution. For further discussion, see Section 12.10 on the Student CD-ROM that accompanies this book.

# SUMMARY

Figure 12.28 presents a roadmap for this chapter. First, you used hypothesis testing for analyzing categorical response data from two samples (independent and related) and from more than two independent samples. In addition, the rules of probability from Section 4.2 were extended to the hypothesis of independence in the joint responses to two categorical variables. You applied these methods to the surveys conducted by T.C. Resort Properties. You concluded that a greater proportion of guests are willing to return to the Beachcomber Hotel than to the Windsurfer; that the Golden Palm, Palm Royale, and Palm Princess hotels are different with respect to the proportion of guests who are likely to return; and that the reasons given for not returning to a hotel are dependent on the hotel the guests visited. These inferences will allow T.C. Resort Properties to improve the quality of service it provides.

You also used the chi-square distribution to test a variance or standard deviation. In addition to the chi-square tests, you studied four nonparametric tests. You used the Wilcoxon rank sum test when the assumptions of the $t$ test for two independent samples were violated, the Wilcoxon signed ranks test when the assumptions of the paired $t$ test were violated, the Kruskal-Wallis rank test when the assumptions of the one-way ANOVA $F$ test were violated, and the Friedman rank test when assumptions of the randomized block $F$ test were violated.

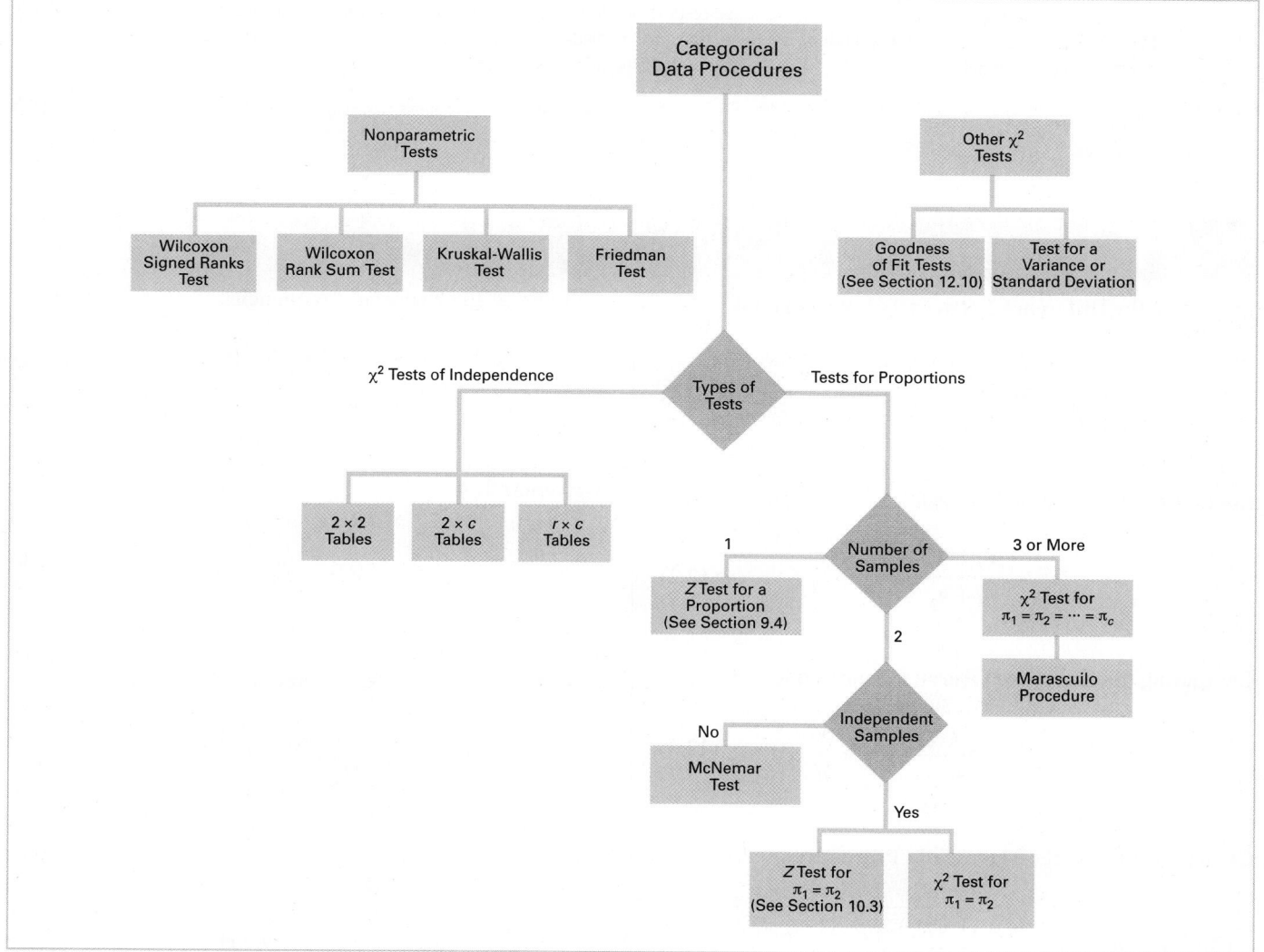

**FIGURE 12.28** Roadmap of Chapter 12

## "Coming Attractions" Revisited

Way back in the Chapter 1 *From the Authors' Desktop* "Coming Attractions," we declared that understanding inferential statistical concepts covered in Chapters 8 through 12 would allow you to fully answer questions such as "How can you make decisions about the many based on a few?" By this point in the book, you've learned how useful sample data can be in reaching conclusions about populations. By reviewing and rehearsing the methods you have learned about to this point, you can now begin to solve business problems in a way similar to how a prior student solved hers in the *From the Authors' Desktop* in Chapter 10 (see page 399).

You would begin by designing a plan for doing an experiment. (The prior student who called divided recent hires into two groups.) Then you would collect and store the data and decide what program you want to use for your analysis, perhaps Microsoft Excel or Minitab. Then you are ready to ask a series of questions about your data.

**Question 1:** What type of variables do I have? In the prior student's case, the variable was customer satisfaction scores, a numerical (not categorical) variable.

**Question 2:** What types of tests should I use? The variable type (numerical or categorical) determines this answer. In the prior student's case, having a numerical variable meant eliminating from consideration any tests related to categorical variables.

**Question 3:** Do I have independent groups or related groups? The prior student had independent groups because the new hires were divided into two groups that were provided with different training. That eliminated any tests for related groups from consideration.

**Question 4:** At this point, what remain are those tests that relate to the central tendency (the mean or median) of two independent groups. If the prior student decided to use a *t* test for the difference between the means, she needs to ask should she use a pooled-variance *t* test or a separate-variance *t* test? Using an *F* test of the ratio of the variances (or a Levene test) would help determine that answer.

**Question 5:** Are my assumptions about my data reasonable? For the prior student's case, is the assumption that the customer satisfaction scores are normally distributed reasonable? If she has any doubts about that, she can conduct a Wilcoxon rank sum test.

With all these questions answered, she will be able to reach conclusions about the effect of the new training program on the customer satisfaction scores. These questions serve as a roadmap for you to use in applying the confidence interval and hypothesis-testing methods that you have learned in these chapters. Answering these questions will help you apply statistics productively in future jobs.

# KEY EQUATIONS

**$\chi^2$ Test for the Difference Between Two Proportions**

$$\chi^2_{STAT} = \sum_{all\ cells} \frac{(f_o - f_e)^2}{f_e} \qquad (12.1)$$

**Computing the Estimated Overall Proportion for 2 Groups**

$$\bar{p} = \frac{X_1 + X_2}{n_1 + n_2} = \frac{X}{n} \qquad (12.2)$$

**Computing the Estimated Overall Proportion for $c$ Groups**

$$\bar{p} = \frac{X_1 + X_2 + \cdots + X_c}{n_1 + n_2 + \cdots + n_c} = \frac{X}{n} \qquad (12.3)$$

**Critical Range for the Marascuilo Procedure**

$$\text{Critical range} = \sqrt{\chi^2_\alpha} \sqrt{\frac{p_j(1-p_j)}{n_j} + \frac{p_{j'}(1-p_{j'})}{n_{j'}}} \qquad (12.4)$$

**Computing the Expected Frequencies**

$$f_e = \frac{\text{row total} \times \text{column total}}{n} \qquad (12.5)$$

**McNemar Test**

$$Z_{STAT} = \frac{B - C}{\sqrt{B + C}} \qquad (12.6)$$

**$\chi^2$ Test for the Variance or Standard Deviation**

$$\chi^2_{STAT} = \frac{(n-1)S^2}{\sigma^2} \qquad (12.7)$$

**Checking the Rankings**

$$T_1 + T_2 = \frac{n(n+1)}{2} \qquad (12.8)$$

**Large Sample Wilcoxon Rank Sum Test**

$$Z_{STAT} = \frac{T_1 - \frac{n_1(n+1)}{2}}{\sqrt{\frac{n_1 n_2 (n+1)}{12}}} \qquad \textbf{(12.9)}$$

**Wilcoxon Signed Ranks Test**

$$W = \sum_{i=1}^{n'} R_i^{(+)} \qquad \textbf{(12.10)}$$

**Large-Sample Wilcoxon Signed Ranks Test**

$$Z_{STAT} = \frac{W - \frac{n'(n'+1)}{4}}{\sqrt{\frac{n'(n'+1)(2n'+1)}{24}}} \qquad \textbf{(12.11)}$$

**Kruskal-Wallis Rank Test for Differences Among $c$ Medians**

$$H = \left[ \frac{12}{n(n+1)} \sum_{j=1}^{c} \frac{T_j^2}{n_j} \right] - 3(n+1) \qquad \textbf{(12.12)}$$

**Friedman Rank Test for Differences Among $c$ Medians**

$$F_R = \frac{12}{rc(c+1)} \sum_{j=1}^{c} R_{.j}^2 - 3r(c+1) \qquad \textbf{(12.13)}$$

**Checking the Rankings in the Friedman Test**

$$R_{.1} + R_{.2} + R_{.3} + R_{.4} = \frac{rc(c+1)}{2} \qquad \textbf{(12.14)}$$

# KEY TERMS

chi-square ($\chi^2$) distribution   506
chi-square ($\chi^2$) test of
   independence   520
chi-square ($\chi^2$) test for the variance or
   standard deviation   530
chi-square ($\chi^2$) test for the difference
   between two proportions   505

contingency table   504
expected frequency ($f_e$)   506
Friedman rank test   552
Kruskal-Wallis rank test   546
Marascuilo procedure   517
McNemar test   526

observed frequency ($f_o$)   506
$2 \times c$ contingency table   513
$2 \times 2$ contingency table   505
Wilcoxon rank sum test   533
Wilcoxon signed ranks test   540

# CHAPTER REVIEW PROBLEMS

## Checking Your Understanding

**12.94** Under what conditions should you use the $\chi^2$ test to determine whether there is a difference between the proportions of two independent populations?

**12.95** Under what conditions should you use the $\chi^2$ test to determine whether there is a difference between the proportions of more than two independent populations?

**12.96** Under what conditions should you use the $\chi^2$ test of independence?

**12.97** Under what conditions should you use the McNemar test?

**12.98** Under what conditions should you use the Wilcoxon rank sum test?

**12.99** Under what conditions should you use the Wilcoxon signed ranks test?

**12.100** Under what conditions should you use the Kruskal-Wallis rank test?

**12.101** Under what conditions should you use the Friedman rank test?

## Applying the Concepts

**12.102** Undergraduate students at Miami University in Oxford, Ohio, were surveyed in order to evaluate the effect of gender and price on purchasing a pizza from Pizza Hut. Students were told to suppose that they were planning on having a large two-topping pizza delivered to their residence that evening. The students had to decide between ordering from Pizza Hut at a reduced price of $8.49 (the regular price for a large two-topping pizza from the Oxford Pizza Hut at this time was $11.49) and ordering a pizza from a different pizzeria. The results from this question are summarized in the following contingency table:

| | PIZZERIA | | |
|---|---|---|---|
| GENDER | Pizza Hut | Other | Total |
| Female | 4 | 13 | 17 |
| Male | 6 | 12 | 18 |
| Total | 10 | 25 | 35 |

The survey also evaluated purchase decisions at other prices. These results are summarized in the following contingency table:

| | PRICE | | | |
|---|---|---|---|---|
| PIZZERIA | $8.49 | $11.49 | $14.49 | Total |
| Pizza Hut | 10 | 5 | 2 | 17 |
| Other | 25 | 23 | 27 | 75 |
| Total | 35 | 28 | 29 | 92 |

a. Using a 0.05 level of significance and using the data in the first contingency table, is there evidence of a significant relationship between a student's gender and his or her pizzeria selection?
b. What is your answer to (a) if nine of the male students selected Pizza Hut and nine selected other?
c. Using a 0.05 level of significance and using the data in the second contingency table, is there evidence of a difference in pizzeria selection based on price?
d. Determine the $p$-value in (c) and interpret its meaning.
e. If appropriate, use the Marascuilo procedure and $\alpha = 0.05$ to determine which prices are different in terms of pizzeria preference.

**12.103** Many companies are finding that customers are using various types of online content before purchasing products (extracted from K. Spors, "How Are We Doing?" *The Wall Street Journal*, November 13, 2006, p. R9). The following results are the percentages of older adults (over age 45), younger adults (21–45), and youths (below 21) who use various sources of online content. Suppose the survey was based on 100 older adults, 100 younger adults, and 100 youths.

| | USE ONLINE CONTENT | | |
|---|---|---|---|
| TYPE OF ONLINE CONTENT | Older Adults | Younger Adults | Youth |
| Customer product ratings/reviews | 71 | 78 | 81 |
| For sale listings with seller ratings | 69 | 72 | 77 |
| For sale listings without seller ratings | 58 | 60 | 65 |
| Online classified ads | 57 | 59 | 66 |
| Message-board posts | 57 | 65 | 71 |
| Webblogs | 55 | 61 | 67 |
| Dating site profiles/ personals | 49 | 52 | 59 |
| Peer-generated and peer-reference information | 49 | 55 | 68 |
| Peer-posted event listings | 46 | 53 | 71 |

For each type of online content,

a. is there a significant difference among the age groups in the proportion who use the type of online content? (Use $\alpha = 0.05$.)
b. If appropriate, apply the Marascuilo procedure to (a), using $\alpha = 0.05$.

**12.104** A company is considering an organizational change by adopting the use of self-managed work teams. To assess the attitudes of employees of the company toward this change, a sample of 400 employees is selected and asked whether they favor the institution of self-managed work teams in the organization. Three responses are permitted: favor, neutral, or oppose. The results of the survey, cross-classified by type of job and attitude toward self-managed work teams, are summarized as follows:

| | SELF-MANAGED WORK TEAMS | | | |
|---|---|---|---|---|
| TYPE OF JOB | Favor | Neutral | Oppose | Total |
| Hourly worker | 108 | 46 | 71 | 225 |
| Supervisor | 18 | 12 | 30 | 60 |
| Middle management | 35 | 14 | 26 | 75 |
| Upper management | 24 | 7 | 9 | 40 |
| Total | 185 | 79 | 136 | 400 |

a. At the 0.05 level of significance, is there evidence of a relationship between attitude toward self-managed work teams and type of job?

The survey also asked respondents about their attitudes toward instituting a policy whereby an employee could take one additional vacation day per month without pay. The results, cross-classified by type of job, are as follows:

### VACATION TIME WITHOUT PAY

| TYPE OF JOB | Favor | Neutral | Oppose | Total |
|---|---|---|---|---|
| Hourly worker | 135 | 23 | 67 | 225 |
| Supervisor | 39 | 7 | 14 | 60 |
| Middle management | 47 | 6 | 22 | 75 |
| Upper management | 26 | 6 | 8 | 40 |
| Total | 247 | 42 | 111 | 400 |

b. At the 0.05 level of significance, is there evidence of a relationship between attitude toward vacation time without pay and type of job?

**12.105** A company that produces and markets videotaped continuing education programs for the financial industry has traditionally mailed sample tapes that contain previews of the programs to prospective customers. Customers then agree to purchase the program tapes or return the sample tapes. A group of sales representatives studied how to increase sales and found that many prospective customers believed it was difficult to tell from a sample tape alone whether the educational programs would meet their needs. The sales representatives performed an experiment to test whether sending the complete program tapes for review by customers would increase sales. They selected 80 customers from the mailing list and randomly assigned 40 to receive the sample tapes and 40 to receive the full-program tapes for review. They then determined the number of tapes that were purchased and returned in each group. The results of the experiment are as follows:

### TYPE OF VIDEOTAPE RECEIVED

| ACTION | Sample | Full | Total |
|---|---|---|---|
| Purchased | 6 | 14 | 20 |
| Returned | 34 | 26 | 60 |
| Total | 40 | 40 | 80 |

a. At the 0.05 level of significance, is there evidence of a difference in the proportion of tapes purchased on the basis of the type of tape sent to the customer?
b. On the basis of the results of (a), which tape do you think a representative should send in the future? Explain the rationale for your decision.

The sales representatives also wanted to determine which of three initial sales approaches result in the most sales: (1) a video sales-information tape mailed to prospective customers, (2) a personal sales call to prospective customers, and (3) a telephone call to prospective customers. A random sample of 300 prospective customers was selected, and 100 were randomly assigned to each of the three sales approaches. The results, in terms of purchases of the full-program tapes, are as follows:

### SALES APPROACH

| ACTION | Videotape | Personal Sales Call | Telephone | Total |
|---|---|---|---|---|
| Purchase | 19 | 27 | 14 | 60 |
| Don't purchase | 81 | 73 | 86 | 240 |
| Total | 100 | 100 | 100 | 300 |

c. At the 0.05 level of significance, is there evidence of a difference in the proportion of tapes purchased on the basis of the sales strategy used?
d. If appropriate, use the Marascuilo procedure and $\alpha = 0.05$ to determine which sales approaches are different.
e. On the basis of the results of (c) and (d), which sales approach do you think a representative should use in the future? Explain the rationale for your decision.

**12.106** A market researcher investigated consumer preferences for Coca-Cola and Pepsi before a taste test and after a taste test. The following table summarizes the results from a sample of 200 consumers:

| PREFERENCE BEFORE TASTE TEST | PREFERENCE AFTER TASTE TEST | | |
|---|---|---|---|
| | Coca-Cola | Pepsi | Total |
| Coca-Cola | 104 | 6 | 110 |
| Pepsi | 14 | 76 | 90 |
| Total | 118 | 82 | 200 |

a. Is there evidence of a difference in the proportion of respondents who prefer Coca-Cola before and after the taste tests? (Use $\alpha = 0.10$.)
b. Compute the $p$-value and interpret its meaning.
c. Show how the following table was derived from the table above:

### SOFT DRINK

| PREFERENCE | Coca-Cola | Pepsi | Total |
|---|---|---|---|
| Before taste test | 110 | 90 | 200 |
| After taste test | 118 | 82 | 200 |
| Total | 228 | 172 | 400 |

d. Using the second table, is there evidence of a difference in preference for Coca-Cola before and after the taste test? (Use $\alpha = 0.05$.)

e. Determine the $p$-value and interpret its meaning.

f. Explain the difference in the results of (a) and (d). One of the methods is incorrect. Which method of analyzing the data should you use? Why?

**12.107** A market researcher was interested in studying the effect of advertisements on brand preference of new car buyers. Prospective purchasers of new cars were first asked whether they preferred Toyota or GM and then watched video advertisements of comparable models of the two manufacturers. After viewing the ads, the prospective customers again indicated their preferences. The results are summarized in the following table:

| PREFERENCE BEFORE ADS | PREFERENCE AFTER ADS | | |
|---|---|---|---|
| | Toyota | GM | Total |
| Toyota | 97 | 3 | 100 |
| GM | 11 | 89 | 100 |
| Total | 108 | 92 | 200 |

a. Is there evidence of a difference in the proportion of respondents who prefer Toyota before and after viewing the ads? (Use $\alpha = 0.05$.)

b. Compute the $p$-value and interpret its meaning.

c. Show how the following table was derived from the table above.

| PREFERENCE | MANUFACTURER | | |
|---|---|---|---|
| | Toyota | GM | Total |
| Before ad | 100 | 100 | 200 |
| After ad | 108 | 92 | 200 |
| Total | 208 | 192 | 400 |

d. Using the second table, is there evidence of a difference in preference for Toyota before and after viewing the ads? (Use $\alpha = 0.05$.)

e. Determine the $p$-value and interpret its meaning.

f. Explain the difference in the results of (a) and (d). One of the methods is incorrect. Which method of analyzing the data should you use? Why?

**12.108** Researchers studied the goals and outcomes of 349 work teams from various manufacturing companies in Ohio. In the first table, teams are categorized as to whether they had specified environmental improvements as a goal and also according to one of four types of manufacturing processes that best described their workplace. The following three tables indicate different outcomes the teams accomplished, based on whether the team had specified cost cutting as one of the team goals.

| TYPE OF MANUFACTURING PROCESS | ENVIRONMENTAL GOAL | | |
|---|---|---|---|
| | Yes | No | Total |
| **Job shop or batch** | 2 | 42 | 44 |
| **Repetitive batch** | 4 | 57 | 61 |
| **Discrete process** | 15 | 147 | 162 |
| **Continuous process** | 17 | 65 | 82 |
| Total | 38 | 311 | 349 |

| OUTCOME | COST-CUTTING GOAL | | |
|---|---|---|---|
| | Yes | No | Total |
| **Improved environmental performance** | 77 | 52 | 129 |
| **Environmental performance not improved** | 91 | 129 | 220 |
| Total | 168 | 181 | 349 |

| OUTCOME | COST-CUTTING GOAL | | |
|---|---|---|---|
| | Yes | No | Total |
| **Improved profitability** | 70 | 68 | 138 |
| **Profitability not improved** | 98 | 113 | 211 |
| Total | 168 | 181 | 349 |

| OUTCOME | COST-CUTTING GOAL | | |
|---|---|---|---|
| | Yes | No | Total |
| **Improved morale** | 67 | 55 | 122 |
| **Morale not improved** | 101 | 126 | 227 |
| Total | 168 | 181 | 349 |

Source: *Extracted from M. Hanna, W. Newman, and P. Johnson, "Linking Operational and Environmental Improvement Thru Employee Involvement,"* International Journal of Operations and Production Management, *2000, 20, pp. 148–165.*

a. At the 0.05 level of significance, determine whether there is evidence of a significant relationship between the presence of environmental goals and the type of manufacturing process.

b. Determine the $p$-value in (a) and interpret its meaning.

c. At the 0.05 level of significance, is there evidence of a difference in improved environmental performance for teams with a specified goal of cutting costs?

d. Determine the $p$-value in (c) and interpret its meaning.

e. At the 0.05 level of significance, is there evidence of a difference in improved profitability for teams with a specified goal of cutting costs?

f. Determine the $p$-value in (e) and interpret its meaning.

g. At the 0.05 level of significance, is there evidence of a difference in improved morale for teams with a specified goal of cutting costs?

h. Determine the $p$-value in (g) and interpret its meaning.

## Team Project

The data file Mutual Funds contains information regarding nine variables from a sample of 868 mutual funds. The variables are:

Category—Type of stocks comprising the mutual fund (small cap, mid cap, or large cap)

Objective—Objective of stocks comprising the mutual fund (growth or value)

Assets—In millions of dollars

Fees—Sales charges (no or yes)

Expense ratio—Ratio of expenses to net assets in percentage

2006 return—Twelve-month return in 2006

Three-year return—Annualized return, 2004–2006

Five-year return—Annualized return, 2002–2006

Risk—Risk-of-loss factor of the mutual fund (low, average, or high)

**12.109 a.** Construct a 2 × 2 contingency table, using fees as the row variable and objective as the column variable.

**b.** At the 0.05 level of significance, is there evidence of a significant relationship between the objective of a mutual fund and whether there is a fee?

**12.110 a.** Construct a 2 × 3 contingency table, using fees as the row variable and risk as the column variable.

**b.** At the 0.05 level of significance, is there evidence of a significant relationship between the perceived risk of a mutual fund and whether there is a fee?

**12.111 a.** Construct a 3 × 2 contingency table, using risk as the row variable and objective as the column variable.

**b.** At the 0.05 level of significance, is there evidence of a significant relationship between the objective of a mutual fund and its perceived risk?

**12.112 a.** Construct a 3 × 3 contingency table, using risk as the row variable and category as the column variable.

**b.** At the 0.05 level of significance, is there evidence of a significant relationship between the category of a mutual fund and its perceived risk?

### Student Survey Data Base

**12.113** Problem 1.27 on page 14 describes a survey of 50 undergraduate students (see the file Undergradsurvey). For these data, construct contingency tables, using gender, major, plans to go to graduate school, and employment status. (You need to construct six tables, taking two variables at a time.) Analyze the data at the 0.05 level of significance to determine whether any significant relationships exist among these variables.

**12.114** Problem 1.27 on page 14 describes a survey of 50 undergraduate students (see the file Undergradsurvey).
**a.** Select a sample of 50 undergraduate students at your school and conduct a similar survey for those students.
**b.** For the data collected in (a), repeat Problem 12.113.
**c.** Compare the results of (b) to those of Problem 12.113.

**12.115** Problem 1.28 on page 14 describes a survey of 40 MBA students (see the file Gradsurvey). For these data, construct contingency tables, using gender, undergraduate major, graduate major, and employment status. (You need to construct six tables, taking two variables at a time.) Analyze the data at the 0.05 level of significance to determine whether any significant relationships exist among these variables.

**12.116** Problem 1.28 on page 14 describes a survey of 40 MBA students (see the file Gradsurvey).
**a.** Select a sample of 40 graduate students in your MBA program and conduct a similar survey for those students.
**b.** For the data collected in (a), repeat Problem 12.115.
**c.** Compare the results of (b) to those of Problem 12.115.

# MANAGING THE *SPRINGVILLE HERALD*

### Phase 1

Reviewing the results of its research, the marketing department team concluded that a segment of Springville households might be interested in a discounted trial home subscription to the *Herald*. The team decided to test various discounts before determining the type of discount to offer during the trial period. It decided to conduct an experiment using three types of discounts plus a plan that offered no discount during the trial period:

1. No discount for the newspaper. Subscribers would pay $4.50 per week for the newspaper during the 90-day trial period.

2. Moderate discount for the newspaper. Subscribers would pay $4.00 per week for the newspaper during the 90-day trial period.

3. Substantial discount for the newspaper. Subscribers would pay $3.00 per week for the newspaper during the 90-day trial period.

4. Discount restaurant card. Subscribers would be given a card providing a discount of 15% at selected restaurants in Springville during the trial period.

Each participant in the experiment was randomly assigned to a discount plan. A random sample of 100 subscribers to each plan during the trial period was tracked to determine how many would continue to subscribe to the *Herald* after the trial period. Table SH12.1 summarizes the results.

## TABLE SH12.1
Number of Subscribers Who Continue Subscriptions After Trial Period with Four Discount Plans

| CONTINUE SUBSCRIPTIONS AFTER TRIAL PERIOD | DISCOUNT PLANS | | | | |
|---|---|---|---|---|---|
| | No Discount | Moderate Discount | Substantial Discount | Restaurant Card | Total |
| Yes | 34 | 37 | 38 | 61 | 170 |
| No | 66 | 63 | 62 | 39 | 230 |
| Total | 100 | 100 | 100 | 100 | 400 |

## EXERCISE

SH12.1  Analyze the results of the experiment. Write a report to the team that includes your recommendation for which discount plan to use. Be prepared to discuss the limitations and assumptions of the experiment.

DO NOT CONTINUE UNTIL THE PHASE 1 EXERCISE HAS BEEN COMPLETED.

## Phase 2

The marketing department team discussed the results of the survey presented in Chapter 8, on pages 333–334. The team realized that the evaluation of individual questions was providing only limited information. In order to further understand the market for home-delivery subscriptions, the data were organized in the following contingency tables:

### READ OTHER NEWSPAPER

| HOME DELIVERY | Yes | No | Total |
|---|---|---|---|
| Yes | 61 | 75 | 136 |
| No | 77 | 139 | 216 |
| Total | 138 | 214 | 352 |

### RESTAURANT CARD

| HOME DELIVERY | Yes | No | Total |
|---|---|---|---|
| Yes | 26 | 110 | 136 |
| No | 40 | 176 | 216 |
| Total | 66 | 286 | 352 |

### MONDAY–SATURDAY PURCHASE BEHAVIOR

| INTEREST IN TRIAL SUBSCRIPTION | Every Day | Most Days | Occasionally or Never | Total |
|---|---|---|---|---|
| Yes | 29 | 14 | 3 | 46 |
| No | 49 | 81 | 40 | 170 |
| Total | 78 | 95 | 43 | 216 |

### SUNDAY PURCHASE BEHAVIOR

| INTEREST IN TRIAL SUBSCRIPTION | Every Sunday | 2–3 Times/ Month | No More Than Once/ Month | Total |
|---|---|---|---|---|
| Yes | 35 | 10 | 1 | 46 |
| No | 103 | 44 | 23 | 170 |
| Total | 138 | 54 | 24 | 216 |

| WHERE PURCHASED | INTEREST IN TRIAL SUBSCRIPTION | | |
|---|---|---|---|
| | Yes | No | Total |
| Convenience store | 12 | 62 | 74 |
| Newsstand/candy store | 15 | 80 | 95 |
| Vending machine | 10 | 11 | 21 |
| Supermarket | 5 | 8 | 13 |
| Other locations | 4 | 9 | 13 |
| Total | 46 | 170 | 216 |

### MONDAY–SATURDAY PURCHASE BEHAVIOR

| SUNDAY PURCHASE BEHAVIOR | Every Day | Most Days | Occasionally or Never | Total |
|---|---|---|---|---|
| Every Sunday | 55 | 65 | 18 | 138 |
| 2–3 times/month | 19 | 23 | 12 | 54 |
| Once/month | 4 | 7 | 13 | 24 |
| Total | 78 | 95 | 43 | 216 |

## EXERCISE

SH12.2  Analyze the results of the contingency tables. Write a report for the marketing department team and discuss the marketing implications of the results for the *Springville Herald*.

# WEB CASE

*Apply your knowledge of testing for the difference between two proportions in this Web Case, which extends the T.C. Resort Properties Using Statistics scenario of this chapter.*

As T.C. Resort Properties seeks to improve its customer service, the company faces new competition from SunLow Resorts. SunLow has recently opened resort hotels on the islands where T.C. Resort Properties has its five hotels. SunLow is currently advertising that a random survey of 300 customers revealed that about 60% percent of the customers preferred its "Concierge Class" travel reward program over the T.C. Resorts "TCPass Plus" program. Visit the SunLow Web site, **www.prenhall.com/Springville/ SunLowHome.htm** (or open the `SunLowHome.htm` file in

the Student CD-ROM Web Case folder), and examine the survey data. Then answer the following:

1. Are the claims made by SunLow valid?
2. What analyses of the survey data would lead to a more favorable impression about T.C. Resort Properties?
3. Perform one of the analyses identified in your answer to step 2.
4. Review the data about the T.C. Resorts Properties customers presented in this chapter. Are there any other questions that you might include in a future survey of travel reward programs? Explain.

# REFERENCES

1. Conover, W. J., Practical Nonparametric Statistics, 3rd ed. (New York: Wiley, 2000).
2. Daniel, W. W., *Applied Nonparametric Statistics*, 2nd ed. (Boston: PWS Kent, 1990).
3. Dixon, W. J., and F. J. Massey, Jr., *Introduction to Statistical Analysis*, 4th ed. (New York: McGraw-Hill, 1983).
4. Goldstein, S. G., "Using Statistics to Improve Satisfaction," *Quality Progress*, March 2007, pp. 28–33.
5. Hollander, M., and D. A. Wolfe, *Nonparametric Statistical Methods*, 2nd ed. (New York: Wiley, 1999).
6. Lewontin, R. C., and J. Felsenstein, "Robustness of Homogeneity Tests in 2 × n Tables," *Biometrics* 21 (March 1965): pp. 19–33.
7. Marascuilo, L. A., "Large-Sample Multiple Comparisons," *Psychological Bulletin* 65 (1966): pp. 280–290.
8. Marascuilo, L. A., and M. McSweeney, *Nonparametric and Distribution-Free Methods for the Social Sciences* (Monterey, CA: Brooks/Cole, 1977).
9. *Microsoft Excel 2007* (Redmond, WA: Microsoft Corp., 2007).
10. *Minitab for Windows Version 15* (State College, PA: Minitab, Inc., 2006).
11. Solomon, H., and M. A. Stephens, "Sample Variance," in *Encyclopedia of Statistical Sciences*, vol. 9, pp. 477–480, edited by S. Kotz and N. L. Johnson. New York: Wiley, 1988.
12. Winer, B. J., D. R. Brown, and K. M. Michels, *Statistical Principles in Experimental Design*, 3rd ed. (New York: McGraw-Hill, 1989).

# Appendix E12
## Using Microsoft Excel for Chi-Square and Nonparametric Tests

## E12.1 Using the Chi-Square Test for the Difference Between Two Proportions

You perform the chi-square test for the difference between two proportions by making entries in the **ChiSquare2P** worksheet of the `Chi-Square.xls` workbook. This worksheet (see Figure

12.3 on page 509) uses the **CHIINV(*level of significance, degrees of freedom*)** and **CHIDIST($\chi^2$ *test statistic, degrees of freedom*)** functions to compute the critical value and *p*-value, respectively, for the Section 12.1 guest satisfaction example. To adapt this worksheet to other problems, enter the problem's contingency table data into the rows 4 through 7 Observed

Frequencies area, the level of significance in cell B18, and enter a new title in cell A1. To examine all formulas in this worksheet, including the ones not shown in Figure 12.3, open to the **ChiSquare2PFormulas** worksheet in the same workbook.

## E12.2 Using the Chi-Square Test for the Difference Among More Than Two Proportions

You perform the chi-square test for the difference among more than two proportions by making entries in one of the worksheets in the **Chi-Square Worksheets.xls** workbook. Open the workbook to the worksheet that contains the appropriate $2 \times c$ observed frequency table for your problem. For example, for the Section 12.2 guest satisfaction example that requires a $2 \times 3$ table, open to the **ChiSquare2x3** worksheet. Worksheets with empty observed frequencies table will display the message #DIV/0! in many cells. This is not an error and these messages will disappear once you enter your contingency table data.

All $2 \times c$ worksheets contain formulas similar to those in the ChiSquare2P worksheet discussed in Section E12.1. To examine all formulas in the ChiSquare2x3 worksheet, including those not shown in Figure 12.7 on page 516, open to the **ChiSquare2x3Formulas** worksheet.

Each $2 \times c$ Chi-Square worksheet is linked to a companion Marascuilo worksheet in the **Chi-Square Worksheets.xls** workbook. Marascuilo worksheet names echo the ChiSquare worksheet to which they are linked, so that **Marascuilo2x3** is linked to **ChiSquare2x3**. (The Marascuilo2x3 worksheet is shown in Figure 12.9 on page 518.) All Marascuilo worksheets compare the absolute differences and critical range values for each pair of groups and display either "Significant" or Not Significant" in column D.

The **Marascuilo2x3Formulas** worksheet displays the formulas of the Marascuilo2x3 worksheet. If you examine this worksheet, note that the formulas for level of significance, the square root of the critical value, the sample proportions, and the critical range all use one or more values from the ChiSquare2x3 worksheet.

## E12.3 Using the Chi-Square Test of Independence

You perform the chi-square test of independence by making entries in one of the worksheets in the **Chi-Square Worksheets.xls** workbook. The workbook contains worksheets for $3 \times 4$, $4 \times 3$, $7 \times 3$, and $8 \times 3$ tables, in addition to the $2 \times c$ worksheets discussed in Section E12.2. Figure 12.12 on page 524 uses the ChiSquare4x3 worksheet.

## E12.4 Using the McNemar Test

You perform the McNemar test by making entries in either the **McNemar_TT** or the **McNemar_All** worksheets of

the **McNemar.xls** workbook. These worksheets use the **NORMSINV($P<X$)** function to determine the lower and upper critical values and use the **NORMSDIST(Z *value*)** function to compute the $p$-values from the $Z$ value calculated in cell B16.

The **McNemar_TT** worksheet (see Figure 12.15 on page 528) uses the two-tail test for the Section 12.4 consumer preference example. The **McNemar_All** worksheet also includes the one-tail tests. To adapt these worksheets to other problems, change the observed frequency table data and labels in rows 4 through 7, the level of significance, and the title. To examine all formulas in this worksheet, open to the **McNemarFormulas** worksheet in the same workbook.

## E12.5 Using the Chi-Square Test for the Variance or Standard Deviation

You perform the chi-square test for the variance or standard deviation by making entries in the **Chi-Square Variance** worksheet of the **Chi-Square Variance.xls** workbook. This worksheet (see Figure 12.17 on page 532) uses the **CHIINV(*level of significance, degrees of freedom*)** and **CHIDIST($\chi^2$ *test statistic, degrees of freedom*)** functions to compute the critical values and $p$-value, respectively, for the Section 12.5 cereal-filling process example. To adapt this worksheet to other problems, change the null hypothesis, level of significance, sample size, and sample standard deviation, and enter a new title in cell A1.

## E12.6 Using the Wilcoxon Rank Sum Test (summarized data)

For summarized data, you perform the Wilcoxon rank sum test by making entries in either the **Wilcoxon_TT** or the **Wilcoxon_All** worksheets of the **Wilcoxon.xls** workbook. These worksheets use the **NORMSINV($P<X$)** function to determine the lower and upper critical values and use the **NORMSDIST(Z *value*)** function to compute the $p$-values from the $Z$ value calculated in cell B18.

The **Wilcoxon_TT** worksheet (see Figure 12.19 on page 537) uses the two-tail test for the Section 12.6 BLK Cola sales example. The **Wilcoxon_All** worksheet also includes the one-tail tests. To adapt these worksheets to other problems, change the level of significance and the sample size and sum of ranks for both samples.

## E12.7 Using the Wilcoxon Rank Sum Test (unsummarized data)

For unsummarized data, you perform the Wilcoxon rank sum test by summarizing your data and then using the instructions of Section E12.6. To summarize your data, you use the **COUNTIF(*cell range for matching, value to be*** *matched*) and **SUMIF**(*cell range for matching, value to be matched, cell range for summing*) functions to compute the sample size and sum of ranks of each population.

To use these functions, place your unsummarized data in unstacked order. Sort the data worksheet in ascending order using the column holding the values (not the population labels). Next add a column of ranks, breaking ties using the method stated at the top of page 534. Then use a formula in the form =**COUNTIF**(*cell range of all population labels, "population 1 name"*) to count the sample size of the first sample, and a formula in the form =**SUMIF**(*cell range of all population labels, "population 1 name", cell range of all sorted values*) to sum the ranks of the first sample. (The population 1 name must appear in a set of double quotation marks.) Create another pair of formulas and use the name of the second population as the *value to be matched* to count the sample size and sum the ranks of the second sample.

For example, the formulas =**COUNTIF(A1:A21, "EndAisle")** and =**SUMIF(A1:A21, "EndAisle", C1:C21)** would compute the sample size and the sum of ranks for the BLK Cola end-aisle sales if placed in empty cells of the **ColaSortedStacked** worksheet of the `Cola.xls` workbook. The formulas =**COUNTIF(A1:A21, "Normal")** and =**SUMIF(A1:A21, "Normal", C1:C21)** would do the same things for the other population sample.

## E12.8 Using the Kruskal-Wallis Rank Test

You perform the Kruskal-Wallis rank test by making entries in one of the worksheets in the `Kruskal-Wallis Worksheets.xls` workbook. Open the workbook to the worksheet that contains the appropriate number of groups for your problem. For example, for the Section 12.8 parachute tensile-strength example that contains four different groups, open to the **Kruskal-Wallis4** worksheet (shown in Figure 12.24 on page 549).

Kruskal-Wallis worksheets use the **CHIINV**(*level of significance, degrees of freedom*) and **CHIDIST**($\chi^2$ *test statistic, degrees of freedom*) functions to compute the critical value and *p*-value, respectively. When you open to a worksheet, enter the sample size, sum of ranks, and mean ranks values in the tinted cells in columns E through G, the level of significance value in cell B4, and a title in cell A1 to complete the worksheet. (#DIV/0! messages that may appear in several cells will disappear after you enter your data. This is not an error.)

If you have unsummarized data, you can use the PHStat2 Kruskal-Wallis Rank Test procedure.

## E12.9 Using the Friedman Rank Test

You perform the Friedman rank test by making entries in one of the worksheets in the `Friedman.xls` workbook. Open the workbook to the worksheet that contains the appropriate number of blocks and groups for your problem. For example, for the Section 12.9 fast-food study example that contains six blocks and four groups, open to the **Friedman6x4** worksheet.

Friedman worksheets use the **RANK**(*value, set of block values, order*) function to rank the values for each block. This function is used twice in each formula in the rank table that begins in row 12, once with *order* set to 1 (ascending order) and then again set to 0 (descending) in a shortcut, to rank values in both ascending and descending order. (This is done to allow the table to break ties.) The worksheets also use the **CHIINV**(*level of significance, degrees of freedom*) and **CHIDIST**($\chi^2$ *test statistic, degrees of freedom*) functions to compute the critical value and *p*-value, respectively.

When you open to a worksheet, enter the data in the table that starts in row 3 and enter the level of significance value in cell B24. (#NA! messages that appear in many cells will disappear after you enter your data. This is not an error.)

# Appendix P12
## Using PHStat2 for Chi-Square and Nonparametric Tests

## P12.1 Using the Chi-Square Test for the Difference Between Two Proportions

To perform the chi-square test for the difference between two proportions, use **PHStat → Two-Sample Tests → Chi-Square Test for Differences in Two**

**Proportions**. This procedure creates a new worksheet similar to Figure 12.3 on page 509 into which you enter observed frequency table data. Before you enter your data, many worksheet cells will display the message #DIV/0!. This is not an error.

## P12.2 Using the Chi-Square Test for the Difference Among More Than Two Proportions

To perform the chi-square test for the difference among more than two proportions, use **PHStat → Multiple-Sample Tests → Chi-Square Test**. This procedure creates a worksheet based on the number of rows and number of columns that you specify, similar in design to Figure 12.7 on page 516, into which you enter observed frequency table data. Before you enter your data, many worksheet cells will display the message #DIV/0!. This is not an error.

If you enter **2** as the **Number of Rows**, you will be able to click the **Marascuilo Procedure** Output Option. Clicking this option creates a second worksheet, similar in design to Figure 12.9 on page 518.

## P12.3 Using the Chi-Square Test of Independence

To perform the chi-square test of independence, use **PHStat → Multiple-Sample Tests → Chi-Square Test**. For more information about this procedure, see Section P12.2.

## P12.4 Using the McNemar Test

To perform the McNemar test, use **PHStat → Two-Sample Tests → McNemar Test**. This procedure creates a worksheet similar to Figure 12.15 on page 528 based on the level of significance and test option you specify. Before you enter your data, many worksheet cells will display the message #DIV/0!. This is not an error.

## P12.5 Using the Chi-Square Test for the Variance or Standard Deviation

To perform the chi-square test for the variance or standard deviation, use **PHStat → One-Sample Tests → Chi-Square Test for a Variance**. This procedure creates a worksheet similar to Figure 12.17 on page 532 based on the null hypothesis, level of significance, sample size, and sample standard deviation values and the test option that you specify.

## P12.6 Using the Wilcoxon Rank Sum Test

To perform the Wilcoxon rank sum test, use **PHStat →
Two-Sample Tests → Wilcoxon Rank Sum Test**. The procedure first calculates the rank sums for the unsummarized,
unstacked data in the **Population 1 Sample Cell Range** and
the **Population 2 Sample Cell Range**. Then it creates a
worksheet similar to Figure 12.19 on page 537 based on the
level of significance and the test option that you specify.

The worksheet created uses the COUNTIF and SUMIF
functions to determine the sample size and sum of ranks
for each sample (see Section E12.7 for more information
about these functions).

## P12.7 Using the Kruskal-Wallis Rank Test

To perform the Kruskal-Wallis rank test, use **PHStat →
Multiple-Sample Tests → Kruskal-Wallis Rank Test**.
This procedure first calculates the rank sums of unsummarized, unstacked data in the **Sample Data Cell Range**. It
then creates a worksheet similar to Figure 12.24 on page
549 based on the level of significance and the test option
that you specify.

# Appendix M12
## Using Minitab for Chi-Square and Nonparametric Tests

## M12.1 Using Chi-Square Tests (unsummarized data)

To create a two-way contingency table from unsummarized
data:

1. Open the worksheet of interest.
2. Select **Stat → Tables → Cross Tabulation and Chi-
   Square**.

In the Cross Tabulation and Chi-Square dialog box (see
Figure M12.1 on page 570):

3. Enter the row variable in the **For rows** box and the column variable in the **For columns** box.
4. Click **Counts, Row percents, Column percents**, and
   **Total percents**.
5. Click **Chi-Square**.

**FIGURE M12.1** Minitab Cross Tabulation and Chi-Square dialog box

In the Cross Tabulation - Chi-Square dialog box (see Figure M12.2),

6. Click **Chi-Square analysis, Expected cell counts**, and **Each cell's contribution to the Chi-Square statistic**.
7. Click **OK**.
8. Back in the original dialog box, click **OK** again.

**FIGURE M12.2** Minitab Cross Tabulation - Chi-Square dialog box

## M12.2 Using Chi-Square Tests (summarized data)

To create a 2 × c contingency table from summarized data, enter the set of cell frequencies that summarize the data into a new worksheet. For example, to enter Table 12.2 on page 505 (the 2 × 2 Contingency Table for the Hotel Guest Satisfaction Survey):

1. Open a new worksheet. (If necessary, select **File → New** and in the New dialog box, click **Minitab Worksheet** and then click **OK**.)

2. Enter **163** and **64** in column C1 rows 1 and 2
3. Enter **154** and **108** in column C2, rows 1 and 2.
4. Enter **Beachcomber** as the name of column C1 and **Windsurfer** as the name of column C2.
5. Select **Stat → Tables → Chi-Square Test (Two-Way Table in Worksheet)**.

In the Chi-Square Test (Table in Worksheet) dialog box (see Figure M12.3):

6. Enter **Beachcomber** and **Windsurfer** in the **Columns containing the table** box.
7. Click **OK**.

**FIGURE M12.3** Minitab Chi-Square Test (Table in Worksheet) dialog box

## M12.3 Using the Wilcoxon Rank Sum Test

To illustrate the Wilcoxon rank sum test:

1. Open the **Cola.mtw** worksheet. (This worksheet contains data in unstacked and stacked formats. If you open a worksheet that contains only stacked data, first unstack the data using the instructions of Section M10.1 on page 439.)
2. Select **Stat → Nonparametrics → Mann-Whitney**.

Note that Minitab performs the Mann-Whitney test, which is equivalent to the Wilcoxon rank sum test. In the Mann-Whitney dialog box (see Figure M12.4):

3. Enter **Normal** in the **First Sample** box.
4. Enter **EndAisle** in the **Second Sample** box.
5. Enter **95.0** in the **Confidence level** box.
6. Select **not equal** in the Alternative drop-down list to perform a two-tail test.
7. Click **OK**.

**FIGURE M12.4** Minitab Mann-Whitney dialog box

**FIGURE M12.5** Minitab 1-Sample Wilcoxon dialog box

## M12.4 Using the Wilcoxon Signed Ranks Test

To illustrate the Wilcoxon signed ranks test:

1.  Open the `AAAmileage.mtw` worksheet.

To compute the differences between the current and new packages:

2.  Enter **Difference** as the C3 column label.
3.  Select **Calc → Calculator**.
4.  Enter **Difference** in the **Store result in variable** box.
5.  Enter **Owner – Government** in the **Expression** box.
6.  Click **OK**.
7.  Select **Stat → Nonparametrics → 1-Sample Wilcoxon**.

In the 1-Sample Wilcoxon dialog box (see Figure M12.5):

8.  Enter **Difference** in the **Variables** box.
9.  Click **Test median** and enter **0.0** in its box.
10. Select **not equal** from the **Alternative** drop-down list to perform the two-tail test.
11. Click **OK**.

## M12.5 Using the Kruskal-Wallis Rank Test

To illustrate the Kruskal-Wallis rank test:

1.  Open the `ParachuteStacked.mtw` worksheet. (This worksheet contains stacked data. If you open a worksheet that contains unstacked data, first stack the data using the instructions of Section M10.1 on page 439.).
2.  Select **Stat → Nonparametrics → Kruskal-Wallis**.

In the Kruskal-Wallis dialog box (see Figure M12.6):

3.  Enter **Strength** in the **Response** box.
4.  Enter **Suppliers** in the **Factor** box.
5.  Click **OK**.

**FIGURE M12.6** Minitab Kruskal-Wallis dialog box

## M12.6 Using the Friedman Rank Test

To illustrate the Friedman rank test:

1. Open the `FFChain.mtw` worksheet.
2. Select **Stat → Nonparametrics → Friedman**.

In the Friedman dialog box (see Figure M12.7):

3. Enter **Rating** in the **Response** box.
4. Enter **Restrat** in the **Treatment** box.
5. Enter **Raters** in the **Blocks** box.
6. Click **OK**.

**FIGURE M12.7** Minitab Friedman dialog box

# LEARNING OBJECTIVES

## In this chapter, you learn:

- To use regression analysis to predict the value of a dependent variable based on an independent variable
- The meaning of the regression coefficients $b_0$ and $b_1$
- To evaluate the assumptions of regression analysis and know what to do if the assumptions are violated
- To make inferences about the slope and correlation coefficient
- To estimate mean values and predict individual values

# USING STATISTICS @ Sunflowers Apparel

The sales for Sunflowers Apparel, a chain of upscale clothing stores for women, have increased during the past 12 years as the chain has expanded the number of stores open. Until now, Sunflowers managers selected sites based on subjective factors, such as the availability of a good lease or the perception that a location seemed ideal for an apparel store. As the new director of planning, you need to develop a systematic approach that will lead to making better decisions during the site selection process. As a starting point, you believe that the size of the store significantly contributes to store sales, and you want to use this relationship in the decision-making process. How can you use statistics so that you can forecast the annual sales of a proposed store based on the size of that store?

In this chapter and the next two chapters, you learn how **regression analysis** enables you to develop a model to predict the values of a numerical variable, based on the value of other variables.

In regression analysis, the variable you wish to predict is called the **dependent variable**. The variables used to make the prediction are called **independent variables**. In addition to predicting values of the dependent variable, regression analysis also allows you to identify the type of mathematical relationship that exists between a dependent and an independent variable, to quantify the effect that changes in the independent variable have on the dependent variable, and to identify unusual observations. For example, as the director of planning, you may wish to predict sales for a Sunflowers store, based on the size of the store. Other examples include predicting the monthly rent of an apartment, based on its size, and predicting the monthly sales of a product in a supermarket, based on the amount of shelf space devoted to the product.

This chapter discusses **simple linear regression**, in which a *single* numerical independent variable, $X$, is used to predict the numerical dependent variable $Y$, such as using the size of a store to predict the annual sales of the store. Chapters 14 and 15 discuss *multiple regression models*, which use *several* independent variables to predict a numerical dependent variable, $Y$. For example, you could use the amount of advertising expenditures, price, and the amount of shelf space devoted to a product to predict its monthly sales.

## 13.1   TYPES OF REGRESSION MODELS

In Section 2.5, you used a **scatter plot** (also known as a **scatter diagram**) to examine the relationship between an $X$ variable on the horizontal axis and a $Y$ variable on the vertical axis. The nature of the relationship between two variables can take many forms, ranging from simple to extremely complicated mathematical functions. The simplest relationship consists of a straight-line or **linear relationship**. Figure 13.1 illustrates a straight-line relationship.

**FIGURE 13.1**

A straight-line
relationship

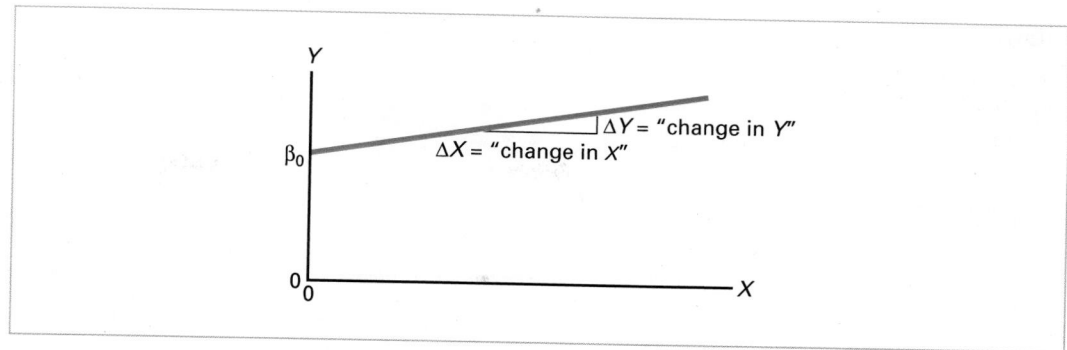

Equation (13.1) represents the straight-line (linear) model.

## Simple Linear Regression Model

$$Y_i = \beta_0 + \beta_1 X_i + \varepsilon_i \qquad\qquad \textbf{(13.1)}$$

where

$\beta_0 = Y$ intercept for the population

$\beta_1 =$ slope for the population

$\varepsilon_i =$ random error in $Y$ for observation $i$

$Y_i =$ dependent variable (sometimes referred to as the **response variable**) for observation $i$

$X_i =$ independent variable (sometimes referred to as the **explanatory variable**) for observation $i$

The portion $Y_i = \beta_0 + \beta_1 X_i$ of the simple linear regression model expressed in Equation (13.1) is a straight line. The **slope** of the line, $\beta_1$, represents the expected change in $Y$ per unit change in $X$. It represents the mean amount that $Y$ changes (either positively or negatively) for a one-unit change in $X$. The **Y intercept**, $\beta_0$, represents the mean value of $Y$ when $X$ equals 0. The last component of the model, $\varepsilon_i$, represents the random error in $Y$ for each observation, $i$. In other words, $\varepsilon_i$ is the vertical distance of the actual value of $Y_i$ above or below the expected value of $Y_i$ on the line.

The selection of the proper mathematical model depends on the distribution of the $X$ and $Y$ values on the scatter plot. In Panel A of Figure 13.2 on page 576, the values of $Y$ are generally increasing linearly as $X$ increases. This panel is similar to Figure 13.3 on page 577, which illustrates the positive relationship between the square footage of the store and the annual sales at branches of the Sunflowers Apparel women's clothing store chain.

Panel B is an example of a negative linear relationship. As $X$ increases, the values of $Y$ are generally decreasing. An example of this type of relationship might be the price of a particular product and the amount of sales.

The data in Panel C show a positive curvilinear relationship between $X$ and $Y$. The values of $Y$ increase as $X$ increases, but this increase tapers off beyond certain values of $X$. An example of a positive curvilinear relationship might be the age and maintenance cost of a machine. As a machine gets older, the maintenance cost may rise rapidly at first, but then level off beyond a certain number of years.

Panel D shows a U-shaped relationship between $X$ and $Y$. As $X$ increases, at first $Y$ generally decreases; but as $X$ continues to increase, $Y$ not only stops decreasing but actually increases above its minimum value. An example of this type of relationship might be the number of errors per hour at a task and the number of hours worked. The number of errors per hour

**FIGURE 13.2**

Six types of relationships found in scatter plots

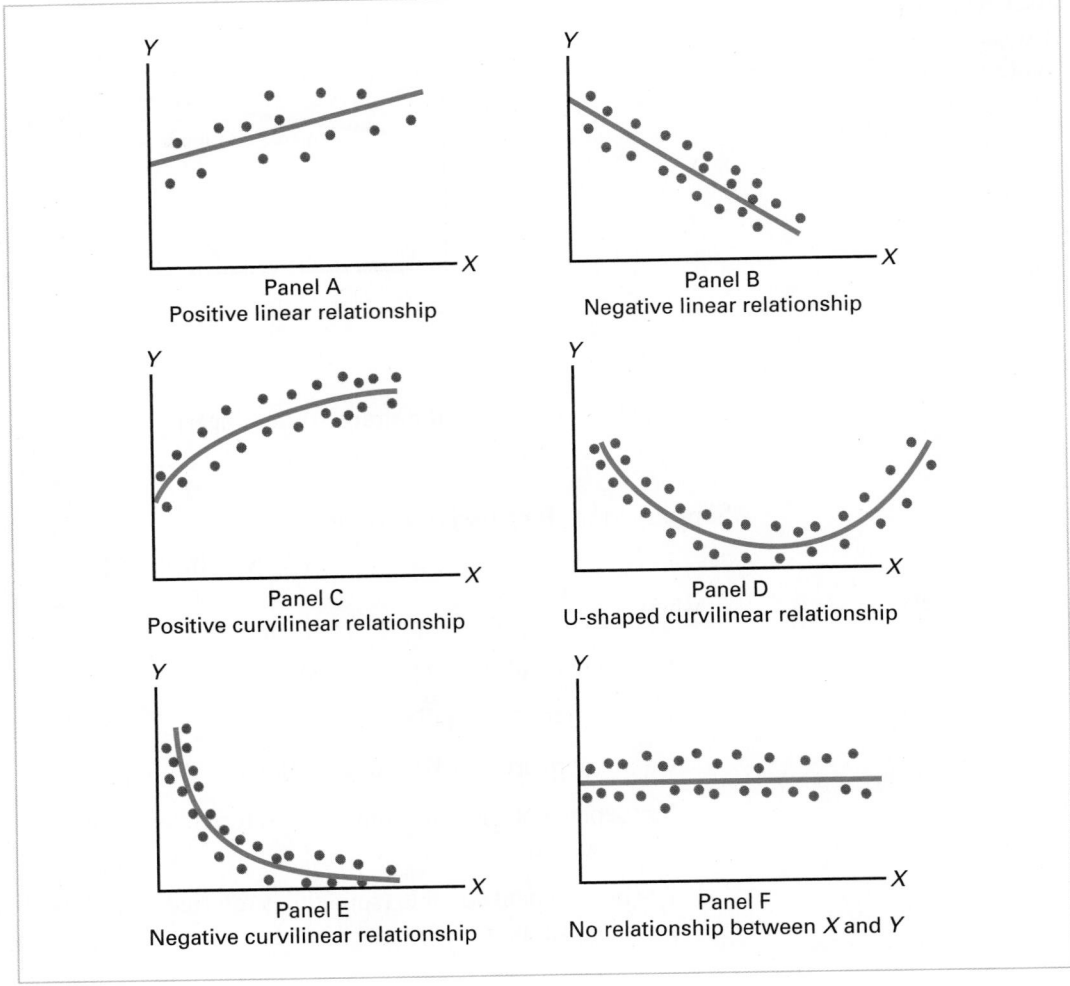

Panel A
Positive linear relationship

Panel B
Negative linear relationship

Panel C
Positive curvilinear relationship

Panel D
U-shaped curvilinear relationship

Panel E
Negative curvilinear relationship

Panel F
No relationship between $X$ and $Y$

decreases as the individual becomes more proficient at the task, but then it increases beyond a certain point because of factors such as fatigue and boredom.

Panel E indicates an exponential relationship between $X$ and $Y$. In this case, $Y$ decreases very rapidly as $X$ first increases, but then it decreases much less rapidly as $X$ increases further. An example of an exponential relationship could be the resale value of an automobile and its age. The resale value drops drastically from its original price in the first year, but decreases much less rapidly in subsequent years.

Finally, Panel F shows a set of data in which there is very little or no relationship between $X$ and $Y$. High and low values of $Y$ appear at each value of $X$.

In this section, a variety of different models that represent the relationship between two variables were briefly examined. Although scatter plots are useful in visually displaying the mathematical form of a relationship, more sophisticated statistical procedures are available to determine the most appropriate model for a set of variables. The rest of this chapter discusses the model used when there is a *linear* relationship between variables.

## 13.2   DETERMINING THE SIMPLE LINEAR REGRESSION EQUATION

In the Using Statistics scenario on page 574, the stated goal is to forecast annual sales for all new stores, based on store size. To examine the relationship between the store size in square feet and its annual sales, a sample of 14 stores was selected. Table 13.1 summarizes the results for these 14 stores, which are stored in the file Site.

**TABLE 13.1**

Square Footage (in Thousands of Square Feet) and Annual Sales (in Millions of Dollars) for a Sample of 14 Branches of Sunflowers Apparel

| Store | Square Feet (Thousands) | Annual Sales (in Millions of Dollars) | Store | Square Feet (Thousands) | Annual Sales (in Millions of Dollars) |
|---|---|---|---|---|---|
| 1 | 1.7 | 3.7 | 8 | 1.1 | 2.7 |
| 2 | 1.6 | 3.9 | 9 | 3.2 | 5.5 |
| 3 | 2.8 | 6.7 | 10 | 1.5 | 2.9 |
| 4 | 5.6 | 9.5 | 11 | 5.2 | 10.7 |
| 5 | 1.3 | 3.4 | 12 | 4.6 | 7.6 |
| 6 | 2.2 | 5.6 | 13 | 5.8 | 11.8 |
| 7 | 1.3 | 3.7 | 14 | 3.0 | 4.1 |

Figure 13.3 displays the scatter plot for the data in Table 13.1. Observe the increasing relationship between square feet ($X$) and annual sales ($Y$). As the size of the store increases, annual sales increase approximately as a straight line. Thus, you can assume that a straight line provides a useful mathematical model of this relationship. Now you need to determine the specific straight line that is the *best* fit to these data.

**FIGURE 13.3**

Microsoft Excel scatter plot for the Sunflowers Apparel data

*See Section E2.13 or P13.2 to create this. (Minitab users, see Section M2.9 to create an equivalent chart.)*

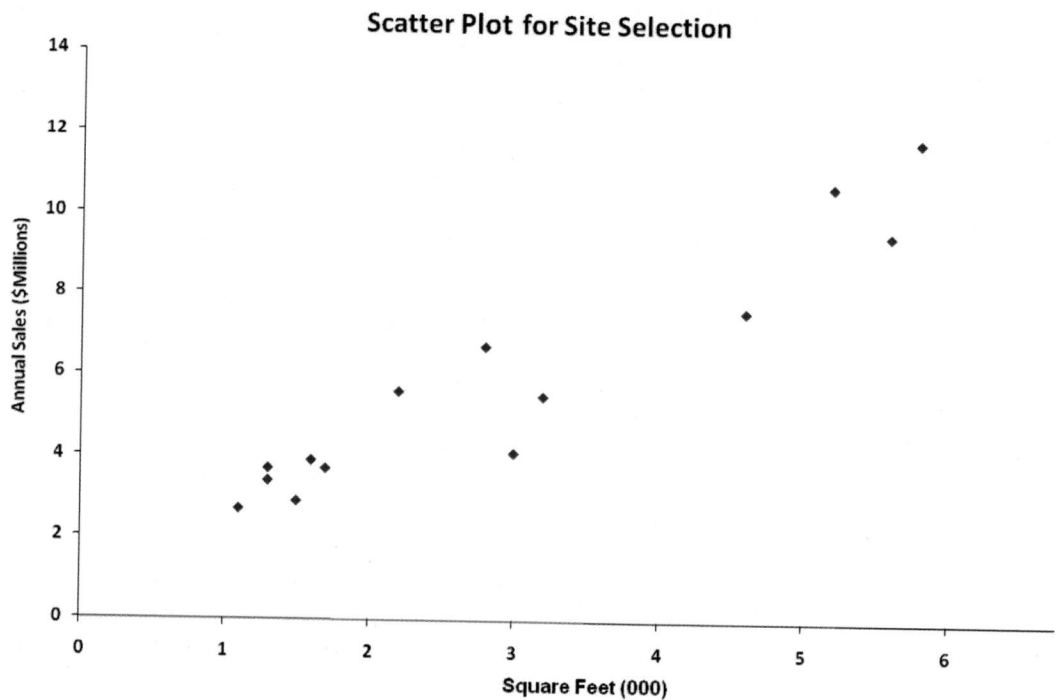

## The Least-Squares Method

In the preceding section, a statistical model is hypothesized to represent the relationship between two variables, square footage and sales, in the entire population of Sunflowers Apparel stores. However, as shown in Table 13.1, the data are from only a random sample of stores. If certain assumptions are valid (see Section 13.4), you can use the sample $Y$ intercept, $b_0$, and the sample slope, $b_1$, as estimates of the respective population parameters, $\beta_0$ and $\beta_1$. Equation (13.2) uses these estimates to form the **simple linear regression equation**. This straight line is often referred to as the **prediction line**.

Simple Linear Regression Equation: The Prediction Line
The predicted value of $Y$ equals the $Y$ intercept plus the slope times the value of $X$.

$$\hat{Y}_i = b_0 + b_1 X_i \tag{13.2}$$

where

$\hat{Y}_i$ = predicted value of $Y$ for observation $i$

$X_i$ = value of $X$ for observation $i$

$b_0$ = sample $Y$ intercept

$b_1$ = sample slope

Equation (13.2) requires the determination of two **regression coefficients**—$b_0$ (the sample $Y$ intercept) and $b_1$ (the sample slope). The most common approach to finding $b_0$ and $b_1$ is the method of least squares. This method minimizes the sum of the squared differences between the actual values ($Y_i$) and the predicted values ($\hat{Y}_i$) using the simple linear regression equation [i.e., the prediction line; see Equation (13.2)]. This sum of squared differences is equal to

$$\sum_{i=1}^{n}(Y_i - \hat{Y}_i)^2$$

Because $\hat{Y}_i = b_0 + b_1 X_i$,

$$\sum_{i=1}^{n}(Y_i - \hat{Y}_i)^2 = \sum_{i=1}^{n}[Y_i - (b_0 + b_1 X_i)]^2$$

Because this equation has two unknowns, $b_0$ and $b_1$, the sum of squared differences depends on the sample $Y$ intercept, $b_0$, and the sample slope, $b_1$. The **least-squares method** determines the values of $b_0$ and $b_1$ that minimize the sum of squared differences around the prediction line. Any values for $b_0$ and $b_1$ other than those determined by the least-squares method result in a greater sum of squared differences between the actual values ($Y_i$) and the predicted values ($\hat{Y}_i$). In this book, Microsoft Excel and Minitab are used to perform the computations involved in the least-squares method. For the data of Table 13.1, Figure 13.4 presents results from Microsoft Excel and Figure 13.5 shows Minitab results.

To understand how the results are computed, many of the computations involved are illustrated in Examples 13.3 and 13.4 on pages 582–583 and 590–591. In Figure 13.4 or 13.5, observe that $b_0 = 0.9645$ and $b_1 = 1.6699$. Thus, the prediction line [see Equation (13.2) above] for these data is

$$\hat{Y}_i = 0.9645 + 1.6699 X_i$$

The slope, $b_1$, is +1.6699. This means that for each increase of 1 unit in $X$, the mean value of $Y$ is estimated to increase by 1.6699 units. In other words, for each increase of 1.0 thousand

**FIGURE 13.4**

Microsoft Excel results worksheet for the Sunflowers Apparel data

*See Section E13.1 or P13.1 to create this.*

| | A | B | C | D | E | F | G |
|---|---|---|---|---|---|---|---|
| 1 | Site Selection Analysis | | | | | | |
| 2 | | | | | | | |
| 3 | *Regression Statistics* | | | | | | |
| 4 | Multiple R | 0.9509 | | | | | |
| 5 | R Square | 0.9042 | | | | | |
| 6 | Adjusted R Square | 0.8962 | | | | | |
| 7 | Standard Error | 0.9664 | | | | | |
| 8 | Observations | 14 | | | | | |
| 9 | | | | | | | |
| 10 | ANOVA | | | | | | |
| 11 | | *df* | *SS* | *MS* | *F* | *Significance F* | |
| 12 | Regression | 1 | 105.7476 | 105.7476 | 113.2335 | 0.0000 | |
| 13 | Residual | 12 | 11.2067 | 0.9339 | | | |
| 14 | Total | 13 | 116.9543 | | | | |
| 15 | | | | | | | |
| 16 | | *Coefficients* | *Standard Error* | *t Stat* | *P-value* | *Lower 95%* | *Upper 95%* |
| 17 | Intercept | 0.9645 | 0.5262 | 1.8329 | 0.0917 | -0.1820 | 2.1110 |
| 18 | Square Feet | 1.6699 | 0.1569 | 10.6411 | 0.0000 | 1.3280 | 2.0118 |

**FIGURE 13.5**

Minitab results for the Sunflowers Apparel data

*See Section M13.1 to create this.*

```
The regression equation is
Annual Sales = 0.964 + 1.67 Square Feet


Predictor        Coef   SE Coef      T      P
Constant       0.9645    0.5262   1.83  0.092
Square Feet    1.6699    0.1569  10.64  0.000


S = 0.966380   R-Sq = 90.4%   R-Sq(adj) = 89.6%

Analysis of Variance

Source          DF      SS      MS       F      P
Regression       1  105.75  105.75  113.23  0.000
Residual Error  12   11.21    0.93
Total           13  116.95

Predicted Values for New Observations

New
Obs    Fit  SE Fit       95% CI          95% PI
  1  7.644   0.309  (6.971, 8.317)  (5.433, 9.854)
```

square feet in the size of the store, the mean annual sales are estimated to increase by 1.6699 millions of dollars. Thus, the slope represents the portion of the annual sales that are estimated to vary according to the size of the store.

The $Y$ intercept, $b_0$, is +0.9645. The $Y$ intercept represents the mean value of $Y$ when $X$ equals 0. Because the square footage of the store cannot be 0, this $Y$ intercept has little or no practical interpretation. Also, the $Y$ intercept for this example is outside the range of the observed values of the $X$ variable, and therefore interpretations of the value of $b_0$ should be made cautiously. Figure 13.6 displays the actual observations and the prediction line. To illustrate a situation in which there is a direct interpretation for the $Y$ intercept, $b_0$, see Example 13.1.

**FIGURE 13.6**

Microsoft Excel scatter plot and prediction line for Sunflowers Apparel data

*See Section E13.2 or P13.2 to create this. (Minitab users, see Section M13.2 to create an equivalent chart.)*

**EXAMPLE 13.1**

INTERPRETING THE Y INTERCEPT, $b_0$, AND THE SLOPE, $b_1$

A statistics professor wants to use the number of hours a student studies for a statistics final exam $(X)$ to predict the final exam score $(Y)$. A regression model was fit based on data collected for a class during the previous semester, with the following results:

$$\hat{Y}_i = 35.0 + 3X_i$$

What is the interpretation of the $Y$ intercept, $b_0$, and the slope, $b_1$?

**SOLUTION** The $Y$ intercept $b_0 = 35.0$ indicates that when the student does not study for the final exam, the predicted final exam score is 35.0. The slope $b_1 = 3$ indicates that for each increase of one hour in studying time, the mean change in the final exam score is predicted to be +3.0. In other words, the final exam score is predicted to increase by 3 points for each one-hour increase in studying time.

Return to the Using Statistics scenario on page 574 concerning the Sunflowers Apparel stores. Example 13.2 illustrates how you use the prediction equation to predict the mean annual sales.

**EXAMPLE 13.2**

PREDICTING MEAN ANNUAL SALES, BASED ON SQUARE FOOTAGE

Use the prediction line to predict the mean annual sales for a store with 4,000 square feet.

**SOLUTION** You can determine the predicted value by substituting $X = 4$ (thousands of square feet) into the simple linear regression equation:

$$\hat{Y}_i = 0.9645 + 1.6699X_i$$

$$\hat{Y}_i = 0.9645 + 1.6699(4) = 7.644 \text{ or } \$7,644,000$$

Thus, the predicted mean annual sales of a store with 4,000 square feet is $7,644,000.

## Predictions in Regression Analysis: Interpolation versus Extrapolation

When using a regression model for prediction purposes, you need to consider only the **relevant range** of the independent variable in making predictions. This relevant range includes all values from the smallest to the largest X used in developing the regression model. Hence, when predicting Y for a given value of X, you can interpolate within this relevant range of the X values, but you should not extrapolate beyond the range of X values. When you use the square footage to predict annual sales, the square footage (in thousands of square feet) varies from 1.1 to 5.8 (see Table 13.1 on page 577). Therefore, you should predict annual sales *only* for stores whose size is between 1.1 and 5.8 thousands of square feet. Any prediction of annual sales for stores outside this range assumes that the observed relationship between sales and store size for store sizes from 1.1 to 5.8 thousand square feet is the same as for stores outside this range. For example, you cannot extrapolate the linear relationship beyond 5,800 square feet in Example 13.2. It would be improper to use the prediction line to forecast the sales for a new store containing 8,000 square feet because it is quite possible that store size has a point of diminishing returns. If that is true, as square footage increases beyond 5,800 square feet, the effect on sales becomes smaller and smaller.

## Computing the Y Intercept, $b_0$, and the Slope, $b_1$

For small data sets, you can use a hand calculator to compute the least-squares regression coefficients. Equations (13.3) and (13.4) give the values of $b_0$ and $b_1$, which minimize

$$\sum_{i=1}^{n}(Y_i - \hat{Y}_i)^2 = \sum_{i=1}^{n}[Y_i - (b_0 + b_1X_i)]^2$$

Computational Formula for the Slope, $b_1$

$$b_1 = \frac{SSXY}{SSX} \tag{13.3}$$

where

$$SSXY = \sum_{i=1}^{n}(X_i - \bar{X})(Y_i - \bar{Y}) = \sum_{i=1}^{n}X_iY_i - \frac{\left(\sum_{i=1}^{n}X_i\right)\left(\sum_{i=1}^{n}Y_i\right)}{n}$$

$$SSX = \sum_{i=1}^{n}(X_i - \bar{X})^2 = \sum_{i=1}^{n}X_i^2 - \frac{\left(\sum_{i=1}^{n}X_i\right)^2}{n}$$

Computational Formula for the Y Intercept, $b_0$

$$b_0 = \bar{Y} - b_1\bar{X} \qquad (13.4)$$

where

$$\bar{Y} = \frac{\sum_{i=1}^{n} Y_i}{n}$$

$$\bar{X} = \frac{\sum_{i=1}^{n} X_i}{n}$$

**EXAMPLE 13.3**

COMPUTING THE Y INTERCEPT, $b_0$, AND THE SLOPE, $b_1$

Compute the Y intercept, $b_0$, and the slope, $b_1$, for the Sunflowers Apparel data.

**SOLUTION** Examining Equations (13.3) and (13.4), you see that five quantities must be calculated to determine $b_1$ and $b_0$. These are $n$, the sample size; $\sum_{i=1}^{n} X_i$, the sum of the $X$ values; $\sum_{i=1}^{n} Y_i$, the sum of the $Y$ values; $\sum_{i=1}^{n} X_i^2$, the sum of the squared $X$ values; and $\sum_{i=1}^{n} X_i Y_i$, the sum of the product of $X$ and $Y$. For the Sunflowers Apparel data, the number of square feet is used to predict the annual sales in a store. Table 13.2 presents the computations of the various sums needed for the site selection problem. The table also includes $\sum_{i=1}^{n} Y_i^2$, the sum of the squared $Y$ values that will be used to compute $SST$ in Section 13.3.

**TABLE 13.2**

Computations for the Sunflowers Apparel Data

| Store | Square Feet ($X$) | Annual Sales ($Y$) | $X^2$ | $Y^2$ | $XY$ |
|-------|-------------------|---------------------|-------|-------|------|
| 1 | 1.7 | 3.7 | 2.89 | 13.69 | 6.29 |
| 2 | 1.6 | 3.9 | 2.56 | 15.21 | 6.24 |
| 3 | 2.8 | 6.7 | 7.84 | 44.89 | 18.76 |
| 4 | 5.6 | 9.5 | 31.36 | 90.25 | 53.20 |
| 5 | 1.3 | 3.4 | 1.69 | 11.56 | 4.42 |
| 6 | 2.2 | 5.6 | 4.84 | 31.36 | 12.32 |
| 7 | 1.3 | 3.7 | 1.69 | 13.69 | 4.81 |
| 8 | 1.1 | 2.7 | 1.21 | 7.29 | 2.97 |
| 9 | 3.2 | 5.5 | 10.24 | 30.25 | 17.60 |
| 10 | 1.5 | 2.9 | 2.25 | 8.41 | 4.35 |
| 11 | 5.2 | 10.7 | 27.04 | 114.49 | 55.64 |
| 12 | 4.6 | 7.6 | 21.16 | 57.76 | 34.96 |
| 13 | 5.8 | 11.8 | 33.64 | 139.24 | 68.44 |
| 14 | 3.0 | 4.1 | 9.00 | 16.81 | 12.30 |
| Totals | 40.9 | 81.8 | 157.41 | 594.90 | 302.30 |

Using Equations (13.3) and (13.4), you can compute the values of $b_0$ and $b_1$:

$$SSXY = \sum_{i=1}^{n}(X_i - \bar{X})(Y_i - \bar{Y}) = \sum_{i=1}^{n} X_i Y_i - \frac{\left(\sum_{i=1}^{n} X_i\right)\left(\sum_{i=1}^{n} Y_i\right)}{n}$$

$$SSXY = 302.3 - \frac{(40.9)(81.8)}{14}$$

$$= 302.3 - 238.97285$$

$$= 63.32715$$

$$SSX = \sum_{i=1}^{n}(X_i - \bar{X})^2 = \sum_{i=1}^{n} X_i^2 - \frac{\left(\sum_{i=1}^{n} X_i\right)^2}{n}$$

$$= 157.41 - \frac{(40.9)^2}{14}$$

$$= 157.41 - 119.48642$$

$$= 37.92358$$

Therefore,

$$b_1 = \frac{SSXY}{SSX}$$

$$= \frac{63.32715}{37.92358}$$

$$= 1.6699$$

And,

$$\bar{Y} = \frac{\sum_{i=1}^{n} Y_i}{n} = \frac{81.8}{14} = 5.842857$$

$$\bar{X} = \frac{\sum_{i=1}^{n} X_i}{n} = \frac{40.9}{14} = 2.92143$$

Therefore,

$$b_0 = \bar{Y} - b_1 \bar{X}$$

$$= 5.842857 - (1.6699)(2.92143)$$

$$= 0.9645$$

# VISUAL EXPLORATIONS: Exploring Simple Linear Regression Coefficients

Use the Visual Explorations Simple Linear Regression procedure to create a prediction line that is as close as possible to the prediction line defined by the least-squares solution. Open the Visual Explorations.xla add-in workbook and select **VisualExplorations → Simple Linear Regression** (Excel 97–2003) or **Add-ins → VisualExplorations → Simple Linear Regression** (Excel 2007).

The procedure displays a scatter plot of the Sunflowers Apparel data of Table 13.1 on page 577, along with an initial prediction line (see illustration below). In the Simple Linear Regression dialog box, click the spinner buttons to change the values for $b_1$, the slope of the prediction line, and $b_0$, the $Y$ intercept of the prediction line to change the prediction line.

Try to create a prediction line that is as close as possible to the prediction line defined by the least-squares estimates, using the chart display as visual feedback and try to make the Difference from Target SSE value as small as possible (see page 592 for an explanation of SSE). At any time, click **Reset** to reset the $b_1$ and $b_0$ values or **Solution** to reveal the prediction line defined by the least-squares method. Click **Finish** when you are finished with this exercise.

*Using Your Own Regression Data*

To use Visual Explorations to find a prediction line for your own data, select **VisualExplorations → Simple**

**Linear Regression with your worksheet data** (Excel 97–2003) or **Add-ins → VisualExplorations → Simple Linear Regression with your worksheet data** (Excel 2007). In the procedure's dialog box (shown below), enter your $Y$ variable cell range as the **Y Variable Cell Range** and your $X$ variable cell range as the **X Variable Cell Range**. Click **First cells in both ranges contain a label**, enter a title as the **Title**, and click **OK**. When the scatter plot with an initial prediction line appears, use the instructions in the first part of this section to try to produce the prediction line defined by the least-squares plot.

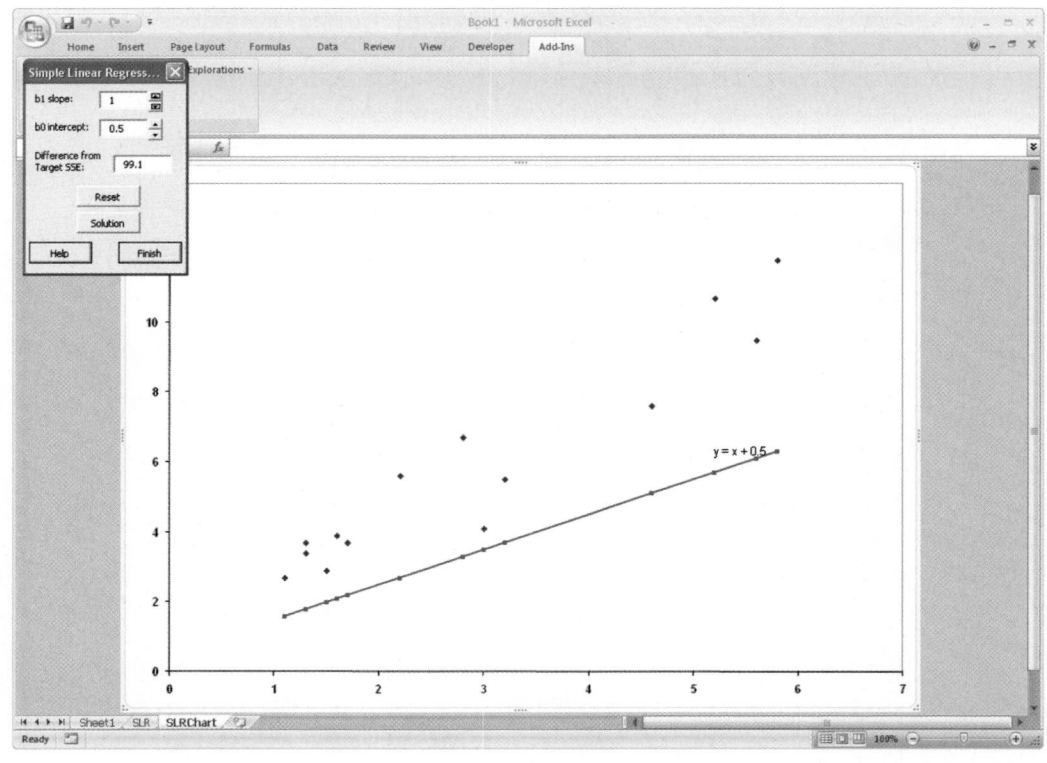

# PROBLEMS FOR SECTION 13.2

## Learning the Basics

**13.1** Fitting a straight line to a set of data yields the following prediction line:

$$\hat{Y}_i = 2 + 5X_i$$

**a.** Interpret the meaning of the $Y$ intercept, $b_0$.
**b.** Interpret the meaning of the slope, $b_1$.
**c.** Predict the mean value of $Y$ for $X = 3$.

**13.2** If the values of $X$ in Problem 13.1 range from 2 to 25, should you use this model to predict the mean value of $Y$ when $X$ equals
**a.** 3?
**b.** −3?
**c.** 0?
**d.** 24?

**13.3** Fitting a straight line to a set of data yields the following prediction line:

$$\hat{Y}_i = 16 - 0.5X_i$$

**a.** Interpret the meaning of the $Y$ intercept, $b_0$.
**b.** Interpret the meaning of the slope, $b_1$.
**c.** Predict the mean value of $Y$ for $X = 6$.

## Applying the Concepts

**SELF Test** **13.4** The marketing manager of a large supermarket chain would like to use shelf space to predict the sales of pet food. A random sample of 12 equal-sized stores is selected, with the following results (stored in the file **Petfood**):

| Store | Shelf Space (X) (Feet) | Weekly Sales (Y) ($) |
|---|---|---|
| 1 | 5 | 160 |
| 2 | 5 | 220 |
| 3 | 5 | 140 |
| 4 | 10 | 190 |
| 5 | 10 | 240 |
| 6 | 10 | 260 |
| 7 | 15 | 230 |
| 8 | 15 | 270 |
| 9 | 15 | 280 |
| 10 | 20 | 260 |
| 11 | 20 | 290 |
| 12 | 20 | 310 |

**a.** Construct a scatter plot.
For these data, $b_0 = 145$ and $b_1 = 7.4$.
**b.** Interpret the meaning of the slope, $b_1$, in this problem.
**c.** Predict the mean weekly sales of pet food for stores with 8 feet of shelf space for pet food.

**13.5** Circulation is the lifeblood of the publishing business. The larger the sales of a magazine, the more it can charge advertisers. Recently, a circulation gap has appeared between the publishers' reports of magazines' newsstand sales and subsequent audits by the Audit Bureau of Circulations. The data in the file **Circulation** represent the reported and audited newsstand sales (in thousands) in 2001 for the following 10 magazines:

| Magazine | Reported (X) | Audited (Y) |
|---|---|---|
| YM | 621.0 | 299.6 |
| CosmoGirl | 359.7 | 207.7 |
| Rosie | 530.0 | 325.0 |
| Playboy | 492.1 | 336.3 |
| Esquire | 70.5 | 48.6 |
| TeenPeople | 567.0 | 400.3 |
| More | 125.5 | 91.2 |
| Spin | 50.6 | 39.1 |
| Vogue | 353.3 | 268.6 |
| Elle | 263.6 | 214.3 |

Source: *Extracted from M. Rose, "In Fight for Ads, Publishers Often Overstate Their Sales," The Wall Street Journal, August 6, 2003, pp. A1, A10.*

**a.** Construct a scatter plot.
For these data, $b_0 = 26.724$ and $b_1 = 0.5719$.
**b.** Interpret the meaning of the slope, $b_1$, in this problem.
**c.** Predict the mean audited newsstand sales for a magazine that reports newsstand sales of 400,000.

**13.6** The owner of a moving company typically has his most experienced manager predict the total number of labor hours that will be required to complete an upcoming move. This approach has proved useful in the past, but he would like to be able to develop a more accurate method of predicting labor hours by using the number of cubic feet moved. In a preliminary effort to provide a more accurate method, he has collected data for 36 moves in which the origin and destination were within the borough of Manhattan in New York City and in which the travel time was an insignificant portion of the hours worked. The data are stored in the file **Moving**.
**a.** Construct a scatter plot.
**b.** Assuming a linear relationship, use the least-squares method to find the regression coefficients $b_0$ and $b_1$.

c. Interpret the meaning of the slope, $b_1$, in this problem.
d. Predict the mean labor hours for moving 500 cubic feet.

**13.7** A critically important aspect of customer service in a supermarket is the waiting time at the checkout (defined as the time the customer enters the line until he or she is served). Data were collected during time periods where there were a given number of checkout counters open. The total number of customers in the store and the waiting times (in minutes) were recorded. The results are stored in the Supermarket file.
a. Construct a scatter plot.
b. Assuming a linear relationship, use the least-squares method to find the regression coefficients $b_0$ and $b_1$.
c. Interpret the meaning of the slope, $b_1$, in this problem.
d. Predict the mean waiting time when there are 20 customers in the store.

**13.8** The value of a sports franchise is directly related to the amount of revenue that a franchise can generate. The data in the file BBrevenue represent the value in 2005 (in millions of dollars) and the annual revenue (in millions of dollars) for 30 baseball franchises. Suppose you want to develop a simple linear regression model to predict franchise value based on annual revenue generated.
a. Construct a scatter plot.
b. Use the least-squares method to find the regression coefficients $b_0$ and $b_1$.
c. Interpret the meaning of $b_0$ and $b_1$ in this problem.
d. Predict the mean value of a baseball franchise that generates $150 million of annual revenue.

**13.9** An agent for a residential real estate company in a large city would like to be able to predict the monthly rental cost for apartments, based on the size of the apartment, as defined by square footage. A sample of 25 apartments (stored in the file Rent) in a particular residential neighborhood was selected, and the information gathered revealed the following:
a. Construct a scatter plot.
b. Use the least-squares method to find the regression coefficients $b_0$ and $b_1$.
c. Interpret the meaning of $b_0$ and $b_1$ in this problem.
d. Predict the mean monthly rent for an apartment that has 1,000 square feet.

| Apartment | Monthly Rent ($) | Size (Square Feet) | Apartment | Monthly Rent ($) | Size (Square Feet) |
|---|---|---|---|---|---|
| 1 | 950 | 850 | 14 | 1,800 | 1,369 |
| 2 | 1,600 | 1,450 | 15 | 1,400 | 1,175 |
| 3 | 1,200 | 1,085 | 16 | 1,450 | 1,225 |
| 4 | 1,500 | 1,232 | 17 | 1,100 | 1,245 |
| 5 | 950 | 718 | 18 | 1,700 | 1,259 |
| 6 | 1,700 | 1,485 | 19 | 1,200 | 1,150 |
| 7 | 1,650 | 1,136 | 20 | 1,150 | 896 |
| 8 | 935 | 726 | 21 | 1,600 | 1,361 |
| 9 | 875 | 700 | 22 | 1,650 | 1,040 |
| 10 | 1,150 | 956 | 23 | 1,200 | 755 |
| 11 | 1,400 | 1,100 | 24 | 800 | 1,000 |
| 12 | 1,650 | 1,285 | 25 | 1,750 | 1,200 |
| 13 | 2,300 | 1,985 | | | |

e. Why would it not be appropriate to use the model to predict the monthly rent for apartments that have 500 square feet?
f. Your friends Jim and Jennifer are considering signing a lease for an apartment in this residential neighborhood. They are trying to decide between two apartments, one with 1,000 square feet for a monthly rent of $1,275 and the other with 1,200 square feet for a monthly rent of $1,425. Based on (a) through (d), which apartment do you think is a better deal?

**13.10** A company that holds the DVD distribution rights to movies previously released only in theaters wants to estimate sales of DVDs based on box office success. Data are available in the file Movie that indicate the box office gross (in $millions) for each of 30 movies and the number of DVDs sold (in thousands). For these data:
a. Construct a scatter plot.
b. Assuming a linear relationship, use the least-squares method to find the regression coefficients $b_0$ and $b_1$.
c. Interpret the meaning of the slope, $b_1$, in this problem.
d. Predict the mean sales for a movie that had a box office gross of $75 million.

## 13.3   MEASURES OF VARIATION

When using the least-squares method to determine the regression coefficients for a set of data, you need to compute three important measures of variation. The first measure, the **total sum of squares (SST)**, is a measure of variation of the $Y_i$ values around their mean, $\bar{Y}$. The **total variation** or total sum of squares is subdivided into **explained variation** and **unexplained**

**variation**. The explained variation or **regression sum of squares (SSR)** is due to the relationship between $X$ and $Y$, and the unexplained variation, or **error sum of squares (SSE)**, is due to factors other than the relationship between $X$ and $Y$. Figure 13.7 shows these different measures of variation.

**FIGURE 13.7**

Measures of variation

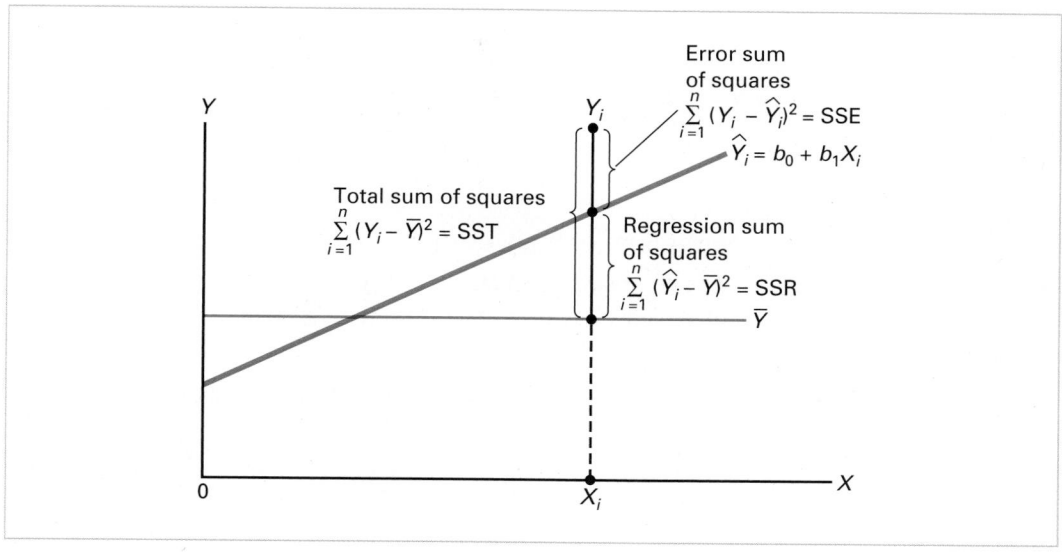

## Computing the Sum of Squares

The regression sum of squares ($SSR$) is based on the difference between $\hat{Y}_i$ (the predicted value of $Y$ from the prediction line) and $\bar{Y}$ (the mean value of $Y$). The error sum of squares ($SSE$) represents the part of the variation in $Y$ that is not explained by the regression. It is based on the difference between $Y_i$ and $\hat{Y}_i$. Equations (13.5), (13.6), (13.7), and (13.8) define these measures of variation.

---

**Measures of Variation in Regression**

The total sum of squares is equal to the regression sum of squares plus the error sum of squares.

$$SST = SSR + SSE \tag{13.5}$$

---

**Total Sum of Squares (SST)**

The total sum of squares ($SST$) is equal to the sum of the squared differences between each observed value of $Y$ and the mean value of $Y$.

$$SST = \text{Total sum of squares}$$

$$= \sum_{i=1}^{n}(Y_i - \bar{Y})^2 \tag{13.6}$$

## Regression Sum of Squares (SSR)

The regression sum of squares (SSR) is equal to the sum of the squared differences between each predicted value of Y and the mean value of Y.

$$SSR = \text{Explained variation or regression of squares}$$

$$= \sum_{i=1}^{n}(\hat{Y}_i - \bar{Y})^2 \tag{13.7}$$

## Error Sum of Squares (SSE)

The error sum of squares (SSE) is equal to the sum of the squared differences between each observed value of Y and the predicted value of Y.

$$SSE = \text{Unexplained variation or error sum of squares}$$

$$= \sum_{i=1}^{n}(Y_i - \hat{Y}_i)^2 \tag{13.8}$$

Figure 13.8 shows the sum of squares portion of the worksheet containing the Microsoft Excel results for the Sunflowers Apparel data, and Figure 13.9 shows Minitab results. The total variation, SST, is equal to 116.9543. This amount is subdivided into the sum of squares explained by the regression (SSR), equal to 105.7476, and the sum of squares unexplained by the regression (SSE), equal to 11.2067. From Equation (13.5) on page 587:

$$SST = SSR + SSE$$

$$116.9543 = 105.7476 + 11.2067$$

**FIGURE 13.8**

Microsoft Excel sum of squares for the Sunflowers Apparel data

*See Section E13.1 or P13.1 to create the worksheet that contains this area.*

| | A | B | C | D | E | F | G |
|---|---|---|---|---|---|---|---|
| 10 | ANOVA | | | | | | |
| 11 | | df | SS | MS | F | Significance F | |
| 12 | Regression | 1 | 105.7476 | 105.7476 | 113.2335 | 0.0000 | |
| 13 | Residual | 12 | 11.2067 | 0.9339 | | | |
| 14 | Total | 13 | 116.9543 | | | | |
| 15 | | | | | | | |
| 16 | | Coefficients | Standard Error | t Stat | P-value | Lower 95% | Upper 95% |
| 17 | Intercept | 0.9645 | 0.5262 | 1.8329 | 0.0917 | -0.1820 | 2.1110 |
| 18 | Square Feet | 1.6699 | 0.1569 | 10.6411 | 0.0000 | 1.3280 | 2.0118 |

**FIGURE 13.9**

Minitab sum of squares for the Sunflowers Apparel data

*See Section M13.1 to create this.*

```
Analysis of Variance

Source          DF     SS      MS      F      P
Regression       1  105.75  105.75  113.23  0.000
Residual Error  12   11.21    0.93
Total           13  116.95
```

In a data set that has a large number of significant digits, the results of a regression analysis are sometimes displayed using a numerical format known as *scientific notation*. This type of format is used to display very small or very large values. The number after the letter E represents the number of digits that the decimal point needs to be moved to the left (for a negative number) or to the right (for a positive number). For example, the number 3.7431E+02 means that the decimal point should be moved two places to the right, producing the number 374.31. The number 3.7431E−02 means that the decimal point should be moved two places to the left, producing the number 0.037431. When scientific notation is used, fewer significant digits are usually displayed, and the numbers may appear to be rounded.

## The Coefficient of Determination

By themselves, *SSR*, *SSE*, and *SST* provide little information. However, the ratio of the regression sum of squares (*SSR*) to the total sum of squares (*SST*) measures the proportion of variation in *Y* that is explained by the independent variable *X* in the regression model. This ratio is called the coefficient of determination, $r^2$, and is defined in Equation (13.9).

Coefficient of Determination

The coefficient of determination is equal to the regression sum of squares (i.e., explained variation) divided by the total sum of squares (i.e., total variation).

$$r^2 = \frac{\text{Regression sum of squares}}{\text{Total sum of squares}} = \frac{SSR}{SST} \qquad (13.9)$$

The **coefficient of determination** measures the proportion of variation in *Y* that is explained by the independent variable *X* in the regression model.

For the Sunflowers Apparel data, with *SSR* = 105.7476, *SSE* = 11.2067, and *SST* = 116.9543,

$$r^2 = \frac{105.7476}{116.9543} = 0.9042$$

Therefore, 90.42% of the variation in annual sales is explained by the variability in the size of the store as measured by the square footage. This large $r^2$ indicates a strong linear relationship between these two variables because the use of a regression model has reduced the variability in predicting annual sales by 90.42%. Only 9.58% of the sample variability in annual sales is due to factors other than what is accounted for by the linear regression model that uses square footage.

Figure 13.10 presents the coefficient of determination portion of the Microsoft Excel results for the Sunflowers Apparel data, and Figure 13.11 shows Minitab results.

**FIGURE 13.10**

Partial Microsoft Excel regression results for the Sunflowers Apparel data

*See Section E13.1 or P13.1 to create the worksheet that contains this.*

| | A | B |
|---|---|---|
| 3 | *Regression Statistics* | |
| 4 | Multiple R | 0.9509 |
| 5 | R Square | 0.9042 |
| 6 | Adjusted R Square | 0.8962 |
| 7 | Standard Error | 0.9664 |
| 8 | Observations | 14 |

**FIGURE 13.11**

Partial Minitab regression results for the Sunflowers Apparel data

*See Section M13.1 to create this.*

```
Predictor        Coef   SE Coef      T      P
Constant       0.9645    0.5262   1.83  0.092
Square Feet    1.6699    0.1569  10.64  0.000


S = 0.966380    R-Sq = 90.4%    R-Sq(adj) = 89.6%
```

**EXAMPLE 13.4**   COMPUTING THE COEFFICIENT OF DETERMINATION

Compute the coefficient of determination, $r^2$, for the Sunflowers Apparel data.

**SOLUTION** You can compute *SST, SSR*, and *SSE*, that are defined in Equations (13.6), (13.7), and (13.8) on pages 587 and 588, by using Equations (13.10), (13.11), and (13.12).

Computational Formula for SST

$$SST = \sum_{i=1}^{n}(Y_i - \overline{Y})^2 = \sum_{i=1}^{n}Y_i^2 - \frac{\left(\sum_{i=1}^{n}Y_i\right)^2}{n} \tag{13.10}$$

Computational Formula for *SSR*

$$SSR = \sum_{i=1}^{n}(\hat{Y}_i - \overline{Y})^2 \tag{13.11}$$

$$= b_0 \sum_{i=1}^{n}Y_i + b_1 \sum_{i=1}^{n}X_iY_i - \frac{\left(\sum_{i=1}^{n}Y_i\right)^2}{n}$$

Computational Formula for *SSE*

$$SSE = \sum_{i=1}^{n}(Y_i - \hat{Y})^2 = \sum_{i=1}^{n}Y_i^2 - b_0 \sum_{i=1}^{n}Y_i - b_1 \sum_{i=1}^{n}X_iY_i \tag{13.12}$$

Using the summary results from Table 13.2 on page 582,

$$SST = \sum_{i=1}^{n}(Y_i - \overline{Y})^2 = \sum_{i=1}^{n}Y_i^2 - \frac{\left(\sum_{i=1}^{n}Y_i\right)^2}{n}$$

$$= 594.9 - \frac{(81.8)^2}{14}$$

$$= 594.9 - 477.94571$$

$$= 116.95429$$

$$SSR = \sum_{i=1}^{n} (\hat{Y}_i - \bar{Y})^2$$

$$= b_0 \sum_{i=1}^{n} Y_i + b_1 \sum_{i=1}^{n} X_i Y_i - \frac{\left(\sum_{i=1}^{n} Y_i\right)^2}{n}$$

$$= (0.964478)(81.8) + (1.66986)(302.3) - \frac{(81.8)^2}{14}$$

$$= 105.74726$$

$$SSE = \sum_{i=1}^{n} (Y_i - \hat{Y}_i)^2$$

$$= \sum_{i=1}^{n} Y_i^2 - b_0 \sum_{i=1}^{n} Y_i - b_1 \sum_{i=1}^{n} X_i Y_i$$

$$= 594.9 - (0.964478)(81.8) - (1.66986)(302.3)$$

$$= 11.2067$$

Therefore,

$$r^2 = \frac{105.74726}{116.95429} = 0.9042$$

## Standard Error of the Estimate

Although the least-squares method results in the line that fits the data with the minimum amount of error, unless all the observed data points fall on a straight line, the prediction line is not a perfect predictor. Just as all data values cannot be expected to be exactly equal to their mean, neither can all the values in a regression analysis be expected to fall exactly on the prediction line. Figure 13.6 on page 580 illustrates the variability around the prediction line for the Sunflowers Apparel data. Observe that, although many of the actual values of $Y$ fall near the prediction line, none of the values are exactly on the line.

The **standard error of the estimate** measures the variability of the actual $Y$ values from the predicted $Y$ values in the same way that the standard deviation in Chapter 3 measures the variability of each value around the sample mean. In other words, the standard error of the estimate is the standard deviation *around* the prediction line, whereas the standard deviation in Chapter 3 is the standard deviation *around* the sample mean. Equation (13.13) defines the standard error of the estimate, represented by the symbol $S_{YX}$.

Standard Error of the Estimate

$$S_{YX} = \sqrt{\frac{SSE}{n-2}} = \sqrt{\frac{\sum_{i=1}^{n} (Y_i - \hat{Y}_i)^2}{n-2}} \qquad (13.13)$$

where

$$Y_i = \text{actual value of } Y \text{ for a given } X_i$$

$$\hat{Y}_i = \text{predicted value of } Y \text{ for a given } X_i$$

$$SSE = \text{error sum of squares}$$

From Equation (13.8) and Figure 13.8 or Figure 13.9 on page 588, $SSE = 11.2067$. Thus,

$$S_{YX} = \sqrt{\frac{11.2067}{14 - 2}} = 0.9664$$

This standard error of the estimate, equal to 0.9664 millions of dollars (i.e., \$966,400), is labeled Standard Error in the Microsoft Excel results shown in Figure 13.10 and $S$ in the Minitab results in Figure 13.11 on page 590. The standard error of the estimate represents a measure of the variation around the prediction line. It is measured in the same units as the dependent variable $Y$. The interpretation of the standard error of the estimate is similar to that of the standard deviation. Just as the standard deviation measures variability around the mean, the standard error of the estimate measures variability around the prediction line. For Sunflowers Apparel, the typical difference between actual annual sales at a store and the predicted annual sales using the regression equation is approximately \$966,400.

## PROBLEMS FOR SECTION 13.3

### Learning the Basics

**13.11** How do you interpret a coefficient of determination, $r^2$, equal to 0.80?

**13.12** If $SSR = 36$ and $SSE = 4$, determine $SST$ and then compute the coefficient of determination, $r^2$, and interpret its meaning.

**13.13** If $SSR = 66$ and $SST = 88$, compute the coefficient of determination, $r^2$, and interpret its meaning.

**13.14** If $SSE = 10$ and $SSR = 30$, compute the coefficient of determination, $r^2$, and interpret its meaning.

**13.15** If $SSR = 120$, why is it impossible for $SST$ to equal 110?

### Applying the Concepts

**✓SELF Test** **13.16** In Problem 13.4 on page 585, the marketing manager used shelf space for pet food to predict weekly sales (stored in the file **Petfood**). For that data, $SSR = 20,535$ and $SST = 30,025$.
**a.** Determine the coefficient of determination, $r^2$, and interpret its meaning.
**b.** Determine the standard error of the estimate.
**c.** How useful do you think this regression model is for predicting sales?

**13.17** In Problem 13.5 on page 585, you used reported magazine newsstand sales to predict audited sales (stored in the file **Circulation**). For that data, $SSR = 130,301.41$ and $SST = 144,538.64$.
**a.** Determine the coefficient of determination, $r^2$, and interpret its meaning.
**b.** Determine the standard error of the estimate.
**c.** How useful do you think this regression model is for predicting audited sales?

**13.18** In Problem 13.6 on page 585, an owner of a moving company wanted to predict labor hours, based on the cubic feet moved (stored in the file **Moving**). Using the results of that problem,
**a.** determine the coefficient of determination, $r^2$, and interpret its meaning.
**b.** determine the standard error of the estimate.
**c.** How useful do you think this regression model is for predicting labor hours?

**13.19** In Problem 13.7 on page 586, you used the number of customers to predict the waiting time at the checkout line in a supermarket (stored in the file **Supermarket**). Using the results of that problem,
**a.** determine the coefficient of determination, $r^2$, and interpret its meaning.
**b.** find the standard error of the estimate.

**c.** How useful do you think this regression model is for predicting the waiting time at the checkout line in a supermarket?

**13.20** In Problem 13.8 on page 586, you used annual revenues to predict the value of a baseball franchise (stored in the file **BBrevenue**). Using the results of that problem,
**a.** determine the coefficient of determination, $r^2$, and interpret its meaning.
**b.** determine the standard error of the estimate.
**c.** How useful do you think this regression model is for predicting the value of a baseball franchise?

**13.21** In Problem 13.9 on page 586, an agent for a real estate company wanted to predict the monthly rent for apartments, based on the size of the apartment (stored in the file **Rent**). Using the results of that problem,
**a.** determine the coefficient of determination, $r^2$, and interpret its meaning.

**b.** determine the standard error of the estimate, and interpret its meaning.
**c.** How useful do you think this regression model is for predicting the monthly rent?
**d.** Can you think of other variables that might explain the variation in monthly rent?

**13.22** In Problem 13.10 on page 586, you used box office gross to predict sales of DVDs (stored in the file **Movie**). Using the results of that problem,
**a.** determine the coefficient of determination, $r^2$, and interpret its meaning.
**b.** find the standard error of the estimate, and interpret its meaning.
**c.** How useful do you think this regression model is for predicting sales of DVDs?
**d.** Can you think of other variables that might explain the variation in DVD sales?

## 13.4    ASSUMPTIONS

The discussion of hypothesis testing and the analysis of variance emphasized the importance of the assumptions to the validity of any conclusions reached. The assumptions necessary for regression are similar to those of the analysis of variance because both topics fall in the general category of *linear models* (reference 4).

The four **assumptions of regression** (known by the acronym LINE) are as follows:

- **L**inearity
- **I**ndependence of errors
- **N**ormality of error
- **E**qual variance

The first assumption, **linearity**, states that the relationship between variables is linear. Relationships between variables that are not linear are discussed in Chapter 15.

The second assumption, **independence of errors**, requires that the errors ($\varepsilon_i$) are independent of one another. This assumption is particularly important when data are collected over a period of time. In such situations, the errors for a specific time period are sometimes correlated with those of the previous time period.

The third assumption, **normality**, requires that the errors ($\varepsilon_i$) are normally distributed at each value of $X$. Like the $t$ test and the ANOVA $F$ test, regression analysis is fairly robust against departures from the normality assumption. As long as the distribution of the errors at each level of $X$ is not extremely different from a normal distribution, inferences about $\beta_0$ and $\beta_1$ are not seriously affected.

The fourth assumption, **equal variance** or **homoscedasticity**, requires that the variance of the errors ($\varepsilon_i$) are constant for all values of $X$. In other words, the variability of $Y$ values is the same when $X$ is a low value as when $X$ is a high value. The equal variance assumption is important when making inferences about $\beta_0$ and $\beta_1$. If there are serious departures from this assumption, you can use either data transformations or weighted least-squares methods (see reference 4).

## 13.5 RESIDUAL ANALYSIS

In Section 13.1, regression analysis was introduced. In Sections 13.2 and 13.3, a regression model was developed using the least-squares approach for the Sunflowers Apparel data. Is this the correct model for these data? Are the assumptions introduced in Section 13.4 valid? In this section, a graphical approach called **residual analysis** is used to evaluate the assumptions and determine whether the regression model selected is an appropriate model.

The **residual** or estimated error value, $e_i$, is the difference between the observed ($Y_i$) and predicted ($\hat{Y}_i$) values of the dependent variable for a given value of $X_i$. Graphically, a residual appears on a scatter plot as the vertical distance between an observed value of $Y$ and the prediction line. Equation (13.14) defines the residual.

Residual

The residual is equal to the difference between the observed value of $Y$ and the predicted value of $Y$.

$$e_i = Y_i - \hat{Y}_i \qquad \textbf{(13.14)}$$

### Evaluating the Assumptions

Recall from Section 13.4 that the four assumptions of regression (known by the acronym LINE) are linearity, independence, normality, and equal variance.

***Linearity*** To evaluate linearity, you plot the residuals on the vertical axis against the corresponding $X_i$ values of the independent variable on the horizontal axis. If the linear model is appropriate for the data, there is no apparent pattern in this plot. However, if the linear model is not appropriate, there is a relationship between the $X_i$ values and the residuals, $e_i$. You can see such a pattern in Figure 13.12. Panel A shows a situation in which, although there is an increasing trend in $Y$ as $X$ increases, the relationship seems curvilinear because the upward trend decreases for increasing values of $X$. This quadratic effect is highlighted in Panel B, where there is a clear relationship between $X_i$ and $e_i$. By plotting the residuals, the linear trend of $X$ with $Y$ has been removed, thereby exposing the lack of fit in the simple linear model. Thus, a quadratic model is a better fit and should be used in place of the simple linear model. (See Section 15.1 for further discussion of fitting quadratic models.)

**FIGURE 13.12**

Studying the appropriateness of the simple linear regression model

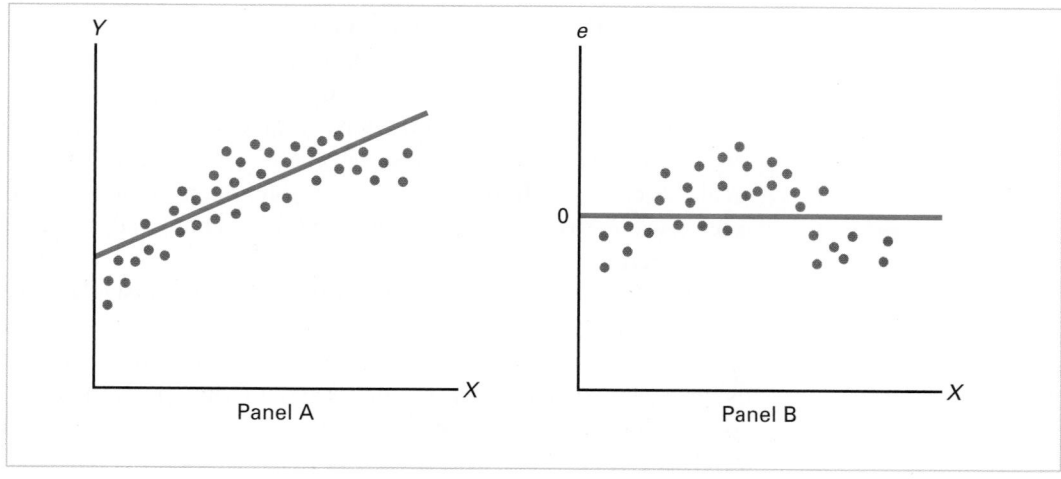

Panel A                    Panel B

To determine whether the simple linear regression model is appropriate, return to the evaluation of the Sunflowers Apparel data. Figure 13.13 provides the predicted values and residuals computed by Microsoft Excel. To assess linearity, the residuals are plotted against the independent variable (store size, in thousands of square feet) in Figure 13.14. Although there is widespread scatter in the residual plot, there is no apparent pattern or relationship between the residuals and $X_i$. The residuals appear to be evenly spread above and below 0 for the differing values of $X$. You can conclude that the linear model is appropriate for the Sunflowers Apparel data.

**FIGURE 13.13**

Microsoft Excel residual output area for the Sunflowers Apparel data

*See Sections E13.3 or P13.3 to create the worksheet that contains this. (Minitab users, see Section M13.1 to create equivalent results.)*

|    | A | B | C |
|----|---|---|---|
| 22 | **RESIDUAL OUTPUT** | | |
| 23 | | | |
| 24 | *Observation* | *Predicted Annual Sales* | *Residuals* |
| 25 | 1 | 3.803239598 | -0.103239598 |
| 26 | 2 | 3.636253367 | 0.263746633 |
| 27 | 3 | 5.640088147 | 1.059911853 |
| 28 | 4 | 10.31570263 | -0.815702635 |
| 29 | 5 | 3.135294672 | 0.264705328 |
| 30 | 6 | 4.638170757 | 0.961829243 |
| 31 | 7 | 3.135294672 | 0.564705328 |
| 32 | 8 | 2.801322208 | -0.101322208 |
| 33 | 9 | 6.308033074 | -0.808033074 |
| 34 | 10 | 3.469267135 | -0.569267135 |
| 35 | 11 | 9.647757708 | 1.052242292 |
| 36 | 12 | 8.645840318 | -1.045840318 |
| 37 | 13 | 10.6496751 | 1.150324902 |
| 38 | 14 | 5.974060611 | -1.874060611 |

**FIGURE 13.14**

Microsoft Excel plot of residuals against the square footage of a store for the Sunflowers Apparel data

*See Sections E2.13 and E13.3 or P13.1 and P13.3 to create this. (Minitab users, see Section M13.1 to create an equivalent chart.)*

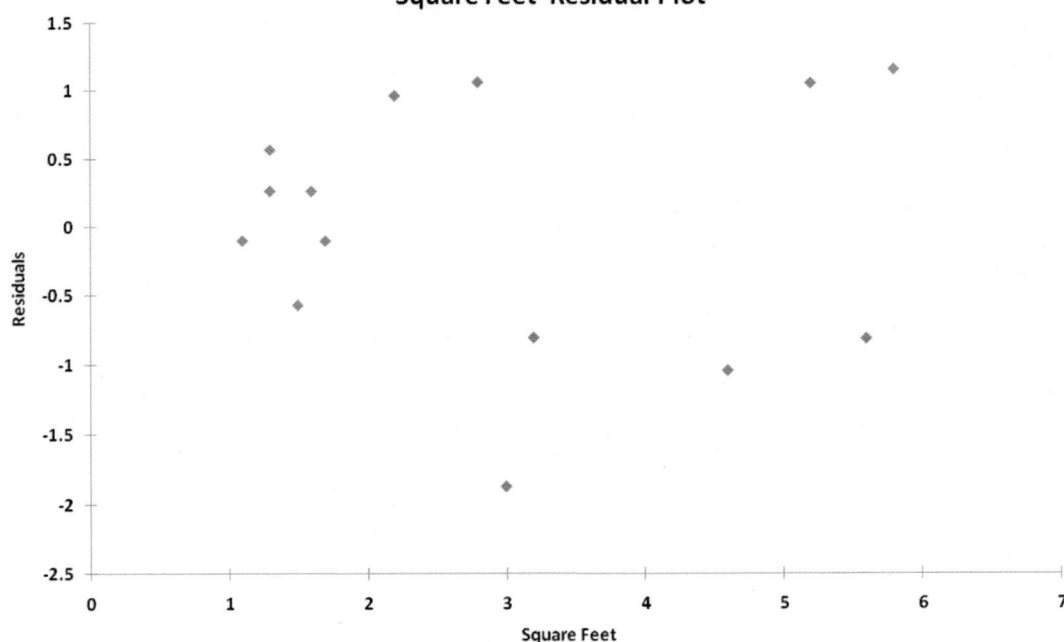

***Independence***   You can evaluate the assumption of independence of the errors by plotting the residuals in the order or sequence in which the data were collected. Data collected over periods of time sometimes exhibit an autocorrelation effect among successive observations. In these instances, there is a relationship between consecutive residuals. If this relationship exists (which violates the assumption of independence), it is apparent in the plot of the residuals versus the time in which the data were collected. You can also test for autocorrelation by using the Durbin-Watson statistic, which is the subject of Section 13.6. Because the Sunflowers Apparel data were collected during the same time period, you do not need to evaluate the independence assumption.

*Normality*    You can evaluate the assumption of normality in the errors by tallying the residuals into a frequency distribution and displaying the results in a histogram (see Section 2.3). For the Sunflowers Apparel data, the residuals have been tallied into a frequency distribution in Table 13.3. (There is an insufficient number of values, however, to construct a histogram.) You can also evaluate the normality assumption by comparing the actual versus theoretical values of the residuals or by constructing a boxplot (see Section 3.5) or normal probability plot (see Section 6.3) of the residuals. Figure 13.15 is a normal probability plot of the residuals for the Sunflower Apparel data.

**TABLE 13.3**

Frequency Distribution of 14 Residual Values for the Sunflowers Apparel Data

| Residuals | Frequency |
|---|---|
| −2.25 but less than −1.75 | 1 |
| −1.75 but less than −1.25 | 0 |
| −1.25 but less than −0.75 | 3 |
| −0.75 but less than −0.25 | 1 |
| −0.25 but less than +0.25 | 2 |
| +0.25 but less than +0.75 | 3 |
| +0.75 but less than +1.25 | 4 |
| | 14 |

**FIGURE 13.15**

Microsoft Excel normal probability plot of the residuals for the Sunflowers Apparel data

*See Section E6.2 or P6.2 to create this. (Minitab users, see Section M6.2 to create an equivalent chart.)*

**Normal Probability Plot of the Residuals**

It is difficult to evaluate the normality assumption for a sample of only 14 values, regardless of whether you use a histogram, stem-and-leaf display, boxplot, or normal probability plot. You can see from Figure 13.15 that the data do not appear to depart substantially from a normal distribution. The robustness of regression analysis with modest departures from normality enables you to conclude that you should not be overly concerned about departures from this normality assumption in the Sunflowers Apparel data.

***Equal Variance***   You can evaluate the assumption of equal variance from a plot of the residuals with $X_i$. For the Sunflowers Apparel data of Figure 13.14 on page 595, there do not appear to be major differences in the variability of the residuals for different $X_i$ values. Thus, you can conclude that there is no apparent violation in the assumption of equal variance at each level of $X$.

To examine a case in which the equal variance assumption is violated, observe Figure 13.16, which is a plot of the residuals with $X_i$ for a hypothetical set of data. In this plot, the variability of the residuals increases dramatically as $X$ increases, demonstrating the lack of homogeneity in the variances of $Y_i$ at each level of $X$. For these data, the equal variance assumption is invalid.

**FIGURE 13.16**

Violation of equal variance

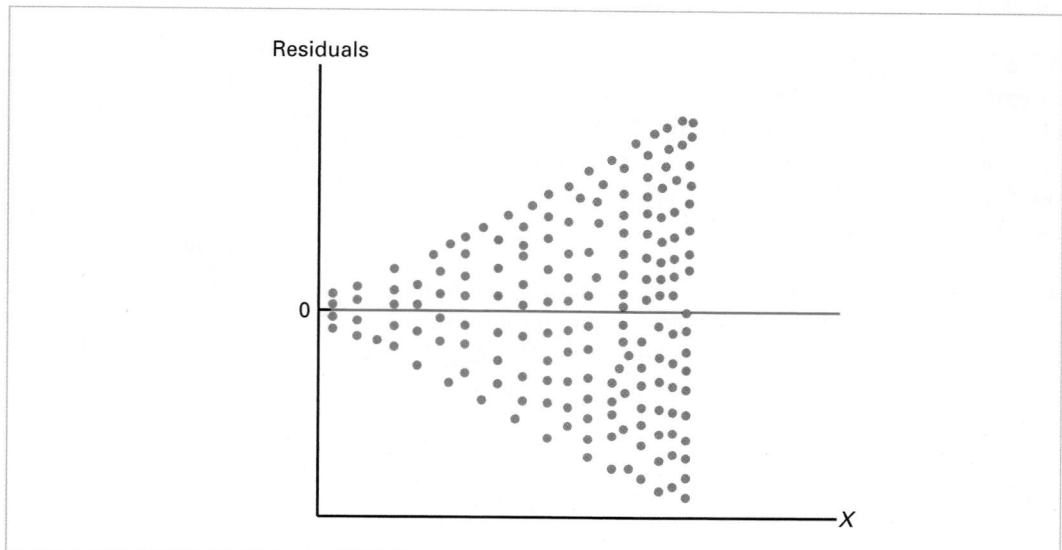

# PROBLEMS FOR SECTION 13.5

## Learning the Basics

**13.23** The results below provide the $X$ values, residuals, and a residual plot from a regression analysis:

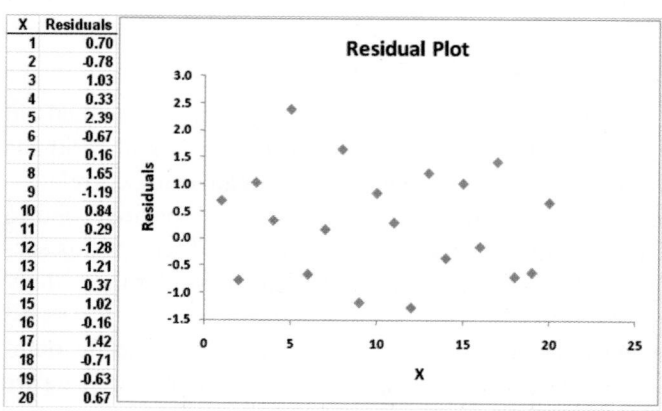

| X | Residuals |
|---|---|
| 1 | 0.70 |
| 2 | -0.78 |
| 3 | 1.03 |
| 4 | 0.33 |
| 5 | 2.39 |
| 6 | -0.67 |
| 7 | 0.16 |
| 8 | 1.65 |
| 9 | -1.19 |
| 10 | 0.84 |
| 11 | 0.29 |
| 12 | -1.28 |
| 13 | 1.21 |
| 14 | -0.37 |
| 15 | 1.02 |
| 16 | -0.16 |
| 17 | 1.42 |
| 18 | -0.71 |
| 19 | -0.63 |
| 20 | 0.67 |

Is there any evidence of a pattern in the residuals? Explain.

**13.24** The results below show the $X$ values, residuals, and a residual plot from a regression analysis:

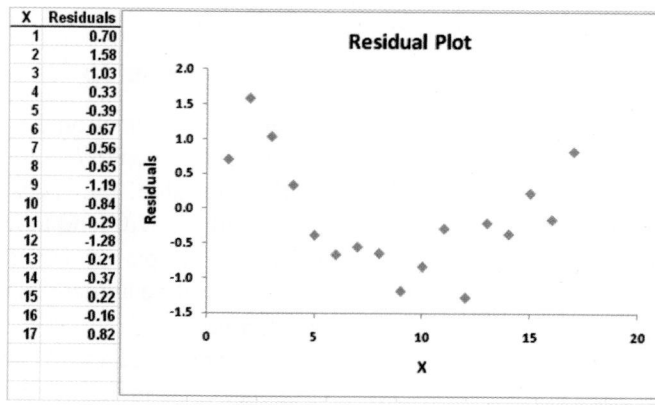

| X | Residuals |
|---|---|
| 1 | 0.70 |
| 2 | 1.58 |
| 3 | 1.03 |
| 4 | 0.33 |
| 5 | -0.39 |
| 6 | -0.67 |
| 7 | -0.56 |
| 8 | -0.65 |
| 9 | -1.19 |
| 10 | -0.84 |
| 11 | -0.29 |
| 12 | -1.28 |
| 13 | -0.21 |
| 14 | -0.37 |
| 15 | 0.22 |
| 16 | -0.16 |
| 17 | 0.82 |

Is there any evidence of a pattern in the residuals? Explain.

## Applying the Concepts

**13.25** In Problem 13.5 on page 585, you used reported magazine newsstand sales to predict audited sales. The data are stored in the file `Circulation`. Perform a residual analysis for these data. Evaluate whether the assumptions of regression have been seriously violated.

**SELF Test** **13.26** In Problem 13.4 on page 585, the marketing manager used shelf space for pet food to predict weekly sales. The data are stored in the file `Petfood`. Perform a residual analysis for these data. Evaluate whether the assumptions of regression have been seriously violated.

**13.27** In Problem 13.7 on page 586, you used the number of customers to predict the waiting time at a supermarket checkout. The data are stored in the file `Supermarket`. Perform a residual analysis for these data. Based on these results, evaluate whether the assumptions of regression have been seriously violated.

**13.28** In Problem 13.6 on page 585, the owner of a moving company wanted to predict labor hours based on the cubic feet moved. The data are stored in the file `Moving`.

Perform a residual analysis for these data. Based on these results, evaluate whether the assumptions of regression have been seriously violated.

**13.29** In Problem 13.9 on page 586, an agent for a real estate company wanted to predict the monthly rent for apartments, based on the size of the apartments. The data are stored in the file `Rent`. Perform a residual analysis for these data. Based on these results, evaluate whether the assumptions of regression have been seriously violated.

**13.30** In Problem 13.8 on page 586, you used annual revenues to predict the value of a baseball franchise. The data are stored in the file `Bbrevenue`. Perform a residual analysis for these data. Based on these results, evaluate whether the assumptions of regression have been seriously violated.

**13.31** In Problem 13.10 on page 586, you used box office gross to predict the sales of DVDs. The data are stored in the file `Movies`. Perform a residual analysis for these data. Based on these results, evaluate whether the assumptions of regression have been seriously violated.

## 13.6 MEASURING AUTOCORRELATION: THE DURBIN-WATSON STATISTIC

One of the basic assumptions of the regression model is the independence of the errors. This assumption is sometimes violated when data are collected over sequential time periods because a residual at any one time period may tend to be similar to residuals at adjacent time periods. This pattern in the residuals is called **autocorrelation**. When a set of data has substantial autocorrelation, the validity of a regression model is in serious doubt.

### Residual Plots to Detect Autocorrelation

As mentioned in Section 13.5, one way to detect autocorrelation is to plot the residuals in time order. If a positive autocorrelation effect is present, there will be clusters of residuals with the same sign, and you will readily detect an apparent pattern. If negative autocorrelation exists, residuals will tend to jump back and forth from positive to negative to positive, and so on. This type of pattern is very rarely seen in regression analysis. Thus, the focus of this section is on positive autocorrelation. To illustrate positive autocorrelation, consider the following example.

The manager of a package delivery store wants to predict weekly sales, based on the number of customers making purchases for a period of 15 weeks. In this situation, because data are collected over a period of 15 consecutive weeks at the same store, you need to determine whether autocorrelation is present. Table 13.4 presents the data (stored in the file `Custsale`). Figure 13.17 illustrates Microsoft Excel results for these data and Figure 13.18 shows Minitab results.

**TABLE 13.4**

Customers and Sales for a Period of 15 Consecutive Weeks

| Week | Customers | Sales (Thousands of Dollars) | Week | Customers | Sales (Thousands of Dollars) |
|------|-----------|------------------------------|------|-----------|------------------------------|
| 1 | 794 | 9.33 | 9 | 880 | 12.07 |
| 2 | 799 | 8.26 | 10 | 905 | 12.55 |
| 3 | 837 | 7.48 | 11 | 886 | 11.92 |
| 4 | 855 | 9.08 | 12 | 843 | 10.27 |
| 5 | 845 | 9.83 | 13 | 904 | 11.80 |
| 6 | 844 | 10.09 | 14 | 950 | 12.15 |
| 7 | 863 | 11.01 | 15 | 841 | 9.64 |
| 8 | 875 | 11.49 | | | |

**FIGURE 13.17**

Microsoft Excel regression results worksheet for the package delivery store data of Table 13.4

*See Section E13.1 or P13.1 to create this.*

| | A | B | C | D | E | F | G |
|---|---|---|---|---|---|---|---|
| 1 | Package Delivery Store Sales Analysis | | | | | | |
| 2 | | | | | | | |
| 3 | *Regression Statistics* | | | | | | |
| 4 | Multiple R | 0.8108 | | | | | |
| 5 | R Square | 0.6574 | | | | | |
| 6 | Adjusted R Square | 0.6311 | | | | | |
| 7 | Standard Error | 0.9360 | | | | | |
| 8 | Observations | 15 | | | | | |
| 9 | | | | | | | |
| 10 | ANOVA | | | | | | |
| 11 | | *df* | *SS* | *MS* | *F* | *Significance F* | |
| 12 | Regression | 1 | 21.8604 | 21.8604 | 24.9501 | 0.0002 | |
| 13 | Residual | 13 | 11.3901 | 0.8762 | | | |
| 14 | Total | 14 | 33.2506 | | | | |
| 15 | | | | | | | |
| 16 | | *Coefficients* | *Standard Error* | *t Stat* | *P-value* | *Lower 95%* | *Upper 95%* |
| 17 | Intercept | -16.0322 | 5.3102 | -3.0192 | 0.0099 | -27.5041 | -4.5603 |
| 18 | Customers | 0.0308 | 0.0062 | 4.9950 | 0.0002 | 0.0175 | 0.0441 |

**FIGURE 13.18**

Minitab results for the package delivery store data of Table 13.4

*See Section M13.1 to create this.*

```
The regression equation is
sales = - 16.0 + 0.0308 customer

|

Predictor      Coef    SE Coef      T      P
Constant    -16.032      5.310   -3.02  0.010
customer   0.030760   0.006158    5.00  0.000


S = 0.936037   R-Sq = 65.7%   R-Sq(adj) = 63.1%


Analysis of Variance

Source         DF      SS      MS      F      P
Regression      1  21.860  21.860  24.95  0.000
Residual Error 13  11.390   0.876
Total          14  33.251


Durbin-Watson statistic = 0.883003
```

From Figure 13.17 or Figure 13.18, observe that $r^2$ is 0.6574, indicating that 65.74% of the variation in sales is explained by variation in the number of customers. In addition, the $Y$ intercept, $b_0$, is $-16.0322$, and the slope, $b_1$, is 0.0308. However, before using this model for prediction, you must perform a proper residual analysis. Because the data have been collected over a consecutive period of 15 weeks, in addition to checking the linearity, normality, and equal-variance assumptions, you must investigate the independence-of-errors assumption. You can plot the residuals versus time to help you see whether a pattern exists. In Figure 13.19, you can see that the residuals tend to fluctuate up and down in a cyclical pattern. This cyclical pattern provides strong cause for concern about the autocorrelation of the residuals and, hence, a violation of the independence-of-errors assumption.

**FIGURE 13.19**

Microsoft Excel residual plot for the package delivery store data of Table 13.4

*See Section E13.3 or P13.3 to create this. (Minitab users, see Section M13.1 to create an equivalent plot.)*

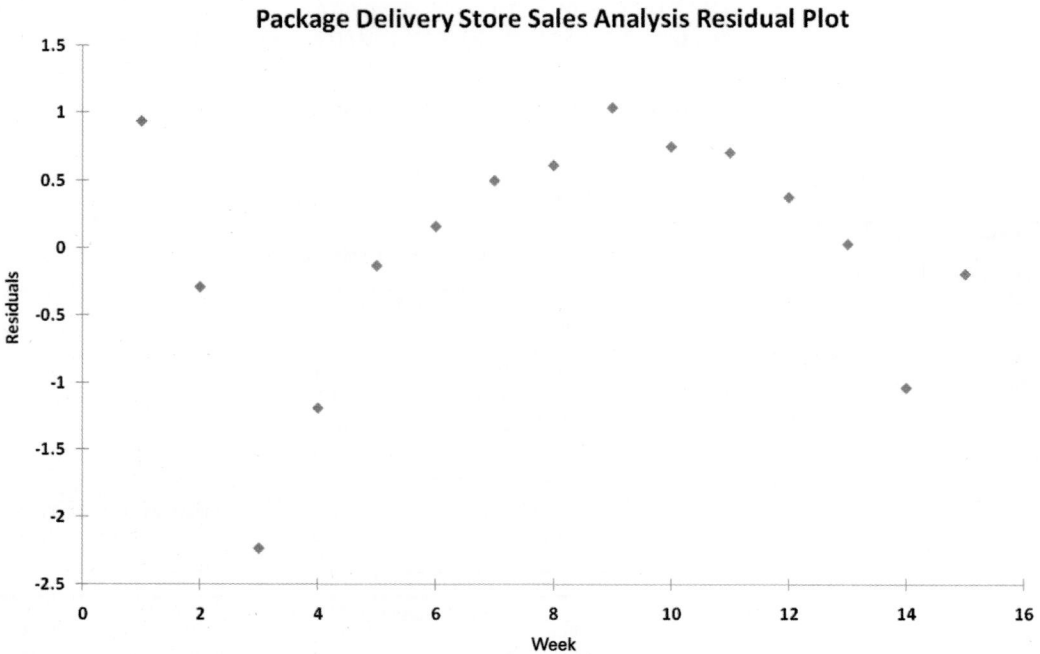

## The Durbin-Watson Statistic

The **Durbin-Watson statistic** is used to measure autocorrelation. This statistic measures the correlation between each residual and the residual for the previous time period. Equation (13.15) defines the Durbin-Watson statistic.

Durbin-Watson Statistic

$$D = \frac{\sum_{i=2}^{n} (e_i - e_{i-1})^2}{\sum_{i=1}^{n} e_i^2} \qquad (13.15)$$

where

$$e_i = \text{residual at the time period } i$$

To better understand the Durbin-Watson statistic, $D$, you can examine Equation (13.15). The numerator, $\sum_{i=2}^{n} (e_i - e_{i-1})^2$, represents the squared difference between two successive residuals, summed from the second value to the $n$th value. The denominator, $\sum_{i=1}^{n} e_i^2$, represents the sum of the squared residuals. When successive residuals are positively autocorrelated, the value of $D$ approaches 0. If the residuals are not correlated, the value of $D$ will be close to 2. (If there is negative autocorrelation, $D$ will be greater than 2 and could even approach its maximum value of 4.) For the package delivery store data, as shown in the Microsoft Excel results of Figure 13.20 or the Minitab results of Figure 13.18 on page 599, the Durbin-Watson statistic, $D$, is 0.8830.

**FIGURE 13.20**

Microsoft Excel worksheet for the Durbin-Watson statistic for the package delivery store data

*See Section E13.4 or P13.4 to create this. See Section E13.4 for an explanation of the SLR worksheet that is referenced in the cell B3 and B4 formulas.*

| | A | B | |
|---|---|---|---|
| 1 | Durbin-Watson Calculations | | |
| 2 | | | |
| 3 | Sum of Squared Difference of Residuals | 10.0575 | =SUMXMY2(SLR!C26:C39, SLR!C25:C38) |
| 4 | Sum of Squared Residuals | 11.3901 | =SUMSQ(SLR!C25:C39) |
| 5 | | | |
| 6 | Durbin-Watson Statistic | 0.8830 | =B3/B4 |

You need to determine when the autocorrelation is large enough to make the Durbin-Watson statistic, $D$, fall sufficiently below 2 to conclude that there is significant positive autocorrelation. After computing $D$, you compare it to the critical values of the Durbin-Watson statistic found in Table E.11, a portion of which is presented in Table 13.5. The critical values depend on $\alpha$, the significance level chosen, $n$, the sample size, and $k$, the number of independent variables in the model (in simple linear regression, $k = 1$).

**TABLE 13.5**

Finding Critical Values of the Durbin-Watson Statistic

| | | | | | | | | | | |
|---|---|---|---|---|---|---|---|---|---|---|
| | | | | | | $\alpha = .05$ | | | | |
| | $k = 1$ | | $k = 2$ | | $k = 3$ | | $k = 4$ | | $k = 5$ | |
| $n$ | $d_L$ | $d_U$ | $d_L$ | $d_U$ | $d_L$ | $d_U$ | $d_L$ | $d_U$ | $d_L$ | $d_U$ |
| 15 | 1.08 | 1.36 | .95 | 1.54 | .82 | 1.75 | .69 | 1.97 | .56 | 2.21 |
| 16 | 1.10 | 1.37 | .98 | 1.54 | .86 | 1.73 | .74 | 1.93 | .62 | 2.15 |
| 17 | 1.13 | 1.38 | 1.02 | 1.54 | .90 | 1.71 | .78 | 1.90 | .67 | 2.10 |
| 18 | 1.16 | 1.39 | 1.05 | 1.53 | .93 | 1.69 | .82 | 1.87 | .71 | 2.06 |

In Table 13.5, two values are shown for each combination of $\alpha$ (level of significance), $n$ (sample size), and $k$ (number of independent variables in the model). The first value, $d_L$, represents the lower critical value. If $D$ is below $d_L$, you conclude that there is evidence of positive autocorrelation among the residuals. If this occurs, the least-squares method used in this chapter is inappropriate, and you should use alternative methods (see reference 4). The second value, $d_U$, represents the upper critical value of $D$, above which you would conclude that there is no evidence of positive autocorrelation among the residuals. If $D$ is between $d_L$ and $d_U$, you are unable to arrive at a definite conclusion.

For the package delivery store data, with one independent variable ($k = 1$) and 15 values ($n = 15$), $d_L = 1.08$ and $d_U = 1.36$. Because $D = 0.8830 < 1.08$, you conclude that there is positive autocorrelation among the residuals. The least-squares regression analysis of the data is inappropriate because of the presence of significant positive autocorrelation among the residuals. In other words, the independence-of-errors assumption is invalid. You need to use alternative approaches discussed in reference 4.

# PROBLEMS FOR SECTION 13.6

## Learning the Basics

**13.32** The residuals for 10 consecutive time periods are as follows:

| Time Period | Residual | Time Period | Residual |
|---|---|---|---|
| 1 | −5 | 6 | +1 |
| 2 | −4 | 7 | +2 |
| 3 | −3 | 8 | +3 |
| 4 | −2 | 9 | +4 |
| 5 | −1 | 10 | +5 |

**a.** Plot the residuals over time. What conclusion can you reach about the pattern of the residuals over time?
**b.** Based on (a), what conclusion can you reach about the autocorrelation of the residuals?

**13.33** The residuals for 15 consecutive time periods are as follows:

| Time Period | Residual | Time Period | Residual |
|---|---|---|---|
| 1 | +4 | 9 | +6 |
| 2 | −6 | 10 | −3 |
| 3 | −1 | 11 | +1 |
| 4 | −5 | 12 | +3 |
| 5 | +2 | 13 | 0 |
| 6 | +5 | 14 | −4 |
| 7 | −2 | 15 | −7 |
| 8 | +7 | | |

**a.** Plot the residuals over time. What conclusion can you reach about the pattern of the residuals over time?
**b.** Compute the Durbin-Watson statistic. At the 0.05 level of significance, is there evidence of positive autocorrelation among the residuals?
**c.** Based on (a) and (b), what conclusion can you reach about the autocorrelation of the residuals?

## Applying the Concepts

**13.34** In Problem 13.4 on page 585 concerning pet food sales, the marketing manager used shelf space for pet food to predict weekly sales.
**a.** Is it necessary to compute the Durbin-Watson statistic in this case? Explain.
**b.** Under what circumstances is it necessary to compute the Durbin-Watson statistic before proceeding with the least-squares method of regression analysis?

**13.35** The owner of a single-family home in a suburban county in the northeastern United States would like to develop a model to predict electricity consumption in his all-electric house (lights, fans, heat, appliances, etc.), based on average atmospheric temperature (in degrees Fahrenheit).

Monthly kilowatt usage and temperature data are available for a period of 24 consecutive months in the file **Elecuse**.
**a.** Assuming a linear relationship, use the least-squares method to find the regression coefficients $b_0$ and $b_1$.
**b.** Predict the mean kilowatt usage when the average atmospheric temperature is 50° Fahrenheit.
**c.** Plot the residuals versus the time period.
**d.** Compute the Durbin-Watson statistic. At the 0.05 level of significance, is there evidence of positive autocorrelation among the residuals?
**e.** Based on the results of (c) and (d), is there reason to question the validity of the model?

**SELF Test** **13.36** A mail-order catalog business that sells personal computer supplies, software, and hardware maintains a centralized warehouse for the distribution of products ordered. Management is currently examining the process of distribution from the warehouse and is interested in studying the factors that affect warehouse distribution costs. Currently, a small handling fee is added to the order, regardless of the amount of the order. Data have been collected over the past 24 months, indicating the warehouse distribution costs and the number of orders received. They are stored in the file **Warecost**. The results are as follows:

| Months | Distribution Cost (Thousands of Dollars) | Number of Orders |
|---|---|---|
| 1 | 52.95 | 4,015 |
| 2 | 71.66 | 3,806 |
| 3 | 85.58 | 5,309 |
| 4 | 63.69 | 4,262 |
| 5 | 72.81 | 4,296 |
| 6 | 68.44 | 4,097 |
| 7 | 52.46 | 3,213 |
| 8 | 70.77 | 4,809 |
| 9 | 82.03 | 5,237 |
| 10 | 74.39 | 4,732 |
| 11 | 70.84 | 4,413 |
| 12 | 54.08 | 2,921 |
| 13 | 62.98 | 3,977 |
| 14 | 72.30 | 4,428 |
| 15 | 58.99 | 3,964 |
| 16 | 79.38 | 4,582 |
| 17 | 94.44 | 5,582 |
| 18 | 59.74 | 3,450 |
| 19 | 90.50 | 5,079 |
| 20 | 93.24 | 5,735 |
| 21 | 69.33 | 4,269 |
| 22 | 53.71 | 3,708 |
| 23 | 89.18 | 5,387 |
| 24 | 66.80 | 4,161 |

**a.** Assuming a linear relationship, use the least-squares method to find the regression coefficients $b_0$ and $b_1$.

**b.** Predict the monthly warehouse distribution costs when the number of orders is 4,500.

**c.** Plot the residuals versus the time period.

**d.** Compute the Durbin-Watson statistic. At the 0.05 level of significance, is there evidence of positive autocorrelation among the residuals?

**e.** Based on the results of (c) and (d), is there reason to question the validity of the model?

**13.37** A freshly brewed shot of espresso has three distinct components: the heart, body, and crema. The separation of these three components typically lasts only 10 to 20 seconds. To use the espresso shot in making a latte, cappuccino, or other drinks, the shot must be poured into the beverage during the separation of the heart, body, and crema. If the shot is used after the separation occurs, the drink becomes excessively bitter and acidic, ruining the final drink. Thus, a longer separation time allows the drink-maker more time to pour the shot and ensure that the beverage will meet expectations. An employee at a coffee shop hypothesized that the harder the espresso grounds were tamped down into the portafilter before brewing, the longer the separation time would be. An experiment using 24 observations was conducted to test this relationship. The independent variable Tamp measures the distance, in inches, between the espresso grounds and the top of the portafilter (i.e., the harder the tamp, the larger the distance). The dependent variable Time is the number of seconds the heart, body, and crema are separated (i.e., the amount of time after the shot is poured before it must be used for the customer's beverage). The data are stored in the file Espresso:

**a.** Determine the prediction line, using Time as the dependent variable and Tamp as the independent variable.

**b.** Predict the mean separation time for a Tamp distance of 0.50 inch.

| Shot | Tamp | Time | Shot | Tamp | Time |
|------|------|------|------|------|------|
| 1 | 0.20 | 14 | 13 | 0.50 | 18 |
| 2 | 0.50 | 14 | 14 | 0.50 | 13 |
| 3 | 0.50 | 18 | 15 | 0.35 | 19 |
| 4 | 0.20 | 16 | 16 | 0.35 | 19 |
| 5 | 0.20 | 16 | 17 | 0.20 | 17 |
| 6 | 0.50 | 13 | 18 | 0.20 | 18 |
| 7 | 0.20 | 12 | 19 | 0.20 | 15 |
| 8 | 0.35 | 15 | 20 | 0.20 | 16 |
| 9 | 0.50 | 9 | 21 | 0.35 | 18 |
| 10 | 0.35 | 15 | 22 | 0.35 | 16 |
| 11 | 0.50 | 11 | 23 | 0.35 | 14 |
| 12 | 0.50 | 16 | 24 | 0.35 | 16 |

**c.** Plot the residuals versus the time order of experimentation. Are there any noticeable patterns?

**d.** Compute the Durbin-Watson statistic. At the 0.05 level of significance, is there evidence of positive autocorrelation among the residuals?

**e.** Based on the results of (c) and (d), is there reason to question the validity of the model?

**13.38** The owner of a chain of ice cream stores would like to study the effect of atmospheric temperature on sales during the summer season. A sample of 21 consecutive days is selected, with the results stored in the data file Icecream.

(*Hint:* Determine which are the independent and dependent variables.)

**a.** Assuming a linear relationship, use the least-squares method to find the regression coefficients $b_0$ and $b_1$.

**b.** Predict the sales for a day in which the temperature is 83°F.

**c.** Plot the residuals versus the time period.

**d.** Compute the Durbin-Watson statistic. At the 0.05 level of significance, is there evidence of positive autocorrelation among the residuals?

**e.** Based on the results of (c) and (d), is there reason to question the validity of the model?

## 13.7 INFERENCES ABOUT THE SLOPE AND CORRELATION COEFFICIENT

In Sections 13.1 through 13.3, regression was used solely for descriptive purposes. You learned how the least-squares method determines the regression coefficients and how to predict $Y$ for a given value of $X$. In addition, you learned how to compute and interpret the standard error of the estimate and the coefficient of determination.

When residual analysis, as discussed in Section 13.5, indicates that the assumptions of a least-squares regression model are not seriously violated and that the straight-line model is appropriate, you can make inferences about the linear relationship between the variables in the population.

## t Test for the Slope

To determine the existence of a significant linear relationship between the $X$ and $Y$ variables, you test whether $\beta_1$ (the population slope) is equal to 0. The null and alternative hypotheses are as follows:

$H_0$: $\beta_1 = 0$ [There is no linear relationship (the slope is zero).]
$H_1$: $\beta_1 \neq 0$ [There is a linear relationship (the slope is not zero).]

If you reject the null hypothesis, you conclude that there is evidence of a linear relationship. Equation (13.16) defines the test statistic.

Testing a Hypothesis for a Population Slope, $\beta_1$, Using the t Test

The $t_{STAT}$ test statistic equals the difference between the sample slope and hypothesized value of the population slope divided by the standard error of the slope.

$$t_{STAT} = \frac{b_1 - \beta_1}{S_{b_1}}$$ (13.16)

where

$$S_{b_1} = \frac{S_{YX}}{\sqrt{SSX}}$$

$$SSX = \sum_{i=1}^{n}(X_i - \bar{X})^2$$

The $t_{STAT}$ test statistic follows a $t$ distribution with $n - 2$ degrees of freedom.

Return to the Using Statistics scenario on page 574 concerning Sunflowers Apparel. To test whether there is a significant linear relationship between the size of the store and the annual sales at the 0.05 level of significance, refer to the Microsoft Excel worksheet for the $t$ test presented in Figure 13.21 or the Minitab results shown in Figure 13.22.

*See Section E13.1 or P13.1 to create the worksheet that contains this area.*

| | A | B | C | D | E | F | G |
|---|---|---|---|---|---|---|---|
| 16 | | Coefficients | Standard Error | t Stat | P-value | Lower 95% | Upper 95% |
| 17 | Intercept | 0.9645 | 0.5262 | 1.8329 | 0.0917 | -0.1820 | 2.1110 |
| 18 | Square Feet | 1.6699 | 0.1569 | 10.6411 | 0.0000 | 1.3280 | 2.0118 |

**FIGURE 13.21** Microsoft Excel t-test results of the slope for the Sunflowers Apparel data

*See Section M13.1 to create this worksheet.*

| Predictor | Coef | SE Coef | T | P |
|---|---|---|---|---|
| Constant | 0.9645 | 0.5262 | 1.83 | 0.092 |
| Square Feet | 1.6699 | 0.1569 | 10.64 | 0.000 |

**FIGURE 13.22** Minitab t-test results of the slope for the Sunflowers Apparel data

From Figure 13.21 or Figure 13.22,

$$b_1 = +1.6699 \quad n = 14 \quad S_{b_1} = 0.1569$$

and

$$t_{STAT} = \frac{b_1 - \beta_1}{S_{b_1}}$$

$$= \frac{1.6699 - 0}{0.1569} = 10.64$$

Microsoft Excel labels this $t_{STAT}$ test statistic $t$ Stat (see Figure 13.21) whereas Minitab labels it T (see Figure 13.22). Using the 0.05 level of significance, the critical value of $t$ with $n - 2 = 12$ degrees of freedom is 2.1788. Because $t_{STAT} = 10.6411 > 2.1788$, you reject $H_0$ (see Figure 13.23). Using the $p$-value, you reject $H_0$ because the $p$-value is approximately 0, which is less than $\alpha = 0.05$. Hence, you can conclude that there is a significant linear relationship between mean annual sales and the size of the store.

**FIGURE 13.23**

Testing a hypothesis about the population slope at the 0.05 level of significance, with 12 degrees of freedom

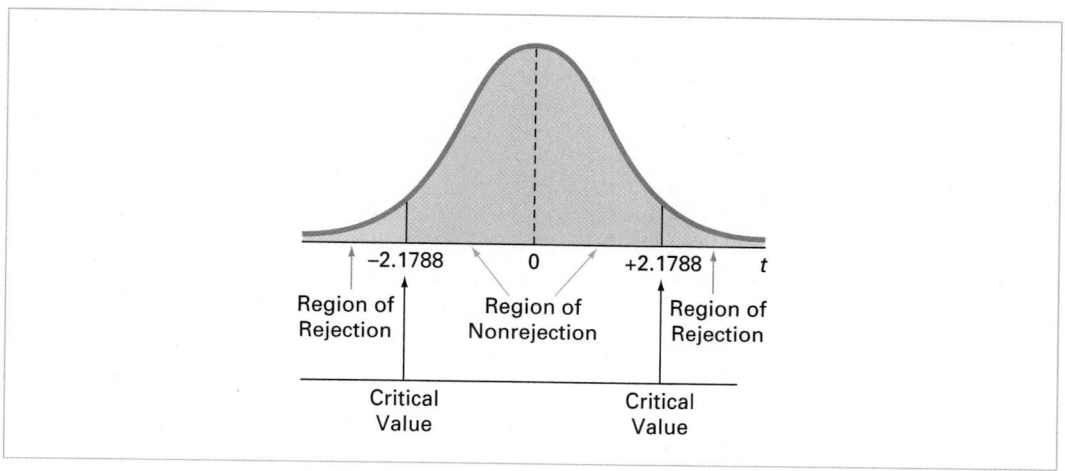

## F Test for the Slope

As an alternative to the $t$ test, you can use an $F$ test to determine whether the slope in simple linear regression is statistically significant. In Section 10.4, you used the $F$ distribution to test the ratio of two variances. Equation (13.17) defines the $F$ test for the slope as the ratio of the variance that is due to the regression ($MSR$) divided by the error variance ($MSE = S_{YX}^2$).

Testing a Hypothesis for a Population Slope, $\beta_1$, Using the $F$ Test

The $F_{STAT}$ test statistic is equal to the regression mean square ($MSR$) divided by the error mean square ($MSE$).

$$F_{STAT} = \frac{MSR}{MSE} \tag{13.17}$$

where

$$MSR = \frac{SSR}{k}$$

$$MSE = \frac{SSE}{n - k - 1}$$

$k$ = number of independent variables in the regression model

The $F_{STAT}$ test statistic follows an $F$ distribution with $k$ and $n - k - 1$ degrees of freedom.

Using a level of significance $\alpha$, the decision rule is

$$\text{Reject } H_0 \text{ if } F_{STAT} > F_\alpha;$$

$$\text{otherwise, do not reject } H_0.$$

Table 13.6 organizes the complete set of results into an Analysis of Variance (ANOVA) table.

**TABLE 13.6**

ANOVA Table for Testing the Significance of a Regression Coefficient

| Source | df | Sum of Squares | Mean Square (Variance) | F |
|---|---|---|---|---|
| Regression | $k$ | $SSR$ | $MSR = \dfrac{SSR}{k}$ | $F_{STAT} = \dfrac{MSR}{MSE}$ |
| Error | $n - k - 1$ | $SSE$ | $MSE = \dfrac{SSE}{n - k - 1}$ | |
| Total | $n - 1$ | $SST$ | | |

The completed ANOVA table is also part of the Microsoft Excel results shown in Figure 13.24 or the Minitab results shown in Figure 13.25. These figures show that the computed $F_{STAT}$ test statistic is 113.2335 and the $p$-value is approximately 0.

**FIGURE 13.24**

Microsoft Excel F-test results for the Sunflowers Apparel data

*See Section E13.1 or P13.1 to create the worksheet that contains this.*

| | A | B | C | D | E | F | G |
|---|---|---|---|---|---|---|---|
| 10 | ANOVA | | | | | | |
| 11 | | df | SS | MS | F | Significance F | |
| 12 | Regression | 1 | 105.7476 | 105.7476 | 113.2335 | 0.0000 | |
| 13 | Residual | 12 | 11.2067 | 0.9339 | | | |
| 14 | Total | 13 | 116.9543 | | | | |
| 15 | | | | | | | |
| 16 | | Coefficients | Standard Error | t Stat | P-value | Lower 95% | Upper 95% |
| 17 | Intercept | 0.9645 | 0.5262 | 1.8329 | 0.0917 | -0.1820 | 2.1110 |
| 18 | Square Feet | 1.6699 | 0.1569 | 10.6411 | 0.0000 | 1.3280 | 2.0118 |

**FIGURE 13.25**

Minitab F-test results for the Sunflowers Apparel data

*See Section M13.1 to create this.*

```
Analysis of Variance

Source           DF    SS       MS           F       P
Regression        1   105.75   105.75 MSR   113.23   0.000
Residual Error   12    11.21     0.93 MSE
Total            13   116.95
```

Using a level of significance of 0.05, from Table E.5, the critical value of the $F$ distribution, with 1 and 12 degrees of freedom, is 4.75 (see Figure 13.26). Because $F_{STAT} = 113.2335 > 4.75$ or because the $p$-value $= 0.0000 < 0.05$, you reject $H_0$ and conclude that the size of the store is significantly related to annual sales. Because the $F$ test in Equation (13.17) on page 605 is equivalent to the $t$ test in Equation (13.16) on page 604, you reach the same conclusion.

**FIGURE 13.26**

Regions of rejection and nonrejection when testing for significance of slope at the 0.05 level of significance, with 1 and 12 degrees of freedom

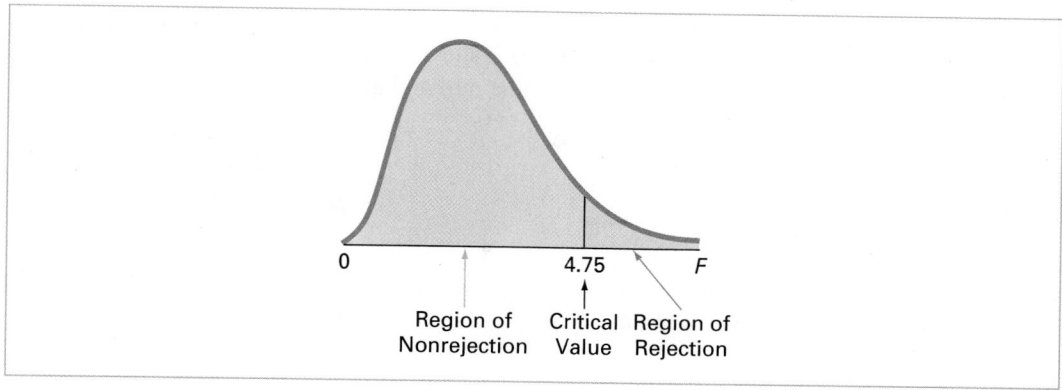

## Confidence Interval Estimate for the Slope

In testing for the existence of a linear relationship between the variables, you can construct a confidence interval estimate of $\beta_1$ using Equation (13.18).

> **Confidence Interval Estimate of the Slope, $\beta_1$**
>
> The confidence interval estimate for the population slope can be constructed by taking the sample slope, $b_1$, and adding and subtracting the critical $t$ value multiplied by the standard error of the slope.
>
> $$b_1 \pm t_{\alpha/2} S_{b_1} \qquad\qquad (13.18)$$
>
> where $t_{\alpha/2}$ is the critical value corresponding to an upper-tail probability of $\alpha/2$ from the $t$ distribution with $n - 2$ degrees of freedom (i.e., a cumulative area of $1 - \alpha/2$).

From the Microsoft Excel results of Figure 13.21 or the Minitab results of Figure 13.22 on page 604,

$$b_1 = 1.6699 \quad n = 14 \quad S_{b_1} = 0.1569$$

To construct a 95% confidence interval estimate, $\alpha/2 = 0.025$, and from Table E.3, $t_{\alpha/2} = 2.1788$. Thus,

$$b_1 \pm t_{\alpha/2} S_{b_1} = 1.6699 \pm (2.1788)(0.1569)$$

$$= 1.6699 \pm 0.3419$$

$$1.3280 \le \beta_1 \le 2.0118$$

Therefore, you estimate with 95% confidence that the population slope is between 1.3280 and 2.0118. Because these values are above 0, you conclude that there is a significant linear relationship between annual sales and the size of the store. Had the interval included 0, you would have concluded that no significant relationship exists between the variables. The confidence interval indicates that for each increase of 1,000 square feet, mean annual sales are estimated to increase by at least $1,328,000 but no more than $2,011,800.

## $t$ Test for the Correlation Coefficient

In Section 3.6 on page 125, the strength of the relationship between two numerical variables was measured, using the **correlation coefficient**, $r$. The values of the coefficient of correlation range from $-1$ for a perfect negative correlation to $+1$ for a perfect positive correlation. You can use the correlation coefficient to determine whether there is a statistically significant linear relationship between $X$ and $Y$. To do so, you hypothesize that the population correlation coefficient, $\rho$, is 0. Thus, the null and alternative hypotheses are

$$H_0: \rho = 0 \text{ (no correlation)}$$

$$H_1: \rho \neq 0 \text{ (correlation)}$$

Equation (13.19) defines the test statistic for determining the existence of a significant correlation.

### Testing for the Existence of Correlation

$$t_{STAT} = \frac{r - \rho}{\sqrt{\dfrac{1 - r^2}{n - 2}}} \qquad \textbf{(13.19a)}$$

where

$$r = +\sqrt{r^2} \ \text{ if } b_1 > 0$$

$$r = -\sqrt{r^2} \ \text{ if } b_1 < 0$$

The $t_{STAT}$ test statistic follows a $t$ distribution with $n - 2$ degrees of freedom.

An alternative method to calculate $r$ is given below:

$$r = \frac{\text{cov}(X, Y)}{S_X S_Y} \qquad \textbf{(13.19b)}$$

where

$$\text{cov}(X, Y) = \frac{\displaystyle\sum_{i=1}^{n}(X_i - \bar{X})(Y_i - \bar{Y})}{n - 1}$$

$$S_X = \sqrt{\frac{\displaystyle\sum_{i=1}^{n}(X_i - \bar{X})^2}{n - 1}}$$

$$S_Y = \sqrt{\frac{\displaystyle\sum_{i=1}^{n}(Y_i - \bar{Y})^2}{n - 1}}$$

In the Sunflowers Apparel problem, $r^2 = 0.9042$ and $b_1 = +1.6699$ (see Figure 13.4 or 13.5 on page 579). Because $b_1 > 0$, the correlation coefficient for annual sales and store size is the positive square root of $r^2$, that is, $r = +\sqrt{0.9042} = +0.9509$. Using Equation

(13.19a) to test the null hypothesis that there is no correlation between these two variables results in the following observed $t$ statistic:

$$t_{STAT} = \frac{r - 0}{\sqrt{\dfrac{1 - r^2}{n - 2}}}$$

$$= \frac{0.9509 - 0}{\sqrt{\dfrac{1 - (0.9509)^2}{14 - 2}}} = 10.6411$$

Using the 0.05 level of significance, because $t_{STAT} = 10.6411 > 2.1788$, you reject the null hypothesis. You conclude that there is evidence of an association between annual sales and store size. This $t_{STAT}$ test statistic is equivalent to the $t_{STAT}$ test statistic found when testing whether the population slope, $\beta_1$, is equal to zero.

# PROBLEMS FOR SECTION 13.7

## Learning the Basics

**13.39** You are testing the null hypothesis that there is no linear relationship between two variables, $X$ and $Y$. From your sample of $n = 10$, you determine that $r = 0.80$.
a. What is the value of $t_{STAT}$?
b. At the $\alpha = 0.05$ level of significance, what are the critical values?
c. Based on your answers to (a) and (b), what statistical decision should you make?

**13.40** You are testing the null hypothesis that there is no relationship between two variables, $X$ and $Y$. From your sample of $n = 18$, you determine that $b_1 = +4.5$ and $S_{b_1} = 1.5$.
a. What is the value of $t_{STAT}$?
b. At the $\alpha = 0.05$ level of significance, what are the critical values?
c. Based on your answers to (a) and (b), what statistical decision should you make?
d. Construct a 95% confidence interval estimate of the population slope, $\beta_1$.

**13.41** You are testing the null hypothesis that there is no relationship between two variables, $X$ and $Y$. From your sample of $n = 20$, you determine that $SSR = 60$ and $SSE = 40$.
a. What is the value of $F_{STAT}$?
b. At the $\alpha = 0.05$ level of significance, what is the critical value?
c. Based on your answers to (a) and (b), what statistical decision should you make?
d. Compute the correlation coefficient by first computing $r^2$ and assuming that $b_1$ is negative.

e. At the 0.05 level of significance, is there a significant correlation between $X$ and $Y$?

## Applying the Concepts

✓SELF **13.42** In Problem 13.4 on page 585, the marketing
Test manager used shelf space for pet food to predict weekly sales. The data are stored in the file **Petfood**. From the results of that problem, $b_1 = 7.4$ and $S_{b_1} = 1.59$.
a. At the 0.05 level of significance, is there evidence of a linear relationship between shelf space and sales?
b. Construct a 95% confidence interval estimate of the population slope, $\beta_1$.

**13.43** In Problem 13.5 on page 585, you used reported magazine newsstand sales to predict audited sales. The data are stored in the file **Circulation**. Using the results of that problem, $b_1 = 0.5719$ and $S_{b_1} = 0.0668$.
a. At the 0.05 level of significance, is there evidence of a linear relationship between reported sales and audited sales?
b. Construct a 95% confidence interval estimate of the population slope, $\beta_1$.

**13.44** In Problem 13.6 on page 585, the owner of a moving company wanted to predict labor hours, based on the number of cubic feet moved. The data are stored in the file **Moving**. Using the results of that problem,
a. at the 0.05 level of significance, is there evidence of a linear relationship between the number of cubic feet moved and labor hours?
b. construct a 95% confidence interval estimate of the population slope, $\beta_1$.

**13.45** In Problem 13.7 on page 586, you used the number of customers to predict the waiting time on the checkout line. The data are stored in the file Supermarket. Using the results of that problem,

a. at the 0.05 level of significance, is there evidence of a linear relationship between the number of customers and the waiting time on the checkout line?

b. construct a 95% confidence interval estimate of the population slope, $\beta_1$.

**13.46** In Problem 13.8 on page 586, you used annual revenues to predict the value of a baseball franchise. The data are stored in the file Bbrevenue. Using the results of that problem,

a. at the 0.05 level of significance, is there evidence of a linear relationship between annual revenue and franchise value?

b. construct a 95% confidence interval estimate of the population slope, $\beta_1$.

**13.47** In Problem 13.9 on page 586, an agent for a real estate company wanted to predict the monthly rent for apartments, based on the size of the apartment. The data are stored in the file Rent. Using the results of that problem,

a. at the 0.05 level of significance, is there evidence of a linear relationship between the size of the apartment and the monthly rent?

b. construct a 95% confidence interval estimate of the population slope, $\beta_1$.

**13.48** In Problem 13.10 on page 586, you used box office gross to predict the sales of DVDs. The data are stored in the file Movie. Using the results of that problem,

a. at the 0.05 level of significance, is there evidence of a linear relationship between box office gross and sales of DVDs?

b. construct a 95% confidence interval estimate of the population slope, $\beta_1$.

**13.49** The volatility of a stock is often measured by its beta value. You can estimate the beta value of a stock by developing a simple linear regression model, using the percentage weekly change in the stock as the dependent variable and the percentage weekly change in a market index as the independent variable. The S&P 500 Index is a common index to use. For example, if you wanted to estimate the beta for Disney, you could use the following model, which is sometimes referred to as a *market model*:

(% weekly change in Disney) = $\beta_0$
    + $\beta_1$ (% weekly change in S & P 500 index) + $\varepsilon$

The least-squares regression estimate of the slope $b_1$ is the estimate of the beta value for Disney. A stock with a beta value of 1.0 tends to move the same as the overall market.

A stock with a beta value of 1.5 tends to move 50% more than the overall market, and a stock with a beta value of 0.6 tends to move only 60% as much as the overall market. Stocks with negative beta values tend to move in a direction opposite that of the overall market. The following table gives some beta values for some widely held stocks:

| Company | Ticker Symbol | Beta |
|---|---|---|
| AT&T | T | 0.43 |
| Disney Company | DIS | 0.81 |
| Alcoa | AA | 1.21 |
| LSI Logic | LSI | 2.76 |
| Wave Systems | WAVX | 5.22 |

Source: *Extracted from* **finance.yahoo.com**, *May 31, 2007.*

a. For each of the five companies, interpret the beta value.

b. How can investors use the beta value as a guide for investing?

**13.50** Index funds are mutual funds that try to mimic the movement of leading indexes, such as the S&P 500 Index, the NASDAQ 100 Index, or the Russell 2000 Index. The beta values (as described in Problem 13.49) for these funds are therefore approximately 1.0. The estimated market models for these funds are approximately

(% weekly change in index fund) = 0.0
    + 1.0 (% weekly change in the index)

Leveraged index funds are designed to magnify the movement of major indexes. An article in *Mutual Funds* (L. O'Shaughnessy, "Reach for Higher Returns," *Mutual Funds*, July 1999, pp. 44–49) described some of the risks and rewards associated with these funds and gave details on some of the most popular leveraged funds, including those in the following table:

| Name (Ticker Symbol) | Fund Description |
|---|---|
| Potomac Small Cap Plus (POSCX) | 125% of Russell 2000 Index |
| Rydex "Inv" Nova (RYNVX) | 150% of the S&P 500 Index |
| ProFund UltraOTC "Inv" (UOPIX) | Double (200%) the NASDAQ 100 Index |

Thus, estimated market models for these funds are approximately

(% weekly change in POSCX) = 0.0
    + 1.25 (% weekly change in the Russell 2000 Index)

(% weekly change in RYNVX) = 0.0
    + 1.50 (% weekly change in the S&P 500 Index)

(% weekly change in UOPIX fund) = 0.0
    + 2.0 (% weekly change in the NASDAQ 100 Index)

Thus, if the Russell 2000 Index gains 10% over a period of time, the leveraged mutual fund POSCX gains approximately 12.5%. On the downside, if the same index loses 20%, POSCX loses approximately 25%.

**a.** Consider the leveraged mutual fund ProFund UltraOTC "Inv" (UOPIX), whose description is 200% of the performance of the S&P 500 Index. What is its approximate market model?

**b.** If the NASDAQ gains 30% in a year, what return do you expect UOPIX to have?

**c.** If the NASDAQ loses 35% in a year, what return do you expect UOPIX to have?

**d.** What type of investors should be attracted to leveraged funds? What type of investors should stay away from these funds?

**13.51** The data in the file `Coffeedrink` represent the calories and fat (in grams) of 16-ounce iced coffee drinks at Dunkin' Donuts and Starbucks:

| Product | Calories | Fat |
|---|---|---|
| Dunkin' Donuts Iced Mocha Swirl latte (whole milk) | 240 | 8.0 |
| Starbucks Coffee Frappuccino blended coffee | 260 | 3.5 |
| Dunkin' Donuts Coffee Coolatta (cream) | 350 | 22.0 |
| Starbucks Iced Coffee Mocha Espresso (whole milk and whipped cream) | 350 | 20.0 |
| Starbucks Mocha Frappuccino blended coffee (whipped cream) | 420 | 16.0 |
| Starbucks Chocolate Brownie Frappuccino blended coffee (whipped cream) | 510 | 22.0 |
| Starbucks Chocolate Frappuccino Blended Crème (whipped cream) | 530 | 19.0 |

Source: *Extracted from "Coffee as Candy at Dunkin' Donuts and Starbucks," Consumer Reports, June 2004, p. 9.*

**a.** Compute and interpret the coefficient of correlation, $r$.

**b.** At the 0.05 level of significance, is there a significant linear relationship between calories and fat?

**13.52** There are several methods for calculating fuel economy. The following table (contained in the file `Mileage`) indicates the mileage as calculated by owners and by current government standards:

| Vehicle | Owner | Government Standards |
|---|---|---|
| 2005 Ford F-150 | 14.3 | 16.8 |
| 2005 Chevrolet Silverado | 15.0 | 17.8 |
| 2002 Honda Accord LX | 27.8 | 26.2 |
| 2002 Honda Civic | 27.9 | 34.2 |
| 2004 Honda Civic Hybrid | 48.8 | 47.6 |
| 2002 Ford Explorer | 16.8 | 18.3 |
| 2005 Toyota Camry | 23.7 | 28.5 |
| 2003 Toyota Corolla | 32.8 | 33.1 |
| 2005 Toyota Prius | 37.3 | 56.0 |

**a.** Compute and interpret the coefficient of correlation, $r$.

**b.** At the 0.05 level of significance, is there a significant linear relationship between the mileage as calculated by owners and by current government standards?

**13.53** College basketball is big business, with coaches' salaries, revenues, and expenses in millions of dollars. The data in the file `Colleges-basketball` represent the coaches' salaries and revenues for college basketball at selected schools in a recent year (extracted from R. Adams, "Pay for Playoffs," *The Wall Street Journal*, March 11–12, 2006, pp. P1, P8).

**a.** Compute and interpret the coefficient of correlation, $r$.

**b.** At the 0.05 level of significance, is there a significant linear relationship between a coach's salary and revenue?

**13.54** College football players trying out for the NFL are given the Wonderlic standardized intelligence test. The data in the file `Wonderlic` represent the average Wonderlic scores of football players trying out for the NFL and the graduation rates for football players at selected schools (extracted from S. Walker, "The NFL's Smartest Team," *The Wall Street Journal*, September 30, 2005, pp. W1, W10).

**a.** Compute and interpret the coefficient of correlation, $r$.

**b.** At the 0.05 level of significance, is there a significant linear relationship between the average Wonderlic score of football players trying out for the NFL and the graduation rates for football players at selected schools?

**c.** What conclusions can you reach about the relationship between the average Wonderlic score of football players trying out for the NFL and the graduation rates for football players at selected schools?

## 13.8 ESTIMATION OF MEAN VALUES AND PREDICTION OF INDIVIDUAL VALUES

This section presents methods of making inferences about the mean of $Y$ and predicting individual values of $Y$.

### The Confidence Interval Estimate

In Example 13.2 on pages 580–581, you used the prediction line to predict the value of $Y$ for a given $X$. The mean annual sales for stores with 4,000 square feet was predicted to be 7.644 millions of dollars ($7,644,000). This estimate, however, is a *point estimate* of the population mean. In Chapter 8, you studied the concept of the confidence interval as an estimate of the population mean. In a similar fashion, Equation (13.20) defines the **confidence interval estimate for the mean response** for a given $X$.

---

**Confidence Interval Estimate for the Mean of $Y$**

$$\hat{Y}_i \pm t_{\alpha/2} S_{YX} \sqrt{h_i}$$

$$\hat{Y}_i - t_{\alpha/2} S_{YX} \sqrt{h_i} \le \mu_{Y|X=X_i} \le \hat{Y}_i + t_{\alpha/2} S_{YX} \sqrt{h_i} \qquad (13.20)$$

$$h_i = \frac{1}{n} + \frac{(X_i - \bar{X})^2}{SSX}$$

where

$$\hat{Y}_i = \text{predicted value of Y; } \hat{Y}_i = b_0 + b_1 X_i$$

$$S_{YX} = \text{standard error of the estimate}$$

$$n = \text{sample size}$$

$$X_i = \text{given value of } X$$

$$\mu_{Y|X=X_i} = \text{mean value of } Y \text{ when } X = X_i$$

$$SSX = \sum_{i=1}^{n}(X_i - \bar{X})^2$$

$t_{\alpha/2}$ is the critical value corresponding to an upper-tail probability of $\alpha/2$ from the $t$ distribution with $n - 1$ degrees of freedom (i.e., a cumulative area of $1 - \alpha/2$).

---

The width of the confidence interval in Equation (13.20) depends on several factors. Increased variation around the prediction line, as measured by the standard error of the estimate, results in a wider interval. However, as you would expect, increased sample size reduces the width of the interval. In addition, the width of the interval also varies at different values of $X$. When you predict $Y$ for values of $X$ close to $\bar{X}$, the interval is narrower than for predictions for $X$ values more distant from $\bar{X}$.

In the Sunflowers Apparel example, suppose you want to construct a 95% confidence interval estimate of the mean annual sales for the entire population of stores that contain 4,000 square feet ($X = 4$). Using the simple linear regression equation,

$$\hat{Y}_i = 0.9645 + 1.6699X_i$$

$$= 0.9645 + 1.6699(4) = 7.6439 \text{ (millions of dollars)}$$

Also, given the following:

$$\bar{X} = 2.9214 \quad S_{YX} = 0.9664$$

$$SSX = \sum_{i=1}^{n}(X_i - \bar{X})^2 = 37.9236$$

From Table E.3, $t_{\alpha/2} = 2.1788$. Thus,

$$\hat{Y}_i \pm t_{\alpha/2}S_{YX}\sqrt{h_i}$$

where

$$h_i = \frac{1}{n} + \frac{(X_i - \bar{X})^2}{SSX}$$

so that

$$\hat{Y}_i \pm t_{\alpha/2}S_{YX}\sqrt{\frac{1}{n} + \frac{(X_i - \bar{X})^2}{SSX}}$$

$$= 7.6439 \pm (2.1788)(0.9664)\sqrt{\frac{1}{14} + \frac{(4 - 2.9214)^2}{37.9236}}$$

$$= 7.6439 \pm 0.6728$$

so

$$6.9711 \le \mu_{Y|X=4} \le 8.3167$$

Therefore, the 95% confidence interval estimate is that the mean annual sales are between $6,971,100 and $8,316,700 for the population of stores with 4,000 square feet.

## The Prediction Interval

Often it is important to predict the response for an individual value. In addition to calculating the predicted value $\hat{Y}$, you can construct a prediction interval. Although the form of the prediction interval is similar to that of the confidence interval estimate of Equation (13.20), the prediction interval is predicting an individual value, not estimating a parameter. Equation (13.21) defines the **prediction interval for an individual response, $Y$,** at a particular value, $X_i$, denoted by $Y_{X=X_i}$.

Prediction Interval for an Individual Response, $Y$

$$\hat{Y}_i \pm t_{\alpha/2}S_{YX}\sqrt{1 + h_i}$$

$$\hat{Y}_i - t_{\alpha/2}S_{YX}\sqrt{1 + h_i} \le Y_{X=X_i} \le \hat{Y}_i + t_{\alpha/2}S_{YX}\sqrt{1 + h_i}$$

**(13.21)**

where $h_i$, $\hat{Y}_i$, $S_{YX}$, $n$, and $X_i$ are defined as in Equation (13.20) on page 612 and $Y_{X=X_i}$ is a future value of $Y$ when $X = X_i$.

$t_{\alpha/2}$ is the critical value corresponding to an upper-tail probability of $\alpha/2$ from the $t$ distribution with $n - 1$ degrees of freedom (i.e., a cumulative area of $1 - \alpha/2$).

To construct a 95% prediction interval of the annual sales for an individual store that contains 4,000 square feet ($X = 4$), you first compute $\hat{Y}_i$. Using the prediction line:

$$\hat{Y}_i = 0.9645 + 1.6699 X_i$$
$$= 0.9645 + 1.6699(4)$$
$$= 7.6439 \text{ (millions of dollars)}$$

Also, given the following:

$$\bar{X} = 2.9214 \quad S_{YX} = 0.9664$$

$$SSX = \sum_{i=1}^{n}(X_i - \bar{X})^2 = 37.9236$$

From Table E.3, $t_{\alpha/2} = 2.1788$. Thus,

$$\hat{Y}_i \pm t_{\alpha/2} S_{YX} \sqrt{1 + h_i}$$

where

$$h_i = \frac{1}{n} + \frac{(X_i - \bar{X})^2}{\sum_{i=1}^{n}(X_i - \bar{X})^2}$$

so that

$$\hat{Y}_i \pm t_{\alpha/2} S_{YX} \sqrt{1 + \frac{1}{n} + \frac{(X_i - \bar{X})^2}{SSX}}$$

$$= 7.6439 \pm (2.1788)(0.9664)\sqrt{1 + \frac{1}{14} + \frac{(4 - 2.9214)^2}{37.9236}}$$

$$= 7.6439 \pm 2.2104$$

so

$$5.4335 \leq Y_{X=4} \leq 9.8543$$

Therefore, with 95% confidence, you predict that the annual sales for an individual store with 4,000 square feet is between \$5,433,500 and \$9,854,300.

Figure 13.27 is a Microsoft Excel worksheet that illustrates the confidence interval estimate and the prediction interval for the Sunflowers Apparel problem and Figure 13.28 contains Minitab results. If you compare the results of the confidence interval estimate and the prediction interval, you see that the width of the prediction interval for an individual store is much wider than the confidence interval estimate for the mean. Remember that there is much more variation in predicting an individual value than in estimating a mean value.

**FIGURE 13.27**

Microsoft Excel confidence interval estimate and prediction interval worksheet for the Sunflowers Apparel data

*See Section E13.5 or P13.5 to create this. See Section E13.5 for an explanation of the DataCopy worksheet that is referenced in several formulas.*

| | A | B | |
|---|---|---|---|
| 1 | Site Selection Analysis | | |
| 2 | | | |
| 3 | **Data** | | |
| 4 | X Value | 4 | |
| 5 | Confidence Level | 95% | |
| 6 | | | |
| 7 | Intermediate Calculations | | |
| 8 | Sample Size | 14 | =DataCopy!F2 |
| 9 | Degrees of Freedom | 12 | =B8 - 2 |
| 10 | t Value | 2.1788 | =TINV(1 - B5, B9) |
| 11 | Sample Mean | 2.9214 | =DataCopy!F3 |
| 12 | Sum of Squared Difference | 37.9236 | =DataCopy!F4 |
| 13 | Standard Error of the Estimate | 0.9664 | from regression worksheet cell B7 |
| 14 | h Statistic | 0.1021 | =1/B8 + (B4 - B11)^2/B12 |
| 15 | Predicted Y (YHat) | 7.6439 | =DataCopy!F5 |
| 16 | | | |
| 17 | For Average Y | | |
| 18 | Interval Half Width | 0.6728 | =B10 * B13 * SQRT(B14) |
| 19 | **Confidence Interval Lower Limit** | 6.9711 | =B15 - B18 |
| 20 | **Confidence Interval Upper Limit** | 8.3167 | =B15 + B18 |
| 21 | | | |
| 22 | For Individual Response Y | | |
| 23 | Interval Half Width | 2.2104 | =B10 * B13 * SQRT(1 + B14) |
| 24 | **Prediction Interval Lower Limit** | 5.4335 | =B15 - B23 |
| 25 | **Prediction Interval Upper Limit** | 9.8544 | =B15 + B23 |

**FIGURE 13.28**

Minitab confidence interval estimate and prediction interval for the Sunflowers Apparel data

*See Section M13.1 to create this.*

```
Predicted Values for New Observations

New
Obs    Fit   SE Fit      95% CI           95% PI
  1  7.644   0.309   (6.971, 8.317)   (5.433, 9.854)


Values of Predictors for New Observations

New   Square
Obs    Feet
  1    4.00
```

# PROBLEMS FOR SECTION 13.8

## Learning the Basics

**13.55** Based on a sample of $n = 20$, the least-squares method was used to develop the following prediction line: $\hat{Y}_i = 5 + 3X_i$. In addition,

$$S_{YX} = 1.0 \quad \bar{X} = 2 \quad \sum_{i=1}^{n}(X_i - \bar{X})^2 = 20$$

a. Construct a 95% confidence interval estimate of the population mean response for $X = 2$.
b. Construct a 95% prediction interval of an individual response for $X = 2$.

**13.56** Based on a sample of $n = 20$, the least-squares method was used to develop the following prediction line: $\hat{Y}_i = 5 + 3X_i$. In addition,

$$S_{YX} = 1.0 \quad \bar{X} = 2 \quad \sum_{i=1}^{n}(X_i - \bar{X})^2 = 20$$

a. Construct a 95% confidence interval estimate of the population mean response for $X = 4$.
b. Construct a 95% prediction interval of an individual response for $X = 4$.
c. Compare the results of (a) and (b) with those of Problem 13.55(a) and (b). Which interval is wider? Why?

## Applying the Concepts

**13.57** In Problem 13.5 on page 585, you used reported sales to predict audited sales of magazines. The data are stored in the file **Circulation**. For these data $S_{YX} = 42.186$ and $h_i = 0.108$ when $X = 400$.

a. Construct a 95% confidence interval estimate of the mean audited sales for magazines that report newsstand sales of 400,000.

b. Construct a 95% prediction interval of the audited sales for an individual magazine that reports newsstand sales of 400,000.

c. Explain the difference in the results in (a) and (b).

**✓SELF** **13.58** In Problem 13.4 on page 585, the market-
**Test** ing manager used shelf space for pet food to pre-
dict weekly sales. The data are stored in the file **Petfood**.
For these data $S_{YX} = 30.81$ and $h_i = 0.1373$ when $X = 8$.

a. Construct a 95% confidence interval estimate of the mean weekly sales for all stores that have 8 feet of shelf space for pet food.

b. Construct a 95% prediction interval of the weekly sales of an individual store that has 8 feet of shelf space for pet food.

c. Explain the difference in the results in (a) and (b).

**13.59** In Problem 13.7 on page 586, you used the total number of customers in the store to predict the waiting time at the checkout counter. The data are stored in the file **Supermarket**.

a. Construct a 95% confidence interval estimate of the mean waiting time for all customers when there are 20 customers in the store.

b. Construct a 95% prediction interval of the waiting time for an individual customer when there are 20 customers in the store.

c. Why is the interval in (a) narrower than the interval in (b)?

**13.60** In Problem 13.6 on page 585, the owner of a moving company wanted to predict labor hours based on the number of cubic feet moved. The data are stored in the file **Moving**.

a. Construct a 95% confidence interval estimate of the mean labor hours for all moves of 500 cubic feet.

b. Construct a 95% prediction interval of the labor hours of an individual move that has 500 cubic feet.

c. Why is the interval in (a) narrower than the interval in (b)?

**13.61** In Problem 13.9 on page 586, an agent for a real estate company wanted to predict the monthly rent for apartments, based on the size of the apartment. The data are stored in the file **Rent**.

a. Construct a 95% confidence interval estimate of the mean monthly rental for all apartments that are 1,000 square feet in size.

b. Construct a 95% prediction interval of the monthly rental of an individual apartment that is 1,000 square feet in size.

c. Explain the difference in the results in (a) and (b).

**13.62** In Problem 13.8 on page 586, you predicted the value of a baseball franchise, based on current revenue. The data are stored in the file **Bbrevenue**.

a. Construct a 95% confidence interval estimate of the mean value of all baseball franchises that generate $150 million of annual revenue.

b. Construct a 95% prediction interval of the value of an individual baseball franchise that generates $150 million of annual revenue.

c. Explain the difference in the results in (a) and (b).

**13.63** In Problem 13.10 on page 586, you used box office gross to predict the number of DVDs sold. The data are stored in the file **Movie**. The company is about to release a movie on DVD that had a box office gross of $30 million.

a. What is the predicted number of DVDs that the company will sell?

b. Which interval is more useful here, the confidence interval estimate of the mean or the predicted interval for an individual response? Explain.

c. Construct and interpret the interval you selected in (b).

## 13.9  PITFALLS IN REGRESSION

Some of the pitfalls involved in using regression analysis are as follows:

- Lacking an awareness of the assumptions of least-squares regression
- Not knowing how to evaluate the assumptions of least-squares regression
- Not knowing what the alternatives are to least-squares regression if a particular assumption is violated
- Using a regression model without knowledge of the subject matter
- Extrapolating outside the relevant range
- Concluding that a significant relationship identified in an observational study is due to a cause-and-effect relationship

The widespread availability of spreadsheet and statistical software has made regression analysis much more feasible. However, for many users, this enhanced availability of software has not been accompanied by an understanding of how to use regression analysis properly. Someone who is not familiar with either the assumptions of regression or how to evaluate the assumptions cannot be expected to know what the alternatives to least-squares regression are if a particular assumption is violated.

The data in Table 13.7 (stored in the file **Anscombe**) illustrate the importance of using scatter plots and residual analysis to go beyond the basic number crunching of computing the $Y$ intercept, the slope, and $r^2$.

**TABLE 13.7**

Four Sets of Artificial Data

| Data Set A | | Data Set B | | Data Set C | | Data Set D | |
|---|---|---|---|---|---|---|---|
| $X_i$ | $Y_i$ | $X_i$ | $Y_i$ | $X_i$ | $Y_i$ | $X_i$ | $Y_i$ |
| 10 | 8.04 | 10 | 9.14 | 10 | 7.46 | 8 | 6.58 |
| 14 | 9.96 | 14 | 8.10 | 14 | 8.84 | 8 | 5.76 |
| 5 | 5.68 | 5 | 4.74 | 5 | 5.73 | 8 | 7.71 |
| 8 | 6.95 | 8 | 8.14 | 8 | 6.77 | 8 | 8.84 |
| 9 | 8.81 | 9 | 8.77 | 9 | 7.11 | 8 | 8.47 |
| 12 | 10.84 | 12 | 9.13 | 12 | 8.15 | 8 | 7.04 |
| 4 | 4.26 | 4 | 3.10 | 4 | 5.39 | 8 | 5.25 |
| 7 | 4.82 | 7 | 7.26 | 7 | 6.42 | 19 | 12.50 |
| 11 | 8.33 | 11 | 9.26 | 11 | 7.81 | 8 | 5.56 |
| 13 | 7.58 | 13 | 8.74 | 13 | 12.74 | 8 | 7.91 |
| 6 | 7.24 | 6 | 6.13 | 6 | 6.08 | 8 | 6.89 |

Source: *Extracted from F. J. Anscombe, "Graphs in Statistical Analysis,"* American Statistician, *vol. 27 (1973), pp. 17–21.*

Anscombe (reference 1) showed that all four data sets given in Table 13.7 have the following identical results:

$$\hat{Y}_i = 3.0 + 0.5X_i$$

$$S_{YX} = 1.237$$

$$S_{b_1} = 0.118$$

$$r^2 = 0.667$$

$$SSR = \text{Explained variation} = \sum_{i=1}^{n}(\hat{Y}_i - \bar{Y})^2 = 27.51$$

$$SSE = \text{Unexplained variation} = \sum_{i=1}^{n}(Y_i - \hat{Y}_i)^2 = 13.76$$

$$SST = \text{Total variation} = \sum_{i=1}^{n}(Y_i - \bar{Y})^2 = 41.27$$

Thus, with respect to these statistics associated with a simple linear regression analysis, the four data sets are identical. Were you to stop the analysis at this point, you would fail to observe the important differences among the four data sets.

From the scatter plots of Figure 13.29 and the residual plots of Figure 13.30 on page 618, you see how different the data sets are. Each has a different relationship between $X$ and $Y$. The only data set that seems to approximately follow a straight line is data set A. The residual plot for data set A does not show any obvious patterns or outlying residuals. This is certainly not true for data sets B, C, and D. The scatter plot for data set B shows that a quadratic regression model (see Section 15.1) is more appropriate. This conclusion is reinforced by the residual plot for data set B. The scatter plot and the residual plot for data set C clearly show an outlying observation. If this is the case, you may want to remove the outlier and reestimate the regression model (see reference 4). Similarly, the scatter plot for data set D represents the situation in

**FIGURE 13.29**
Scatter plots for four data sets

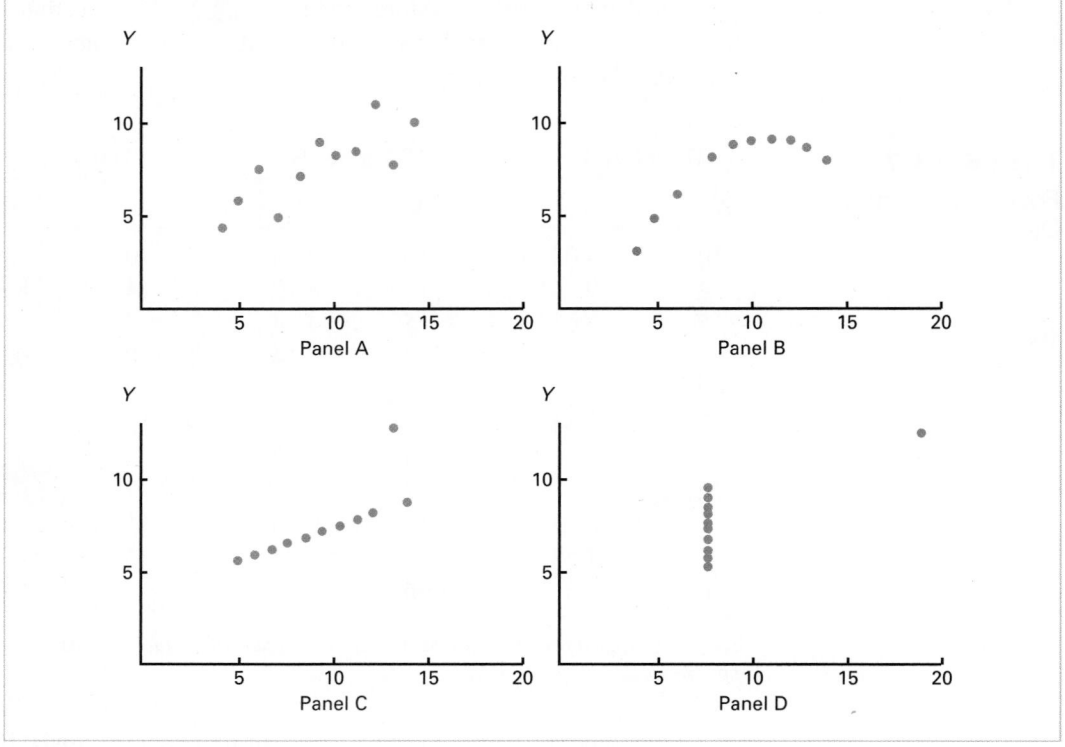

**FIGURE 13.30**
Residual plots for four data sets

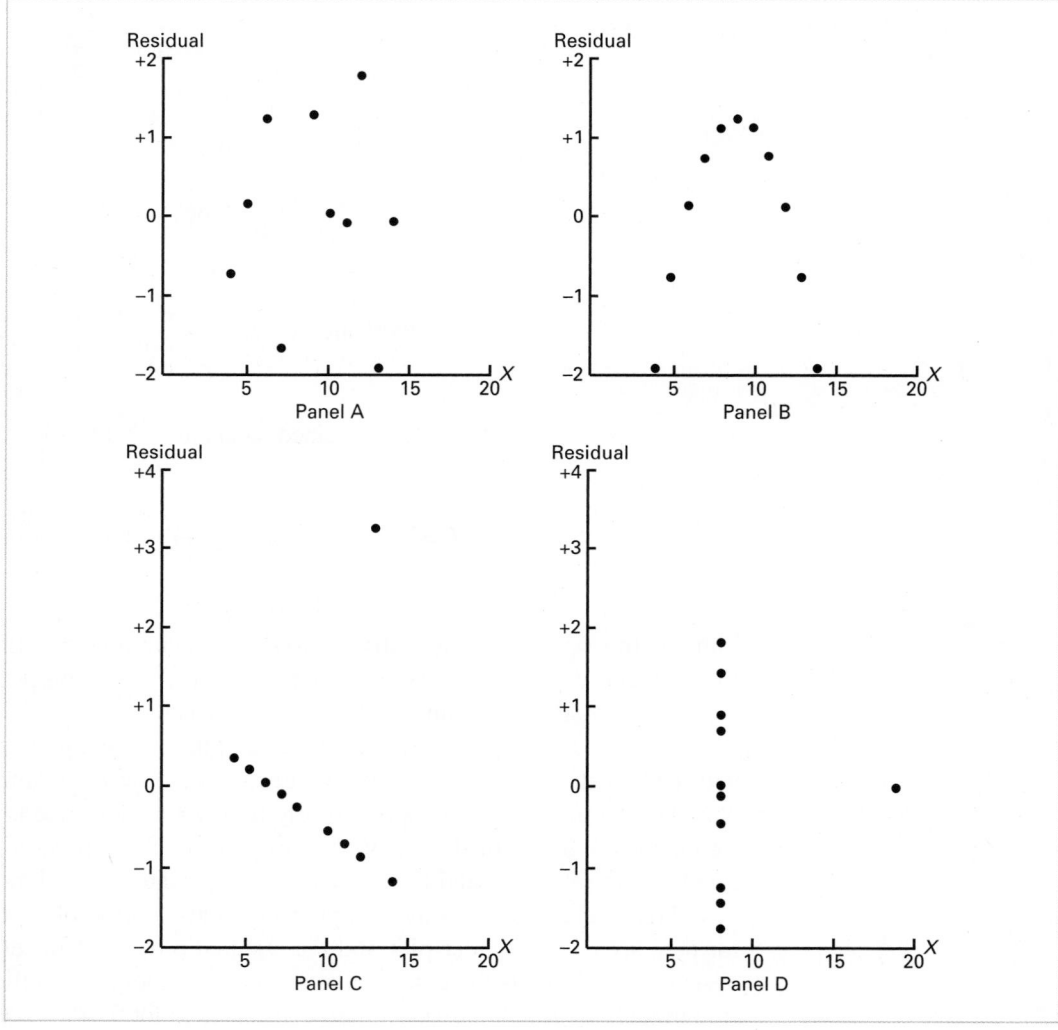

which the model is heavily dependent on the outcome of a single response ($X_8 = 19$ and $Y_8 = 12.50$). You would have to cautiously evaluate any regression model because its regression coefficients are heavily dependent on a single observation.

In summary, scatter plots and residual plots are of vital importance to a complete regression analysis. The information they provide is so basic to a credible analysis that you should always include these graphical methods as part of a regression analysis. Thus, a strategy that you can use to help avoid the pitfalls of regression is as follows:

1. Start with a scatter plot to observe the possible relationship between $X$ and $Y$.
2. Check the assumptions of regression (**L**inearity, **I**ndependence, **N**ormality, **E**qual variance) by performing a residual analysis that includes:

   a. Plotting the residuals versus the independent variable to determine whether the linear model is appropriate and to check for equal variance.
   b. Constructing a histogram, stem-and-leaf display, boxplot, or normal probability plot of the residuals to check for normality.
   c. Plotting the residuals versus time and performing the Durbin-Watson test to check for independence (this step is necessary only if the data are collected over time).

3. If there are violations of the assumptions, use alternative methods to least-squares regression or alternative least-squares models.
4. If there are no violations of the assumptions, carry out tests for the significance of the regression coefficients and develop confidence and prediction intervals.
5. Avoid making predictions and forecasts outside the relevant range of the independent variable.
6. Keep in mind that the relationships identified in observational studies may or may not be due to cause-and-effect relationships. Remember that, although causation implies correlation, correlation does not imply causation.

## America's Top Models

*From the Authors' Desktop*

Perhaps you are familiar with the TV competition produced by Tyra Banks to find "America's top model." You may be less familiar with another set of top models that are emerging from the business world.

In a *Business Week* article from its January 23, 2006, edition (S. Baker, "Why Math Will Rock Your World: More Math Geeks Are Calling the Shots in Business. Is Your Industry Next?" *Business Week*, pp. 54–62), Stephen Baker talks about how "quants" turned finance upside down and are moving on to other business fields. The name *quants* derives from the "quantitative methods" that "math geeks" use to develop models and forecasts. These methods are built on the principles of regression analysis discussed in this chapter, although the actual models are much more complicated than the simple linear models discussed in this chapter.

Regression-based models have become the top models for many types of business analyses. Some examples include:

- **Advertising and marketing** Managers use econometric models (in other words, regression models) to determine the effect of an advertisement on sales, based on a set of factors. Also, managers use data mining to predict patterns of behavior of what customers will buy in the future, based on historic information about the consumer.
- **Finance** Any time you read about a financial "model," you should understand that some type of regression model is being used. For example, a *New York Times* article on June 18, 2006, titled "An Old Formula That Points to New Worry" by Mark Hulbert (p. BU8) discusses a market timing model that predicts the return of stocks in the next three to five years, based on the dividend yield of the stock market and the interest rate of 90-day Treasury bills.
- **Food and beverage** Believe it or not, Enologix, a California consulting company, has developed a "formula" (a regression model) that predicts a wine's quality index, based on a set of chemical compounds found in the wine (see D. Darlington, "The Chemistry of a 90+ Wine," *The New York Times Magazine*, August 7, 2005, pp. 36–39).
- **Publishing** A study of the effect of price changes on sales at Amazon.com and BN.com (again, regression analysis) found that a 1% price increase at BN.com pushed sales down 4%, but the same price increase at Amazon.com pushed sales down only 0.5%.
- **Transportation** Farecast.com uses data mining and predictive technologies to objectively predict airfare pricing (see D. Darlin, "Airfares Made Easy (Or Easier)," *The New York Times*, July 1, 2006, pp. C1, C6).
- **Real estate** Zillow.com uses information about the features contained in a home and its location to develop estimates about the market value of the home, using a "formula" built with a proprietary algorithm.

In the *Business Week* article, Baker stated that statistics and probability will become core skills for businesspeople and consumers. Those who are successful will know how to use statistics, whether they are building financial models or making marketing plans. He also strongly endorsed the need for people in business to know how to use Microsoft Excel to perform statistical analysis and create reports.

# SUMMARY

As you can see from the chapter roadmap in Figure 13.31, this chapter develops the simple linear regression model and discusses the assumptions and how to evaluate them. Once you are assured that the model is appropriate, you can predict values by using the prediction line and test for the significance of the slope.

You have learned how the director of planning for a chain of clothing stores can use regression analysis to investigate the relationship between the size of a store and its annual sales. You have used this analysis to make better decisions when selecting new sites for stores as well as to forecast sales for existing stores. In Chapter 14, regression analysis is extended to situations in which more than one independent variable is used to predict the value of a dependent variable.

**FIGURE 13.31**
Roadmap for simple
linear regression

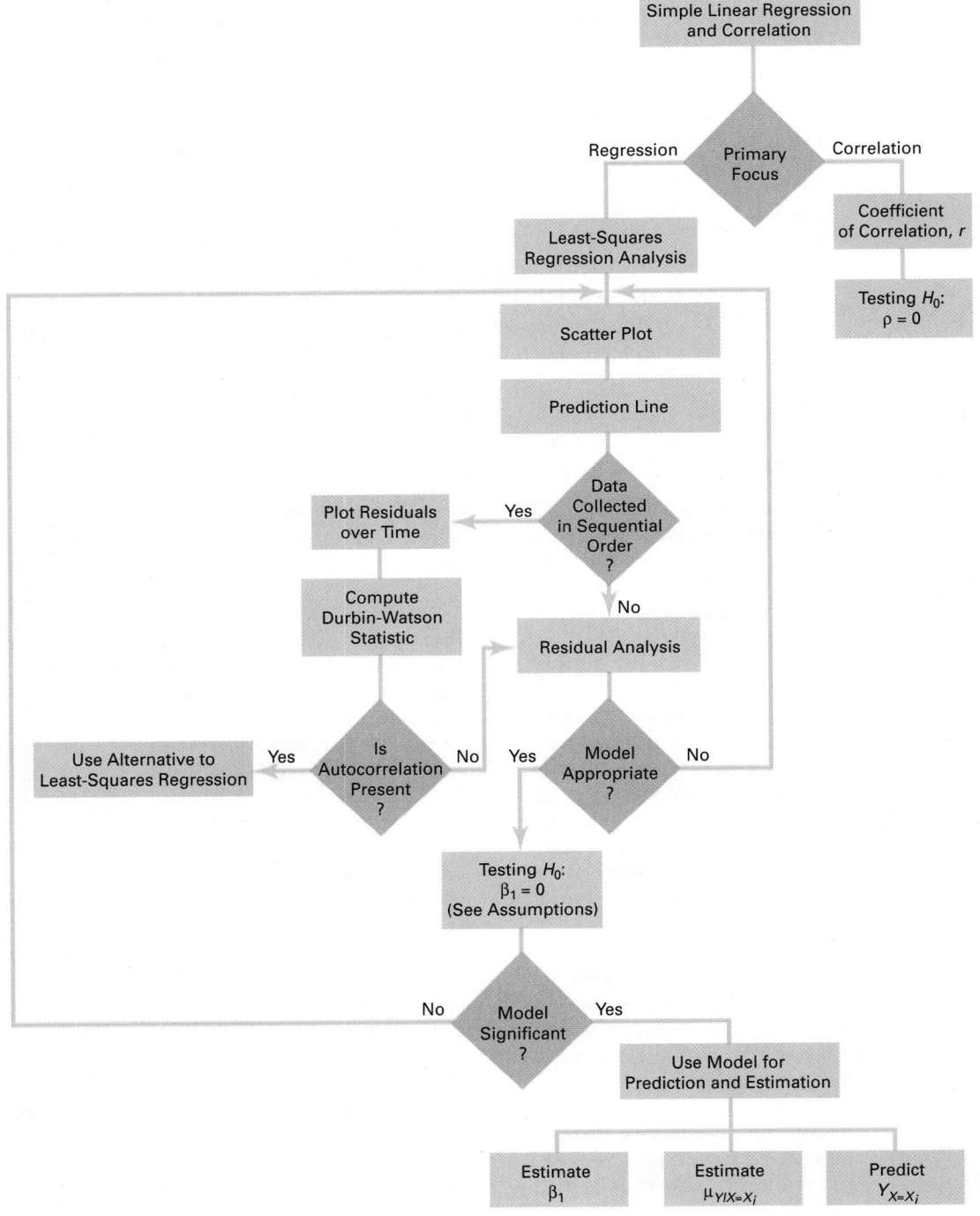

# KEY EQUATIONS

**Simple Linear Regression Model**

$$Y_i = \beta_0 + \beta_1 X_i + \varepsilon_i \qquad (13.1)$$

**Simple Linear Regression Equation: The Prediction Line**

$$\hat{Y}_i = b_0 + b_1 X_i \qquad (13.2)$$

**Computational Formula for the Slope, $b_1$**

$$b_1 = \frac{SSXY}{SSX} \qquad (13.3)$$

**Computational Formula for the $Y$ Intercept, $b_0$**

$$b_0 = \bar{Y} - b_1 \bar{X} \qquad (13.4)$$

**Measures of Variation in Regression**

$$SST = SSR + SSE \qquad (13.5)$$

**Total Sum of Squares ($SST$)**

$$SST = \text{Total sum of squares} = \sum_{i=1}^{n}(Y_i - \bar{Y})^2 \qquad (13.6)$$

**Regression Sum of Squares ($SSR$)**

$SSR$ = Explained variation or regression sum of squares

$$= \sum_{i=1}^{n}(\hat{Y}_i - \bar{Y})^2 \qquad (13.7)$$

**Error Sum of Squares ($SSE$)**

$SSE$ = Unexplained variation or error sum of squares

$$= \sum_{i=1}^{n}(Y_i - \hat{Y}_i)^2 \qquad (13.8)$$

**Coefficient of Determination**

$$r^2 = \frac{\text{Regression sum of squares}}{\text{Total sum of squares}} = \frac{SSR}{SST} \qquad (13.9)$$

**Computational Formula for $SST$**

$$SST = \sum_{i=1}^{n}(Y_i - \bar{Y})^2 = \sum_{i=1}^{n}Y_i^2 - \frac{\left(\sum_{i=1}^{n}Y_i\right)^2}{n} \qquad (13.10)$$

**Computational Formula for $SSR$**

$$SSR = \sum_{i=1}^{n}(\hat{Y}_i - \bar{Y})^2$$

$$= b_0\sum_{i=1}^{n}Y_i + b_1\sum_{i=1}^{n}X_iY_i - \frac{\left(\sum_{i=1}^{n}Y_i\right)^2}{n} \qquad (13.11)$$

**Computational Formula for $SSE$**

$$SSE = \sum_{i=1}^{n}(Y_i - \hat{Y})^2 = \sum_{i=1}^{n}Y_i^2 - b_0\sum_{i=1}^{n}Y_i - b_1\sum_{i=1}^{n}X_iY_i \qquad (13.12)$$

**Standard Error of the Estimate**

$$S_{YX} = \sqrt{\frac{SSE}{n-2}} = \sqrt{\frac{\sum_{i=1}^{n}(Y_i - \hat{Y}_i)^2}{n-2}} \qquad (13.13)$$

**Residual**

$$e_i = Y_i - \hat{Y}_i \qquad (13.14)$$

**Durbin-Watson Statistic**

$$D = \frac{\sum_{i=2}^{n}(e_i - e_{i-1})^2}{\sum_{i=1}^{n}e_i^2} \qquad (13.15)$$

**Testing a Hypothesis for a Population Slope, $\beta_1$, Using the $t$ Test**

$$t_{STAT} = \frac{b_1 - \beta_1}{S_{b_1}} \qquad (13.16)$$

**Testing a Hypothesis for a Population Slope, $\beta_1$, Using the $F$ Test**

$$F_{STAT} = \frac{MSR}{MSE} \qquad (13.17)$$

**Confidence Interval Estimate of the Slope, $\beta_1$**

$$b_1 \pm t_{\alpha/2}S_{b_1}$$

$$b_1 - t_{\alpha/2}S_{b_1} \le \beta_1 \le b_1 + t_{\alpha/2}S_{b_1} \qquad (13.18)$$

**Testing for the Existence of Correlation**

$$t_{STAT} = \frac{r - \rho}{\sqrt{\dfrac{1 - r^2}{n - 2}}} \qquad \text{(13.19a)}$$

$$r = \frac{\text{cov}(X, Y)}{S_X S_Y} \qquad \text{(13.19b)}$$

**Confidence Interval Estimate for the Mean of $Y$**

$$\hat{Y}_i \pm t_{\alpha/2} S_{YX} \sqrt{h_i}$$

$$\hat{Y}_i - t_{\alpha/2} S_{YX} \sqrt{h_i} \leq \mu_{Y|X=X_i} \leq \hat{Y}_i + t_{\alpha/2} S_{YX} \sqrt{h_i} \qquad \text{(13.20)}$$

**Prediction Interval for an Individual Response, $Y$**

$$\hat{Y}_i \pm t_{\alpha/2} S_{YX} \sqrt{1 + h_i}$$

$$\hat{Y}_i - t_{\alpha/2} S_{YX} \sqrt{1 + h_i} \leq Y_{X=X_i} \leq \hat{Y}_i + t_{\alpha/2} S_{YX} \sqrt{1 + h_i} \qquad \text{(13.21)}$$

# KEY TERMS

# CHAPTER REVIEW PROBLEMS

## Checking Your Understanding

**13.64** What is the interpretation of the $Y$ intercept and the slope in the simple linear regression equation?

**13.65** What is the interpretation of the coefficient of determination?

**13.66** When is the unexplained variation (i.e., error sum of squares) equal to 0?

**13.67** When is the explained variation (i.e., regression sum of squares) equal to 0?

**13.68** Why should you always carry out a residual analysis as part of a regression model?

**13.69** What are the assumptions of regression analysis?

**13.70** How do you evaluate the assumptions of regression analysis?

**13.71** When and how do you use the Durbin-Watson statistic?

**13.72** What is the difference between a confidence interval estimate of the mean response, $\mu_{Y|X=X_i}$, and a prediction interval of $Y_{X=X_i}$?

## Applying the Concepts

**13.73** Researchers from the Lubin School of Business at Pace University in New York City conducted a study on Internet-supported courses. In one part of the study, four numerical variables were collected on 108 students in an introductory management course that met once a week for an entire semester. One variable collected was *hit consistency*. To measure hit consistency, the researchers did the following: If a student did not visit the Internet site between classes, the student was given a 0 for that time period. If a student visited the Internet site one or more times between classes, the student was given a 1 for that time period. Because there were 13 time periods, a student's score on hit consistency could range from 0 to 13.

The other three variables included the student's course average, the student's cumulative grade point average (GPA), and the total number of hits the student had on the Internet site supporting the course. The following table gives the correlation coefficient for all pairs of variables. Note that correlations marked with an * are statistically significant, using $\alpha = 0.001$:

| Variable | Correlation |
|---|---|
| Course Average, Cumulative GPA | 0.72* |
| Course Average, Total Hits | 0.08 |
| Course Average, Hit Consistency | 0.37* |
| Cumulative GPA, Total Hits | 0.12 |
| Cumulative GPA, Hit Consistency | 0.32* |
| Total Hits, Hit Consistency | 0.64* |

Source: *Extracted from D. Baugher, A. Varanelli, and E. Weisbord, "Student Hits in an Internet-Supported Course: How Can Instructors Use Them and What Do They Mean?"* Decision Sciences Journal of Innovative Education, *Fall 2003, 1(2), pp. 159–179.*

a. What conclusions can you reach from this correlation analysis?

b. Are you surprised by the results, or are they consistent with your own observations and experiences?

**13.74** Management of a soft-drink bottling company wants to develop a method for allocating delivery costs to customers. Although one cost clearly relates to travel time within a particular route, another variable cost reflects the time required to unload the cases of soft drink at the delivery point. A sample of 20 deliveries within a territory was selected. The delivery times and the number of cases delivered were recorded in the Delivery file:

| Customer | Number of Cases | Delivery Time (Minutes) | Customer | Number of Cases | Delivery Time (Minutes) |
|---|---|---|---|---|---|
| 1 | 52 | 32.1 | 11 | 161 | 43.0 |
| 2 | 64 | 34.8 | 12 | 184 | 49.4 |
| 3 | 73 | 36.2 | 13 | 202 | 57.2 |
| 4 | 85 | 37.8 | 14 | 218 | 56.8 |
| 5 | 95 | 37.8 | 15 | 243 | 60.6 |
| 6 | 103 | 39.7 | 16 | 254 | 61.2 |
| 7 | 116 | 38.5 | 17 | 267 | 58.2 |
| 8 | 121 | 41.9 | 18 | 275 | 63.1 |
| 9 | 143 | 44.2 | 19 | 287 | 65.6 |
| 10 | 157 | 47.1 | 20 | 298 | 67.3 |

Develop a regression model to predict delivery time, based on the number of cases delivered.

a. Use the least-squares method to compute the regression coefficients $b_0$ and $b_1$.

b. Interpret the meaning of $b_0$ and $b_1$ in this problem.

c. Predict the delivery time for 150 cases of soft drink.

d. Should you use the model to predict the delivery time for a customer who is receiving 500 cases of soft drink? Why or why not?

e. Determine the coefficient of determination, $r^2$, and explain its meaning in this problem.

f. Perform a residual analysis. Is there any evidence of a pattern in the residuals? Explain.

g. At the 0.05 level of significance, is there evidence of a linear relationship between delivery time and the number of cases delivered?

h. Construct a 95% confidence interval estimate of the mean delivery time for 150 cases of soft drink.

i. Construct a 95% prediction interval of the delivery time for a single delivery of 150 cases of soft drink.

j. Construct a 95% confidence interval estimate of the population slope.

k. Explain how the results in (a) through (j) can help allocate delivery costs to customers.

**13.75** A brokerage house wants to predict the number of trade executions per day, using the number of incoming phone calls as a predictor variable. Data were collected over a period of 35 days and are stored in the file Trades.

a. Use the least-squares method to compute the regression coefficients $b_0$ and $b_1$.

b. Interpret the meaning of $b_0$ and $b_1$ in this problem.

c. Predict the number of trades executed for a day in which the number of incoming calls is 2,000.

d. Should you use the model to predict the number of trades executed for a day in which the number of incoming calls is 5,000? Why or why not?

e. Determine the coefficient of determination, $r^2$, and explain its meaning in this problem.

f. Plot the residuals against the number of incoming calls and also against the days. Is there any evidence of a pattern in the residuals with either of these variables? Explain.

g. Determine the Durbin-Watson statistic for these data.

h. Based on the results of (f) and (g), is there reason to question the validity of the model? Explain.

i. At the 0.05 level of significance, is there evidence of a linear relationship between the volume of trade executions and the number of incoming calls?

j. Construct a 95% confidence interval estimate of the mean number of trades executed for days in which the number of incoming calls is 2,000.

k. Construct a 95% prediction interval of the number of trades executed for a particular day in which the number of incoming calls is 2,000.

l. Construct a 95% confidence interval estimate of the population slope.

m. Based on the results of (a) through (l), do you think the brokerage house should focus on a strategy of increasing the total number of incoming calls or on a strategy that relies on trading by a small number of heavy traders? Explain.

**13.76** You want to develop a model to predict the selling price of homes based on assessed value. A sample of 30 recently sold single-family houses in a small city is selected to study the relationship between selling price (in thousands of dollars) and assessed value (in thousands of dollars). The houses in the city had been reassessed at full value one year prior to the study. The results are in the file House1.

(*Hint:* First, determine which are the independent and dependent variables.)

a. Construct a scatter plot and, assuming a linear relationship, use the least-squares method to compute the regression coefficients $b_0$ and $b_1$.

b. Interpret the meaning of the $Y$ intercept, $b_0$, and the slope, $b_1$, in this problem.

c. Use the prediction line developed in (a) to predict the selling price for a house whose assessed value is $170,000.

d. Determine the coefficient of determination, $r^2$, and interpret its meaning in this problem.

e. Perform a residual analysis on your results and evaluate the regression assumptions.

f. At the 0.05 level of significance, is there evidence of a linear relationship between selling price and assessed value?

g. Construct a 95% confidence interval estimate of the mean selling price for houses with an assessed value of $170,000.

h. Construct a 95% prediction interval of the selling price of an individual house with an assessed value of $170,000.

i. Construct a 95% confidence interval estimate of the population slope.

**13.77** You want to develop a model to predict the assessed value of houses, based on heating area. A sample of 15 single-family houses is selected in a city. The assessed value (in thousands of dollars) and the heating area of the houses (in thousands of square feet) are recorded, with the following results, stored in the file House2:

| House | Assessed Value ($000) | Heating Area of Dwelling (Thousands of Square Feet) |
|---|---|---|
| 1 | 184.4 | 2.00 |
| 2 | 177.4 | 1.71 |
| 3 | 175.7 | 1.45 |
| 4 | 185.9 | 1.76 |
| 5 | 179.1 | 1.93 |
| 6 | 170.4 | 1.20 |
| 7 | 175.8 | 1.55 |
| 8 | 185.9 | 1.93 |
| 9 | 178.5 | 1.59 |
| 10 | 179.2 | 1.50 |
| 11 | 186.7 | 1.90 |
| 12 | 179.3 | 1.39 |
| 13 | 174.5 | 1.54 |
| 14 | 183.8 | 1.89 |
| 15 | 176.8 | 1.59 |

(*Hint:* First, determine which are the independent and dependent variables.)

a. Construct a scatter plot and, assuming a linear relationship, use the least-squares method to compute the regression coefficients $b_0$ and $b_1$.

b. Interpret the meaning of the $Y$ intercept, $b_0$, and the slope, $b_1$, in this problem.

c. Use the prediction line developed in (a) to predict the assessed value for a house whose heating area is 1,750 square feet.

d. Determine the coefficient of determination, $r^2$, and interpret its meaning in this problem.

e. Perform a residual analysis on your results and evaluate the regression assumptions.

f. At the 0.05 level of significance, is there evidence of a linear relationship between assessed value and heating area?

g. Construct a 95% confidence interval estimate of the mean assessed value for houses with a heating area of 1,750 square feet.

h. Construct a 95% prediction interval of the assessed value of an individual house with a heating area of 1,750 square feet.

i. Construct a 95% confidence interval estimate of the population slope.

**13.78** The director of graduate studies at a large college of business would like to predict the grade point average (GPA) of students in an MBA program based on the Graduate Management Admission Test (GMAT) score. A sample of 20 students who had completed 2 years in the program is selected. The results are stored in the file Gpigmat:

| Observation | GMAT Score | GPA | Observation | GMAT Score | GPA |
|---|---|---|---|---|---|
| 1 | 688 | 3.72 | 11 | 567 | 3.07 |
| 2 | 647 | 3.44 | 12 | 542 | 2.86 |
| 3 | 652 | 3.21 | 13 | 551 | 2.91 |
| 4 | 608 | 3.29 | 14 | 573 | 2.79 |
| 5 | 680 | 3.91 | 15 | 536 | 3.00 |
| 6 | 617 | 3.28 | 16 | 639 | 3.55 |
| 7 | 557 | 3.02 | 17 | 619 | 3.47 |
| 8 | 599 | 3.13 | 18 | 694 | 3.60 |
| 9 | 616 | 3.45 | 19 | 718 | 3.88 |
| 10 | 594 | 3.33 | 20 | 759 | 3.76 |

(*Hint:* First, determine which are the independent and dependent variables.)

a. Construct a scatter plot and, assuming a linear relationship, use the least-squares method to compute the regression coefficients $b_0$ and $b_1$.

b. Interpret the meaning of the $Y$ intercept, $b_0$, and the slope, $b_1$, in this problem.

c. Use the prediction line developed in (a) to predict the GPA for a student with a GMAT score of 600.

d. Determine the coefficient of determination, $r^2$, and interpret its meaning in this problem.

e. Perform a residual analysis on your results and evaluate the regression assumptions.

f. At the 0.05 level of significance, is there evidence of a linear relationship between GMAT score and GPA?

g. Construct a 95% confidence interval estimate of the mean GPA of students with a GMAT score of 600.

h. Construct a 95% prediction interval of the GPA for a particular student with a GMAT score of 600.

i. Construct a 95% confidence interval estimate of the population slope.

**13.79** An accountant for a large department store would like to develop a model to predict the amount of time it takes to process invoices. Data are collected from the last 32 working days, and the number of invoices processed and completion time (in hours) is stored in the file Invoice. (*Hint:* First, determine which are the independent and dependent variables.)

a. Assuming a linear relationship, use the least-squares method to compute the regression coefficients $b_0$ and $b_1$.
b. Interpret the meaning of the $Y$ intercept, $b_0$, and the slope, $b_1$, in this problem.
c. Use the prediction line developed in (a) to predict the amount of time it would take to process 150 invoices.
d. Determine the coefficient of determination, $r^2$, and interpret its meaning.
e. Plot the residuals against the number of invoices processed and also against time.
f. Based on the plots in (e), does the model seem appropriate?
g. Compute the Durbin-Watson statistic and, at the 0.05 level of significance, determine whether there is any autocorrelation in the residuals. If you believe autocorrelation exists, discuss, within the context of the problem, the nature and possible causes of the autocorrelation.
h. Based in the results of (e) through (g) what conclusions can you make about the validity of the prediction made in (c)?

**13.80** On January 28, 1986, the space shuttle *Challenger* exploded, and seven astronauts were killed. Prior to the launch, the predicted atmospheric temperature was for freezing weather at the launch site. Engineers for Morton Thiokol (the manufacturer of the rocket motor) prepared charts to make the case that the launch should not take place due to the cold weather. These arguments were rejected, and the launch tragically took place. Upon investigation after the tragedy, experts agreed that the disaster occurred because of leaky rubber O-rings that did not seal properly due to the cold temperature. Data indicating the atmospheric temperature at the time of 23 previous launches and the O-ring damage index (stored in the file O-ring) are as follows:

| Flight Number | Temperature (°F) | O-Ring Damage Index |
|---|---|---|
| 1 | 66 | 0 |
| 2 | 70 | 4 |
| 3 | 69 | 0 |
| 5 | 68 | 0 |
| 6 | 67 | 0 |
| 7 | 72 | 0 |
| 8 | 73 | 0 |
| 9 | 70 | 0 |
| 41-B | 57 | 4 |
| 41-C | 63 | 2 |
| 41-D | 70 | 4 |
| 41-G | 78 | 0 |

| Flight Number | Temperature (°F) | O-Ring Damage Index |
|---|---|---|
| 51-A | 67 | 0 |
| 51-B | 75 | 0 |
| 51-C | 53 | 11 |
| 51-D | 67 | 0 |
| 51-F | 81 | 0 |
| 51-G | 70 | 0 |
| 51-I | 67 | 0 |
| 51-J | 79 | 0 |
| 61-A | 75 | 4 |
| 61-B | 76 | 0 |
| 61-C | 58 | 4 |

*Note:* Data from flight 4 is omitted due to unknown O-ring condition.

Source: *Extracted from Report of the Presidential Commission on the Space Shuttle Challenger Accident,* Washington, DC, 1986, Vol. II (H1-H3) and Vol. IV (664), and *Post Challenger Evaluation of Space Shuttle Risk Assessment and Management,* Washington, DC, 1988, pp. 135–136.

a. Construct a scatter plot for the seven flights in which there was O-ring damage (O-ring damage index $\neq 0$). What conclusions, if any, can you draw about the relationship between atmospheric temperature and O-ring damage?
b. Construct a scatter plot for all 23 flights.
c. Explain any differences in the interpretation of the relationship between atmospheric temperature and O-ring damage in (a) and (b).
d. Based on the scatter plot in (b), provide reasons why a prediction should not be made for an atmospheric temperature of 31°F, the temperature on the morning of the launch of the *Challenger*.
e. Although the assumption of a linear relationship may not be valid for the set of 23 flights, fit a simple linear regression model to predict O-ring damage, based on atmospheric temperature.
f. Include the prediction line found in (e) on the scatter plot developed in (b).
g. Based on the results of (f), do you think a linear model is appropriate for these data? Explain.
h. Perform a residual analysis. What conclusions do you reach?

**13.81** Crazy Dave, a well-known baseball analyst, would like to study various team statistics for the 2006 baseball season to determine which variables might be useful in predicting the number of wins achieved by teams during the season. He has decided to begin by using a team's earned run average (ERA), a measure of pitching performance, to predict the number of wins. The data for the 30 Major League Baseball teams are in the file BB2006.

(*Hint:* First, determine which are the independent and dependent variables.)

a. Assuming a linear relationship, use the least-squares method to compute the regression coefficients $b_0$ and $b_1$.

**b.** Interpret the meaning of the $Y$ intercept, $b_0$, and the slope, $b_1$, in this problem.

**c.** Use the prediction line developed in (a) to predict the number of wins for a team with an ERA of 4.50.

**d.** Compute the coefficient of determination, $r^2$, and interpret its meaning.

**e.** Perform a residual analysis on your results and determine the adequacy of the fit of the model.

**f.** At the 0.05 level of significance, is there evidence of a linear relationship between the number of wins and the ERA?

**g.** Construct a 95% confidence interval estimate of the mean number of wins expected for teams with an ERA of 4.50.

**h.** Construct a 95% prediction interval of the number of wins for an individual team that has an ERA of 4.50.

**i.** Construct a 95% confidence interval estimate of the population slope.

**j.** The 30 teams constitute a population. In order to use statistical inference, as in (f) through (i), the data must be assumed to represent a random sample. What "population" would this sample be drawing conclusions about?

**k.** What other independent variables might you consider for inclusion in the model?

**13.82** College football players trying out for the NFL are given the Wonderlic standardized intelligence test. The data in the file `Wonderlic` contains the average Wonderlic scores of football players trying out for the NFL and the graduation rates for football players at selected schools (extracted from S. Walker, "The NFL's Smartest Team," *The Wall Street Journal*, September 30, 2005, pp. W1, W10). You plan to develop a regression model to predict the Wonderlic scores for football players trying out for the NFL, based on the graduation rate of the school they attended.

**a.** Assuming a linear relationship, use the least-squares method to compute the regression coefficients $b_0$ and $b_1$.

**b.** Interpret the meaning of the $Y$ intercept, $b_0$, and the slope, $b_1$, in this problem.

**c.** Use the prediction line developed in (a) to predict the Wonderlic score for football players trying out for the NFL from a school that has a graduation rate of 50%.

**d.** Compute the coefficient of determination, $r^2$, and interpret its meaning.

**e.** Perform a residual analysis on your results and evaluate the regression assumptions.

**f.** At the 0.05 level of significance, is there evidence of a linear relationship between the Wonderlic score for a football player trying out for the NFL from a school and the school's graduation rate?

**g.** Construct a 95% confidence interval estimate of the mean Wonderlic score for football players trying out for the NFL from a school that has a graduation rate of 50%.

**h.** Construct a 95% prediction interval of the Wonderlic score for a football player trying out for the NFL from a school that has a graduation rate of 50%.

**i.** Construct a 95% confidence interval estimate of the population slope.

**13.83** College basketball is big business, with coaches' salaries, revenues, and expenses in millions of dollars. The data in the file `Colleges-basketball` contains the coaches' salaries and revenues for college basketball at selected schools in a recent year (extracted from R. Adams, "Pay for Playoffs," *The Wall Street Journal*, March 11–12, 2006, pp. P1, P8). You plan to develop a regression model to predict a coach's salary based on revenue.

**a.** Assuming a linear relationship, use the least-squares method to compute the regression coefficients $b_0$ and $b_1$.

**b.** Interpret the meaning of the $Y$ intercept, $b_0$, and the slope, $b_1$, in this problem.

**c.** Use the prediction line developed in (a) to predict the coach's salary for a school that has revenue of $7 million.

**d.** Compute the coefficient of determination, $r^2$, and interpret its meaning.

**e.** Perform a residual analysis on your results and evaluate the regression assumptions.

**f.** At the 0.05 level of significance, is there evidence of a linear relationship between the coach's salary and revenue?

**g.** Construct a 95% confidence interval estimate of the mean salary of coaches at schools that have revenue of $7 million.

**h.** Construct a 95% prediction interval of the coach's salary for a school that has revenue of $7 million.

**i.** Construct a 95% confidence interval estimate of the population slope.

**13.84** During the fall harvest season in the United States, pumpkins are sold in large quantities at farm stands. Often, instead of weighing the pumpkins prior to sale, the farm stand operator will just place the pumpkin in the appropriate circular cutout on the counter. When asked why this was done, one farmer replied, "I can tell the weight of the pumpkin from its circumference." To determine whether this was really true, a sample of 23 pumpkins were measured for circumference and weighed, with the following results, stored in the file `Pumpkin`:

| Circumference (cm) | Weight (Grams) | Circumference (cm) | Weight (Grams) |
|---|---|---|---|
| 50 | 1,200 | 57 | 2,000 |
| 55 | 2,000 | 66 | 2,500 |
| 54 | 1,500 | 82 | 4,600 |
| 52 | 1,700 | 83 | 4,600 |
| 37 | 500 | 70 | 3,100 |
| 52 | 1,000 | 34 | 600 |
| 53 | 1,500 | 51 | 1,500 |
| 47 | 1,400 | 50 | 1,500 |
| 51 | 1,500 | 49 | 1,600 |
| 63 | 2,500 | 60 | 2,300 |
| 33 | 500 | 59 | 2,100 |
| 43 | 1,000 | | |

**a.** Assuming a linear relationship, use the least-squares method to compute the regression coefficients $b_0$ and $b_1$.

**b.** Interpret the meaning of the slope, $b_1$, in this problem.

**c.** Predict the weight for a pumpkin that is 60 centimeters in circumference.

**d.** Do you think it is a good idea for the farmer to sell pumpkins by circumference instead of weight? Explain.

**e.** Determine the coefficient of determination, $r^2$, and interpret its meaning.

**f.** Perform a residual analysis for these data and evaluate the regression assumptions.

**g.** At the 0.05 level of significance, is there evidence of a linear relationship between the circumference and the weight of a pumpkin?

**h.** Construct a 95% confidence interval estimate of the population slope, $\beta_1$.

**i.** Construct a 95% confidence interval estimate of the population mean weight for pumpkins that have a circumference of 60 centimeters.

**j.** Construct a 95% prediction interval of the weight for an individual pumpkin that has a circumference of 60 centimeters.

**13.85** Can demographic information be helpful in predicting sales at sporting goods stores? The data stored in the file **Sporting** are the monthly sales totals from a random sample of 38 stores in a large chain of nationwide sporting goods stores. All stores in the franchise, and thus within the sample, are approximately the same size and carry the same merchandise. The county or, in some cases, counties in which the store draws the majority of its customers is referred to here as the customer base. For each of the 38 stores, demographic information about the customer base is provided. The data are real, but the name of the franchise is not used at the request of the company. The variables in the data set are:

  Sales—Latest one-month sales total (dollars)
  Age—Median age of customer base (years)
  HS—Percentage of customer base with a high school diploma
  College—Percentage of customer base with a college diploma
  Growth—Annual population growth rate of customer base over the past 10 years
  Income—Median family income of customer base (dollars)

**a.** Construct a scatter plot, using sales as the dependent variable and median family income as the independent variable. Discuss the scatter plot.

**b.** Assuming a linear relationship, use the least-squares method to compute the regression coefficients $b_0$ and $b_1$.

**c.** Interpret the meaning of the $Y$ intercept, $b_0$, and the slope, $b_1$, in this problem.

**d.** Compute the coefficient of determination, $r^2$, and interpret its meaning.

**e.** Perform a residual analysis on your results and determine the adequacy of the fit of the model.

**f.** At the 0.05 level of significance, is there evidence of a linear relationship between the independent variable and the dependent variable?

**g.** Construct a 95% confidence interval estimate of the population slope and interpret its meaning.

**13.86** For the data of Problem 13.85, repeat (a) through (g), using median age as the independent variable.

**13.87** For the data of Problem 13.85, repeat (a) through (g), using high school graduation rate as the independent variable.

**13.88** For the data of Problem 13.85, repeat (a) through (g), using college graduation rate as the independent variable.

**13.89** For the data of Problem 13.85, repeat (a) through (g), using population growth as the independent variable.

**13.90** Zagat's publishes restaurant ratings for various locations in the United States. The data file **Restaurants** contains the Zagat rating for food, decor, service, and the price per person for a sample of 50 restaurants located in an urban area (New York City) and 50 restaurants located in a suburb of New York City. Develop a regression model to predict the price per person, based on a variable that represents the sum of the ratings for food, decor, and service.

Source: *Extracted from* Zagat Survey 2006 New York City Restaurants *and* Zagat Survey 2005–2006, Long Island Restaurants.

**a.** Assuming a linear relationship, use the least-squares method to compute the regression coefficients $b_0$ and $b_1$.

**b.** Interpret the meaning of the $Y$ intercept, $b_0$, and the slope, $b_1$, in this problem.

**c.** Use the prediction line developed in (a) to predict the price per person for a restaurant with a summated rating of 50.

**d.** Compute the coefficient of determination, $r^2$, and interpret its meaning.

**e.** Perform a residual analysis on your results and evaluate the regression assumptions.

**f.** At the 0.05 level of significance, is there evidence of a linear relationship between the price per person and the summated rating?

**g.** Construct a 95% confidence interval estimate of the mean price per person for all restaurants with a summated rating of 50.

**h.** Construct a 95% prediction interval of the price per person for a restaurant with a summated rating of 50.

**i.** Construct a 95% confidence interval estimate of the population slope.

**j.** How useful do you think the summated rating is as a predictor of price? Explain.

**13.91** Refer to the discussion of beta values and market models in Problem 13.49 on page 610. The S&P 500 Index tracks the overall movement of the stock market by considering the stock prices of 500 large corporations. The data file **Stocks2006** contains weekly data for this index as well as the weekly closing stock price for three companies during 2006. The variables included are:

  WEEK—Week ending on date given
  S&P—Weekly closing value for the S&P 500 Index

GE—Weekly closing stock price for General Electric
TARGET—Weekly closing stock price for Target
SARA LEE—Weekly closing stock price for Sara Lee

Source: *Extracted from* **finance.yahoo.com**, *April 3, 2007.*

**a.** Estimate the market model for GE. (*Hint:* Use the percentage change in the S&P 500 Index as the independent variable and the percentage change in GE's stock price as the dependent variable.)
**b.** Interpret the beta value for GE.
**c.** Repeat (a) and (b) for Target.
**d.** Repeat (a) and (b) for Sara Lee.
**e.** Write a brief summary of your findings.

**13.92** The data file Stocks2006 contains the stock prices of three companies, collected weekly in 2006. The variables are:

WEEK—Week ending on date given
GE—Weekly closing stock price for General Electric
TARGET—Weekly closing stock price for Target
SARA LEE—Weekly closing stock price for Sara Lee

Source: *Extracted from* **finance.yahoo.com**, *April 3, 2007.*

**a.** Calculate the correlation coefficient, $r$, for each pair of stocks. (There are three of them.)
**b.** Interpret the meaning of $r$ for each pair.

**c.** Is it a good idea to have all the stocks in an individual's portfolio be strongly positively correlated among each other? Explain.

**13.93** Is the daily performance of stocks and bonds correlated? The data file Stocks & bonds contains information concerning the closing value of the Dow Jones Industrial Average and the Vanguard Long-Term Bond Index Fund for the first six months of 2007. The variables included are:
Date—Current day
Bonds—Closing price of Vanguard Long-Term Bond Index Fund
Stocks—Closing price of the Dow Jones Industrial Average

Source: *Extracted from* **finance.yahoo.com**, *July 3, 2007.*

**a.** Compute and interpret the correlation coefficient, $r$, for the daily closing price of Stocks and of Bonds.
**b.** At the 0.05 level of significance, is there a relationship between these two variables? Explain.

## Report Writing Exercises

**13.94** In Problems 13.85–13.89 on page 627, you developed regression models to predict monthly sales at a sporting goods store. Now, write a report based on the models you developed. Append to your report all appropriate charts and statistical information.

# MANAGING THE *SPRINGVILLE HERALD*

To ensure that as many trial subscriptions as possible are converted to regular subscriptions, the *Herald* marketing department works closely with the distribution department to accomplish a smooth initial delivery process for the trial subscription customers. To assist in this effort, the marketing department needs to accurately forecast the number of new regular subscriptions for the coming months.

A team consisting of managers from the marketing and distribution departments was convened to develop a better method of forecasting new subscriptions. Previously, after examining new subscription data for the prior three months, a group of three managers would develop a subjective forecast of the number of new subscriptions. Lauren Hall, who was recently hired by the company to provide special skills in quantitative forecasting methods, suggested that the department look for factors that might help in predicting new subscriptions.

Members of the team found that the forecasts in the past year had been particularly inaccurate because in some months, much more time was spent on telemarketing than in other months. In particular, in the past month, only 1,055 hours were completed because callers were busy during the first week of the month attending training sessions on the personal but formal greeting style and a new standard presentation guide (see "Managing the *Springville Herald*"

in Chapter 11). Lauren collected data (stored in the file SH13) for the number of new subscriptions and hours spent on telemarketing for each month for the past two years.

## EXERCISES

SH13.1 What criticism can you make concerning the method of forecasting that involved taking the new subscriptions data for the prior three months as the basis for future projections?

SH13.2 What factors other than number of telemarketing hours spent might be useful in predicting the number of new subscriptions? Explain.

SH13.3 **a.** Analyze the data and develop a regression model to predict the mean number of new subscriptions for a month, based on the number of hours spent on telemarketing for new subscriptions.
**b.** If you expect to spend 1,200 hours on telemarketing per month, estimate the mean number of new subscriptions for the month. Indicate the assumptions on which this prediction is based. Do you think these assumptions are valid? Explain.
**c.** What would be the danger of predicting the number of new subscriptions for a month in which 2,000 hours were spent on telemarketing?

# WEB CASE

*Apply your knowledge of simple linear regression in this Web Case, which extends the Sunflowers Apparel Using Statistics scenario from this chapter.*

Leasing agents from the Triangle Mall Management Corporation have suggested that Sunflowers consider several locations in some of Triangle's newly renovated lifestyle malls that cater to shoppers with higher-than-mean disposable income. Although the locations are smaller than the typical Sunflowers location, the leasing agents argue that higher-than-mean disposable income in the surrounding community is a better predictor of higher sales than store size. The leasing agents maintain that sample data from 14 Sunflowers stores prove that this is true.

Review the leasing agents' proposal and supporting documents that describe the data at the company's Web site, **www.prenhall.com/Springville/Triangle_Sunflower.htm** (or open the `Triangle_Sunflower.htm` file from the Student CD-ROM's Web Case folder), and then answer the following:

1. Should mean disposable income be used to predict sales based on the sample of 14 Sunflowers stores?
2. Should the management of Sunflowers accept the claims of Triangle's leasing agents? Why or why not?
3. Is it possible that the mean disposable income of the surrounding area is not an important factor in leasing new locations? Explain.
4. Are there any other factors not mentioned by the leasing agents that might be relevant to the store leasing decision?

# REFERENCES

1. Anscombe, F. J., "Graphs in Statistical Analysis," *The American Statistician*, 27 (1973): 17–21.
2. Hoaglin, D. C., and R. Welsch, "The Hat Matrix in Regression and ANOVA," *The American Statistician* 32 (1978): 17–22.
3. Hocking, R. R., "Developments in Linear Regression Methodology: 1959–1982," *Technometrics* 25 (1983): 219–250.
4. Kutner, M. H., C. J. Nachtsheim, J. Neter, and W. Li, *Applied Linear Statistical Models*, 5th ed. (New York: McGraw-Hill/Irwin, 2005).
5. *Microsoft Excel 2007* (Redmond, WA: Microsoft Corp., 2007).
6. *Minitab for Windows Version 15* (State College, PA: Minitab, Inc., 2006).

# Appendix E13
## Using Microsoft Excel for Simple Linear Regression

## E13.1 Performing Simple Linear Regression Analyses

You perform simple linear regression analyses by using the ToolPak Regression procedure.

Open to the worksheet containing the data for the regression analysis. Select **Tools → Data Analysis** (Excel 97–2003) or **Data → Data Analysis** (Excel 2007). Then select **Regression** from the Data Analysis list and click **OK**. In the procedure's dialog box (at right), enter the cell range of the *Y* variable data as the **Input Y Range** and enter the cell range of the *X* variable data as the **Input X Range**. Click **Labels**, click **Confidence Level** and enter a value in its box, and then click **OK**. Results similar to Figure 13.4 on page 579 appear on a new worksheet.

## E13.2 Creating a Prediction Line on Scatter Plots: Overview

You create a prediction line on a scatter plot by first using Excel charting features to create a scatter plot and then using the **Trendline** charting option to add a prediction line.

## E13.2A Creating a Prediction Line on Scatter Plots (Excel 97–2003)

Open to the scatter plot or use the instructions of Section E2.13 on page 78 to first create a scatter plot. With your workbook open to the plot, select **Chart ➜ Add Trendline**. In the Add Trendline dialog box (see Figure E13.1), click the **Type** tab and then click **Linear**. Click the **Options** tab and select the **Automatic** option. Click **Display equation on chart** and **Display R-squared value on chart** and then click **OK**. If your data range contains a label, that label and not the label **Series1** shown in Figure E13.1 will appear in the Options tab.

**FIGURE E13.1** Add Trendline dialog box (Excel 97–2003)

If there are $Y$ axis values that are less than zero, the $X$ axis will most likely not be placed at the bottom of the plot. To relocate the $X$ axis to this position, right-click the **Y-axis**, and click **Format Axis** from the shortcut menu. In the Format Axis dialog box that appears, click the **Scale** tab and enter the value found in the **Minimum** box as the **Value (X) axis Crosses at** value. Then click **OK**.

## E13.2B Creating a Prediction Line on Scatter Plots (Excel 2007)

Open to the scatter plot or use the instructions of Section E2.13 on page 79 to first create a scatter plot. With your workbook open to the plot, select **Layout ➜ Trendline** and in the Trendline gallery (not shown), select **More Trendline Options**. In the Format Trendline dialog box that appears (shown in Figure E13.2), click **Trendline Options** in the left panel. In the right panel, click **Linear, Display equation on chart** and **Display R-squared value on chart**, and then click **Close**.

**FIGURE E13.2** Format Trendline dialog box (Excel 2007)

If there are $Y$ axis values that are less than zero, the $X$ axis will most likely not be placed at the bottom of the plot. To relocate the $X$ axis to this position, right-click the **Y axis**, and click **Format Axis** from the shortcut menu. In the Format Axis dialog box that appears, click **Axis Options** in the left panel. In the right panel, click **Axis value** and in its box enter the value shown in the dimmed **Minimum** box at the top of the panel. Then click **Close**.

## E13.3 Performing Residual Analyses

You perform residual analysis by modifying the instructions of Section E13.1 to click **Residuals** and **Residual Plots** in the Regression dialog box before your click **OK**.

## E13.4 Computing the Durbin-Watson Statistic

You compute the Durbin-Watson statistic by first using the instructions of Section E13.3 to perform a simple linear regression analysis with a residuals table (similar to the table shown in Figure 13.13 on page 595) and then by making entries in the **DurbinWatson** worksheet of the `Durbin-Watson.xls` workbook.

Open the `Durbin-Watson.xls` workbook and copy the regression results worksheet (containing the residuals table) to the workbook. Next, open to the **DurbinWatson** worksheet. This worksheet (see Figure 13.20 on page 601) uses the **SUMXMY2** (*cell range 1, cell range 2*) function in cell B3 to compute the sum of squared differences of the residuals and the **SUMSQ** (*residuals cell range*) function in cell B4 to compute the sum of squared residuals. By setting *cell range 2* to the cell range of the first residual through the second-to-last residual and *cell range 1* to the cell range of the second residual through the last residual, the SUMXMY2 function computes the squared differences between two successive residuals, the numerator term in Equation (13.15) on page 600.

In Figure 13.20 on page 601, **SLR** is the name of the worksheet that contains the regression results worksheet for the Section 13.6 package delivery store example (some of which is shown in Figure 13.17 on page 599). Because the residuals appear in the cell range SLR!C25:C39, *cell range 1* is set to **SLR!C26:C39** and *cell range 2* is set to **SLR!C25:C38**, as shown in Figure 13.20.

To adapt the Durbin-Watson workbook to other problems, first create a simple linear regression results work- sheet that contains a residuals table and copy the worksheet to the **Durbin-Watson** workbook. Then, open to the **DurbinWatson** worksheet and edit the formulas in cells B3 and B4 so that they refer to the correct cell ranges.

## E13.5 Estimating Mean Values and Predicting Individual Values

You estimate the mean of $Y$ and predict individual values of $Y$ by making entries in the `CIEandPIforSLR.xls` workbook. Open to the **CIEandPI** worksheet and, in cell B13, enter the standard error of the estimate. This value always appears labeled as the **Standard Error** in cell B7 of a regression results worksheet such as the one shown in Figure 13.4 on page 579.

With the standard error value entered, open to the **DataCopy** worksheet. This worksheet contains the $Y$ and $X$ values in column A and B and formulas in column C and F. Noteworthy is the cell F5 formula that uses the **TREND(Y** *variable cell range,* **X** *variable cell range,* **X** *value*) function to calculate the predicted $Y$ value.

Initially, the DataCopy worksheet contains the data for the Section 13.8 Sunflowers Apparel example. To change this worksheet for other problems, follow the instructions in the worksheet for adding or deleting rows of data. (Following those instructions will ensure that the formulas in column F of the DataCopy worksheet are properly updated.)

When you are finished updating the DataCopy worksheet, return to the CIEandPI worksheet and note the results. To predict an individual $Y$ value, enter a $X$ value in cell B4.

# Appendix P13
## Using PHStat2 for Simple Linear Regression

### P13.1 Performing Simple Linear Regression Analyses

To perform simple linear regression analyses, use **PHStat → Regression → Simple Linear Regression**. This procedure creates a worksheet based on sample data and a confidence level that you specify. The procedure uses the ToolPak Regression procedure to perform the regression analysis and creates a worksheet similar to Figure 13.4 on page 579 if you leave **Regression Statistics Table** and **ANOVA and Coefficients Table** checked.

Other sections of this PHStat2 appendix explain the use of the other Output Options to create charts and worksheets related to the regression analysis.

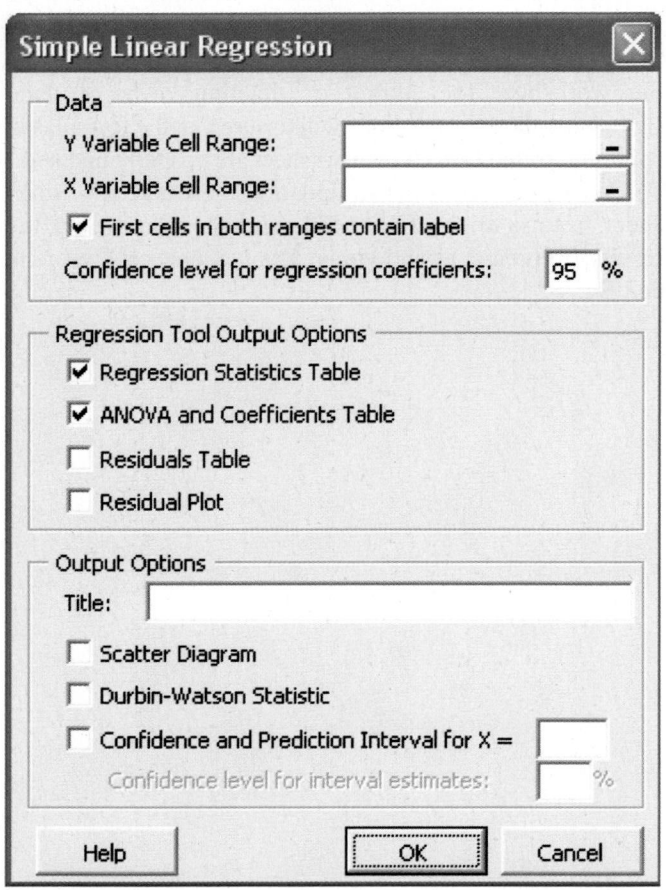

### P13.2 Creating a Prediction Line on Scatter Plots

To create a prediction line on a scatter plot, click **Scatter Plot** when using the Simple Linear Regression procedure (see Section P13.1). After the scatter plot is created, use instructions in either Section E13.2A or E13.2B on page 620 to add a prediction line.

### P13.3 Performing Residual Analyses

To perform residual analysis, use the Section P13.1 instructions but click **Residuals Table** and **Residual Plot** before you click **OK** in the Simple Linear Regression dialog box.

### P13.4 Computing the Durbin-Watson Statistic

To compute the Durbin-Watson statistic, use the Section P13.1 instructions but click **Durbin-Watson Statistic** before you click **OK** in the Simple Linear Regression dialog box. (Clicking this option will cause PHStat2 to create a Residuals Table even if you did not check the **Residuals Table** output option.)

### P13.5 Estimating Mean Values and Predicting Individual Values

To estimate the mean of $Y$ and predict individual values of $Y$, use the Section P13.1 instructions but click **Confidence and Prediction Interval for X =** and enter values for the $X$ value and the **Confidence level for interval estimates** before you click **OK** in the Simple Linear Regression dialog box.

# Appendix M13
## Using Minitab for Simple Linear Regression

### M13.1 Performing Simple Linear Regression Analyses

To illustrate performing simple linear regression analyses:

1. Open the `Site.mtw` worksheet. (This worksheet contains the Sunflowers Apparel data used in examples throughout Chapter 13.)
2. Select **Stat → Regression → Regression**.

In the Regression dialog box (see Figure M13.1):

3. Enter **'Annual Sales'** in the **Response** box.
4. Enter **'Square Feet'** in the **Predictors** box.
5. Click **Graphs**.

**FIGURE M13.1** Minitab Regression dialog box

In the Regression - Graphs dialog box (see Figure M13.2):

6. Click **Regular**.
7. Click **Individual Plots** and then click **Histogram of residuals**, **Normal plot of residuals**, and **Residuals versus fits**. (If the data were in time order, you would also click **Residuals versus order**.)
8. Enter **'Square Feet'** in the **Residuals versus the variables** box.
9. Click **OK**.

**FIGURE M13.2** Minitab Regression - Graphs dialog box

10. Back in the Regression dialog box, click **Results**.

In the Regression - Results dialog box (see Figure M13.3):

11. Click **Regression equation, table of coefficients, s, R-squared, and basic analysis of variance**.
12. Click **OK**.
13. Back in the Regression dialog box, click **Options**.

**FIGURE M13.3** Minitab Regression - Results dialog box

In the Regression - Options dialog box (see Figure M13.4):

14. Leave all of the **Display** check boxes unchecked because the site selection data was not collected over

time. If you were using data that had been collected over time, you would click **Durbin-Watson statistic**.

15. Enter **4** in the **Prediction intervals for new observations** box.
16. Enter **95** in the **Confidence level** box.
17. Click **OK**.
18. Back in the Regression dialog box, click **OK** to perform the analysis.

**FIGURE M13.4** Minitab Regression - Options dialog box

## M13.2 Creating a Prediction Line on Scatter Plots

To illustrate creating a prediction line on a scatter plot:

1. Open the `Site.mtw` worksheet.
2. Select **Graph → Scatterplot**.

In the Scatterplots dialog box (see Figure M13.5):

3. Click **With Regression**.
4. Click **OK**.

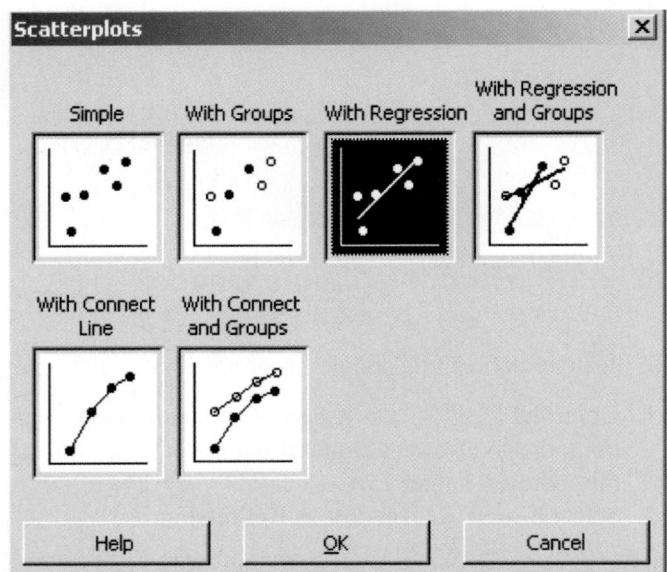

**FIGURE M13.5** Minitab Scatterplots dialog box

In the Scatterplot - With Regression dialog box (see Figure M13.6):

5. Enter **'Annual Sales'** in the row 1 Y variables column.
6. Enter **'Square Feet'** in the row 1 X variables column.
7. Click **OK**.

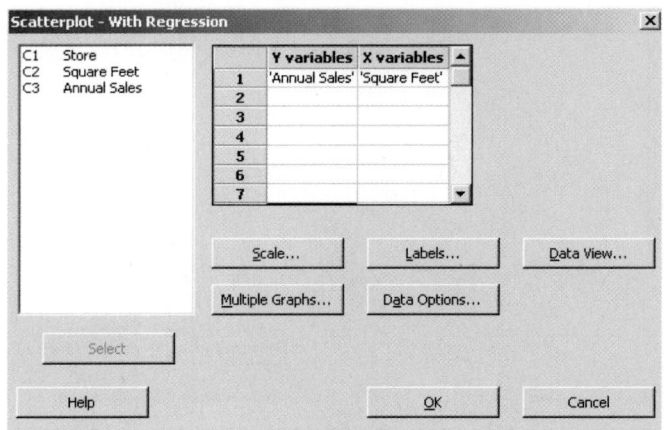

**FIGURE M13.6** Minitab Scatterplot - With Regression dialog box

# CHAPTER
# FOURTEEN
## INTRODUCTION TO MULTIPLE REGRESSION

## LEARNING OBJECTIVES

### In this chapter, you learn:

- How to develop a multiple regression model
- How to interpret the regression coefficients
- How to determine which independent variables to include in the regression model
- How to determine which independent variables are most important in predicting a dependent variable
- How to use categorical independent variables in a regression model
- How to predict a categorical dependent variable using logistic regression

# USING STATISTICS @ OmniFoods

You are the marketing manager for OmniFoods, a large food products company. The company is planning a nationwide introduction of OmniPower, a new high-energy bar. Although originally marketed to runners, mountain climbers, and other athletes, high-energy bars are now popular with the general public. OmniFoods is anxious to capture a share of this thriving market.

Because the marketplace already contains several successful energy bars, you need to develop an effective marketing strategy. In particular, you need to determine the effect that price and in-store promotions will have on the sales of OmniPower. Before marketing the bar nationwide, you plan to conduct a test-market study of OmniPower sales using a sample of 34 stores in a supermarket chain. How can you extend the linear regression methods discussed in Chapter 13 to incorporate the effects of price *and* promotion into the same model? How can you use this model to improve the success of the nationwide introduction of OmniPower?

Chapter 13 focused on simple linear regression models that use *one* numerical independent variable, $X$, to predict the value of a numerical dependent variable, $Y$. Often you can make better predictions by using *more than one* independent variable. This chapter introduces you to **multiple regression models** that use two or more independent variables to predict the value of a dependent variable.

## 14.1 DEVELOPING A MULTIPLE REGRESSION MODEL

A sample of 34 stores in a supermarket chain is selected for a test-market study of OmniPower. All the stores selected have approximately the same monthly sales volume. Two independent variables are considered here—the price of an OmniPower bar, as measured in cents ($X_1$), and the monthly budget for in-store promotional expenditures, measured in dollars ($X_2$). In-store promotional expenditures typically include signs and displays, in-store coupons, and free samples. The dependent variable $Y$ is the number of OmniPower bars sold in a month. Table 14.1 presents the results (stored in the file **OmniPower**) of the test-market study.

**TABLE 14.1**

Monthly OmniPower Sales, Price, and Promotional Expenditures

| Store | Sales | Price | Promotion | Store | Sales | Price | Promotion |
|-------|-------|-------|-----------|-------|-------|-------|-----------|
| 1 | 4,141 | 59 | 200 | 18 | 2,730 | 79 | 400 |
| 2 | 3,842 | 59 | 200 | 19 | 2,618 | 79 | 400 |
| 3 | 3,056 | 59 | 200 | 20 | 4,421 | 79 | 400 |
| 4 | 3,519 | 59 | 200 | 21 | 4,113 | 79 | 600 |
| 5 | 4,226 | 59 | 400 | 22 | 3,746 | 79 | 600 |
| 6 | 4,630 | 59 | 400 | 23 | 3,532 | 79 | 600 |
| 7 | 3,507 | 59 | 400 | 24 | 3,825 | 79 | 600 |
| 8 | 3,754 | 59 | 400 | 25 | 1,096 | 99 | 200 |
| 9 | 5,000 | 59 | 600 | 26 | 761 | 99 | 200 |
| 10 | 5,120 | 59 | 600 | 27 | 2,088 | 99 | 200 |
| 11 | 4,011 | 59 | 600 | 28 | 820 | 99 | 200 |
| 12 | 5,015 | 59 | 600 | 29 | 2,114 | 99 | 400 |
| 13 | 1,916 | 79 | 200 | 30 | 1,882 | 99 | 400 |
| 14 | 675 | 79 | 200 | 31 | 2,159 | 99 | 400 |
| 15 | 3,636 | 79 | 200 | 32 | 1,602 | 99 | 400 |
| 16 | 3,224 | 79 | 200 | 33 | 3,354 | 99 | 600 |
| 17 | 2,295 | 79 | 400 | 34 | 2,927 | 99 | 600 |

With two independent variables and a dependent variable, the data are in three dimensions. Figure 14.1 presents a three-dimensional plot constructed by Minitab.

**FIGURE 14.1**

Minitab three-dimensional plot of monthly OmniPower sales, price, and promotional expenditures

*See Section M14.1 to create this.*

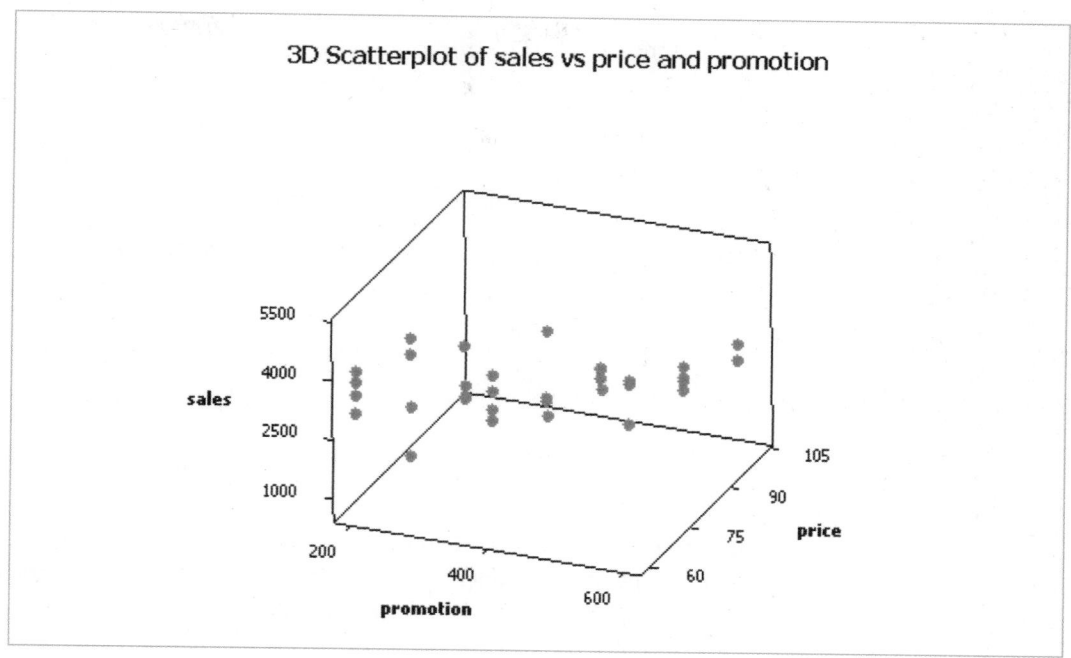

## Interpreting the Regression Coefficients

When there are several independent variables, you can extend the simple linear regression model of Equation (13.1) on page 575 by assuming a linear relationship between each independent variable and the dependent variable. For example, with $k$ independent variables, the multiple regression model is expressed in Equation (14.1).

---

Multiple Regression Model with $k$ Independent Variables

$$Y_i = \beta_0 + \beta_1 X_{1i} + \beta_2 X_{2i} + \beta_3 X_{3i} + \cdots + \beta_k X_{ki} + \varepsilon_i \qquad (14.1)$$

where

$\beta_0 = Y$ intercept

$\beta_1 = $ slope of $Y$ with variable $X_1$, holding variables $X_2, X_3, \ldots, X_k$ constant

$\beta_2 = $ slope of $Y$ with variable $X_2$, holding variables $X_1, X_3, \ldots, X_k$ constant

$\beta_3 = $ slope of $Y$ with variable $X_3$, holding variables $X_1, X_2, X_4, \ldots, X_k$ constant

.

.

.

$\beta_k = $ slope of $Y$ with variable $X_k$, holding variables $X_1, X_2, X_3, \ldots, X_{k-1}$ constant

$\varepsilon_i = $ random error in $Y$ for observation $i$

Equation (14.2) defines the multiple regression model with two independent variables.

Multiple Regression Model with Two Independent Variables

$$Y_i = \beta_0 + \beta_1 X_{1i} + \beta_2 X_{2i} + \varepsilon_i \qquad (14.2)$$

where

$\beta_0 = Y$ intercept

$\beta_1 =$ slope of $Y$ with variable $X_1$, holding variable $X_2$ constant

$\beta_2 =$ slope of $Y$ with variable $X_2$, holding variable $X_1$ constant

$\varepsilon_i =$ random error in $Y$ for observation $i$

Compare the multiple regression model to the simple linear regression model [Equation (13.1) on page 575]:

$$Y_i = \beta_0 + \beta_1 X_i + \varepsilon_i$$

In the simple linear regression model, the slope, $\beta_1$, represents the change in the mean of $Y$ per unit change in $X$ and does not take into account any other variables. In the multiple regression model with two independent variables [Equation (14.2)], the slope, $\beta_1$, represents the change in the mean of $Y$ per unit change in $X_1$, taking into account the effect of $X_2$.

As in the case of simple linear regression, you use the sample regression coefficients ($b_0$, $b_1$, and $b_2$) as estimates of the population parameters ($\beta_0$, $\beta_1$, and $\beta_2$). Equation (14.3) defines the regression equation for a multiple regression model with two independent variables.

Multiple Regression Equation with Two Independent Variables

$$\hat{Y}_i = b_0 + b_1 X_{1i} + b_2 X_{2i} \qquad (14.3)$$

You can use Microsoft Excel or Minitab to compute the values of the three regression coefficients for the OmniPower sales data (see Figure 14.2 or 14.3).

**FIGURE 14.2**

Partial Microsoft Excel regression results worksheet for OmniPower sales data

*See Section E14.1 or P14.1 to create this.*

| | A | B | C | D | E | F | G |
|---|---|---|---|---|---|---|---|
| 1 | **OmniPower Sales Analysis** | | | | | | |
| 2 | | | | | | | |
| 3 | ***Regression Statistics*** | | | | | | |
| 4 | **Multiple R** | 0.8705 | | | | | |
| 5 | **R Square** | 0.7577 | | | | | |
| 6 | **Adjusted R Square** | 0.7421 | | | | | |
| 7 | **Standard Error** | 638.0653 | | | | | |
| 8 | **Observations** | 34 | | | | | |
| 9 | | | | | | | |
| 10 | **ANOVA** | | | | | | |
| 11 | | *df* | *SS* | *MS* | *F* | *Significance F* | |
| 12 | **Regression** | 2 | 39472730.77 | 19736365.387 | 48.4771 | 2.86258E-10 | |
| 13 | **Residual** | 31 | 12620946.67 | 407127.312 | | | |
| 14 | **Total** | 33 | 52093677.44 | | | | |
| 15 | | | | | | | |
| 16 | | *Coefficients* | *Standard Error* | *t Stat* | *P-value* | *Lower 95%* | *Upper 95%* |
| 17 | **Intercept** | 5837.5208 | 628.1502 | 9.2932 | 1.791E-10 | 4556.3992 | 7118.6423 |
| 18 | **Price** | -53.2173 | 6.8522 | -7.7664 | 9.200E-09 | -67.1925 | -39.2421 |
| 19 | **Promotion** | 3.6131 | 0.6852 | 5.2728 | 9.822E-06 | 2.2155 | 5.0106 |

**FIGURE 14.3**

Partial Minitab results for OmniPower sales data

*See Section M14.2 to create this.*

```
The regression equation is
sales = 5838 - 53.2 price + 3.61 promotion

Predictor      Coef   SE Coef      T      P
Constant     5837.5     628.2   9.29  0.000
price       -53.217     6.852  -7.77  0.000
promotion    3.6131    0.6852   5.27  0.000

S = 638.065   R-Sq = 75.8%   R-Sq(adj) = 74.2%

Analysis of Variance

Source         DF        SS        MS      F      P
Regression      2  39472731  19736365  48.48  0.000
Residual Error 31  12620947    407127
Total          33  52093677

Predicted Values for New Observations
New
Obs   Fit  SE Fit      95% CI          95% PI
  1  3079     110  (2854, 3303)  (1758, 4399)
```

From Figure 14.2 or 14.3, the computed values of the regression coefficients are

$$b_0 = 5,837.5208 \quad b_1 = -53.2173 \quad b_2 = 3.6131$$

Therefore, the multiple regression equation is

$$\hat{Y}_i = 5,837.5208 - 53.2173X_{1i} + 3.6131X_{2i}$$

where

$\hat{Y}_i$ = predicted monthly sales of OmniPower bars for store $i$

$X_{1i}$ = price of OmniPower bar (in cents) for store $i$

$X_{2i}$ = monthly in-store promotional expenditures (in dollars) for store $i$

The sample $Y$ intercept ($b_0 = 5,837.5208$) estimates the number of OmniPower bars sold in a month if the price is $0.00 and the total amount spent on promotional expenditures is also $0.00. Because these values of price and promotion are outside the range of price and promotion used in the test-market study, and are nonsensical, the value of $b_0$ has little or no practical interpretation.

The slope of price with OmniPower sales ($b_1 = -53.2173$) indicates that, for a given amount of monthly promotional expenditures, the mean sales of OmniPower are estimated to decrease by 53.2173 bars per month for each 1-cent increase in the price. The slope of monthly promotional expenditures with OmniPower sales ($b_2 = 3.6131$) indicates that, for a given price, the mean sales of OmniPower are estimated to increase by 3.6131 bars for each additional $1 spent on promotions. These estimates allow you to better understand the likely effect that price and promotion decisions will have in the marketplace. For example, a 10-cent decrease in price is estimated to increase mean sales by 532.173 bars, with a fixed amount of monthly promotional expenditures. A $100 increase in promotional expenditures is estimated to increase mean sales by 361.31 bars, for a given price.

Regression coefficients in multiple regression are called **net regression coefficients**; they estimate the mean change in $Y$ per unit change in a particular $X$, *holding constant the effect of the other X variables*. For example, in the study of OmniPower bar sales, for a store with a given amount of promotional expenditures, the mean sales are estimated to decrease by 53.2173 bars per month for each 1-cent increase in the price of an OmniPower bar. Another way to interpret this "net effect" is to think of two stores with an equal amount of promotional expenditures. If the first store charges 1 cent more than the other store, the net effect of this difference is that the first store is predicted to sell 53.2173 fewer bars per month than the second store. To interpret the net effect of promotional expenditures, you can consider two stores that are charging the same price. If the first store spends $1 more on promotional expenditures, the net effect of this difference is that the first store is predicted to sell 3.6131 more bars per month than the second store.

## Predicting the Dependent Variable Y

You can use the multiple regression equation computed by Microsoft Excel or Minitab to predict values of the dependent variable. For example, what are the predicted sales for a store charging 79 cents during a month in which promotional expenditures are $400? Using the multiple regression equation,

$$\hat{Y}_i = 5,837.5208 - 53.2173X_{1i} + 3.6131X_{2i}$$

with $X_{1i} = 79$ and $X_{2i} = 400$,

$$\hat{Y}_i = 5,837.5208 - 53.2173(79) + 3.6131(400)$$
$$= 3,078.57$$

**FIGURE 14.4**

Microsoft Excel confidence interval estimate and prediction interval worksheet for the OmniPower sales data

*See Section E14.3 or P14.3 to create this.*

| | A | B | C | D |
|---|---|---|---|---|
| 1 | **Confidence Interval Estimate and Prediction Interval** | | | |
| 2 | | | | |
| 3 | **Data** | | | |
| 4 | **Confidence Level** | 95% | | |
| 5 | | 1 | | |
| 6 | **Price given value** | 79 | | |
| 7 | **Promotion given value** | 400 | | |
| 8 | | | | |
| 9 | X'X | 34 | 2646 | 13200 |
| 10 | | 2646 | 214674 | 1018800 |
| 11 | | 13200 | 1018800 | 6000000 |
| 12 | | | | |
| 13 | Inverse of X'X | 0.969163 | -0.00941 | -0.00053 |
| 14 | | -0.009408 | 0.000115 | 1.12E-06 |
| 15 | | -0.000535 | 1.12E-06 | 1.15E-06 |
| 16 | | | | |
| 17 | X'G times Inverse of X'X | 0.012054 | 0.000149 | 1.49E-05 |
| 18 | | | | |
| 19 | [X'G times Inverse of X'X] times XG | 0.029762 | =MMULT(B17:D17, B5:B7) | |
| 20 | t Statistic | 2.0395 | =TINV(1 - B4, MR!B13) | |
| 21 | **Predicted Y (YHat)** | 3078.57 | {=MMULT(TRANSPOSE(B5:B7), MR!B17:B19)} | |
| 22 | | | | |
| 23 | **For Average Predicted Y (YHat)** | | | |
| 24 | **Interval Half Width** | 224.50 | =B20 * SQRT(B19 ) * MR!B7 | |
| 25 | **Confidence Interval Lower Limit** | 2854.07 | =B21 - B24 | |
| 26 | **Confidence Interval Upper Limit** | 3303.08 | =B21 + B24 | |
| 27 | | | | |
| 28 | **For Individual Response Y** | | | |
| 29 | **Interval Half Width** | 1320.57 | =B20 * SQRT(1 + B19 ) * MR!B7 | |
| 30 | **Prediction Interval Lower Limit** | 1758.01 | =B21 - B29 | |
| 31 | **Prediction Interval Upper Limit** | 4399.14 | =B21 + B29 | |

Thus, your sales prediction for stores charging 79 cents and spending $400 in promotional expenditures is 3,078.57 OmniPower bars per month.

After you have predicted $Y$ and done a residual analysis (see Section 14.3), the next step often involves a confidence interval estimate of the mean predicted value and a prediction interval for an individual value. The computation of these intervals is too complex to do by hand, and you should use Microsoft Excel or Minitab to perform the calculations. Figure 14.3 on page 639 presents a confidence interval and a prediction interval computed by Minitab. Figure 14.4 on page 640 illustrates Microsoft Excel results.

The 95% confidence interval estimate of the mean OmniPower sales for all stores charging 79 cents and spending $400 in promotional expenditures is 2,854.07 to 3,303.08 bars. The prediction interval for an individual store is 1,758.01 to 4,399.14 bars.

# PROBLEMS FOR SECTION 14.1

## Learning the Basics

**14.1** For this problem, use the following multiple regression equation:

$$\hat{Y}_i = 10 + 5X_{1i} + 3X_{2i}$$

**a.** Interpret the meaning of the slopes.
**b.** Interpret the meaning of the $Y$ intercept.

**14.2** For this problem, use the following multiple regression equation:

$$\hat{Y}_i = 50 - 2X_{1i} + 7X_{2i}$$

**a.** Interpret the meaning of the slopes.
**b.** Interpret the meaning of the $Y$ intercept.

## Applying the Concepts

**14.3** A marketing analyst for a shoe manufacturer is considering the development of a new brand of running shoes. The marketing analyst wants to determine which variables to use in predicting durability (i.e., the effect of long-term impact). Two independent variables under consideration are $X_1$ (FOREIMP), a measurement of the forefoot shock-absorbing capability, and $X_2$ (MIDSOLE), a measurement of the change in impact properties over time. The dependent variable $Y$ is LTIMP, a measure of the shoe's durability after a repeated impact test. A random sample of 15 types of currently manufactured running shoes was selected for testing, with the following results:

| Variable | Coefficients | Standard Error | $t$ Statistic | $p$-Value |
|---|---|---|---|---|
| INTERCEPT | −0.02686 | 0.06905 | −0.39 | 0.7034 |
| FOREIMP | 0.79116 | 0.06295 | 12.57 | 0.0000 |
| MIDSOLE | 0.60484 | 0.07174 | 8.43 | 0.0000 |

**a.** State the multiple regression equation.
**b.** Interpret the meaning of the slopes, $b_1$ and $b_2$, in this problem.

**SELF Test** **14.4** A mail-order catalog business selling personal computer supplies, software, and hardware maintains a centralized warehouse. Management is currently examining the process of distribution from the warehouse and wants to study the factors that affect warehouse distribution costs. Currently, a small handling fee is added to each order, regardless of the amount of the order. Data collected over the past 24 months (stored in the file **Warecost**) indicate the warehouse distribution costs (in thousands of dollars), the sales (in thousands of dollars), and the number of orders received.

**a.** State the multiple regression equation.
**b.** Interpret the meaning of the slopes, $b_1$ and $b_2$, in this problem.
**c.** Explain why the regression coefficient, $b_0$, has no practical meaning in the context of this problem.
**d.** Predict the mean monthly warehouse distribution cost when sales are $400,000 and the number of orders is 4,500.
**e.** Construct a 95% confidence interval estimate for the mean monthly warehouse distribution cost when sales are $400,000 and the number of orders is 4,500.
**f.** Construct a 95% prediction interval for the monthly warehouse distribution cost for a particular month when sales are $400,000 and the number of orders is 4,500.
**g.** Explain why the interval in (e) is narrower than the interval in (f).

**14.5** A consumer organization wants to develop a regression model to predict gasoline mileage (as measured by miles per gallon) based on the horsepower of the car's engine and the weight of the car (in pounds). A sample of 50 recent car models was selected, with the results recorded in the file **Auto**.

a. State the multiple regression equation.
b. Interpret the meaning of the slopes, $b_1$ and $b_2$, in this problem.
c. Explain why the regression coefficient, $b_0$, has no practical meaning in the context of this problem.
d. Predict the mean miles per gallon for cars that have 60 horsepower and weigh 2,000 pounds.
e. Construct a 95% confidence interval estimate for the mean miles per gallon for cars that have 60 horsepower and weigh 2,000 pounds.
f. Construct a 95% prediction interval for the miles per gallon for an individual car that has 60 horsepower and weighs 2,000 pounds.

**14.6** A consumer products company wants to measure the effectiveness of different types of advertising media in the promotion of its products. Specifically, the company is interested in the effectiveness of radio advertising and newspaper advertising (including the cost of discount coupons). A sample of 22 cities with approximately equal populations is selected for study during a test period of one month. Each city is allocated a specific expenditure level both for radio advertising and for newspaper advertising. The sales of the product (in thousands of dollars) and also the levels of media expenditure (in thousands of dollars) during the test month are recorded, with the following results stored in the file **Advertise** :

| City | Sales ($000) | Radio Advertising ($000) | Newspaper Advertising ($000) |
|---|---|---|---|
| 1 | 973 | 0 | 40 |
| 2 | 1,119 | 0 | 40 |
| 3 | 875 | 25 | 25 |
| 4 | 625 | 25 | 25 |
| 5 | 910 | 30 | 30 |
| 6 | 971 | 30 | 30 |
| 7 | 931 | 35 | 35 |
| 8 | 1,177 | 35 | 35 |
| 9 | 882 | 40 | 25 |
| 10 | 982 | 40 | 25 |
| 11 | 1,628 | 45 | 45 |
| 12 | 1,577 | 45 | 45 |
| 13 | 1,044 | 50 | 0 |
| 14 | 914 | 50 | 0 |
| 15 | 1,329 | 55 | 25 |
| 16 | 1,330 | 55 | 25 |
| 17 | 1,405 | 60 | 30 |
| 18 | 1,436 | 60 | 30 |
| 19 | 1,521 | 65 | 35 |
| 20 | 1,741 | 65 | 35 |
| 21 | 1,866 | 70 | 40 |
| 22 | 1,717 | 70 | 40 |

a. State the multiple regression equation.
b. Interpret the meaning of the slopes, $b_1$ and $b_2$, in this problem.
c. Interpret the meaning of the regression coefficient, $b_0$.
d. Which type of advertising is more effective? Explain.

**14.7** The director of broadcasting operations for a television station wants to study the issue of standby hours (i.e., hours in which unionized graphic artists at the station are paid but are not actually involved in any activity). The variables in the study include:

Standby hours ($Y$)—Total number of standby hours in a week

Total staff present ($X_1$)—Weekly total of people-days

Remote hours ($X_2$)—Total number of hours worked by employees at locations away from the central plant

The results for a period of 26 weeks are in the data file **Standby**.

a. State the multiple regression equation.
b. Interpret the meaning of the slopes, $b_1$ and $b_2$, in this problem.
c. Explain why the regression coefficient, $b_0$, has no practical meaning in the context of this problem.
d. Predict the mean standby hours for a week in which the total staff present have 310 people-days and the remote hours are 400.
e. Construct a 95% confidence interval estimate for the mean standby hours for weeks in which the total staff present have 310 people-days and the remote hours are 400.
f. Construct a 95% prediction interval for the standby hours for a single week in which the total staff present have 310 people-days and the remote hours are 400.

**14.8** Nassau County is located approximately 25 miles east of New York City. Data in the file **GlenCove** include the appraised value, land area of the property in acres, and age, in years, for a sample of 30 single-family homes located in Glen Cove, a small city in Nassau County. Develop a multiple linear regression model to predict appraised value based on land area of the property and age, in years.

a. State the multiple regression equation.
b. Interpret the meaning of the slopes, $b_1$ and $b_2$, in this problem.
c. Explain why the regression coefficient, $b_0$, has no practical meaning in the context of this problem.
d. Predict the mean appraised value for a house that has a land area of 0.25 acres and is 45 years old.
e. Construct a 95% confidence interval estimate for the mean appraised value for houses that have a land area of 0.25 acres and are 45 years old.
f. Construct a 95% prediction interval estimate for the appraised value for an individual house that has a land area of 0.25 acres and is 45 years old.

## 14.2   $r^2$, ADJUSTED $r^2$, AND THE OVERALL $F$ TEST

This section discusses three methods you can use to evaluate the overall multiple regression model: the coefficient of multiple determination $r^2$, the adjusted $r^2$, and the overall $F$ test.

### Coefficient of Multiple Determination

Recall from Section 13.3 that the coefficient of determination, $r^2$, measures the proportion of the variation in $Y$ that is explained by the independent variable $X$ in the simple linear regression model. In multiple regression, the **coefficient of multiple determination** represents the proportion of the variation in $Y$ that is explained by the set of independent variables. Equation (14.4) defines the coefficient of multiple determination for a multiple regression model with two or more independent variables.

**Coefficient of Multiple Determination**

The coefficient of multiple determination is equal to the regression sum of squares ($SSR$) divided by the total sum of squares ($SST$).

$$r^2 = \frac{\text{Regression sum of squares}}{\text{Total sum of squares}} = \frac{SSR}{SST} \qquad (14.4)$$

where

$$SSR = \text{regression sum of squares}$$

$$SST = \text{total sum of squares}$$

In the OmniPower example, from Figure 14.2 or 14.3 on pages 638–639, $SSR = 39,472,730.77$ and $SST = 52,093,677.44$. Thus,

$$r^2 = \frac{SSR}{SST} = \frac{39,472,730.77}{52,093,677.44} = 0.7577$$

The coefficient of multiple determination ($r^2 = 0.7577$) indicates that 75.77% of the variation in sales is explained by the variation in the price and in the promotional expenditures. You can also find the coefficient of multiple determination directly from the Microsoft Excel results in Figure 14.2 on page 638, labeled "R Square"; or from the Minitab results in Figure 14.3 on page 639, labeled "R-Sq."

### Adjusted $r^2$

When considering multiple regression models, some statisticians suggest that you should use the **adjusted $r^2$** to reflect both the number of independent variables in the model and the sample size. Reporting the adjusted $r^2$ is extremely important when you are comparing two or more regression models that predict the same dependent variable but have a different number of independent variables. Equation (14.5) defines the adjusted $r^2$.

Adjusted $r^2$

$$r_{adj}^2 = 1 - \left[(1 - r^2)\frac{n-1}{n-k-1}\right] \qquad (14.5)$$

where $k$ is the number of independent variables in the regression equation.

Thus, for the OmniPower data, because $r^2 = 0.7577$, $n = 34$, and $k = 2$,

$$r_{adj}^2 = 1 - \left[(1 - 0.7577)\frac{34-1}{(34-2-1)}\right]$$
$$= 1 - \left[(0.2423)\frac{33}{31}\right]$$
$$= 1 - 0.2579$$
$$= 0.7421$$

Hence, 74.21% of the variation in sales is explained by the multiple regression model—adjusted for number of independent variables and sample size. You can also find the adjusted $r^2$ directly from the Microsoft Excel results in Figure 14.2 on page 638, labeled "Adjusted R Square"; or from the Minitab results in Figure 14.3 on page 639, labeled "R-Sq(adj)."

## Test for the Significance of the Overall Multiple Regression Model

You use the **overall $F$ test** to test whether there is a significant relationship between the dependent variable and the entire set of independent variables (the overall multiple regression model). Because there is more than one independent variable, you use the following null and alternative hypotheses:

$H_0$: $\beta_1 = \beta_2 = \cdots = \beta_k = 0$ (There is no linear relationship between the dependent variable and the independent variables.)

$H_1$: At least one $\beta_j \neq 0$, $j = 1, 2, \ldots, k$ (There is a linear relationship between the dependent variable and at least one of the independent variables.)

Equation (14.6) defines the statistic for the overall $F$ test. Table 14.2 presents the associated ANOVA summary table.

Overall $F$ Test

The $F_{STAT}$ test statistic is equal to the regression mean square ($MSR$) divided by the mean square error ($MSE$).

$$F_{STAT} = \frac{MSR}{MSE} \qquad (14.6)$$

where

$F_{STAT}$ = test statistic from an $F$ distribution with $k$ and $n - k - 1$ degrees of freedom

$k$ = number of independent variables in the regression model

**TABLE 14.2**

ANOVA Summary Table for the Overall $F$ Test

| Source | Degrees of Freedom | Sum of Squares | Mean Square (Variance) | $F$ |
|---|---|---|---|---|
| Regression | $k$ | $SSR$ | $MSR = \dfrac{SSR}{k}$ | $F_{STAT} = \dfrac{MSR}{MSE}$ |
| Error | $n - k - 1$ | $SSE$ | $MSE = \dfrac{SSE}{n - k - 1}$ | |

The decision rule is

Reject $H_0$ at the $\alpha$ level of significance if $F_{STAT} > F_\alpha$;

otherwise, do not reject $H_0$.

Using a 0.05 level of significance, the critical value of the $F$ distribution with 2 and 31 degrees of freedom found from Table E.5 is approximately 3.32 (see Figure 14.5 below). From Figure 14.2 or 14.3 on pages 638–639, the $F_{STAT}$ test statistic given in the ANOVA summary table is 48.4771. Because 48.4771 > 3.32, or because the $p$-value = 0.000 < 0.05, you reject $H_0$ and conclude that at least one of the independent variables (price and/or promotional expenditures) is related to sales.

**FIGURE 14.5**

Testing for the significance of a set of regression coefficients at the 0.05 level of significance, with 2 and 31 degrees of freedom

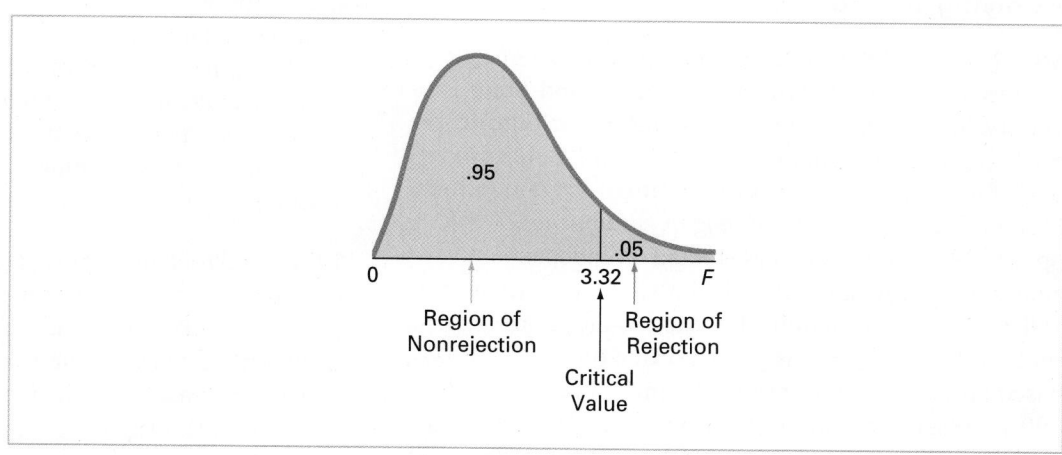

## PROBLEMS FOR SECTION 14.2

### Learning the Basics

**14.9** The following ANOVA summary table is for a multiple regression model with two independent variables:

| Source | Degrees of Freedom | Sum of Squares | Mean Squares | $F$ |
|---|---|---|---|---|
| Regression | 2 | 60 | | |
| Error | 18 | 120 | | |
| Total | 20 | 180 | | |

**a.** Determine the regression mean square ($MSR$) and the mean square error ($MSE$).

**b.** Compute the overall $F_{STAT}$ test statistic.

**c.** Determine whether there is a significant relationship between $Y$ and the two independent variables at the 0.05 level of significance.

**d.** Compute the coefficient of multiple determination, $r^2$, and interpret its meaning.

**e.** Compute the adjusted $r^2$.

**14.10** The following ANOVA summary table is for a multiple regression model with two independent variables:

| Source | Degrees of Freedom | Sum of Squares | Mean Squares | F |
|---|---|---|---|---|
| Regression | 2 | 30 | | |
| Error | 10 | 120 | | |
| Total | 12 | 150 | | |

**a.** Determine the regression mean square (*MSR*) and the mean square error (*MSE*).
**b.** Compute the overall $F_{STAT}$ test statistic.
**c.** Determine whether there is a significant relationship between $Y$ and the two independent variables at the 0.05 level of significance.
**d.** Compute the coefficient of multiple determination, $r^2$, and interpret its meaning.
**e.** Compute the adjusted $r^2$.

## Applying the Concepts

**14.11** Eileen M. Van Aken and Brian M. Kleiner, professors at Virginia Polytechnic Institute and State University, investigated the factors that contribute to the effectiveness of teams (extracted from "Determinants of Effectiveness for Cross-Functional Organizational Design Teams," *Quality Management Journal*, 1997, 4, pp. 51–79). The researchers studied 34 independent variables, such as team skills, diversity, meeting frequency, and clarity in expectations. For each of the teams studied, each of the variables was given a value of 1 through 100, based on the results of interviews and survey data, where 100 represents the highest rating. The dependent variable, team performance, was also given a value of 1 through 100, with 100 representing the highest rating. Many different regression models were explored, including the following:

**Model 1**

$$\text{Team performance} = b_0 + b_1(\text{Team skills}) + \varepsilon,$$

$$r^2_{adj} = 0.68$$

**Model 2**

$$\text{Team performance} = b_0 + b_1(\text{Clarity in expectations}) + \varepsilon,$$

$$r^2_{adj} = 0.78$$

**Model 3**

$$\text{Team performance} = b_0 + b_1(\text{Team skills}) +$$
$$b_2(\text{Clarity in expectations}) + \varepsilon,$$

$$r^2_{adj} = 0.97$$

**a.** Interpret the adjusted $r^2$ for each of the three models.
**b.** Which of these three models do you think is the best predictor of team performance?

**14.12** In Problem 14.3 on page 641, you predicted the durability of a brand of running shoe, based on the forefoot shock-absorbing capability and the change in impact properties over time. The regression analysis resulted in the following ANOVA summary table:

| Source | Degrees of Freedom | Sum of Squares | Mean Squares | F | p-value |
|---|---|---|---|---|---|
| Regression | 2 | 12.61020 | 6.30510 | 97.69 | 0.0001 |
| Error | 12 | 0.77453 | 0.06454 | | |
| Total | 14 | 13.38473 | | | |

**a.** Determine whether there is a significant relationship between durability and the two independent variables at the 0.05 level of significance.
**b.** Interpret the meaning of the *p*-value.
**c.** Compute the coefficient of multiple determination, $r^2$, and interpret its meaning.
**d.** Compute the adjusted $r^2$.

**14.13** In Problem 14.5 on page 641, you used horsepower and weight to predict gasoline mileage (see the Auto file). Using the results from that problem,
**a.** determine whether there is a significant relationship between gasoline mileage and the two independent variables (horsepower and weight) at the 0.05 level of significance.
**b.** interpret the meaning of the *p*-value.
**c.** compute the coefficient of multiple determination, $r^2$, and interpret its meaning.
**d.** compute the adjusted $r^2$.

**14.14** In Problem 14.4 on page 641, you used sales and number of orders to predict distribution costs at a mail-order catalog business (see the Warecost file). Using the results from that problem,
**a.** determine whether there is a significant relationship between distribution costs and the two independent variables (sales and number of orders) at the 0.05 level of significance.
**b.** interpret the meaning of the *p*-value.

**c.** compute the coefficient of multiple determination, $r^2$, and interpret its meaning.

**d.** compute the adjusted $r^2$.

**14.15** In Problem 14.7 on page 642, you used the total staff present and remote hours to predict standby hours (see the file **Standby**). Using the results from that problem,

**a.** determine whether there is a significant relationship between standby hours and the two independent variables (total staff present and remote hours) at the 0.05 level of significance.

**b.** interpret the meaning of the $p$-value.

**c.** compute the coefficient of multiple determination, $r^2$, and interpret its meaning.

**d.** compute the adjusted $r^2$.

**14.16** In Problem 14.6 on page 642, you used radio advertising and newspaper advertising to predict sales (see the **Advertise** file). Using the results from that problem,

**a.** determine whether there is a significant relationship between sales and the two independent variables (radio advertising and newspaper advertising) at the 0.05 level of significance.

**b.** interpret the meaning of the $p$-value.

**c.** compute the coefficient of multiple determination, $r^2$, and interpret its meaning.

**d.** compute the adjusted $r^2$.

**14.17** In Problem 14.8 on page 642, you used the land area of a property and the age of a house to predict appraised value (see the **GlenCove** file). Using the results from that problem,

**a.** determine whether there is a significant relationship between appraised value and the two independent variables (land area of a property and age of a house) at the 0.05 level of significance.

**b.** interpret the meaning of the $p$-value.

**c.** compute the coefficient of multiple determination, $r^2$, and interpret its meaning.

**d.** compute the adjusted $r^2$.

## 14.3  RESIDUAL ANALYSIS FOR THE MULTIPLE REGRESSION MODEL

In Section 13.5, you used residual analysis to evaluate the simple linear regression model for a set of data. For the multiple regression model with two independent variables, you need to construct and analyze the following residual plots:

1. Residuals versus $\hat{Y}_i$
2. Residuals versus $X_{1i}$
3. Residuals versus $X_{2i}$
4. Residuals versus time

The first residual plot examines the pattern of residuals versus the predicted values of $Y$. If the residuals show a pattern for different predicted values of $Y$, there is evidence of a possible quadratic effect in at least one independent variable, a possible violation of the assumption of equal variance (see Figure 13.16 on page 597), and/or the need to transform the $Y$ variable.

The second and third residual plots involve the independent variables. Patterns in the plot of the residuals versus an independent variable may indicate the existence of a quadratic effect and, therefore, the need to add a quadratic independent variable to the multiple regression model. The fourth plot is used to investigate patterns in the residuals in order to validate the independence assumption when the data are collected in time order. Associated with this residual plot, as in Section 13.6, you can compute the Durbin-Watson statistic to determine the existence of positive autocorrelation among the residuals.

Figure 14.6 illustrates the Microsoft Excel residual plots for the OmniPower sales example. There is very little or no pattern in the relationship between the residuals and the predicted value of $Y$, the value of $X_1$ (price), or the value of $X_2$ (promotional expenditures). Thus, you can conclude that the multiple regression model is appropriate for predicting sales. There is no need to plot the residuals versus time since the data were not collected in time order.

**FIGURE 14.6**

Microsoft Excel residual plots for the OmniPower sales data: Panel *A*, residuals versus predicted *Y*; Panel *B*, residuals versus price; Panel *C*, residuals versus promotional expenditures

*See Section E14.2 or P14.2 to create this. Minitab users, see Section M14.2 to create equivalent charts.*

Panel *A*

Panel *B*

Panel *C*

## PROBLEMS FOR SECTION 14.3

### Applying the Concepts

**14.18** In Problem 14.4 on page 641, you used sales and number of orders to predict distribution costs at a mail-order catalog business (see the Warecost file).
a. Plot the residuals versus $\hat{Y}_i$.
b. Plot the residuals versus $X_{1i}$.
c. Plot the residuals versus $X_{2i}$.
d. Plot the residuals versus time.
e. In the residuals plots created in (a) through (d), is there any evidence of a violation to the regression assumptions? Explain.
f. Determine the Durbin-Watson statistic.
g. At the 0.05 level of significance, is there evidence of positive autocorrelation in the residuals?

**14.19** In Problem 14.5 on page 641, you used horsepower and weight to predict gasoline mileage (see the Auto file).
a. Plot the residuals versus $\hat{Y}_i$.
b. Plot the residuals versus $X_{1i}$.
c. Plot the residuals versus $X_{2i}$.
d. In the residuals plots created in (a) through (c), is there any evidence of a violation to the regression assumptions? Explain.
e. Should you compute the Durbin-Watson statistic for these data? Explain.

**14.20** In Problem 14.6 on page 642, you used radio advertising and newspaper advertising to predict sales (see the Advertise file).
a. Perform a residual analysis on your results.
b. If appropriate, perform the Durbin-Watson test using $\alpha = 0.05$.
c. Are the regression assumptions valid for these data?

**14.21** In Problem 14.7 on page 642, you used the total staff present and remote hours to predict standby hours (see the Standby file).
a. Perform a residual analysis on your results.
b. If appropriate, perform the Durbin-Watson test using $\alpha = 0.05$.
c. Are the regression assumptions valid for these data?

**14.22** In Problem 14.8 on page 642, you used the land area of a property and the age of a house to predict appraised value (see the GlenCove file).
a. Perform a residual analysis on your results.
b. If appropriate, perform the Durbin-Watson test using $\alpha = 0.05$.
c. Are the regression assumptions valid for these data?

## 14.4 INFERENCES CONCERNING THE POPULATION REGRESSION COEFFICIENTS

In Section 13.7, you tested the slope in a simple linear regression model to determine the significance of the relationship between $X$ and $Y$. In addition, you constructed a confidence interval estimate of the population slope. This section extends those procedures to multiple regression.

### Tests of Hypothesis

In a simple linear regression model, to test a hypothesis concerning the population slope, $\beta_1$, you used Equation (13.16) on page 597:

$$t_{STAT} = \frac{b_1 - \beta_1}{S_{b_1}}$$

Equation (14.7) generalizes this equation for multiple regression.

Testing for the Slope in Multiple Regression

$$t_{STAT} = \frac{b_j - \beta_j}{S_{b_j}} \qquad (14.7)$$

where

$b_j$ = slope of variable $j$ with $Y$, holding constant the effects of all other independent variables

$S_{b_j}$ = standard error of the regression coefficient $b_j$

$t_{STAT}$ = test statistic for a $t$ distribution with $n - k - 1$ degrees of freedom

$k$ = number of independent variables in the regression equation

$\beta_j$ = hypothesized value of the population slope for variable $j$, holding constant the effects of all other independent variables

To determine whether variable $X_2$ (amount of promotional expenditures) has a significant effect on sales, taking into account the price of OmniPower bars, the null and alternative hypotheses are

$$H_0: \beta_2 = 0$$

$$H_1: \beta_2 \neq 0$$

From Equation (14.7) and Figures 14.2 or 14.3 on pages 638–639,

$$t_{STAT} = \frac{b_2 - \beta_2}{S_{b_2}}$$

$$= \frac{3.6131 - 0}{0.6852} = 5.2728$$

If you select a level of significance of 0.05, the critical values of $t$ for 31 degrees of freedom from Table E.3 are $-2.0395$ and $+2.0395$ (see Figure 14.7).

**FIGURE 14.7**

Testing for significance of a regression coefficient at the 0.05 level of significance, with 31 degrees of freedom

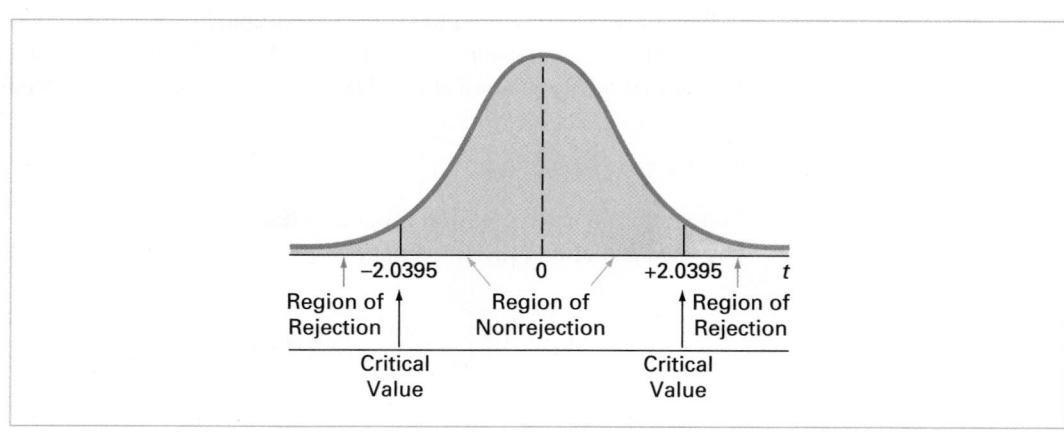

From Figure 14.2 or 14.3 on pages 638–639, observe that the computed $t_{STAT}$ test statistic is 5.2728. Because $t_{STAT} = 5.2728 > 2.0395$, you reject $H_0$ and conclude that there is a significant relationship between the variable $X_2$ (promotional expenditures) and sales, taking into account the price, $X_1$. Using the $p$-value approach, note that the $p$-value is approximately zero. This extremely small $p$-value allows you to strongly reject the null hypothesis that there is no linear relationship between sales and promotional expenditures. Example 14.1 presents the test for the significance of $\beta_1$, the slope of sales with price.

**EXAMPLE 14.1**    TESTING FOR THE SIGNIFICANCE OF THE SLOPE OF SALES WITH PRICE

At the 0.05 level of significance, is there evidence that the slope of sales with price is different from zero?

**SOLUTION** From Figure 14.2 or 14.3 on pages 638–639, $t_{STAT} = -7.7664 < -2.0395$ (the critical value for $\alpha = 0.05$) or the $p$-value $= 0.0000000092 < 0.05$. Thus, there is a significant relationship between price, $X_1$, and sales, taking into account the promotional expenditures, $X_2$.

As seen with each of the two $X$ variables, the test of significance for a specific regression coefficient is actually a test for the significance of adding that variable into a regression model, given that the other variable is included. Therefore, the $t$ test for the regression coefficient is equivalent to testing for the contribution of each independent variable.

## Confidence Interval Estimation

Instead of testing the significance of a population slope, you may want to estimate the value of a population slope. Equation (14.8) defines the confidence interval estimate for a population slope in multiple regression.

---

Confidence Interval Estimate for the Slope

$$b_j \pm t_{\alpha/2} S_{b_j} \tag{14.8}$$

where $t_{\alpha/2}$ is the critical value corresponding to an upper-tail probability of $\alpha/2$ from the $t$ distribution with $n - k - 1$ degrees of freedom (i.e., a cumulative area of $1 - \alpha/2$), and $k$ is the number of independent variables.

---

To construct a 95% confidence interval estimate of the population slope, $\beta_1$ (the effect of price, $X_1$, on sales, $Y$, holding constant the effect of promotional expenditures, $X_2$), the critical value of $t$ at the 95% confidence level with 31 degrees of freedom is 2.0395 (see Table E.3). Then, using Equation (14.8) and Figure 14.2 or 14.3 on pages 638–639,

$$b_1 \pm t_{\alpha/2} S_{b_1}$$

$$-53.2173 \pm (2.0395)(6.8522)$$

$$-53.2173 \pm 13.9752$$

$$-67.1925 \le \beta_1 \le -39.2421$$

Taking into account the effect of promotional expenditures, the estimated effect of a 1-cent increase in price is to reduce mean sales by approximately 39.2 to 67.2 bars. You have 95% confidence that this interval correctly estimates the relationship between these variables. From a hypothesis-testing viewpoint, because this confidence interval does not include 0, you conclude that the regression coefficient, $\beta_1$, has a significant effect.

Example 14.2 constructs and interprets a confidence interval estimate for the slope of sales with promotional expenditures.

**EXAMPLE 14.2**      CONSTRUCTING A CONFIDENCE INTERVAL ESTIMATE FOR THE SLOPE OF SALES WITH PROMOTIONAL EXPENDITURES

Construct a 95% confidence interval estimate of the population slope of sales with promotional expenditures.

**SOLUTION** The critical value of $t$ at the 95% confidence level, with 31 degrees of freedom, is 2.0395 (see Table E.3). Using Equation (14.8) and Figure 14.2 or 14.3 on pages 638–639,

$$b_2 \pm t_{\alpha/2} S_{b_2}$$

$$3.6131 \pm (2.0395)(0.6852)$$

$$3.6131 \pm 1.3975$$

$$2.2156 \leq \beta_2 \leq 5.0106$$

Thus, taking into account the effect of price, the estimated effect of each additional dollar of promotional expenditures is to increase mean sales by approximately 2.2 to 5.0 bars. You have 95% confidence that this interval correctly estimates the relationship between these variables. From a hypothesis-testing viewpoint, because this confidence interval does not include 0, you can conclude that the regression coefficient, $\beta_2$, has a significant effect.

## PROBLEMS FOR SECTION 14.4

### Learning the Basics

**14.23** Given the following information from a multiple regression analysis:

$$n = 25 \quad b_1 = 5 \quad b_2 = 10 \quad S_{b_1} = 2 \quad S_{b_2} = 8$$

a. Which variable has the largest slope, in units of a $t$ statistic?
b. Construct a 95% confidence interval estimate of the population slope, $\beta_1$.
c. At the 0.05 level of significance, determine whether each independent variable makes a significant contribution to the regression model. On the basis of these results, indicate the independent variables to include in this model.

**14.24** Given the following information from a multiple regression analysis:

$$n = 20 \quad b_1 = 4 \quad b_2 = 3 \quad S_{b_1} = 1.2 \quad S_{b_2} = 0.8$$

a. Which variable has the largest slope, in units of a $t$ statistic?
b. Construct a 95% confidence interval estimate of the population slope, $\beta_1$.
c. At the 0.05 level of significance, determine whether each independent variable makes a significant contribution to the regression model. On the basis of these results, indicate the independent variables to include in this model.

### Applying the Concepts

**14.25** In Problem 14.3 on page 641, you predicted the durability of a brand of running shoe, based on the forefoot shock-absorbing capability (FOREIMP) and the change in impact properties over time (MIDSOLE) for a sample of 15 pairs of shoes. Use the following results:

| Variable | Coefficient | Standard Error | $t$ Statistic | $p$-Value |
|---|---|---|---|---|
| INTERCEPT | −0.02686 | 0.06905 | −0.39 | 0.7034 |
| FOREIMP | 0.79116 | 0.06295 | 12.57 | 0.0000 |
| MIDSOLE | 0.60484 | 0.07174 | 8.43 | 0.0000 |

a. Construct a 95% confidence interval estimate of the population slope between durability and forefoot shock-absorbing capability.
b. At the 0.05 level of significance, determine whether each independent variable makes a significant contribution to the regression model. On the basis of these results, indicate the independent variables to include in this model.

✓ **SELF Test** **14.26** In Problem 14.4 on page 641, you used sales and number of orders to predict distribution costs at a mail-order catalog business (see the **Warecost** file). Using the results from that problem,

**a.** construct a 95% confidence interval estimate of the population slope between distribution cost and sales.

**b.** at the 0.05 level of significance, determine whether each independent variable makes a significant contribution to the regression model. On the basis of these results, indicate the independent variables to include in this model.

**14.27** In Problem 14.5 on page 641, you used horsepower and weight to predict gasoline mileage (see the Auto file). Using the results from that problem,

**a.** construct a 95% confidence interval estimate of the population slope between gasoline mileage and horsepower.

**b.** at the 0.05 level of significance, determine whether each independent variable makes a significant contribution to the regression model. On the basis of these results, indicate the independent variables to include in this model.

**14.28** In Problem 14.6 on page 642, you used radio advertising and newspaper advertising to predict sales (see the Advertise file). Using the results from that problem,

**a.** construct a 95% confidence interval estimate of the population slope between sales and radio advertising.

**b.** at the 0.05 level of significance, determine whether each independent variable makes a significant contribution to the regression model. On the basis of these results, indicate the independent variables to include in this model.

**14.29** In Problem 14.7 on page 642, you used the total number of staff present and remote hours to predict standby hours (see the Standby file). Using the results from that problem,

**a.** construct a 95% confidence interval estimate of the population slope between standby hours and total number of staff present.

**b.** at the 0.05 level of significance, determine whether each independent variable makes a significant contribution to the regression model. On the basis of these results, indicate the independent variables to include in this model.

**14.30** In Problem 14.8 on page 642, you used land area of a property and age of a house to predict appraised value (see the GlenCove file). Using the results from that problem,

**a.** construct a 95% confidence interval estimate of the population slope between appraised value and land area of a property.

**b.** at the 0.05 level of significance, determine whether each independent variable makes a significant contribution to the regression model. On the basis of these results, indicate the independent variables to include in this model.

## 14.5   TESTING PORTIONS OF THE MULTIPLE REGRESSION MODEL

In developing a multiple regression model, you want to use only those independent variables that significantly reduce the error in predicting the value of a dependent variable. If an independent variable does not improve the prediction, you can delete it from the multiple regression model and use a model with fewer independent variables.

The **partial $F$ test** is an alternative method to the $t$ test discussed in Section 14.4 for determining the contribution of an independent variable. It involves determining the contribution to the regression sum of squares made by each independent variable after all the other independent variables have been included in the model. The new independent variable is included only if it significantly improves the model.

To conduct partial $F$ tests for the OmniPower sales example, you need to evaluate the contribution of promotional expenditures $(X_2)$ after price $(X_1)$ has been included in the model, and also evaluate the contribution of price $(X_1)$ after promotional expenditures $(X_2)$ have been included in the model.

In general, if there are several independent variables, you determine the contribution of each independent variable by taking into account the regression sum of squares of a model that includes all independent variables except the one of interest, $j$. This regression sum of squares is denoted $SSR$(all $X$s except $j$). Equation (14.9) determines the contribution of variable $j$, assuming that all other variables are already included.

Determining the Contribution of an Independent Variable
to the Regression Model

$$SSR(X_j \mid \text{All } Xs \text{ except } j) = SSR \text{ (All } Xs) - SSR \text{ (All } Xs \text{ except } j) \qquad \textbf{(14.9)}$$

If there are two independent variables, you use Equations (14.10a) and (14.10b) to determine the contribution of each.

Contribution of Variable $X_1$, Given that $X_2$ Has Been Included

$$SSR(X_1 \mid X_2) = SSR(X_1 \text{ and } X_2) - SSR(X_2) \qquad \textbf{(14.10a)}$$

Contribution of Variable $X_2$, Given that $X_1$ Has Been Included

$$SSR(X_2 \mid X_1) = SSR(X_1 \text{ and } X_2) - SSR(X_1) \qquad \textbf{(14.10b)}$$

The term $SSR(X_2)$ represents the sum of squares that is due to regression for a model that includes only the independent variable $X_2$ (promotional expenditures). Similarly, $SSR(X_1)$ represents the sum of squares that is due to regression for a model that includes only the independent variable $X_1$ (price). Figures 14.8 and 14.9 present Microsoft Excel results and Figures 14.10 and 14.11 show Minitab results for these two models.

**FIGURE 14.8**

Microsoft Excel regression results worksheet for a simple linear regression analysis for sales and promotional expenditures, $SSR(X_2)$

*See Section E13.1 or P13.1 to create this.*

| | A | B | C | D | E | F | G |
|---|---|---|---|---|---|---|---|
| 1 | **Sales & Promotional Expenses Analysis** | | | | | | |
| 2 | | | | | | | |
| 3 | *Regression Statistics* | | | | | | |
| 4 | **Multiple R** | 0.5351 | | | | | |
| 5 | **R Square** | 0.2863 | | | | | |
| 6 | **Adjusted R Square** | 0.2640 | | | | | |
| 7 | **Standard Error** | 1077.8721 | | | | | |
| 8 | **Observations** | 34 | | | | | |
| 9 | | | | | | | |
| 10 | **ANOVA** | | | | | | |
| 11 | | *df* | *SS* | *MS* | *F* | *Significance F* | |
| 12 | **Regression** | 1 | 14915814.102 | 14915814.102 | 12.8384 | 0.0011 | |
| 13 | **Residual** | 32 | 37177863.339 | 1161808.229 | | | |
| 14 | **Total** | 33 | 52093677.441 | | | | |
| 15 | | | | | | | |
| 16 | | *Coefficients* | *Standard Error* | *t Stat* | *P-value* | *Lower 95%* | *Upper 95%* |
| 17 | **Intercept** | 1496.0161 | 483.9789 | 3.0911 | 0.0041 | 510.1843 | 2481.8480 |
| 18 | **Promotion** | 4.1281 | 1.1521 | 3.5831 | 0.0011 | 1.7813 | 6.4748 |

**FIGURE 14.9**

Microsoft Excel regression results worksheet for a simple linear regression model for sales and price, $SSR(X_1)$

*See Section E13.1 or P13.1 to create this.*

| | A | B | C | D | E | F | G |
|---|---|---|---|---|---|---|---|
| 1 | **Sales & Price Analysis** | | | | | | |
| 2 | | | | | | | |
| 3 | *Regression Statistics* | | | | | | |
| 4 | **Multiple R** | 0.7351 | | | | | |
| 5 | **R Square** | 0.5404 | | | | | |
| 6 | **Adjusted R Square** | 0.5261 | | | | | |
| 7 | **Standard Error** | 864.9457 | | | | | |
| 8 | **Observations** | 34 | | | | | |
| 9 | | | | | | | |
| 10 | **ANOVA** | | | | | | |
| 11 | | *df* | *SS* | *MS* | *F* | *Significance F* | |
| 12 | **Regression** | 1 | 28153486.15 | 28153486.15 | 37.6318 | 7.35855E-07 | |
| 13 | **Residual** | 32 | 23940191.29 | 748130.98 | | | |
| 14 | **Total** | 33 | 52093677.44 | | | | |
| 15 | | | | | | | |
| 16 | | *Coefficients* | *Standard Error* | *t Stat* | *P-value* | *Lower 95%* | *Upper 95%* |
| 17 | **Intercept** | 7512.3480 | 734.6189 | 10.2262 | 1.30793E-11 | 6015.9796 | 9008.7164 |
| 18 | **Price** | -56.7138 | 9.2451 | -6.1345 | 7.35855E-07 | -75.5455 | -37.8822 |

**FIGURE 14.10**

Minitab results for a simple linear regression analysis for sales and promotional expenditures, $SSR(X_2)$

*See Section M13.1 to create this.*

```
The regression equation is
sales = 1496 + 4.13 promotion


Predictor    Coef    SE Coef    T      P
Constant    1496.0    484.0    3.09   0.004
promotion    4.128    1.152    3.58   0.001


S = 1077.87   R-Sq = 28.6%   R-Sq(adj) = 26.4%


Analysis of Variance

Source          DF        SS         MS        F      P
Regression       1    14915814    14915814   12.84   0.001
Residual Error  32    37177863     1161808
Total           33    52093677
```

**FIGURE 14.11**

Minitab results of a simple linear regression model for sales and price, $SSR(X_1)$

*See Section M13.1 to create this.*

```
The regression equation is
sales = 7512 - 56.7 price


Predictor    Coef     SE Coef     T      P
Constant    7512.3     734.6    10.23  0.000
price      -56.714     9.245    -6.13  0.000


S = 864.946   R-Sq = 54.0%   R-Sq(adj) = 52.6%


Analysis of Variance

Source          DF        SS         MS        F      P
Regression       1    28153486    28153486   37.63   0.000
Residual Error  32    23940191     748131
Total           33    52093677
```

From Figure 14.8 or 14.10, $SSR(X_2) = 14{,}915{,}814.102$ and from Figure 14.2 or 14.3 on pages 638–639, $SSR(X_1 \text{ and } X_2) = 39{,}472{,}730.77$. Then, using Equation (14.10a),

$$SSR(X_1 \mid X_2) = SSR(X_1 \text{ and } X_2) - SSR(X_2)$$

$$= 39{,}472{,}730.77 - 14{,}915{,}814.102$$

$$= 24{,}556{,}916.67$$

To determine whether $X_1$ significantly improves the model after $X_2$ has been included, you divide the regression sum of squares into two component parts, as shown in Table 14.3.

**TABLE 14.3**

ANOVA Table Dividing the Regression Sum of Squares into Components to Determine the Contribution of Variable $X_1$

| Source | Degrees of Freedom | Sum of Squares | Mean Square (Variance) | F |
|---|---|---|---|---|
| Regression | 2 | 39,472,730.77 | 19,736,365.39 | |
| $\left\{\begin{array}{c} X_2 \\ X_1 \mid X_2 \end{array}\right.$ | $\left\{\begin{array}{c} 1 \\ 1 \end{array}\right.$ | $\left\{\begin{array}{c} 14,915,814.10 \\ 24,556,916.67 \end{array}\right.$ | 24,556,916.67 | 60.32 |
| Error | 31 | 12,620,946.67 | 407,127.31 | |
| Total | 33 | 52,093,677.44 | | |

The null and alternative hypotheses to test for the contribution of $X_1$ to the model are

$H_0$: Variable $X_1$ does not significantly improve the model after variable $X_2$ has been included.
$H_1$: Variable $X_1$ significantly improves the model after variable $X_2$ has been included.

Equation (14.11) defines the partial $F$ test statistic for testing the contribution of an independent variable.

**Partial F Test**

$$F_{STAT} = \frac{SSR(X_j \mid \text{All } Xs \text{ except } j)}{MSE} \qquad (14.11)$$

The partial $F_{STAT}$ test statistic follows an $F$ distribution with 1 and $n - k - 1$ degrees of freedom.

From Table 14.3,

$$F_{STAT} = \frac{24,556,916.67}{407,127.31} = 60.32$$

The partial $F_{STAT}$ test statistic has 1 and $n - k - 1 = 34 - 2 - 1 = 31$ degrees of freedom. Using a level of significance of 0.05, the critical value from Table E.5 is approximately 4.17 (see Figure 14.12).

**FIGURE 14.12**

Testing for the contribution of a regression coefficient to a multiple regression model at the 0.05 level of significance, with 1 and 31 degrees of freedom

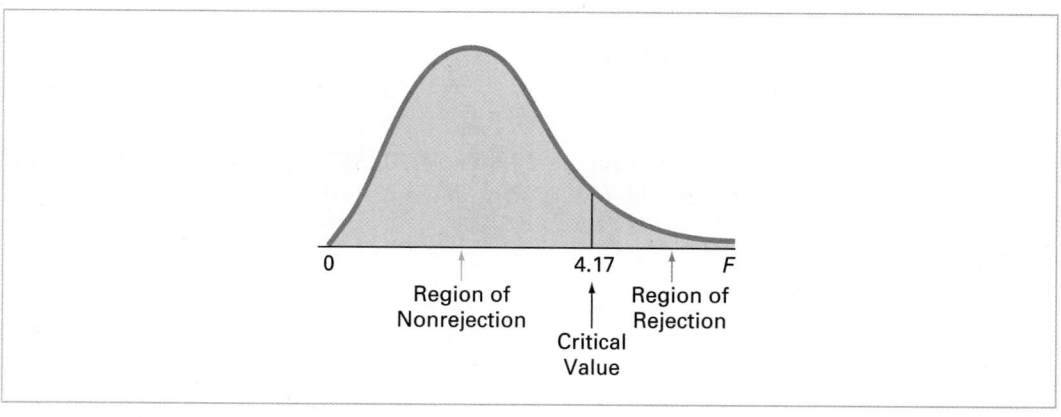

Because the computed partial $F_{STAT}$ test statistic is greater than this critical $F$ value (60.32 > 4.17), reject $H_0$. You can conclude that the addition of variable $X_1$ (price) significantly improves a regression model that already contains variable $X_2$ (promotional expenditures).

To evaluate the contribution of variable $X_2$ (promotional expenditures) to a model in which variable $X_1$ (price) has been included, you need to use Equation (14.10b). First, from Figure 14.9 or 14.11 on pages 654–655, observe that $SSR(X_1) = 28,153,486.15$. Second, from Table 14.3, observe that $SSR(X_1 \text{ and } X_2) = 39,472,730.77$. Then, using Equation (14.10b) on page 654,

$$SSR(X_2 \mid X_1) = 39,472,730.77 - 28,153,486.15 = 11,319,244.62$$

To determine whether $X_2$ significantly improves a model after $X_1$ has been included, you can divide the regression sum of squares into two component parts, as shown in Table 14.4.

**TABLE 14.4**

ANOVA Table Dividing the Regression Sum of Squares into Components to Determine the Contribution of Variable $X_2$

| Source | Degrees of Freedom | Sum of Squares | Mean Square (Variance) | F |
|---|---|---|---|---|
| Regression | 2 | 39,472,730.77 | 19,736,365.39 | |
| $\left\{\begin{array}{c} X_1 \\ X_2 \mid X_1 \end{array}\right\}$ | $\left\{\begin{array}{c} 1 \\ 1 \end{array}\right\}$ | $\left\{\begin{array}{c} 28,153,486.15 \\ 11,319,244.62 \end{array}\right\}$ | 11,319,244.62 | 27.80 |
| Error | 31 | 12,620,946.67 | 407,127.31 | |
| Total | 33 | 52,093,677.44 | | |

The null and alternative hypotheses to test for the contribution of $X_2$ to the model are

$H_0$: Variable $X_2$ does not significantly improve the model after variable $X_1$ has been included.
$H_1$: Variable $X_2$ significantly improves the model after variable $X_1$ has been included.

Using Equation (14.11) and Table 14.4,

$$F_{STAT} = \frac{11,319,244.62}{407,127.31} = 27.80$$

In Figure 14.12, you can see that, using a 0.05 level of significance, the critical value of $F$, with 1 and 31 degrees of freedom, is approximately 4.17. Because the computed partial $F_{STAT}$ test statistic is greater than this critical value (27.80 > 4.17), reject $H_0$. You can conclude that the addition of variable $X_2$ (promotional expenditures) significantly improves the multiple regression model already containing $X_1$ (price).

Thus, by testing for the contribution of each independent variable after the other has been included in the model, you determine that each of the two independent variables significantly improves the model. Therefore, the multiple regression model should include both price, $X_1$, and promotional expenditures, $X_2$.

The partial $F$-test statistic developed in this section and the $t$-test statistic of Equation (14.7) on page 000 are both used to determine the contribution of an independent variable to a multiple regression model. In fact, the hypothesis tests associated with these two statistics always result in the same decision (i.e., the $p$-values are identical). The $t_{STAT}$ test statistics for the OmniPower regression model are $-7.7664$ and $+5.2728$, and the corresponding $F_{STAT}$ test statistics are 60.32 and 27.80. Equation (14.12) illustrates the relationship between $t$ and $F$.

Relationship Between a $t$ Statistic and an $F$ Statistic

$$t^2_{STAT} = F_{STAT} \qquad\qquad (14.12)$$

## Coefficients of Partial Determination

Recall from Section 14.2 that the coefficient of multiple determination, $r^2$, measures the proportion of the variation in $Y$ that is explained by variation in the independent variables. The **coefficients of partial determination** ($r_{Y1.2}^2$ and $r_{Y2.1}^2$) measure the proportion of the variation in the dependent variable that is explained by each independent variable while controlling for, or holding constant, the other independent variable. Equation (14.13) defines the coefficients of partial determination for a multiple regression model with two independent variables.

Coefficients of Partial Determination for a Multiple Regression Model Containing Two Independent Variables

$$r_{Y1.2}^2 = \frac{SSR(X_1 \mid X_2)}{SST - SSR(X_1 \text{ and } X_2) + SSR(X_1 \mid X_2)} \quad \textbf{(14.13a)}$$

and

$$r_{Y2.1}^2 = \frac{SSR(X_2 \mid X_1)}{SST - SSR(X_1 \text{ and } X_2) + SSR(X_2 \mid X_1)} \quad \textbf{(14.13b)}$$

where

$SSR(X_1 \mid X_2)$ = sum of squares of the contribution of variable $X_1$ to the regression model, given that variable $X_2$ has been included in the model

$SST$ = total sum of squares for $Y$

$SSR(X_1 \text{ and } X_2)$ = regression sum of squares when variables $X_1$ and $X_2$ are both included in the multiple regression model

$SSR(X_2 \mid X_1)$ = sum of squares of the contribution of variable $X_2$ to the regression model, given that variable $X_1$ has been included in the model

For the OmniPower sales example,

$$r_{Y1.2}^2 = \frac{24,556,916.67}{52,093,677.44 - 39,472,730.77 + 24,556,916.67}$$

$$= 0.6605$$

$$r_{Y2.1}^2 = \frac{11,319,244.62}{52,093,677.44 - 39,472,730.77 + 11,319,244.62}$$

$$= 0.4728$$

The coefficient of partial determination $r_{Y2.1}^2$, of variable $Y$ with $X_1$ while holding $X_2$ constant is 0.6605. Thus, for a given (constant) amount of promotional expenditures, 66.05% of the variation in OmniPower sales is explained by the variation in the price. The coefficient of partial determination $r_{Y2.1}^2$, of variable $Y$ with $X_2$ while holding $X_1$ constant is 0.4728. Thus, for a given (constant) price, 47.28% of the variation in sales of OmniPower bars is explained by variation in the amount of promotional expenditures.

Equation (14.14) defines the coefficient of partial determination for the $j$th variable in a multiple regression model containing several ($k$) independent variables.

---

**Coefficient of Partial Determination for a Multiple Regression Model Containing $k$ Independent Variables**

$$r^2_{Y_{j.} \, (\text{All } Xs \text{ except } j)} = \frac{SSR(X_j \mid \text{All } Xs \text{ except } j)}{SST - SSR(\text{All } Xs) + SSR(X_j \mid \text{All } Xs \text{ except } j)}$$

(14.14)

---

# PROBLEMS FOR SECTION 14.5

## Learning the Basics

**14.31** The following is the ANOVA summary table for a multiple regression model with two independent variables:

| Source | Degrees of Freedom | Sum of Squares | Mean Squares | F |
|---|---|---|---|---|
| Regression | 2 | 60 | | |
| Error | 18 | 120 | | |
| Total | 20 | 180 | | |

If $SSR(X_1) = 45$ and $SSR(X_2) = 25$,
a. determine whether there is a significant relationship between $Y$ and each independent variable at the 0.05 level of significance.
b. compute the coefficients of partial determination, $r^2_{Y1.2}$ and $r^2_{Y2.1}$, and interpret their meaning.

**14.32** The following is the ANOVA summary table for a multiple regression model with two independent variables:

| Source | Degrees of Freedom | Sum of Squares | Mean Squares | F |
|---|---|---|---|---|
| Regression | 2 | 30 | | |
| Error | 10 | 120 | | |
| Total | 12 | 150 | | |

If $SSR(X_1) = 20$ and $SSR(X_2) = 15$,
a. determine whether there is a significant relationship between $Y$ and each independent variable at the 0.05 level of significance.
b. compute the coefficients of partial determination, $r^2_{Y1.2}$ and $r^2_{Y2.1}$, and interpret their meaning.

## Applying the Concepts

**14.33** In Problem 14.5 on page 641, you used horsepower and weight to predict gasoline mileage (see the **Auto** file). Using the results from that problem,

a. at the 0.05 level of significance, determine whether each independent variable makes a significant contribution to the regression model. On the basis of these results, indicate the most appropriate regression model for this set of data.
b. compute the coefficients of partial determination, $r^2_{Y1.2}$ and $r^2_{Y2.1}$, and interpret their meaning.

**✓ SELF Test** **14.34** In Problem 14.4 on page 641, you used sales and number of orders to predict distribution costs at a mail-order catalog business (see the **Warecost** file). Using the results from that problem,
a. at the 0.05 level of significance, determine whether each independent variable makes a significant contribution to the regression model. On the basis of these results, indicate the most appropriate regression model for this set of data.
b. compute the coefficients of partial determination, $r^2_{Y1.2}$ and $r^2_{Y2.1}$, and interpret their meaning.

**14.35** In Problem 14.7 on page 642, you used the total staff present and remote hours to predict standby hours (see the **Standby** file). Using the results from that problem,
a. at the 0.05 level of significance, determine whether each independent variable makes a significant contribution to the regression model. On the basis of these results, indicate the most appropriate regression model for this set of data.
b. compute the coefficients of partial determination, $r^2_{Y1.2}$ and $r^2_{Y2.1}$, and interpret their meaning.

**14.36** In Problem 14.6 on page 642, you used radio advertising and newspaper advertising to predict sales (see the **Advertise** file). Using the results from that problem,
a. at the 0.05 level of significance, determine whether each independent variable makes a significant contribution to the regression model. On the basis of these results, indicate the most appropriate regression model for this set of data.
b. compute the coefficients of partial determination, $r^2_{Y1.2}$ and $r^2_{Y2.1}$, and interpret their meaning.

**14.37** In Problem 14.8 on page 642, you used land area of a property and age of a house to predict appraised value (see the GlenCove file). Using the results from that problem,

a. at the 0.05 level of significance, determine whether each independent variable makes a significant contribution to the regression model. On the basis of these results, indicate the most appropriate regression model for this set of data.

b. compute the coefficients of partial determination, $r_{Y1.2}^2$ and $r_{Y2.1}^2$, and interpret their meaning.

## 14.6  USING DUMMY VARIABLES AND INTERACTION TERMS IN REGRESSION MODELS

The multiple regression models discussed in Sections 14.1 through 14.5 assumed that each independent variable is numerical. However, in some situations, you might need to include categorical independent variablesin the regression model. For example, in Section 14.1, you used price and promotional expenditures to predict the monthly sales of OmniPower high-energy bars. In addition to these numerical independent variables, you may need to include the effect of the shelf location in the store (e.g., end-aisle display or no end-aisle display) when developing a model to predict OmniPower sales.

The use of **dummy variables** allows you to include categorical independent variables in the regression model. If a given categorical independent variable has two categories, then you need only one dummy variable to represent the two categories. A dummy variable, $X_d$, is defined as

$$X_d = 0 \text{ if the observation is in category 1}$$

$$X_d = 1 \text{ if the observation is in category 2}$$

To illustrate the application of dummy variables in regression, consider a model for predicting the assessed value from a sample of 15 houses, based on the size of the house (in thousands of square feet) and whether the house has a fireplace. To include the categorical variable concerning the presence of a fireplace, the dummy variable $X_2$ is defined as

$$X_2 = 0 \text{ if the house does not have a fireplace}$$

$$X_2 = 1 \text{ if the house has a fireplace}$$

Table 14.5 presents the data, which are also stored in the file House3. In the last column of Table 14.5, you can see how the categorical data are converted to numerical values.

**TABLE 14.5**

Predicting Assessed Value, Based on Size of the House and Presence of a Fireplace

| Assessed Value | Size | Fireplace | Fireplace Coded |
|---|---|---|---|
| 234.4 | 2.00 | Yes | 1 |
| 227.4 | 1.71 | No | 0 |
| 225.7 | 1.45 | No | 0 |
| 235.9 | 1.76 | Yes | 1 |
| 229.1 | 1.93 | No | 0 |
| 220.4 | 1.20 | Yes | 1 |
| 225.8 | 1.55 | Yes | 1 |
| 235.9 | 1.93 | Yes | 1 |
| 228.5 | 1.59 | Yes | 1 |
| 229.2 | 1.50 | Yes | 1 |
| 236.7 | 1.90 | Yes | 1 |
| 229.3 | 1.39 | Yes | 1 |
| 224.5 | 1.54 | No | 0 |
| 233.8 | 1.89 | Yes | 1 |
| 226.8 | 1.59 | No | 0 |

Assuming that the slope of assessed value with the size of the house is the same for houses that have and do not have a fireplace, the multiple regression model is

$$Y_i = \beta_0 + \beta_1 X_{1i} + \beta_2 X_{2i} + \varepsilon_i$$

where

$Y_i$ = assessed value in thousands of dollars for house $i$

$\beta_0$ = $Y$ intercept

$X_{1i}$ = size of the house, in thousands of square feet, for house $i$

$\beta_1$ = slope of assessed value with size of the house, holding constant the presence or absence of a fireplace

$X_{2i}$ = dummy variable representing the presence or absence of a fireplace for house $i$

$\beta_2$ = net effect of the presence of a fireplace on assessed value, holding constant the size of the house

$\varepsilon_i$ = random error in $Y$ for house $i$

Figure 14.13 illustrates the Microsoft Excel results for this model. Figure 14.14 shows Minitab results.

**FIGURE 14.13**

Microsoft Excel regression results worksheet for the regression model that includes size of the house and presence of fireplace

*See Section E14.5 and either E14.1 or P14.1 to create this.*

| | A | B | C | D | E | F | G |
|---|---|---|---|---|---|---|---|
| 1 | **Assessed Value Analysis** | | | | | | |
| 2 | | | | | | | |
| 3 | **Regression Statistics** | | | | | | |
| 4 | Multiple R | 0.9006 | | | | | |
| 5 | R Square | 0.8111 | | | | | |
| 6 | Adjusted R Square | 0.7796 | | | | | |
| 7 | Standard Error | 2.2626 | | | | | |
| 8 | Observations | 15 | | | | | |
| 9 | | | | | | | |
| 10 | ANOVA | | | | | | |
| 11 | | df | SS | MS | F | Significance F | |
| 12 | Regression | 2 | 263.7039 | 131.8520 | 25.7557 | 0.0000 | |
| 13 | Residual | 12 | 61.4321 | 5.1193 | | | |
| 14 | Total | 14 | 325.1360 | | | | |
| 15 | | | | | | | |
| 16 | | Coefficients | Standard Error | t Stat | P-value | Lower 95% | Upper 95% |
| 17 | Intercept | 200.0905 | 4.3517 | 45.9803 | 0.0000 | 190.6090 | 209.5719 |
| 18 | Size | 16.1858 | 2.5744 | 6.2871 | 0.0000 | 10.5766 | 21.7951 |
| 19 | FireplaceCoded | 3.8530 | 1.2412 | 3.1042 | 0.0091 | 1.1486 | 6.5574 |

**FIGURE 14.14**

Minitab results for the regression model that includes size of the house and presence of fireplace

*See Sections M14.2 and M14.3 to create this.*

```
The regression equation is
Value = 200 + 16.2 Size + 3.85 Fireplace Coded


Predictor           Coef  SE Coef       T      P
Constant         200.090    4.352   45.98  0.000
Size              16.186    2.574    6.29  0.000
Fireplace Coded    3.853    1.241    3.10  0.009


S = 2.26260   R-Sq = 81.1%   R-Sq(adj) = 78.0%


Analysis of Variance

Source         DF     SS      MS      F      P
Regression      2  263.70  131.85  25.76  0.000
Residual Error 12   61.43    5.12
Total          14  325.14
```

From Figure 14.13 or 14.14, the regression equation is

$$\hat{Y}_i = 200.0905 + 16.1858X_{1i} + 3.8530X_{2i}$$

For houses without a fireplace, you substitute $X_2 = 0$ into the regression equation:

$$\hat{Y}_i = 200.0905 + 16.1858X_{1i} + 3.8530X_{2i}$$
$$= 200.0905 + 16.1858X_{1i} + 3.8530(0)$$
$$= 200.0905 + 16.1858X_{1i}$$

For houses with a fireplace, you substitute $X_2 = 1$ into the regression equation:

$$\hat{Y}_i = 200.0905 + 16.1858X_{1i} + 3.8530X_{2i}$$
$$= 200.0905 + 16.1858X_{1i} + 3.8530(1)$$
$$= 203.9435 + 16.1858X_{1i}$$

In this model, the regression coefficients are interpreted as follows:

1. Holding constant whether a house has a fireplace, for each increase of 1.0 thousand square feet in the size of the house, the mean assessed value is estimated to increase by 16.1858 thousand dollars (i.e., $16,185.80).
2. Holding constant the size of the house, the presence of a fireplace is estimated to increase the mean assessed value of the house by 3.8530 thousand dollars (i.e. $3,853).

In Figure 14.13 or 14.14, the $t_{STAT}$ test statistic for the slope of the size of the house with assessed value is 6.2871, and the $p$-value is approximately 0.000; the $t_{STAT}$ test statistic for presence of a fireplace is 3.1042, and the $p$-value is 0.0091. Thus, each of the two variables makes a significant contribution to the model at a level of significance of 0.01. In addition, the coefficient of multiple determination indicates that 81.11% of the variation in assessed value is explained by variation in the size of the house and whether the house has a fireplace.

---

**EXAMPLE 14.3**    MODELING A THREE-LEVEL CATEGORICAL VARIABLE

Define a multiple regression model using sales as the dependent variable and package design and price as independent variables. Package design is a three-level categorical variable with designs $A$, $B$, or $C$.

**SOLUTION**  To model a three-level categorical variable, two dummy variables are needed:

$$X_{1i} = 1 \text{ if package design } A \text{ is used in observation } i; 0 \text{ otherwise}$$

$$X_{2i} = 1 \text{ if package design } B \text{ is used in observation } i; 0 \text{ otherwise}$$

If observation $i$ is for package design $A$, then $X_{1i} = 1$ and $X_{2i} = 0$; for package design $B$, then $X_{1i} = 0$ and $X_{2i} = 1$; and for package design $C$, then $X_{1i} = X_{2i} = 0$. A third independent variable is used for price:

$$X_{3i} = \text{price for observation } i$$

Thus, the regression model for this example is

$$Y_i = \beta_0 + \beta_1 X_{1i} + \beta_2 X_{2i} + \beta_3 X_{3i} + \varepsilon_i$$

where

$$Y_i = \text{sales for observation } i$$

$\beta_0 = Y \text{ intercept}$

$\beta_1 =$ difference between the mean sales of design $A$ and the mean sales of design $C$, holding the price constant

$\beta_2 =$ difference between the mean sales of design $B$ and the mean sales of design $C$, holding the price constant

$\beta_3 =$ slope of sales with price, holding the package design constant

$\varepsilon_i =$ random error in $Y$ for observation $i$

## Interactions

In all the regression models discussed so far, the *effect* an independent variable has on the dependent variable was assumed to be statistically independent of the other independent variables in the model. An **interaction** occurs if the effect of an independent variable on the dependent variable is affected by the *value* of a second independent variable. For example, it is possible for advertising to have a large effect on the sales of a product when the price of a product is low. However, if the price of the product is too high, increases in advertising will not dramatically change sales. In this case, price and advertising are said to interact. In other words, you cannot make general statements about the effect of advertising on sales. The effect that advertising has on sales is *dependent* on the price. You use an **interaction term** (sometimes referred to as a **cross-product term**) to model an interaction effect in a regression model.

To illustrate the concept of interaction and use of an interaction term, return to the example concerning the assessed values of homes discussed on pages 660–662. In the regression model, you assumed that the effect the size of the home has on the assessed value is independent of whether the house has a fireplace. In other words, you assumed that the slope of assessed value with size is the same for houses with fireplaces as it is for houses without fireplaces. If these two slopes are different, an interaction between the size of the home and the fireplace exists.

To evaluate the possibility of an interaction, you first define an interaction term that equals the product of the independent variable $X_1$ (size of house) and the dummy variable $X_2$ (fireplace). You then test whether this interaction variable makes a significant contribution to the regression model. If the interaction is significant, you cannot use the original model for prediction. For the data of Table 14.5 on page 660, let

$$X_3 = X_1 \times X_2$$

Figure 14.15 on page 664 illustrates Microsoft Excel results for this regression model (and Figure 14.16 on page 664 displays Minitab results), which includes the size of the house, $X_1$, the presence of a fireplace, $X_2$, and the interaction of $X_1$ and $X_2$ (which is defined as $X_3$).

To test for the existence of an interaction, you use the null hypothesis

$$H_0: \beta_3 = 0$$

versus the alternative hypothesis

$$H_1: \beta_3 \neq 0.$$

**FIGURE 14.15**

Microsoft Excel regression results worksheet for a regression model that includes size, presence of fireplace, and interaction of size and fireplace

*See Sections E14.5 and E14.6 and either E14.1 or P14.1 to create this.*

| | A | B | C | D | E | F | G |
|---|---|---|---|---|---|---|---|
| 1 | Assessed Value Analysis | | | | | | |
| 2 | | | | | | | |
| 3 | *Regression Statistics* | | | | | | |
| 4 | Multiple R | 0.9179 | | | | | |
| 5 | R Square | 0.8426 | | | | | |
| 6 | Adjusted R Square | 0.7996 | | | | | |
| 7 | Standard Error | 2.1573 | | | | | |
| 8 | Observations | 15 | | | | | |
| 9 | | | | | | | |
| 10 | ANOVA | | | | | | |
| 11 | | df | SS | MS | F | Significance F | |
| 12 | Regression | 3 | 273.9441 | 91.3147 | 19.6215 | 0.0001 | |
| 13 | Residual | 11 | 51.1919 | 4.6538 | | | |
| 14 | Total | 14 | 325.1360 | | | | |
| 15 | | | | | | | |
| 16 | | Coefficients | Standard Error | t Stat | P-value | Lower 95% | Upper 95% |
| 17 | Intercept | 212.9522 | 9.6122 | 22.1544 | 0.0000 | 191.7959 | 234.1084 |
| 18 | Size | 8.3624 | 5.8173 | 1.4375 | 0.1784 | -4.4414 | 21.1662 |
| 19 | FireplaceCoded | -11.8404 | 10.6455 | -1.1122 | 0.2898 | -35.2710 | 11.5902 |
| 20 | Size * FireplaceCoded | 9.5180 | 6.4165 | 1.4834 | 0.1661 | -4.6046 | 23.6406 |

**FIGURE 14.16**

Minitab results for a regression model that includes size, presence of fireplace, and interaction of size and fireplace

*See Sections M14.2– M14.4 to create this.*

```
The regression equation is
Value = 213 + 8.36 Size - 11.8 Fireplace Coded + 9.52 Size*Fireplace


Predictor          Coef   SE Coef      T      P
Constant        212.952     9.612  22.15  0.000
Size              8.362     5.817   1.44  0.178
Fireplace Coded  -11.84     10.65  -1.11  0.290
Size*Fireplace    9.518     6.416   1.48  0.166


S = 2.15727   R-Sq = 84.3%   R-Sq(adj) = 80.0%


Analysis of Variance

Source         DF      SS      MS      F      P
Regression      3  273.944  91.315  19.62  0.000
Residual Error 11   51.192   4.654
Total          14  325.136
```

In Figure 14.15 or 14.16, the $t_{STAT}$ test statistic for the interaction of size and fireplace is 1.4834. Because $t_{STAT} = 1.4834 < 2.201$ or the *p*-value = 0.1661 > 0.05, you do not reject the null hypothesis. Therefore, the interaction does not make a significant contribution to the model, given that size and presence of a fireplace are already included. You can conclude that the slope of assessed value with size is the same for houses with fireplaces and without fireplaces.

Regression models can have several numerical independent variables. Example 14.4 illustrates a regression model in which there are two numerical independent variables as well as a categorical independent variable.

**EXAMPLE 14.4**

STUDYING A REGRESSION MODEL THAT CONTAINS A DUMMY VARIABLE

A real estate developer wants to predict heating oil consumption in single-family houses, based on atmospheric temperature, $X_1$, and the amount of attic insulation, $X_2$. Suppose that, of 15 houses selected, houses 1, 4, 6, 7, 8, 10, and 12 are ranch-style houses. The data are stored in the file **Htngoil**. Develop and analyze an appropriate regression model, using these three independent variables, $X_1$, $X_2$, and $X_3$ (the dummy variable for ranch-style houses).

**SOLUTION**  Define $X_3$, a dummy variable for ranch-style house, as follows:

$$X_3 = 0 \text{ if the style is not ranch}$$

$$X_3 = 1 \text{ if the style is ranch}$$

Assuming that the slope between heating oil consumption and atmospheric temperature, $X_1$, and between heating oil consumption and the amount of attic insulation, $X_2$, is the same for both styles of houses, the regression model is

$$Y_i = \beta_0 + \beta_1 X_{1i} + \beta_2 X_{2i} + \beta_3 X_{3i} + \varepsilon_i$$

where

$Y_i$ = monthly heating oil consumption, in gallons, for house $i$

$\beta_0$ = $Y$ intercept

$\beta_1$ = slope of heating oil consumption with atmospheric temperature, holding constant the effect of attic insulation and the style of the house

$\beta_2$ = slope of heating oil consumption with attic insulation, holding constant the effect of atmospheric temperature and the style of the house

$\beta_3$ = incremental effect of the presence of a ranch-style house, holding constant the effect of atmospheric temperature and attic insulation

$\varepsilon_i$ = random error in $Y$ for house $i$

Figure 14.17 displays Microsoft Excel results. Figure 14.18 on page 666 displays Minitab results.

**FIGURE 14.17**

Microsoft Excel regression results worksheet for a regression model that includes temperature, insulation, and style for the heating oil data

*See Sections E14.5 and either E14.1 or P14.1 to create this.*

| | A | B | C | D | E | F | G |
|---|---|---|---|---|---|---|---|
| 1 | **Heating Oil Consumption Analysis** | | | | | | |
| 2 | | | | | | | |
| 3 | **Regression Statistics** | | | | | | |
| 4 | **Multiple R** | 0.9942 | | | | | |
| 5 | **R Square** | 0.9884 | | | | | |
| 6 | **Adjusted R Square** | 0.9853 | | | | | |
| 7 | **Standard Error** | 15.7489 | | | | | |
| 8 | **Observations** | 15 | | | | | |
| 9 | | | | | | | |
| 10 | **ANOVA** | | | | | | |
| 11 | | *df* | *SS* | *MS* | *F* | *Significance F* | |
| 12 | **Regression** | 3 | 233406.9094 | 77802.3031 | 313.6822 | 6.21548E-11 | |
| 13 | **Residual** | 11 | 2728.3200 | 248.0291 | | | |
| 14 | **Total** | 14 | 236135.2293 | | | | |
| 15 | | | | | | | |
| 16 | | *Coefficients* | *Standard Error* | *t Stat* | *P-value* | *Lower 95%* | *Upper 95%* |
| 17 | **Intercept** | 592.5401 | 14.3370 | 41.3295 | 2.02317E-13 | 560.9846 | 624.0956 |
| 18 | **Temperature** | -5.5251 | 0.2044 | -27.0267 | 2.07188E-11 | -5.9751 | -5.0752 |
| 19 | **Insulation** | -21.3761 | 1.4480 | -14.7623 | 1.34816E-08 | -24.5632 | -18.1891 |
| 20 | **Ranch-style** | -38.9727 | 8.3584 | -4.6627 | 0.0007 | -57.3695 | -20.5759 |

From the results in Figure 14.17 or 14.18, the regression equation is

$$\hat{Y}_i = 592.5401 - 5.5251X_{1i} - 21.3761X_{2i} - 38.9727X_{3i}$$

**FIGURE 14.18**

Minitab results for a regression model that includes temperature, insulation, and style for the heating oil data

*See Sections M14.2 and M14.3 to create this.*

```
The regression equation is
Gallons = 593 - 5.53 Temp(F) - 21.4 Insulation - 39.0 Style


Predictor        Coef   SE Coef       T       P
Constant       592.54     14.34   41.33   0.000
Temp(F)        -5.5251    0.2044  -27.03   0.000
Insulation    -21.376     1.448  -14.76   0.000
Style         -38.973     8.358   -4.66   0.001


S = 15.7489    R-Sq = 98.8%    R-Sq(adj) = 98.5%


Analysis of Variance

Source           DF      SS      MS        F       P
Regression        3  233407   77802   313.68   0.000
Residual Error   11    2728     248
Total            14  236135
```

For houses that are not ranch style, because $X_3 = 0$, the regression equation reduces to

$$\hat{Y}_i = 592.5401 - 5.5251X_{1i} - 21.3761X_{2i}$$

For houses that are ranch style, because $X_3 = 1$, the regression equation reduces to

$$\hat{Y}_i = 553.5674 - 5.5251X_{1i} - 21.3761X_{2i}$$

The regression coefficients are interpreted as follows:

1. Holding constant the attic insulation and the house style, for each additional 1°F increase in atmospheric temperature, you estimate that the mean heating oil consumption decreases by 5.5251 gallons.
2. Holding constant the atmospheric temperature and the house style, for each additional 1-inch increase in attic insulation, you estimate that the mean heating oil consumption decreases by 21.3761 gallons.
3. $b_3$ measures the effect on oil consumption of having a ranch-style house ($X_3 = 1$) compared with having a house that is not ranch style ($X_3 = 0$). Thus, with atmospheric temperature and attic insulation held constant, you estimate that the mean heating oil consumption is 38.9727 gallons less for a ranch-style house than for a house that is not ranch style.

The three $t_{STAT}$ test statistics representing the slopes for temperature, insulation, and ranch style are $-27.0267$, $-14.7623$, and $-4.6627$. Each of the corresponding $p$-values is extremely small, all being less than 0.001. Thus, each of the three variables makes a significant contribution to the model. In addition, the coefficient of multiple determination indicates that 98.84% of the variation in oil usage is explained by variation in the temperature, insulation, and whether the house is ranch style.

Before you can use the model in Example 14.4, you need to determine whether the independent variables interact with each other. In Example 14.5, three interaction terms are added to the model.

**EXAMPLE 14.5**

### EVALUATING A REGRESSION MODEL WITH SEVERAL INTERACTIONS

For the data of Example 14.4, determine whether adding the interaction terms make a significant contribution to the regression model.

**SOLUTION** To evaluate possible interactions between the independent variables, three interaction terms are constructed. Let $X_4 = X_1 \times X_2$, $X_5 = X_1 \times X_3$, and $X_6 = X_2 \times X_3$. The regression model is now

$$Y_i = \beta_0 + \beta_1 X_{1i} + \beta_2 X_{2i} + \beta_3 X_{3i} + \beta_4 X_{4i} + \beta_5 X_{5i} + \beta_6 X_{6i} + \varepsilon_i$$

where $X_1$ is temperature, $X_2$ is insulation, $X_3$ is the dummy variable ranch style, $X_4$ is the interaction between temperature and insulation, $X_5$ is the interaction between temperature and ranch style, and $X_6$ is the interaction between insulation and ranch style. Figure 14.19 presents Microsoft Excel results and Figure 14.20 provides Minitab results.

To test whether the three interactions significantly improve the regression model, you use the partial $F$ test. The null and alternative hypotheses are

$H_0$: $\beta_4 = \beta_5 = \beta_6 = 0$ (There are no interactions among $X_1$, $X_2$, and $X_3$.)
$H_1$: $\beta_4 \neq 0$ and/or $\beta_5 \neq 0$ and/or $\beta_6 \neq 0$ ($X_1$ interacts with $X_2$, and/or $X_1$ interacts with $X_3$, and/or $X_2$ interacts with $X_3$.)

From Figure 14.19 or 14.20,

$$SSR(X_1, X_2, X_3, X_4, X_5, X_6) = 234,510.582 \text{ with 6 degrees of freedom}$$

and from Figure 14.17 or 14.18 on pages 665–666, $SSR(X_1, X_2, X_3) = 233,406.9094$ with 3 degrees of freedom.

**FIGURE 14.19**

Microsoft Excel regression results worksheet for a model that includes temperature, $X_1$; insulation, $X_2$; the dummy variable ranch style, $X_3$; the interaction of temperature and insulation, $X_4$; the interaction of temperature and ranch style, $X_5$; and the interaction of insulation and ranch style, $X_6$

See Sections E14.5 and E14.6 and either E14.1 or P14.1 to create this.

| | A | B | C | D | E | F | G |
|---|---|---|---|---|---|---|---|
| 1 | **Heating Oil Consumption Analysis** | | | | | | |
| 2 | | | | | | | |
| 3 | **Regression Statistics** | | | | | | |
| 4 | Multiple R | 0.9966 | | | | | |
| 5 | R Square | 0.9931 | | | | | |
| 6 | Adjusted R Square | 0.9880 | | | | | |
| 7 | Standard Error | 14.2506 | | | | | |
| 8 | Observations | 15 | | | | | |
| 9 | | | | | | | |
| 10 | ANOVA | | | | | | |
| 11 | | df | SS | MS | F | Significance F | |
| 12 | Regression | 6 | 234510.582 | 39085.097 | 192.4607 | 3.32423E-08 | |
| 13 | Residual | 8 | 1624.647 | 203.081 | | | |
| 14 | Total | 14 | 236135.229 | | | | |
| 15 | | | | | | | |
| 16 | | Coefficients | Standard Error | t Stat | P-value | Lower 95% | Upper 95% |
| 17 | Intercept | 642.8867 | 26.7059 | 24.0728 | 9.45284E-09 | 581.3027 | 704.4707 |
| 18 | Temperature | -6.9263 | 0.7531 | -9.1969 | 1.58014E-05 | -8.6629 | -5.1896 |
| 19 | Insulation | -27.8825 | 3.5801 | -7.7882 | 5.29456E-05 | -36.1383 | -19.6268 |
| 20 | Style | -84.6088 | 29.9956 | -2.8207 | 0.0225 | -153.7788 | -15.4389 |
| 21 | Temperature * Insulation | 0.1702 | 0.0886 | 1.9204 | 0.0911 | -0.0342 | 0.3746 |
| 22 | Temperature * Ranch-style | 0.6596 | 0.4617 | 1.4286 | 0.1910 | -0.4051 | 1.7242 |
| 23 | Insulation * Ranch-style | 4.9870 | 3.5137 | 1.4193 | 0.1936 | -3.1156 | 13.0895 |

**FIGURE 14.20**

Minitab results for a regression model that includes temperature, $X_1$; insulation, $X_2$; the dummy variable ranch style, $X_3$; the interaction of temperature and insulation, $X_4$; the interaction of temperature and ranch style, $X_5$; and the interaction of insulation and ranch style, $X_6$

*See Sections M14.2–M14.4 to create this.*

```
The regression equation is
Gallons = 643 - 6.93 Temp(F) - 27.9 Insulation - 84.6 Style
          + 0.170 Temp*Insulation + 0.660 Temp*Style + 4.99 Insulation*Style

Predictor            Coef   SE Coef       T       P
Constant           642.89     26.71   24.07   0.000
Temp(F)           -6.9263    0.7531   -9.20   0.000
Insulation        -27.883     3.580   -7.79   0.000
Style              -84.61     30.00   -2.82   0.022
Temp*Insulation   0.17021   0.08863    1.92   0.091
Temp*Style         0.6596    0.4617    1.43   0.191
Insulation*Style    4.987     3.514    1.42   0.194

S = 14.2506    R-Sq = 99.3%    R-Sq(adj) = 98.8%

Analysis of Variance

Source           DF      SS      MS       F       P
Regression        6  234511   39085  192.46   0.000
Residual Error    8    1625     203
Total            14  236135
```

Thus, $SSR(X_1, X_2, X_3, X_4, X_5, X_6) - SSR(X_1, X_2, X_3) = 234{,}510.582 - 233{,}406.9094 = 1{,}103.67$. The difference in degrees of freedom is $6 - 3 = 3$.

To use the partial $F$ test for the simultaneous contribution of three variables to a model, you use an extension of Equation (14.11) on page 656.[1] The partial $F_{STAT}$ test statistic is

[1] *In general, if a model has several independent variables and you want to test whether an additional set of independent variables contribute to the model, the numerator of the F test is SSR(for all independent variables) – SSR(for the initial set of variables) divided by the number of independent variables whose contribution is being tested.*

$$F_{STAT} = \frac{[SSR(X_1, X_2, X_3, X_4, X_5, X_6) - SSR(X_1, X_2, X_3)]/3}{MSE(X_1, X_2, X_3, X_4, X_5, X_6)} = \frac{1{,}103.67/3}{203.08} = 1.81$$

You compare the computed $F_{STAT}$ test statistic to the critical $F$ value for 3 and 8 degrees of freedom. Using a level of significance of 0.05, the critical $F$ value from Table E.5 is 4.07. Because $F_{STAT} = 1.81 < 4.07$, you conclude that the interactions do not make a significant contribution to the model, given that the model already includes temperature, $X_1$; insulation, $X_2$; and whether the house is ranch style, $X_3$. Therefore, the multiple regression model using $X_1$, $X_2$, and $X_3$ but no interaction terms is the better model. If you rejected this null hypothesis, you would then test the contribution of each interaction separately in order to determine which interaction terms to include in the model.

## PROBLEMS FOR SECTION 14.6

### Learning the Basics

**14.38** Suppose $X_1$ is a numerical variable and $X_2$ is a dummy variable and the regression equation for a sample of $n = 20$ is

$$\hat{Y}_i = 6 + 4X_{1i} + 2X_{2i}$$

**a.** Interpret the regression coefficient associated with variable $X_1$.
**b.** Interpret the regression coefficient associated with variable $X_2$.

**c.** Suppose that the $t_{STAT}$ test statistic for testing the contribution of variable $X_2$ is 3.27. At the 0.05 level of significance, is there evidence that variable $X_2$ makes a significant contribution to the model?

### Applying the Concepts

**14.39** The chair of the accounting department wants to develop a regression model to predict the grade point average in accounting for graduating accounting majors, based on the student's SAT score and whether the student received a grade of B or higher in the introductory statistics course (0 = no and 1 = yes).

**a.** Explain the steps involved in developing a regression model for these data. Be sure to indicate the particular models you need to evaluate and compare.

**b.** Suppose the regression coefficient for the variable of whether the student received a grade of B or higher in the introductory statistics course is +0.30. How do you interpret this result?

**14.40** A real estate association in a suburban community would like to study the relationship between the size of a single-family house (as measured by the number of rooms) and the selling price of the house (in thousands of dollars). Two different neighborhoods are included in the study, one on the east side of the community (= 0) and the other on the west side (=1). A random sample of 20 houses was selected, with the results given in the file **Neighbor**. For (a) through (k) do not include an interaction term.

**a.** State the multiple regression equation that predicts the selling price based on the number of rooms and the neighborhood.

**b.** Interpret the regression coefficients in (a).

**c.** Predict the mean selling price for a house with nine rooms that is located in an east-side neighborhood. Construct a 95% confidence interval estimate and a 95% prediction interval.

**d.** Perform a residual analysis on the results and determineif the regression assumptions are valid.

**e.** Is there a significant relationship between selling price and the two independent variables (rooms and neighborhood) at the 0.05 level of significance?

**f.** At the 0.05 level of significance, determine whether each independent variable makes a contribution to the regression model. Indicate the most appropriate regression model for this set of data.

**g.** Construct and interpret a 95% confidence interval estimate of the population slope for the relationship between selling price and number of rooms.

**h.** Construct and interpret a 95% confidence interval estimate of the population slope for the relationship between selling price and neighborhood.

**i.** Compute and interpret the adjusted $r^2$.

**j.** Compute the coefficients of partial determination and interpret their meaning.

**k.** What assumption do you need to make about the slope of selling price with number of rooms?

**l.** Add an interaction term to the model and, at the 0.05 level of significance, determine whether it makes a significant contribution to the model.

**m.** On the basis of the results of (f) and (l), which model is most appropriate? Explain.

**14.41** The marketing manager of a large supermarket chain would like to determine the effect of shelf space and whether the product was placed at the front (=1) or back

(=0) of the aisle on the sales of pet food. A random sample of 12 equal-sized stores is selected, with the following results (stored in the file **Petfood**):

| Store | Shelf Space (Feet) | Location | Weekly Sales (Dollars) |
|---|---|---|---|
| 1 | 5 | Back | 160 |
| 2 | 5 | Front | 220 |
| 3 | 5 | Back | 140 |
| 4 | 10 | Back | 190 |
| 5 | 10 | Back | 240 |
| 6 | 10 | Front | 260 |
| 7 | 15 | Back | 230 |
| 8 | 15 | Back | 270 |
| 9 | 15 | Front | 280 |
| 10 | 20 | Back | 260 |
| 11 | 20 | Back | 290 |
| 12 | 20 | Front | 310 |

For (a) through (m), do not include an interaction term.

**a.** State the multiple regression equation that predicts sales based on shelf space and location.

**b.** Interpret the regression coefficients in (a).

**c.** Predict the mean weekly sales of pet food for a store with 8 feet of shelf space situated at the back of the aisle. Construct a 95% confidence interval estimate and a 95% prediction interval.

**d.** Perform a residual analysis on the results and determine if the regression assumptions are valid.

**e.** Is there a significant relationship between sales and the two independent variables (shelf space and aisle position) at the 0.05 level of significance?

**f.** At the 0.05 level of significance, determine whether each independent variable makes a contribution to the regression model. Indicate the most appropriate regression model for this set of data.

**g.** Construct and interpret a 95% confidence interval estimates of the population slope for the relationship between sales and shelf space and between sales and aisle location.

**h.** Compare the slope in (b) with the slope for the simple linear regression model of Problem 13.4 on page 585. Explain the difference in the results.

**i.** Computer and interpret the meaning of the coefficient of multiple determination, $r^2$.

**j.** Compute and interpret the adjusted $r^2$.

**k.** Compare $r^2$ with the $r^2$ value computed in Problem 13.16(a) on page 592.

**l.** Compute the coefficients of partial determination and interpret their meaning.

**m.** What assumption about the slope of shelf space with sales do you need to make in this problem?

**n.** Add an interaction term to the model and, at the 0.05 level of significance, determine whether it makes a significant contribution to the model.

**o.** On the basis of the results of (f) and (n), which model is most appropriate? Explain.

**14.42** In mining engineering, holes are often drilled through rock, using drill bits. As the drill hole gets deeper, additional rods are added to the drill bit to enable additional drilling to take place. It is expected that drilling time increases with depth. This increased drilling time could be caused by several factors, including the mass of the drill rods that are strung together. A key question relates to whether drilling is faster using dry drilling holes or wet drilling holes. Using dry drilling holes involves forcing compressed air down the drill rods to flush the cuttings and drive the hammer. Using wet drilling holes involves forcing water rather than air down the hole. The data file Drill contains measurements for a sample of 50 drill holes of the time to drill each additional 5 feet (in minutes), the depth (in feet), and whether the hole was a dry drilling hole or a wet drilling hole. Develop a model to predict additional drilling time, based on depth and type of drilling hole (dry or wet). For (a) through (k) do not include an interaction term.

Source: *Extracted from R. Penner and D. G. Watts, "Mining Information," The American Statistician, 45, 1991, pp. 4–9.*

**a.** State the multiple regression equation.

**b.** Interpret the regression coefficients in (a).

**c.** Predict the mean additional drilling time for a dry drilling hole at a depth of 100 feet. Construct a 95% confidence interval estimate and a 95% prediction interval.

**d.** Perform a residual analysis on the results and determine if the regression assumptions are valid.

**e.** Is there a significant relationship between additional drilling time and the two independent variables (depth and type of drilling hole) at the 0.05 level of significance?

**f.** At the 0.05 level of significance, determine whether each independent variable makes a contribution to the regression model. Indicate the most appropriate regression model for this set of data.

**g.** Construct a 95% confidence interval estimate of the population slope for the relationship between additional drilling time and depth.

**h.** Construct a 95% confidence interval estimate of the population slope for the relationship between additional drilling time and the type of hole drilled.

**i.** Compute and interpret the adjusted $r^2$.

**j.** Compute the coefficients of partial determination and interpret their meaning.

**k.** What assumption do you need to make about the slope of additional drilling time with depth?

**l.** Add an interaction term to the model and, at the 0.05 level of significance, determine whether it makes a significant contribution to the model.

**m.** On the basis of the results of (f) and (l), which model is most appropriate? Explain.

**14.43** The owner of a moving company typically has his most experienced manager predict the total number of labor hours that will be required to complete an upcoming move. This approach has proved useful in the past, but the owner would like to be able to develop a more accurate method of predicting the labor hours by using the number of cubic feet moved and whether there is an elevator in the apartment building. In a preliminary effort to provide a more accurate method, he has collected data for 36 moves in which the origin and destination were within the borough of Manhattan in New York City and the travel time was an insignificant portion of the hours worked. The data are stored in the file Moving. For (a) through (k) do not include an interaction term.

**a.** State the multiple regression equation for predicting labor hours using the number of cubic feet moved and whether there is an elevator.

**b.** Interpret the regression coefficients in (a).

**c.** Predict the mean labor hours for moving 500 cubic feet in an apartment building that has an elevator, and construct a 95% confidence interval estimate and a 95% prediction interval.

**d.** Perform a residual analysis on the results and determine if the regression assumptions are valid.

**e.** Is there a significant relationship between labor hours and the two independent variables (cubic feet moved and whether there is an elevator in the apartment building) at the 0.05 level of significance?

**f.** At the 0.05 level of significance, determine whether each independent variable makes a contribution to the regression model. Indicate the most appropriate regression model for this set of data.

**g.** Construct a 95% confidence interval estimate of the population slope for the relationship between labor hours and cubic feet moved.

**h.** Construct a 95% confidence interval estimate for the relationship between labor hours and the presence of an elevator.

**i.** Compute and interpret the adjusted $r^2$.

**j.** Compute the coefficients of partial determination and interpret their meaning.

**k.** What assumption about the slope of labor hours with cubic feet moved do you need to make?

**l.** Add an interaction term to the model and, at the 0.05 level of significance, determine whether it makes a significant contribution to the model.

**m.** On the basis of the results of (f) and (l), which model is most appropriate? Explain.

**SELF** ✓ **Test** **14.44** In Problem 14.4 on page 641, you used sales and orders to predict distribution cost (see the file **Warecost**). Develop a regression model to predict distribution cost that includes the sales, orders, and the interaction of sales and orders.
a. At the 0.05 level of significance, is there evidence that the interaction term makes a significant contribution to the model?
b. Which regression model is more appropriate, the one used in (a) or the one used in Problem 14.4? Explain.

**14.45** Zagat's publishes restaurant ratings for various locations in the United States. The data file **Restaurants** contains the Zagat rating for food, décor, service, and the price per person for a sample of 50 restaurants located in an urban area and 50 restaurants located in a suburban area. Develop a regression model to predict the price per person based on a variable that represents the sum of the ratings for food, décor, and service and a dummy variable concerning location (urban versus suburban). For (a) through (m) do not include an interaction term.
Source: *Extracted from* Zagat Survey 2006 New York City Restaurants *and* Zagat Survey 2005–2006 Long Island Restaurants.
a. State the multiple regression equation.
b. Interpret the regression coefficients in (a).
c. Predict the mean price for a restaurant with a summated rating of 60 that is located in an urban area and construct a 95% confidence interval estimate and a 95% prediction interval.
d. Perform a residual analysis on the results and determine if the regression assumptions are satisfied.
e. Is there a significant relationship between price and the two independent variables (summated rating and location) at the 0.05 level of significance?
f. At the 0.05 level of significance, determine whether each independent variable makes a contribution to the regression model. Indicate the most appropriate regression model for this set of data.
g. Construct a 95% confidence interval estimate of the population slope for the relationship between price and summated rating.
h. Compare the slope in (b) with the slope for the simple linear regression model of Problem 13.90 on page 627. Explain the difference in the results.
i. Compute and interpret the meaning of the coefficient of multiple determination.

j. Compute and interpret the adjusted $r^2$.
k. Compare $r^2$ with the $r^2$ value computed in Problem 13.90(d) on page 627.
l. Compute the coefficients of partial determination and interpret their meaning.
m. What assumption about the slope of price with summated rating do you need to make in this problem?
n. Add an interaction term to the model and, at the 0.05 level of significance, determine whether it makes a significant contribution to the model.
o. On the basis of the results of (f) and (n), which model is most appropriate? Explain.

**14.46** In Problem 14.6 on page 642, you used radio advertising and newspaper advertising to predict sales (see the file **Advertise**). Develop a regression model to predict sales that includes radio advertising, newspaper advertising, and the interaction of radio advertising and newspaper advertising.
a. At the 0.05 level of significance, is there evidence that the interaction term makes a significant contribution to the model?
b. Which regression model is more appropriate, the one used in this problem or the one used in Problem 14.6? Explain.

**14.47** In Problem 14.5 on page 641, horsepower and weight were used to predict miles per gallon (see the file **Auto**). Develop a regression model that includes horsepower, weight, and the interaction of horsepower and weight to predict miles per gallon.
a. At the 0.05 level of significance, is there evidence that the interaction term makes a significant contribution to the model?
b. Which regression model is more appropriate, the one used in this problem or the one used in Problem 14.5? Explain.

**14.48** In Problem 14.7 on page 642, you used total staff present and remote hours to predict standby hours (see the file **Standby**). Develop a regression model to predict standby hours that includes total staff present, remote hours, and the interaction of total staff present and remote hours.
a. At the 0.05 level of significance, is there evidence that the interaction term makes a significant contribution to the model?
b. Which regression model is more appropriate, the one used in this problem or the one used in Problem 14.7? Explain.

## 14.7  LOGISTIC REGRESSION

The discussion of the simple linear regression model in Chapter 13 and the multiple regression models in Sections 14.1 through 14.6 only considered *numerical* dependent variables. However, in many instances, the dependent variable is a *categorical* variable that takes on one of only two possible values such as a customer prefers Brand *A* or a customer prefers Brand *B*. The use of simple or multiple least-squares regression for a categorical dependent variable violates the normality assumption and can predict *Y* values that are impossible.

An alternative approach originally applied to survival data in the health sciences (see reference 2), **logistic regression**, enables you to use regression models to predict the probability of a particular categorical response for a given set of independent variables. The logistic regression model is based on the **odds ratio**, which represents the probability of an event of interest compared with the probability of not having an event of interest. Equation (14.15) defines the odds ratio.

Odds Ratio

$$\text{Odds ratio} = \frac{\text{probability of an event of interest}}{1 - \text{probability of an event of interest}} \qquad \textbf{(14.15)}$$

Using Equation (14.15), if the probability of an event of interest is 0.50, the odds ratio is

$$\text{Odds ratio} = \frac{0.50}{1 - 0.50} = 1.0, \text{ or 1 to 1}$$

If the probability of an event of interest is 0.75, the odds ratio is

$$\text{Odds ratio} = \frac{0.75}{1 - 0.75} = 3.0, \text{ or 3 to 1}$$

[2]*For more information on logarithms see Appendix A.3.*

The logistic regression model is based on the natural logarithm (ln) of this odds ratio.[2] Equation (14.16) defines the logistic regression model for *k* independent variables.

Logistic Regression Model

$$\ln(\text{odds ratio}) = \beta_0 + \beta_1 X_{1i} + \beta_2 X_{2i} + \cdots + \beta_k X_{ki} + \varepsilon_i \qquad \textbf{(14.16)}$$

where

$k$ = number of independent variables in the model

$\varepsilon_i$ = random error in observation *i*

In Sections 13.2 and 14.1, the method of least squares was used to develop a regression equation. In logistic regression, a mathematical method called *maximum likelihood estimation* is usually used to develop a regression equation to predict the natural logarithm of this odds ratio. Equation (14.17) defines the logistic regression equation.

Logistic Regression Equation

$$\ln(\text{estimated odds ratio}) = b_0 + b_1 X_{1i} + b_2 X_{2i} + \cdots + b_k X_{ki} \qquad \textbf{(14.17)}$$

Once you have determined the logistic regression equation, you use Equation (14.18) to compute the estimated odds ratio.

**Estimated Odds Ratio**

$$\text{Estimated odds ratio} = e^{\ln(\text{estimated odds ratio})} \qquad \textbf{(14.18)}$$

Once you have computed the estimated odds ratio, you use Equation (14.19) to find the estimated probability of an event of interest.

**Estimated Probability of an Event of Interest**

$$\text{Estimated probability of an event of interest} = \frac{\text{estimated odds ratio}}{1 + \text{estimated odds ratio}} \qquad \textbf{(14.19)}$$

To illustrate the logistic regression model, the marketing department for a credit card company is about to embark on a campaign to convince existing holders of the company's standard credit card to upgrade to the company's premium card for a nominal annual fee. A major question facing the marketing department is "Which of the existing standard credit cardholders should be the target for the campaign?" Data available from a sample of 30 cardholders who were contacted during last year's campaign indicate whether the cardholder upgraded to a premium card (0 = no, 1 = yes). The marketing department wants to predict the categorical variable purchase behavior (i.e., did the customer upgrade to a premium card?) using two independent variables: total amount of credit card purchases (in thousands of dollars) in the prior year ($X_1$), and whether the cardholder possesses additional credit cards (which involves an extra cost) for other members of the household ($X_2$: 0 = no, 1 = yes). The data are stored in the `Logpurch` file.

Figure 14.21 presents Minitab results for the logistic regression model.

**FIGURE 14.21**

Minitab logistic regression results for the credit card data

*See Section M14.5 to create this.*

```
Logistic Regression Table

                                                Odds        95% CI
Predictor       Coef       SE Coef    Z      P  Ratio  Lower   Upper
Constant      -6.93984     2.94712  -2.35  0.019
Spending       0.139469    0.0680641  2.05  0.040  1.15   1.01    1.31
Extra
1              2.77434     1.19267   2.33  0.020  16.03  1.55  166.00


Log-Likelihood = -10.038
Test that all slopes are zero: G = 20.977, DF = 2, P-Value = 0.000


Goodness-of-Fit Tests

Method           Chi-Square  DF     P
Pearson            18.5186   27  0.887
Deviance           20.0769   27  0.828
Hosmer-Lemeshow     6.5174    8  0.589
```

The regression coefficients $b_0$, $b_1$, and $b_2$ are interpreted as follows:

1. The regression constant $b_0$ is −6.940. Thus, for a credit cardholder who did not charge any purchases last year and who does not have additional cards, the estimated natural logarithm of the odds ratio of purchasing the premium card is −6.940.
2. The regression coefficient $b_1$ is 0.13947. Therefore, holding constant the effect of whether the credit cardholder has additional cards for members of the household, for each increase of \$1,000 in annual credit card spending using the company's card, the estimated natural logarithm of the odds ratio of purchasing the premium card increases by 0.13947. Therefore, cardholders who charged more in the previous year are more likely to upgrade to a premium card.
3. The regression coefficient $b_2$ is 2.774. Therefore, holding constant the annual credit card spending, the estimated natural logarithm of the odds ratio of purchasing the premium card increases by 2.774 for a credit cardholder who has additional cards for members of the household compared with one who does not have additional cards. Therefore, cardholders possessing additional cards for other members of the household are much more likely to upgrade to a premium card.

Based on 2 and 3 above, the credit card company should develop a marketing campaign that targets cardholders who tend to charge large amounts to their cards, and to households that possess more than one card.

As was the case with least-squares regression models, a main purpose of performing logistic regression analysis is to provide predictions of a dependent variable. For example, consider a cardholder who charged \$36,000 last year and possesses additional cards for members of the household. What is the probability the cardholder will upgrade to the premium card during the marketing campaign? Using $X_1 = 36$, $X_2 = 1$, Equation (14.17) on page 672, and the results displayed in Figure 14.21 on page 673,

$$\text{ln(estimated odds of purchasing versus not purchasing)} = -6.94 + (0.13947)(36) + (2.774)(1)$$

$$= 0.85492$$

Then, using Equation (14.18) on page 673,

$$\text{estimated odds ratio} = e^{0.85492} = 2.3512$$

Therefore, the odds are 2.3512 to 1 that a credit cardholder who spent \$36,000 last year and has additional cards will purchase the premium card during the campaign. Using Equation (14.19) on page 673, you can convert this odds ratio to a probability.

$$\text{estimated probability of purchasing premium card} = \frac{2.3512}{1 + 2.3512}$$

$$= 0.7016$$

Thus, the estimated probability is 0.7016 that a credit cardholder who spent \$36,000 last year and has additional cards will purchase the premium card during the campaign. In other words, you predict 70.16% of such individuals will purchase the premium card.

Now that you have used the logistic regression model for prediction, you need to determine whether or not the model is a good-fitting model. The **deviance statistic** is frequently used to determine whether or not the current model provides a good fit to the data. This statistic measures the fit of the current model compared with a model that has as many parameters as there are data points (what is called a *saturated* model). The deviance statistic follows a chi-square distribution with $n - k - 1$ degrees of freedom. The null and alternative hypotheses are:

$H_0$: The model is a good-fitting model.
$H_1$: The model is not a good-fitting model.

When using the deviance statistic for logistic regression, the null hypothesis represents a good-fitting model, which is the opposite of the null hypothesis when using the overall $F$ test for the multiple regression model (see Section 14.2). Using the $\alpha$ level of significance, the decision rule is:

Reject $H_0$ if deviance $> \chi_\alpha^2$ with $n - k - 1$ degrees of freedom;

otherwise, do not reject $H_0$.

The critical value for a $\chi^2$ statistic with $n - k - 1 = 30 - 2 - 1 = 27$ degrees of freedom is 40.113 (see Table E.4). From Figure 14.21 on page 673, the deviance $= 20.08 < \chi_\alpha^2 = 40.113$, or the $p$-value $= 0.828 > 0.05$. Thus, you do not reject $H_0$, and you conclude that the model is a good-fitting one.

Now that you have concluded that the model is a good-fitting one, you need to evaluate whether each of the independent variables makes a significant contribution to the model in the presence of the others. As was the case with linear regression in Sections 13.7 and 14.4, the test statistic is based on the ratio of the regression coefficient to the standard error of the regression coefficient. In logistic regression, this ratio is defined by the **Wald statistic**, which approximately follows the normal distribution. From Figure 14.21, the Wald statistic (labeled $Z$) is 2.05 for $X_1$ and 2.33 for $X_2$. Each of these is greater than the critical value of $+1.96$ for the normal distribution at the 0.05 level of significance (the $p$-values are 0.04 and 0.02). You can conclude that each of the two independent variables makes a contribution to the model in the presence of the other. Therefore, you should include both these independent variables in the model.

# A New Mining for the Twenty-First Century

*From the Authors' Desktop*

The authors of the recent book *Competing on Analytics: The New Science of Winning* (see reference 1) argue that using sophisticated quantitative analyses should be part of the competitive strategy of an organization. Already today, many businesses use *data mining* as one such technique. The online *Concise Encyclopedia Britannica* (**Britannica.com**) defines data mining as a type of analysis "that attempts to discover useful patterns or relationships in a group of data." The following applications of logistic regression, discussed in Section 14.7, are examples of data mining in use today (see reference 6):

## Banking and Financial Services

- **Mortgage acceptance and default**—predicting which applicants will qualify for a specific type of mortgage and which will default on their mortgage

- **Retention**—examining who will remain a customer of the financial services company

## Retailing and Marketing

- **Response to promotions**—predicting which customers will respond to promotions
- **Brand loyalty**—predicting which customers will remain loyal to the product or service
- **Purchasing sequence**—predicting which customers are ready to purchase a specific product at a certain time

## Quality and Warranty Management

- **Product failure**—Predicting the type of product that will fail during a warranty period

- **Warranty fraud**—Detecting the type of individual who might be involved in fraudulent activities concerning the warranty of the product

## Insurance

- **Fraud detection**—predicting the characteristics of a claim and an individual that indicate a fraudulent claim
- **Claim submission**—predicting the characteristics of an individual who will file a specific type of claim

# PROBLEMS FOR SECTION 14.7

## Learning the Basics

**14.49** Interpret the meaning of a logistic regression slope coefficient equal to 0.8.

**14.50** Interpret the meaning of a logistic regression slope coefficient equal to 2.2.

**14.51** Given an estimated odds ratio of 2.5, find the estimated probability of an event of interest.

**14.52** Given an estimated odds ratio of 0.75, find the estimated probability of an event of interest.

**14.53** Consider the following logistic regression equation:

$$\ln(\text{estimated odds ratio}) = 0.1 + 0.5X_{1i} + 0.2X_{2i}$$

**a.** Interpret the meaning of the logistic regression coefficients.
**b.** If $X_1 = 2$ and $X_2 = 1.5$, find the estimated odds ratio and interpret its meaning.
**c.** On the basis of the results of (b), compute the estimated probability of an event of interest.

## Applying the Concepts

 **14.54** Refer to Figure 14.21 on page 673.
**a.** Predict the probability that a cardholder who charged \$36,000 last year and does not have any additional credit cards for members of the household will purchase the premium card during the marketing campaign.
**b.** Compare the results in (a) with those for a person with additional credit cards.
**c.** Predict the probability that a cardholder who charged \$18,000 and does not have any additional credit cards for members of the household will purchase the premium card during the marketing campaign.
**d.** Compare the results of (a) and (c) and indicate what implications these results might have for the strategy for the marketing campaign.

**14.55** Researchers at John Carroll University investigated reasons companies adopt electronic data interchange (EDI) with their supply chain partners (extracted from Charles A. Watts, Patrick T. Hogan, and Mark D. Treleven, "Issues Influencing Use of Electronic Data Interchange Technology: An Empirical Study," *Mid-American Journal of Business*, Fall 1998, 13(2): 7–13). The researchers used a logistic regression model to predict whether a firm adopts EDI. The dependent variable was equal to 1 if a company uses EDI and 0 otherwise. Independent variables in their logistic regression model are:

$X_1$ = The company's resistance to change (the larger the value of $X_1$, the more resistance to change present in the organization)
$X_2$ = The importance a company places on technology infrastructure (the larger the value of $X_2$, the more importance placed on technology within the organization)
$X_3$ = The financial hurdles involved in implementing EDI (the larger the value of $X_3$, the more expensive it is for a company to implement EDI)
$X_4$ = The amount of opinion leadership (the larger the value of $X_4$, the more contact the company has with sources that have previous experience with EDI such as customers and user groups)

A partial listing of the logistic regression results is given in the following table.

| Variable | Coefficient Estimates | $p$-Value |
|---|---|---|
| $X_1$ | $-0.95$ | $< 0.01$ |
| $X_2$ | $0.06$ | $> 0.05$ |
| $X_3$ | $0.73$ | $< 0.05$ |
| $X_4$ | $-0.53$ | $> 0.05$ |

Explain the meaning of the regression coefficient estimates. Be sure to write your answers in a business context.

**14.56** The director of graduate studies at a college of business wants to predict the success of students in an MBA program using two independent variables, undergraduate grade point average (GPA) and GMAT score. A random sample of 30 students (stored in the file **MBA**) indicates that 20 successfully completed the program (coded as 1) and 10 did not (coded as 0).
**a.** Use Minitab to estimate a logistic regression model to predict the probability of successful completion of the MBA program based on undergraduate grade point average and GMAT score.
**b.** Explain the meaning of the regression coefficients for the model in (a).
**c.** Predict the probability of successful completion of the program for a student with an undergraduate grade point average of 3.25 and a GMAT score of 600.

| Success in MBA Program | Under-graduate GPA | GMAT Score | Success in MBA Program | Under-graduate GPA | GMAT Score |
|---|---|---|---|---|---|
| 0 | 2.93 | 617 | 1 | 3.17 | 639 |
| 0 | 3.05 | 557 | 1 | 3.24 | 632 |
| 0 | 3.11 | 599 | 1 | 3.41 | 639 |
| 0 | 3.24 | 616 | 1 | 3.37 | 619 |
| 0 | 3.36 | 594 | 1 | 3.46 | 665 |
| 0 | 3.41 | 567 | 1 | 3.57 | 694 |
| 0 | 3.45 | 542 | 1 | 3.62 | 641 |
| 0 | 3.60 | 551 | 1 | 3.66 | 594 |
| 0 | 3.64 | 573 | 1 | 3.69 | 678 |
| 0 | 3.57 | 536 | 1 | 3.70 | 624 |
| 1 | 2.75 | 688 | 1 | 3.78 | 654 |
| 1 | 2.81 | 647 | 1 | 3.84 | 718 |
| 1 | 3.03 | 652 | 1 | 3.77 | 692 |
| 1 | 3.10 | 608 | 1 | 3.79 | 632 |
| 1 | 3.06 | 680 | 1 | 3.97 | 784 |

**d.** At the 0.05 level of significance, is there evidence that a logistic regression model that uses undergraduate grade point average and GMAT score to predict probability of success in the MBA program is a good-fitting model?

**e.** At the 0.05 level of significance, is there evidence that undergraduate grade point average and GMAT score each make a significant contribution to the logistic regression model?

**f.** Use Minitab to estimate a logistic regression model that includes only undergraduate grade point average to predict probability of success in the MBA program.

**g.** Use Minitab to estimate a logistic regression model that includes only GMAT score to predict probability of success in the MBA program.

**h.** Compare the models in (a), (f), and (g). Evaluate the differences among the models.

**14.57** A hotel has designed a new system for room service delivery of breakfast that allows the customer to select a specific delivery time. The difference between the actual and requested delivery times was recorded (a negative time means that the breakfast was delivered before the requested time) for 30 deliveries on a particular day along with whether the customer had previously stayed at the hotel. The data are stored in the file Satisfaction.

**a.** Use Minitab to estimate a logistic regression model to predict the probability that the customer will be satisfied (0 = unfavorable, 1 = favorable) based on the delivery time difference and whether the customer had previously stayed at the hotel.

**b.** Explain the meaning of the regression coefficients for the model in (a).

**c.** Predict the probability that the customer will be satisfied if the delivery time difference is 3 minutes and he or she did not previously stay at the hotel.

**d.** At the 0.05 level of significance, is there evidence that a logistic regression model that uses delivery time difference and whether the customer had previously stayed at the hotel is a good-fitting model?

**e.** At the 0.05 level of significance, is there evidence that both independent variables (delivery time difference and whether the customer had previously stayed at the hotel) make a significant contribution to the logistic regression model?

# SUMMARY

In this chapter, you learned how a marketing manager can use multiple regression analysis to understand the effects of price and promotional expenses on the sales of a new product. You also learned how to include categorical independent variables and interaction terms in regression models. In addition, you used the logistic regression model to predict a dependent variable that is categorical and not numerical. Figure 14.22 on page 678 presents a road map of the chapter.

**FIGURE 14.22**
Roadmap for multiple
regression

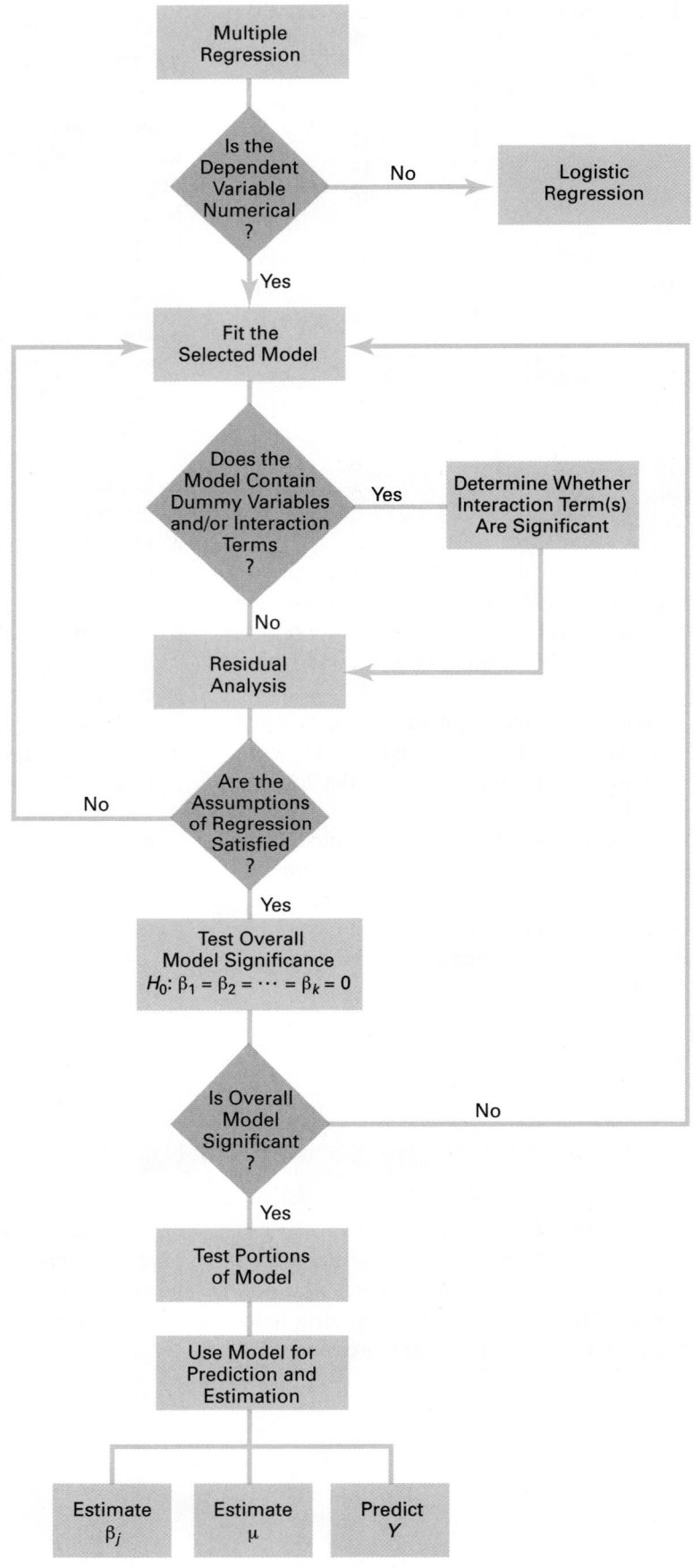

# KEY EQUATIONS

**Multiple Regression Model with $k$ Independent Variables**

$$Y_i = \beta_0 + \beta_1 X_{1i} + \beta_2 X_{2i} + \beta_3 X_{3i} + \cdots + \beta_k X_{ki} + \varepsilon_i \quad \text{(14.1)}$$

**Multiple Regression Model with Two Independent Variables**

$$Y_i = \beta_0 + \beta_1 X_{1i} + \beta_2 X_{2i} + \varepsilon_i \quad \text{(14.2)}$$

**Multiple Regression Equation with Two Independent Variables**

$$\hat{Y}_i = b_0 + b_1 X_{1i} + b_2 X_{2i} \quad \text{(14.3)}$$

**Coefficient of Multiple Determination**

$$r^2 = \frac{\text{Regression sum of squares}}{\text{Total sum of squares}} = \frac{SSR}{SST} \quad \text{(14.4)}$$

**Adjusted $r^2$**

$$r^2_{\text{adj}} = 1 - \left[ (1 - r^2) \frac{n-1}{n-k-1} \right] \quad \text{(14.5)}$$

**Overall $F$ Test**

$$F_{STAT} = \frac{MSR}{MSE} \quad \text{(14.6)}$$

**Testing for the Slope in Multiple Regression**

$$t_{STAT} = \frac{b_j - \beta_j}{S_{b_j}} \quad \text{(14.7)}$$

**Confidence Interval Estimate for the Slope**

$$b_j \pm t_{\alpha/2} S_{b_j} \quad \text{(14.8)}$$

**Determining the Contribution of an Independent Variable to the Regression Model**

$$SSR(X_j \mid \text{All } Xs \text{ except } j) = SSR \,(\text{All } Xs) - SSR \,(\text{All } Xs \text{ except } j) \quad \text{(14.9)}$$

**Contribution of Variable $X_1$, Given That $X_2$ Has Been Included**

$$SSR(X_1 \mid X_2) = SSR(X_1 \text{ and } X_2) - SSR(X_2) \quad \text{(14.10a)}$$

**Contribution of Variable $X_2$, Given That $X_1$ Has Been Included**

$$SSR(X_2 \mid X_1) = SSR(X_1 \text{ and } X_2) - SSR(X_1) \quad \text{(14.10b)}$$

**Partial $F$ Test**

$$F_{STAT} = \frac{SSR(X_j \mid \text{All } Xs \text{ except } j)}{MSE} \quad \text{(14.11)}$$

**Relationship Between a $t$ Statistic and an $F$ Statistic**

$$t^2_{STAT} = F_{STAT} \quad \text{(14.12)}$$

**Coefficients of Partial Determination for a Multiple Regression Model Containing Two Independent Variables**

$$r^2_{Y1.2} = \frac{SSR(X_1 \mid X_2)}{SST - SSR(X_1 \text{ and } X_2) + SSR(X_1 \mid X_2)} \quad \text{(14.13a)}$$

and

$$r^2_{Y2.1} = \frac{SSR(X_2 \mid X_1)}{SST - SSR(X_1 \text{ and } X_2) + SSR(X_2 \mid X_1)} \quad \text{(14.13b)}$$

**Coefficient of Partial Determination for a Multiple Regression Model Containing $k$ Independent Variables**

$$r^2_{Y_j.\,(\text{All } Xs \text{ except } j)} = \frac{SSR(X_j \mid \text{All } Xs \text{ except } j)}{SST - SSR(\text{All } Xs) + SSR(X_j \mid \text{All } Xs \text{ except } j)} \quad \text{(14.14)}$$

**Odds Ratio**

$$\text{Odds ratio} = \frac{\text{probability of an event of interest}}{1 - \text{probability of an event of interest}} \quad \text{(14.15)}$$

**Logistic Regression Model**

$$\ln(\text{odds ratio}) = \beta_0 + \beta_1 X_{1i} + \beta_2 X_{2i} + \cdots + \beta_k X_{ki} + \varepsilon_i \quad \text{(14.16)}$$

**Logistic Regression Equation**

$$\ln(\text{estimated odds ratio}) = b_0 + b_1 X_{1i} + b_2 X_{2i} + \cdots + b_k X_{ki} \quad \text{(14.17)}$$

**Estimated Odds Ratio**

$$\text{Estimated odds ratio} = e^{\ln(\text{estimated odds ratio})} \quad \text{(14.18)}$$

**Estimated Probability of an Event of Interest**

$$\text{Estimated probability of an event of interest} = \frac{\text{estimated odds ratio}}{1 + \text{estimated odds ratio}} \quad \text{(14.19)}$$

# KEY TERMS

adjusted $r^2$   643
coefficient of multiple
    determination   643
coefficients of partial
    determination   658
cross-product term   663

deviance statistic   674
dummy variables   660
interaction   663
interaction term   663
logistic regression   672
multiple regression model   636

net regression
    coefficients   639
odds ratio   672
overall $F$ test   644
partial $F$ test   653
Wald statistic   675

# CHAPTER REVIEW PROBLEMS

## Checking Your Understanding

**14.58** What is the difference between $r^2$ and the adjusted $r^2$?

**14.59** How does the interpretation of the regression coefficients differ in multiple regression and simple linear regression?

**14.60** How does testing the significance of the entire multiple regression model differ from testing the contribution of each independent variable?

**14.61** How do the coefficients of partial determination differ from the coefficient of multiple determination?

**14.62** Why and how do you use dummy variables?

**14.63** How can you evaluate whether the slope of the dependent variable with an independent variable is the same for each level of the dummy variable?

**14.64** Under what circumstances do you include an interaction term in a regression model?

**14.65** When a dummy variable is included in a regression model that has one numerical independent variable, what assumption do you need to make concerning the slope between the dependent variable, $Y$, and the numerical independent variable, $X$?

**14.66** When do you use logistic regression?

## Applying the Concepts

**14.67** Increasing customer satisfaction typically results in increased purchase behavior. For many products, there is more than one measure of customer satisfaction. In many of these instances, purchase behavior can increase dramatically with an increase in any one of the customer satisfaction measures, not necessarily all of them at the same time. Gunst and Barry ("One Way to Moderate Ceiling Effects," *Quality Progress*, October 2003, pp. 83–85) consider a product with two satisfaction measures, $X_1$ and $X_2$, that range from the lowest level of satisfaction, 1, to the highest level of satisfaction, 7. The dependent variable, $Y$, is a measure of purchase behavior, with the highest value generating the most sales. The following regression equation is presented:

$$\hat{Y}_i = -3.888 + 1.449 X_{1i} + 1.462 X_{2i} - 0.190 X_{1i} X_{2i}$$

Suppose that $X_1$ is the perceived quality of the product and $X_2$ is the perceived value of the product. (*Note:* If the product is overpriced in the view of the customer, he or she perceives it to be of low value and vice versa.)
a. What is the predicted purchase behavior when $X_1 = 2$ and $X_2 = 2$?
b. What is the predicted purchase behavior when $X_1 = 2$ and $X_2 = 7$?
c. What is the predicted purchase behavior when $X_1 = 7$ and $X_2 = 2$?
d. What is the predicted purchase behavior when $X_1 = 7$ and $X_2 = 7$?
e. What is the regression equation when $X_2 = 2$? What is the slope for $X_1$ now?
f. What is the regression equation when $X_2 = 7$? What is the slope for $X_1$ now?
g. What is the regression equation when $X_1 = 2$? What is the slope for $X_2$ now?
h. What is the regression equation when $X_1 = 7$? What is the slope for $X_2$ now?
i. Discuss the implications of (a) through (h) within the context of increasing sales for this product with two customer satisfaction measures.

**14.68** The owner of a moving company typically has his most experienced manager predict the total number of labor hours that will be required to complete an upcoming move. This approach has proved useful in the past, but the owner would like to be able to develop a more accurate method of predicting the labor hours by using the number of cubic feet moved and the number of pieces of large furniture. In a preliminary effort to provide a more accurate method, he has collected data for 36 moves in which the origin and destination were within the borough of Manhattan in New York City and the travel time was an insignificant portion of the hours worked. The data are stored in the file Moving.
a. State the multiple regression equation.
b. Interpret the meaning of the slopes in this equation.
c. Predict the mean labor hours for moving 500 cubic feet with two large pieces of furniture.

**d.** Perform a residual analysis on your results and determine if the regression assumptions are valid.

**e.** Determine whether there is a significant relationship between labor hours and the two independent variables (the amount of cubic feet moved and the number of pieces of large furniture) at the 0.05 level of significance.

**f.** Determine the $p$-value in (e) and interpret its meaning.

**g.** Interpret the meaning of the coefficient of multiple determination in this problem.

**h.** Determine the adjusted $r^2$.

**i.** At the 0.05 level of significance, determine whether each independent variable makes a significant contribution to the regression model. Indicate the most appropriate regression model for this set of data.

**j.** Determine the $p$-values in (i) and interpret their meaning.

**k.** Construct a 95% confidence interval estimate of the population slope between labor hours and the number of cubic feet moved. How does the interpretation of the slope here differ from that in Problem 13.44 on page 609?

**l.** Compute and interpret the coefficients of partial determination.

**14.69** Professional basketball has truly become a sport that generates interest among fans around the world. More and more players come from outside the United States to play in the National Basketball Association (NBA). You want to develop a regression model to predict the number of wins achieved by each NBA team, based on field goal (shots made) percentage for the team and for the opponent. The data are stored in the file **NBA2007**.

**a.** State the multiple regression equation.

**b.** Interpret the meaning of the slopes in this equation.

**c.** Predict the mean number of wins for a team that has a field goal percentage of 45% and an opponent field goal percentage of 44%.

**d.** Perform a residual analysis on your results and determine if the regression assumptions are valid.

**e.** Is there a significant relationship between number of wins and the two independent variables (field goal percentage for the team and for the opponent) at the 0.05 level of significance?

**f.** Determine the $p$-value in (e) and interpret its meaning.

**g.** Interpret the meaning of the coefficient of multiple determination in this problem.

**h.** Determine the adjusted $r^2$.

**i.** At the 0.05 level of significance, determine whether each independent variable makes a significant contribution to the regression model. Indicate the most appropriate regression model for this set of data.

**j.** Determine the $p$-values in (i) and interpret their meaning.

**k.** Compute and interpret the coefficients of partial determination.

**14.70** A sample of 30 recently sold single-family houses in a small city is selected. Develop a model to predict the

selling price (in thousands of dollars), using the assessed value (in thousands of dollars) as well as time period (in months since reassessment). The houses in the city had been reassessed at full value one year prior to the study. The results are contained in the file **House1**.

**a.** State the multiple regression equation.

**b.** Interpret the meaning of the slopes in this equation.

**c.** Predict the mean selling price for a house that has an assessed value of $170,000 and was sold in time period 12.

**d.** Perform a residual analysis on your results and determine if the regression assumptions are valid.

**e.** Determine whether there is a significant relationship between selling price and the two independent variables (assessed value and time period) at the 0.05 level of significance.

**f.** Determine the $p$-value in (e) and interpret its meaning.

**g.** Interpret the meaning of the coefficient of multiple determination in this problem.

**h.** Determine the adjusted $r^2$.

**i.** At the 0.05 level of significance, determine whether each independent variable makes a significant contribution to the regression model. Indicate the most appropriate regression model for this set of data.

**j.** Determine the $p$-values in (i) and interpret their meaning.

**k.** Construct a 95% confidence interval estimate of the population slope between selling price and assessed value. How does the interpretation of the slope here differ from that in Problem 13.76 on page 623?

**l.** Compute and interpret the coefficients of partial determination.

**14.71** Measuring the height of a California redwood tree is very difficult because these trees grow to heights of over 300 feet. People familiar with these trees understand that the height of a California redwood tree is related to other characteristics of the tree, including the diameter of the tree at the breast height of a person and the thickness of the bark of the tree. The data in the file **Redwood** represent the height, diameter at breast height of a person, and bark thickness for a sample of 21 California redwood trees.

**a.** State the multiple regression equation that predicts the height of a tree based on the tree's diameter at breast height and the thickness of the bark.

**b.** Interpret the meaning of the slopes in this equation.

**c.** Predict the mean height for a tree that has a breast diameter of 25 inches and a bark thickness of 2 inches.

**d.** Interpret the meaning of the coefficient of multiple determination in this problem.

**e.** Perform a residual analysis on the results and determine if the regression assumptions are valid.

**f.** Determine whether there is a significant relationship between the height of redwood trees and the two independent variables (breast-height diameter and the bark thickness) at the 0.05 level of significance.

**g.** Construct a 95% confidence interval estimate of the population slope between the height of redwood trees and breast-height diameter and between the height of redwood trees and the bark thickness.

**h.** At the 0.05 level of significance, determine whether each independent variable makes a significant contribution to the regression model. Indicate the independent variables to include in this model.

**i.** Construct a 95% confidence interval estimate of the mean height for trees that have a breast-height diameter of 25 inches and a bark thickness of 2 inches along with a prediction interval for an individual tree.

**j.** Compute and interpret the coefficients of partial determination.

**14.72** Develop a model to predict the assessed value (in thousands of dollars), using the size of the houses (in thousands of square feet) and the age of the houses (in years) from the following table (whose data are stored in the file House2):

| House | Assessed Value ($000) | Size of House (Thousands of Square Feet) | Age (Years) |
|---|---|---|---|
| 1 | 184.4 | 2.00 | 3.42 |
| 2 | 177.4 | 1.71 | 11.50 |
| 3 | 175.7 | 1.45 | 8.33 |
| 4 | 185.9 | 1.76 | 0.00 |
| 5 | 179.1 | 1.93 | 7.42 |
| 6 | 170.4 | 1.20 | 32.00 |
| 7 | 175.8 | 1.55 | 16.00 |
| 8 | 185.9 | 1.93 | 2.00 |
| 9 | 178.5 | 1.59 | 1.75 |
| 10 | 179.2 | 1.50 | 2.75 |
| 11 | 186.7 | 1.90 | 0.00 |
| 12 | 179.3 | 1.39 | 0.00 |
| 13 | 174.5 | 1.54 | 12.58 |
| 14 | 183.8 | 1.89 | 2.75 |
| 15 | 176.8 | 1.59 | 7.17 |

**a.** State the multiple regression equation.

**b.** Interpret the meaning of the slopes in this equation.

**c.** Predict the mean assessed value for a house that has a size of 1,750 square feet and is 10 years old.

**d.** Perform a residual analysis on the results and determine if the regression assumptions are valid.

**e.** Determine whether there is a significant relationship between assessed value and the two independent variables (size and age) at the 0.05 level of significance.

**f.** Determine the p-value in (e) and interpret its meaning.

**g.** Interpret the meaning of the coefficient of multiple determination in this problem.

**h.** Determine the adjusted $r^2$.

**i.** At the 0.05 level of significance, determine whether each independent variable makes a significant contribution to the regression model. Indicate the most appropriate regression model for this set of data.

**j.** Determine the p-values in (i) and interpret their meaning.

**k.** Construct a 95% confidence interval estimate of the population slope between assessed value and size. How does the interpretation of the slope here differ from that of Problem 13.77 on page 624?

**l.** Compute and interpret the coefficients of partial determination.

**m.** The real estate assessor's office has been publicly quoted as saying that the age of a house has no bearing on its assessed value. Based on your answers to (a) through (l), do you agree with this statement? Explain.

**14.73** Crazy Dave, a well-known baseball analyst, wants to determine which variables are important in predicting a team's wins in a given season. He has collected data related to wins, earned run average (ERA), and runs scored for the 2006 season (stored in the file BB2006). Develop a model to predict the number of wins based on ERA and runs scored.

**a.** State the multiple regression equation.

**b.** Interpret the meaning of the slopes in this equation.

**c.** Predict the mean number of wins for a team that has an ERA of 4.50 and has scored 750 runs.

**d.** Perform a residual analysis on the results and determine if the regression assumptions are valid.

**e.** Is there a significant relationship between number of wins and the two independent variables (ERA and runs scored) at the 0.05 level of significance?

**f.** Determine the p-value in (e) and interpret its meaning.

**g.** Interpret the meaning of the coefficient of multiple determination in this problem.

**h.** Determine the adjusted $r^2$.

**i.** At the 0.05 level of significance, determine whether each independent variable makes a significant contribution to the regression model. Indicate the most appropriate regression model for this set of data.

**j.** Determine the p-values in (i) and interpret their meaning.

**k.** Construct a 95% confidence interval estimate of the population slope between wins and ERA.

**l.** Compute and interpret the coefficients of partial determination.

**m.** Which is more important in predicting wins—pitching, as measured by ERA, or offense, as measured by runs scored? Explain.

**14.74** Referring to Problem 14.73, suppose that in addition to using ERA to predict the number of wins, Crazy Dave wants to include the league (American vs. National) as an independent variable. Develop a model to predict wins based on ERA and league. For (a)-(k), do not include an interaction term.

**a.** State the multiple regression equation.

**b.** Interpret the regression coefficients in (a).

**c.** Predict the mean number of wins for a team with an ERA of 4.50 in the American League. Construct a 95% confidence interval estimate for all teams and a 95% prediction interval for an individual team.

**d.** Perform a residual analysis on the results and determine if the regression assumptions are valid.

**e.** Is there a significant relationship between wins and the two independent variables (ERA and league) at the 0.05 level of significance?

**f.** At the 0.05 level of significance, determine whether each independent variable makes a contribution to the regression model. Indicate the most appropriate regression model for this set of data.

**g.** Construct a 95% confidence interval estimate of the population slope for the relationship between wins and ERA.

**h.** Construct a 95% confidence interval estimate of the population slope for the relationship between wins and league.

**i.** Compute and interpret the adjusted $r^2$.

**j.** Compute and interpret the coefficients of partial determination.

**k.** What assumption do you have to make about the slope of wins with ERA?

**l.** Add an interaction term to the model and, at the 0.05 level of significance, determine whether it makes a significant contribution to the model.

**m.** On the basis of the results of (f) and (l), which model is most appropriate? Explain.

**14.75** You are a real estate broker who wants to compare property values in Glen Cove and Roslyn (which are located approximately 8 miles apart). In order to do so, you will analyze the data in the `GCRoslyn` file that includes samples of houses from Glen Cove and Roslyn. Making sure to include the dummy variable for location (Glen Cove or Roslyn), develop a regression model to predict appraised value, based on the land area of a property, the age of a house, and location. Be sure to determine whether any interaction terms need to be included in the model.

**14.76** Undergraduate students at Miami University in Oxford, Ohio, were surveyed in order to evaluate the effect of price on the purchase of a pizza from Pizza Hut. The students were asked to suppose that they were going to have a large 2-topping pizza delivered to their residence. Then they were asked to select from either Pizza Hut or another pizzeria of their choice. The price they would have to pay to get a Pizza Hut pizza differed from survey to survey. For example, some surveys used the price currently charged by the Oxford Pizza Hut, $11.49. Other prices investigated were $8.49, $9.49, $10.49, $12.49, $13.49, and $14.49. The dependent variable for this study is whether or not a student will select Pizza Hut. Possible independent variables are the price of Pizza Hut and the gender of the student. The data set `Pizzahut` has 220 observations and 3 variables:

Gender (1 = male, 0 = female)
Price (8.49, 9.49, 10.49, 11.49, 12.49, 13.49, or 14.49)
Purchase (1 = the student selected Pizza Hut, 0 = the student selected another pizzeria)

**a.** Use Minitab to develop a logistic regression model to predict the probability that a student selects Pizza Hut based on the price of the pizza. Is price an important indicator of purchase selection?

**b.** Use Minitab to develop a logistic regression model to predict the probability that a student selects Pizza Hut based on the price of the pizza and the gender of the student. Is price an important indicator of purchase selection? Is gender an important indicator of purchase selection?

**c.** Compare the results from (a) and (b). Which model would you choose? Discuss.

**d.** Using the model selected in (c), predict the probability that a student will select Pizza Hut if the price is $8.99.

**e.** Using the model selected in (c), predict the probability that a student will select Pizza Hut if the price is $11.49.

**f.** Using the model selected in (c), predict the probability that a student will select Pizza Hut if the price is $13.99.

**14.77** The director of a training program for a large insurance company is evaluating three different methods of training underwriters. The three methods are traditional, CD-ROM based, and Web based. She divides 30 trainees into three randomly assigned groups of 10. Before the start of the training, each trainee is given a proficiency exam that measures mathematics and computer skills. At the end of the training, all students take the same end-of-training exam. The results are stored in the file `Underwriting`.

Develop a multiple regression model to predict the score on the end-of-training exam, based on the score on the proficiency exam and the method of training used. For (a) through (k) do not include an interaction term.

**a.** State the multiple regression equation.

**b.** Interpret the regression coefficients in (a).

**c.** Predict the mean end-of-training exam score for a student with a proficiency exam score of 100 who had Web-based training.

**d.** Perform a residual analysis on your results and determine if the regression assumptions are valid.

**e.** Is there a significant relationship between the end-of-training exam score and the independent variables (proficiency score and training method) at the 0.05 level of significance?

**f.** At the 0.05 level of significance, determine whether each independent variable makes a contribution to the regression model. Indicate the most appropriate regression model for this set of data.

**g.** Construct and interpret a 95% confidence interval estimate of the population slope for the relationship between end-of-training exam score and the proficiency exam.

**h.** Construct and interpret a 95% confidence interval estimate of the population slope for the relationship between end-of-training exam score and type of training method.

**i.** Compute and interpret the adjusted $r^2$.

**j.** Compute the coefficients of partial determination and interpret their meaning.

**k.** What assumption about the slope of proficiency score with end-of-training exam score do you need to make in this problem?

**l.** Add interaction terms to the model and, at the 0.05 level of significance, determine whether any interaction terms make a significant contribution to the model.

**m.** On the basis of the results of (f) and (l), which model is most appropriate? Explain.

# MANAGING THE *SPRINGVILLE HERALD*

In its continuing study of the home-delivery subscription solicitation process, a marketing department team wants to test the effects of two types of structured sales presentations (personal formal and personal informal) and the number of hours spent on telemarketing on the number of new subscriptions. The staff has recorded these data in the file `SH14` for the past 24 weeks. You can find this data set at **www.prenhall.com/HeraldCase/EffectsData.htm** and in

the `EffectsData.htm` file in the **Herald Case** folder on the Student CD-ROM that accompanies this book.

Analyze these data and develop a multiple regression model to predict the number of new subscriptions for a week, based on the number of hours spent on telemarketing and the sales presentation type. Write a report, giving detailed findings concerning the regression model used.

# WEB CASE

*Apply your knowledge of multiple regression models in this Web Case, which extends the Using Statistics OmniFoods scenario from this chapter.*

To ensure a successful test marketing of its OmniPower energy bars, the OmniFoods marketing department has contracted with In-Store Placements Group (ISPG), a merchandising consultancy. ISPG will work with the grocery store chain that is conducting the test-market study. Using the same 34-store sample used in the test-market study, ISPG claims that the choice of shelf location and the presence of in-store OmniPower coupon dispensers each increase sale of the energy bars.

Review the ISPG claims and supporting data at the OmniFoods internal Web page, **www.prenhall.com/Springville/Omni_ISPGMemo.htm** (or open the

`Omni_ISPGMemo.htm` file from the Student CD-ROM Web Case folder) and then answer the following:

**1.** Are the supporting data consistent with ISPG's claims? Perform an appropriate statistical analysis to confirm (or discredit) the stated relationship between sales and the two independent variables of product shelf location and the presence of in-store OmniPower coupon dispensers.

**2.** If you were advising OmniFoods, would you recommend using a specific shelf location and in-store coupon dispensers to sell OmniPower bars?

**3.** What additional data would you advise collecting in order to determine the effectiveness of the sales promotion techniques used by ISPG?

# REFERENCES

1. Davenport, T., and J. Harris, *Competing on Analytics: The New Science of Winning* (Boston, MA: Harvard Business School Press, 2007).

2. Hosmer, D. W., and S. Lemeshow, *Applied Logistic Regression*, 2nd ed. (New York: Wiley, 2001).

3. Kutner, M., C. Nachtsheim, J. Neter, and W. Li, *Applied Linear Statistical Models*, 5th ed. (New York: McGraw-Hill/Irwin, 2005).

4. *Microsoft Excel 2007* (Redmond, WA: Microsoft Corp., 2007).

5. *Minitab for Windows Version 15* (State College, PA: Minitab, Inc., 2006).

6. **www.britannica.com/ebc/article-9362293**.

# Appendix E14
## Using Microsoft Excel for Multiple Regression Models

### E14.1 Performing Multiple Regression Analyses

You perform a multiple regression analysis by using the ToolPak Regression procedure.

Open to the worksheet that contains data for the $Y$ variable and the $X$ variables. Data for the $X$ variables must be placed in contiguous columns. (Use cut-and-paste to rearrange the data, if necessary.) Select **Tools → Data Analysis** (Excel 97–2003) or **Data → Data Analysis** (Excel 2007). Then select **Regression** from the Data Analysis list, and click **OK**. In the procedure's dialog box (see below), enter the cell range of the $Y$ variable data as the **Input Y Range**, the cell range of the $X$ variables data as the **Input X Range**, and click **Labels**. Click **Confidence Level**, enter a value in its box, and then click **OK**. Results appear on a new worksheet similar to Figure 14.2 on page 638.

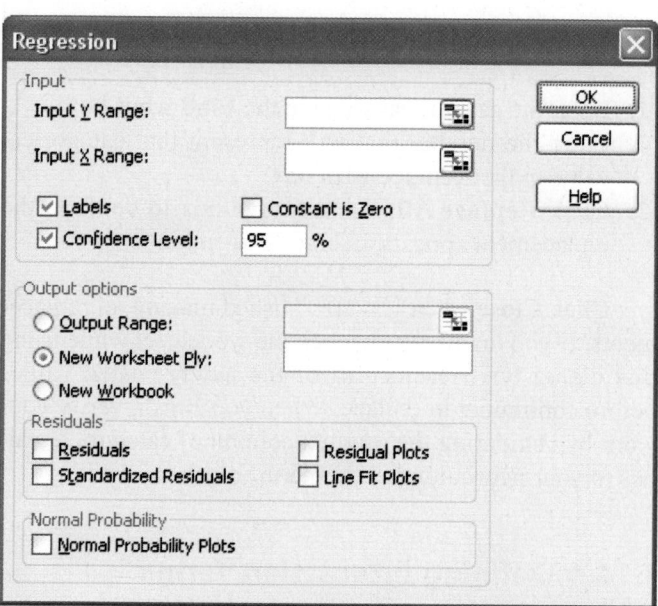

### E14.2 Performing Multiple Regression Residual Analysis

You perform multiple regression residual analysis using a two-step process. You first modify the instructions of Section E14.1, clicking **Residuals** in the Regression dialog

box before you click **OK**. This option adds a residual table similar to the one shown in Figure E14.1 (the residuals for the OmniPower sales analysis). You then use Excel charting features to do a residual analysis of a multiple regression model. (Although the Regression dialog box contains a **Residuals Plots** option, this option will create only the residual plots for each independent variable.)

| | A | B | C |
|---|---|---|---|
| 23 | **RESIDUAL OUTPUT** | | |
| 24 | | | |
| 25 | **Observation** | **Predicted Sales** | **Residuals** |
| 26 | 1 | 3420.3095 | 720.6905 |
| 27 | 2 | 3420.3095 | 421.6905 |
| 28 | 3 | 3420.3095 | -364.3095 |
| 29 | 4 | 3420.3095 | 98.6905 |
| 30 | 5 | 4142.9211 | 83.0789 |
| 31 | 6 | 4142.9211 | 487.0789 |
| 32 | 7 | 4142.9211 | -635.9211 |
| 33 | 8 | 4142.9211 | -388.9211 |
| 34 | 9 | 4865.5327 | 134.4673 |
| 35 | 10 | 4865.5327 | 254.4673 |
| 36 | 11 | 4865.5327 | -854.5327 |
| 37 | 12 | 4865.5327 | 149.4673 |
| 38 | 13 | 2355.9628 | -439.9628 |
| 39 | 14 | 2355.9628 | -1680.9628 |
| 40 | 15 | 2355.9628 | 1280.0372 |
| 41 | 16 | 2355.9628 | 868.0372 |
| 42 | 17 | 3078.5744 | -783.5744 |
| 43 | 18 | 3078.5744 | -348.5744 |
| 44 | 19 | 3078.5744 | -460.5744 |
| 45 | 20 | 3078.5744 | 1342.4256 |
| 46 | 21 | 3801.1860 | 311.8140 |
| 47 | 22 | 3801.1860 | -55.1860 |
| 48 | 23 | 3801.1860 | -269.1860 |
| 49 | 24 | 3801.1860 | 23.8140 |
| 50 | 25 | 1291.6161 | -195.6161 |
| 51 | 26 | 1291.6161 | -530.6161 |
| 52 | 27 | 1291.6161 | 796.3839 |
| 53 | 28 | 1291.6161 | -471.6161 |
| 54 | 29 | 2014.2277 | 99.7723 |
| 55 | 30 | 2014.2277 | -132.2277 |
| 56 | 31 | 2014.2277 | 144.7723 |
| 57 | 32 | 2014.2277 | -412.2277 |
| 58 | 33 | 2736.8393 | 617.1607 |
| 59 | 34 | 2736.8393 | 190.1607 |

**FIGURE E14.1**

Residual Output table

The residuals output table allows you to create the residual plot of the residuals versus $\hat{Y}_i$, the predicted values of $Y$. Apply the instructions of Section E2.13 on pages

78–79 to create this residual plot, using the cell range of the residuals (C25:C59 in Figure E14.1) as the $Y$ variable and the cell range of the predicted $Y$ (B25:B59 in Figure E14.1) as the $X$ variable.

Residual plots of residuals versus $X_{1i}$, $X_{2i}$, or *Observation* require more work as initially data for these plots will not be in proper order ($X$ variable first, then $Y$ variable) or will not appear together on one worksheet, as required when creating scatter plots.

For these plots, first copy the Residuals cell range column (C25:C59 in Figure E14.1) to column A of a new worksheet and then copy the $X_{1i}$ $X_{2i}$ or *Observation* values to column B. The $X_{1i}$ and $X_{2i}$ values appear on your original data worksheet and the *Observation* values appear on the regression results worksheet (cell range A25:A59 in Figure E14.1). Then apply the instructions of Section E2.13 to create a residual plot, using the column A (residuals) cell range as the $Y$ variable and the column B cell range as the $X$ variable.

## E14.3 Computing the Confidence Interval Estimate of the Mean Response and the Prediction Interval

You compute the confidence interval estimate of the mean response and the prediction interval using Excel techniques that are beyond the scope of this book. If you are an advanced Excel user, you can use the **CIEandPI** worksheet of the `CIEandPIforMR.xls` workbook (shown in Figure 14.4 on page 640) as a model for your own solutions. This worksheet uses the **TINV(1-*confidence level, degrees of freedom*)** function to compute the $t$ statistic in cell B20 and uses the **TRANSPOSE(*cell range*), MMULT(*cell range 1, cell range 2*)**, and **MINVERSE(*cell range*)** array functions to perform advanced matrix mathematics. Some worksheet formulas reference a regression results worksheet named **MR**, whereas others, not shown in Figure 14.4, refer to a **DC** worksheet that contains a copy of the regression data and a column of all 1's. (Review the **CIEandPIFormulas** worksheet to see all of the formulas in the **CIEandPI** worksheet.)

## E14.4 Computing the Coefficients of Partial Determination

You compute the coefficients of partial determination using a two-step process. You first use the instructions of Section E14.1 to create all possible regression results worksheets. For example, if you have two independent variables, you perform three regression analyses: $Y$ with $X_1$ and $X_2$, $Y$ with $X_1$, and $Y$ with $X_2$. You then open the `CPD.xls` workbook and transfer values from the regression results worksheets to the CPD worksheet that matches your model.

For example, if you have two independent variables, you would make entries in the **CPD_2** worksheet.

Further instructions for using the CPD worksheets appear on the worksheets themselves. (The #DIV/0! messages that may appear in several cells will disappear after you enter your data. This is not an error.)

## E14.5 Creating Dummy Variables

You create dummy variables by using the Excel find-and-replace command to "find" each categorical value and "replace" it with a number.

Open the worksheet that contains your data. Copy all of the values of the categorical variable for which you are creating a dummy variable and paste the values into the first empty column of your worksheet.

Select all of the newly pasted values and press **Crtl+H**, the keyboard shortcut that displays the Find and Replace dialog box (shown below). For each unique categorical value in the column:

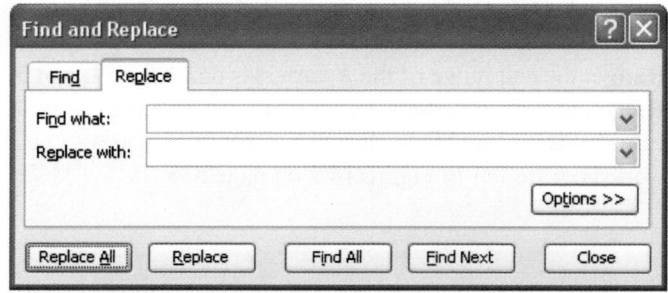

1. Enter the categorical value in the **Find what** box.
2. Enter the number that will represent that categorical value in the **Replace with** box.
3. Click **Replace All**. If a message box to confirm the replacement appears, click **OK** to continue.

Click **Close** when you are finished making all replacements. If you inadvertently click the worksheet while using this dialog box, reselect all of the newly pasted values before continuing to replace. When you finish, verify your work by comparing the original column of categorical values to your new column of numeric values.

## E14.6 Defining Interaction Terms

You define the interaction term of an independent variable $X_1$ and a second independent variable $X_2$ by creating a column of formulas that multiply the $X_1$ variable by the $X_2$ variable. For example, if the first independent variable appeared in column B and the second independent variable appeared in column C, you would enter the formula **=B2*C2** in the row 2 cell of an empty column and then copy the formula down through all rows of data.

# Appendix P14
## Using PHStat2 for Multiple Regression Models

### P14.1 Performing Multiple Regression Analyses

To perform a multiple regression analysis, use **PHStat → Regression → Multiple Regression**. This procedure creates a regression results worksheet based on sample data and a confidence level that you specify. The procedure uses the ToolPak Regression procedure to perform the regression analysis and creates a worksheet similar to Figure 14.2 on page 638 if you leave **Regression Statistics Table** and **ANOVA and Coefficients Table** checked. Other sections of this PHStat2 appendix explain the use of the other Output Options to create charts and worksheets related to the regression analysis.

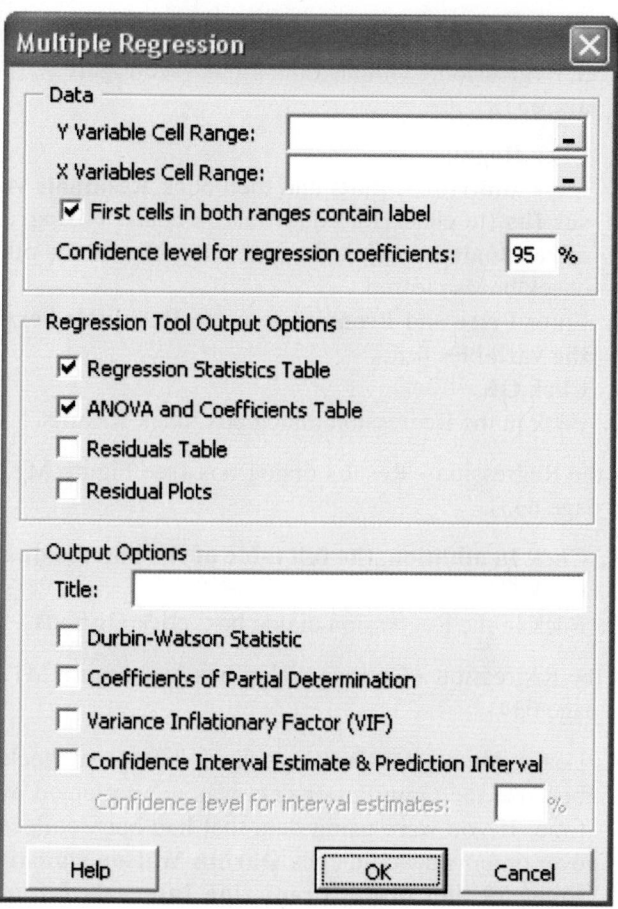

### P14.2 Performing Multiple Regression Residual Analyses

To perform a multiple regression residual analysis, use the Section P14.1 instructions but click **Residuals Table** and **Residual Plots** before you click **OK** in the Multiple Regression dialog box.

### P14.3 Computing the Confidence Interval Estimate of the Mean and the Prediction Interval

To compute the confidence interval estimate of the mean and the prediction interval, use the Section P14.1 instructions, but click **Confidence Interval Estimate & Prediction Interval** and enter a value for the **Confidence level for interval estimates** before you click **OK** in the Multiple Regression dialog box. PHStat2 will compute the confidence interval estimate and prediction interval on a separate, second worksheet that will be similar to Figure 14.4 on page 640.

### P14.4 Computing the Coefficients of Partial Determination

To compute the coefficients of partial determination, use the Section P14.1 instructions, but click **Coefficients of Partial Determination** before you click **OK** in the Multiple Regression dialog box. PHStat2 will compute the coefficients on a separate, second worksheet that will be similar to one of the CPD worksheets in the CPD.xls workbook.

# Appendix M14
## Using Minitab for Multiple Regression Models

### M14.1 Creating Three-Dimensional Plots

To illustrate creating a three-dimensional plot (for use only when there are two independent variables in the regression model):

1. Open the **OmniPower.mtw** worksheet.
2. Select **Graph → 3D Scatterplot**.
3. In the 3D Scatterplots dialog box (see Figure M14.1), click **Simple** and then **OK** (to proceed to the next dialog box).

**FIGURE M14.1**

Minitab 3D Scatterplots dialog box

In the 3D Scatterplot - Simple dialog box (see Figure M14.2):

4. Enter **Sales** in the **Z variable** box.
5. Enter **Price** in the **Y variable** box.
6. Enter **Promotion** in the **X variable** box.
7. Click **OK**.

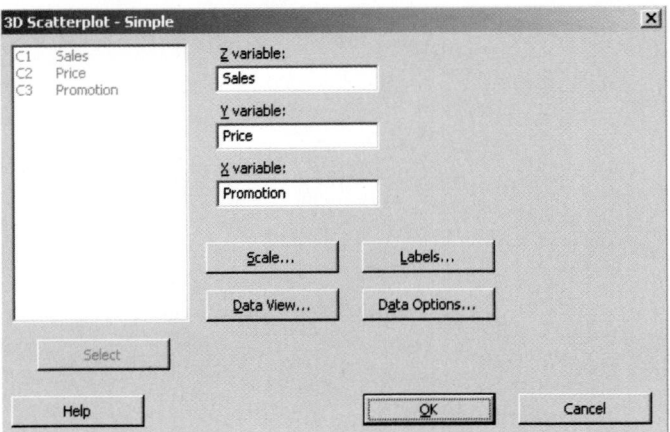

**FIGURE M14.2**

Minitab 3D Scatterplot - Simple dialog box

### M14.2 Performing Multiple Regression Analyses

In Minitab, performing a multiple regression analysis is similar to performing a simple linear regression (see Section M13.1 on page 633). To illustrate performing a multiple regression analysis:

1. Open the **OmniPower.mtw** worksheet.
2. Select **Stat → Regression → Regression**.

In the Regression dialog box (see Figure M13.1 on page 633):

3. Enter **Sales** in the **Response** box.
4. Enter **Price** and **Promotion** in the **Predictors** box.
5. Click **Graphs**.

In the Regression - Graphs dialog box (see Figure M13.2 on page 633):

6. Click **Regular**.
7. Click **Individual plots** and then click **Residuals versus fits** (to check for equal variance) and **Histogram of residuals** (to check for normality). Leave the other check boxes cleared.
8. Enter **Price** and **Promotion** in the **Residuals versus the variables** box.
9. Click **OK**.
10. Back in the Regression dialog box, click **Results**.

In the Regression - Results dialog box (see Figure M13.3 on page 633):

11. Click **In addition, the full table of fits and residuals**.
12. Click **OK**.
13. Back in the Regression dialog box, click **Options**.

In the Regression - Options dialog box (see Figure M13.4 on page 634):

14. Leave all of the **Display** check boxes unchecked because the OmniPower data was not collected over time. If you were using data that had been collected over time, you would click **Durbin-Watson statistic**.
15. Enter **79 400** in the **Prediction intervals for new observations** box.
16. Enter **95** in the **Confidence level** box.
17. Click **OK**.
18. Back in the Regression dialog box, click **OK** (to perform the analysis).

## M14.3 Creating Dummy Variables

To illustrate creating a dummy variable using the data of Table 14.5 on page 660:

1. Open the **House3.mtw** worksheet. (The fireplace variable in column C3 of this worksheet is entered as Yes and No values.)
2. Enter **FireplaceCoded** as the name of the blank column **C4**.
3. Select **Data → Code → Text to Numeric**.

In the Code - Text to Numeric dialog box:

4. Enter **Fireplace** in the **Code data from columns** box.
5. Enter **FireplaceCoded** in the **Store coded data in columns** box.
6. In the first **Original values** box, enter **Yes**.
7. In the first **New** box, enter **1**.
8. In the second **Original values** box, enter **No**.
9. In the second **New** box, enter **0**.
10. Click **OK**.

## M14.4 Defining Interaction Terms

To illustrate defining an interaction term using the data of Table 14.5 on page 660:

1. Use the instructions for Section M14.3 to create the **FireplaceCoded** column in the **House3.mtw** worksheet.
2. Select **Calc → Calculator**.
3. Enter **C5** in the **Store result in variable** box.
4. Enter **Size * FireplaceCoded** in the **Expression** box.
5. Click **OK**.
6. Enter **Size * FireplaceCoded** as the name for column **C5**.

## M14.5 Performing Logistic Regression

To illustrate performing logistic regression:

1. Open the **Logpurch.mtw** worksheet, containing the data of the credit card upgrade example on page 673.
2. Select **Stat → Regression → Binary Logistic Regression**.

In the Binary Logistic Regression dialog box (see Figure M14.3):

3. Click **Response in response/frequency format**.
4. Enter **Purchase** in the **Response** box.
5. Enter **Spending** and **Extra** in the **Model** box.
6. Enter **Extra** in the **Factors (optional)** box (because **Extra** is a categorical variable).
7. Click **OK**.

**FIGURE M14.3**

Minitab Binary Logistic Regression dialog box

# CHAPTER
# FIFTEEN

## MULTIPLE REGRESSION MODEL BUILDING

# LEARNING OBJECTIVES

## In this chapter, you learn:

- To use quadratic terms in a regression model
- To use transformed variables in a regression model
- To measure the correlation among independent variables
- To build a regression model, using either the stepwise or best-subsets approach
- To avoid the pitfalls involved in developing a multiple regression model

# USING STATISTICS @ WTT-TV

As part of your job as the operations manager at WTT-TV, you look for ways to reduce labor expenses. Currently, the unionized graphic artists at the station receive hourly pay for a significant number of hours during which they are idle. These hours are called standby hours. You have collected data concerning standby hours and four factors that you suspect are related to the excessive number of standby hours the station is currently experiencing: the total number of staff present, remote hours, Dubner hours, and total labor hours.

You plan to build a multiple regression model to help determine which factors most heavily affect standby hours. You believe that an appropriate model will help you to predict the number of future standby hours, identify the root causes for excessive numbers of standby hours, and allow you to reduce the total number of future standby hours. How do you build the model with the most appropriate mix of independent variables? Are there statistical techniques to help you identify a "best" model without having to consider all possible models? How do you begin?

In Chapter 14, you focused on multiple regression models with two independent variables. In this chapter, regression analysis is extended to models containing more than two independent variables. In order to help you learn to develop the best model when confronted with a large set of data (such as the one described in the Using Statistics scenario), this chapter introduces you to various topics related to model building. These topics include quadratic independent variables, transformations of either the dependent or independent variables, stepwise regression, and best-subsets regression.

## 15.1    THE QUADRATIC REGRESSION MODEL

The simple regression model discussed in Chapter 13 and the multiple regression model discussed in Chapter 14 assumed that the relationship between $Y$ and each independent variable is linear. However, in Section 13.1, several different types of nonlinear relationships between variables were introduced. One of the most common nonlinear relationships is a quadratic relationship between two variables in which $Y$ increases (or decreases) at a changing rate for various values of $X$ (see Figure 13.2, Panels C–E, on page 576). You can use the quadratic regression model defined in Equation (15.1) to analyze this type of relationship between $X$ and $Y$.

Quadratic Regression Model

$$Y_i = \beta_0 + \beta_1 X_{1i} + \beta_2 X_{1i}^2 + \varepsilon_i \qquad (15.1)$$

where

$\beta_0 = Y$ intercept

$\beta_1 =$ coefficient of the linear effect on $Y$

$\beta_2 =$ coefficient of the quadratic effect on $Y$

$\varepsilon_i =$ random error in $Y$ for observation $i$

This **quadratic regression model** is similar to the multiple regression model with two independent variables [see Equation (14.2) on page 638] except that the second independent variable is the square of the first independent variable. Once again, you use the sample regression coefficients ($b_0$, $b_1$, and $b_2$) as estimates of the population parameters ($\beta_0$, $\beta_1$, and $\beta_2$). Equation (15.2) defines the regression equation for the quadratic model with one independent variable ($X_1$) and a dependent variable ($Y$).

Quadratic Regression Equation

$$\hat{Y}_i = b_0 + b_1 X_{1i} + b_2 X_{1i}^2 \tag{15.2}$$

In Equation (15.2), the first regression coefficient, $b_0$, represents the $Y$ intercept; the second regression coefficient, $b_1$, represents the linear effect; and the third regression coefficient, $b_2$, represents the quadratic effect.

## Finding the Regression Coefficients and Predicting Y

To illustrate the quadratic regression model, consider a study that investigated how adding fly ash affected the strength of concrete. (Fly ash is an inexpensive industrial waste by-product that can be used as a substitute for Portland cement, a more expensive ingredient of concrete.) Batches of concrete were prepared in which the percentage of fly ash ranged from 0% to 60%. Table 15.1 summarizes a sample drawn from 18 different batches (these data can be found in the file Flyash).

**TABLE 15.1**

Fly Ash Percentage and Strength of 18 Batches of 28-Day-Old Concrete

| Fly Ash % | Strength (psi) | Fly Ash % | Strength (psi) |
|-----------|----------------|-----------|----------------|
| 0 | 4,779 | 40 | 5,995 |
| 0 | 4,706 | 40 | 5,628 |
| 0 | 4,350 | 40 | 5,897 |
| 20 | 5,189 | 50 | 5,746 |
| 20 | 5,140 | 50 | 5,719 |
| 20 | 4,976 | 50 | 5,782 |
| 30 | 5,110 | 60 | 4,895 |
| 30 | 5,685 | 60 | 5,030 |
| 30 | 5,618 | 60 | 4,648 |

The scatter plot in Figure 15.1 on page 694 can help you select the proper model for expressing the relationship between fly ash percentage and strength. Figure 15.1 indicates an initial increase in the strength of the concrete as the percentage of fly ash increases. The strength appears to level off and then drop after achieving maximum strength at about 40% fly ash. Strength for 50% fly ash is slightly below strength at 40%, but strength at 60% is substantially below strength at 50%. Therefore, a quadratic model is a more appropriate choice than a linear model to estimate strength based on fly ash percentage.

Figure 15.2 on page 694 shows the Excel worksheet for these data and Figure 15.3 on page 694 displays Minitab results.

From Figure 15.2 or 15.3,

$$b_0 = 4{,}486.3611 \quad b_1 = 63.0052 \quad b_2 = -0.8765$$

Therefore, the quadratic regression equation is

$$\hat{Y}_i = 4{,}486.3611 + 63.0052 X_{1i} - 0.8765 X_{1i}^2$$

where

$$\hat{Y}_i = \text{predicted strength for sample } i$$

$$X_{1i} = \text{percentage of fly ash for sample } i$$

**FIGURE 15.1**

Microsoft Excel scatter plot of fly ash percentage (X) and strength (Y)

*See Section E2.12 or P2.12 to create this. Minitab users, see Section M2.9 to create an equivalent chart.*

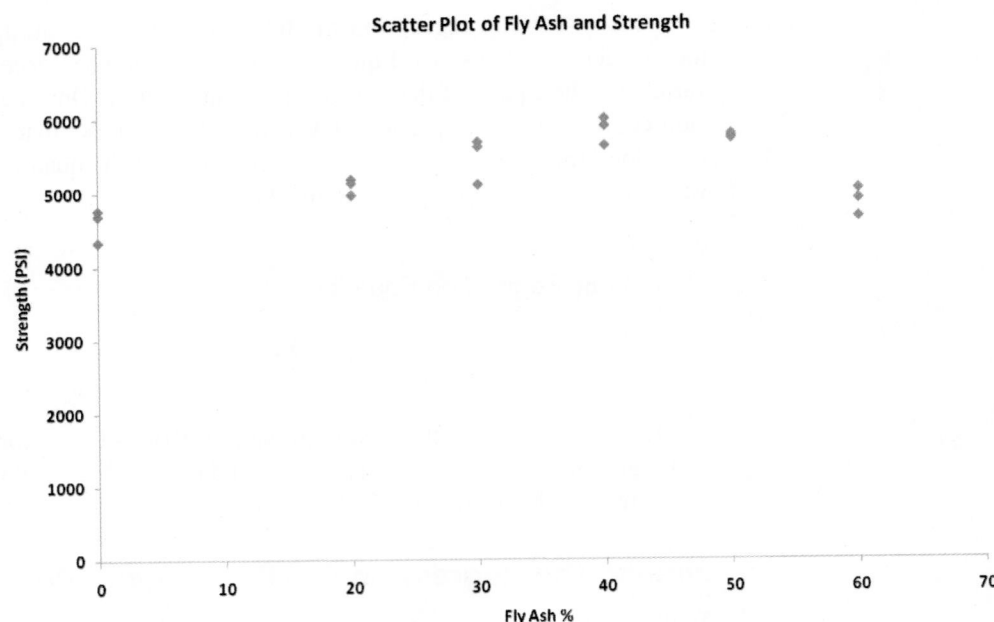

**FIGURE 15.2**

Microsoft Excel regression results worksheet for the concrete strength data

*See Section E15.1 and either E14.1 or P14.1 to create this.*

|   | A | B | C | D | E | F | G |
|---|---|---|---|---|---|---|---|
| 1 | **Concrete Strength Analysis** | | | | | | |
| 2 | | | | | | | |
| 3 | *Regression Statistics* | | | | | | |
| 4 | Multiple R | 0.8053 | | | | | |
| 5 | R Square | 0.6485 | | | | | |
| 6 | Adjusted R Square | 0.6016 | | | | | |
| 7 | Standard Error | 312.1129 | | | | | |
| 8 | Observations | 18 | | | | | |
| 9 | | | | | | | |
| 10 | ANOVA | | | | | | |
| 11 | | *df* | *SS* | *MS* | *F* | *Significance F* | |
| 12 | Regression | 2 | 2695473.49 | 1347736.745 | 13.8351 | 0.0004 | |
| 13 | Residual | 15 | 1461217.01 | 97414.4674 | | | |
| 14 | Total | 17 | 4156690.5 | | | | |
| 15 | | | | | | | |
| 16 | | Coefficients | Standard Error | t Stat | P-value | Lower 95% | Upper 95% |
| 17 | Intercept | 4486.3611 | 174.7531 | 25.6726 | 0.0000 | 4113.8834 | 4858.8389 |
| 18 | Fly Ash% | 63.0052 | 12.3725 | 5.0923 | 0.0001 | 36.6338 | 89.3767 |
| 19 | Fly Ash% ^2 | -0.8765 | 0.1966 | -4.4578 | 0.0005 | -1.2955 | -0.4574 |

**FIGURE 15.3**

Minitab results for the concrete strength data

*See Sections M15.1 and M14.2 to create this.*

```
The regression equation is
PSI = 4486 + 63.0 %flyash - 0.876 Flyashsquared


Predictor        Coef    SE Coef      T      P
Constant        4486.4     174.8   25.67  0.000
%flyash          63.01     12.37    5.09  0.000
Flyashsquared  -0.8765    0.1966   -4.46  0.000


S = 312.113    R-Sq = 64.8%    R-Sq(adj) = 60.2%


Analysis of Variance

Source           DF       SS        MS       F      P
Regression        2  2695473   1347737   13.84  0.000
Residual Error   15  1461217     97414
Total            17  4156690
```

Figure 15.4 plots this quadratic regression equation on the scatter plot to show the fit of the quadratic regression model to the original data.

**FIGURE 15.4**

Microsoft Excel scatter plot expressing the quadratic relationship between fly ash percentage and strength for the concrete data

*See Section E2.13 or P2.9 to create this. Minitab users, see Section M13.2 to create an equivalent chart.*

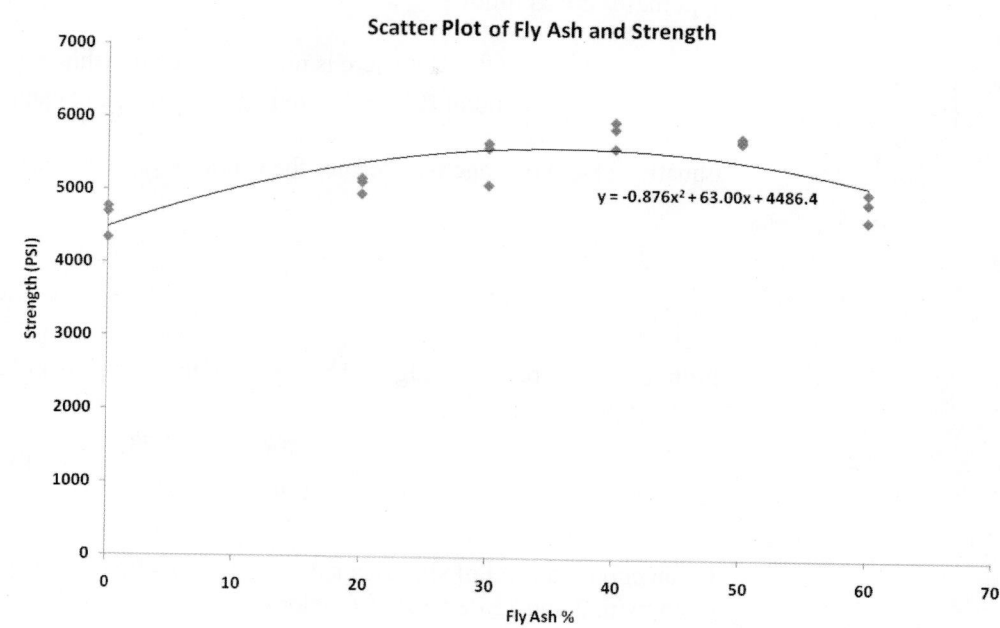

From the quadratic regression equation and Figure 15.4, the $Y$ intercept ($b_0 = 4{,}486.3611$) is the predicted strength when the percentage of fly ash is 0. To interpret the coefficients $b_1$ and $b_2$, observe that after an initial increase, strength decreases as fly ash percentage increases. This nonlinear relationship is further demonstrated by predicting the strength for fly ash percentages of 20, 40, and 60. Using the quadratic regression equation,

$$\hat{Y}_i = 4{,}486.3611 + 63.0052 X_{1i} - 0.8765 X_{1i}^2$$

for $X_{1i} = 20$,

$$\hat{Y}_i = 4{,}486.3611 + 63.0052(20) - 0.8765(20)^2 = 5{,}395.865$$

for $X_{1i} = 40$,

$$\hat{Y}_i = 4{,}486.3611 + 63.0052(40) - 0.8765(40)^2 = 5{,}604.169$$

and for $X_{1i} = 60$,

$$\hat{Y}_i = 4{,}486.3611 + 63.0052(60) - 0.8765(60)^2 = 5{,}111.273$$

Thus, the predicted concrete strength for 40% fly ash is 208.304 psi above the predicted strength for 20% fly ash, but the predicted strength for 60% fly ash is 492.896 psi below the predicted strength for 40% fly ash.

## Testing for the Significance of the Quadratic Model

After you calculate the quadratic regression equation, you can test whether there is a significant overall relationship between strength, $Y$, and fly ash percentage, $X_1$. The null and alternative hypotheses are as follows:

$H_0$: $\beta_1 = \beta_2 = 0$ (There is no overall relationship between $X_1$ and $Y$.)
$H_1$: $\beta_1$ and/or $\beta_2 \neq 0$ (There is an overall relationship between $X_1$ and $Y$.)

Equation (14.6) on page 644 defines the overall $F_{STAT}$ test statistic used for this test:

$$F_{STAT} = \frac{MSR}{MSE}$$

From the Excel results in Figure 15.2 or the Minitab results in Figure 15.3 on page 694,

$$F_{STAT} = \frac{MSR}{MSE} = \frac{1,347,736.745}{97,414.4674} = 13.8351$$

If you choose a level of significance of 0.05, from Table E.5, the critical value of the $F$ distribution, with 2 and 15 degrees of freedom, is 3.68 (see Figure 15.5). Because $F_{STAT} = 13.8351 > 3.68$, or because the $p$-value $= 0.0004 < 0.05$, you reject the null hypothesis ($H_0$) and conclude that there is a significant overall relationship between strength and fly ash percentage.

**FIGURE 15.5**

Testing for the existence of the overall relationship at the 0.05 level of significance, with 2 and 15 degrees of freedom

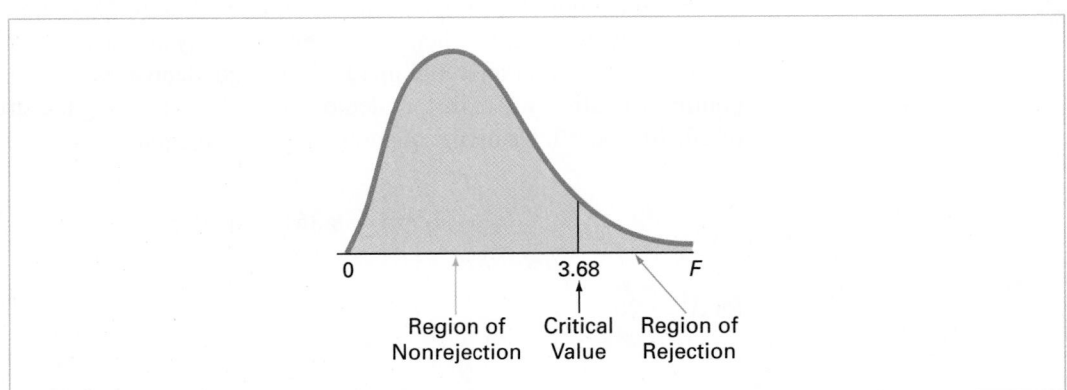

0    3.68    $F$

Region of Nonrejection    Critical Value    Region of Rejection

## Testing the Quadratic Effect

In using a regression model to examine a relationship between two variables, you want to find not only the most accurate model, but also the simplest model that expresses that relationship. Therefore, you need to examine whether there is a significant difference between the quadratic model:

$$Y_i = \beta_0 + \beta_1 X_{1i} + \beta_2 X_{1i}^2 + \varepsilon_i$$

and the linear model:

$$Y_i = \beta_0 + \beta_1 X_{1i} + \varepsilon_i$$

In Section 14.4, you used the $t$ test to determine whether each independent variable makes a significant contribution to the regression model. To test the significance of the contribution of the quadratic effect, you use the following null and alternative hypotheses:

$H_0$: Including the quadratic effect does not significantly improve the model ($\beta_2 = 0$).
$H_1$: Including the quadratic effect significantly improves the model ($\beta_2 \neq 0$).

The standard error of each regression coefficient and its corresponding $t_{STAT}$ test statistic are part of the Excel or Minitab results (see Figure 15.2 or 15.3 on page 694). Equation (14.7) on page 649 defines the $t_{STAT}$ test statistic:

$$t_{STAT} = \frac{b_2 - \beta_2}{S_{b_2}}$$

$$= \frac{-0.8765 - 0}{0.1966} = -4.4578$$

If you select the 0.05 level of significance, then from Table E.3, the critical values for the $t$ distribution with 15 degrees of freedom are $-2.1315$ and $+2.1315$ (see Figure 15.6).

**FIGURE 15.6**

Testing for the contribution of the quadratic effect to a regression model at the 0.05 level of significance, with 15 degrees of freedom

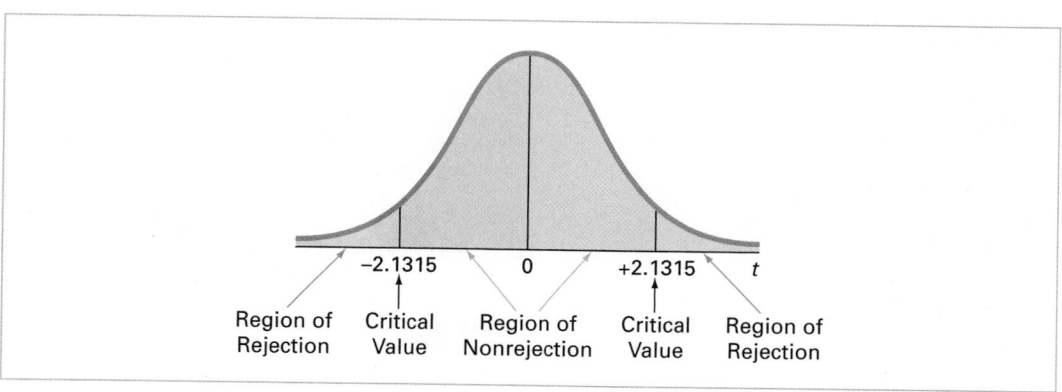

Because $t_{STAT} = -4.4578 < -2.1315$ or because the $p$-value $= 0.0005 < 0.05$, you reject $H_0$ and conclude that the quadratic model is significantly better than the linear model for representing the relationship between strength and fly ash percentage.

Example 15.1 provides an additional illustration of a possible quadratic effect.

**EXAMPLE 15.1**

STUDYING THE QUADRATIC EFFECT IN A MULTIPLE REGRESSION MODEL

A real estate developer studying the effect of atmospheric temperature and the amount of attic insulation on the consumption of heating oil selects a random sample of 15 single-family houses. The data are stored in the file Htngoil. Figure 15.7 on page 698 shows the Excel results for a multiple regression model using the two independent variables, atmospheric temperature and attic insulation. Figure 15.8 on page 698 displays Minitab results.

The residual plot for attic insulation (not shown here) contained some evidence of a quadratic effect. Thus, the real estate developer reanalyzed the data by adding a quadratic term for attic insulation to the multiple regression model. At the 0.05 level of significance, is there evidence of a significant quadratic effect for attic insulation?

**SOLUTION** Figure 15.9 on page 698 shows the Excel results for this regression model and Figure 15.10 on page 699 displays Minitab results.

**FIGURE 15.7**

Microsoft Excel worksheet for the multiple linear regression model predicting monthly consumption of heating oil

*See Section E14.1 or P14.1 to create this.*

| | A | B | C | D | E | F | G |
|---|---|---|---|---|---|---|---|
| 1 | Heating Oil Consumption Analysis | | | | | | |
| 2 | | | | | | | |
| 3 | *Regression Statistics* | | | | | | |
| 4 | Multiple R | 0.9827 | | | | | |
| 5 | R Square | 0.9656 | | | | | |
| 6 | Adjusted R Square | 0.9599 | | | | | |
| 7 | Standard Error | 26.0138 | | | | | |
| 8 | Observations | 15 | | | | | |
| 9 | | | | | | | |
| 10 | ANOVA | | | | | | |
| 11 | | *df* | *SS* | *MS* | *F* | *Significance F* | |
| 12 | Regression | 2 | 228014.6263 | 114007.3132 | 168.4712 | 1.65411E-09 | |
| 13 | Residual | 12 | 8120.6030 | 676.7169 | | | |
| 14 | Total | 14 | 236135.2293 | | | | |
| 15 | | | | | | | |
| 16 | | *Coefficients* | *Standard Error* | *t Stat* | *P-value* | *Lower 95%* | *Upper 95%* |
| 17 | Intercept | 562.1510 | 21.0931 | 26.6509 | 4.77868E-12 | 516.1931 | 608.1089 |
| 18 | Temperature | -5.4366 | 0.3362 | -16.1699 | 1.64178E-09 | -6.1691 | -4.7040 |
| 19 | Insulation | -20.0123 | 2.3425 | -8.5431 | 1.90731E-06 | -25.1162 | -14.9084 |

**FIGURE 15.8**

Minitab results for the multiple linear regression model predicting monthly consumption of heating oil

*See Section M14.2 to create this.*

```
The regression equation is
Gallons = 562 - 5.44 Temp(F) - 20.0 Insulation


Predictor        Coef   SE Coef        T      P
Constant       562.15     21.09    26.65  0.000
Temp(F)       -5.4366    0.3362   -16.17  0.000
Insulation    -20.012     2.343    -8.54  0.000


S = 26.0138    R-Sq = 96.6%   R-Sq(adj) = 96.0%


Analysis of Variance

Source          DF       SS       MS       F       P
Regression       2   228015   114007  168.47   0.000
Residual Error  12     8121      677
Total           14   236135
```

**FIGURE 15.9**

Microsoft Excel worksheet for the multiple regression model with a quadratic term for attic insulation

*See Section E15.1 and either Section E14.1 or P14.1 to create this.*

| | A | B | C | D | E | F | G |
|---|---|---|---|---|---|---|---|
| 1 | Quadratic Effect for Insulation Variable? | | | | | | |
| 2 | | | | | | | |
| 3 | *Regression Statistics* | | | | | | |
| 4 | Multiple R | 0.9862 | | | | | |
| 5 | R Square | 0.9725 | | | | | |
| 6 | Adjusted R Square | 0.9650 | | | | | |
| 7 | Standard Error | 24.2938 | | | | | |
| 8 | Observations | 15 | | | | | |
| 9 | | | | | | | |
| 10 | ANOVA | | | | | | |
| 11 | | *df* | *SS* | *MS* | *F* | *Significance F* | |
| 12 | Regression | 3 | 229643.2 | 76547.7215 | 129.7006 | 7.26403E-09 | |
| 13 | Residual | 11 | 6492.1 | 590.1877 | | | |
| 14 | Total | 14 | 236135.2 | | | | |
| 15 | | | | | | | |
| 16 | | *Coefficients* | *Standard Error* | *t Stat* | *P-value* | *Lower 95%* | *Upper 95%* |
| 17 | Intercept | 624.5864 | 42.4352 | 14.7186 | 1.39085E-08 | 531.1872 | 717.9856 |
| 18 | Temperature | -5.3626 | 0.3171 | -16.9099 | 3.20817E-09 | -6.0606 | -4.6646 |
| 19 | Insulation | -44.5868 | 14.9547 | -2.9815 | 0.0125 | -77.5019 | -11.6717 |
| 20 | Insulation ^2 | 1.8667 | 1.1238 | 1.6611 | 0.1249 | -0.6067 | 4.3401 |

**FIGURE 15.10**

Minitab results for the multiple regression model with a quadratic term for attic insulation

*See Section M15.1 and M14.2 to create this.*

```
The regression equation is
Gallons = 625 - 5.36 Temp(F) - 44.6 Insulation + 1.87 InsulationSquared


Predictor              Coef  SE Coef      T      P
Constant             624.59    42.44  14.72  0.000
Temp(F)             -5.3626   0.3171 -16.91  0.000
Insulation           -44.59    14.95  -2.98  0.012
InsulationSquared     1.867    1.124   1.66  0.125


S = 24.2938   R-Sq = 97.3%   R-Sq(adj) = 96.5%


Analysis of Variance

Source           DF      SS     MS      F      P
Regression        3  229643  76548 129.70  0.000
Residual Error   11    6492    590
Total            14  236135
```

The multiple regression equation is

$$\hat{Y}_i = 624.5864 - 5.3626 X_{1i} - 44.5868 X_{2i} + 1.8667 X_{2i}^2$$

To test for the significance of the quadratic effect,

$H_0$: Including the quadratic effect does not significantly improve the model ($\beta_3 = 0$).
$H_1$: Including the quadratic effect significantly improves the model ($\beta_3 \neq 0$).

From Figure 15.9 or Figure 15.10 and Table E.3, $-2.2010 < t_{STAT} = 1.661 < 2.2010$. Therefore, you do not reject the null hypothesis. You get the same result using the $p$-value approach because the $p$-value = 0.1249 > 0.05. You conclude that there is insufficient evidence that the quadratic effect for attic insulation is different from zero. In the interest of keeping the model as simple as possible, you should use the multiple regression equation computed in Figure 15.7 or Figure 15.8:

$$\hat{Y}_i = 562.1510 - 5.4366 X_{1i} - 20.0123 X_{2i}$$

## The Coefficient of Multiple Determination

In the multiple regression model, the coefficient of multiple determination, $r^2$ (see Section 14.2), represents the proportion of variation in $Y$ that is explained by variation in the independent variables. Consider the quadratic regression model you used to predict the strength of concrete using fly ash and fly ash squared. You compute $r^2$ by using Equation (14.4) on page 643:

$$r^2 = \frac{SSR}{SST}$$

From Figure 15.2 or Figure 15.3 on page 694,

$$SSR = 2,695,473.49 \quad SST = 4,156,690.5$$

Thus,

$$r^2 = \frac{SSR}{SST} = \frac{2,695,473.49}{4,156,690.5} = 0.6485$$

This coefficient of multiple determination indicates that 64.85% of the variation in strength is explained by the quadratic relationship between strength and the percentage of fly ash. You should also compute $r_{adj}^2$ to account for the number of independent variables and the sample size. In the quadratic regression model, $k = 2$ because there are two independent variables, $X_1$ and $X_1^2$. Thus, using Equation (14.5) on page 644,

$$r_{adj}^2 = 1 - \left[ (1 - r^2) \frac{(n-1)}{(n-k-1)} \right]$$

$$= 1 - \left[ (1 - 0.6485) \frac{17}{15} \right]$$

$$= 1 - 0.3984$$

$$= 0.6016$$

# PROBLEMS FOR SECTION 15.1

## Learning the Basics

**15.1** The following quadratic regression equation is for a sample of $n = 25$:

$$\hat{Y}_i = 5 + 3X_{1i} + 1.5X_{1i}^2$$

**a.** Predict $Y$ for $X_1 = 2$.
**b.** Suppose that the computed $t_{STAT}$ test statistic for the quadratic regression coefficient is 2.35. At the 0.05 level of significance, is there evidence that the quadratic model is better than the linear model?
**c.** Suppose that the computed $t_{STAT}$ test statistic for the quadratic regression coefficient is 1.17. At the 0.05 level of significance, is there evidence that the quadratic model is better than the linear model?
**d.** Suppose the regression coefficient for the linear effect is $-3.0$. Predict $Y$ for $X_1 = 2$.

## Applying the Concepts

**15.2** Businesses actively recruit business students with well-developed higher-order cognitive skills (HOCS) such as problem identification, analytical reasoning, and integrating content. Researchers conducted a study to see if improvement in students' HOCS was related to the students' GPA (extracted from R. V. Bradley, C. S. Sankar, H. R. Clayton, V. W. Mbarika, and P. K. Raju, "A Study on the Impact of GPA on Perceived Improvement of Higher-Order Cognitive Skills," *Decision Sciences Journal of Innovative Education*, January 2007, 5(1), pp 151–168). The researchers conducted a study in which business students were taught via the case study method. Using data

collected from 300 business students, the following quadratic regression equation was derived:

$$HOCS = -3.48 + 4.53(GPA) - 0.68(GPA)^2$$

where the dependent variable HOCS measured the improvement in higher-order cognitive skills with 1 being the lowest improvement in HOCS and 5 being the highest improvement in HOCS.

**a.** Construct a table of predicted HOCS using GPA equal to 2.0, 2.1, 2.2, ..., 4.0.
**b.** Plot the values in the table constructed in (a) with GPA on the horizontal axis and predicted HOCS on the vertical axis.
**c.** Discuss the curvilinear relationship between students' GPA and their predicted improvement in HOCS.
**d.** The researchers reported that the model had an $r^2$ of 0.07 and an adjusted $r^2$ of 0.06. What does this tell you about the scatter of individual HOCS scores around the curvilinear relationship plotted in (b) and discussed in (c)?

**15.3** The following market research study was conducted by a national chain of consumer electronics stores. To promote sales, the chain relies heavily on local newspaper advertising to support its modest exposure in nationwide television commercials. A sample of 20 cities with similar populations and monthly sales totals were assigned different newspaper advertising budgets for one month. The following table (with the results stored in the file **Advertising**) summarizes the sales (in $millions) and the newspaper advertising budgets (in $000) observed during the study.

| Sales | Newspaper Advertising | Sales | Newspaper Advertising |
|-------|------------------------|-------|------------------------|
| 6.14 | 5 | 6.84 | 15 |
| 6.04 | 5 | 6.66 | 15 |
| 6.21 | 5 | 6.95 | 20 |
| 6.32 | 5 | 6.65 | 20 |
| 6.42 | 10 | 6.83 | 20 |
| 6.56 | 10 | 6.81 | 20 |
| 6.67 | 10 | 7.03 | 25 |
| 6.35 | 10 | 6.88 | 25 |
| 6.76 | 15 | 6.84 | 25 |
| 6.79 | 15 | 6.99 | 25 |

a. Construct a scatter plot for advertising and sales.

b. Fit a quadratic regression model and state the quadratic regression equation.

c. Predict the mean monthly sales for a city with newspaper advertising of $20,000.

d. Perform a residual analysis on the results and determine if the regression assumptions are valid.

e. At the 0.05 level of significance, is there a significant quadratic relationship between monthly sales and newspaper advertising?

f. At the 0.05 level of significance, determine whether the quadratic model is a better fit than the linear model.

g. Interpret the meaning of the coefficient of multiple determination.

h. Compute the adjusted $r^2$.

**15.4** Is the number of calories in a beer related to the number of carbohydrates and/or the percentage of alcohol in the beer? Data concerning 71 of the best-selling domestic beers in the United States are located in the file Domesticbeer. The values for three variables are included: the number of calories per 12 ounces, the alcohol percentage, and the number of carbohydrates (in grams) per 12 ounces (extracted from **www.Beer100.com**, May 4, 2007).

a. Perform a multiple linear regression analysis, using calories as the dependent variable and percentage alcohol and the number of carbohydrates as the independent variables.

b. Add quadratic terms for alcohol percentage and the number of carbohydrates.

c. Which model is better, the one in (a) or (b)?

d. Write a short summary concerning the relationship between the number of calories in a beer and the alcohol percentage and number of carbohydrates.

**15.5** The marketing department of a large supermarket chain wants to study the effect of price on the sales of packages of disposable razors. A sample of 15 stores with equivalent store traffic and product placement (i.e., at the checkout counter) is selected. Five stores are randomly assigned to each of three price levels (79, 99, and 119 cents) for the package of razors. The number of packages sold over a full week and the price at each store are in the following table (and in the file Dispraz):

| Sales | Price (Cents) | Sales | Price (Cents) |
|-------|---------------|-------|---------------|
| 142 | 79 | 115 | 99 |
| 151 | 79 | 126 | 99 |
| 163 | 79 | 77 | 119 |
| 168 | 79 | 86 | 119 |
| 176 | 79 | 95 | 119 |
| 91 | 99 | 100 | 119 |
| 100 | 99 | 106 | 119 |
| 107 | 99 | | |

a. Construct a scatter plot for price and sales.

b. Fit a quadratic regression model and state the quadratic regression equation.

c. Predict the mean weekly sales for a price per package of 79 cents.

d. Perform a residual analysis on the results and determine if the regression models are valid.

e. At the 0.05 level of significance, is there a significant quadratic relationship between weekly sales and price?

f. At the 0.05 level of significance, determine whether the quadratic model is a better fit than the linear model.

g. Interpret the meaning of the coefficient of multiple determination.

h. Compute the adjusted $r^2$.

**SELF Test 15.6** An agronomist designed a study in which tomatoes were grown using six different amounts of fertilizer: 0, 20, 40, 60, 80, and 100 pounds per 1,000 square feet. These fertilizer application rates were then randomly assigned to plots of land. The results including the yield of tomatoes (in pounds) were as follows (see the file Tomato):

| Plot | Fertilizer Application Rate | Yield | Plot | Fertilizer Application Rate | Yield |
|------|------|-------|------|------|-------|
| 1 | 0 | 6 | 7 | 60 | 46 |
| 2 | 0 | 9 | 8 | 60 | 50 |
| 3 | 20 | 19 | 9 | 80 | 48 |
| 4 | 20 | 24 | 10 | 80 | 54 |
| 5 | 40 | 32 | 11 | 100 | 52 |
| 6 | 40 | 38 | 12 | 100 | 58 |

a. Construct a scatter plot for fertilizer application rate and yield.

b. Fit a quadratic regression model and state the quadratic regression equation.

c. Predict the mean yield for a plot of land fertilized with 70 pounds per 1,000 square feet.

**d.** Perform a residual analysis on the results and determine if the regression models are valid.

**e.** At the 0.05 level of significance, is there a significant overall relationship between the fertilizer application rate and tomato yield?

**f.** What is the $p$-value in (e)? Interpret its meaning.

**g.** At the 0.05 level of significance, determine whether there is a significant quadratic effect.

**h.** What is the $p$-value in (g)? Interpret its meaning.

**i.** Interpret the meaning of the coefficient of multiple determination.

**j.** Compute the adjusted $r^2$.

**15.7** An auditor for a county government would like to develop a model to predict county taxes, based on the age of single-family houses. She selects a random sample of 19 single-family houses, and the results are in the data file Taxes .

**a.** Construct a scatter plot of age and county taxes.

**b.** Fit a quadratic regression model and state the quadratic regression equation.

**c.** Predict the mean county taxes for a house that is 20 years old.

**d.** Perform a residual analysis on the results and determine if the regression assumptions are valid.

**e.** At the 0.05 level of significance, is there a significant overall relationship between age and county taxes?

**f.** What is the $p$-value in (e)? Interpret its meaning.

**g.** At the 0.05 level of significance, determine whether the quadratic model is superior to the linear model.

**h.** What is the $p$-value in (g)? Interpret its meaning.

**i.** Interpret the meaning of the coefficient of multiple determination.

**j.** Compute the adjusted $r^2$.

## 15.2  USING TRANSFORMATIONS IN REGRESSION MODELS

This section introduces regression models in which the independent variable, the dependent variable, or both are transformed in order to either overcome violations of the assumptions of regression or to make a model linear in form. Among the many transformations available (see reference 1) are the square-root transformation and transformations involving the common logarithm (base 10) and the natural logarithm (base $e$).[1]

[1]For more information on logarithms, see Appendix A.3.

### The Square-Root Transformation

The **square-root transformation** is often used to overcome violations of the equal-variance assumption as well as to transform a model that is not linear in form into one that is linear. Equation (15.3) shows a regression model that uses a square-root transformation of the independent variable.

> Regression Model with a Square-Root Transformation
> $$Y_i = \beta_0 + \beta_1\sqrt{X_{1i}} + \varepsilon_i \qquad (15.3)$$

Example 15.2 illustrates the use of a square-root transformation.

---

**EXAMPLE 15.2**     USING THE SQUARE-ROOT TRANSFORMATION

Given the following values for $Y$ and $X$, use a square-root transformation for the $X$ variable:

| Y | X | Y | X |
|---|---|---|---|
| 42.7 | 1 | 100.4 | 3 |
| 50.4 | 1 | 104.7 | 4 |
| 69.1 | 2 | 112.3 | 4 |
| 79.8 | 2 | 113.6 | 5 |
| 90.0 | 3 | 123.9 | 5 |

Construct a scatter plot for $X$ and $Y$ and for the square root of $X$ and $Y$.

**SOLUTION** Figure 15.11, Panel A, displays the scatter plot of $X$ and $Y$; Panel B shows the square root of $X$ versus $Y$.

**FIGURE 15.11**

Panel *A*: Scatter plot of *X* with *Y*

Panel *B*: Scatter plot of the square root of *X* and *Y*

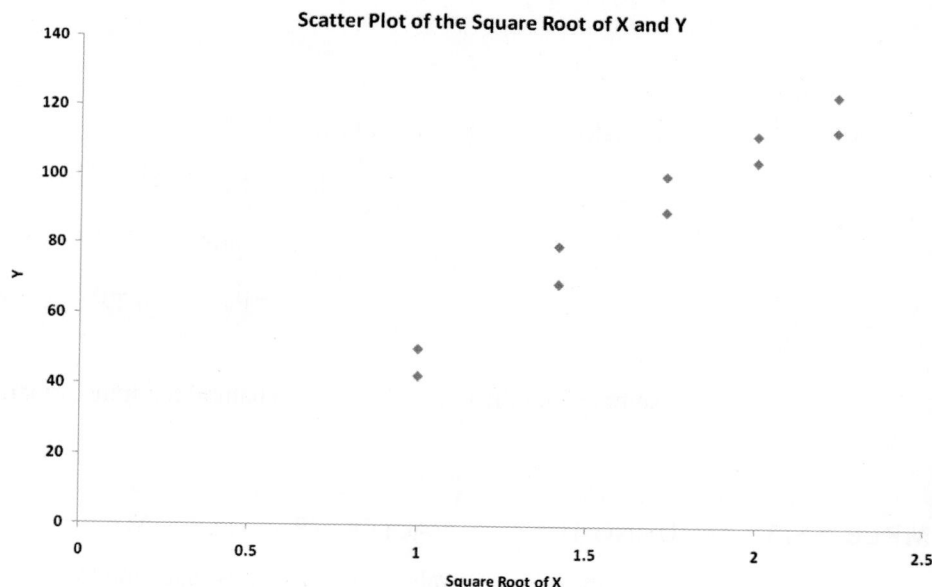

You can see that the square-root transformation has transformed a nonlinear relationship into a linear relationship.

## The Log Transformation

The **logarithmic transformation** is often used to overcome violations to the equal-variance assumption. You can also use the logarithmic transformation to change a nonlinear model into a linear model. Equation (15.4) shows a multiplicative model.

**Original Multiplicative Model**

$$Y_i = \beta_0 X_{1i}^{\beta_1} X_{2i}^{\beta_2} \varepsilon_i \qquad (15.4)$$

By taking base 10 logarithms of both the dependent and independent variables, you can transform Equation (15.4) to the model shown in Equation (15.5).

**Transformed Multiplicative Model**

$$\log Y_i = \log(\beta_0 X_{1i}^{\beta_1} X_{2i}^{\beta_2} \varepsilon_i) \qquad (15.5)$$
$$= \log \beta_0 + \log(X_{1i}^{\beta_1}) + \log(X_{2i}^{\beta_2}) + \log \varepsilon_i$$
$$= \log \beta_0 + \beta_1 \log X_{1i} + \beta_2 \log X_{2i} + \log \varepsilon_i$$

Thus, Equation (15.5) is linear in the logarithms. Similarly, you can transform the exponential model shown in Equation (15.6) to linear form by taking the natural logarithm of both sides of the equation. Equation (15.7) is the transformed model.

**Original Exponential Model**

$$Y_i = e^{\beta_0 + \beta_1 X_{1i} + \beta_2 X_{2i}} \varepsilon_i \qquad (15.6)$$

**Transformed Exponential Model**

$$\ln Y_i = \ln(e^{\beta_0 + \beta_1 X_{1i} + \beta_2 X_{2i}} \varepsilon_i) \qquad (15.7)$$
$$= \ln(e^{\beta_0 + \beta_1 X_{1i} + \beta_2 X_{2i}}) + \ln \varepsilon_i$$
$$= \beta_0 + \beta_1 X_{1i} + \beta_2 X_{2i} + \ln \varepsilon_i$$

Example 15.3 illustrates the use of a natural log transformation.

---

**EXAMPLE 15.3**

**USING THE NATURAL LOG TRANSFORMATION**

Given the following values for $Y$ and $X$, use a natural logarithm transformation for the $Y$ variable:

| Y | X | Y | X |
|-----|-----|------|-----|
| 0.7 | 1 | 4.8 | 3 |
| 0.5 | 1 | 12.9 | 4 |
| 1.6 | 2 | 11.5 | 4 |
| 1.8 | 2 | 32.1 | 5 |
| 4.2 | 3 | 33.9 | 5 |

Construct a scatter plot for $X$ and $Y$ and for $X$ and the natural logarithm of $Y$.

**SOLUTION** As shown in Figure 15.12, the natural logarithm transformation has transformed a nonlinear relationship into a linear relationship.

**FIGURE 15.12**

Panel A: Scatter plot of X and Y

Panel B: Scatter plot of X and the natural logarithm of Y

---

# PROBLEMS FOR SECTION 15.2

## Learning the Basics

**15.8** Consider the following regression equation:

$$\log \hat{Y}_i = \log 3.07 + 0.9 \log X_{1i} + 1.41 \log X_{2i}$$

**a.** Predict the value of Y when $X_1 = 8.5$ and $X_2 = 5.2$.
**b.** Interpret the meaning of the regression coefficients $b_0$, $b_1$, and $b_2$.

**15.9** Consider the following regression equation:

$$\ln \hat{Y}_i = 4.62 + 0.5 X_{1i} + 0.7 X_{2i}$$

**a.** Predict the value of Y when $X_1 = 8.5$ and $X_2 = 5.2$.
**b.** Interpret the meaning of the regression coefficients $b_0$, $b_1$, and $b_2$.

## Applying the Concepts

✓ **SELF Test** **15.10** Referring to the data of Problem 15.4 on page 701 and using the file **Domesticbeer**, perform a square-root transformation on each of the independent variables (percentage alcohol and the number of carbohydrates). Using calories as the dependent variable and the transformed independent variables, perform a multiple regression analysis.

**a.** State the regression equation.
**b.** Perform a residual analysis of the results and determine if the regression assumptions are valid.
**c.** At the 0.05 level of significance, is there a significant relationship between calories and the square root of the percentage of alcohol and the square root of the number of carbohydrates?

**d.** Interpret the meaning of the coefficient of determination, $r^2$, in this problem.

**e.** Compute the adjusted $r^2$.

**f.** Compare your results with those in Problem 15.4. Which model is better? Why?

**15.11** Referring to the data of Problem 15.4 on page 701 and using the file **Domesticbeer**, perform a natural logarithmic transformation of the dependent variable (calories). Using the transformed dependent variable and the percentage of alcohol and the number of carbohydrates as the independent variables, perform a multiple regression analysis.

**a.** State the regression equation.

**b.** Perform a residual analysis of the results and determine if the regression assumptions are valid.

**c.** At the 0.05 level of significance, is there a significant relationship between the natural logarithm of calories and the percentage of alcohol and the number of carbohydrates?

**d.** Interpret the meaning of the coefficient of determination, $r^2$, in this problem.

**e.** Compute the adjusted $r^2$.

**f.** Compare your results with those in Problems 15.4 and 15.10. Which model is best? Why?

**15.12** Referring to the data of Problem 15.6 on page 701 and using the file **Tomato**, perform a natural logarithm transformation of the dependent variable (yield). Using the transformed dependent variable and the fertilizer application rate as the independent variable, perform a regression analysis.

**a.** State the regression equation.

**b.** Predict the mean yield when 55 pounds of fertilizer is applied per 1,000 square feet.

**c.** Perform a residual analysis of the results and determine if the regression assumptions are valid.

**d.** At the 0.05 level of significance, is there a significant relationship between the natural logarithm of yield and the fertilizer application rate?

**e.** Interpret the meaning of the coefficient of determination, $r^2$, in this problem.

**f.** Compute the adjusted $r^2$.

**g.** Compare your results with those in Problem 15.6. Which model is better? Why?

**15.13** Referring to the data of Problem 15.6 on page 701 and using the file **Tomato**, perform a square-root transformation of the independent variable (fertilizer application rate). Using yield as the dependent variable and the transformed independent variable, perform a regression analysis.

**a.** State the regression equation.

**b.** Predict the mean yield when 55 pounds of fertilizer is applied per 1,000 square feet.

**c.** Perform a residual analysis of the results and determine if the regression assumptions are valid.

**d.** At the 0.05 level of significance, is there a significant relationship between yield and the square root of the fertilizer application rate?

**e.** Interpret the meaning of the coefficient of determination, $r^2$, in this problem.

**f.** Compute the adjusted $r^2$.

**g.** Compare your results with those of Problems 15.6 and 15.12. Which model is best? Why?

**h.** How much fertilizer should you apply in order to grow the most tomatoes?

## 15.3 COLLINEARITY

One important problem in the application of multiple regression analysis involves the possible **collinearity** of the independent variables. This condition refers to situations in which one or more of the independent variables are highly correlated with each other. In such situations, collinear variables do not provide unique information, and it becomes difficult to separate the effects of such variables on the dependent variable. When collinearity exists, the values of the regression coefficients for the correlated variables may fluctuate drastically, depending on which independent variables are included in the model.

One method of measuring collinearity is the **variance inflationary factor (VIF)** for each independent variable. Equation (15.8) defines $VIF_j$, the variance inflationary factor for variable $j$.

Variance Inflationary Factor

$$VIF_j = \frac{1}{1 - R_j^2} \tag{15.8}$$

where $R_j^2$ is the coefficient of multiple determination from a regression model using variable $X_j$ as the dependent variable and all other $X$ variables serving as independent variables.

If there are only two independent variables, $R_1^2$ is the coefficient of determination between $X_1$ and $X_2$. It is identical to $R_2^2$, which is the coefficient of determination between $X_2$ and $X_1$. If there are three independent variables, then $R_1^2$ is the coefficient of multiple determination of $X_1$ with $X_2$ and $X_3$; $R_2^2$ is the coefficient of multiple determination of $X_2$ with $X_1$ and $X_3$; and $R_3^2$ is the coefficient of multiple determination of $X_3$ with $X_1$ and $X_2$.

If a set of independent variables is uncorrelated, each $VIF_j$ is equal to 1. If the set is highly correlated, then a $VIF_j$ might even exceed 10. Marquardt (see reference 2) suggests that if $VIF_j$ is greater than 10, there is too much correlation between the variable $X_j$ and the other independent variables. However, other statisticians suggest a more conservative criterion. Snee (see reference 5) recommends using alternatives to least-squares regression if the maximum $VIF_j$ exceeds 5.

You need to proceed with extreme caution when using a multiple regression model that has one or more large $VIF$ values. You can use the model to predict values of the dependent variable *only* in the case where the values of the independent variables used in the prediction are in the relevant range of the values in the data set. However, you cannot extrapolate to values of the independent variables not observed in the sample data. And because the independent variables contain overlapping information, you should always avoid interpreting the regression coefficient estimates separately because there is no way to accurately estimate the individual effects of the independent variables. One solution to the problem is to delete the variable with the largest $VIF$ value. The reduced model (i.e., the model with the independent variable with the largest $VIF$ value deleted) is often free of collinearity problems. If you determine that all the independent variables are needed in the model, you can use methods discussed in reference 1.

In the OmniPower sales data (see Section 14.1), the correlation between the two independent variables, price and promotional expenditure, is −0.0968. Because there are only two independent variables in the model, from Equation (15.8) on page 706:

$$VIF_1 = VIF_2 = \frac{1}{1-(-0.0968)^2}$$

$$= 1.009$$

Thus, you can conclude that there is no problem with collinearity for the OmniPower sales data.

In models containing quadratic and interaction terms, collinearity is usually present. The linear and quadratic terms of an independent variable are usually highly correlated with each other, and an interaction term is often correlated with one or both of the independent variables making up the interaction. Thus, you cannot interpret individual parameter estimates separately. You need to interpret the linear and quadratic parameter estimates together in order to understand the nonlinear relationship. Likewise, you need to interpret an interaction parameter estimate in conjunction with the two parameter estimates associated with the variables comprising the interaction. In summary, large $VIF$s in quadratic or interaction models do not necessarily mean that the model is a poor one. They do, however, require you to carefully interpret the parameter estimates.

# PROBLEMS FOR SECTION 15.3

## Learning the Basics

**15.14** If the coefficient of determination between two independent variables is 0.20, what is the $VIF$?

**15.15** If the coefficient of determination between two independent variables is 0.50, what is the $VIF$?

## Applying the Concepts

✓ SELF Test **15.16** Refer to Problem 14.4 on page 641. Perform a multiple regression analysis using the file Warecost and determine the $VIF$ for each independent variable in the model. Is there reason to suspect the existence of collinearity?

**15.17** Refer to Problem 14.5 on page 641. Perform a multiple regression analysis using the file Auto and determine the *VIF* for each independent variable in the model. Is there reason to suspect the existence of collinearity?

**15.18** Refer to Problem 14.6 on page 642. Perform a multiple regression analysis using the file Advertise and determine the *VIF* for each independent variable in the model. Is there reason to suspect the existence of collinearity?

**15.19** Refer to Problem 14.7 on page 642. Perform a multiple regression analysis using the file Standby and determine the *VIF* for each independent variable in the model. Is there reason to suspect the existence of collinearity?

**15.20** Refer to Problem 14.8 on page 642. Perform a multiple regression analysis using the file GlenCove and determine the *VIF* for each independent variable in the model. Is there reason to suspect the existence of collinearity?

## 15.4   MODEL BUILDING

This chapter and Chapter 14 have introduced you to many different topics in regression analysis, including quadratic terms, dummy variables, and interaction terms. In this section, you will learn a structured approach to building the most appropriate regression model. As you will see, successful model building incorporates many of the topics you have studied so far.

To begin, refer to the Using Statistics scenario introduced on page 692, in which four independent variables (total staff present, remote hours, Dubner hours, and total labor hours) are considered in developing a regression model to predict standby hours of unionized graphic artists. Table 15.2 presents the data, which are contained in the file Standby.

**TABLE 15.2**

Predicting Standby Hours Based on Total Staff Present, Remote Hours, Dubner Hours, and Total Labor Hours

| Week | Standby Hours | Total Staff Present | Remote Hours | Dubner Hours | Total Labor Hours |
|---|---|---|---|---|---|
| 1 | 245 | 338 | 414 | 323 | 2,001 |
| 2 | 177 | 333 | 598 | 340 | 2,030 |
| 3 | 271 | 358 | 656 | 340 | 2,226 |
| 4 | 211 | 372 | 631 | 352 | 2,154 |
| 5 | 196 | 339 | 528 | 380 | 2,078 |
| 6 | 135 | 289 | 409 | 339 | 2,080 |
| 7 | 195 | 334 | 382 | 331 | 2,073 |
| 8 | 118 | 293 | 399 | 311 | 1,758 |
| 9 | 116 | 325 | 343 | 328 | 1,624 |
| 10 | 147 | 311 | 338 | 353 | 1,889 |
| 11 | 154 | 304 | 353 | 518 | 1,988 |
| 12 | 146 | 312 | 289 | 440 | 2,049 |
| 13 | 115 | 283 | 388 | 276 | 1,796 |
| 14 | 161 | 307 | 402 | 207 | 1,720 |
| 15 | 274 | 322 | 151 | 287 | 2,056 |
| 16 | 245 | 335 | 228 | 290 | 1,890 |
| 17 | 201 | 350 | 271 | 355 | 2,187 |
| 18 | 183 | 339 | 440 | 300 | 2,032 |
| 19 | 237 | 327 | 475 | 284 | 1,856 |
| 20 | 175 | 328 | 347 | 337 | 2,068 |
| 21 | 152 | 319 | 449 | 279 | 1,813 |
| 22 | 188 | 325 | 336 | 244 | 1,808 |
| 23 | 188 | 322 | 267 | 253 | 1,834 |
| 24 | 197 | 317 | 235 | 272 | 1,973 |
| 25 | 261 | 315 | 164 | 223 | 1,839 |
| 26 | 232 | 331 | 270 | 272 | 1,935 |

Before you develop a model to predict standby hours, you need to consider the principle of parsimony.

> The principle of **parsimony** is the belief that you should select the simplest model that gets the job done adequately.

Regression models with fewer independent variables are simpler and easier to interpret, particularly because they are less likely to be affected by collinearity problems (described in Section 15.3).

The selection of an appropriate model when many independent variables are under consideration involves complexities that are not present with a model that has only two independent variables. The evaluation of all possible regression models is more computationally complex. And, although you can quantitatively evaluate competing models, there may not be a *uniquely* best model but several *equally appropriate* models.

To begin analyzing the standby-hours data, you compute the variance inflationary factors [see Equation (15.8) on page 706] to measure the amount of collinearity among the independent variables. Figure 15.13 shows an Excel worksheet that summarizes the *VIF* computations (Panel *A*), the multiple regression prediction equation worksheet using the four independent variables, and the Durbin-Watson statistic for this model (Panel *B*). Figure 15.14 on page 710 shows Minitab results.

**FIGURE 15.13**

Microsoft Excel worksheets for predicting standby hours based on four independent variables

See Sections E15.3, E14.1 and E13.4 or P15.1, P14.1 and P13.4 to create this.

| | A | B | C | D | E |
|---|---|---|---|---|---|
| 1 | **Standby Hours Analysis** | | | | |
| 2 | | *Regression Statistics* | | | |
| 3 | | Total Staff and all other X | Remote and all other X | Dubner and all other X | Total Labor and all other X |
| 4 | **Multiple R** | 0.64368 | 0.43490 | 0.56099 | 0.70698 |
| 5 | **R Square** | 0.41433 | 0.18914 | 0.31471 | 0.49982 |
| 6 | **Adjusted R Square** | 0.33446 | 0.07856 | 0.22126 | 0.43161 |
| 7 | **Standard Error** | 16.47151 | 124.93921 | 57.55254 | 114.41183 |
| 8 | **Observations** | 26 | 26 | 26 | 26 |
| 9 | **VIF** | 1.70743 | 1.23325 | 1.45924 | 1.99928 |

| | A | B | C | D | E | F | G |
|---|---|---|---|---|---|---|---|
| 1 | **Standby Hours Analysis** | | | | | | |
| 2 | | | | | | | |
| 3 | *Regression Statistics* | | | | | | |
| 4 | **Multiple R** | 0.7894 | | | | | |
| 5 | **R Square** | 0.6231 | | | | | |
| 6 | **Adjusted R Square** | 0.5513 | | | | | |
| 7 | **Standard Error** | 31.8350 | | | | | |
| 8 | **Observations** | 26 | | | | | |
| 9 | | | | | | | |
| 10 | **ANOVA** | | | | | | |
| 11 | | | *df* | *SS* | *MS* | *F* | *Significance F* |
| 12 | **Regression** | | 4 | 35181.7937 | 8795.4484 | 8.6786 | 0.0003 |
| 13 | **Residual** | | 21 | 21282.8217 | 1013.4677 | | |
| 14 | **Total** | | 25 | 56464.6154 | | | |
| 15 | | | | | | | |
| 16 | | | Coefficients | Standard Error | t Stat | P-value | Lower 95% | Upper 95% |
| 17 | **Intercept** | | -330.8318 | 110.8954 | -2.9833 | 0.0071 | -561.4514 | -100.2123 |
| 18 | **Total Staff** | | 1.2456 | 0.4121 | 3.0229 | 0.0065 | 0.3887 | 2.1026 |
| 19 | **Remote** | | -0.1184 | 0.0543 | -2.1798 | 0.0408 | -0.2314 | -0.0054 |
| 20 | **Dubner** | | -0.2971 | 0.1179 | -2.5189 | 0.0199 | -0.5423 | -0.0518 |
| 21 | **Total Labor** | | 0.1305 | 0.0593 | 2.2004 | 0.0391 | 0.0072 | 0.2539 |

| | A | B |
|---|---|---|
| 1 | **Durbin-Watson Calculations** | |
| 2 | | |
| 3 | Sum of Squared Difference of Residuals | 47241.6126 |
| 4 | Sum of Squared Residuals | 21282.8217 |
| 5 | | |
| 6 | **Durbin-Watson Statistic** | 2.2197 |

Observe that all the *VIF* values are relatively small, ranging from a high of 1.999 for the total labor hours to a low of 1.233 for remote hours. Thus, on the basis of the criteria developed by Snee that all *VIF* values should be less than 5.0 (see reference 5), there is little evidence of collinearity among the set of independent variables.

**FIGURE 15.14**

Minitab results for predicting standby hours based on four independent variables

*See Sections M14.3 and M15.3 to create this.*

```
The regression equation is
Standby = - 331 + 1.25 Staff - 0.118 Remote - 0.297 Dubner + 0.131 Labor


Predictor        Coef   SE Coef       T      P     VIF
Constant       -330.8     110.9   -2.98  0.007
Staff          1.2456    0.4121    3.02  0.006   1.707
Remote       -0.11842   0.05432   -2.18  0.041   1.233
Dubner        -0.2971    0.1179   -2.52  0.020   1.459
Labor         0.13053   0.05932    2.20  0.039   1.999


S = 31.8350   R-Sq = 62.3%   R-Sq(adj) = 55.1%

Analysis of Variance

Source           DF      SS     MS      F      P
Regression        4   35182   8795   8.68  0.000
Residual Error   21   21283   1013
Total            25   56465

Durbin-Watson statistic = 2.21971
```

## The Stepwise Regression Approach to Model Building

You continue your analysis of the standby-hours data by attempting to determine whether a subset of all independent variables yields an adequate and appropriate model. The first approach described here is **stepwise regression**, which attempts to find the "best" regression model without examining all possible models.

The first step of stepwise regression is to find the best model that uses one independent variable. The next step is to find the best of the remaining independent variables to add to the model selected in the first step. An important feature of the stepwise approach is that an independent variable that has entered into the model at an early stage may subsequently be removed after other independent variables are considered. Thus, in stepwise regression, variables are either added to or deleted from the regression model at each step of the model-building process. The partial $F_{STAT}$ test statistic (see Section 14.5) is used to determine whether variables are added or deleted. The stepwise procedure terminates with the selection of a best-fitting model when no additional variables can be added to or deleted from the last model evaluated. Figure 15.15 on page 711 represents Microsoft Excel stepwise regression results for the standby-hours data. Figure 15.16 on page 711 presents Minitab results.

For this example, a significance level of 0.05 is used to enter a variable into the model or to delete a variable from the model. The first variable entered into the model is total staff, the variable that correlates most highly with the dependent variable standby hours. Because the $p$-value of 0.0011 is less than 0.05, total staff is included in the regression model.

The next step involves selecting a second independent variable for the model. The second variable chosen is one that makes the largest contribution to the model, given that the first variable has been selected. For this model, the second variable is remote hours. Because the $p$-value of 0.0269 for remote hours is less than 0.05, remote hours is included in the regression model.

After remote hours is entered into the model, the stepwise procedure determines whether total staff is still an important contributing variable or whether it can be eliminated from the model. Because the $p$-value of 0.0001 for total staff is less than 0.05, total staff remains in the regression model.

The next step involves selecting a third independent variable for the model. Because none of the other variables meets the 0.05 criterion for entry into the model, the stepwise procedure terminates with a model that includes total staff present and the number of remote hours.

**FIGURE 15.15**

PHStat2 stepwise regression results worksheet for the standby-hours data

*See Section P15.2 to create this.*

| | | df | SS | MS | F | Significance F | |
|---|---|---|---|---|---|---|---|
| 1 | Stepwise Analysis for Standby Hours | | | | | | |
| 2 | Table of Results for General Stepwise | | | | | | |
| 4 | Total Staff entered. | | | | | | |
| 6 | | df | SS | MS | F | Significance F | |
| 7 | Regression | 1 | 20667.3980 | 20667.3980 | 13.8563 | 0.0011 | |
| 8 | Residual | 24 | 35797.2174 | 1491.5507 | | | |
| 9 | Total | 25 | 56464.6154 | | | | |

| | | Coefficients | Standard Error | t Stat | P-value | Lower 95% | Upper 95% |
|---|---|---|---|---|---|---|---|
| 11 | | Coefficients | Standard Error | t Stat | P-value | Lower 95% | Upper 95% |
| 12 | Intercept | -272.3816 | 124.2402 | -2.1924 | 0.0383 | -528.8008 | -15.9625 |
| 13 | Total Staff | 1.4241 | 0.3826 | 3.7224 | 0.0011 | 0.6345 | 2.2136 |

| | | df | SS | MS | F | Significance F | |
|---|---|---|---|---|---|---|---|
| 16 | Remote entered. | | | | | | |
| 18 | | df | SS | MS | F | Significance F | |
| 19 | Regression | 2 | 27662.5429 | 13831.2714 | 11.0450 | 0.0004 | |
| 20 | Residual | 23 | 28802.0725 | 1252.2640 | | | |
| 21 | Total | 25 | 56464.6154 | | | | |

| | | Coefficients | Standard Error | t Stat | P-value | Lower 95% | Upper 95% |
|---|---|---|---|---|---|---|---|
| 23 | | Coefficients | Standard Error | t Stat | P-value | Lower 95% | Upper 95% |
| 24 | Intercept | -330.6748 | 116.4802 | -2.8389 | 0.0093 | -571.6322 | -89.7175 |
| 25 | Total Staff | 1.7649 | 0.3790 | 4.6562 | 0.0001 | 0.9808 | 2.5490 |
| 26 | Remote | -0.1390 | 0.0588 | -2.3635 | 0.0269 | -0.2606 | -0.0173 |

| 29 | No other variables could be entered into the model. Stepwise ends. |

**FIGURE 15.16**

Minitab stepwise regression results for the standby-hours data

*See Section M15.4 to create this.*

```
Alpha-to-Enter: 0.05   Alpha-to-Remove: 0.05


Response is Standby on 4 predictors, with N = 26


Step             1       2
Constant     -272.4  -330.7

Staff          1.42    1.76
T-Value        3.72    4.66
P-Value       0.001   0.000

Remote                -0.139
T-Value               -2.36
P-Value                0.027

S              38.6    35.4
R-Sq          36.60   48.99
R-Sq(adj)     33.96   44.56
Mallows Cp     13.3     8.4
```

This stepwise regression approach to model building was originally developed more than four decades ago, when regression analysis on mainframe computers involved the costly use of large amounts of processing time. Under such conditions, stepwise regression became widely used, although it provides a limited evaluation of alternative models. With today's extremely fast personal computers, the evaluation of many different regression models is completed quickly, at a very small cost. Thus, a more general way of evaluating alternative regression models, in this era of fast computers, is the best-subsets approach discussed next. Stepwise regression is not obsolete, however. Today, many businesses use stepwise regression as part of a research technique called **data mining**, in which huge data sets are explored to discover significant statistical relationships among a large number of variables. These data sets are so large that the best-subsets approach is impractical.

## The Best-Subsets Approach to Model Building

The **best-subsets approach** evaluates all possible regression models for a given set of independent variables. Figure 15.17 presents PHStat2 results of all possible regression models for the standby-hours data. Figure 15.18 displays Minitab results.

**FIGURE 15.17**

PHStat2 best-subsets regression results worksheet for the standby-hours data

*See Section P15.3 to create this.*

| | A | B | C | D | E | F |
|---|---|---|---|---|---|---|
| 1 | **Best Subsets Analysis for Standby Hours** | | | | | |
| 2 | | | | | | |
| 3 | **Intermediate Calculations** | | | | | |
| 4 | R2T | 0.6231 | | | | |
| 5 | 1 - R2T | 0.3769 | | | | |
| 6 | n | 26 | | | | |
| 7 | T | 5 | | | | |
| 8 | n - T | 21 | | | | |
| 9 | | | | | | |
| 10 | **Model** | Cp | k+1 | R Square | Adj. R Square | Std. Error |
| 11 | X1 | 13.3215 | 2 | 0.3660 | 0.3396 | 38.6206 |
| 12 | X1X2 | 8.4193 | 3 | 0.4899 | 0.4456 | 35.3873 |
| 13 | X1X2X3 | 7.8418 | 4 | 0.5362 | 0.4729 | 34.5029 |
| 14 | X1X2X3X4 | 5.0000 | 5 | 0.6231 | 0.5513 | 31.8350 |
| 15 | X1X2X4 | 9.3449 | 4 | 0.5092 | 0.4423 | 35.4921 |
| 16 | X1X3 | 10.6486 | 3 | 0.4499 | 0.4021 | 36.7490 |
| 17 | X1X3X4 | 7.7517 | 4 | 0.5378 | 0.4748 | 34.4426 |
| 18 | X1X4 | 14.7982 | 3 | 0.3754 | 0.3211 | 39.1579 |
| 19 | X2 | 33.2078 | 2 | 0.0091 | -0.0322 | 48.2836 |
| 20 | X2X3 | 32.3067 | 3 | 0.0612 | -0.0205 | 48.0087 |
| 21 | X2X3X4 | 12.1381 | 4 | 0.4591 | 0.3853 | 37.2608 |
| 22 | X2X4 | 23.2481 | 3 | 0.2238 | 0.1563 | 43.6540 |
| 23 | X3 | 30.3884 | 2 | 0.0597 | 0.0205 | 47.0345 |
| 24 | X3X4 | 11.8231 | 3 | 0.4288 | 0.3791 | 37.4466 |
| 25 | X4 | 24.1846 | 2 | 0.1710 | 0.1365 | 44.1619 |

**FIGURE 15.18**

Minitab best-subsets regression results for the standby-hours data

*See Section M15.5 to create this.*

```
Best Subsets Regression: Standby versus Staff, Remote, Dubner, Labor

Response is Standby

                                      R D
                                      S e u L
                                      t m b a
                                      a o n b
                        Mallows       f t e o
Vars  R-Sq  R-Sq(adj)     Cp      S   f e r r
  1   36.6    34.0       13.3  38.621  X
  1   17.1    13.7       24.2  44.162       X
  1    6.0     2.1       30.4  47.035          X
  2   49.0    44.6        8.4  35.387  X X
  2   45.0    40.2       10.6  36.749  X    X
  2   42.9    37.9       11.8  37.447       X X
  3   53.8    47.5        7.8  34.443  X  X X
  3   53.6    47.3        7.8  34.503  X X X
  3   50.9    44.2        9.3  35.492  X X    X
  4   62.3    55.1        5.0  31.835  X X X X
```

A criterion often used in model building is the adjusted $r^2$, which adjusts the $r^2$ of each model to account for the number of independent variables in the model as well as for the sample size (see Section 14.2). Because model building requires you to compare models with different numbers of independent variables, the adjusted $r^2$ is more appropriate than $r^2$.

Referring to Figure 15.17 or Figure 15.18, you see that the adjusted $r^2$ reaches a maximum value of 0.5513 (or 55.13%) when all four independent variables plus the intercept term (for a total of five estimated parameters) are included in the model.

A second criterion often used in the evaluation of competing models is the $C_p$ statistic developed by Mallows (see reference 1). The **$C_p$ statistic**, defined in Equation (15.9), measures the differences between a fitted regression model and a *true* model, along with random error.

## $C_p$ Statistic

$$C_p = \frac{(1 - R_k^2)(n - T)}{1 - R_T^2} - [n - 2(k + 1)] \qquad \textbf{(15.9)}$$

where

$k$ = number of independent variables included in a regression model

$T$ = total number of parameters (including the intercept) to be estimated in the full regression model

$R_k^2$ = coefficient of multiple determination for a regression model that has $k$ independent variables

$R_T^2$ = coefficient of multiple determination for a full regression model that contains all $T$ estimated parameters

Using Equation (15.9) to compute $C_p$ for the model containing total staff and remote hours,

$$n = 26 \quad k = 2 \quad T = 4 + 1 = 5 \quad R_k^2 = 0.4899 \quad R_T^2 = 0.6231$$

so that

$$C_p = \frac{(1 - 0.4899)(26 - 5)}{1 - 0.6231} - [26 - 2(2 + 1)]$$
$$= 8.4193$$

When a regression model with $k$ independent variables contains only random differences from a *true* model, the mean value of $C_p$ is $k + 1$, the number of parameters. Thus, in evaluating many alternative regression models, the goal is to find models whose $C_p$ is close to or less than $k + 1$. In Figure 15.17 or Figure 15.18 on page 712, you see that only the model with all four independent variables considered contains a $C_p$ value close to or below $k + 1$. Therefore, using the $C_p$ criterion you should choose that model.

Although it was not the case here, the $C_p$ statistic often provides several alternative models for you to evaluate in greater depth. Moreover, the best model or models using the $C_p$ criterion might differ from the model selected using the adjusted $r^2$ and/or the model selected using the stepwise procedure. (Note here that the model selected using stepwise regression has a $C_p$ value of 8.4193, which is substantially above the suggested criterion of $k + 1 = 3$ for that model.) Remember that there may not be a uniquely best model, but several equally appropriate models. Final model selection often involves using more subjective criteria, such as parsimony, interpretability, and departure from model assumptions (as evaluated by residual analysis).

When you have finished selecting the independent variables to include in the model, you should perform a residual analysis to evaluate the regression assumptions, and because the data were collected in time order, you also need to compute the Durbin-Watson statistic to determine whether there is autocorrelation in the residuals (see Section 13.6). From Panel $B$ of Figure 15.13 on page 709 or from Figure 15.14 on page 710, you see that the Durbin-Watson statistic, $D$, is 2.2197. Because $D$ is greater than 2.0, there is no indication of positive correlation in the residuals. Figure 15.19 presents Microsoft Excel residual plots used in the residual analysis.

**FIGURE 15.19**

Microsoft Excel residual plots for the standby-hours data

*See Section E14.2 or P14.2 to create this. Minitab users see Section M14.2 to create an equivalent chart.*

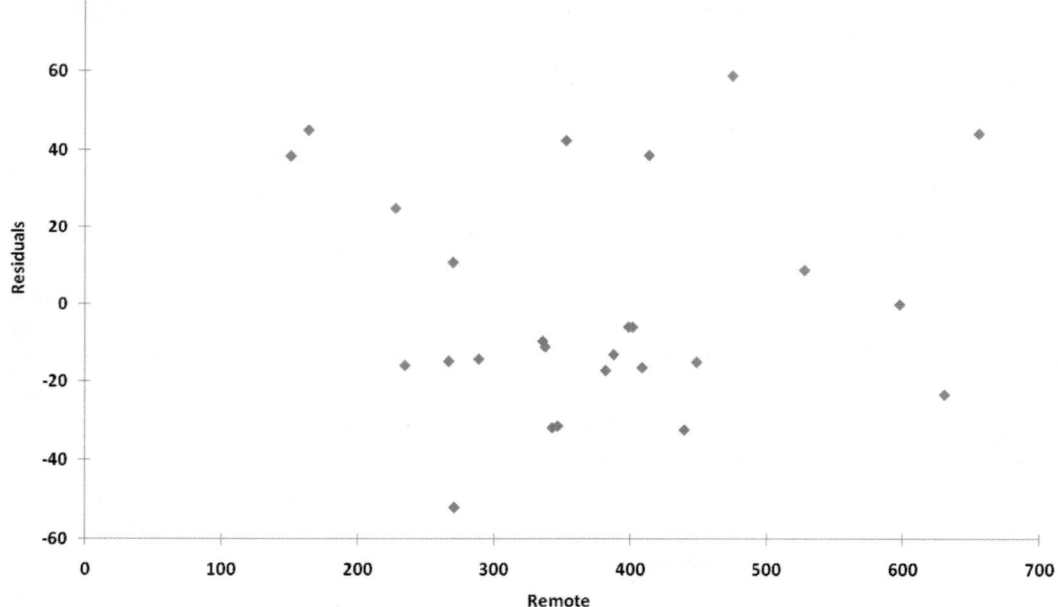

None of the residual plots versus the total staff, the remote hours, the Dubner hours, and the total labor hours reveal apparent patterns. In addition, a histogram of the residuals (not shown here) indicates only moderate departure from normality, and a plot of the residuals versus the predicted values of $Y$ (also not shown here) does not show evidence of unequal variance. Thus, from Figure 15.13 or 15.14 on pages 709–710, the regression equation is

$$\hat{Y}_i = -330.8318 + 1.2456X_{1i} - 0.1184X_{2i} - 0.2971X_{3i} + 0.1305X_{4i}$$

Example 15.4 presents a situation in which there are several alternative models in which the $C_p$ statistic is close to or less than $k + 1$.

**FIGURE 15.19**
(*Continued*)

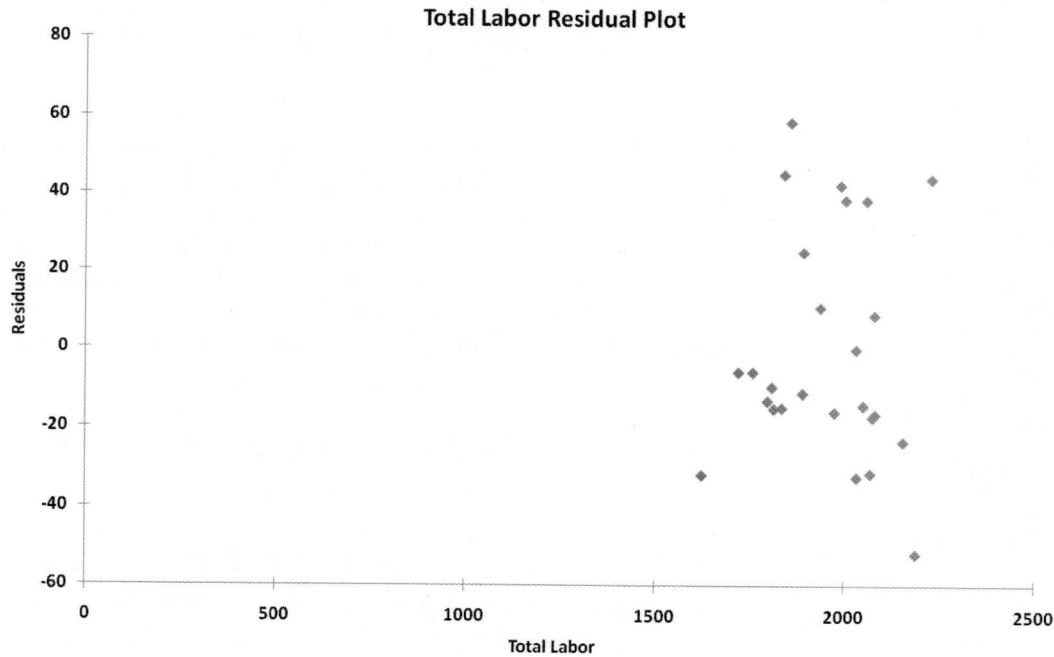

**EXAMPLE 15.4**    CHOOSING AMONG ALTERNATIVE REGRESSION MODELS

Table 15.3 on page 716 shows results from a best-subsets regression analysis of a regression model with seven independent variables. Determine which regression model you would choose as the *best* model.

**SOLUTION** From Table 15.3, you need to determine which models have $C_p$ values that are less than or close to $k + 1$. Two models meet this criterion. The model with six independent variables ($X_1, X_2, X_3, X_4, X_5, X_6$) has a $C_p$ value of 6.8, which is less than $k + 1 = 6 + 1 = 7$, and the full model with seven independent variables ($X_1, X_2, X_3, X_4, X_5, X_6, X_7$) has a $C_p$ value of 8.0. One way you can choose among the two models is to select the model with the largest adjusted $r^2$, that is, the model with six independent variables. Another way to select a final

**TABLE 15.3**

Partial Results from
Best-Subsets
Regression

| Number of Variables | $r^2$ (%) | Adjusted $r^2$ (%) | $C_p$ | Variables Included |
|---|---|---|---|---|
| 1 | 12.1 | 11.9 | 113.9 | $X_4$ |
| 1 | 9.3 | 9.0 | 130.4 | $X_1$ |
| 1 | 8.3 | 8.0 | 136.2 | $X_3$ |
| 2 | 21.4 | 21.0 | 62.1 | $X_3, X_4$ |
| 2 | 19.1 | 18.6 | 75.6 | $X_1, X_3$ |
| 2 | 18.1 | 17.7 | 81.0 | $X_1, X_4$ |
| 3 | 28.5 | 28.0 | 22.6 | $X_1, X_3, X_4$ |
| 3 | 26.8 | 26.3 | 32.4 | $X_3, X_4, X_5$ |
| 3 | 24.0 | 23.4 | 49.0 | $X_2, X_3, X_4$ |
| 4 | 30.8 | 30.1 | 11.3 | $X_1, X_2, X_3, X_4$ |
| 4 | 30.4 | 29.7 | 14.0 | $X_1, X_3, X_4, X_6$ |
| 4 | 29.6 | 28.9 | 18.3 | $X_1, X_3, X_4, X_5$ |
| 5 | 31.7 | 30.8 | 8.2 | $X_1, X_2, X_3, X_4, X_5$ |
| 5 | 31.5 | 30.6 | 9.6 | $X_1, X_2, X_3, X_4, X_6$ |
| 5 | 31.3 | 30.4 | 10.7 | $X_1, X_3, X_4, X_5, X_6$ |
| 6 | 32.3 | 31.3 | 6.8 | $X_1, X_2, X_3, X_4, X_5, X_6$ |
| 6 | 31.9 | 30.9 | 9.0 | $X_1, X_2, X_3, X_4, X_5, X_7$ |
| 6 | 31.7 | 30.6 | 10.4 | $X_1, X_2, X_3, X_4, X_6, X_7$ |
| 7 | 32.4 | 31.2 | 8.0 | $X_1, X_2, X_3, X_4, X_5, X_6, X_7$ |

model is to determine whether the models contain a subset of variables that are common. Then you test whether the contribution of the additional variables is significant. In this case, because the models differ only by the inclusion of variable $X_7$ in the full model, you test whether variable $X_7$ makes a significant contribution to the regression model, given that the variables $X_1, X_2, X_3, X_4, X_5$, and $X_6$ are already included in the model. If the contribution is statistically significant, then you should include variable $X_7$ in the regression model. If variable $X_7$ does not make a statistically significant contribution, you should not include it in the model.

Exhibit 15.1 summarizes the steps involved in model building.

**EXHIBIT 15.1  STEPS INVOLVED IN MODEL BUILDING**

1. Compile a listing of all independent variables under consideration.
2. Fit a regression model that includes all the independent variables under consideration and determine the *VIF* for each independent variable. Three possible results can occur:
   a. None of the independent variables have a *VIF* > 5; in this case, proceed to Step 3.
   b. One of the independent variables has a *VIF* > 5; in this case, eliminate that independent variable and proceed to Step 3.
   c. More than one of the independent variables has a *VIF* > 5; in this case, eliminate the independent variable that has the highest *VIF* and repeat Step 2.
3. Perform a best-subsets regression with the remaining independent variables and determine the $C_p$ statistic and/or the adjusted $r^2$ for each model.
4. List all models that have $C_p$ close to or less than $k + 1$ and/or a high adjusted $r^2$.
5. From those models listed in Step 4, choose a best model.
6. Perform a complete analysis of the model chosen, including a residual analysis.
7. Depending on the results of the residual analysis, add quadratic and/or interaction terms, transform variables, and reanalyze the data.
8. Use the selected model for prediction and inference.

Figure 15.20 represents a roadmap for the steps involved in model building.

**FIGURE 15.20**

Roadmap for model building

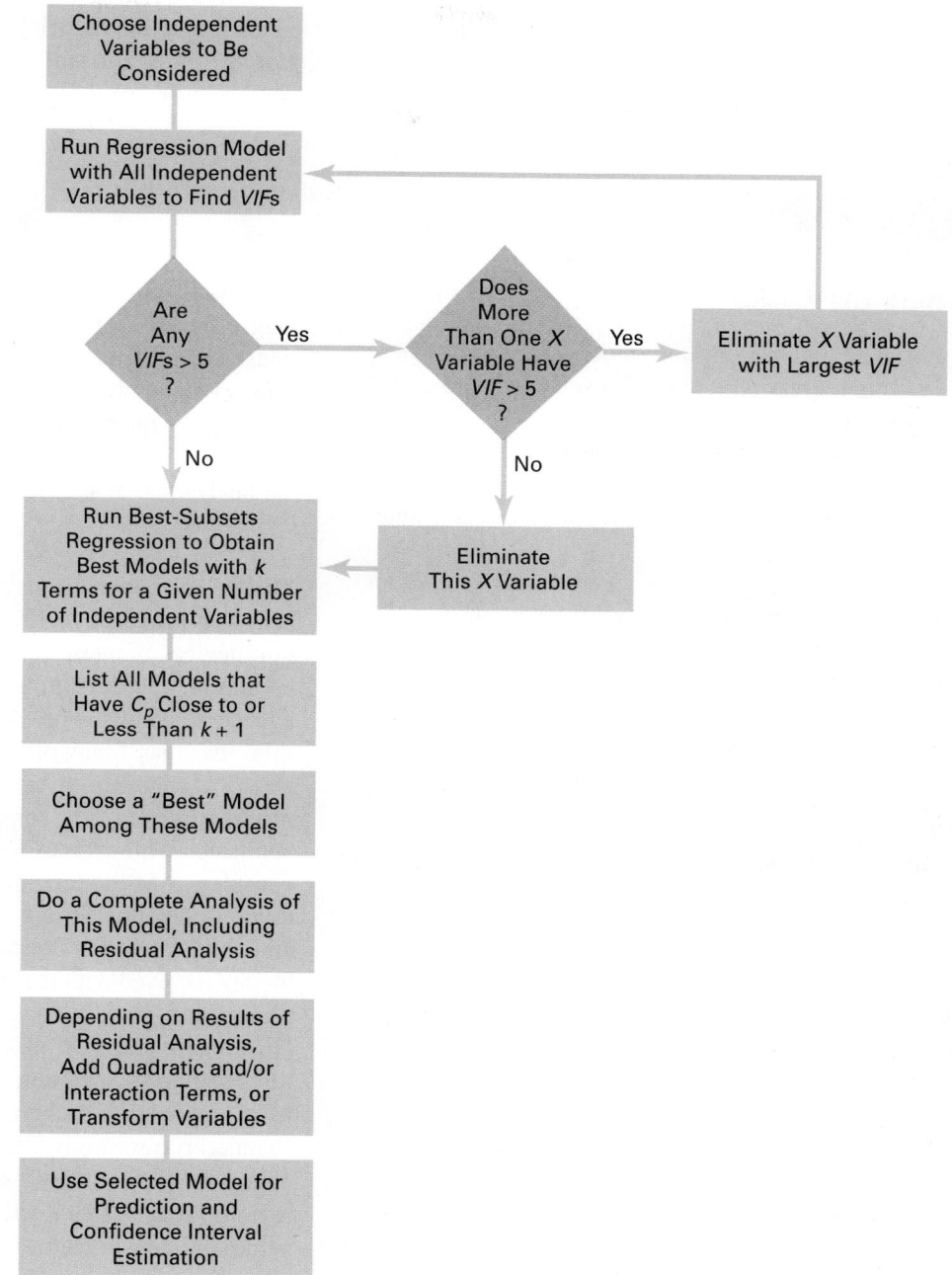

## Model Validation

The final step in the model-building process is to validate the selected regression model. This step involves checking the model against data that were not part of the sample analyzed. Several ways of validating a regression model are:

- Collect new data and compare the results.
- Compare the results of the regression model to previous results.
- If the data set is large, split the data into two parts and cross-validate the results.

Perhaps the best way of validating a regression model is by collecting new data. If the results with new data are consistent with the selected regression model, you have strong reason to believe that the fitted regression model is applicable in a wide set of circumstances.

If it is not possible to collect new data, you can use one of the two other approaches. In one approach, you compare your regression coefficients and predictions to previous results. If the data set is large, you can use **cross-validation**. First, you split the data into two parts. Then you use the first part of the data to develop the regression model. You then use the second part of the data to evaluate the predictive ability of the regression model.

# PROBLEMS FOR SECTION 15.4

## Learning the Basics

**15.21** You are considering four independent variables for inclusion in a regression model. You select a sample of 30 observations, with the following results:

1. The model that includes independent variables $A$ and $B$ has a $C_p$ value equal to 4.6.
2. The model that includes independent variables $A$ and $C$ has a $C_p$ value equal to 2.4.
3. The model that includes independent variables $A$, $B$, and $C$ has a $C_p$ value equal to 2.7.

**a.** Which models meet the criterion for further consideration? Explain.

**b.** How would you compare the model that contains independent variables $A$, $B$, and $C$ to the model that contains independent variables $A$ and $B$? Explain.

**15.22** You are considering six independent variables for inclusion in a regression model. You select a sample of 40 observations, with the following results:

$$n = 40 \quad k = 2 \quad T = 6 + 1 = 7 \quad R_k^2 = 0.274 \quad R_T^2 = 0.653$$

**a.** Compute the $C_p$ value for this two-independent-variable model.

**b.** Based on your answer to (a), does this model meet the criterion for further consideration as the best model? Explain.

## Applying the Concepts

**15.23** In Problems 13.85–13.89 on page 627, you constructed simple linear regression models to investigate the relationship between demographic information and monthly sales for a chain of sporting goods stores (see the file **Sporting**). Develop the most appropriate multiple regression model to predict a store's monthly sales. Be sure to include a thorough residual analysis. In addition, provide a detailed explanation of the results, including a comparison of the most appropriate multiple regression model to the best simple linear regression model.

**✓SELF Test** **15.24** You need to develop a model to predict the selling price of houses, based on assessed value, time period in which a house is sold, and whether the

house is new (0 = no; 1 = yes). A sample of 30 recently sold single-family houses in a small city is selected. (The houses in the city were reassessed at full value one year prior to the study.) The results are in the data file **House1**. Develop the most appropriate multiple regression model to predict selling price. Be sure to perform a thorough residual analysis. In addition, provide a detailed explanation of the results.

**15.25** The human resources (HR) director for a large company that produces highly technical industrial instrumentation devices is interested in using regression modeling to help in making recruiting decisions concerning sales managers. The company has 45 sales regions, each headed by a sales manager. Many of the sales managers have degrees in electrical engineering, and due to the technical nature of the product line, several company officials believe that only applicants with degrees in electrical engineering should be considered. At the time of their application, candidates are asked to take the Strong-Campbell Interest Inventory Test and the Wonderlic Personnel Test. Due to the time and money involved with the testing, some discussion has taken place about dropping one or both of the tests. To start, the HR director gathered information on each of the 45 current sales managers, including years of selling experience, electrical engineering background, and the scores from both the Wonderlic and Strong-Campbell tests. The dependent variable was "sales index" score, which is the ratio of the regions' actual sales divided by the target sales. The target values are constructed each year by upper management, in consultation with the sales managers, and are based on past performance and market potential within each region. The data file **Managers** contains information on the 45 current sales managers. The variables included are:

Sales—Ratio of yearly sales divided by the target sales value for that region. The target values were mutually agreed-upon "realistic expectations."

Wonder—Score from the Wonderlic Personnel Test. The higher the score, the higher the applicant's perceived ability to manage.

SC—Score on the Strong-Campbell Interest Inventory Test. The higher the score, the higher the applicant's perceived interest in sales.

Experience—Number of years of selling experience prior to becoming a sales manager.

Engineer—Dummy variable that equals 1 if the sales manager has a degree in electrical engineering and 0 otherwise.

**a.** Develop the most appropriate regression model to predict sales.

**b.** Do you think that the company should continue administering both the Wonderlic and Strong-Campbell tests? Explain.

**c.** Do the data support the argument that electrical engineers outperform the other sales managers? Would you support the idea to hire only electrical engineers? Explain.

**d.** How important is prior selling experience in this case? Explain.

**e.** Discuss in detail how the HR director should incorporate the regression model you developed into the recruiting process.

## More About A New Type of Mining for the Twenty-First Century

*From the Authors' Desktop*

In the *From the Authors' Desktop* on page 675, you were introduced to data mining, a sophisticated approach used to find patterns or relationships in large databases. That section discussed how data miners used logistic regression when the dependent variables were *categorical* responses. Data mining is also used to make predictions of *quantitative* dependent variables. Because of the large number of possible independent variables in these databases, model-building techniques are needed to find the best regression model. Regression applications of data mining in business include predicting stock and currency values, forecasting operations, detecting fraudulent transactions, determining the most profitable credit card customers, risk analysis, sales forecasting, inventory forecasting, customer traffic patterns, and warranty cost control.

## 15.5 PITFALLS IN MULTIPLE REGRESSION AND ETHICAL ISSUES

### Pitfalls in Multiple Regression

Model building is an art as well as a science. Different individuals may not always agree on the best multiple regression model. To try to find a best regression model, you should use the process described in Exhibit 15.1 on pages 716–717. In doing so, you must avoid certain pitfalls that can interfere with the development of a useful model. Section 13.9 discussed pitfalls in simple linear regression and strategies for avoiding them. Now that you have studied a variety of multiple regression models, you need to take some additional precautions. To avoid pitfalls in multiple regression, you also need to:

- Interpret the regression coefficient for a particular independent variable from a perspective in which the values of all other independent variables are held constant.
- Evaluate residual plots for each independent variable.
- Evaluate interaction and quadratic terms.

- Compute the *VIF* for each independent variable before determining which independent variables to include in the model.
- Examine several alternative models using best-subsets regression.
- Validate the model before implementing it.

### Ethical Issues

Ethical issues arise when a user who wants to make predictions manipulates the development process of the multiple regression model. The key here is intent. In addition to the situations discussed in Section 13.9, unethical behavior occurs when someone uses multiple regression analysis and *willfully fails* to remove from consideration variables that exhibit a high collinearity with other independent variables or *willfully fails* to use methods other than least-squares regression when the assumptions necessary for least-squares regression are seriously violated.

## 15.6   (CD-ROM TOPIC) INFLUENCE ANALYSIS

Influence analysis measures the influence of individual observations on a regression model. To study this topic, go to the `Section 15.6.pdf` file located on the Student CD-ROM that accompanies this book.

# SUMMARY

In this chapter, various multiple regression topics were considered (see Figure 15.21), including quadratic regression models, transformations, collinearity, and model building. From the Using Statistic scenario on page 642, you have learned how an operations manager for a television station can build a multiple regression model as an aid in reducing labor expenses.

# KEY EQUATIONS

**Quadratic Regression Model**

$$Y_i = \beta_0 + \beta_1 X_{1i} + \beta_2 X_{1i}^2 + \varepsilon_i \qquad (15.1)$$

**Quadratic Regression Equation**

$$\hat{Y}_i = b_0 + b_1 X_{1i} + b_2 X_{1i}^2 \qquad (15.2)$$

**Regression Model with a Square-Root Transformation**

$$Y_i = \beta_0 + \beta_1 \sqrt{X_{1i}} + \varepsilon_i \qquad (15.3)$$

**Original Multiplicative Model**

$$Y_i = \beta_0 X_{1i}^{\beta_1} X_{2i}^{\beta_2} \varepsilon_i \qquad (15.4)$$

**Transformed Multiplicative Model**

$$\log Y_i = \log(\beta_0 X_{1i}^{\beta_1} X_{2i}^{\beta_2} \varepsilon_i)$$

$$= \log \beta_0 + \log(X_{1i}^{\beta_1}) + \log(X_{2i}^{\beta_2}) + \log \varepsilon_i \qquad (15.5)$$

$$= \log \beta_0 + \beta_1 \log X_{1i} + \beta_2 \log X_{2i} + \log \varepsilon_i$$

**Original Exponential Model**

$$Y_i = e^{\beta_0 + \beta_1 X_{1i} + \beta_2 X_{2i}} \varepsilon_i \qquad (15.6)$$

**Transformed Exponential Model**

$$\ln Y_i = \ln(e^{\beta_0 + \beta_1 X_{1i} + \beta_2 X_{2i}} \varepsilon_i)$$

$$= \ln(e^{\beta_0 + \beta_1 X_{1i} + \beta_2 X_{2i}}) + \ln \varepsilon_i \qquad (15.7)$$

$$= \beta_0 + \beta_1 X_{1i} + \beta_2 X_{2i} + \ln \varepsilon_i$$

**Variance Inflationary Factor**

$$VIF_j = \frac{1}{1 - R_j^2} \qquad (15.8)$$

**$C_p$ Statistic**

$$C_p = \frac{(1 - R_k^2)(n - T)}{1 - R_T^2} - [n - 2(k + 1)] \qquad (15.9)$$

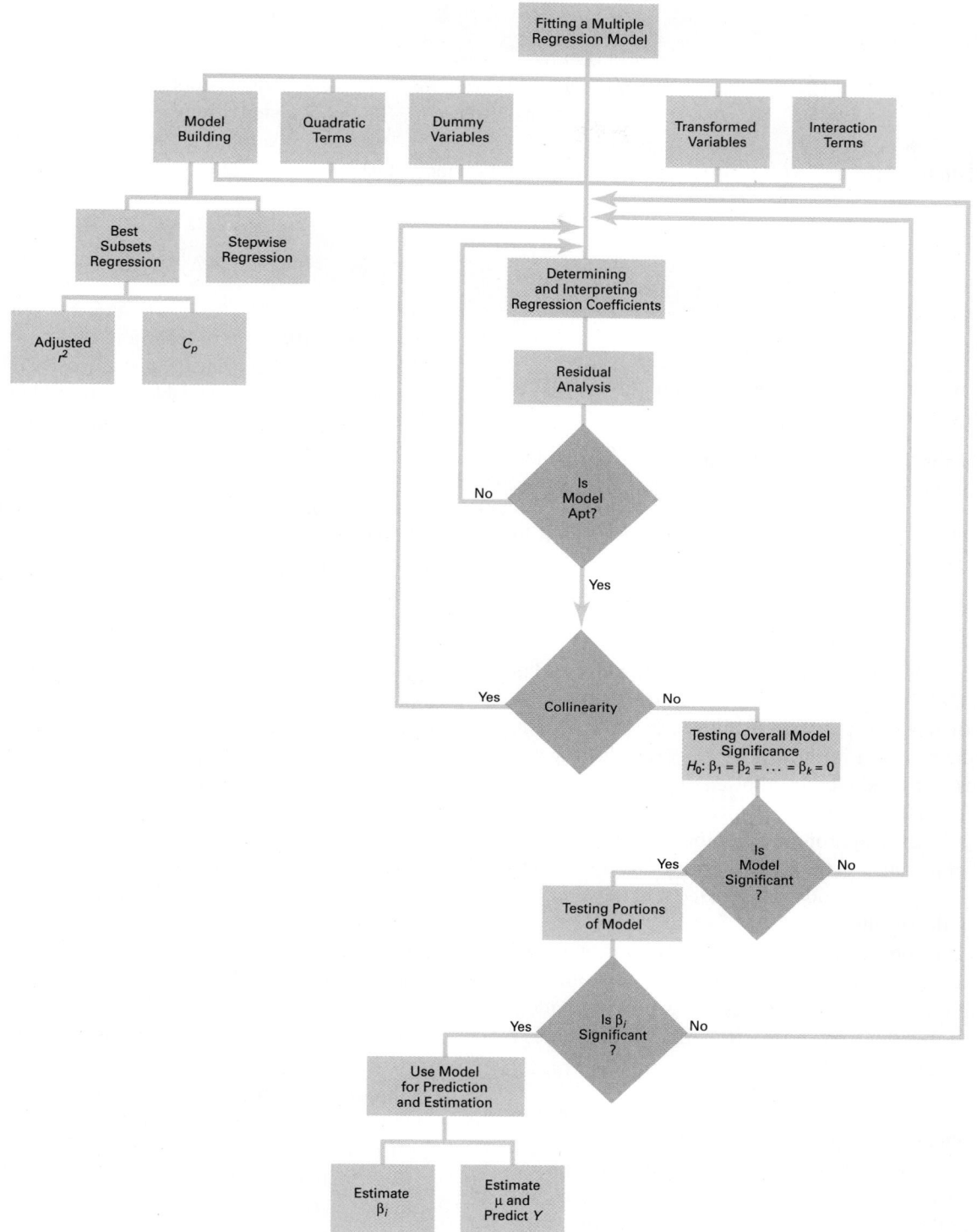

**FIGURE 15.21**
Roadmap for multiple regression

# KEY TERMS

| | | |
|---|---|---|
| best-subsets approach   712 | data mining   711 | square-root transformation   702 |
| $C_p$ statistic   712 | logarithmic transformation   703 | stepwise regression   710 |
| collinearity   706 | parsimony   709 | variance inflationary factor (*VIF*)   706 |
| cross-validation   718 | quadratic regression model   693 | |

# CHAPTER REVIEW PROBLEMS

## Checking Your Understanding

**15.26** How can you evaluate whether a multiple regression model suffers from collinearity?

**15.27** What is the difference between stepwise regression and best-subsets regression?

**15.28** How do you choose among models according to the $C_p$ statistic in best-subsets regression?

## Applying the Concepts

**15.29** Crazy Dave has expanded his analysis, presented in Problem 14.73 on page 682, of which variables are important in predicting a team's wins in a given baseball season. He has collected data in the file BB2006 related to wins, ERA, saves, runs scored, hits allowed, walks allowed, and errors for the 2005 season.

**a.** Develop the most appropriate multiple regression model to predict a team's wins. Be sure to include a thorough residual analysis. In addition, provide a detailed explanation of the results.

**b.** Develop the most appropriate multiple regression model to predict a team's ERA on the basis of hits allowed, walks allowed, errors, and saves. Be sure to include a thorough residual analysis. In addition, provide a detailed explanation of the results.

**15.30** Professional basketball has truly become a sport that generates interest among fans around the world. More and more players come from outside the United States to play in the National Basketball Association (NBA). Many factors could impact the number of wins achieved by each NBA team. In addition to the number of wins, the data file NBA2007 contains team statistics for points per game (for team, opponent, and the difference between team and opponent), field goal (shots made) percentage (for team, opponent, and the difference between team and opponent), turnovers (losing the ball before a shot is taken) per game (for team, opponent, and the difference between team and opponent), offensive rebound percentage, and defensive rebound percentage.

**a.** Consider team points per game, opponent points per game, team field goal percentage, opponent field goal percentage, difference in team and opponent turnovers, offensive rebound percentage, and defensive rebound percentage as independent variables for possible inclusion in the multiple regression model. Develop the most appropriate multiple regression model to predict the number of wins.

**b.** Consider the difference between team points and opponent points per game, the difference between team field goal percentage and opponent field goal percentage, the difference in team and opponent turnovers, offensive rebound percentage, and defensive rebound percentage as independent variables for possible inclusion in the multiple regression model. Develop the most appropriate multiple regression model to predict the number of wins.

**c.** Compare the results of (a) and (b). Which model is better for predicting the number of wins? Explain.

**15.31** Hemlock Farms is a community located in the Pocono Mountains area of eastern Pennsylvania. The data file Hemlockfarms contains information on homes that were for sale as of July 4, 2006. The variables included were

    List Price—Asking price of the house
    Hot Tub—Whether the house has a hot tub, with 0 = No and 1 = Yes
    Lake View—Whether the house has a lake view, with 0 = No and 1 = Yes
    Bathrooms—Number of bathrooms
    Bedrooms—Number of bedrooms
    Loft/Den—Whether the house has a loft or den, with 0 = No and 1 = Yes
    Finished basement—Whether the house has a finished basement, with 0 = No and 1 = Yes
    Acres—Number of acres for the property

Develop the most appropriate multiple regression model to predict the asking price. Be sure to perform a thorough residual analysis. In addition, provide a detailed explanation of your results.

**15.32** Nassau County is located approximately 25 miles east of New York City. Data in the file GlenCove are from a sample of 30 single-family homes located in Glen Cove. Variables included are the appraised value, land area of the

property (acres), interior size (square feet), age (years), number of rooms, number of bathrooms, and number of cars that can be parked in the garage.
a. Develop the most appropriate multiple regression model to predict appraised value.
b. Compare the results in (a) with those of Problems 15.33 (a) and 15.34(a).

**15.33** Data similar to those in Problem 15.32 are available for homes located in Roslyn and are stored in the file Roslyn.
a. Perform an analysis similar to that of Problem 15.32.
b. Compare the results in (a) with those of Problems 15.32 (a) and 15.34(a).

**15.34** Data similar to Problem 15.32 are available for homes located in Freeport and are stored in the file Freeport.
a. Perform an analysis similar to that of Problem 15.32.
b. Compare the results in (a) with those of Problems 15.32(a) and 15.33(a).

**15.35** You are a real estate broker who wants to compare property values in Glen Cove and Roslyn (which are located approximately 8 miles apart). Use the data in the file GCroslyn. Make sure to include the dummy variable for location (Glen Cove or Roslyn) in the regression model.
a. Develop the most appropriate multiple regression model to predict appraised value.
b. What conclusions can you reach concerning the differences in appraised value between Glen Cove and Roslyn?

**15.36** You are a real estate broker who wants to compare property values in Glen Cove, Freeport, and Roslyn. Use the data in the file GCFreeRoslyn.
a. Develop the most appropriate multiple regression model to predict appraised value.
b. What conclusions can you reach concerning the differences in appraised value between Glen Cove, Freeport, and Roslyn?

**15.37** Over the past 30 years, public awareness and concern about air pollution have escalated dramatically. Venturi scrubbers are used for the removal of submicron particulate matter from smoke stacks. An experiment was conducted to determine the effect of air flow rate, water flow rate (liters/minute), recirculating water flow rate (liters/minute), and orifice size (mm) in the air side of the pneumatic nozzle on the performance of the scrubber, as measured by the number of transfer units. The results are provided in the file Scrubber.

Develop the most appropriate multiple regression model to predict the number of transfer units. Be sure to perform a thorough residual analysis. In addition, provide a detailed explanation of your results.

Source: *Extracted from D. A. Marshall, R. J. Sumner, and C. A. Shook, "Removal of SiO$_2$ Particles with an Ejector Venturi Scrubber," Environmental Progress, 14, 1995, pp. 28–32.*

**15.38** A flux chamber is a Plexiglas dome about two feet in diameter that is placed over contaminated soil to sample soil gases. A study was carried out at a suspected radon hot spot to predict radon concentration (pCi/L) based on solar radiation (Ly/Day), soil temperature (°F), vapor pressure (mBar), wind speed (mph), relative humidity (%), dew point (°F), and ambient air temperature (°F). The data are contained in the Radon file.

Develop the most appropriate multiple regression model to predict radon concentration. Be sure to perform a thorough residual analysis. In addition, provide a detailed explanation of your results.

**15.39** A headline on page 1 of *The New York Times* of March 4, 1990, read: "Wine equation puts some noses out of joint." The article explained that Professor Orley Ashenfelter, a Princeton University economist, had developed a multiple regression model to predict the quality of French Bordeaux, based on the amount of winter rain, the average temperature during the growing season, and the harvest rain. The multiple regression equation is

$$Q = -12.145 + 0.00117WR + 0.6164TMP - 0.00386HR$$

where

$Q$ = logarithmic index of quality
$WR$ = winter rain (October through March), in millimeters
$TMP$ = average temperature during the growing season (April through September), in degrees Celsius
$HR$ = harvest rain (August to September), in millimeters

You are at a cocktail party, sipping a glass of wine, when one of your friends mentions to you that she has read the article. She asks you to explain the meaning of the coefficients in the equation and also asks you about analyses that might have been done and were not included in the article. What is your reply?

## Report Writing Exercises

**15.40** In Problem 15.23 on page 718, you developed a multiple regression model to predict monthly sales at sporting goods stores for the data in the file Sporting. Your task is to write a report based on the model you developed. Append all appropriate charts and statistical information to your report.

## Team Project

**15.41** The data file Mutual Funds contains information regarding nine variables from a sample of 868 mutual funds. The variables are:
Category—Type of stocks comprising the mutual fund (small cap, mid cap, or large cap)
Objective—Objective of stocks comprising the mutual fund (growth or value)

Assets—In millions of dollars

Fees—Sales charges (no or yes)

Expense ratio—Ratio of expenses to net assets, in percentage

2006 return—Twelve-month return in 2006

Three-year return—Annualized return, 2004–2006

Five-year return—Annualized return, 2002–2006

Risk—Risk-of-loss factor of the mutual fund (low, average, or high)

Develop regression models to predict the 2006 return, the three-year return, and the five-year return, based on fees, expense ratio, objective, and risk. (For the purpose of this analysis, combine low risk and average risk into one category.) Be sure to perform a thorough residual analysis. In addition, provide a detailed explanation of your results. Append all appropriate charts and statistical information to your report.

# THE MOUNTAIN STATES POTATO COMPANY

Mountain States Potato Company sells a by-product of its potato-processing operation, called a filter cake, to area feedlots as cattle feed. Recently, the feedlot owners have noticed that the cattle are not gaining weight as quickly as they once were. They believe that the root cause of the problem is that the percentage of solids in the filter cake is too low.

Historically, the percentage of solids in the filter cakes ran slightly above 12%. Lately, however, the solids are running in the 11% range. What is actually affecting the solids is a mystery, but something has to be done quickly. Individuals involved in the process were asked to identify variables that might affect the percentage of solids. This review turned up the six variables (in addition to the percentage of solids) listed below in the following table. Data collected by monitoring the process several times daily for 20 days are stored in the `Potato` file.

| Variable | Comments |
| --- | --- |
| SOLIDS | Percentage solids in the filter cake. |
| PH | Acidity. This measure of acidity indicates bacterial action in the clarifier and is controlled by the amount of downtime in the |

system. As bacterial action progresses, organic acids are produced that can be measured using pH.

| | |
| --- | --- |
| LOWER | Pressure of the vacuum line below the fluid line on the rotating drum. |
| UPPER | Pressure of the vacuum line above the fluid line on the rotating drum. |
| THICK | Filter cake thickness, measured on the drum. |
| VARIDRIV | Setting used to control the drum speed. May differ from DRUMSPD due to mechanical inefficiencies. |
| DRUMSPD | Speed at which the drum is rotating when collecting the filter cake. Measured with a stopwatch. |

1. Thoroughly analyze the data and develop a regression model to predict the percentage of solids.
2. Write an executive summary concerning your findings to the president of the Mountain States Potato Company. Include specific recommendations on how to get the percentage of solids back above 12%.

# WEB CASE

*Apply your knowledge of multiple regression model building in this Web Case, which extends the Using Statistics scenario concerning OmniPower energy bars from Chapter 14.*

Still concerned about ensuring a successful test marketing of its OmniPower energy bars, the marketing department of OmniFoods has contacted Connect2Coupons (C2C), another merchandising consultancy. C2C suggests that earlier analysis done by In-Store Placements Group (ISPG) was faulty because it did not use the correct type of data. C2C claims that its Internet-based viral marketing will have an even greater effect on OmniPower energy bar sales, as new data from the same 34-store sample will show. In

response, ISPG says its earlier claims are valid and has reported to the OmniFoods marketing department that it can discern no simple relationship between C2C's viral marketing and increased OmniPower sales.

Review all these claims on the message board at the OmniFoods internal Web site, **www.prenhall.com/ Springville/Omni_OmniPowerMB.htm** (or open the `Omni_OmniPowerMB.htm` file from the Student CD-ROM Web Case folder) and then answer the following:

1. Which of the claims are true? false? true but misleading? Support your answer by performing an appropriate statistical analysis.

**2.** If the grocery store chain allowed OmniFoods to use an unlimited number of sales techniques, which techniques should it use? Explain.

**3.** If the grocery store chain allowed OmniFoods to use only one sales technique, which technique should it use? Explain.

# REFERENCES

1. Kutner, M., C. Nachtsheim, J. Neter, and W. Li, *Applied Linear Statistical Models*, 5th ed. (New York: McGraw-Hill/Irwin, 2005).
2. Marquardt, D. W., "You Should Standardize the Predictor Variables in Your Regression Models," discussion of "A Critique of Some Ridge Regression Methods," by G. Smith and F. Campbell, *Journal of the American Statistical Association* 75 (1980): 87–91.
3. *Microsoft Excel 2007* (Redmond, WA: Microsoft Corp., 2007).
4. *Minitab for Windows Version 15* (State College, PA: Minitab, Inc., 2006).
5. Snee, R. D., "Some Aspects of Nonorthogonal Data Analysis, Part I. Developing Prediction Equations," *Journal of Quality Technology* 5 (1973): 67–79.

# Appendix E15
## Using Microsoft Excel for Multiple Regression Model Building

## E15.1 Creating Quadratic Terms

You create quadratic terms by creating a new column of formulas that compute the square of the linear term.

Open to the worksheet that contains your data. Locate the column to the right of the column that contains the data for the linear term. If this column is not blank, select the column, right-click the column, and select **Insert** from the shortcut menu to create a (new) blank column.

In the row 1 cell of this column, enter a column heading. Then, starting in row 2, enter formulas in the form *=Previous Column's Cell^2* down the column through all the data rows. For example, if column C contains the data for your linear term and column D is blank, enter the formula =**C2^2** in cell D2 and copy the formula down through all the data rows to create the data for the quadratic term.

With your expanded regression data worksheet, use the instructions of Section E14.1 (see page 685) to perform a multiple regression analysis that includes both the linear and quadratic terms.

## E15.2 Creating Transformations

To create a transformation, enter formulas in the form *=FUNCTION(Previous Column's Cell)* in a blank column to the right of the column containing the data you want to transform. If the column to the right is not blank, select the column, right-click the column, and select **Insert** from the shortcut menu to create a (new) blank column.

*FUNCTION* can be the SQRT (square root), LOG (common logarithm), or LN (natural logarithm) functions. For example, to create a square root transformation in a blank column D for an independent variable in column C, enter the formula =**SQRT(C2)** in cell D2 and copy the formula down through all data rows.

## E15.3 Computing Variance Inflationary Factors (VIFs)

You compute the variance inflationary factors using a two-step process. You first use the instructions of Section E14.1 (see page 685) to perform a regression analysis for every combination of X variables. Then, in each of the regression results worksheets, enter the label **VIF** in cell A9 and enter the formula =**1/(1-B5)** in cell **B9** to compute the VIF.

# Appendix P15
## Using PHStat2 for Multiple Regression Model Building

### P15.1 Computing Variance Inflationary Factors (VIFs)

To compute the variance inflationary factor, use the Section P14.1 instructions on page 687, but click **Variance Inflationary Factor (VIF)** before you click **OK** in the Multiple Regression dialog box. The VIF will appear in cell B9 of the regression results worksheets, as seen in Figure 15.13 on page 709.

### P15.2 Using Stepwise Regression

To use a stepwise regression approach to model building, use **PHStat → Regression → Stepwise Regression**. This procedure creates a stepwise analysis worksheet based on stepwise criteria and options and a confidence level that you specify. The procedure uses the ToolPak Regression procedure to perform a series of regressions that are then summarized on the stepwise analysis worksheet. (The options and *p*-values shown in the illustration at the right were used to create the stepwise regression worksheet shown in Figure 15.15 on page 711.)

This procedure may take a number of seconds to complete on older or entry-level computer systems. The procedure finishes when the statement "Stepwise ends" (seen in row 29 in Figure 15.15) is added to the stepwise analysis worksheet.

### P15.3 Using Best-Subsets Regression

To use a best-subsets approach to model building, use **PHStat → Regression → Best Subsets**. This procedure creates a best-subsets analysis worksheet based on the confidence level that you specify. The procedure uses the ToolPak Regression procedure to perform a series of regressions that are then summarized on the best-subsets analysis worksheet.

# Appendix M15
## Using Minitab for Multiple Regression Model Building

## M15.1 Creating Quadratic Terms

To create a new $X$ variable that is the square of another $X$ variable:

1. Enter the variable name for the new variable in a blank column.
2. Select **Calc → Calculator**.

In the Calculator dialog box:

3. Enter the new variable name in the **Store result in variable** box.
4. Enter the name of the $X$ variable you wish to square, *, and the name of the $X$ variable you wish to square again, in the **Expression** box. For example, if your variable was named **FlyAsh**, you would enter **FlyAsh*FlyAsh**.
5. Click **OK**.

To perform a regression analysis using this new variable, see the instructions of Section M14.2 on page 688.

## M15.2 Creating Transformations

To transform a variable:

1. Enter the variable name for the new variable in a blank column.
2. Select **Calc → Calculator**.

In the Calculator dialog box:

3. Enter the new variable name in the **Store result in variable** box.
4. Enter an expression in the form *FUNCTION(variable to transform)* in the **Expression** box. *FUNCTION* can be either **SQRT** for a square root transformation, **LOGTEN** for a common logarithm transformation, or **LN** for a natural logarithm transformation. For example, **SQRT(Y)** creates a square root transformation for a variable named **Y**.
5. Click **OK**.

To perform a regression analysis using this new variable, see the instructions of Section M14.2 on page 688.

## M15.3 Computing Variance Inflationary Factors (VIFs)

To illustrate computing the Variance Inflationary factors (VIFs):

1. Open the Standby.mtw worksheet.
2. Select **Stat → Regression → Regression**.

In the Regression dialog box (see Section M13.1 on page 633):

3. Enter **Standby** in the **Response** box.
4. Enter **Staff-Labor** in the **Predictors** box. (This enters the four variables **Staff, Remote, Dubner**, and **Labor**.)

In addition to the other selections in the Regression dialog box (see Section M14.2 on page 688):

5. Click **Options**.

In the Options dialog box:

6. Click **Variance inflation factors**.
7. Click **OK**.
8. Back in the Regression dialog box, click **OK**.

## M15.4 Using Stepwise Regression

To illustrate a stepwise regression approach to model building:

1. Open the Standby.mtw worksheet.
2. Select **Stat → Regression → Stepwise**.

In the Stepwise Regression dialog box (see Figure M15.1 on page 728):

3. Enter **Standby** in the **Response** box.
4. Enter **Staff-Labor** in the **Predictors** box.
5. Click **Methods**.

In the Stepwise - Methods dialog box (see Figure M15.2 on page 728):

6. Click **Use alpha values**.
7. Click **Stepwise**.
8. Enter **0.05** in the **Alpha to enter** box and **0.05** in the **Alpha to remove** box.
9. Click **OK**.
10. Back in the Stepwise Regression dialog box, click **OK**.

**FIGURE M15.1**
Minitab Stepwise Regression dialog box

**FIGURE M15.2**
Minitab Stepwise - Methods dialog box

**FIGURE M15.3**
Minitab Best Subsets Regression dialog box

In the Best Subsets Regression - Options dialog box (see Figure M15.4),

6. Enter **3** in the **Models of each size to print** box.
7. Click **OK**.
8. Back in the Best Subsets Regression dialog box, click **OK**.

**FIGURE M15.4**
Minitab Best Subsets Regression - Options dialog box

## M15.5 Using Best-Subsets Regression

To illustrate a best-subsets approach to model building:

1. Open the `Standby.mtw` worksheet.
2. Select **Stat → Regression → Best Subsets**.

In the Best Subsets Regression dialog box (see Figure M15.3):

3. Enter **Standby** in the **Response** box.
4. Enter **Staff-Labor** in the **Free predictors** box.
5. Click **Options**.

# CHAPTER SIXTEEN

## TIME-SERIES FORECASTING AND INDEX NUMBERS

## LEARNING OBJECTIVES

### In this chapter, you learn:

- About different time-series forecasting models: moving averages, exponential smoothing, the linear trend, the quadratic trend, the exponential trend, the autoregressive, and the least-squares models for seasonal data
- To choose the most appropriate time-series forecasting model
- About price indexes and the difference between aggregated and unaggregated indexes

# USING STATISTICS @ The Principled

You are a financial analyst for The Principled, a large financial services company. You need to forecast revenues for three companies in order to better evaluate investment opportunities for your clients. To assist in the forecasting, you have collected time-series data on three companies: Cabot Corporation, Wm. Wrigley Jr. Company, and Wal-Mart. Each time series has unique characteristics due to the different types of business activities and growth patterns experienced by the three companies. You understand that you can use several different types of forecasting models. How do you decide which type of forecasting model is best for each company? How do you use the information gained from the forecasting models to evaluate investment opportunities for your clients?

In Chapters 13 through 15, you used regression analysis as a tool for model building and prediction. In this chapter, regression analysis and other statistical methodologies are applied to time-series data. A **time series** is a set of numerical data collected over time. Due to differences in the features of data for various companies such as the three companies described in the Using Statistics scenario, you need to consider several different approaches to forecasting time-series data.

This chapter begins with an introduction to the importance of business forecasting (see Section 16.1) and a description of the components of time-series models (see Section 16.2). The coverage of forecasting *models* begins with annual time-series data. Two techniques for smoothing a series are illustrated in Section 16.3: moving averages and exponential smoothing. The analysis of annual time series continues, with the use of least-squares trend fitting and forecasting (see Section 16.4) and other more sophisticated forecasting methods (see Section 16.5) before discussing how to choose among alternative forecasting models in Section 16.6. These trend-fitting and forecasting models are then extended to monthly or quarterly time series (see Section 16.7). This chapter concludes with Section 16.8 that discusses several types of index numbers.

## 16.1   THE IMPORTANCE OF BUSINESS FORECASTING

**Forecasting** is done by monitoring changes that occur over time and projecting into the future. Forecasting is commonly used in both the for-profit and not-for-profit sectors of the economy. For example, marketing executives of a retailing corporation forecast product demand, sales revenues, consumer preferences, inventory, and so on in order to make timely decisions regarding promotions and strategic planning. Government officials forecast unemployment, inflation, industrial production, and revenues from income taxes in order to formulate policies. And the administrators of a college or university forecast student enrollment in order to plan for the construction of dormitories and academic facilities, plan for student and faculty recruitment, and make assessments of other needs.

There are two common approaches to forecasting: *qualitative* and *quantitative*. **Qualitative forecasting methods** are especially important when historical data are unavailable. Qualitative forecasting methods are considered to be highly subjective and judgmental.

**Quantitative forecasting methods** make use of historical data. The goal of these methods is to use past data to predict future values. Quantitative forecasting methods are subdivided into two types: *time series* and *causal*. **Time-series forecasting methods** involve forecasting future values based entirely on the past and present values of a variable. For example, the daily closing prices of a particular stock on the New York Stock Exchange constitute a time series. Other examples of economic or business time series are the monthly publication of the consumer price index (CPI), the quarterly gross domestic product (GDP), and the annual sales revenues of a particular company.

**Causal forecasting methods** involve the determination of factors that relate to the variable you are trying to forecast. These include multiple regression analysis with lagged variables, econometric modeling, leading indicator analysis, diffusion indexes, and other economic barometers that are beyond the scope of this text (see references 2–4). The primary emphasis in this chapter is on time-series forecasting methods.

## 16.2 COMPONENT FACTORS OF TIME-SERIES MODELS

The basic assumption of time-series forecasting is that the factors that have influenced activities in the past and present will continue to do so in approximately the same way in the future. Thus, the major goals of time-series forecasting are to identify and isolate these influencing factors in order to make predictions. Four effects or components are often considered in time-series models:

1. Trend
2. Cyclical effect
3. Irregular or random effect
4. Seasonal effect

A **trend** is an overall long-term upward or downward movement in a time series. Trend is not the only component factor that can influence data in a time series. The **cyclical component** depicts the up-and-down swings or movements through the series. Cyclical movements vary in length, usually lasting from 2 to 10 years. They differ in intensity and are often correlated with a business cycle. In some time periods, the values are higher than would be predicted by a trend line (i.e., they are at or near the peak of a cycle). In other time periods, the values are lower than would be predicted by a trend line (i.e., they are at or near the bottom of a cycle). Any data that do not follow the trend modified by the cyclical component are considered part of the **irregular** or **random component**. When you have monthly or quarterly data, an additional component, the **seasonal component**, is considered along with the trend, cyclical, and irregular components.

Your first step in a time-series analysis is to plot the data and observe any patterns that occur over time. You must determine whether there is a long-term upward or downward movement in the series (i.e., a trend). If there is no obvious long-term upward or downward trend, then you can use the method of moving averages or the method of exponential smoothing to smooth the series and provide an overall long-term impression (see Section 16.3). If a trend is present, you can consider several time-series forecasting methods (see Sections 16.4 and 16.5 for forecasting annual data and Section 16.7 for forecasting monthly or quarterly time series).

## 16.3 SMOOTHING AN ANNUAL TIME SERIES

One of the companies of interest in the Using Statistics scenario is the Cabot Corporation. The Cabot Corporation is a Boston-based manufacturer and distributor of chemicals, performance materials, specialty fluids, microelectronic materials, and liquefied natural gas. The company operates 36 manufacturing facilities in 21 countries and its stock is traded on the New York Stock Exchange with the ticker symbol CBT. Revenues in 2006 were approximately $2.5 billion. Table 16.1 gives the total revenues, in millions of dollars, for 1982 to 2006 (see the file Cabot). Figure 16.1 presents the time-series plot.

**TABLE 16.1**

Revenues (in Millions of Dollars) for the Cabot Corporation from 1982 to 2006

| Year | Revenue | Year | Revenue | Year | Revenue |
|------|---------|------|---------|------|---------|
| 1982 | 1,588 | 1991 | 1,488 | 1999 | 1,699 |
| 1983 | 1,558 | 1992 | 1,562 | 2000 | 1,698 |
| 1984 | 1,753 | 1993 | 1,619 | 2001 | 1,523 |
| 1985 | 1,408 | 1994 | 1,687 | 2002 | 1,557 |
| 1986 | 1,310 | 1995 | 1,841 | 2003 | 1,795 |
| 1987 | 1,424 | 1996 | 1,865 | 2004 | 1,934 |
| 1988 | 1,677 | 1997 | 1,637 | 2005 | 2,125 |
| 1989 | 1,937 | 1998 | 1,653 | 2006 | 2,543 |
| 1990 | 1,685 | | | | |

Source: *Extracted from* Moody's Handbook of Common Stocks, 1992, Mergent's Handbook of Common Stocks, 2006, *and* **wl.cabot-corp.com**.

**FIGURE 16.1**

Microsoft Excel plot of revenues (in millions of dollars) for the Cabot Corporation (1982–2006)

*See Section E2.13 to create this. (Minitab users, see Section M2.9 to create an equivalent chart.)*

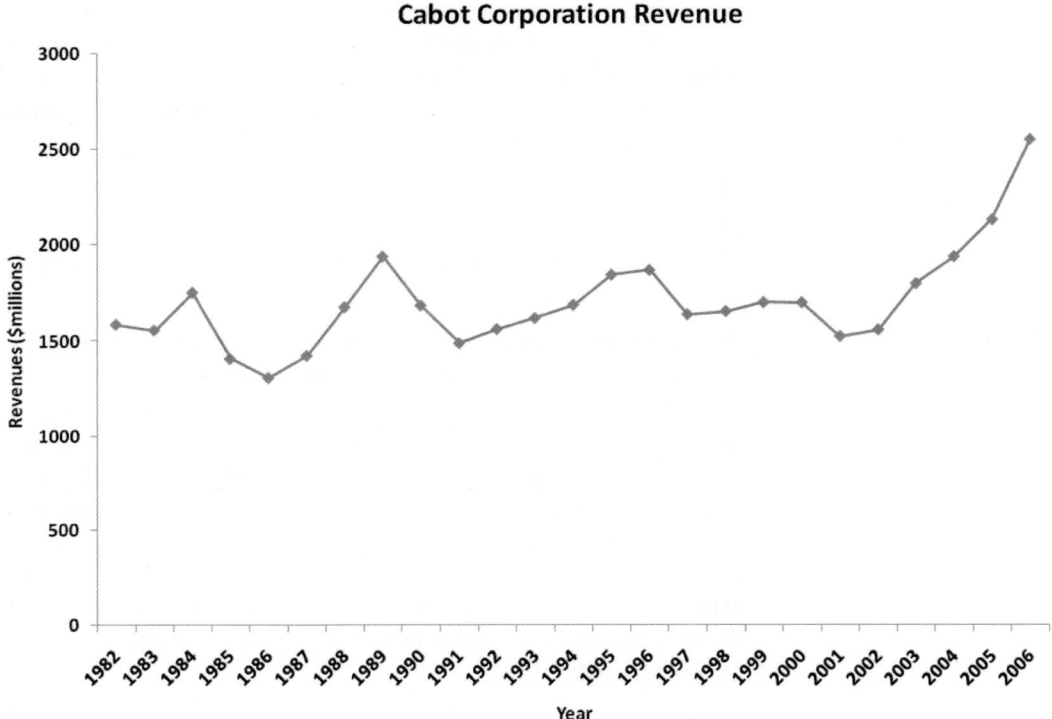

When you examine annual data, your visual impression of the long-term trend in the series is sometimes obscured by the amount of variation from year to year. Often, you cannot judge whether any long-term upward or downward trend exists in the series. To get a better overall impression of the pattern of movement in the data over time, you can use the methods of moving averages or exponential smoothing.

## Moving Averages

> **Moving averages** for a chosen period of length $L$ consist of a series of means computed over time such that each mean is calculated for a sequence of $L$ observed values. Moving averages are represented by the symbol $MA(L)$.

To illustrate, suppose you want to compute five-year moving averages from a series that has $n = 11$ years. Because $L = 5$, the five-year moving averages consist of a series of means computed by averaging consecutive sequences of five values. You compute the first five-year moving average by summing the values for the first five years in the series and dividing by 5:

$$MA(5) = \frac{Y_1 + Y_2 + Y_3 + Y_4 + Y_5}{5}$$

You compute the second five-year moving average by summing the values of years 2 through 6 in the series and then dividing by 5:

$$MA(5) = \frac{Y_2 + Y_3 + Y_4 + Y_5 + Y_6}{5}$$

You continue this process until you have computed the last of these five-year moving averages by summing the values of the last 5 years in the series (i.e., years 7 through 11) and then dividing by 5:

$$MA(5) = \frac{Y_7 + Y_8 + Y_9 + Y_{10} + Y_{11}}{5}$$

When you are dealing with annual time-series data, $L$, the length of the period chosen for constructing the moving averages, should be an *odd* number of years. By following this rule, you are not able to compute any moving averages for the first $(L - 1)/2$ years or the last $(L - 1)/2$ years of the series. Thus, for a five-year moving average, you cannot make computations for the first two years or the last two years of the series.

When plotting moving averages, you plot each of the computed values against the middle year of the sequence of years used to compute it. If $n = 11$ and $L = 5$, the first moving average is centered on the third year, the second moving average is centered on the fourth year, and the last moving average is centered on the ninth year. Example 16.1 illustrates the computation of five-year moving averages.

**EXAMPLE 16.1**

COMPUTING FIVE-YEAR MOVING AVERAGES

The following data represent total revenues for a fast-food store over the 11-year period 1997 to 2007:

| 4.0 | 5.0 | 7.0 | 6.0 | 8.0 | 9.0 | 5.0 | 2.0 | 3.5 | 5.5 | 6.5 |

Compute the five-year moving averages for this annual time series.

**SOLUTION** To compute the five-year moving averages, you first compute the five-year moving total and then divide this total by 5. The first of the five-year moving averages is

$$MA(5) = \frac{Y_1 + Y_2 + Y_3 + Y_4 + Y_5}{5} = \frac{4.0 + 5.0 + 7.0 + 6.0 + 8.0}{5} = \frac{30.0}{5} = 6.0$$

The moving average is then centered on the middle value—the third year of this time series. To compute the second of the five-year moving averages, you compute the moving total of the second through sixth years and divide this value by 5:

$$MA(5) = \frac{Y_2 + Y_3 + Y_4 + Y_5 + Y_6}{5} = \frac{5.0 + 7.0 + 6.0 + 8.0 + 9.0}{5} = \frac{35.0}{5} = 7.0$$

This moving average is centered on the new middle value—the fourth year of the time series. The remaining moving averages are

$$MA(5) = \frac{Y_3 + Y_4 + Y_5 + Y_6 + Y_7}{5} = \frac{7.0 + 6.0 + 8.0 + 9.0 + 5.0}{5} = \frac{35.0}{5} = 7.0$$

$$MA(5) = \frac{Y_4 + Y_5 + Y_6 + Y_7 + Y_8}{5} = \frac{6.0 + 8.0 + 9.0 + 5.0 + 2.0}{5} = \frac{30.0}{5} = 6.0$$

$$MA(5) = \frac{Y_5 + Y_6 + Y_7 + Y_8 + Y_9}{5} = \frac{8.0 + 9.0 + 5.0 + 2.0 + 3.5}{5} = \frac{27.5}{5} = 5.5$$

$$MA(5) = \frac{Y_6 + Y_7 + Y_8 + Y_9 + Y_{10}}{5} = \frac{9.0 + 5.0 + 2.0 + 3.5 + 5.5}{5} = \frac{25.0}{5} = 5.0$$

$$MA(5) = \frac{Y_7 + Y_8 + Y_9 + Y_{10} + Y_{11}}{5} = \frac{5.0 + 2.0 + 3.5 + 5.5 + 6.5}{5} = \frac{22.5}{5} = 4.5$$

These moving averages are then centered on their respective middle values—the fifth, sixth, seventh, eighth, and ninth years in the time series. By using the five-year moving averages, you are unable to compute a moving average for the first two or last two values in the time series.

In practice, you should use Microsoft Excel or Minitab when computing moving averages to avoid the tedious computations. Figure 16.2 presents the annual Cabot Corporation revenue data for the 25-year period from 1982 through 2006, the computations for 3- and 7-year moving averages, and a plot of the original data and the moving averages.

**FIGURE 16.2**

Microsoft Excel worksheet for the three-year and seven-year moving averages for Cabot Corporation revenues

*See Section E16.1 or P16.1 to create this. (Minitab users, see Sections M2.9 and M16.1 to create an equivalent chart.)*

In Figure 16.2, there is no three-year moving average for the first and the last year and no seven-year moving average for the first three years and last three years. You can see that the seven-year moving averages smooth the series a great deal more than the three-year moving averages because the period is longer. Unfortunately, the longer the period, the fewer the number of moving averages you can compute. Therefore, selecting moving averages that are longer than seven years is usually undesirable because too many moving average values are missing at the beginning and end of the series. This makes it more difficult to get an overall impression of the entire series.

The selection of $L$, the length of the period used for constructing the averages, is highly subjective. If cyclical fluctuations are present in the data, you should choose an integer value of

$L$ that corresponds to (or is a multiple of) the estimated length of a cycle in the series. If no obvious cyclical fluctuations are present, then the most common choices are three-year, five-year, or seven-year moving averages, depending on the amount of smoothing desired and the amount of data available.

## Exponential Smoothing

**Exponential smoothing** is another method used to smooth a time series. In addition to smoothing, you can use exponential smoothing to compute short-term (one period into the future) forecasts when the presence and type of long-term trend in a time series is questionable. The name *exponential smoothing* comes from the fact that this method consists of a series of *exponentially weighted* moving averages. The weights assigned to the values change so that the most recent value receives the highest weight, the previous value receives the second-highest weight, and so on, with the first value receiving the lowest weight. Throughout the series, each exponentially smoothed value depends on all previous values, which is another advantage of exponential smoothing over the method of moving averages. Although the computations involved in exponential smoothing seem formidable, you can use Microsoft Excel or Minitab to perform the computations.

The equation developed for exponentially smoothing a series in any time period, $i$, is based on only three terms—the current value in the time series, $Y_i$; the previously computed exponentially smoothed value, $E_{i-1}$; and an assigned weight or smoothing coefficient, $W$.[1] You use Equation (16.1) to exponentially smooth a time series.

[1] *The damping factor used by Microsoft Excel is equal to 1 − W.*

Computing an Exponentially Smoothed Value in Time Period $i$

$$E_1 = Y_1$$
$$E_i = WY_i + (1-W)E_{i-1} \quad i = 2,3,4,\ldots \tag{16.1}$$

where

$E_i$ = value of the exponentially smoothed series being computed in time period $i$

$E_{i-1}$ = value of the exponentially smoothed series already computed in time period $i-1$

$Y_i$ = observed value of the time series in period $i$

$W$ = subjectively assigned weight or smoothing coefficient (where $0 < W < 1$).
  Although $W$ can approach 1.0, in virtually all business applications, $W \leq 0.5$.

Choosing the weight or smoothing coefficient (i.e., $W$) that you assign to the time series is critical. Unfortunately, this selection is somewhat subjective. If your goal is only to smooth a series by eliminating unwanted cyclical and irregular variations, you should select a small value for $W$ (close to 0). If your goal is forecasting, you should choose a large value for $W$ (close to 0.5). In the former case, the overall long-term tendencies of the series will be more apparent; in the latter case, future short-term directions may be more adequately predicted.

Figure 16.3 presents the Microsoft Excel exponentially smoothed values (with smoothing coefficients of $W = 0.50$ and $W = 0.25$) for annual revenue of the Cabot Corporation over the 25-year period 1982 to 2006, along with a plot of the original data and the two exponentially smoothed time series.

To illustrate these exponential smoothing computations for a smoothing coefficient of $W = 0.25$, you begin with the initial value $Y_{1982} = 1,588$ as the first smoothed value ($E_{1982} = 1,588$).

**FIGURE 16.3**

Microsoft Excel
worksheet for the
exponentially smoothed
series ($W = 0.50$ and
$W = 0.25$) of the Cabot
Corporation revenues

*See Section E16.3 to create
this. (Minitab users, see
Section M16.2 to create
equivalent results.)*

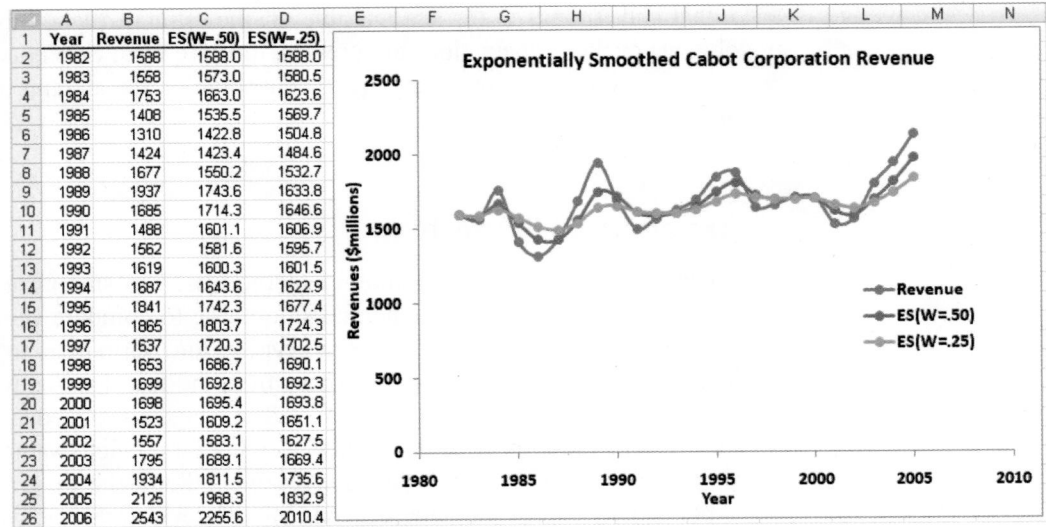

| Year | Revenue | ES(W=.50) | ES(W=.25) |
|------|---------|-----------|-----------|
| 1982 | 1588 | 1588.0 | 1588.0 |
| 1983 | 1558 | 1573.0 | 1580.5 |
| 1984 | 1753 | 1663.0 | 1623.6 |
| 1985 | 1408 | 1535.5 | 1569.7 |
| 1986 | 1310 | 1422.8 | 1504.8 |
| 1987 | 1424 | 1423.4 | 1484.6 |
| 1988 | 1677 | 1550.2 | 1532.7 |
| 1989 | 1937 | 1743.6 | 1633.8 |
| 1990 | 1685 | 1714.3 | 1646.6 |
| 1991 | 1488 | 1601.1 | 1606.9 |
| 1992 | 1562 | 1581.6 | 1595.7 |
| 1993 | 1619 | 1600.3 | 1601.5 |
| 1994 | 1687 | 1643.6 | 1622.9 |
| 1995 | 1841 | 1742.3 | 1677.4 |
| 1996 | 1865 | 1803.7 | 1724.3 |
| 1997 | 1637 | 1720.3 | 1702.5 |
| 1998 | 1653 | 1686.7 | 1690.1 |
| 1999 | 1699 | 1692.8 | 1692.3 |
| 2000 | 1698 | 1695.4 | 1693.8 |
| 2001 | 1523 | 1609.2 | 1651.1 |
| 2002 | 1557 | 1583.1 | 1627.5 |
| 2003 | 1795 | 1689.1 | 1669.4 |
| 2004 | 1934 | 1811.5 | 1735.6 |
| 2005 | 2125 | 1968.3 | 1832.9 |
| 2006 | 2543 | 2255.6 | 2010.4 |

Then, using the value of the time series for 1983 ($Y_{1983} = 1,558$), you smooth the series for 1983 by computing

$$E_{1983} = WY_{1983} + (1-W)E_{1982}$$
$$= (0.25)(1,558) + (0.75)(1,588) = 1,580.5$$

To smooth the series for 1984:

$$E_{1984} = WY_{1984} + (1-W)E_{1983}$$
$$= (0.25)(1,753) + (0.75)(1,580.5) = 1,623.6$$

To smooth the series for 1985:

$$E_{1985} = WY_{1985} + (1-W)E_{1984}$$
$$= (0.25)(1,408) + (0.75)(1,623.6) = 1,569.7$$

You continue this process until you have computed the exponentially smoothed values for all 25 years in the series, as shown in Figure 16.3.

To use exponential smoothing for forecasting, you use the smoothed value in the current time period as the forecast of the value in the following period.

**Forecasting Time Period $i + 1$**

$$\hat{Y}_{i+1} = E_i \qquad (16.2)$$

To forecast the revenue of Cabot Corporation during 2007, using a smoothing coefficient of $W = 0.25$, you use the smoothed value for 2006 as its estimate. Figure 16.3 shows that this value is $2,010.4 million. (How close is this forecast? Look up Cabot Corporation's revenue at **www.w1.cabot-corp.com** to find out.) When the value for 2007 becomes available, you can use Equation (16.1) to make a forecast for 2008 by computing the smoothed value for 2007, as follows:

Current smoothed value = $(W)$(Current value) + $(1-W)$(previous smoothed value)

$$E_{2007} = WY_{2007} + (1-W)E_{2006}$$

Or, in terms of forecasting, you compute the following:

New forecast = $(W)$(Current value) + $(1-W)$(Current forecast)

$$\hat{Y}_{2008} = WY_{2007} + (1-W)\hat{Y}_{2007}$$

# PROBLEMS FOR SECTION 16.3

## Learning the Basics

**16.1** If you are using exponential smoothing for forecasting an annual time series of revenues, what is your forecast for next year if the smoothed value for this year is $32.4 million?

**16.2** Consider a nine-year moving average used to smooth a time series that was first recorded in 1955.
**a.** Which year serves as the first centered value in the smoothed series?
**b.** How many years of values in the series are lost when computing all the nine-year moving averages?

**16.3** You are using exponential smoothing on an annual time series concerning total revenues (in millions of dollars). You decide to use a smoothing coefficient of $W = 0.20$ and the exponentially smoothed value for 2007 is $E_{2007} = (0.20)(12.1) + (0.80)(9.4)$.
**a.** What is the smoothed value of this series in 2007?
**b.** What is the smoothed value of this series in 2008 if the value of the series in that year is 11.5 million dollars?

## Applying the Concepts

✓**SELF** **16.4** The following data (stored in the file **Movies**) represent the yearly movie attendance (in billions) from 1999 to 2006:

| Year | Attendance | Year | Attendance |
|------|------------|------|------------|
| 1999 | 1.47 | 2003 | 1.57 |
| 2000 | 1.42 | 2004 | 1.53 |
| 2001 | 1.49 | 2005 | 1.41 |
| 2002 | 1.63 | 2006 | 1.45 |

Source: *Extracted from C. Passy, "Good Night and Good Luck," Palm Beach Post, February 5, 2006, p. 1J.*

**a.** Plot the time series.
**b.** Fit a three-year moving average to the data and plot the results.
**c.** Using a smoothing coefficient of $W = 0.50$, exponentially smooth the series and plot the results.
**d.** Repeat (c), using $W = 0.25$.
**e.** Compare the results of (c) and (d).

**16.5** The following data, contained in the file **Deals**, provide the number of mergers and acquisitions made during January 1 through January 11 of each year from 1995 to 2006 (extracted from "Back of the Envelope," *The New York Times*, January 13, 2006, p. C7):

| Year | Deals | Year | Deals |
|------|-------|------|-------|
| 1995 | 715 | 2001 | 1,031 |
| 1996 | 865 | 2002 | 893 |
| 1997 | 708 | 2003 | 735 |
| 1998 | 861 | 2004 | 759 |
| 1999 | 931 | 2005 | 1,013 |
| 2000 | 939 | 2006 | 622 |

**a.** Plot the time series.
**b.** Fit a three-year moving average to the data and plot the results.
**c.** Using a smoothing coefficient of $W = 0.50$, exponentially smooth the series and plot the results.
**d.** Repeat (c), using $W = 0.25$.
**e.** Compare the results of (c) and (d).

**16.6** The NASDAQ stock market includes small- and medium-sized companies, many of which are in high-tech industries. Because of the nature of these companies, the NASDAQ tends to be more volatile than the Dow Jones Industrial Average or the S&P 500. The daily closing values for the NASDAQ during the first 70 trading days in 2007 are listed in the data file **DailyNASDAQ** (extracted from **finance.yahoo.com**):
**a.** Plot the time series.
**b.** Fit a three-period moving average to the data and plot the results.
**c.** Using a smoothing coefficient of $W = 0.50$, exponentially smooth the series and plot the results.
**d.** Repeat (c), using $W = 0.25$.
**e.** What conclusions can you reach concerning the presence or absence of trends during the first 70 trading days in 2007?

**16.7** The following data (in the file **Treasury**) represent the three-month Treasury bill rates in the United States from 1991 to 2006:

| Year | Rate | Year | Rate |
|------|------|------|------|
| 1991 | 5.38 | 1999 | 4.64 |
| 1992 | 3.43 | 2000 | 5.82 |
| 1993 | 3.00 | 2001 | 3.40 |
| 1994 | 4.25 | 2002 | 1.61 |
| 1995 | 5.49 | 2003 | 1.01 |
| 1996 | 5.01 | 2004 | 1.37 |
| 1997 | 5.06 | 2005 | 3.15 |
| 1998 | 4.78 | 2006 | 4.73 |

Source: *Board of Governors of the Federal Reserve System,* **www.federalreserve.gov**.

a. Plot the data.
b. Fit a three-year moving average to the data and plot the results.
c. Using a smoothing coefficient of $W = 0.50$, exponentially smooth the series and plot the results.
d. What is your exponentially smoothed forecast for 2007?
e. Repeat (c) and (d), using a smoothing coefficient of $W = 0.25$.
f. Compare the results of (d) and (e).

**SELF** ✓**Test** **Electricity** **16.8** The following data (stored in the file **Electricity**) represent the average residential prices of electricity, in cost per kilowatt hour, in the October–March winter months from 1994–1995 to 2005–2006.
a. Plot the data.
b. Fit a three-year moving average to the data and plot the results.
c. Using a smoothing coefficient of $W = 0.50$, exponentially smooth the series and plot the results.

| Year | Cost | Year | Cost |
|------|------|------|------|
| 1994–1995 | 8.16 | 2000–2001 | 8.11 |
| 1995–1996 | 8.10 | 2001–2002 | 8.37 |
| 1996–1997 | 8.17 | 2002–2003 | 8.20 |
| 1997–1998 | 8.12 | 2003–2004 | 8.49 |
| 1998–1999 | 7.94 | 2004–2005 | 8.78 |
| 1999–2000 | 7.98 | 2005–2006 | 9.67 |

Source: *Energy Information Administration, Department of Energy,* **www.eia.doe.gov**.

d. What is your exponentially smoothed forecast for 2006–2007?
e. Repeat (c) and (d), using a smoothing coefficient of $W = 0.25$.
f. Compare the results of (d) and (e).

## 16.4    LEAST-SQUARES TREND FITTING AND FORECASTING

The component factor of a time series most often studied is trend. You study trend in order to make intermediate and long-range forecasts. To get a visual impression of the overall long-term movements in a time series, you construct a time-series plot. If a straight-line trend adequately fits the data, you can use a linear trend model [see Equation (16.3) and Section 13.2]. If the time-series data indicate some long-run downward or upward quadratic movement, you can use a quadratic trend model [see Equation (16.4) and Section 15.1]. When the time-series data increase at a rate such that the percentage difference from value to value is constant, you can use an exponential trend model [see Equation (16.5)].

### The Linear Trend Model

The **linear trend model**:

$$Y_i = \beta_0 + \beta_1 X_i + \varepsilon_i$$

is the simplest forecasting model. Equation (16.3) defines the linear trend forecasting equation.

> **Linear Trend Forecasting Equation**
>
> $$\hat{Y}_i = b_0 + b_1 X_i \qquad\qquad \textbf{(16.3)}$$

Recall that in linear regression analysis, you use the method of least squares to compute the sample slope, $b_1$, and the sample $Y$ intercept, $b_0$. You then substitute the values for $X$ into Equation (16.3) to predict $Y$.

When using the least-squares method for fitting trends in a time series, you can simplify the interpretation of the coefficients by coding the $X$ values so that the first value is assigned a code of $X = 0$. You then assign all successive values consecutively increasing integer codes: 1,

2, 3, . . . , so that the *n*th and last value in the series has code $n - 1$. For example, for time-series data recorded annually over 23 years, you assign the first year a coded value of 0, the second year a coded value of 1, the third year a coded value of 2, and so on, with the final (23rd) year assigned a coded value of 22.

In the Using Statistics scenario on page 730, one of the companies of interest is the Wm. Wrigley Jr. Company. Wrigley's is the world's largest manufacturer and marketer of chewing gum. The Chicago-based firm operates factories in 12 countries and markets its products in more than 150 countries. Revenues in 2006 topped $4.6 billion (Wm. Wrigley Jr. Company, **www.wrigley.com**). Table 16.2 lists the actual gross revenues (in millions of dollars) from 1984 to 2006 (see the file Wrigley).

**TABLE 16.2**

Revenues (in Millions of Dollars) for the Wm. Wrigley Jr. Company (1984–2006)

| Year | Revenue | Year | Revenue |
|------|---------|------|---------|
| 1984 | 591 | 1996 | 1,851 |
| 1985 | 620 | 1997 | 1,954 |
| 1986 | 699 | 1998 | 2,023 |
| 1987 | 781 | 1999 | 2,079 |
| 1988 | 891 | 2000 | 2,146 |
| 1989 | 993 | 2001 | 2,430 |
| 1990 | 1,111 | 2002 | 2,746 |
| 1991 | 1,149 | 2003 | 3,069 |
| 1992 | 1,301 | 2004 | 3,649 |
| 1993 | 1,440 | 2005 | 4,159 |
| 1994 | 1,661 | 2006 | 4,686 |
| 1995 | 1,770 | | |

Source: *Extracted from* Moody's Handbook of Common Stocks, 1992, Mergent's Handbook of Common Stocks, 2006, *and* **www.wrigley.com**.

Coding the consecutive *X* values from 0 through 22 and then using Microsoft Excel or Minitab to perform a simple linear regression analysis on the adjusted time series (see Figure 16.4 or 16.5) results in the following linear trend forecasting equation:

$$\hat{Y}_i = 174.1413 + 157.2875 X_i$$

where year coded zero is 1984.

**FIGURE 16.4**

Microsoft Excel regression results worksheet for a linear trend model to forecast revenues (in millions of dollars) at Wm. Wrigley Jr. Company

*See Section E16.6 or P16.1 to create this.*

| | A | B | C | D | E | F | G |
|---|---|---|---|---|---|---|---|
| 1 | Linear Trend Model for Wm. Wrigley Jr. Company Revenue | | | | | | |
| 2 | | | | | | | |
| 3 | Regression Statistics | | | | | | |
| 4 | Multiple R | 0.9436 | | | | | |
| 5 | R Square | 0.8904 | | | | | |
| 6 | Adjusted R Square | 0.8852 | | | | | |
| 7 | Standard Error | 383.0643 | | | | | |
| 8 | Observations | 23 | | | | | |
| 9 | | | | | | | |
| 10 | ANOVA | | | | | | |
| 11 | | df | SS | MS | F | Significance F | |
| 12 | Regression | 1 | 25036245.6769 | 25036245.6769 | 170.6184 | 0.0000 | |
| 13 | Residual | 21 | 3081503.1927 | 146738.2473 | | | |
| 14 | Total | 22 | 28117748.8696 | | | | |
| 15 | | | | | | | |
| 16 | | Coefficients | Standard Error | t Stat | P-value | Lower 95% | Upper 95% |
| 17 | Intercept | 174.1413 | 154.6762 | 1.1258 | 0.2729 | -147.5254 | 495.8080 |
| 18 | Coded Year | 157.2875 | 12.0415 | 13.0621 | 0.0000 | 132.2458 | 182.3293 |

**FIGURE 16.5**

Minitab results for a linear regression model to forecast revenues at Wm. Wrigley Jr. Company

*See Section M16.3 to create this.*

```
The regression equation is
Revenue = 174 + 157 Coded Year


Predictor      Coef   SE Coef      T      P
Constant      174.1     154.7   1.13  0.273
Coded Year   157.29     12.04  13.06  0.000


S = 383.064   R-Sq = 89.0%   R-Sq(adj) = 88.5%


Analysis of Variance

Source          DF         SS        MS       F      P
Regression       1   25036246  25036246  170.62  0.000
Residual Error  21    3081503    146738
Total           22   28117749
```

You interpret the regression coefficients as follows:

- The $Y$ intercept, $b_0 = 174.1413$, is the predicted revenues (in millions of dollars) at Wm. Wrigley Jr. during the origin or base year, 1984.
- The slope, $b_1 = 157.2875$, indicates that revenues are predicted to increase by 157.2875 million dollars per year.

To project the trend in the revenues at Wm. Wrigley Jr. to 2007, you substitute $X_{24} = 23$, the code for 2007, into the linear trend forecasting equation:

$$\hat{Y}_i = 174.1413 + 157.2875(23) = 3,791.7538 \text{ millions of dollars}$$

The trend line is plotted in Figure 16.6, along with the observed values of the time series. There is a strong upward linear trend, and the adjusted $r^2$ is 0.8852, indicating that more than 88% of the variation in revenues is explained by the linear trend over the time series. To investigate whether a different trend model might provide an even better fit, a *quadratic* trend model and an *exponential* trend model are presented next.

**FIGURE 16.6**

Microsoft Excel plot of the least-squares trend line for Wm. Wrigley Jr. Company revenues data

*See Section E16.6 or P16.1 to create this. (Minitab users, see Section M16.3 to create an equivalent chart.)*

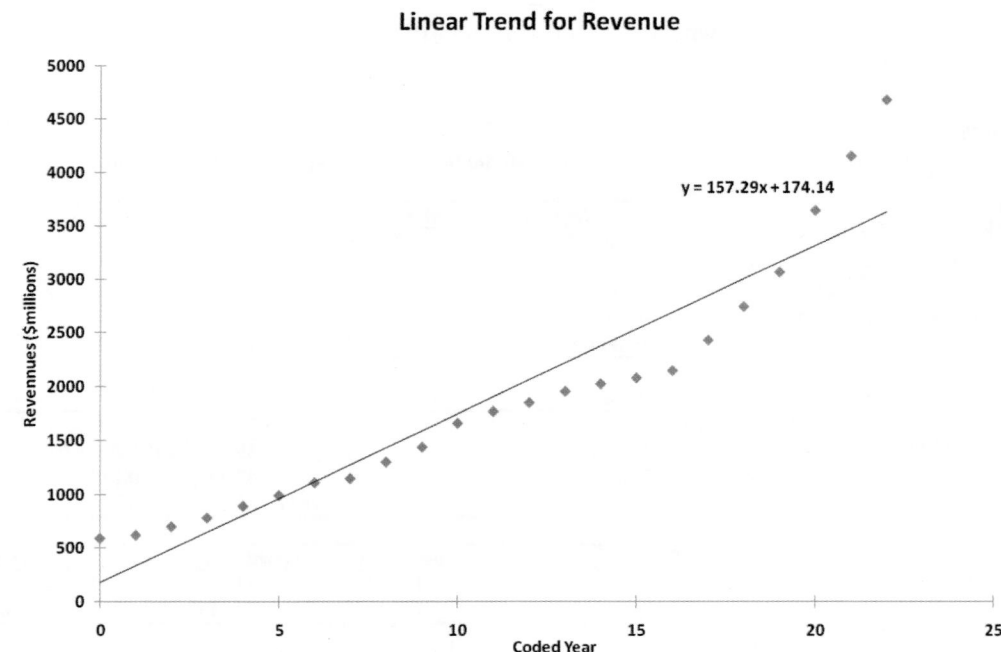

## The Quadratic Trend Model

A **quadratic trend model**:

$$\hat{Y}_i = \beta_0 + \beta_1 X_i + \beta_2 X_i^2 + \varepsilon_i$$

is the simplest nonlinear model. Using the least-squares method described in Section 15.1, you can develop a quadratic trend forecasting equation, as presented in Equation (16.4).

> **Quadratic Trend Forecasting Equation**
>
> $$\hat{Y}_i = b_0 + b_1 X_i + b_2 X_i^2 \qquad (16.4)$$
>
> where
>
> $b_0$ = estimated $Y$ intercept
>
> $b_1$ = estimated *linear* effect on $Y$
>
> $b_2$ = estimated *quadratic* effect on $Y$

Once again, you use Microsoft Excel or Minitab to compute the quadratic trend forecasting equation. Figure 16.7 provides Microsoft Excel results for the quadratic trend model used to forecast revenues at the Wm. Wrigley Jr. Company. Figure 16.8 shows Minitab results.

**FIGURE 16.7**

Microsoft Excel regression results worksheet for the quadratic trend model to forecast Wm. Wrigley Jr. Company revenues

*See Section E16.7 or P16.2 to create this.*

**FIGURE 16.8**

Minitab results for a quadratic regression model to forecast revenues at Wm. Wrigley Jr. Company

*See Section M16.3 to create this.*

In Figure 16.7 or 16.8,

$$\hat{Y}_i = 759.7217 - 10.0211X_i + 7.6049X_i^2$$

where year coded zero is 1984.

To compute a forecast using the quadratic trend equation, you substitute the appropriate coded $X$ value into this equation. For example, to forecast the trend in revenues for 2007 (i.e., $X_{24} = 23$),

$$\hat{Y}_i = 759.7217 - 10.0211(23) + 7.6049(23)^2 = 4,552.2285 \text{ millions of dollars}$$

Figure 16.9 plots the quadratic trend forecasting equation along with the time series for the actual data. This quadratic trend model provides a better fit (adjusted $r^2 = 0.9596$) to the time series than does the linear trend model. The $t_{STAT}$ test statistic for the contribution of the quadratic term to the model is 6.2978 ($p$-value = 0.0000).

**FIGURE 16.9**

Microsoft Excel plot to fit a quadratic trend forecasting equation for the Wm. Wrigley Jr. Company revenues data using Microsoft Excel

*See Section E16.7 or P16.2 to create this. (Minitab users, see Section M16.3 to create an equivalent chart.)*

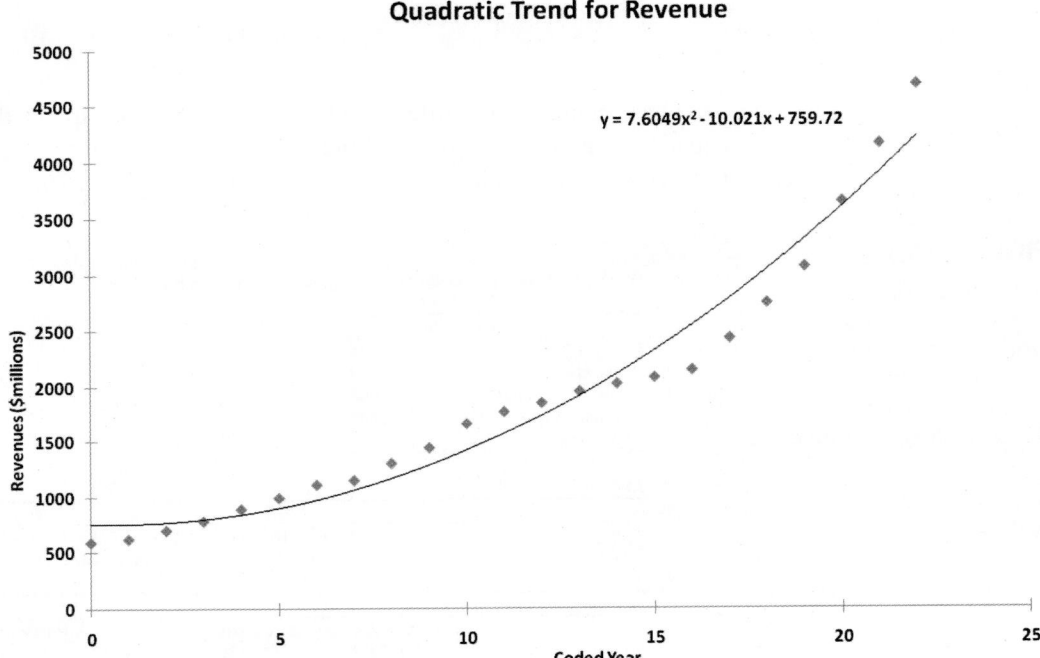

## The Exponential Trend Model

When a time series increases at a rate such that the percentage difference from value to value is constant, an exponential trend is present. Equation (16.5) defines the **exponential trend model**.

Exponential Trend Model

$$Y_i = \beta_0 \beta_1^{X_i} \varepsilon_i \tag{16.5}$$

where

$$\beta_0 = Y \text{ intercept}$$

$(\beta_1 - 1) \times 100\%$ is the annual compound growth rate (in %)

[2] Alternatively, you can use base e logarithms. For more information on logarithms, see Appendix A.3.

The model in Equation (16.5) is not in the form of a linear regression model. To transform this nonlinear model to a linear model, you use a base 10 logarithm transformation.[2] Taking the logarithm of each side of Equation (16.5) results in Equation (16.6).

### Transformed Exponential Trend Model

$$\log(Y_i) = \log(\beta_0 \beta_1^{X_i} \varepsilon_i)$$

$$= \log(\beta_0) + \log(\beta_1^{X_i}) + \log(\varepsilon_i)$$

$$= \log(\beta_0) + X_i \log(\beta_1) + \log(\varepsilon_i) \qquad (16.6)$$

Equation (16.6) is a linear model you can estimate using the least-squares method, with $\log(Y_i)$ as the dependent variable and $X_i$ as the independent variable. This results in Equation (16.7).

### Exponential Trend Forecasting Equation

$$\log(\hat{Y}_i) = b_0 + b_1 X_i \qquad (16.7a)$$

where

$$b_0 = \text{estimate of } \log(\beta_0) \text{ and thus } 10^{b_0} = \hat{\beta}_0$$
$$b_1 = \text{estimate of } \log(\beta_1) \text{ and thus } 10^{b_1} = \hat{\beta}_1$$

therefore,

$$\hat{Y}_i = \hat{\beta}_0 \hat{\beta}_1^{X_i} \qquad (16.7b)$$

where

$(\hat{\beta}_1 - 1) \times 100\%$ is the estimated annual compound growth rate (in %)

Figure 16.10 shows an Excel results worksheet for an exponential trend model of revenues at the Wm. Wrigley Jr. Company. Figure 16.11 shows Minitab results

**FIGURE 16.10**

Microsoft Excel regression results worksheet for an exponential model to forecast Wm. Wrigley Jr. Company revenues

See Section E16.8 or P16.3 to create this.

| | A | B | C | D | E | F | G |
|---|---|---|---|---|---|---|---|
| 1 | Exponential Trend Model for Wm. Wrigley Jr. Company Revenue | | | | | | |
| 2 | | | | | | | |
| 3 | Regression Statistics | | | | | | |
| 4 | Multiple R | 0.9922 | | | | | |
| 5 | R Square | 0.9845 | | | | | |
| 6 | Adjusted R Square | 0.9838 | | | | | |
| 7 | Standard Error | 0.0331 | | | | | |
| 8 | Observations | 23 | | | | | |
| 9 | | | | | | | |
| 10 | ANOVA | | | | | | |
| 11 | | df | SS | MS | F | Significance F | |
| 12 | Regression | 1 | 1.4626 | 1.4626 | 1333.0690 | 0.0000 | |
| 13 | Residual | 21 | 0.0230 | 0.0011 | | | |
| 14 | Total | 22 | 1.4856 | | | | |
| 15 | | | | | | | |
| 16 | | Coefficients | Standard Error | t Stat | P-value | Lower 95% | Upper 95% |
| 17 | Intercept | 2.7893 | 0.0134 | 208.5522 | 0.0000 | 2.7615 | 2.8171 |
| 18 | Coded Year | 0.0380 | 0.0010 | 36.5112 | 0.0000 | 0.0359 | 0.0402 |

**FIGURE 16.11**

Minitab results for an exponential regression model to forecast revenues for the Wm. Wrigley Jr. Company

*See Section M16.3 to create this.*

```
The regression equation is
Log(Revenue) = 2.79 + 0.0380 Coded Year


Predictor        Coef    SE Coef        T       P
Constant      2.78930    0.01337   208.55   0.000
Coded Year   0.038016   0.001041    36.51   0.000


S = 0.0331230    R-Sq = 98.4%    R-Sq(adj) = 98.4%


Analysis of Variance

Source          DF        SS       MS        F       P
Regression       1    1.4626   1.4626  1333.07   0.000
Residual Error  21    0.0230   0.0011
Total           22    1.4856
```

Using Equation (16.7a) and the results from Figure 16.10 or 16.11,

$$\log(\hat{Y}_i) = 2.7893 + 0.0380 X_i$$

where year coded zero is 1984.

You compute the values for $\hat{\beta}_0$ and $\hat{\beta}_1$ by taking the antilog of the regression coefficients ($b_0$ and $b_1$):

$$\hat{\beta}_0 = \text{antilog } b_0 = \text{antilog}(2.7893) = 10^{2.7893} = 615.602$$

$$\hat{\beta}_1 = \text{antilog } b_1 = \text{antilog}(0.0380) = 10^{0.0380} = 1.0914$$

Thus, using Equation (16.7b), the exponential trend forecasting equation is

$$\hat{Y}_i = (615.602)(1.0914)^{X_i}$$

where year coded zero is 1984.

The $Y$ intercept, $\hat{\beta}_0 = 615.602$ millions of dollars, is the revenue forecast for the base year 1984. The value $(\hat{\beta}_1 - 1) \times 100\% = 9.14\%$ is the annual compound growth rate in revenues at the Wm. Wrigley Jr. Company.

For forecasting purposes, you substitute the appropriate coded $X$ values into either Equation (16.7a) or Equation (16.7b). For example, to forecast revenues for 2007 (i.e., $X_{24} = 23$) using Equation (16.7a),

$$\log(\hat{Y}_i) = 2.7893 + 0.0380(23) = 3.6633$$

$$\hat{Y}_i = \text{antilog}(3.6633) = 10^{3.6633} = 4,605.7461 \text{ millions of dollars}$$

Figure 16.12 plots the exponential trend forecasting equation, along with the time-series data. The adjusted $r^2$ for the exponential trend model (0.9838) is higher than the adjusted $r^2$ for the linear trend model (0.8852) and the quadratic model (0.9596).

**FIGURE 16.12**

Microsoft Excel plot to fit an exponential trend forecasting equation for the Wm. Wrigley Jr. Company revenues

*See Section E16.8 or P16.3 and Section E16.9 to create this. (Minitab users, see Section M16.3 to create an equivalent chart.)*

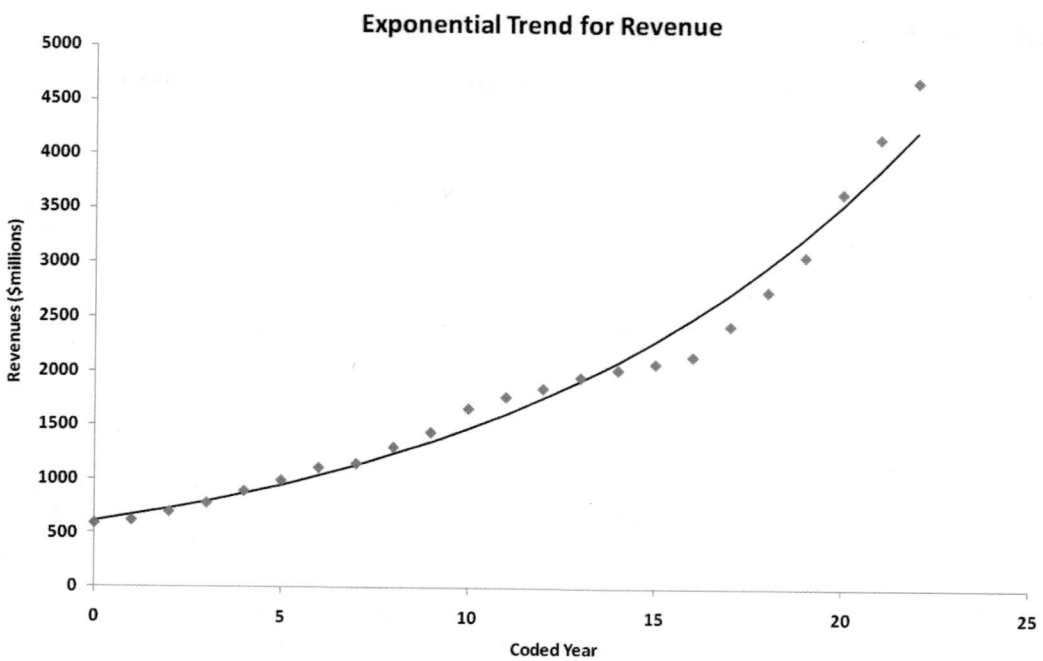

## Model Selection Using First, Second, and Percentage Differences

You have used the linear, quadratic, and exponential models to forecast revenues for the Wm. Wrigley Jr. Company. How can you determine which of these models is the most appropriate model? In addition to visually inspecting time-series plots and comparing adjusted $r^2$ values, you can compute and examine first, second, and percentage differences. The identifying features of linear, quadratic, and exponential trend models are as follows:

- If a linear trend model provides a perfect fit to a time series, then the first differences are constant. Thus, the differences between consecutive values in the series are the same throughout:

$$(Y_2 - Y_1) = (Y_3 - Y_2) = \cdots = (Y_n - Y_{n-1})$$

- If a quadratic trend model provides a perfect fit to a time series, then the second differences are constant. Thus,

$$[(Y_3 - Y_2) - (Y_2 - Y_1)] = [(Y_4 - Y_3) - (Y_3 - Y_2)] = \cdots = [(Y_n - Y_{n-1}) - (Y_{n-1} - Y_{n-2})]$$

- If an exponential trend model provides a perfect fit to a time series, then the percentage differences between consecutive values are constant. Thus,

$$\frac{Y_2 - Y_1}{Y_1} \times 100\% = \frac{Y_3 - Y_2}{Y_2} \times 100\% = \cdots = \frac{Y_n - Y_{n-1}}{Y_{n-1}} \times 100\%$$

Although you should not expect a perfectly fitting model for any particular set of time-series data, you can consider the first differences, second differences, and percentage differences for a given series as guides in choosing an appropriate model. Examples 16.2, 16.3, and 16.4 illustrate applications of linear, quadratic, and exponential trend models having perfect (or nearly perfect) fits to their respective data sets.

**EXAMPLE 16.2**  A LINEAR TREND MODEL WITH A PERFECT FIT

The following time series represents the number of passengers per year (in millions) on ABC Airlines:

| | \multicolumn{10}{c}{Year} |
|---|---|
| | 1998 | 1999 | 2000 | 2001 | 2002 | 2003 | 2004 | 2005 | 2006 | 2007 |
| **Passengers** | 30.0 | 33.0 | 36.0 | 39.0 | 42.0 | 45.0 | 48.0 | 51.0 | 54.0 | 57.0 |

Using first differences, show that the linear trend model provides a perfect fit to these data.

**SOLUTION** The following table shows the solution:

| | \multicolumn{10}{c}{Year} |
|---|---|
| | 1998 | 1999 | 2000 | 2001 | 2002 | 2003 | 2004 | 2005 | 2006 | 2007 |
| **Passengers** | 30.0 | 33.0 | 36.0 | 39.0 | 42.0 | 45.0 | 48.0 | 51.0 | 54.0 | 57.0 |
| **First differences** | | 3.0 | 3.0 | 3.0 | 3.0 | 3.0 | 3.0 | 3.0 | 3.0 | 3.0 |

The differences between consecutive values in the series are the same throughout. Thus, ABC Airlines is exhibiting a linear growth pattern. The number of passengers increases by 3 million per year.

**EXAMPLE 16.3**  A QUADRATIC TREND MODEL WITH A PERFECT FIT

The following time series represents the number of passengers per year (in millions) on XYZ Airlines:

| | \multicolumn{10}{c}{Year} |
|---|---|
| | 1998 | 1999 | 2000 | 2001 | 2002 | 2003 | 2004 | 2005 | 2006 | 2007 |
| **Passengers** | 30.0 | 31.0 | 33.5 | 37.5 | 43.0 | 50.0 | 58.5 | 68.5 | 80.0 | 93.0 |

Using second differences, show that the quadratic trend model provides a perfect fit to these data.

**SOLUTION** The following table shows the solution:

| | \multicolumn{10}{c}{Year} |
|---|---|
| | 1998 | 1999 | 2000 | 2001 | 2002 | 2003 | 2004 | 2005 | 2006 | 2007 |
| **Passengers** | 30.0 | 31.0 | 33.5 | 37.5 | 43.0 | 50.0 | 58.5 | 68.5 | 80.0 | 93.0 |
| **First differences** | | 1.0 | 2.5 | 4.0 | 5.5 | 7.0 | 8.5 | 10.0 | 11.5 | 13.0 |
| **Second differences** | | | 1.5 | 1.5 | 1.5 | 1.5 | 1.5 | 1.5 | 1.5 | 1.5 |

The second differences between consecutive pairs of values in the series are the same throughout. Thus, XYZ airlines is exhibiting a quadratic growth pattern. Its rate of growth is accelerating over time.

**EXAMPLE 16.4**  AN EXPONENTIAL TREND MODEL WITH A PERFECT FIT

The following time series represents the number of passengers per year (in millions) for EXP Airlines:

| | \multicolumn{10}{c}{Year} |
|---|---|
| | 1998 | 1999 | 2000 | 2001 | 2002 | 2003 | 2004 | 2005 | 2006 | 2007 |
| **Passengers** | 30.0 | 31.5 | 33.1 | 34.8 | 36.5 | 38.3 | 40.2 | 42.2 | 44.3 | 46.5 |

Using percentage differences, show that the exponential trend model provides almost a perfect fit to these data.

**SOLUTION**  The following table shows the solution:

| | | | | | Year | | | | | |
|---|---|---|---|---|---|---|---|---|---|---|
| | 1998 | 1999 | 2000 | 2001 | 2002 | 2003 | 2004 | 2005 | 2006 | 2007 |
| Passengers | 30.0 | 31.5 | 33.1 | 34.8 | 36.5 | 38.3 | 40.2 | 42.2 | 44.3 | 46.5 |
| First differences | | 1.5 | 1.6 | 1.7 | 1.7 | 1.8 | 1.9 | 2.0 | 2.1 | 2.2 |
| Percentage differences | | 5.0 | 5.1 | 5.1 | 4.9 | 4.9 | 5.0 | 5.0 | 5.0 | 5.0 |

The percentage differences between consecutive values in the series are approximately the same throughout. Thus, EXP Airlines is exhibiting an exponential growth pattern. Its rate of growth is approximately 5% per year.

Figure 16.13 presents the first, second, and percentage differences for the revenues data at Wm. Wrigley Jr. Company. Neither the first differences, second differences, nor percentage differences are constant across the series. Therefore, other models (including those considered in Section 16.5) may be more appropriate.

**FIGURE 16.13**

Comparing first, second, and percentage differences in revenues (in millions of dollars) for Wm. Wrigley Jr. Company

| | A | B | C | D | E |
|---|---|---|---|---|---|
| 1 | Year | Revenue | First Difference | Second Difference | Percentage Difference |
| 2 | 1984 | 591 | | | |
| 3 | 1985 | 620 | 29 | | 4.91% |
| 4 | 1986 | 699 | 79 | 50 | 12.74% |
| 5 | 1987 | 781 | 82 | 3 | 11.73% |
| 6 | 1988 | 891 | 110 | 28 | 14.08% |
| 7 | 1989 | 993 | 102 | -8 | 11.45% |
| 8 | 1990 | 1111 | 118 | 16 | 11.88% |
| 9 | 1991 | 1149 | 38 | -80 | 3.42% |
| 10 | 1992 | 1301 | 152 | 114 | 13.23% |
| 11 | 1993 | 1440 | 139 | -13 | 10.68% |
| 12 | 1994 | 1661 | 221 | 82 | 15.35% |
| 13 | 1995 | 1770 | 109 | -112 | 6.56% |
| 14 | 1996 | 1851 | 81 | -28 | 4.58% |
| 15 | 1997 | 1954 | 103 | 22 | 5.56% |
| 16 | 1998 | 2023 | 69 | -34 | 3.53% |
| 17 | 1999 | 2079 | 56 | -13 | 2.77% |
| 18 | 2000 | 2146 | 67 | 11 | 3.22% |
| 19 | 2001 | 2430 | 284 | 217 | 13.23% |
| 20 | 2002 | 2746 | 316 | 32 | 13.00% |
| 21 | 2003 | 3069 | 323 | 7 | 11.76% |
| 22 | 2004 | 3649 | 580 | 257 | 18.90% |
| 23 | 2005 | 4159 | 510 | -70 | 13.98% |
| 24 | 2006 | 4686 | 527 | 17 | 12.67% |

# PROBLEMS FOR SECTION 16.4

## Learning the Basics

**16.9** If using the method of least squares for fitting trends in an annual time series containing 25 consecutive yearly values,

**a.** what coded value do you assign to $X$ for the first year in the series?

**b.** what coded value do you assign to $X$ for the fifth year in the series?

**c.** what coded value do you assign to $X$ for the most recent recorded year in the series?

**d.** what coded value do you assign to $X$ if you want to project the trend and make a forecast five years beyond the last observed value?

**16.10** The linear trend forecasting equation for an annual time series containing 22 values (from 1986 to 2007) on total revenues (in millions of dollars) is

$$\hat{Y}_i = 4.0 + 1.5X_i$$

a. Interpret the $Y$ intercept, $b_0$.
b. Interpret the slope, $b_1$.
c. What is the fitted trend value for the fifth year?
d. What is the fitted trend value for the most recent year?
e. What is the projected trend forecast three years after the last value?

**16.11** The linear trend forecasting equation for an annual time series containing 42 values (from 1966 to 2007) on net sales (in billions of dollars) is

$$\hat{Y}_i = 1.2 + 0.5X_i$$

a. Interpret the $Y$ intercept, $b_0$.
b. Interpret the slope, $b_1$.
c. What is the fitted trend value for the tenth year?
d. What is the fitted trend value for the most recent year?
e. What is the projected trend forecast two years after the last value?

## Applying the Concepts

**16.12** The following data (in the file CPI-U) reflect the annual values of the CPI in the United States over the 42-year period 1965 through 2006, using 1982 through 1984 as the base period. This index measures the average change in prices over time in a fixed "market basket" of goods and services purchased by all urban consumers, including urban wage earners (i.e., clerical, professional, managerial, and technical workers; self-employed individuals; and short-term workers), unemployed individuals, and retirees.

| Year | CPI | Year | CPI | Year | CPI |
|------|-----|------|-----|------|-----|
| 1965 | 31.5 | 1979 | 72.6 | 1993 | 144.5 |
| 1966 | 32.4 | 1980 | 82.4 | 1994 | 148.2 |
| 1967 | 33.4 | 1981 | 90.9 | 1995 | 152.4 |
| 1968 | 34.8 | 1982 | 96.5 | 1996 | 156.9 |
| 1969 | 36.7 | 1983 | 99.6 | 1997 | 160.5 |
| 1970 | 38.8 | 1984 | 103.9 | 1998 | 163.0 |
| 1971 | 40.5 | 1985 | 107.6 | 1999 | 166.6 |
| 1972 | 41.8 | 1986 | 109.6 | 2000 | 172.2 |
| 1973 | 44.4 | 1987 | 113.6 | 2001 | 177.1 |
| 1974 | 49.3 | 1988 | 118.3 | 2002 | 179.9 |
| 1975 | 53.8 | 1989 | 124.0 | 2003 | 184.0 |
| 1976 | 56.9 | 1990 | 130.7 | 2004 | 188.9 |
| 1977 | 60.6 | 1991 | 136.2 | 2005 | 195.3 |
| 1978 | 65.2 | 1992 | 140.3 | 2006 | 201.6 |

Source: *Bureau of Labor Statistics, U.S. Department of Labor,* **www.bls.gov**.

a. Plot the data.
b. Describe the movement in this time series over the 42-year period.

**16.13** Gross domestic product (GDP) is a major indicator of a nation's overall economic activity. It consists of personal consumption expenditures, gross domestic investment, net exports of goods and services, and government consumption expenditures. The GDP (in billions of current dollars) for the United States from 1980 to 2006 is in the data file GDP.

Source: *Bureau of Economic Analysis, U.S. Department of Commerce,* **www.bea.gov**.

a. Plot the data.
b. Compute a linear trend forecasting equation and plot the trend line.
c. What are your forecasts for 2007 and 2008?
d. What conclusions can you reach concerning the trend in GDP?

**16.14** The data in the file Fedreceipt represent federal receipts from 1978 through 2006, in billions of current dollars, from individual and corporate income tax, social insurance, excise tax, estate and gift tax, customs duties, and federal reserve deposits.

Source: *Tax Policy Center,* **www.taxpolicycenter.org**.

a. Plot the series of data.
b. Compute a linear trend forecasting equation and plot the trend line.
c. What are your forecasts of the federal receipts for 2007 and 2008?
d. What conclusions can you reach concerning the trend in federal receipts between 1978 and 2006?

**16.15** The data in the file Strategic represent the amount of oil, in billions of barrels, held in the U.S. strategic oil reserve, from 1981 through 2006.

Source: *Energy Information Administration, U.S. Department of Energy,* **www.eia.doe.gov**.

a. Plot the data.
b. Compute a linear trend forecasting equation and plot the trend line.
c. Compute a quadratic trend forecasting equation and plot the results.
d. Compute an exponential trend forecasting equation and plot the results.
e. Which model is the most appropriate?
f. Using the most appropriate model, forecast the number of barrels, in billions, for 2007. Check how accurate your forecast is by locating the true value for 2007 on the Internet or in your library.

 **16.16** The data in the file CocaCola represent the annual net operating revenues (in billions of current dollars) at Coca-Cola Company from 1975 through 2006.

Source: *Extracted from* Moody's Handbook of Common Stocks, 1980, 1989, 1999, *and* Mergent's Handbook of Common Stocks, 2005, *and the Coca-Cola Company,* **www.cocacola.com**.

**a.** Plot the data.

**b.** Compute a linear trend forecasting equation and plot the trend line.

**c.** Compute a quadratic trend forecasting equation and plot the results.

**d.** Compute an exponential trend forecasting equation and plot the results.

**e.** Using the models in (b) through (d), what are your annual trend forecasts of net operating revenues for 2007 and 2008?

**16.17** The data in the following table represent the closing values of the Dow Jones Industrial Average (DJIA) from 1979 through 2006 (see the file **DJIA**):

| Year | DJIA | Year | DJIA | Year | DJIA |
|------|------|------|------|------|------|
| 1979 | 838.7 | 1989 | 2,753.2 | 1998 | 9,181.4 |
| 1980 | 964.0 | 1990 | 2,633.7 | 1999 | 11,497.1 |
| 1981 | 875.0 | 1991 | 3,168.8 | 2000 | 10,788.0 |
| 1982 | 1,046.5 | 1992 | 3,301.1 | 2001 | 10,021.5 |
| 1983 | 1,258.6 | 1993 | 3,754.1 | 2002 | 8,341.6 |
| 1984 | 1,211.6 | 1994 | 3,834.4 | 2003 | 10,453.9 |
| 1985 | 1,546.7 | 1995 | 5,117.1 | 2004 | 10,788.0 |
| 1986 | 1,896.0 | 1996 | 6,448.3 | 2005 | 10,717.5 |
| 1987 | 1,938.8 | 1997 | 7,908.3 | 2006 | 12,463.2 |
| 1988 | 2,168.6 | | | | |

Source: *Extracted from* **finance.yahoo.com**.

**a.** Plot the data.

**b.** Compute a linear trend forecasting equation and plot the trend line.

**c.** Compute a quadratic trend forecasting equation and plot the results.

**d.** Compute an exponential trend forecasting equation and plot the results.

**e.** Which model is the most appropriate?

**f.** Using the most appropriate model, forecast the closing value for the DJIA in 2007. Check the accuracy of your forecast on the Internet or at your library and try to explain the difference between the forecast and the actual value.

**✓SELF Test 16.18** General Electric (GE) is one of the world's largest companies; it develops, manufactures, and markets a wide range of products, including medical diagnostic imaging devices, jet engines, lighting products, and chemicals. Through its affiliate NBC Universal, GE produces and delivers network television and motion pictures. The data in the file **GE** represent the January 1 stock price for the 21-year period from 1987 to 2007.
Source: *Extracted from* **finance.yahoo.com**.

**a.** Plot the data.

**b.** Compute a linear trend forecasting equation and plot the trend line.

**c.** Compute a quadratic trend forecasting equation and plot the results.

**d.** Compute an exponential trend forecasting equation and plot the results.

**e.** Which model is the most appropriate?

**f.** Using the most appropriate model, forecast the stock price for January 1, 2008.

**16.19** Although you should not expect a perfectly fitting model for any time-series data, you can consider the first differences, second differences, and percentage differences for a given series as guides in choosing an appropriate model. For this problem, use each of the time series presented in the following table and stored in the file **Tsmodel1**:

| | Year | | | | |
|---|---|---|---|---|---|
| | 1997 | 1998 | 1999 | 2000 | 2001 |
| Time series I | 10.0 | 15.1 | 24.0 | 36.7 | 53.8 |
| Time series II | 30.0 | 33.1 | 36.4 | 39.9 | 43.9 |
| Time series III | 60.0 | 67.9 | 76.1 | 84.0 | 92.2 |

| | Year | | | | |
|---|---|---|---|---|---|
| | 2002 | 2003 | 2004 | 2005 | 2006 |
| Time series I | 74.8 | 100.0 | 129.2 | 162.4 | 199.0 |
| Time series II | 48.2 | 53.2 | 58.2 | 64.5 | 70.7 |
| Time series III | 100.0 | 108.0 | 115.8 | 124.1 | 132.0 |

**a.** Determine the most appropriate model.

**b.** Compute the forecasting equation.

**c.** Forecast the value for 2007.

**16.20** A time-series plot often helps you determine the appropriate model to use. For this problem, use each of the time series presented in the following table and stored in the file **Tsmodel2.xls**:

| | Year | | | | |
|---|---|---|---|---|---|
| | 1997 | 1998 | 1999 | 2000 | 2001 |
| Time series I | 100.0 | 115.2 | 130.1 | 144.9 | 160.0 |
| Time series II | 100.0 | 115.2 | 131.7 | 150.8 | 174.1 |

| | Year | | | | |
|---|---|---|---|---|---|
| | 2002 | 2003 | 2004 | 2005 | 2006 |
| Time series I | 175.0 | 189.8 | 204.9 | 219.8 | 235.0 |
| Time series II | 200.0 | 230.8 | 266.1 | 305.5 | 351.8 |

**a.** Plot the observed data ($Y$) over time ($X$) and plot the logarithm of the observed data ($\log Y$) over time ($X$) to determine whether a linear trend model or an exponential trend model is more appropriate. (*Hint:* If the plot of

log $Y$ versus $X$ appears to be linear, an exponential trend model provides an appropriate fit.)
b. Compute the appropriate forecasting equation.
c. Forecast the value for 2007.

**16.21** The data in the file `Oysters` represent the bushels of oysters harvested in Chesapeake Bay for 1990–1991 through 2003–2004 (*Source:* Maryland Department of Natural Resources).
a. Compare the first differences, second differences, and percentage differences to determine the most appropriate model.
b. Compute the appropriate forecasting equation.
c. Forecast the number of bushels harvested for 2004–2005 and 2005–2006.
d. What would you say about your forecasting model if you knew that in 1980–1981 there were 2,532,321 bushels harvested?

**SELF**
**Test** **16.22** Bed Bath & Beyond Inc. is a nationwide chain of retail stores that sell a wide assortment of merchandise, principally including domestics merchandise and home furnishings, as well as food, giftware, and health and beauty care items. The following data (stored in the file `BedBath`) show the number of stores open at the end of the fiscal year from 1993 to 2007:

| Year | Stores Open | Year | Stores Open |
|------|-------------|------|-------------|
| 1993 | 38 | 2001 | 311 |
| 1994 | 45 | 2002 | 396 |
| 1995 | 61 | 2003 | 519 |
| 1996 | 80 | 2004 | 629 |
| 1997 | 108 | 2005 | 721 |
| 1998 | 141 | 2006 | 809 |
| 1999 | 186 | 2007 | 815 |
| 2000 | 241 | | |

Source: *Extracted from* Bed Bath & Beyond Annual Report, 2005, May 24, 2006, June 11, 2007.

a. Plot the data.
b. Compute a linear trend forecasting equation and plot the results.
c. Compute a quadratic trend forecasting equation and plot the results.
d. Compute an exponential trend forecasting equation and plot the results.
e. Using the forecasting equations in (b) through (d), what are your annual forecasts of the number of stores open for 2008 and 2009.
f. How can you explain the differences in the three forecasts in (e)? What forecast do you think you should use? Why?

## 16.5 AUTOREGRESSIVE MODELING FOR TREND FITTING AND FORECASTING

[3]The exponential smoothing model described in Section 16.3 and the autoregressive models described in this section are special cases of autoregressive integrated moving average (ARIMA) models developed by Box and Jenkins (reference 2).

Frequently, the values of a time series are highly correlated with the values that precede and succeed them. This type of correlation is called autocorrelation. **Autoregressive modeling**[3] is a technique used to forecast time series with autocorrelation. A **first-order autocorrelation** refers to the association between consecutive values in a time series. A **second-order autocorrelation** refers to the relationship between values that are two periods apart. A ***p*th-order autocorrelation** refers to the correlation between values in a time series that are *p* periods apart. You can take into account the autocorrelation in data by using autoregressive modeling methods.

Equations (16.8), (16.9), and (16.10) define first-order, second-order, and *p*th-order autoregressive models.

First-Order Autoregressive Model

$$Y_i = A_0 + A_1 Y_{i-1} + \delta_i \qquad (16.8)$$

Second-Order Autoregressive Model

$$Y_i = A_0 + A_1 Y_{i-1} + A_2 Y_{i-2} + \delta_i \qquad (16.9)$$

### pth-Order Autoregressive Models

$$Y_i = A_0 + A_1 Y_{i-1} + A_2 Y_{i-2} + \cdots + A_p Y_{i-p} + \delta_i \qquad \textbf{(16.10)}$$

where

$$Y_i = \text{the observed value of the series at time } i$$

$$Y_{i-1} = \text{the observed value of the series at time } i - 1$$

$$Y_{i-2} = \text{the observed value of the series at time } i - 2$$

$$Y_{i-p} = \text{the observed value of the series at time } i - p$$

$$A_0, A_1, A_2, \ldots, A_p = \text{autoregression parameters to be estimated from least-squares regression analysis}$$

$$\delta_i = \text{a nonautocorrelated random error component (with mean} = 0 \text{ and constant variance)}$$

The **first-order autoregressive model** [Equation (16.8)] is similar in form to the simple linear regression model [Equation (13.1) on page 575]. The **second-order autoregressive model** [Equation (16.9)] is similar to the multiple regression model with two independent variables [Equation (14.2) on page 638]. The *pth-order autoregressive model* [Equation (16.10)] is similar to the multiple regression model [Equation (14.1) on page 637]. In the regression models, the regression parameters are given by the symbols $\beta_0, \beta_1, \ldots, \beta_k$, with corresponding estimates denoted by $b_0, b_1, \ldots, b_k$. In the autoregressive models, the parameters are given by the symbols $A_0, A_1, \ldots, A_p$, with corresponding estimates denoted by $a_0, a_1, \ldots, a_p$.

Selecting an appropriate autoregressive model can be complicated. You must weigh the advantages that are due to simplicity against the concern of failing to take into account important autocorrelation in the data. You also must be concerned with selecting a higher-order model requiring the estimation of numerous, unnecessary parameters—especially if $n$, the number of values in the series, is small. The reason for this concern is that when computing an estimate of $A_p$, you lose $p$ out of the $n$ data values when comparing each data value with the data value $p$ periods prior.

Examples 16.5 and 16.6 illustrate this loss of data values.

---

**EXAMPLE 16.5**    COMPARISON SCHEMA FOR A FIRST-ORDER AUTOREGRESSIVE MODEL

Consider the following series of $n = 7$ consecutive annual values:

|  | \multicolumn{7}{c}{Year} |
|---|---|---|---|---|---|---|---|
|  | 1 | 2 | 3 | 4 | 5 | 6 | 7 |
| **Series** | 31 | 34 | 37 | 35 | 36 | 43 | 40 |

Show the comparisons needed for a first-order autoregressive model.

**SOLUTION**

| Year | First-Order Autoregressive Model |
|:---:|:---:|
| $i$ | $(Y_i \text{ vs. } Y_{i-1})$ |
| 1 | $31 \leftrightarrow \cdots$ |
| 2 | $34 \leftrightarrow 31$ |
| 3 | $37 \leftrightarrow 34$ |
| 4 | $35 \leftrightarrow 37$ |
| 5 | $36 \leftrightarrow 35$ |
| 6 | $43 \leftrightarrow 36$ |
| 7 | $40 \leftrightarrow 43$ |

Because there is no value recorded prior to $Y_1$, this value is lost for regression analysis. Therefore, the first-order autoregressive model is based on six pairs of values.

---

**EXAMPLE 16.6**  COMPARISON SCHEMA FOR A SECOND-ORDER AUTOREGRESSIVE MODEL

Consider the following series of $n = 7$ consecutive annual values:

| | Year | | | | | | |
|:---:|:---:|:---:|:---:|:---:|:---:|:---:|:---:|
| | 1 | 2 | 3 | 4 | 5 | 6 | 7 |
| **Series** | 31 | 34 | 37 | 35 | 36 | 43 | 40 |

Show the comparisons needed for a second-order autoregressive model.

**SOLUTION**

| Year | Second-Order Autoregressive Model |
|:---:|:---:|
| $i$ | $(Y_i \text{ vs. } Y_{i-1} \text{ and } Y_i \text{ vs. } Y_{i-2})$ |
| 1 | $31 \leftrightarrow \cdots \text{ and } 31 \leftrightarrow \cdots$ |
| 2 | $34 \leftrightarrow 31 \text{ and } 34 \leftrightarrow \cdots$ |
| 3 | $37 \leftrightarrow 34 \text{ and } 37 \leftrightarrow 31$ |
| 4 | $35 \leftrightarrow 37 \text{ and } 35 \leftrightarrow 34$ |
| 5 | $36 \leftrightarrow 35 \text{ and } 36 \leftrightarrow 37$ |
| 6 | $43 \leftrightarrow 36 \text{ and } 43 \leftrightarrow 35$ |
| 7 | $40 \leftrightarrow 43 \text{ and } 40 \leftrightarrow 36$ |

Because there is no value recorded prior to $Y_1$, two values are lost for regression analysis. Therefore, the second-order autoregressive model is based on five pairs of values.

---

After selecting a model and using the least-squares method to compute estimates of the parameters, you need to determine the appropriateness of the model. Either you can select a particular $p$th-order autoregressive model based on previous experiences with similar data or, as a starting point, you can choose a model with several parameters and then eliminate the higher-order parameters that do not significantly contribute to the model. In this latter approach, you use a $t$ test for the significance of $A_p$, the highest-order autoregressive parameter in the current model under consideration. The null and alternative hypotheses are

$$H_0: A_p = 0$$

$$H_1: A_p \neq 0$$

Equation (16.11) defines the test statistic.

### $t$ Test for Significance of the Highest-Order Autoregressive Parameter, $A_p$

$$t_{STAT} = \frac{a_p - A_p}{S_{a_p}}$$    **(16.11)**

where

$A_p$ = hypothesized value of the highest-order parameter, $A_p$, in the regression model

$a_p$ = the estimate of the highest-order parameter, $A_p$, in the autoregressive model

$S_{a_p}$ = the standard deviation of $a_p$

The $t_{STAT}$ test statistic follows a $t$ distribution with $n - 2p - 1$ degrees of freedom.[4]

[4]In addition to the degrees of freedom lost for each of the p population parameters you are estimating, p additional degrees of freedom are lost because there are p fewer comparisons to be made out of the original n values in the time series.

For a given level of significance $\alpha$, you reject the null hypothesis if the $t_{STAT}$ test statistic is greater than the upper-tail critical value from the $t$ distribution or if the $t_{STAT}$ test statistic is less than the lower-tail critical value from the $t$ distribution. Thus, the decision rule is

Reject $H_0$ if $t_{STAT} < -t_{\alpha/2}$ or if $t_{STAT} > t_{\alpha/2}$;

otherwise, do not reject $H_0$.

Figure 16.14 illustrates the decision rule and regions of rejection and nonrejection.

**FIGURE 16.14**

Rejection regions for a two-tail test for the significance of the highest-order autoregressive parameter, $A_p$

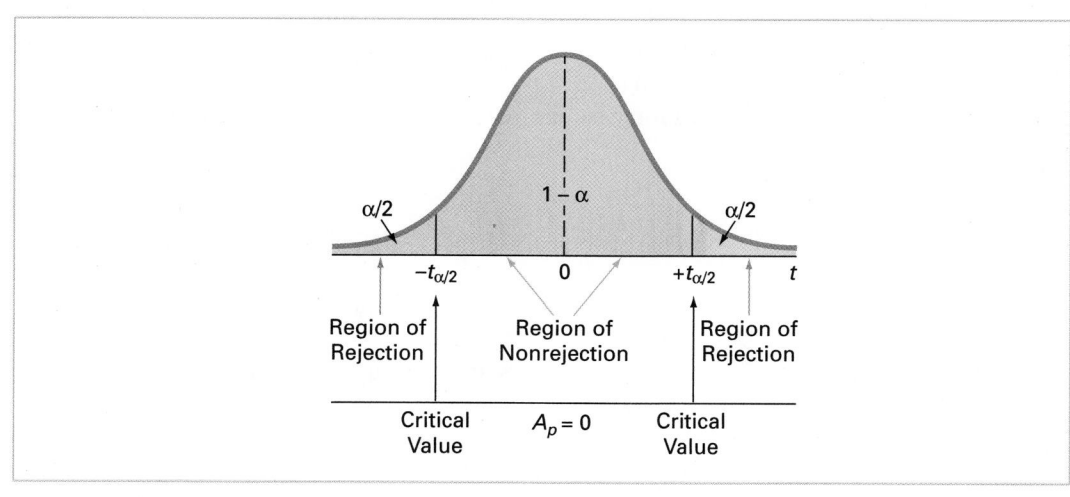

If you do not reject the null hypothesis that $A_p = 0$, you conclude that the selected model contains too many estimated parameters. You then discard the highest-order term and estimate an autoregressive model of order $p - 1$, using the least-squares method. You then repeat the test of the hypothesis that the new highest-order parameter is 0. This testing and modeling continues until you reject $H_0$. When this occurs, you know that the remaining highest-order parameter is significant, and you can use that model for forecasting purposes.

Equation (16.12) defines the fitted $p$th-order autoregressive equation.

---

**Fitted $p$th-Order Autoregressive Equation**

$$\hat{Y}_i = a_0 + a_1 Y_{i-1} + a_2 Y_{i-2} + \cdots + a_p Y_{i-p} \qquad (16.12)$$

where

$$\hat{Y}_i = \text{fitted values of the series at time } i$$

$$Y_{i-1} = \text{observed value of the series at time } i - 1$$

$$Y_{i-2} = \text{observed value of the series at time } i - 2$$

$$Y_{i-p} = \text{observed value of the series at time } i - p$$

$$a_0, a_1, a_2, \ldots, a_p = \text{regression estimates of the parameters } A_0, A_1, A_2, \ldots, A_p$$

---

You use Equation (16.13) to forecast $j$ years into the future from the current $n$th time period.

---

**$p$th-Order Autoregressive Forecasting Equation**

$$\hat{Y}_{n+j} = a_0 + a_1 \hat{Y}_{n+j-1} + a_2 \hat{Y}_{n+j-2} + \cdots + a_p \hat{Y}_{n+j-p} \qquad (16.13)$$

where

$$a_0, a_1, a_2, \ldots, a_p = \text{regression estimates of the parameters } A_0, A_1, A_2, \ldots, A_p$$

$$j = \text{number of years into the future}$$

$$\hat{Y}_{n+j-p} = \text{forecast of } Y_{n+j-p} \text{ from the current time period for } j - p > 0$$

$$\hat{Y}_{n+j-p} = \text{observed value for } Y_{n+j-p} \text{ for } j - p \leq 0$$

---

Thus, to make forecasts $j$ years into the future, using a third-order autoregressive model, you need only the most recent $p = 3$ values ($Y_n$, $Y_{n-1}$, and $Y_{n-2}$) and the regression estimates $a_0$, $a_1$, $a_2$, and $a_3$.

To forecast one year ahead, Equation (16.13) becomes

$$\hat{Y}_{n+1} = a_0 + a_1 Y_n + a_2 Y_{n-1} + a_3 Y_{n-2}$$

To forecast two years ahead, Equation (16.13) becomes

$$\hat{Y}_{n+2} = a_0 + a_1 \hat{Y}_{n+1} + a_2 Y_n + a_3 Y_{n-1}$$

To forecast three years ahead, Equation (16.13) becomes

$$\hat{Y}_{n+3} = a_0 + a_1 \hat{Y}_{n+2} + a_2 \hat{Y}_{n+1} + a_3 Y_n$$

and so on.

Autoregressive modeling is a powerful forecasting technique for time series that have auto-correlation. Although slightly more complicated than other methods, the following step-by-step approach should guide you through the analysis:

1. Choose a value for $p$, the highest-order parameter in the autoregressive model to be evaluated, realizing that the $t$ test for significance is based on $n - 2p - 1$ degrees of freedom.
2. Form a series of $p$ "lagged predictor" variables such that the first variable lags by one time period, the second variable lags by two time periods, and so on and the last predictor variable lags by $p$ time periods (see Figure 16.15).
3. Use Microsoft Excel or Minitab to perform a least-squares analysis of the multiple regression model containing all $p$ lagged predictor variables.
4. Test for the significance of $A_p$, the highest-order autoregressive parameter in the model.
   a. If you do not reject the null hypothesis, discard the $p$th variable and repeat steps 3 and 4. The test for the significance of the new highest-order parameter is based on a $t$ distribution whose degrees of freedom are revised to correspond with the new number of predictors.
   b. If you reject the null hypothesis, select the autoregressive model with all $p$ predictors for fitting [see Equation (16.12)] and forecasting [see Equation (16.13)].

To demonstrate the autoregressive modeling approach, return to the time series concerning the revenues for the Wm. Wrigley Jr. Company over the 23-year period 1984 through 2006. Figure 16.15 displays the revenues and the setup for the first-order, second-order, and third-order autoregressive models. All the columns in this table are needed for fitting the third-order autoregressive model. The last column is omitted when fitting second-order autoregressive models, and the last two columns are omitted when fitting first-order autoregressive models. Thus, out of $n = 23$ values, $p = 1, 2,$ or $3$ values out of $n = 23$ are lost in the comparisons needed for developing the first-order, second-order, and third-order autoregressive models.

**FIGURE 16.15**

Microsoft Excel worksheet for developing first-order, second-order, and third-order autoregressive models on revenues for the Wm. Wrigley Jr. Company (1984–2006)

*See Section E16.10 to create this. (Minitab users, see Section M16.4 to create this.)*

| | A | B | C | D | E |
|---|---|---|---|---|---|
| 1 | Year | Revenue | Lag1 | Lag2 | Lag3 |
| 2 | 1984 | 591 | #N/A | #N/A | #N/A |
| 3 | 1985 | 620 | 591 | #N/A | #N/A |
| 4 | 1986 | 699 | 620 | 591 | #N/A |
| 5 | 1987 | 781 | 699 | 620 | 591 |
| 6 | 1988 | 891 | 781 | 699 | 620 |
| 7 | 1989 | 993 | 891 | 781 | 699 |
| 8 | 1990 | 1111 | 993 | 891 | 781 |
| 9 | 1991 | 1149 | 1111 | 993 | 891 |
| 10 | 1992 | 1301 | 1149 | 1111 | 993 |
| 11 | 1993 | 1440 | 1301 | 1149 | 1111 |
| 12 | 1994 | 1661 | 1440 | 1301 | 1149 |
| 13 | 1995 | 1770 | 1661 | 1440 | 1301 |
| 14 | 1996 | 1851 | 1770 | 1661 | 1440 |
| 15 | 1997 | 1954 | 1851 | 1770 | 1661 |
| 16 | 1998 | 2023 | 1954 | 1851 | 1770 |
| 17 | 1999 | 2079 | 2023 | 1954 | 1851 |
| 18 | 2000 | 2146 | 2079 | 2023 | 1954 |
| 19 | 2001 | 2430 | 2146 | 2079 | 2023 |
| 20 | 2002 | 2746 | 2430 | 2146 | 2079 |
| 21 | 2003 | 3069 | 2746 | 2430 | 2146 |
| 22 | 2004 | 3649 | 3069 | 2746 | 2430 |
| 23 | 2005 | 4159 | 3649 | 3069 | 2746 |
| 24 | 2006 | 4686 | 4159 | 3649 | 3069 |

Selecting an autoregressive model that best fits the annual time series begins with the third-order autoregressive model shown in Figure 16.16 using Microsoft Excel and in Figure 16.17 using Minitab.

**FIGURE 16.16**

Microsoft Excel regression results worksheet for the third-order autoregressive model for the Wm. Wrigley Jr. Company revenues

*See Section E16.12 or P16.5 to create this.*

| | A | B | C | D | E | F | G |
|---|---|---|---|---|---|---|---|
| 1 | **Third-Order Autoregressive Model** | | | | | | |
| 2 | | | | | | | |
| 3 | *Regression Statistics* | | | | | | |
| 4 | Multiple R | 0.9972 | | | | | |
| 5 | R Square | 0.9945 | | | | | |
| 6 | Adjusted R Square | 0.9934 | | | | | |
| 7 | Standard Error | 88.3643 | | | | | |
| 8 | Observations | 20 | | | | | |
| 9 | | | | | | | |
| 10 | ANOVA | | | | | | |
| 11 | | *df* | *SS* | *MS* | *F* | *Significance F* | |
| 12 | Regression | 3 | 22442745.0177 | 7480915.0059 | 958.0788 | 0.0000 | |
| 13 | Residual | 16 | 124931.9323 | 7808.2458 | | | |
| 14 | Total | 19 | 22567676.9500 | | | | |
| 15 | | | | | | | |
| 16 | | *Coefficients* | *Standard Error* | *t Stat* | *P-value* | *Lower 95%* | *Upper 95%* |
| 17 | Intercept | -32.1256 | 49.8581 | -0.6443 | 0.5285 | -137.8200 | 73.5687 |
| 18 | X Variable 1 | 1.6079 | 0.2471 | 6.5082 | 0.0000 | 1.0842 | 2.1317 |
| 19 | X Variable 2 | -0.4466 | 0.4638 | -0.9629 | 0.3499 | -1.4298 | 0.5366 |
| 20 | X Variable 3 | -0.0979 | 0.2850 | -0.3435 | 0.7357 | -0.7021 | 0.5063 |

**FIGURE 16.17**

Minitab results for the third-order autoregressive model for the Wm. Wrigley Jr. Company revenues data

*See Section M16.4 to create this.*

```
The regression equation is
Revenue = - 32.1 + 1.61 Lag1 - 0.447 Lag2 - 0.098 Lag3


20 cases used, 3 cases contain missing values


Predictor      Coef   SE Coef      T      P
Constant     -32.13     49.86   -0.64  0.528
Lag1          1.6079   0.2471    6.51  0.000
Lag2         -0.4466   0.4638   -0.96  0.350
Lag3         -0.0979   0.2850   -0.34  0.736


S = 88.3643   R-Sq = 99.4%   R-Sq(adj) = 99.3%


Analysis of Variance

Source          DF        SS        MS       F      P
Regression       3  22442745   7480915  958.08  0.000
Residual Error  16    124932      7808
Total           19  22567677
```

From Figure 16.16 or 16.17, the fitted third-order autoregressive equation is

$$\hat{Y}_i = -32.1256 + 1.6079Y_{i-1} - 0.4466Y_{i-2} - 0.0979Y_{i-3}$$

where the first year in the series is 1987.

Next, you test for the significance of $A_3$, the highest-order parameter. The highest-order parameter estimate, $a_3$, for the fitted third-order autoregressive model is $-0.0979$, with a standard error of 0.2850.

To test the null hypothesis:

$$H_0: A_3 = 0$$

against the alternative hypothesis:

$$H_1: A_3 \neq 0$$

using Equation (16.11) on page 753 and the Microsoft Excel results given in Figure 16.16 or the Minitab results given in Figure 16.17,

$$t_{STAT} = \frac{a_3 - A_3}{S_{a_3}} = \frac{-0.0979 - 0}{0.2850} = -0.3435$$

Using a 0.05 level of significance, the two-tail $t$ test with 16 degrees of freedom has critical values of $\pm 2.1199$. Because $-2.1199 < t_{STAT} = -0.3435 < +2.1199$ or because the $p$-value $= 0.7357 > 0.05$, you do not reject $H_0$. You conclude that the third-order parameter of the autoregressive model is not significant and can be deleted.

Using Microsoft Excel or Minitab once again (see Figures 16.18 or 16.19), you fit a second-order autoregressive model.

**FIGURE 16.18**

Microsoft Excel regression results worksheet for the second-order autoregressive model for the Wm. Wrigley Jr. Company revenues data

*See Section E16.12 or P16.5 to create this.*

| | A | B | C | D | E | F | G |
|---|---|---|---|---|---|---|---|
| 1 | Second-Order Autoregressive Model | | | | | | |
| 2 | | | | | | | |
| 3 | Regression Statistics | | | | | | |
| 4 | Multiple R | 0.9974 | | | | | |
| 5 | R Square | 0.9947 | | | | | |
| 6 | Adjusted R Square | 0.9942 | | | | | |
| 7 | Standard Error | 84.4696 | | | | | |
| 8 | Observations | 21 | | | | | |
| 9 | | | | | | | |
| 10 | ANOVA | | | | | | |
| 11 | | df | SS | MS | F | Significance F | |
| 12 | Regression | 2 | 24293797.9421 | 12146898.9710 | 1702.4113 | 0.0000 | |
| 13 | Residual | 18 | 128432.0579 | 7135.1143 | | | |
| 14 | Total | 20 | 24422230.0000 | | | | |
| 15 | | | | | | | |
| 16 | | Coefficients | Standard Error | t Stat | P-value | Lower 95% | Upper 95% |
| 17 | Intercept | -25.6968 | 43.8647 | -0.5858 | 0.5653 | -117.8531 | 66.4596 |
| 18 | X Variable 1 | 1.6555 | 0.2020 | 8.1971 | 0.0000 | 1.2312 | 2.0798 |
| 19 | X Variable 2 | -0.5906 | 0.2318 | -2.5485 | 0.0202 | -1.0776 | -0.1037 |

**FIGURE 16.19**

Minitab results for the second-order autoregressive model for the Wm. Wrigley Jr. Company revenues data

*See Section M16.4 to create this.*

```
The regression equation is
Revenue = - 25.7 + 1.66 Lag1 - 0.591 Lag2


21 cases used, 2 cases contain missing values


Predictor      Coef   SE Coef      T      P
Constant     -25.70     43.86  -0.59  0.565
Lag1         1.6555    0.2020   8.20  0.000
Lag2        -0.5906    0.2318  -2.55  0.020


S = 84.4696   R-Sq = 99.5%   R-Sq(adj) = 99.4%


Analysis of Variance

Source           DF        SS        MS       F      P
Regression        2  24293798  12146899  1702.41  0.000
Residual Error   18    128432      7135
Total            20  24422230
```

The fitted second-order autoregressive equation is

$$\hat{Y}_i = -25.6968 + 1.6555 Y_{i-1} - 0.5906 Y_{i-2}$$

where the first year of the series is 1986.

From Figure 16.18 or 16.19, the highest-order parameter estimate is $a_2 = -0.5906$, with a standard error of 0.2318.

To test the null hypothesis:

$$H_0: A_2 = 0$$

against the alternative hypothesis:

$$H_1: A_2 \neq 0$$

using Equation (16.11) on page 753,

$$t_{STAT} = \frac{a_2 - A_2}{S_{a_2}} = \frac{-0.5906 - 0}{0.2318} = -2.5485$$

Using the 0.05 level of significance, the two-tail $t$ test with 18 degrees of freedom has critical values of $\pm 2.1009$. Because $t_{STAT} = -2.5485 < -2.1009$ or because the $p$-value $= 0.0202 < 0.05$, you reject $H_0$. You conclude that the second-order parameter of the autoregressive model is significant and should be included in the model.

The model-building approach has led to the selection of the second-order autoregressive model as the most appropriate for the given data. Using the estimates $a_0 = -25.6968$, $a_1 = 1.6555$, and $a_2 = -0.5906$, as well as the two most recent data values $Y_{23} = 4,686$ and $Y_{22} = 4,159$, the forecasts of revenues at the Wm. Wrigley Jr. Company for 2007 and 2008 from Equation (16.13) on page 754 are

$$\hat{Y}_{n+j} = -25.6968 + 1.6555\hat{Y}_{n+j-1} - 0.5906\hat{Y}_{n+j-2}$$

Therefore,

2007: 1 year ahead, $\hat{Y}_{24} = -25.6968 + 1.6555(4,686) - 0.5906(4,159) = 5,275.6708$ millions of dollars

2008: 2 years ahead, $\hat{Y}_{25} = -25.6968 + 1.6555(5,275.6708) - 0.5906(4,686) = 5,940.6246$ millions of dollars

Figure 16.20 displays the actual and predicted $Y$ values from the second-order autoregressive model.

**FIGURE 16.20**

Microsoft Excel plot of actual and predicted revenues from a second-order autoregressive model at the Wm. Wrigley Jr. Company

*See Section E16.1 or P16.5 to create this. (Minitab users, see Section 16.4 to create an equivalent chart.)*

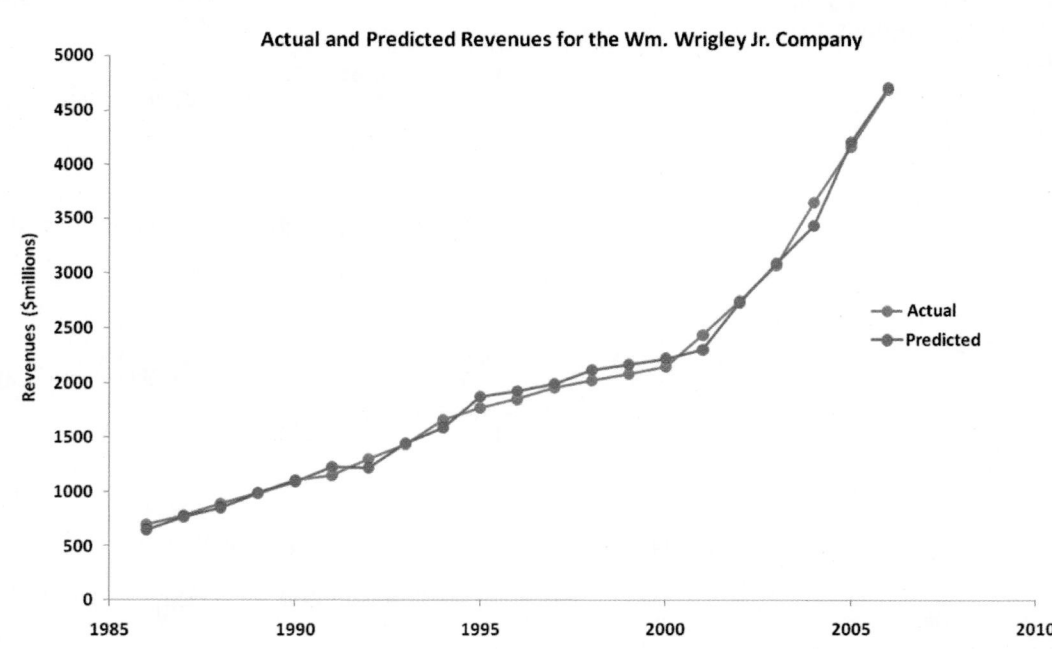

# PROBLEMS FOR SECTION 16.5

## Learning the Basics

**16.23** You are given an annual time series with 40 consecutive values and asked to fit a fifth-order autoregressive model.
a. How many comparisons are lost in the development of the autoregressive model?
b. How many parameters do you need to estimate?
c. Which of the original 40 values do you need for forecasting?
d. State the model.
e. Write an equation to indicate how you would forecast $j$ years into the future.

**16.24** A third-order autoregressive model is fitted to an annual time series with 17 values and has the following estimated parameters and standard errors:

$$a_0 = 4.50 \quad a_1 = 1.80 \quad a_2 = 0.80 \quad a_3 = 0.24$$
$$S_{a_1} = 0.50 \quad S_{a_2} = 0.30 \quad S_{a_3} = 0.10$$

At the 0.05 level of significance, test the appropriateness of the fitted model.

**16.25** Refer to Problem 16.24. The three most recent values are

$$Y_{15} = 23 \quad Y_{16} = 28 \quad Y_{17} = 34$$

Forecast the values for the next year and the following year.

**16.26** Refer to Problem 16.24. Suppose, when testing for the appropriateness of the fitted model, the standard errors are

$$S_{a_1} = 0.45 \quad S_{a_2} = 0.35 \quad S_{a_3} = 0.15$$

a. What conclusions can you make?
b. Discuss how to proceed if forecasting is still your main objective.

## Applying the Concepts

**16.27** Refer to the data given in Problem 16.15 on page 748 that represent the amount of oil (in billions of barrels) held in the U.S. strategic reserve from 1981 through 2006 (see the file Strategic).
a. Fit a third-order autoregressive model to the amount of oil and test for the significance of the third-order autoregressive parameter. (Use $\alpha = 0.05$.)
b. If necessary, fit a second-order autoregressive model to the amount of oil and test for the significance of the second-order autoregressive parameter. (Use $\alpha = 0.05$.)

c. If necessary, fit a first-order autoregressive model to the amount of oil and test for the significance of the first-order autoregressive parameter. (Use $\alpha = 0.05$.)
d. If appropriate, forecast the barrels held in 2007.

**16.28** **SELF Test** Refer to the data introduced in Problem 16.16 on page 748 (and stored in the file CocaCola) concerning annual net operating revenues (in billions of current dollars) at Coca-Cola Company over the 32-year period 1975 through 2006.
a. Fit a third-order autoregressive model to the annual net operating revenues and test for the significance of the third-order autoregressive parameter. (Use $\alpha = 0.05$.)
b. If necessary, fit a second-order autoregressive model to the annual net operating revenues and test for the significance of the second-order autoregressive parameter. (Use $\alpha = 0.05$.)
c. If necessary, fit a first-order autoregressive model to the annual net operating revenues and test for the significance of the first-order autoregressive parameter. (Use $\alpha = 0.05$.)
d. If appropriate, forecast net operating revenues for 2007 and 2008.

**16.29** Refer to the data given in Problem 16.17 on page 749 that represent the closing values of the DJIA from 1979 to 2006 (stored in the file DJIA).
a. Fit a third-order autoregressive model to the DJIA and test for the significance of the third-order autoregressive parameter. (Use $\alpha = 0.05$.)
b. If necessary, fit a second-order autoregressive model to the DJIA and test for the significance of the second-order autoregressive parameter. (Use $\alpha = 0.05$.)
c. If necessary, fit a first-order autoregressive model to the DJIA and test for the significance of the first-order autoregressive parameter. (Use $\alpha = 0.05$.)
d. If appropriate, forecast the DJIA for 2007 and 2008.

**16.30** Refer to the data given in Problem 16.18 on page 749 (stored in the file GE) that represent the stock prices for GE from 1987 through 2007.
a. Fit a third-order autoregressive model to the stock price and test for the significance of the third-order autoregressive parameter. (Use $\alpha = 0.05$.)
b. If necessary, fit a second-order autoregressive model to the stock price and test for the significance of the second-order autoregressive parameter. (Use $\alpha = 0.05$.)
c. If necessary, fit a first-order autoregressive model to the stock price and test for the significance of the first-order autoregressive parameter. (Use $\alpha = 0.05$.)
d. If appropriate, forecast the stock price for January 1, 2008.

**16.31** Refer to the data given in Problem 16.22 on page 750 that represent the number of stores open for Bed Bath & Beyond from 1993 through 2007 (see the file BedBath).

**a.** Fit a third-order autoregressive model to the number of stores and test for the significance of the third-order autoregressive parameter. (Use $\alpha = 0.05$.)

**b.** If necessary, fit a second-order autoregressive model to the number of stores and test for the significance of

the second-order autoregressive parameter. (Use $\alpha = 0.05$.)

**c.** If necessary, fit a first-order autoregressive model to the number of stores and test for the significance of the first-order autoregressive parameter. (Use $\alpha = 0.05$.)

**d.** If appropriate, forecast the number of stores open in 2008 and 2009.

## 16.6 CHOOSING AN APPROPRIATE FORECASTING MODEL

In Sections 16.4 and 16.5, you studied six time-series forecasting methods: the linear trend model, the quadratic trend model, and the exponential trend model in Section 16.4; and the first-order, second-order, and $p$th-order autoregressive models in Section 16.5. Is there a *best* model? Among these models, which one should you select for forecasting? The following guidelines are provided for determining the adequacy of a particular forecasting model. These guidelines are based on a judgment of how well the model fits the past data of a given time series and assumes that future movements in the time series can be projected by a study of the past data:

- Perform a residual analysis.
- Measure the magnitude of the residuals through squared differences.
- Measure the magnitude of the residuals through absolute differences.
- Use the principle of parsimony.

A discussion of these guidelines follows.

### Performing a Residual Analysis

Recall from Sections 13.5 and 14.3 that residuals are the differences between the observed and predicted values. After fitting a particular model to a time series, you plot the residuals over the $n$ time periods. As shown in Panel A of Figure 16.21, if the particular model fits adequately, the residuals represent the irregular component of the time series. Therefore, they should be

**FIGURE 16.21**

Residual analysis for studying error patterns

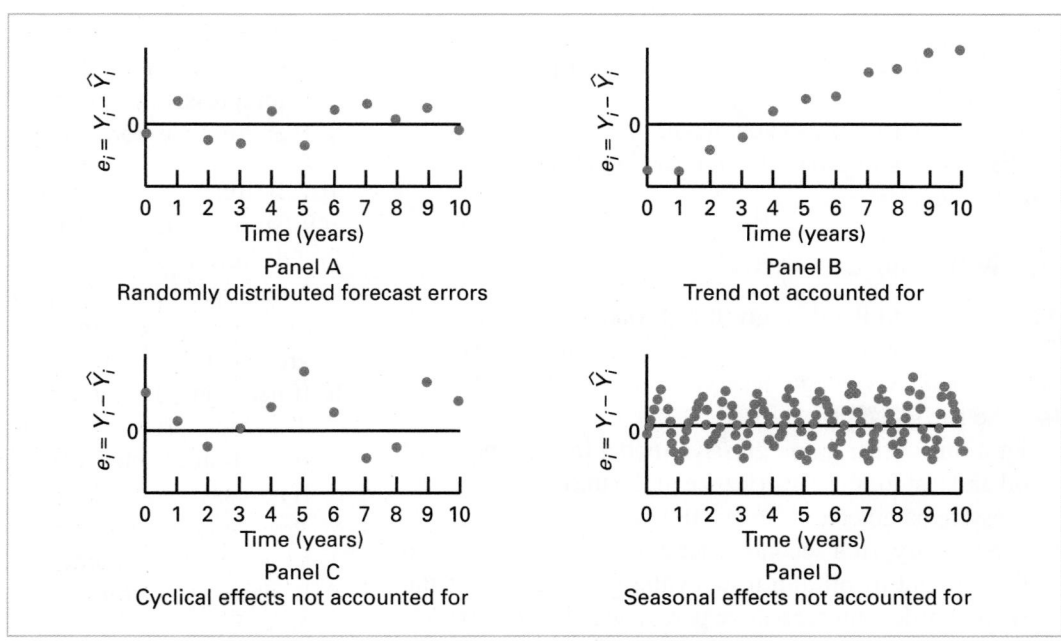

Panel A
Randomly distributed forecast errors

Panel B
Trend not accounted for

Panel C
Cyclical effects not accounted for

Panel D
Seasonal effects not accounted for

randomly distributed throughout the series. However, as illustrated in the three remaining panels of Figure 16.21, if the particular model does not fit adequately, the residuals may show a systematic pattern, such as a failure to account for trend (Panel B), a failure to account for cyclical variation (Panel C), or, with monthly or quarterly data, a failure to account for seasonal variation (Panel D).

## Measuring the Magnitude of the Residuals Through Squared or Absolute Differences

If, after performing a residual analysis, you still believe that two or more models appear to fit the data adequately, you can use additional methods for model selection. Numerous measures based on the residuals are available (see references 1 and 4). However, there is no consensus among statisticians as to which particular measure is best for determining the most appropriate forecasting model.

Based on the principle of least squares, one measure that you have already used in regression analysis (see Section 13.3) is the standard error of the estimate ($S_{YX}$). For a particular model, this measure is based on the sum of squared differences between the actual and predicted values in a time series. If a model fits the time-series data perfectly, then the standard error of the estimate is zero. If a model fits the time-series data poorly, then $S_{YX}$ is large. Thus, when comparing the adequacy of two or more forecasting models, you can select the model with the minimum $S_{YX}$ as most appropriate.

However, a major drawback to using $S_{YX}$ when comparing forecasting models is that whenever there is a large difference between even a single $Y_i$ and $\hat{Y}_i$, the value of $S_{YX}$ becomes inflated through the squaring process. For this reason, many statisticians prefer the **mean absolute deviation ($MAD$)**. Equation (16.14) defines the $MAD$ as the mean of the absolute differences between the actual and predicted values in a time series.

Mean Absolute Deviation

$$MAD = \frac{\sum_{i=1}^{n} |Y_i - \hat{Y}_i|}{n}$$

(16.14)

If a model fits the time-series data perfectly, the $MAD$ is zero. If a model fits the time-series data poorly, the $MAD$ is large. When comparing two or more forecasting models, you can select the one with the minimum $MAD$ as the most appropriate model.

## The Principle of Parsimony

If, after performing a residual analysis and comparing the $S_{YX}$ and $MAD$ measures, you still believe that two or more models appear to adequately fit the data, then you can use the principle of parsimony for model selection.

The principle of **parsimony** is the belief that you should select the simplest model that gets the job done adequately.

Among the six forecasting models studied in this chapter, the least-squares linear and quadratic models and the first-order autoregressive model are regarded by most statisticians as the simplest. The second- and $p$th-order autoregressive models and the least-squares exponential model are considered more complex.

## A Comparison of Four Forecasting Methods

Consider once again the Wm. Wrigley Jr. Company's revenues data. To illustrate the model selection process, you can compare four of the forecasting models used in Sections 16.4 and 16.5: the linear model, the quadratic model, the exponential model, and the second-order autoregressive model. (There is no need to further study the first-order or third-order autoregressive model for this time series because the third-order model did not significantly improve the fit whereas the second-order autoregressive model did improve the fit.)

Figure 16.22 displays the residual plots for the four models. In drawing conclusions from these residual plots, you must use caution because there are only 23 values.

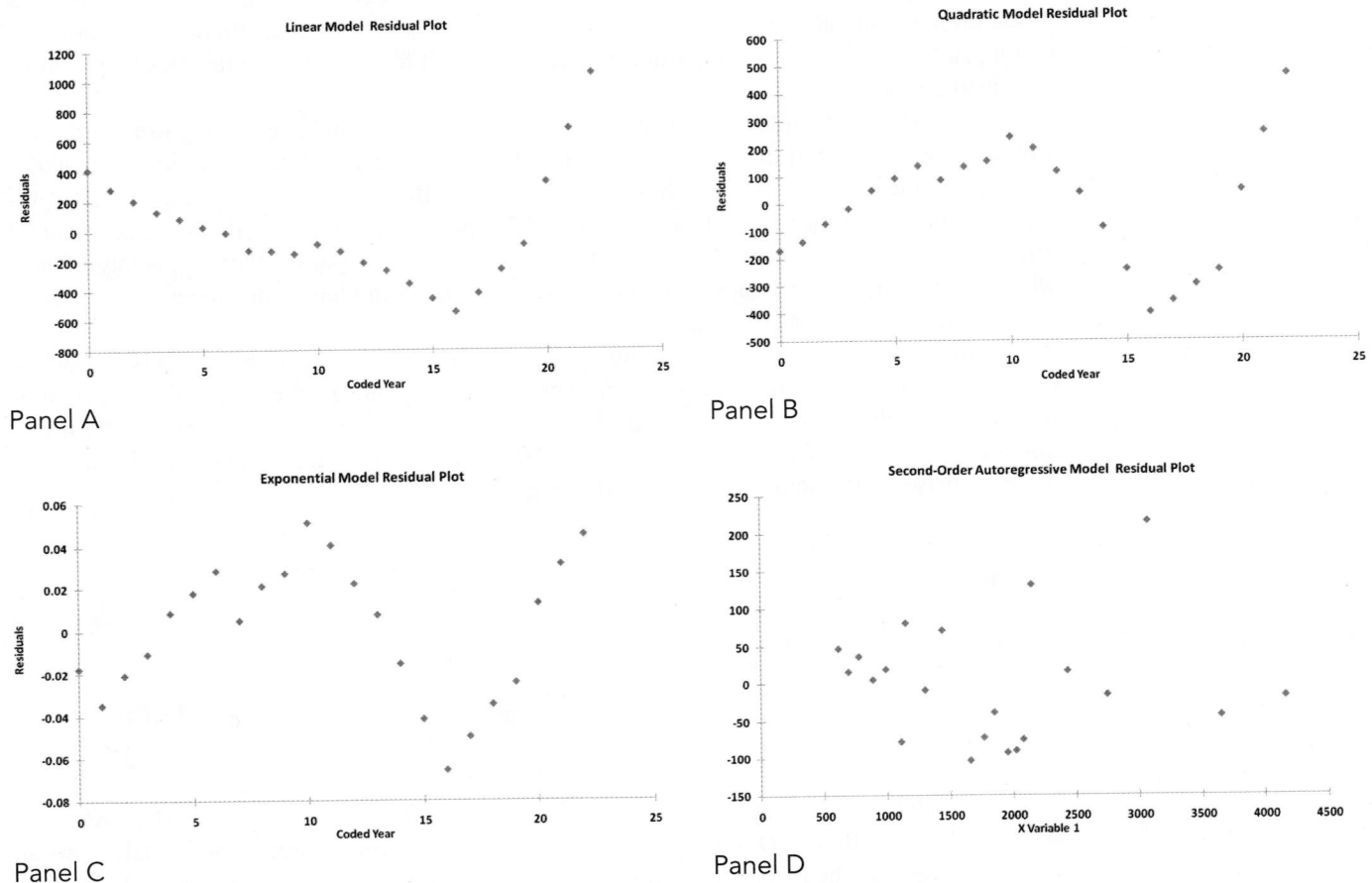

Panel A    Panel B

Panel C    Panel D

**FIGURE 16.22** Microsoft Excel residual plots for four forecasting methods

*See Section E13.3 and E14.2 or P13.3 and P14.2 to create these plots. (Minitab users, see Section M14.2 to create equivalent plots.)*

In Figure 16.22, observe the systematic structure of the residuals in the linear model (Panel A), quadratic model (Panel B), and exponential model (Panel C). For the autoregressive model (Panel D), the residuals appear more random.

To summarize, on the basis of the residual analysis of all four forecasting models, it appears that the second-order autoregressive model is the most appropriate, and the linear, quadratic, and exponential models are less appropriate. For further verification, you can compare the four models with respect to the magnitude of their residuals. Figure 16.23 shows the actual values ($Y_i$) along with the predicted values ($\hat{Y}_i$), the residuals ($e_i$), the error sum of squares (*SSE*), the standard error of the estimate ($S_{YX}$), and the mean absolute deviation (*MAD*) for each of the four models.

For this time series, $S_{YX}$ and *MAD* provide similar results. A comparison of the $S_{YX}$ and *MAD* clearly indicates that the linear model provides the poorest fit. The second-order autoregressive model provides the best fit. Considering the results of the residual analysis and $S_{YX}$ and *MAD*, the choice for the best model is the second-order autoregressive model.

After you select a particular forecasting model, you need to continually monitor your forecasts. If large errors occur between forecasted and actual values, the underlying structure of the time series may have changed. Remember that the forecasting methods presented in this chapter assume that the patterns inherent in the past will continue into the future. Large forecast errors are an indication that an assumption is no longer true.

**FIGURE 16.23**

Microsoft Excel worksheet that compares four forecasting methods, using $S_{YX}$ and MAD

| | A | B | C | D | E | F | G | H | I | J | K | L | M | N |
|---|---|---|---|---|---|---|---|---|---|---|---|---|---|---|
| 1 | | | | Linear | | | Quadratic | | | Exponential | | | Second-Order Autoregressive | |
| 2 | Year | Revenue | | Predicted | Residual | | Predicted | Residual | | Predicted | Residual | | Predicted | Residual |
| 3 | 1984 | 591 | | 174.141 | 416.859 | | 759.722 | -168.722 | | 615.608 | -24.608 | | #N/A | #N/A |
| 4 | 1985 | 620 | | 331.429 | 288.571 | | 757.306 | -137.306 | | 671.924 | -51.924 | | #N/A | #N/A |
| 5 | 1986 | 699 | | 488.716 | 210.284 | | 770.099 | -71.099 | | 733.392 | -34.392 | | 651.640 | 47.360 |
| 6 | 1987 | 781 | | 646.004 | 134.996 | | 798.103 | -17.103 | | 800.483 | -19.483 | | 765.295 | 15.705 |
| 7 | 1988 | 891 | | 803.292 | 87.708 | | 841.316 | 49.684 | | 873.712 | 17.288 | | 854.385 | 36.615 |
| 8 | 1989 | 993 | | 960.579 | 32.421 | | 899.740 | 93.260 | | 953.639 | 39.361 | | 988.057 | 4.943 |
| 9 | 1990 | 1111 | | 1117.867 | -6.867 | | 973.373 | 137.627 | | 1040.878 | 70.122 | | 1091.947 | 19.053 |
| 10 | 1991 | 1149 | | 1275.154 | -126.154 | | 1062.216 | 86.784 | | 1136.098 | 12.902 | | 1227.049 | -78.049 |
| 11 | 1992 | 1301 | | 1432.442 | -131.442 | | 1166.269 | 134.731 | | 1240.029 | 60.971 | | 1220.262 | 80.738 |
| 12 | 1993 | 1440 | | 1589.729 | -149.729 | | 1285.532 | 154.468 | | 1353.467 | 86.533 | | 1449.453 | -9.453 |
| 13 | 1994 | 1661 | | 1747.017 | -86.017 | | 1420.004 | 240.996 | | 1477.283 | 183.717 | | 1589.789 | 71.211 |
| 14 | 1995 | 1770 | | 1904.304 | -134.304 | | 1569.687 | 200.313 | | 1612.425 | 157.575 | | 1873.554 | -103.554 |
| 15 | 1996 | 1851 | | 2061.592 | -210.592 | | 1734.579 | 116.421 | | 1759.931 | 91.069 | | 1923.471 | -72.471 |
| 16 | 1997 | 1954 | | 2218.879 | -264.879 | | 1914.682 | 39.318 | | 1920.930 | 33.070 | | 1993.186 | -39.186 |
| 17 | 1998 | 2023 | | 2376.167 | -353.167 | | 2109.994 | -86.994 | | 2096.657 | -73.657 | | 2115.860 | -92.860 |
| 18 | 1999 | 2079 | | 2533.455 | -454.455 | | 2320.516 | -241.516 | | 2288.460 | -209.460 | | 2169.252 | -90.252 |
| 19 | 2000 | 2146 | | 2690.742 | -544.742 | | 2546.248 | -400.248 | | 2497.809 | -351.809 | | 2221.206 | -75.206 |
| 20 | 2001 | 2430 | | 2848.030 | -418.030 | | 2787.190 | -357.190 | | 2726.309 | -296.309 | | 2299.048 | 130.952 |
| 21 | 2002 | 2746 | | 3005.317 | -259.317 | | 3043.342 | -297.342 | | 2975.713 | -229.713 | | 2729.636 | 16.364 |
| 22 | 2003 | 3069 | | 3162.605 | -93.605 | | 3314.704 | -245.704 | | 3247.932 | -178.932 | | 3085.029 | -16.029 |
| 23 | 2004 | 3649 | | 3319.892 | 329.108 | | 3601.275 | 47.725 | | 3545.054 | 103.946 | | 3433.111 | 215.889 |
| 24 | 2005 | 4159 | | 3477.180 | 681.820 | | 3903.057 | 255.943 | | 3869.357 | 289.643 | | 4202.521 | -43.521 |
| 25 | 2006 | 4686 | | 3634.467 | 1051.533 | | 4220.048 | 465.952 | | 4223.327 | 462.673 | | 4704.250 | -18.250 |
| 26 | | | | SSE: | 3081503.193 | | SSE: | 1032983.128 | | SSE: | 745386.649 | | SSE: | 128432.058 |
| 27 | | | | $S_{YX}$ | 383.064 | | $S_{YX}$ | 227.265 | | $S_{YX}$ | 188.400 | | $S_{YX}$ | 84.470 |
| 28 | | | | MAD: | 281.156 | | MAD: | 175.932 | | MAD: | 130.549 | | MAD: | 60.841 |

# PROBLEMS FOR SECTION 16.6

## Learning the Basics

**16.32** The following residuals are from a linear trend model used to forecast sales:

2.0  -0.5  1.5  1.0  0.0  1.0  -3.0  1.5  -4.5  2.0  0.0  -1.0

**a.** Compute $S_{YX}$ and interpret your findings.
**b.** Compute the MAD and interpret your findings.

**16.33** Refer to Problem 16.32. Suppose the first residual is 12.0 (instead of 2.0) and the last residual is -11.0 (instead of -1.0).
**a.** Compute $S_{YX}$ and interpret your findings
**b.** Compute the MAD and interpret your findings.

## Applying the Concepts

**16.34** Refer to the results in Problem 16.13 on page 748 (see the file GDP).
**a.** Perform a residual analysis.
**b.** Compute the standard error of the estimate ($S_{YX}$).
**c.** Compute the MAD.
**d.** On the basis of (a) through (c), are you satisfied with your linear trend forecasts in Problem 16.13? Discuss.

**16.35** Refer to the results in Problem 16.15 on page 748 and Problem 16.27 on page 759 concerning the number of barrels of oil in the U.S. strategic oil reserve (see the file Strategic).

**a.** Perform a residual analysis for each model.
**b.** Compute the standard error of the estimate ($S_{YX}$) for each model.
**c.** Compute the MAD for each model.
**d.** On the basis of (a) through (c) and the principle of parsimony, which forecasting model would you select? Discuss.

**16.36** Refer to the results in Problem 16.16 on page 748 and Problem 16.28 on page 759 concerning annual net operating revenues at Coca-Cola (see the file CocaCola).
**a.** Perform a residual analysis for each model.
**b.** Compute the standard error of the estimate ($S_{YX}$) for each model.
**c.** Compute the MAD for each model.
**d.** On the basis of (a) through (c) and the principle of parsimony, which forecasting model would you select? Discuss.

**16.37** Refer to the results in Problem 16.17 on page 749 and Problem 16.29 on page 759 concerning the DJIA (see the file DJIA).
**a.** Perform a residual analysis for each model.
**b.** Compute the standard error of the estimate ($S_{YX}$) for each model.
**c.** Compute the MAD for each model.
**d.** On the basis of (a) through (c) and the principle of parsimony, which forecasting model would you select? Discuss.

**16.38** Refer to the results in Problem 16.18 on page 749 and Problem 16.30 on page 759 concerning the price per share for GE stock (see the file **GE**).

**a.** Perform a residual analysis for each model.

**b.** Compute the standard error of the estimate ($S_{YX}$) for each model.

**c.** Compute the *MAD* for each model.

**d.** On the basis of (a) through (c) and the principle of parsimony, which forecasting model would you select? Discuss.

**16.39** Refer to the results in Problem 16.22 on page 750 and Problem 16.31 on page 760 concerning the number of Bed Bath & Beyond stores open (see the data file **BedBath**).

**a.** Perform a residual analysis for each model.

**b.** Compute the standard error of the estimate ($S_{YX}$) for each model.

**c.** Compute the *MAD* for each model.

**d.** On the basis of (a) through (c) and the principle of parsimony, which forecasting model would you select? Discuss.

## 16.7  TIME-SERIES FORECASTING OF SEASONAL DATA

So far, this chapter has focused on forecasting annual data. However, many time series are collected quarterly or monthly, and others are collected weekly, daily, and even hourly. When a time series is collected quarterly or monthly, you must consider the impact of seasonal effects. In this section, regression model building is used to forecast monthly or quarterly data.

One of the companies of interest in the Using Statistics scenario is Wal-Mart Stores, Inc. In 2007, Wal-Mart operated more than 7,000 Wal-Marts, Supercenters, Sam's Clubs, and Neighborhood Markets and had revenues that exceeded $344 billion (Wal-Mart Stores, Inc., **investor.walmartstores.com**). Wal-Mart revenues are highly seasonal, and therefore you need to analyze quarterly revenues. The fiscal year for the company ends on January 31. Thus, the fourth quarter of 2007 includes November and December of 2006 and January of 2007. Table 16.3 lists the quarterly revenues, in billions of dollars, from 2000 to 2007 (see the file **Walmart**). Figure 16.24 displays the time series.

**TABLE 16.3**

Quarterly Revenues for Wal-Mart Stores, Inc., in Billions of Dollars (2000–2007)

| Quarter | 2000 | 2001 | 2002 | 2003 | 2004 | 2005 | 2006 | 2007 |
|---|---|---|---|---|---|---|---|---|
| 1 | 34.7 | 43.0 | 48.6 | 55.0 | 56.7 | 64.8 | 71.6 | 79.6 |
| 2 | 38.2 | 46.1 | 53.3 | 59.7 | 62.6 | 69.7 | 76.8 | 84.5 |
| 3 | 40.4 | 45.7 | 51.8 | 58.8 | 62.4 | 68.5 | 75.4 | 83.5 |
| 4 | 51.4 | 56.6 | 64.2 | 71.1 | 74.5 | 82.2 | 88.6 | 98.1 |

Source: *Extracted from Wal-Mart Stores, Inc.,* **investor.walmartstores.com**.

**FIGURE 16.24**

Microsoft Excel plot of quarterly revenues for Wal-Mart Stores, Inc., in billions of dollars (2000–2007)

*See Section E2.13 to create this. (Minitab users, see Section M2.9 to create an equivalent chart.)*

## Least-Squares Forecasting with Monthly or Quarterly Data

To develop a least-squares regression model that includes trend, seasonal, and irregular components, the approach to least-squares trend fitting in Section 16.4 is combined with the approach to model building using dummy variables (see Section 14.6) to model the seasonal component.

Equation (16.15) defines the exponential trend model for quarterly data.

**Exponential Model with Quarterly Data**

$$Y_i = \beta_0 \beta_1^{X_i} \beta_2^{Q_1} \beta_3^{Q_2} \beta_4^{Q_3} \varepsilon_i \tag{16.15}$$

where

$X_i$ = coded quarterly value, $i = 0, 1, 2, \ldots$

$Q_1 = 1$ if first quarter, 0 if not first quarter

$Q_2 = 1$ if second quarter, 0 if not second quarter

$Q_3 = 1$ if third quarter, 0 if not third quarter

$\beta_0 = Y$ intercept

$(\beta_1 - 1) \times 100\%$ = quarterly compound growth rate (in %)

$\beta_2$ = multiplier for first quarter relative to fourth quarter

$\beta_3$ = multiplier for second quarter relative to fourth quarter

$\beta_4$ = multiplier for third quarter relative to fourth quarter

$\varepsilon_i$ = value of the irregular component for time period $i$

[5] Alternatively, you can use base e logarithms. For more information on logarithms, see Appendix A.3.

The model in Equation (16.15) is not in the form of a linear regression model. To transform this nonlinear model to a linear model, you use a base 10 logarithmic transformation.[5] Taking the logarithm of each side of Equation (16.15) results in Equation (16.16).

**Transformed Exponential Model with Quarterly Data**

$$\log(Y_i) = \log(\beta_0 \beta_1^{X_i} \beta_2^{Q_1} \beta_3^{Q_2} \beta_4^{Q_3} \varepsilon_i)$$

$$= \log(\beta_0) + \log(\beta_1^{X_i}) + \log(\beta_2^{Q_1}) + \log(\beta_3^{Q_2}) + \log(\beta_4^{Q_3}) + \log(\varepsilon_i)$$

$$= \log(\beta_0) + X_i \log(\beta_1) + Q_1 \log(\beta_2) + Q_2 \log(\beta_3) + Q_3 \log(\beta_4) + \log(\varepsilon_i) \tag{16.16}$$

Equation (16.16) is a linear model that you can estimate using least-squares regression. Performing the regression analysis using $\log(Y_i)$ as the dependent variable and $X_i$, $Q_1$, $Q_2$, and $Q_3$ as the independent variables results in Equation (16.17).

## Exponential Growth with Quarterly Data Forecasting Equation

$$\log(\hat{Y}_i) = b_0 + b_1 X_i + b_2 Q_1 + b_3 Q_2 + b_4 Q_3 \qquad (16.17)$$

where

$$b_0 = \text{estimate of } \log(\beta_0) \text{ and thus } 10^{b_0} = \hat{\beta}_0$$
$$b_1 = \text{estimate of } \log(\beta_1) \text{ and thus } 10^{b_1} = \hat{\beta}_1$$
$$b_2 = \text{estimate of } \log(\beta_2) \text{ and thus } 10^{b_2} = \hat{\beta}_2$$
$$b_3 = \text{estimate of } \log(\beta_3) \text{ and thus } 10^{b_3} = \hat{\beta}_3$$
$$b_4 = \text{estimate of } \log(\beta_4) \text{ and thus } 10^{b_4} = \hat{\beta}_4$$

Equation (16.18) is used for monthly data.

## Exponential Model with Monthly Data

$$Y_i = \beta_0 \beta_1^{X_i} \beta_2^{M_1} \beta_3^{M_2} \beta_4^{M_3} \beta_5^{M_4} \beta_6^{M_5} \beta_7^{M_6} \beta_8^{M_7} \beta_9^{M_8} \beta_{10}^{M_9} \beta_{11}^{M_{10}} \beta_{12}^{M_{11}} \varepsilon_i \qquad (16.18)$$

where

$$X_i = \text{coded monthly value, } i = 0, 1, 2, \ldots$$
$$M_1 = 1 \text{ if January, 0 if not January}$$
$$M_2 = 1 \text{ if February, 0 if not February}$$
$$M_3 = 1 \text{ if March, 0 if not March}$$

$$\cdot$$
$$\cdot$$
$$\cdot$$

$$M_{11} = 1 \text{ if November, 0 if not November}$$
$$\beta_0 = Y \text{ intercept}$$
$$(\beta_1 - 1) \times 100\% = \text{monthly compound growth rate (in \%)}$$
$$\beta_2 = \text{multiplier for January relative to December}$$
$$\beta_3 = \text{multiplier for February relative to December}$$
$$\beta_4 = \text{multiplier for March relative to December}$$

$$\cdot$$
$$\cdot$$
$$\cdot$$

$$\beta_{12} = \text{multiplier for November relative to December}$$
$$\varepsilon_i = \text{value of the irregular component for time period } i$$

The model in Equation (16.18) is not in the form of a linear regression model. To transform this nonlinear model to a linear model, you can use a base 10 logarithm transformation. Taking the logarithm of each side of Equation (16.18) results in Equation (16.19).

Transformed Exponential Model with Monthly Data

$$\log(Y_i) = \log(\beta_0 \beta_1^{X_i} \beta_2^{M_1} \beta_3^{M_2} \beta_4^{M_3} \beta_5^{M_4} \beta_6^{M_5} \beta_7^{M_6} \beta_8^{M_7} \beta_9^{M_8} \beta_{10}^{M_9} \beta_{11}^{M_{10}} \beta_{12}^{M_{11}} \varepsilon_i)$$

$$= \log(\beta_0) + X_i \log(\beta_1) + M_1 \log(\beta_2) + M_2 \log(\beta_3) \qquad \textbf{(16.19)}$$

$$+ M_3 \log(\beta_4) + M_4 \log(\beta_5) + M_5 \log(\beta_6) + M_6 \log(\beta_7)$$

$$+ M_7 \log(\beta_8) + M_8 \log(\beta_9) + M_9 \log(\beta_{10}) + M_{10} \log(\beta_{11})$$

$$+ M_{11} \log(\beta_{12}) + \log(\varepsilon_i)$$

Equation (16.19) is a linear model that you can estimate using the least-squares method. Performing the regression analysis using $\log(Y_i)$ as the dependent variable and $X_i, M_1, M_2, \ldots,$ and $M_{11}$ as the independent variables results in Equation (16.20).

Exponential Growth with Monthly Data Forecasting Equation

$$\log(\hat{Y}_i) = b_0 + b_1 X_i + b_2 M_1 + b_3 M_2 + b_4 M_3 + b_5 M_4 + b_6 M_5 + b_7 M_6 \qquad \textbf{(16.20)}$$

$$+ b_8 M_7 + b_9 M_8 + b_{10} M_9 + b_{11} M_{10} + b_{12} M_{11}$$

where

$$b_0 = \text{estimate of } \log(\beta_0) \text{ and thus } 10^{b_0} = \hat{\beta}_0$$

$$b_1 = \text{estimate of } \log(\beta_1) \text{ and thus } 10^{b_1} = \hat{\beta}_1$$

$$b_2 = \text{estimate of } \log(\beta_2) \text{ and thus } 10^{b_2} = \hat{\beta}_2$$

$$b_3 = \text{estimate of } \log(\beta_3) \text{ and thus } 10^{b_3} = \hat{\beta}_3$$

$$\cdot$$
$$\cdot$$
$$\cdot$$

$$b_{12} = \text{estimate of } \log(\beta_{12}) \text{ and thus } 10^{b_{12}} = \hat{\beta}_{12}$$

$Q_1, Q_2,$ and $Q_3$ are the three dummy variables needed to represent the four quarter periods in a quarterly time series. $M_1, M_2, M_3, \ldots, M_{11}$ are the 11 dummy variables needed to represent the 12 months in a monthly time series. In building the model, you use $\log(Y_i)$ instead of $Y_i$ values and then find the regression coefficients by taking the antilog of the regression coefficients developed from Equations (16.17) and (16.20).

Although at first glance these regression models look imposing, when fitting or forecasting in any one time period, the values of all or all but one of the dummy variables in the model are set equal to zero, and the equations simplify dramatically. In establishing the dummy variables for quarterly time-series data, the fourth quarter is the base period and has a coded value of zero for each dummy variable. With a quarterly time series, Equation (16.17) reduces as follows:

For any first quarter:  $\log(\hat{Y}_i) = b_0 + b_1 X_i + b_2$

For any second quarter:  $\log(\hat{Y}_i) = b_0 + b_1 X_i + b_3$

For any third quarter:  $\log(\hat{Y}_i) = b_0 + b_1 X_i + b_4$

For any fourth quarter:  $\log(\hat{Y}_i) = b_0 + b_1 X_i$

When establishing the dummy variables for each month, December serves as the base period and has a coded value of zero for each dummy variable. For example, with a monthly time series, Equation (16.20) reduces as follows:

For any January:     $\log(\hat{Y}_i) = b_0 + b_1 X_i + b_2$
For any February:    $\log(\hat{Y}_i) = b_0 + b_1 X_i + b_3$

.

.

.

For any November:   $\log(\hat{Y}_i) = b_0 + b_1 X_i + b_{12}$
For any December:    $\log(\hat{Y}_i) = b_0 + b_1 X_i$

To demonstrate the process of model building and least-squares forecasting with a quarterly time series, return to the Wal-Mart revenue data (in billions of dollars) originally displayed in Table 16.3 on page 764. The data are from each quarter from the first quarter of 2000 through the last quarter of 2007. Microsoft Excel results for the quarterly exponential trend model are displayed in Figure 16.25. Minitab results are presented in Figure 16.26.

**FIGURE 16.25**

Microsoft Excel regression results worksheet for fitting and forecasting with the quarterly Wal-Mart revenue data

*See Section E14.1 or P14.1 to create this.*

| | A | B | C | D | E | F | G |
|---|---|---|---|---|---|---|---|
| 1 | Quarterly Revenues Regression Model for Wal-Mart Stores | | | | | | |
| 2 | | | | | | | |
| 3 | Regression Statistics | | | | | | |
| 4 | Multiple R | 0.9905 | | | | | |
| 5 | R Square | 0.9812 | | | | | |
| 6 | Adjusted R Square | 0.9784 | | | | | |
| 7 | Standard Error | 0.0166 | | | | | |
| 8 | Observations | 32.0000 | | | | | |
| 9 | | | | | | | |
| 10 | ANOVA | | | | | | |
| 11 | | df | SS | MS | F | Significance F | |
| 12 | Regression | 4 | 0.3879 | 0.0970 | 352.0768 | 0.0000 | |
| 13 | Residual | 27 | 0.0074 | 0.0003 | | | |
| 14 | Total | 31 | 0.3953 | | | | |
| 15 | | | | | | | |
| 16 | | Coefficients | Standard Error | t Stat | P-value | Lower 95% | Upper 95% |
| 17 | Intercept | 1.6680 | 0.0080 | 208.4374 | 0.0000 | 1.6516 | 1.6844 |
| 18 | Coded Quarter | 0.0111 | 0.0003 | 34.5784 | 0.0000 | 0.0104 | 0.0117 |
| 19 | Q1 | -0.0827 | 0.0084 | -9.9047 | 0.0000 | -0.0999 | -0.0656 |
| 20 | Q2 | -0.0590 | 0.0083 | -7.0851 | 0.0000 | -0.0760 | -0.0419 |
| 21 | Q3 | -0.0726 | 0.0083 | -8.7432 | 0.0000 | -0.0896 | -0.0556 |

**FIGURE 16.26**

Minitab results for fitting and forecasting with the quarterly Wal-Mart revenue data

*See Section M14.2 to create this.*

```
The regression equation is
Log(Revenues) = 1.67 + 0.0111 Coded Quarter - 0.0827 Q1 - 0.0590 Q2 - 0.0726 Q3


Predictor          Coef      SE Coef        T       P
Constant        1.66800     0.00800   208.44   0.000
Coded Quarter   0.0110684   0.0003201   34.58   0.000
Q1             -0.082737    0.008353    -9.90   0.000
Q2             -0.058966    0.008323    -7.09   0.000
Q3             -0.072604    0.008304    -8.74   0.000


S = 0.0165957   R-Sq = 98.1%   R-Sq(adj) = 97.8%


Analysis of Variance

Source          DF      SS        MS        F       P
Regression       4   0.387872  0.096968  352.08   0.000
Residual Error  27   0.007436  0.000275
Total           31   0.395308
```

From Figure 16.25 or 16.26, the model fits the data extremely well. The coefficient of determination $r^2 = 0.9812$ and the adjusted $r^2 = 0.9784$, and the overall $F$ test results in an $F_{STAT}$ test statistic of 352.0768 ($p$-value = 0.000). Looking further, at the 0.05 level of significance, each regression coefficient is highly statistically significant and contributes to the model. Taking the antilogs of all the regression coefficients, you have the following summary:

| Regression Coefficient | $b_i = \log\hat{\beta}_i$ | $\hat{\beta}_i = \text{antilog}(b_i) = 10^{b_i}$ |
|---|---|---|
| $b_0$: $Y$ intercept | 1.6680 | 46.5586 |
| $b_1$: coded quarter | 0.0111 | 1.0259 |
| $b_2$: first quarter | −0.0827 | 0.8266 |
| $b_3$: second quarter | −0.0590 | 0.8730 |
| $b_4$: third quarter | −0.0726 | 0.8461 |

The interpretations for $\hat{\beta}_0$, $\hat{\beta}_1$, $\hat{\beta}_2$, $\hat{\beta}_3$, and $\hat{\beta}_4$ are as follows:

- The $Y$ intercept, $\hat{\beta}_0 = 46.5586$ (in billions of dollars), is the *unadjusted* forecast for quarterly revenues in the first quarter of 2000, the initial quarter in the time series. *Unadjusted* means that the seasonal component is not incorporated in the forecast.
- The value $(\hat{\beta}_1 - 1) \times 100\% = 0.0259$, or 2.59%, is the estimated *quarterly compound growth rate* in revenues, after adjusting for the seasonal component.
- $\hat{\beta}_2 = 0.8266$ is the seasonal multiplier for the first quarter relative to the fourth quarter; it indicates that there is 17.34% less revenue for the first quarter as compared with the fourth quarter.
- $\hat{\beta}_3 = 0.8730$ is the seasonal multiplier for the second quarter relative to the fourth quarter; it indicates that there is 12.70% less revenue for the second quarter as compared with the fourth quarter.
- $\hat{\beta}_4 = 0.8461$ is the seasonal multiplier for the third quarter relative to the fourth quarter; it indicates that there is 15.39% less revenue for the third quarter than the fourth quarter. Thus, the fourth quarter, which includes the holiday shopping season, has the strongest sales.

Using the regression coefficients $b_0$, $b_1$, $b_2$, $b_3$, $b_4$, and Equation (16.17) on page 766, you can make forecasts for selected quarters. As an example, to predict revenues for the fourth quarter of 2007 ($X_i = 31$):

$$\log(\hat{Y}_i) = b_0 + b_1 X_i$$
$$= 1.668 + (0.0111)(31)$$
$$= 2.0121$$

Thus,

$$\hat{Y}_i = 10^{2.0121} = 102.8253$$

The predicted revenue for the fourth quarter of fiscal 2007 is $102.8253 billion. To make a forecast for a future time period, such as the first quarter of fiscal 2008 ($X_i = 32$, $Q_1 = 1$):

$$\log(\hat{Y}_i) = b_0 + b_1 X_i + b_2 Q_1$$
$$= 1.6680 + (0.0111)(32) + (-0.0827)(1)$$
$$= 1.9405$$

Thus,

$$\hat{Y}_i = 10^{1.9405} = 87.1967$$

The predicted revenue for the first quarter of fiscal 2008 is $87.1967 billion.

## PROBLEMS FOR SECTION 16.7

### Learning the Basics

**16.40** In forecasting a monthly time series over a five-year period from January 2003 to December 2007, the exponential trend forecasting equation for January is

$$\log \hat{Y}_i = 2.0 + 0.01 X_i + 0.10 (\text{January})$$

Take the antilog of the appropriate coefficient from this equation and interpret the
**a.** $Y$ intercept, $\hat{\beta}_0$.
**b.** monthly compound growth rate.
**c.** January multiplier.

**16.41** In forecasting daily time-series data, how many dummy variables are needed to account for the seasonal component day-of-the-week?

**16.42** In forecasting a quarterly time series over the five-year period from the first quarter of 2003 through the fourth quarter of 2007, the exponential trend forecasting equation is given by

$$\log \hat{Y}_i = 3.0 + 0.10 X_i - 0.25 Q_1 + 0.20 Q_2 + 0.15 Q_3$$

where quarter zero is first quarter of 2003. Take the antilog of the appropriate coefficient from this equation and interpret the
**a.** $Y$ intercept, $\hat{\beta}_0$.
**b.** quarterly compound growth rate.
**c.** second-quarter multiplier.

**16.43** Refer to the exponential model given in Problem 16.42.
**a.** What is the fitted value of the series in the fourth quarter of 2005?
**b.** What is the fitted value of the series in the first quarter of 2005?
**c.** What is the forecast in the fourth quarter of 2007?
**d.** What is the forecast in the first quarter of 2008?

### Applying the Concepts

**16.44** The data given in the file S&Pindex represent the S&P Composite Stock Price Index recorded at the end of each quarter from 1998 through the first quarter of 2007.
Source: *Extracted from* **finance.yahoo.com**.

**a.** Plot the data.
**b.** Develop an exponential trend forecasting equation with quarterly components.
**c.** Interpret the quarterly compound growth rate.
**d.** Interpret the first quarter multiplier.

**e.** What is the fitted value for the first quarter of 2007?
**f.** What are the forecasts for the remaining three quarters of 2007?

**16.45** Are gasoline prices higher during the height of the summer vacation season? The following table contains the mean monthly prices (in dollars per gallon) for unleaded gasoline in the United States from 2000 to 2006 (stored in the file Unleaded):

| Month | Year | | | | | | |
|---|---|---|---|---|---|---|---|
| | 2000 | 2001 | 2002 | 2003 | 2004 | 2005 | 2006 |
| January | 1.301 | 1.472 | 1.139 | 1.473 | 1.592 | 1.823 | 2.315 |
| February | 1.369 | 1.484 | 1.130 | 1.641 | 1.672 | 1.918 | 2.310 |
| March | 1.541 | 1.447 | 1.241 | 1.748 | 1.766 | 2.065 | 2.401 |
| April | 1.506 | 1.564 | 1.407 | 1.659 | 1.833 | 2.283 | 2.757 |
| May | 1.498 | 1.729 | 1.421 | 1.542 | 2.009 | 2.216 | 2.947 |
| June | 1.617 | 1.640 | 1.404 | 1.514 | 2.041 | 2.176 | 2.917 |
| July | 1.593 | 1.482 | 1.412 | 1.524 | 1.939 | 2.316 | 2.999 |
| August | 1.510 | 1.427 | 1.423 | 1.628 | 1.898 | 2.506 | 2.985 |
| September | 1.582 | 1.531 | 1.422 | 1.728 | 1.891 | 2.927 | 2.589 |
| October | 1.559 | 1.362 | 1.449 | 1.603 | 2.029 | 2.785 | 2.272 |
| November | 1.555 | 1.263 | 1.448 | 1.535 | 2.010 | 2.343 | 2.241 |
| December | 1.489 | 1.131 | 1.394 | 1.494 | 1.882 | 2.186 | 2.334 |

Source: *Bureau of Labor Statistics, U.S. Department of Labor,* **www.bls.gov**.

**a.** Construct a time-series plot.
**b.** Develop an exponential trend forecasting equation for monthly data.
**c.** Interpret the monthly compound growth rate.
**d.** Interpret the monthly multipliers.
**e.** Write a short summary of your findings.

**16.46** The U.S. Bureau of Labor Statistics compiles data on a wide variety of workforce issues. The data in the file Unemploy give the monthly seasonally adjusted civilian unemployment rates for the United States from 2000 through 2006.
Source: *Bureau of Labor Statistics, U.S. Department of Labor,* **www.bls.gov**.

**a.** Plot the time-series data.
**b.** Develop an exponential trend forecasting equation with monthly components.
**c.** What is the fitted value in December 2006?
**d.** What are the forecasts for all 12 months of 2007?
**e.** Interpret the monthly compound growth rate.
**f.** Interpret the July multiplier.
**g.** Go to your library or the Internet and locate the actual unemployment rate in 2007. Discuss.

**16.47** The following data (stored in the file **Credit**) are monthly credit card charges (in millions of dollars) for a popular credit card issued by a large bank (the name of which is not disclosed at its request):

| Month | Year 2001 | 2002 | 2003 |
|---|---|---|---|
| January | 31.9 | 39.4 | 45.0 |
| February | 27.0 | 36.2 | 39.6 |
| March | 31.3 | 40.5 | |
| April | 31.0 | 44.6 | |
| May | 39.4 | 46.8 | |
| June | 40.7 | 44.7 | |
| July | 42.3 | 52.2 | |
| August | 49.5 | 54.0 | |
| September | 45.0 | 48.8 | |
| October | 50.0 | 55.8 | |
| November | 50.9 | 58.7 | |
| December | 58.5 | 63.4 | |

**a.** Construct the time-series plot.
**b.** Describe the monthly pattern that is evident in the data.
**c.** In general, would you say that the overall dollar amounts charged on the bank's credit cards is increasing or decreasing? Explain.
**d.** Note that December 2002 charges were more than $63 million, but those for February 2003 were less than $40 million. Was February's total close to what you would have expected?
**e.** Develop an exponential trend forecasting equation with monthly components.
**f.** Interpret the monthly compound growth rate.
**g.** Interpret the January multiplier.
**h.** What is the predicted value for March 2003?
**i.** What is the predicted value for April 2003?
**j.** How can this type of time-series forecasting benefit the bank?

 **16.48** The data in the file **Toys-rev** are quarterly revenues (in millions of dollars) for Toys R Us from 1996 through 2005.

Source: *Extracted from* Standard & Poor's Stock Reports, *November 1995, November 1998, and April 2002. New York: McGraw-Hill, Inc., and Toys R Us, Inc.,* **www.toysrus.com**.

**a.** Do you think that the revenues for Toys R Us are subject to seasonal variation? Explain.
**b.** Plot the data. Does this chart support your answer to (a)?
**c.** Develop an exponential trend forecasting equation with quarterly components.
**d.** Interpret the quarterly compound growth rate.
**e.** Interpret the quarterly multipliers.
**f.** What are the forecasts for all four quarters of 2006?

**16.49** The data in the file **Ford** are quarterly revenues (in millions of dollars) for the Ford Motor Company, from 1996 through 2006.

Source: Standard & Poor's Stock Reports, *November 2000 and April 2002. New York: McGraw-Hill, Inc., and the Ford Motor Company,* **www.ford.com**.

**a.** Do you think that the revenues for the Ford Motor Company are subject to seasonal variation? Explain.
**b.** Plot the data. Does this chart support your answer to (a)?
**c.** Develop an exponential trend forecasting equation with quarterly components.
**d.** Interpret the quarterly compound growth rate.
**e.** Interpret the quarterly multipliers.
**f.** What are the forecasts for all four quarters of 2007?

## 16.8 INDEX NUMBERS

This chapter has presented various methods for forecasting time-series data. In this section, index numbers are used to compare a value of a time series relative to another value of a time series. **Index numbers** measure the value of an item (or group of items) at a particular point in time, as a percentage of the value of an item (or group of items) at another point in time. They are commonly used in business and economics as indicators of changing business or economic activity. There are many kinds of index numbers, including price indexes, quantity indexes, value indexes, and sociological indexes. In this section, only the price index is considered. In addition to allowing comparison of prices at different points in time, price indexes are also used to deflate the effect of inflation on a time series in order to compare values in *real* dollars instead of *actual* dollars.

## Price Indexes

A **price index** compares the price of a commodity in a given period of time to the price paid for that commodity at a particular point of time in the past. A **simple price index** tracks the price of a single commodity. An **aggregate price index** tracks the prices for a group of commodities (called a market basket) at a given period of time to the price paid for that group of commodities at a particular point of time in the past. The **base period** is the point of time in the past against which all comparisons are made. In selecting the base period for a particular index, if possible, you select a period of economic stability rather than one at or near the peak of an expanding economy or the bottom of a recession or declining economy. In addition, the base period should be relatively recent so that comparisons are not greatly affected by changing technology and consumer attitudes and habits. Equation (16.21) defines the simple price index.

Simple Price Index

$$I_i = \frac{P_i}{P_{base}} \times 100 \qquad\qquad (16.21)$$

where

$$I_i = \text{price index for year } i$$

$$P_i = \text{price for year } i$$

$$P_{base} = \text{price for the base year}$$

As an example of the simple price index, consider the price per gallon of unleaded gasoline in the United States from 1980 to 2006. Table 16.4 on page 773 presents the prices plus two sets of index numbers (see the file Gasoline). To illustrate the computation of the simple price index for 1981, using 1980 as the base year, from Equation (16.21) and Table 16.4,

$$I_{1981} = \frac{P_{1981}}{P_{1980}} \times 100 = \frac{1.38}{1.25} \times 100 = 110.4$$

Thus, the price per gallon of unleaded gasoline in the United States in 1981 was 10.4% higher in 1981 than 1980.

To compute the simple price index for 2006,

$$I_{2006} = \frac{P_{2006}}{P_{1980}} \times 100 = \frac{2.59}{1.25} \times 100 = 207.2$$

Therefore, the price per gallon of unleaded gasoline in the United States in 2006 was 107.2% higher than in 1980. An examination of the price indexes for 1980 to 2006 in Table 16.4 indicates that the price of unleaded gasoline increased in 1981 and 1982 over the base year of 1980 but then was below the 1980 price every year until 2000. Because the base period for the index numbers in Table 16.4 is 1980, you should use a base year closer to the present. The price remained fairly constant from 1990 to 1995; thus, it is appropriate to use 1995 as a base year. Equation (16.22) is used to develop index numbers with a new base.

**TABLE 16.4**

Price per Gallon of Unleaded Gasoline in the United States and Simple Price Index, with 1980 and 1995 as the Base Years (1980–2006)

| Year | Gasoline Price | Price Index—1980 | Price Index—1995 |
|------|---------------|------------------|------------------|
| 1980 | 1.25 | 100.0 | 108.7 |
| 1981 | 1.38 | 110.4 | 120.0 |
| 1982 | 1.30 | 104.0 | 113.0 |
| 1983 | 1.24 | 99.2 | 107.8 |
| 1984 | 1.21 | 96.8 | 105.2 |
| 1985 | 1.20 | 96.0 | 104.3 |
| 1986 | 0.93 | 74.4 | 80.9 |
| 1987 | 0.95 | 76.0 | 82.6 |
| 1988 | 0.95 | 76.0 | 82.6 |
| 1989 | 1.02 | 81.6 | 88.7 |
| 1990 | 1.16 | 92.8 | 100.9 |
| 1991 | 1.14 | 91.2 | 99.1 |
| 1992 | 1.14 | 91.2 | 99.1 |
| 1993 | 1.11 | 88.8 | 96.5 |
| 1994 | 1.11 | 88.8 | 96.5 |
| 1995 | 1.15 | 92.0 | 100.0 |
| 1996 | 1.23 | 98.4 | 107.0 |
| 1997 | 1.23 | 98.4 | 107.0 |
| 1998 | 1.06 | 84.8 | 92.2 |
| 1999 | 1.17 | 93.6 | 101.7 |
| 2000 | 1.51 | 120.8 | 131.3 |
| 2001 | 1.46 | 116.8 | 127.0 |
| 2002 | 1.36 | 108.8 | 118.3 |
| 2003 | 1.59 | 127.2 | 138.3 |
| 2004 | 1.88 | 150.4 | 163.5 |
| 2005 | 2.30 | 184.0 | 200.0 |
| 2006 | 2.59 | 207.2 | 225.2 |

Source: *Bureau of Labor Statistics, U.S. Department of Labor,* **www.bls.gov**.

---

Shifting the Base for a Simple Price Index

$$I_{new} = \frac{I_{old}}{I_{new\ base}} \times 100 \tag{16.22}$$

where

$$I_{new} = \text{new price index}$$
$$I_{old} = \text{old price index}$$
$$I_{new\ base} = \text{value of the old price index for the new base year}$$

To change the base year to 1995, $I_{new\ base} = 92.0$. Using Equation (16.22) to find the new price index for 2006,

$$I_{new} = \frac{I_{old}}{I_{new\ base}} \times 100 = \frac{207.2}{92.0} \times 100 = 225.2$$

Thus, the 2006 price for unleaded gasoline in the United States was more than twice the price that it was in 1995. See Table 16.4 for the complete set of price indexes.

## Aggregate Price Indexes

An aggregate price index consists of a group of commodities taken together. The group of commodities under consideration is often called a *market basket*. There are two types of aggregate price indexes: unweighted aggregate price indexes and weighted aggregate price indexes. An **unweighted aggregate price index**, defined in Equation (16.23), places equal weight on all the items in the market basket.

Unweighted Aggregate Price Index

$$I_U^{(t)} = \frac{\sum_{i=1}^{n} P_i^{(t)}}{\sum_{i=1}^{n} P_i^{(0)}} \times 100 \qquad (16.23)$$

where

$t$ = time period (0, 1, 2, . . .)

$i$ = item (1, 2, . . . , $n$)

$n$ = total number of items under consideration

$\sum_{i=1}^{n} P_i^{(t)}$ = sum of the prices paid for each of the $n$ commodities at time period $t$

$\sum_{i=1}^{n} P_i^{(0)}$ = sum of the prices paid for each of the $n$ commodities at time period 0

$I_U^{(t)}$ = value of the unweighted price index at time period $t$

Table 16.5 presents the mean prices for three fruit items for selected periods from 1980 to 2005 (stored in the file Fruit).

**TABLE 16.5**

Prices (in Dollars per Pound) for Three Fruit Items

| | Year | | | | | |
|---|---|---|---|---|---|---|
| **Fruit** | **1980** $P_i^{(0)}$ | **1985** $P_i^{(1)}$ | **1990** $P_i^{(2)}$ | **1995** $P_i^{(3)}$ | **2000** $P_i^{(4)}$ | **2005** $P_i^{(5)}$ |
| **Apples** | 0.692 | 0.684 | 0.719 | 0.835 | 0.927 | 0.966 |
| **Bananas** | 0.342 | 0.367 | 0.463 | 0.490 | 0.509 | 0.838 |
| **Oranges** | 0.365 | 0.533 | 0.570 | 0.625 | 0.638 | 0.490 |

Source: *Bureau of Labor Statistics, U.S. Department of Labor,* **www.bls.gov.**

To calculate the unweighted aggregate price index for the various years, using Equation (16.23) and 1980 as the base period:

$$1980: I_U^{(0)} = \frac{\sum_{i=1}^{3} P_i^{(0)}}{\sum_{i=1}^{3} P_i^{(0)}} \times 100 = \frac{0.692 + 0.342 + 0.365}{0.692 + 0.342 + 0.365} \times 100 = \frac{1.399}{1.399} \times 100 = 100.0$$

$$1985: I_U^{(1)} = \frac{\sum_{i=1}^{3} P_i^{(1)}}{\sum_{i=1}^{3} P_i^{(0)}} \times 100 = \frac{0.684 + 0.367 + 0.533}{0.692 + 0.342 + 0.365} \times 100 = \frac{1.584}{1.399} \times 100 = 113.2$$

$$1990: I_U^{(2)} = \frac{\sum_{i=1}^{3} P_i^{(2)}}{\sum_{i=1}^{3} P_i^{(0)}} \times 100 = \frac{0.719 + 0.463 + 0.570}{0.692 + 0.342 + 0.365} \times 100 = \frac{1.752}{1.399} \times 100 = 125.2$$

$$1995: I_U^{(3)} = \frac{\sum_{i=1}^{3} P_i^{(3)}}{\sum_{i=1}^{3} P_i^{(0)}} \times 100 = \frac{0.835 + 0.490 + 0.625}{0.692 + 0.342 + 0.365} \times 100 = \frac{1.950}{1.399} \times 100 = 139.4$$

$$2000: I_U^{(4)} = \frac{\sum_{i=1}^{3} P_i^{(4)}}{\sum_{i=1}^{3} P_i^{(0)}} \times 100 = \frac{0.927 + 0.509 + 0.638}{0.692 + 0.342 + 0.365} \times 100 = \frac{2.074}{1.399} \times 100 = 148.2$$

$$2005: I_U^{(5)} = \frac{\sum_{i=1}^{3} P_i^{(5)}}{\sum_{i=1}^{3} P_i^{(0)}} \times 100 = \frac{0.966 + 0.838 + 0.490}{0.692 + 0.342 + 0.365} \times 100 = \frac{2.294}{1.399} \times 100 = 164.0$$

Thus, in 2005, the combined price of a pound of apples, a pound of bananas, and a pound of oranges was 64% more than it was in 1980.

An unweighted aggregate price index represents the changes in prices, over time, for an entire group of commodities. However, an unweighted aggregate price index has two shortcomings. First, this index considers each commodity in the group as equally important. Thus, the most expensive commodities per unit are overly influential. Second, not all the commodities are consumed at the same rate. In an unweighted index, changes in the price of the least-consumed commodities are overly influential.

## Weighted Aggregate Price Indexes

Due to the shortcomings of unweighted aggregate price indexes, weighted aggregate price indexes are generally preferable. **Weighted aggregate price indexes** account for differences in the magnitude of prices per unit and differences in the consumption levels of the items in the market basket. Two types of weighted aggregate price indexes are commonly used in business and economics: the Laspeyres price index and the Paasche price index. Equation (16.24) defines the **Laspeyres price index**, which uses the consumption quantities associated with the base year in the calculation of all price indexes in the series.

Laspeyres Price Index

$$I_L^{(t)} = \frac{\sum_{i=1}^{n} P_i^{(t)} Q_i^{(0)}}{\sum_{i=1}^{n} P_i^{(0)} Q_i^{(0)}} \times 100 \qquad (16.24)$$

where

$t$ = time period (0, 1, 2, . . .)

$i$ = item (1, 2, . . . , $n$)

$n$ = total number of items under consideration

$Q_i^{(0)}$ = quantity of item $i$ at time period 0

$I_L^{(t)}$ = value of the Laspeyres price index at time $t$

$P_i^{(t)}$ = price paid for commodity $i$ at time period $t$

$P_i^{(0)}$ = price paid for commodity $i$ at time period 0

Table 16.6 gives the price and per capita consumption, in pounds, for the three fruit items comprising the market basket of interest (see the file Fruit).

**TABLE 16.6**

Prices (in Dollars per Pound) and Quantities (Annual per Capita Consumption, in Pounds) for Three Fruit Items*

| Fruit | Year | | | | | |
|---|---|---|---|---|---|---|
| | 1980 $P_i^{(0)}, Q_i^{(0)}$ | 1985 $P_i^{(1)}, Q_i^{(1)}$ | 1990 $P_i^{(2)}, Q_i^{(2)}$ | 1995 $P_i^{(3)}, Q_i^{(3)}$ | 2000 $P_i^{(4)}, Q_i^{(4)}$ | 2005 $P_i^{(5)}, Q_i^{(5)}$ |
| **Apples** | 0.692, 19.2 | 0.684, 17.3 | 0.719, 19.6 | 0.835, 18.9 | 0.927, 17.5 | 0.966, 16.0 |
| **Bananas** | 0.342, 20.2 | 0.367, 23.5 | 0.463, 24.4 | 0.490, 27.4 | 0.509, 28.5 | 0.838, 26.8 |
| **Oranges** | 0.365, 14.3 | 0.533, 11.6 | 0.570, 12.4 | 0.625, 12.0 | 0.638, 11.7 | 0.490, 10.6 |

Source: *Bureau of Labor Statistics, U.S. Department of Labor,* **www.bls.gov**, *and Statistical Abstract of the United States, U.S. Census Bureau,* **www.census.gov**.
*The 2005 consumption values are preliminary estimates.

Using 1980 as the base year, you calculate the Laspeyres price index for 2005 ($t = 5$) using Equation (16.24):

$$I_L^{(5)} = \frac{\sum_{i=1}^{3} P_i^{(5)} Q_i^{(0)}}{\sum_{i=1}^{3} P_i^{(0)} Q_i^{(0)}} \times 100 = \frac{(0.966 \times 19.2) + (0.838 \times 20.2) + (0.490 \times 14.3)}{(0.692 \times 19.2) + (0.342 \times 20.2) + (0.365 \times 14.3)} \times 100$$

$$= \frac{42.4818}{25.4143} \times 100 = 167.2$$

Thus, the Laspeyres price index is 167.2, indicating that the cost of purchasing these three items in 2005 was 67.2% more than in 1980. This index is more than the unweighted index, 164.0, because the most-purchased item, bananas, increased in price more than apples and oranges in the time span. In other words, in the unweighted index, the least-purchased commodities (apples and oranges) are overly influential.

The **Paasche price index** uses the consumption quantities in the year of interest instead of using the initial quantities. Thus, the Paasche index is a more accurate reflection of total consumption costs at that point in time. However, there are two major drawbacks of the Paasche index. First, accurate consumption values for current purchases are often hard to obtain. Thus, many important indexes, such as the CPI, use the Laspeyres method. Second, if a particular product increases greatly in price compared to the other items in the market basket, consumers will avoid the high-priced item out of necessity, not because of changes in what they might prefer to purchase. Equation (16.25) defines the Paasche price index.

---

**Paasche Price Index**

$$I_P^{(t)} = \frac{\sum_{i=1}^{n} P_i^{(t)} Q_i^{(t)}}{\sum_{i=1}^{n} P_i^{(0)} Q_i^{(t)}} \times 100 \qquad \text{(16.25)}$$

where

$t$ = time period $(0, 1, 2, \ldots)$

$i$ = item $(1, 2, \ldots, n)$

$n$ = total number of items under consideration

$Q_i^{(t)}$ = quantity of item $i$ at time period $t$

$I_P^{(t)}$ = value of the Paasche price index at time period $t$

$P_i^{(t)}$ = price paid for commodity $i$ at time period $t$

$P_i^{(0)}$ = price paid for commodity $i$ at time period 0

---

To calculate the Paasche price index in 2005, using 1980 as a base year, you use $t = 5$ in Equation (16.25):

$$I_P^{(5)} = \frac{\sum_{i=1}^{3} P_i^{(5)} Q_i^{(5)}}{\sum_{i=1}^{3} P_i^{(0)} Q_i^{(5)}} \times 100 = \frac{(0.966 \times 16.0) + (0.838 \times 26.8) + (0.490 \times 10.6)}{(0.692 \times 16.0) + (0.342 \times 26.8) + (0.365 \times 10.6)} \times 100$$

$$= \frac{43.1084}{24.1066} \times 100 = 178.8$$

The Paasche price index for this market basket is 178.8. Thus, the cost of these three fruit items in 2000 was 78.8% higher in 2005 than in 1980, when using 2005 quantities.

## Some Common Price Indexes

Various price indexes are commonly used in business and economics. The CPI is the most familiar index in the United States. This index is officially referred to as the CPI-U to reflect that it measures the prices "urban" residents are subject to, but it is commonly referred to as the CPI. The CPI, published monthly by the U.S. Bureau of Labor Statistics, is the primary measure of changes in the cost of living in the United States. The CPI is a weighted aggregate price index, using the Laspeyres method, for 400 commonly purchased food, clothing, transportation, medical, and housing items. Currently computed using 1982–1984 averages as a base year, the CPI was 201.6 in 2006. (See data file CPI-U for a listing of the CPI-U for 1965–2006.)

Another important price index published by the U.S. Bureau of Labor Statistics is the producer price index (PPI). The PPI is a weighted aggregate price index that also uses the Laspeyres method for prices of commodities sold by wholesalers. The PPI is considered a leading indicator of the CPI. In other words, increases in the PPI tend to precede increases in the CPI, and, similarly, decreases in the PPI tend to precede decreases in the CPI.

Financial indexes such as the DJIA Index, the S&P 500 Index, and the NASDAQ Index are price indexes for different sets of stocks in the United States. Many indexes measure the performance of international stock markets, including the Nikkei Index for Japan, the Dax 30 for Germany, and the SSE Composite for China.

## PROBLEMS FOR SECTION 16.8

### Learning the Basics

**16.50** The simple price index for a commodity in 2007, using 1995 as the base year, is 175. Interpret this index number.

**16.51** The following are prices for a commodity from 2005 to 2007:

2005: $5
2006: $8
2007: $7

**a.** Calculate the simple price indexes for 2005 to 2007, using 2005 as the base year.
**b.** Calculate the simple price indexes for 2005 to 2007, using 2006 as the base year.

**16.52** The following are prices and consumption quantities for three commodities in 1995 and 2007:

| | Year | |
|---|---|---|
| | **1995** | **2007** |
| **Commodity** | **Price, Quantity** | **Price, Quantity** |
| A | $2, 20 | $3, 21 |
| B | $18, 3 | $36, 2 |
| C | $3, 18 | $4, 23 |

**a.** Calculate the unweighted aggregate price index for 2007, using 1995 as the base year.

**b.** Calculate the Laspeyres aggregate price index for 2007, using 1995 as the base year.
**c.** Calculate the Paasche aggregate price index for 2007, using 1995 as the base year.

### Applying the Concepts

**16.53** The data in the file DJIA represent the closing values of the DJIA from 1979 to 2006.
**a.** Calculate the price index for the DJIA with 1979 as the base year.
**b.** Shift the base of the DJIA to 1990 and recalculate the price index.
**c.** Compare the results of (a) and (b). Which price index do you think is more useful in understanding the changes in the DJIA? Explain.

**✓ SELF Test** **16.54** The data in the file Coffeeprice represent the mean price per pound of coffee in the United States from 1980 to 2006.

Source: *Bureau of Labor Statistics, U.S. Department of Labor,* **www.bls.gov**.

**a.** Calculate the simple price indexes for 1980 to 2006, using 1980 as the base year.
**b.** Interpret the simple price index for 2006, using 1980 as the base year.
**c.** Recalculate the simple price indexes found in (a), using Equation (16.22) on page 773, with 1990 as the base year.

**d.** Interpret the simple price index for 2006, using 1990 as the base year.

**e.** Would it be a good idea to use 1995 as the base year? Explain.

**f.** Describe the trends in coffee costs from 1980 to 2006.

**16.55** The following data represent the mean prices per pound of fresh tomatoes in the United States from 1980 to 2006 (see the file Tomatoes):

| Year | Price | Year | Price | Year | Price |
|------|-------|------|-------|------|-------|
| 1980 | 0.703 | 1989 | 0.797 | 1998 | 1.452 |
| 1981 | 0.792 | 1990 | 1.735 | 1999 | 1.904 |
| 1982 | 0.763 | 1991 | 0.912 | 2000 | 1.443 |
| 1983 | 0.726 | 1992 | 0.936 | 2001 | 1.414 |
| 1984 | 0.854 | 1993 | 1.141 | 2002 | 1.451 |
| 1985 | 0.697 | 1994 | 1.604 | 2003 | 1.711 |
| 1986 | 1.104 | 1995 | 1.323 | 2004 | 1.472 |
| 1987 | 0.943 | 1996 | 1.103 | 2005 | 1.660 |
| 1988 | 0.871 | 1997 | 1.213 | 2006 | 2.162 |

Source: *Bureau of Labor Statistics, U.S. Department of Labor,* **www.bls.gov**.

**a.** Calculate the simple price indexes for 1980 to 2006, using 1980 as the base year.

**b.** Interpret the simple price index for 2006, using 1980 as the base year.

**c.** Recalculate the simple price indexes found in (a), using Equation (16.22) on page 773, with 1990 as the base year.

**d.** Interpret the simple price index for 2006, using 1990 as the base year.

**e.** Describe the trends in the cost of fresh tomatoes from 1980 to 2006.

**✓ SELF Test** **16.56** The data in the file Energy2 represent the mean price for three types of energy products in the United States from 1992 to 2006. Included are electricity (dollars per 500 kWH), natural gas (dollars per 40 therms), and fuel oil (dollars per gallon).

Source: *Bureau of Labor Statistics, U.S. Department of Labor,* **www.bls.gov**.

**a.** Calculate the 1992–2006 simple price indexes for electricity, natural gas, and fuel oil, using 1992 as the base year.

**b.** Recalculate the price indexes in (a), using 1996 as the base year.

**c.** Calculate the 1992–2006 unweighted aggregate price indexes for the group of three energy items.

**d.** Calculate the 2006 Laspeyres price index for the group of three energy items for a family that consumed 5,000 kWH of electricity (10 units), 960 therms of natural gas (24 units), and 400 gallons of fuel oil (400 units) in 1992.

**e.** Calculate the 2006 Laspeyres price index for the group of three energy items for a family that consumed 6,500 kWH of electricity, 1,040 therms of natural gas, and 235 gallons of fuel oil in 1992.

# Let the Model User Beware

*From the Authors' Desktop*

Besides the statistical assumptions discussed in Sections 13.4, 13.5, and 14.2, the time-series models developed in this chapter also assume that past data can be used to predict the future. Using the past to predict the future is something that comes naturally to all of us. This is how we go about our everyday lives. But, if using past data to predict the future is a legitimate thing to do, how come a recent investment prospectus received by one of us included the warning "past performance is no guarantee of future results"?

Every so often, a crisis in financial markets illustrates that even though using the past to predict the future is legitimate, doing so is not without risk. The crisis involving hedge funds that occurred in August 2007 is an example of this. Apparently, many hedge fund managers used models that based their investment strategy on trading patterns over long time periods. These models did not—and could not—reflect trading patterns contrary to historical patterns (G. Morgenson, "A Week When Risk Came Home to Roost," *The New York Times*, August 12, 2007, pp. B1, B7). In August 2007, when fund managers needed to sell stocks due to losses in their fixed income portfolios, stocks that were previously stronger became weaker, and weaker ones became stronger—the reverse of what the models expected. In addition, because so many fund managers were using similar models, the effect of the selling pressure was multiplied, an effect that the models had not considered and therefore could not reflect in their results.

Using models does not absolve you of being a thoughtful decision maker. When you use models, you must always review the assumptions built into the model and must always reflect how novel or changing circumstances may render the model less useful. No model can completely remove risk involved in making a decision. Do go ahead and use models—appropriately used they will enhance your decision making—but don't lose sight of their limitations, or else you may lose much more.

## 16.9    ● (CD-ROM TOPIC) THE HOLT-WINTERS METHOD FOR TREND FITTING AND FORECASTING

The Holt-Winters method extends the exponential smoothing approach described in Section 16.3 by including the future trend. For further discussion, see section 16.9.pdf on the Student CD-ROM that accompanies this book.

# SUMMARY

In this chapter, you used time-series methods to develop forecasts for the Wm. Wrigley Jr. Company, Cabot Corporation, and Wal-Mart. You studied smoothing techniques, least-squares trend fitting, autoregressive models, forecasting of seasonal data, and index numbers. Figure 16.27 provides a summary chart for the time-series and index number methods discussed in this chapter.

If you are using time-series forecasting, you need to plot the time series and ask the following question: Is there a trend in the data? If there is a trend, then you can use the autoregressive model or the linear, quadratic, or exponential trend models. If there is no obvious trend in the time-series plot, then you should use moving averages or exponential smoothing to smooth out the effect of the random component and

possible cyclical components. After smoothing the data, if a trend is still not present, then you can use exponential smoothing to forecast future values. If smoothing the data reveals a trend, then you can use the autoregressive model, or the linear, quadratic, or exponential trend models.

If you are developing index numbers, you need to ask the following question: Are you developing an aggregate index of more than one commodity? If the answer is no, then you can use a simple price index. If the answer is yes, then you need to determine whether you will develop a weighted price index. If not, you can develop an unweighted price index. If you are developing a weighted price index, you can use a Laspeyres price index or a Paasche price index.

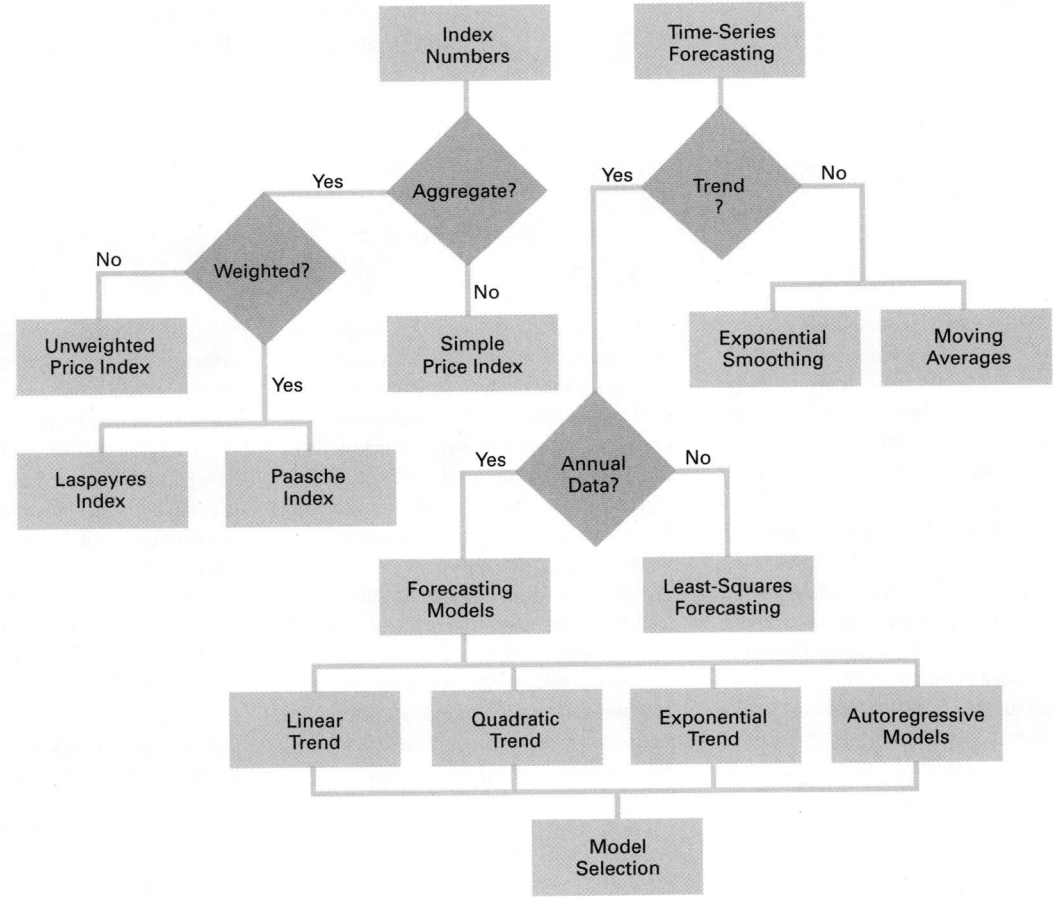

**FIGURE 16.27** Summary chart of time-series forecasting and index number methods

# KEY EQUATIONS

**Computing an Exponentially Smoothed Value in Time Period $i$**

$$E_1 = Y_1$$
$$E_i = WY_i + (1-W)E_{i-1} \quad i = 2, 3, 4, \ldots \qquad (16.1)$$

**Forecasting Time Period $i + 1$**

$$\hat{Y}_{i+1} = E_i \qquad (16.2)$$

**Linear Trend Forecasting Equation**

$$\hat{Y}_i = b_0 + b_1 X_i \qquad (16.3)$$

**Quadratic Trend Forecasting Equation**

$$\hat{Y}_i = b_0 + b_1 X_i + b_2 X_i^2 \qquad (16.4)$$

**Exponential Trend Model**

$$Y_i = \beta_0 \beta_1^{X_i} \varepsilon_i \qquad (16.5)$$

**Transformed Exponential Trend Model**

$$\begin{aligned}
\log(Y_i) &= \log(\beta_0 \beta_i^{X_i} \varepsilon_i) \\
&= \log(\beta_0) + \log(\beta_1^{X_i}) + \log(\varepsilon_i) \\
&= \log(\beta_0) + X_i \log(\beta_1) + \log(\varepsilon_i)
\end{aligned} \qquad (16.6)$$

**Exponential Trend Forecasting Equation**

$$\log(\hat{Y}_i) = b_0 + b_1 X_i \qquad (16.7a)$$

$$\hat{Y}_i = \hat{\beta}_0 \hat{\beta}_1^{X_i} \qquad (16.7b)$$

**First-Order Autoregressive Model**

$$Y_i = A_0 + A_1 Y_{i-1} + \delta_i \qquad (16.8)$$

**Second-Order Autoregressive Model**

$$Y_i = A_0 + A_1 Y_{i-1} + A_2 Y_{i-2} + \delta_i \qquad (16.9)$$

**$p$th-Order Autoregressive Models**

$$Y_i = A_0 + A_1 Y_{i-1} + A_2 Y_{i-2} + \cdots + A_p Y_{i-p} + \delta_i \qquad (16.10)$$

**$t$ Test for Significance of the Highest-Order Autoregressive Parameter, $A_p$**

$$t_{STAT} = \frac{a_p - A_p}{S_{a_p}} \qquad (16.11)$$

**Fitted $p$th-Order Autoregressive Equation**

$$\hat{Y}_i = a_0 + a_1 Y_{i-1} + a_2 Y_{i-2} + \cdots + a_p Y_{i-p} \qquad (16.12)$$

**$p$th-Order Autoregressive Forecasting Equation**

$$\hat{Y}_{n+j} = a_0 + a_1 \hat{Y}_{n+j-1} + a_2 \hat{Y}_{n+j-2} + \cdots + a_p \hat{Y}_{n+j-p} \qquad (16.13)$$

**Mean Absolute Deviation**

$$MAD = \frac{\sum_{i=1}^{n} |Y_i - \hat{Y}_i|}{n} \qquad (16.14)$$

**Exponential Model with Quarterly Data**

$$Y_i = \beta_0 \beta_1^{X_i} \beta_2^{Q_1} \beta_3^{Q_2} \beta_4^{Q_3} \varepsilon_i \qquad (16.15)$$

**Transformed Exponential Model with Quarterly Data**

$$\begin{aligned}
\log(Y_i) &= \log(\beta_0 \beta_1^{X_i} \beta_2^{Q_1} \beta_3^{Q_2} \beta_4^{Q_3} \varepsilon_i) \\
&= \log(\beta_0) + \log(\beta_1^{X_i}) + \log(\beta_2^{Q_1}) + \log(\beta_3^{Q_2}) \\
&\quad + \log(\beta_4^{Q_3}) + \log(\varepsilon_i) \\
&= \log(\beta_0) + X_i \log(\beta_1) + Q_1 \log(\beta_2) \\
&\quad + Q_2 \log(\beta_3) + Q_3 \log(\beta_4) + \log(\varepsilon_i)
\end{aligned} \qquad (16.16)$$

**Exponential Growth with Quarterly Data Forecasting Equation**

$$\log(\hat{Y}_i) = b_0 + b_1 X_i + b_2 Q_1 + b_3 Q_2 + b_4 Q_3 \qquad (16.17)$$

## Exponential Model with Monthly Data

$$Y_i = \beta_0 \beta_1^{X_i} \beta_2^{M_1} \beta_3^{M_2} \beta_4^{M_3} \beta_5^{M_4} \beta_6^{M_5} \beta_7^{M_6} \beta_8^{M_7} \beta_9^{M_8} \beta_{10}^{M_9} \beta_{11}^{M_{10}} \beta_{12}^{M_{11}} \varepsilon_i$$

(16.18)

## Transformed Exponential Model with Monthly Data

$$\begin{aligned}
\log(Y_i) &= \log(\beta_0 \beta_1^{X_i} \beta_2^{M_1} \beta_3^{M_2} \beta_4^{M_3} \beta_5^{M_4} \beta_6^{M_5} \beta_7^{M_6} \beta_8^{M_7} \beta_9^{M_8} \beta_{10}^{M_9} \beta_{11}^{M_{10}} \beta_{12}^{M_{11}} \varepsilon_i) \\
&= \log(\beta_0) + X_i \log(\beta_1) + M_1 \log(\beta_2) + M_2 \log(\beta_3) \\
&\quad + M_3 \log(\beta_4) + M_4 \log(\beta_5) + M_5 \log(\beta_6) + M_6 \log(\beta_7) \\
&\quad + M_7 \log(\beta_8) + M_8 \log(\beta_9) + M_9 \log(\beta_{10}) + M_{10} \log(\beta_{11}) \\
&\quad + M_{11} \log(\beta_{12}) + \log(\varepsilon_i)
\end{aligned}$$

(16.19)

## Exponential Growth with Monthly Data Forecasting Equation

$$\begin{aligned}
\log(\hat{Y}_i) &= b_0 + b_1 X_i + b_2 M_1 + b_3 M_2 + b_4 M_3 + b_5 M_4 + b_6 M_5 \\
&\quad + b_7 M_6 + b_8 M_7 + b_9 M_8 + b_{10} M_9 + b_{11} M_{10} + b_{12} M_{11}
\end{aligned}$$

(16.20)

## Simple Price Index

$$I_i = \frac{P_i}{P_{base}} \times 100$$

(16.21)

## Shifting the Base for a Simple Price Index

$$I_{new} = \frac{I_{old}}{I_{new\ base}} \times 100$$

(16.22)

## Unweighted Aggregate Price Index

$$I_U^{(t)} = \frac{\sum_{i=1}^{n} P_i^{(t)}}{\sum_{i=1}^{n} P_i^{(0)}} \times 100$$

(16.23)

## Laspeyres Price Index

$$I_L^{(t)} = \frac{\sum_{i=1}^{n} P_i^{(t)} Q_i^{(0)}}{\sum_{i=1}^{n} P_i^{(0)} Q_i^{(0)}} \times 100$$

(16.24)

## Paasche Price Index

$$I_P^{(t)} = \frac{\sum_{i=1}^{n} P_i^{(t)} Q_i^{(t)}}{\sum_{i=1}^{n} P_i^{(0)} Q_i^{(t)}} \times 100$$

(16.25)

# KEY TERMS

aggregate price index   772
autoregressive modeling   750
base period   772
causal forecasting methods   731
cyclical component   731
exponential smoothing   735
exponential trend model   742
first-order autocorrelation   750
first-order autoregressive
   model   751
forecasting   730
index numbers   771
irregular component   731

Laspeyres price index   776
linear trend model   738
mean absolute deviation
   (*MAD*)   761
moving averages   732
Paasche price index   777
parsimony   761
price index   772
*p*th-order autocorrelation   750
*p*th-order autoregressive
   model   751
quadratic trend model   741
qualitative forecasting methods   730

quantitative forecasting methods   730
random component   731
seasonal component   731
second-order autocorrelation   750
second-order autoregressive
   model   751
simple price index   772
time series   730
time-series forecasting methods   730
trend   731
unweighted aggregate price
   index   774
weighted aggregate price index   775

# CHAPTER REVIEW PROBLEMS

## Checking Your Understanding

**16.57** What is a time series?

**16.58** What are the different components of a time-series model?

**16.59** What is the difference between moving averages and exponential smoothing?

**16.60** Under what circumstances is the exponential trend model most appropriate?

**16.61** How does the least-squares linear trend forecasting model developed in this chapter differ from the least-squares linear regression model considered in Chapter 13?

**16.62** How does autoregressive modeling differ from the other approaches to forecasting?

**16.63** What are the different approaches to choosing an appropriate forecasting model?

**16.64** What is the major difference between using $S_{YX}$ and *MAD* for evaluating how well a particular model fits the data?

**16.65** How does forecasting for monthly or quarterly data differ from forecasting for annual data?

**16.66** What is an index number?

**16.67** What is the difference between a simple price index and an aggregate price index?

**16.68** What is the difference between a Paasche price index and a Laspeyres price index?

## Applying the Concepts

**16.69** The following table (stored in the file **Polio**) represents the annual incidence rates (per 100,000 persons) of reported acute poliomyelitis recorded over five-year periods from 1915 to 1955:

| Year | 1915 | 1920 | 1925 | 1930 | 1935 | 1940 | 1945 | 1950 | 1955 |
|------|------|------|------|------|------|------|------|------|------|
| Rate | 3.1 | 2.2 | 5.3 | 7.5 | 8.5 | 7.4 | 10.3 | 22.1 | 17.6 |

Source: *Extracted from B. Wattenberg, ed.,* The Statistical History of the United States: From Colonial Times to the Present, *ser. B303 (New York: Basic Books, 1976).*

a. Plot the data.
b. Compute the linear trend forecasting equation and plot the trend line.
c. What are your forecasts for 1960, 1965, and 1970?
d. Using a library or the Internet, find the actually reported incidence rates of acute poliomyelitis for 1960, 1965, and 1970. Record your results.

e. Why are the forecasts you made in (c) not useful? Discuss.

**16.70** The U.S. Department of Labor gathers and publishes statistics concerning the labor market. The data file **Workforce** contains the U.S. civilian noninstitutional population of people 16 years and over (in thousands) and the U.S. civilian noninstitutional workforce of people 16 years and over (in thousands) for 1984–2006. The workforce variable reports the number of people in the population who have a job or are actively looking for a job.

| Year | Population | Workforce | Year | Population | Workforce |
|------|-----------|-----------|------|-----------|-----------|
| 1984 | 176,383 | 113,544 | 1996 | 200,591 | 133,943 |
| 1985 | 178,206 | 115,461 | 1997 | 203,133 | 136,297 |
| 1986 | 180,587 | 117,834 | 1998 | 205,220 | 137,673 |
| 1987 | 182,753 | 119,865 | 1999 | 207,753 | 139,368 |
| 1988 | 184,613 | 121,669 | 2000 | 212,577 | 142,583 |
| 1989 | 186,393 | 123,869 | 2001 | 215,092 | 143,734 |
| 1990 | 189,164 | 125,840 | 2002 | 217,570 | 144,863 |
| 1991 | 190,925 | 126,346 | 2003 | 221,168 | 146,510 |
| 1992 | 192,805 | 128,105 | 2004 | 223,357 | 147,401 |
| 1993 | 194,838 | 129,200 | 2005 | 226,082 | 149,320 |
| 1994 | 196,814 | 131,056 | 2006 | 228,815 | 151,428 |
| 1995 | 198,584 | 132,304 | | | |

Source: *Bureau of Labor Statistics, U.S. Department of Labor,* **www.bls.gov**.

a. Plot the time series for the U.S. civilian noninstitutional population of people 16 years and older.
b. Compute the linear trend forecasting equation.
c. Forecast the U.S. civilian noninstitutional population of people 16 years and older for 2007 and 2008.
d. Repeat (a) through (c) for the U.S. civilian noninstitutional workforce of people 16 years and older.

**16.71** The quarterly price for natural gas (dollars per 40 therms) in the United States from 1994 through 2006 is given in the data file **Naturalgas**.
Source: *Bureau of Labor Statistics, U.S. Department of Labor,* **www.bls.gov**.

a. Do you think the price for natural gas has a seasonal component?
b. Plot the time series. Does this chart support your answer in (a)?
c. Compute an exponential trend forecasting equation for quarterly data.
d. Interpret the quarterly compound growth rate.
e. Interpret the quarter multipliers. Do the multipliers support your answers to (a) and (b)?

**16.72** The data in the following table (stored in the file McDonalds) represent the gross revenues (in billions of current dollars) of McDonald's Corporation from 1975 through 2006:

| Year | Revenues | Year | Revenues | Year | Revenues |
|------|----------|------|----------|------|----------|
| 1975 | 1.0 | 1986 | 4.2 | 1997 | 11.4 |
| 1976 | 1.2 | 1987 | 4.9 | 1998 | 12.4 |
| 1977 | 1.4 | 1988 | 5.6 | 1999 | 13.3 |
| 1978 | 1.7 | 1989 | 6.1 | 2000 | 14.2 |
| 1979 | 1.9 | 1990 | 6.8 | 2001 | 14.8 |
| 1980 | 2.2 | 1991 | 6.7 | 2002 | 15.2 |
| 1981 | 2.5 | 1992 | 7.1 | 2003 | 16.8 |
| 1982 | 2.8 | 1993 | 7.4 | 2004 | 18.6 |
| 1983 | 3.1 | 1994 | 8.3 | 2005 | 19.8 |
| 1984 | 3.4 | 1995 | 9.8 | 2006 | 21.6 |
| 1985 | 3.8 | 1996 | 10.7 | | |

Source: *Extracted from* Moody's Handbook of Common Stocks, 1980, 1989, and 1999, *and* Mergent's Handbook of Common Stocks, Spring 2002 *and* **www.mcdonalds.com**.

a. Plot the data.
b. Compute the linear trend forecasting equation.
c. Compute the quadratic trend forecasting equation.
d. Compute the exponential trend forecasting equation.
e. Find the best-fitting autoregressive model, using $\alpha = 0.05$.
f. Perform a residual analysis for each of the models in (b) through (e).
g. Compute the standard error of the estimate ($S_{YX}$) and the *MAD* for each corresponding model in (f).
h. On the basis of your results in (f) and (g), along with a consideration of the principle of parsimony, which model would you select for purposes of forecasting? Discuss.
i. Using the selected model in (h), forecast gross revenues for 2007.

**16.73** The U.S. Census Bureau tracks the number of new houses that begin construction each quarter. This metric of economic activity is often referred to as "housing starts." The file Housing contains quarterly data from 2000 to 2006.

| Quarter | Units | Quarter | Units | Quarter | Units |
|---------|-------|---------|-------|---------|-------|
| 2000—1 | 278 | 2002—3 | 361 | 2005—1 | 369 |
| 2000—2 | 357 | 2002—4 | 319 | 2005—2 | 485 |
| 2000—3 | 320 | 2003—1 | 304 | 2005—3 | 471 |
| 2000—4 | 275 | 2003—2 | 406 | 2005—4 | 392 |
| 2001—1 | 274 | 2003—3 | 412 | 2006—1 | 382 |
| 2001—2 | 374 | 2003—4 | 377 | 2006—2 | 433 |
| 2001—3 | 341 | 2004—1 | 345 | 2006—3 | 372 |
| 2001—4 | 285 | 2004—2 | 456 | 2006—4 | 278 |
| 2002—1 | 293 | 2004—3 | 440 | | |
| 2002—2 | 386 | 2004—4 | 370 | | |

a. Do you think new housing construction is seasonal? Why or why not?
b. Plot the data.
c. Does your graph in (b) support your answer to (a)?
d. Develop an exponential trend forecasting equation with quarterly data.
e. Based on (d), which quarter has the most housing starts? The least housing starts?
f. Is there a long-term trend from 2000 to 2006 in the number of new houses being built?

**16.74** Teachers' Retirement System of the City of New York offers several types of investments for its members. Among the choices are investments with fixed and variable rates of return. There are currently two categories of variable return investments. Variable *A* consists of investments that are primarily made in stocks, and variable *B* consists of investments in corporate bonds and other types of lower-risk instruments. The following data (stored in the file Trsnyc) represent the value of a unit of each type of variable return investment at the beginning of each year from 1984 to 2007:

| Year | A | B | Year | A | B |
|------|------|------|------|------|------|
| 1984 | 13.111 | 10.342 | 1996 | 39.644 | 17.682 |
| 1985 | 13.176 | 11.073 | 1997 | 45.389 | 18.004 |
| 1986 | 16.526 | 11.925 | 1998 | 54.882 | 18.341 |
| 1987 | 18.652 | 12.694 | 1999 | 64.790 | 18.678 |
| 1988 | 15.564 | 13.352 | 2000 | 74.220 | 18.962 |
| 1989 | 20.827 | 13.919 | 2001 | 67.534 | 19.320 |
| 1990 | 24.738 | 14.557 | 2002 | 57.709 | 19.673 |
| 1991 | 22.678 | 15.213 | 2003 | 44.843 | 19.735 |
| 1992 | 28.549 | 15.883 | 2004 | 55.993 | 19.609 |
| 1993 | 29.829 | 16.510 | 2005 | 60.909 | 19.520 |
| 1994 | 32.199 | 16.970 | 2006 | 63.038 | 19.452 |
| 1995 | 30.830 | 17.351 | 2007 | 70.413 | 19.441 |

Source: *Teachers' Retirement System of the City of New York,* **www.trs.nyc.ny.us**.

For each of the two time series,
a. plot the data.
b. compute the linear trend forecasting equation.
c. compute the quadratic trend forecasting equation.
d. compute the exponential trend forecasting equation.
e. find the best-fitting autoregressive model, using $\alpha = 0.05$.
f. Perform a residual analysis for each of the models in (b) through (e).
g. Compute the standard error of the estimate ($S_{YX}$) and the *MAD* for each corresponding model in (f).
h. On the basis of your results in (f) and (g), along with a consideration of the principle of parsimony, which model would you select for purposes of forecasting? Discuss.
i. Using the selected model in (h), forecast the unit values for 2008.

**j.** Based on the results of (a) through (i), what investment strategy would you recommend for a member of the Teachers' Retirement System of the City of New York? Explain.

**16.75** The data file Basket contains the prices of a basket of food items from 1992 to 2006. Included are the prices (in dollars) for a one-pound loaf of white bread, a pound of beef (ground chuck), a dozen grade A large eggs, and one pound of iceberg lettuce:

| Year | Bread | Beef | Eggs | Lettuce |
|------|-------|------|------|---------|
| 1992 | 0.726 | 1.926 | 0.933 | 0.573 |
| 1993 | 0.748 | 1.970 | 0.898 | 0.625 |
| 1994 | 0.768 | 1.892 | 0.917 | 0.506 |
| 1995 | 0.767 | 1.847 | 0.882 | 0.821 |
| 1996 | 0.860 | 1.799 | 1.155 | 0.769 |
| 1997 | 0.862 | 1.850 | 1.148 | 0.651 |
| 1998 | 0.855 | 1.818 | 1.120 | 1.072 |
| 1999 | 0.872 | 1.834 | 1.053 | 0.649 |
| 2000 | 0.907 | 1.903 | 0.975 | 0.748 |
| 2001 | 0.982 | 2.037 | 1.011 | 0.736 |
| 2002 | 1.001 | 2.151 | 0.973 | 1.003 |
| 2003 | 1.042 | 2.131 | 1.175 | 0.734 |
| 2004 | 0.946 | 2.585 | 1.573 | 0.876 |
| 2005 | 0.997 | 2.478 | 1.211 | 0.817 |
| 2006 | 1.046 | 2.607 | 1.449 | 0.874 |

Source: *Bureau of Labor Statistics, U.S. Department of Labor,* **www.bls.gov**.

**a.** Compute the 1992–2006 simple price indexes for bread, beef, eggs, and lettuce, using 1992 as the base year.

**b.** Recalculate the price indexes in (a), using 1996 as the base year.

**c.** Compute the 1992–2006 unweighted aggregate price indexes for the basket of these four food items.

**d.** Compute the 2006 Laspeyres price index for the basket of these four food items for a family that consumed 50 loaves of bread, 22 pounds of beef, 24 dozen eggs, and 18 pounds of lettuce in 1992.

**e.** Compute the 2006 Paasche price index for the basket of these four food items for a family that consumed 55 loaves of bread, 17 pounds of beef, 20 dozen eggs, and 28 pounds of lettuce in 2006.

### Report Writing Exercises

**16.76** As a consultant to an investment company trading in various currencies, you have been assigned the task of studying the long-term trends in the exchange rates of the Canadian dollar, the Japanese yen, and the English pound. Data have been collected from 1967 to 2006 and are contained in the file Currency, where the Canadian dollar, the Japanese yen, and the English pound are expressed in units per U.S. dollar.

Develop a forecasting model for the exchange rate of each of these three currencies and provide forecasts for 2007 and 2008 for each currency. Write an executive summary for a presentation to be given to the investment company. Append to this executive summary a discussion regarding possible limitations that may exist in these models.

# MANAGING THE *SPRINGVILLE HERALD*

As part of the continuing strategic initiative to increase home-delivery subscriptions, the circulation department is closely monitoring the number of such subscriptions. The circulation department wants to forecast future home-delivery subscriptions. To accomplish this task, the circulation department compiled the number of home-delivery subscriptions for the most recent 24-month period in the file SH16.

### EXERCISE

SH16.1  **a.** Analyze these data and develop a model to forecast home-delivery subscriptions. Present your findings in a report that includes the assumptions of the model and its limitations. Forecast home-delivery subscriptions for the next four months.

**b.** Would you be willing to use the model developed to forecast home-delivery subscriptions one year into the future? Explain.

**c.** Compare the trend in home-delivery subscriptions to the number of new subscriptions per month provided in the data file SH13. What explanation can you provide for any differences?

# WEB CASE

*Apply your knowledge about time-series forecasting in this Web Case, which extends the running "Managing the Springville Herald" case that appears in selected chapters of this book.*

The *Springville Herald* competes for readers in the Tri-Cities area with the newer *Oxford Glen Journal* (*OGJ*). Recently, the circulation staff at the *OGJ* claimed that their newspaper's circulation and subscription base is growing faster than that of the *Herald* and that local advertisers would do better transferring their advertisements from the *Herald* to the *OGJ*. The circulation department of the *Herald* has complained to the Springville Chamber of Commerce about *OGJ*'s claims and has asked the chamber to investigate, a request that was welcomed by *OGJ*'s circulation staff.

Review the circulation dispute information collected by the Springville Chamber of Commerce at the Web page, **www.prenhall.com/Springville/SCC_CirculationDispute. htm** (or open the `SCC_CirculationDispute.htm` file from the Student CD-ROM Web Case folder) and then answer the following:

1. Which newspaper would you say has the right to claim the fastest-growing circulation and subscription base? Support your answer by performing and summarizing an appropriate statistical analysis.

2. What is the single most positive fact about the *Herald*'s circulation and subscription base? What is the single most positive fact about the *OGJ*'s circulation and subscription base? Explain your answers.

3. What additional data would be helpful in investigating the circulation claims made by the staffs of each newspaper?

# REFERENCES

1. Bowerman, B. L., R. T. O'Connell, and A. Koehler, *Forecasting, Time Series, and Regression*, 4th ed. (Belmont, CA: Duxbury Press, 2005).
2. Box, G. E. P., G. M. Jenkins, and G. C. Reinsel, *Time Series Analysis: Forecasting and Control*, 3rd ed. (Upper Saddle River, NJ: Prentice Hall, 1994).
3. Frees, E. W., *Data Analysis Using Regression Models: The Business Perspective* (Upper Saddle River, NJ: Prentice Hall, 1996).
4. Hanke, J. E., D. W. Wichern, and A. G. Reitsch, *Business Forecasting*, 7th ed. (Upper Saddle River, NJ: Prentice Hall, 2001).
5. *Microsoft Excel 2007* (Redmond, WA: Microsoft Corp., 2007).
6. *Minitab for Windows Version 15* (State College, PA: Minitab, Inc., 2006).

# Appendix E16
## Using Microsoft Excel for Time-Series Forecasting and Index Numbers

## E16.1 Computing Moving Averages

You compute a moving average by adding a column whose cells will either contain the special Excel value **#N/A** (not available) or a simple formula using the AVERAGE function. To create such a column, open to a worksheet that contains time-series data in row order (each row is one time period). In a blank column, enter formulas that use the AVERAGE function to average values in the cell range that matches your chosen period of length *L*. Each formula should be entered in the middle row of the cell range that the formula averages. Then enter the special value **#N/A** in the cells at the beginning and end of the column for which no moving average can be computed.

For example, to create three-year and seven-year moving averages for the Cabot Corporation revenue data, open to the **Data** worksheet of the `Cabot.xls` workbook and make

entries in the blank columns C and D. Figure E16.1 shows the entries for the first four and last five data rows of these columns and illustrates how the special value **#N/A** is used at the beginning and end of a moving average column.

| | A | B | C | D |
|---|---|---|---|---|
| 1 | Year | Revenue | MA 3-Year | MA 7-Year |
| 2 | 1982 | 1588 | #N/A | #N/A |
| 3 | 1983 | 1558 | =AVERAGE(B2:B4) | #N/A |
| 4 | 1984 | 1753 | =AVERAGE(B3:B5) | #N/A |
| 5 | 1985 | 1408 | =AVERAGE(B4:B6) | =AVERAGE(B2:B8) |
| 22 | 2002 | 1557 | =AVERAGE(B21:B23) | =AVERAGE(B19:B25) |
| 23 | 2003 | 1795 | =AVERAGE(B22:B24) | =AVERAGE(B20:B26) |
| 24 | 2004 | 1934 | =AVERAGE(B23:B25) | #N/A |
| 25 | 2005 | 2125 | =AVERAGE(B24:B26) | #N/A |
| 26 | 2006 | 2543 | #N/A | #N/A |

**FIGURE E16.1** Moving averages columns (rows 6 through 21 not shown)

## E16.2 Creating Moving-Average Plots: Overview

You create time-series plots by using Excel charting features. Base your plots on a time-series worksheet in which the time periods have been entered into column A.

### E16.2A Creating Moving-Average Plots (Excel 97–2003)

Open to the time-series data worksheet and then select **Insert → Chart** (to begin the Chart Wizard). Make the following entries in the Wizard Step dialog boxes:

**Wizard Step 1**  Click XY (Scatter) from the Standard Types Chart type box. Click the first choice of the third row in the Chart sub-types gallery, described as Scatter with data points connected by lines.

**Wizard Step 2**  Click the **Data Range** tab. Enter the cell range of the original data and the moving-average data as the **Data range** and select the **Columns** option. For example, for the modified Data worksheet shown in Figure E16.1, you would enter **A1:D26** as the Data Range.

**Wizard Step 3**  Click the Titles tab. Enter Moving Averages for the Cabot Corporation as the Chart title, Revenue ($ millions) as the Value (Y) axis title, and Year as the Value (X) axis title. Click the Legend tab and click Show legend. Click, in turn, the Axes, Gridlines, and Data Labels tabs and use the formatting settings given in Section E2.3A (see page 72).

### E16.2B Creating Moving-Average Plots (Excel 2007)

Open to the time-series data worksheet and select the cell range of the original data and the moving-average data. (If you were using the worksheet shown in Figure E16.1, you would select **A1:D26**.) Select **Insert → Scatter → Scatter with Straight Lines and Markers**. Finish by relocating your chart to a chart sheet and customizing your chart using the instructions in Section E.2.3B (see page 73), modifying the instruction for (chart) **Legend** by selecting something other than **None** in order to display a necessary chart legend.

## E16.3 Computing Exponentially Smoothed Values

You create exponentially smoothed values by using the ToolPak Exponential Smoothing procedure. Open to the worksheet containing your time-series data in row-wise order.

Select **Tools → Data Analysis** (Excel 97–2003) or **Data → Data Analysis** (Excel 2007). Then select **Exponential Smoothing** from the Data Analysis list and click **OK**. In the Exponential Smoothing dialog box (shown below), enter the cell range of the time-series variable to be smoothed as the **Input Range**, and enter either **0.5** (for W = .50) *or* **0.75** (for W = 0.25, as 1 − 0.25 equals 0.75) as the **damping factor**. Click **Labels**, enter the column cell range to hold the smoothed values as the **Output Range**, and click **OK**. The column cell range should begin with row 2 so as to leave the row 1 cell blank. (Enter a column heading in the row 1 cell after the procedure creates the column.)

The column of formulas created shows exponentially smoothed values for each time period *i* one row down from the row that displays the time period. To adjust the column so that the exponentially smoothed values appear in the proper (same time period) rows, right-click the **row 2 cell** in that column and select **Delete** from the shortcut menu. In the Delete dialog box, click **Shift cells up** and then click **OK**. Then copy the formula in the second-to-last cell of the column down to the last cell.

## E16.4 Creating Coded X Variables

You create a coded *X* variable by adding a new column that contains an integer series starting with zero to your time-series data worksheet. In a blank column, enter a column label in the row 1 cell and the first integer in the series in the row 2 cell. Automate the entry of the other integers by reselecting the row 2 cell and selecting **Edit → Fill → Series** (Excel 97–2003) or **Home → Fill → Series** (Excel 2007; Fill is in the editing group). In the Series dialog box (shown at the top of page 788), select the **Columns** and **Linear** options, enter the appropriate **Step value** and **Stop value** and click **OK**.

For example, enter **1** as the **Step value** and **23** as the **Stop value** to complete the twenty-four integer series 0 through 23.

## E16.5 Creating Quadratic and Exponential Terms

You create quadratic and exponential terms using the instructions of Sections E15.1 and E15.2 (see page 725). For an exponential term, use the LOG function described in Section E15.2.

## E16.6 Using Least-Squares Linear Trend Fitting

You use least-squares linear trend fitting by modifying the Section E13.1 instructions (see page 629) to use the cell range of the coded variable as the $X$ variable cell range. To plot the linear trend, use the Section E13.2 instructions (see page 630).

## E16.7 Using Least-Squares Quadratic Trend Fitting

You use least-squares quadratic trend fitting by modifying the Section E14.1 instructions (see page 685) to use the cell range of the coded variable and the squared coded variable as the $X$ variables cell range. To plot the quadratic trend, use the Section E13.2 instructions (see page 630), but click **Polynomial** and not Linear as the **Trend/Regression type** (see either Figure E13.1 on page 629 or Figure E13.2 on page 630).

## E16.8 Using Least-Squares Exponential Trend Fitting

You use least-squares exponential trend fitting by modifying the Section E13.1 instructions to use the cell range of the log $Y$ values as the $Y$ variable cell range and the cell range of the coded variable as the $X$ variable cell range. To plot the exponential trend, see the next section. (You cannot modify the instructions of Section E13.2 to plot the exponential trend because the Residual Output table in the regression results worksheet contains the log of the predicted values and not the predicted values themselves.)

## E16.9 Plotting Least-Squares Exponential Trends: Overview

You compute the predicted $Y$ values from the log of the predicated values and then use the Section E2.13 instructions to plot a least-squares exponential trend.

First, create a new column of formulas labeled "**Predicted Y**" in the form =**POWER(***10, log of predicted value***)** to compute the predicted $Y$ values. [The POWER function computes the antilog of a log value or, in plain language, the number from its exponent. For example, POWER(10,2) returns 100, as 100 is $10^2$, that is, 10 raised to the 2nd power.] Place this column on the worksheet that contains the columns for your time variable and original $Y$ variable. Then, optionally, copy these three columns to a new worksheet for later ease of use. Finally, use either the Section E16.9A or E16.9B instructions to create the exponential trend plot.

## E16.9A Plotting Least-Squares Exponential Trends (Excel 97–2003)

Create a scatter plot using the Section E2.13A instructions on page 72. Use the cell range of the time variable, original $Y$ variable, and the predicted $Y$ values as the **Data range** cell range in the Chart Wizard Step 2 dialog box. After the scatter plot is created, right-click any predicted $Y$ data point and select **Format Data Series** from the shortcut menu that appears. In the Format Data Series dialog box, click **Automatic** in the **Line group** and **None** in the **Marker group** of the **Patterns** tab and then click **OK**.

## E16.9B Plotting Least-Squares Exponential Trends (Excel 2007)

Create a scatter plot using the Section E2.13B instructions on page 73, selecting the time variable, the original $Y$ variable, and the predicted $Y$ values before you select **Insert**. After the scatter plot is created, right-click any predicted $Y$ data point and select **Format Data Series** from the shortcut menu that appears. In the Format Data Series dialog box, first click **Line Style** in the left panel and then enter **1** as the **Width** in the Line Style right pane. Then click **Marker Options** in the left pane and click **None** in the Marker Options right pane. Then click **Close**.

## E16.10 Creating Lagged Predictor Variables

You create lagged predictor variables by assigning a column of formulas that refer to a previous row's (previous time period's) $Y$ value. You place the special Excel value

#N/A (not available) in the cells in the column for which lagged values do not apply.

For example, Figure E16.2 (shown below) shows the first five rows and the last row of the worksheet shown in Figure 16.15 on page 755 that contains lagged variables for the first-order, second-order, and third-order autoregressive models. Because cells C2, D2:D3, and E2:E4 do not have lagged values, the value #N/A has been entered into those cells.

| | A | B | C | D | E |
|---|---|---|---|---|---|
| 1 | Year | Revenue | Lag1 | Lag2 | Lag3 |
| 2 | 1984 | 591 | #N/A | #N/A | #N/A |
| 3 | 1985 | 620 | =B2 | #N/A | #N/A |
| 4 | 1986 | 699 | =B3 | =C3 | #N/A |
| 5 | 1987 | 781 | =B4 | =C4 | =D4 |
| 24 | 2006 | 4686 | =B23 | =C23 | =D23 |

**FIGURE E16.2** Lagged predictor variable worksheet

## E16.11 Creating First-Order Autoregressive Models

You create first-order autoregressive models by modifying the Section E13.1 instructions (see page 629) to use the cell range of the first-order lagged variable as the $X$ variable cell range and by *not* clicking **Labels** in the Regression dialog box.

## E16.12 For Second-Order or Third-Order Autoregressive Models

You create second-order or third-order autoregressive models by modifying the Section E14.1 instructions (see page 685) to use the cell range of the lagged variables as the $X$ variables cell range and by *not* clicking **Labels** in the Regression dialog box. Use the cell range of the first-order and second-order lagged variables for a second-order model and use the cell range of the first-order, second-order, and third-order lagged variables for the third-order model.

## E16.13 Computing the Mean Absolute Deviation (*MAD*)

You compute the mean absolute deviation in a two-part process. You first use the instructions of either Section E13.3 or Section E14.2 (see pages 630 and 685) to perform the appropriate regression analysis with residuals output.

For a linear, quadratic, or autoregressive model, you copy the predicted and residuals values found in columns B and C of the residuals table in the regression results worksheet to blank columns in the regression data worksheet. You then add a column of formulas in the form *=ABS(residual cell)* to calculate the absolute value of the residuals. Finally, you add a single formula in the form *=AVERAGE(cell range of residual absolute values)* to calculate the *MAD*.

For an exponential model, you must convert the base 10 logarithms used to report predicted $Y$ values and residuals into their original units. To do this, in the residuals tables, add a column of formulas that use the **POWER(10, Logvalue)** function to convert the logarithms of the predicted $Y$ to the predicted $Y$ values. Then, copy the original $Y$ values into the cells to the right of the POWER function formulas. Continue by adding a third column of formulas in the form *=ABS(Yvaluecell - PredictedYvaluecell)* to calculate the absolute value of the residuals. Finally, add a single formula at the end of this third column in the form *=AVERAGE(cell range of residual absolute values)* to calculate the *MAD*.

## E16.14 Creating Dummy Variables for Quarterly or Monthly Data

You create dummy variables by adding columns of formulas that use the **IF(*comparison, value if comparison is true, value to use if comparison is false*)** function.

Figure E16.3 shows the first four rows of columns F through K of a data worksheet that contains dummy variables. Columns F, G, and H contain the quarterly dummy variables Q1, Q2, and Q3 that are based on column B coded quarter values (not shown). Columns J and K contain the two monthly variables M1 and M6 that are based on column C month values (also not shown).

## E16.15 Computing Index Numbers

You compute index numbers by using the **Unweighted Aggregate PI** and the **Weighted Aggregate PI** worksheets of the `Index Numbers.xls` workbook as models for your own solutions.

| | F | G | H | I | J | K |
|---|---|---|---|---|---|---|
| 1 | Q1 | Q2 | Q3 | | M1 | M6 |
| 2 | =IF(B2 = 1, 1, 0) | =IF(B2 = 2, 1, 0) | =IF(B2 = 3, 1, 0) | | =IF(C2 ="January", 1, 0) | =IF(C2 = "June", 1, 0) |
| 3 | =IF(B3 = 1, 1, 0) | =IF(B3 = 2, 1, 0) | =IF(B3 = 3, 1, 0) | | =IF(C3 ="January", 1, 0) | =IF(C3 = "June", 1, 0) |
| 4 | =IF(B4 = 1, 1, 0) | =IF(B4 = 2, 1, 0) | =IF(B4 = 3, 1, 0) | | =IF(C4 ="January", 1, 0) | =IF(C4 = "June", 1, 0) |

**FIGURE E16.3** Dummy variables for quarterly and monthly data

# Appendix P16
## Using PHStat2 for Time-Series Forecasting

### P16.1 Using Least-Squares Linear Trend Fitting

To use least-squares linear trend fitting, modify the Section P13.1 instructions (see page 632) to use the cell range of the coded variable as the $X$ variable cell range. To plot the linear trend, use the Section E13.2 instructions (see page 630).

### P16.2 Using Least-Squares Quadratic Trend Fitting

To use least-squares quadratic trend fitting, modify the Section P14.1 instructions (see page 687) to use the cell range of the coded variable and the squared coded variable as the $X$ variables cell range. To plot the quadratic trend, use the Section E13.2 instructions (see page 630), but click **Polynomial**, and not Linear, as the **Trend/Regression type** (see either Figure E13.1 on page 630 or Figure E13.2 on page 630).

### P16.3 Using Least-Squares Exponential Trend Fitting

To use least-squares exponential trend fitting, modify the Section P13.1 instructions (see page 632) to use the cell range of the log $Y$ values as the $Y$ variable cell range and the cell range of the coded variable as the $X$ variable cell range. To plot the exponential trend, see Section E16.9.

### P16.4 Creating First-Order Autoregressive Models

To create first-order autoregressive models, modify the Section P13.1 instructions (see page 632) to use the cell range of the first-order lagged variable as the $X$ variable cell range and do *not* click **First cells in both ranges contain label** in the Simple Linear Regression dialog box.

### P16.5 For Second-Order or Third-Order Autoregressive Models

To create second-order or third-order autoregressive models, modify the Section P14.1 instructions to use the cell range of the lagged variables as the $X$ variables cell range and do *not* click **First cells in both ranges contain label** in the Multiple Regression dialog box. Use the cell range of the first-order and second-order lagged variables for a second-order model and use the cell range of the first-order, second-order, and third-order lagged variables for the third-order model.

# Appendix M16
## Using Minitab for Time-Series Forecasting

## M16.1 Computing Moving Averages

To illustrate how to compute moving averages:

1. Open the `Cabot.mtw` worksheet.
2. Select **Stat → Time Series → Moving Average**.

In the Moving Average dialog box (see Figure M16.1):

3. Enter **Revenue** in the **Variable** box.
4. Enter **3** in the **MA length** box (for a 3-year moving average).
5. Click **Center the moving averages**.
6. Click **Results**.
7. In the Moving Average - Results dialog box, click **Summary table and results table** and then click **OK**.
8. Back in the Moving Average dialog box, click **OK**.

**FIGURE M16.1** Minitab Moving Average dialog box

## M16.2 Computing Exponentially Smoothed Values

To illustrate how to compute exponentially smoothed values:

1. Open the `Cabot.mtw` worksheet.
2. Select **Stat → Time Series → Single Exp Smoothing**.

In the Single Exponential Smoothing dialog box (see Figure M16.2):

3. Enter **Revenue** in the **Variable** box.
4. Click **Use** and enter **0.25** in its box (for a $W$ value of 0.25). (Enter **0.50** for a $W$ value of 0.50.)

5. Click **Results**.
6. In the Single Exponential Smoothing - Results dialog box (not shown), click **Summary table and results table** and then click **OK**.
7. Back in the Single Exponential Smoothing dialog box, click **Options**.
8. In the Single Exponential Smoothing - Options dialog box (not shown), enter **1** in the **Use average of first K observations** box and then click **OK**.
9. Back in the Single Exponential Smoothing dialog box, click **OK**.

**FIGURE M16.2** Minitab Single Exponential Smoothing dialog box

## M16.3 Using Least-Squares Trend Fitting

In Chapters 13 through 15, you used Minitab for the simple linear regression model and for a variety of multiple regression models. In this chapter, time-series models were developed assuming either a linear, quadratic, or exponential trend. For the linear trend model, see Section M13.1. For the quadratic model and the exponential model, see Sections M15.1 and M15.2.

## M16.4 Using Autoregressive Modeling

To use Minitab for autoregressive models, you first create lagged variables. To illustrate this:

1. Open the `Wrigley.mtw` worksheet.
2. Select **Stat → Time Series → Lag**.

In the Lag dialog box (see Figure M16.3),

3. Enter **Revenue** in the **Series** box.
4. Enter **C6** in the **Store lags in** box.
5. Enter **1** in the **Lag** box (for a 1-period lag). (For a 2-period lag, enter **2**. For a 3-period lag, enter **3**.)
6. Click **OK**.

Repeat this procedure for 2- and 3-period lags by changing the lags to 2 and then 3, respectively, and then store the lags in columns C7 and C8, respectively. Once the lagged variables have been created, use **Stat → Regression → Regression** as in Appendix M14.2.

**FIGURE M16.3** Minitab Lag dialog box

# CHAPTER
# SEVENTEEN

## DECISION MAKING

**USING STATISTICS @** Reliable Fund

# LEARNING OBJECTIVES

## In this chapter, you learn:

- To use payoff tables and decision trees to evaluate alternative courses of action
- To use several criteria to select an alternative course of action
- To use Bayes' theorem to revise probabilities in light of sample information
- About the concept of utility

# USING STATISTICS @ Reliable Fund

As the manager of The Reliable Fund, you are responsible for purchasing and selling stocks for the fund. The investors in this mutual fund expect a large return on their investment and, at the same time, they want to minimize their risk. At the present time, you need to decide between two stocks to purchase. An economist for your company has evaluated the potential one-year returns for both stocks, under four economic conditions: recession, stability, moderate growth, and boom. She has also estimated the probability of each economic condition occurring. How can you use the information provided by the economist to determine which stock to choose in order to maximize return and minimize risk?

In Chapter 4, you studied various rules of probability and used Bayes' theorem to revise probabilities. In Chapter 5, you learned about discrete probability distributions and how to compute the expected value. In this chapter, these probability rules and probability distributions are applied to a decision-making process for evaluating alternative courses of action. In this context, you can consider the four basic features of a decision-making situation:

- **Alternative courses of action**   The decision maker must have two or more possible choices to evaluate prior to selecting one course of action. For example, as a manager of a mutual fund in the Using Statistics scenario, you must decide whether to purchase stock $A$ or stock $B$.
- **Events or states of the world**   The decision maker must list the events that can occur and consider the probability of occurrence of each event. To aid in selecting which stock to purchase in the Using Statistics scenario, an economist for your company has listed four possible economic conditions and the probability of occurrence of each event in the next year.
- **Payoffs**   In order to evaluate each course of action, the decision maker must associate a value or payoff with the result of each event. In business applications, this payoff is usually expressed in terms of profits or costs, although other payoffs, such as units of satisfaction or utility, are sometimes considered. In the Using Statistics scenario, the payoff is the return on investment.
- **Decision criteria**   The decision maker must determine how to select the best course of action. Section 17.2 discusses five criteria for decision making: maximax payoff, maximin payoff, expected monetary value, expected opportunity loss, and return-to-risk ratio.

## 17.1 PAYOFF TABLES AND DECISION TREES

In order to evaluate the alternative courses of action for a complete set of events, you need to develop a payoff table or construct a decision tree. A **payoff table** contains each possible event that can occur for each alternative course of action and a value or payoff for each combination of an event and course of action. Example 17.1 discusses a payoff table for a marketing manager trying to decide how to market organic salad dressings.

---

**EXAMPLE 17.1**   A PAYOFF TABLE FOR DECIDING HOW TO MARKET ORGANIC SALAD DRESSINGS

You are marketing manager for a food products company who is considering the introduction of a new brand of organic salad dressings. You need to develop a marketing plan for the salad dressings in which you must decide whether you will have a gradual introduction of the salad dressings (with only a few different salad dressings introduced to the market) or a concentrated introduction of the salad dressings (in which a full line of salad dressings will be introduced to the market). You estimate that if there is a low demand for the salad dressings, your first year profit will be $1 million for a gradual introduction and −$5 million (a loss of $5 million) for a concentrated introduction. If there is high demand, you estimate that your first year profit will be $4 million for a gradual introduction and $10 million for a concentrated introduction. Construct a payoff table for these two alternative courses of action.

**SOLUTION** Table 17.1 is a payoff table for the organic salad dressings marketing example.

**TABLE 17.1**

Payoff Table for the Organic Salad Dressings Marketing Example (in Millions of Dollars)

| EVENT, $E_i$ | ALTERNATIVE COURSE OF ACTION | |
| --- | --- | --- |
| | Gradual, $A_1$ | Concentrated, $A_2$ |
| Low demand, $E_1$ | 1 | −5 |
| High demand, $E_2$ | 4 | 10 |

A **decision tree** is another way of representing the events for each alternative course of action. A decision tree pictorially represents the events and courses of action through a set of branches and nodes. Example 17.2 illustrates a decision tree.

**EXAMPLE 17.2**     A DECISION TREE FOR THE ORGANIC SALAD DRESSINGS MARKETING DECISION

Given the payoff table for the organic salad dressings example, construct a decision tree.

**SOLUTION** Figure 17.1 is the decision tree for the payoff table shown in Table 17.1.

**FIGURE 17.1**

Decision tree for the organic salad dressings marketing example (in millions of dollars)

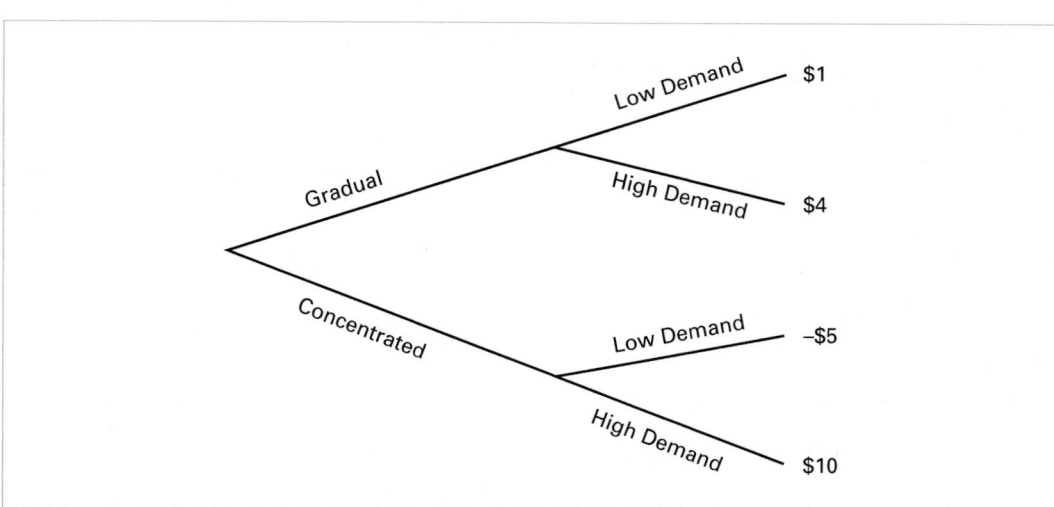

In Figure 17.1, the first set of branches relates to the two alternative courses of action: gradual introduction to the market or concentrated introduction to the market. The second set of branches represents the possible events of low demand and high demand. These events occur for each of the alternative courses of action on the decision tree.

The decision structure for the organic salad dressings marketing example contains only two possible alternative courses of action and two possible events. In general, there can be several alternative courses of action and events. As a manager of The Reliable Fund in the Using

Statistics scenario, you need to decide between two stocks to purchase for a short-term invest-ment of one year. An economist at the company has predicted returns for the two stocks under four economic conditions—recession, stability, moderate growth, and boom. Table 17.2 pre-sents the predicted one-year return of a $1,000 investment in each stock under each economic condition. Figure 17.2 shows the decision tree for this payoff table. The decision (which stock to purchase) is the first branch of the tree, and the second set of branches represents the four events (the economic conditions).

**TABLE 17.2**

Predicted One-Year Return ($) on $1,000 Investment in Each of Two Stocks, Under Four Economic Conditions

| | STOCK | |
| --- | --- | --- |
| ECONOMIC CONDITION | *A* | *B* |
| **Recession** | 30 | −50 |
| **Stable economy** | 70 | 30 |
| **Moderate growth** | 100 | 250 |
| **Boom** | 150 | 400 |

**FIGURE 17.2**

Decision tree for the stock selection payoff table

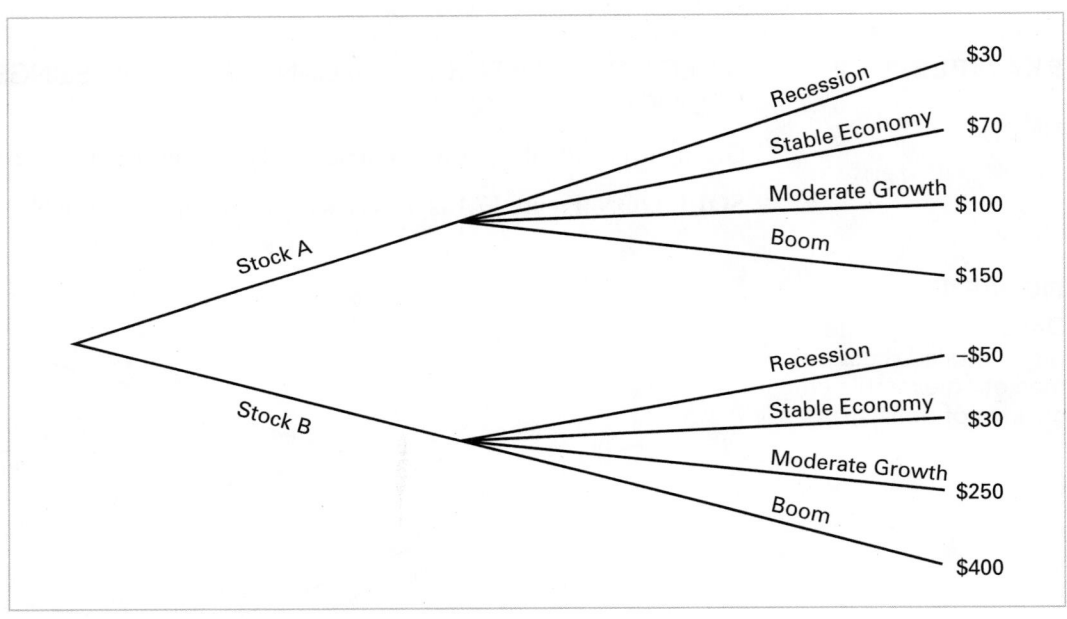

You use payoff tables and decision trees as decision-making tools to help determine the best course of action. For example, when deciding how to market the organic salad dressings, you would use a concentrated introduction to the market if you knew that there would be high demand. You would use a gradual introduction to the market if you knew that there would be low demand. For each event, you can determine the amount of profit that will be lost if the best alternative course of action is not taken. This is called opportu-nity loss.

> The **opportunity loss** is the difference between the highest possible profit for an event and the actual profit for an action taken.

Example 17.3 illustrates the computation of opportunity loss.

**EXAMPLE 17.3**

FINDING OPPORTUNITY LOSS IN THE ORGANIC SALAD DRESSINGS MARKETING EXAMPLE

Using the payoff table from Example 17.1 on page 794, construct an opportunity loss table.

**SOLUTION** For the event "low demand," the maximum profit occurs when there is a gradual introduction to the market (+$1 million). The opportunity that is lost with a concentrated introduction to the market is the difference between $1 million and − $5 million, which is $6 million. If there is a high demand, the best action is to have a concentrated introduction to the market ($10 million profit). The opportunity that is lost by making the incorrect decision of having a gradual introduction to the market is $10 million − $4 million = $6 million. The opportunity loss is always a nonnegative number because it represents the difference between the profit under the best action and any other course of action that is taken for the particular event. Table 17.3 shows the complete opportunity loss table for the organic salad dressings marketing example.

**TABLE 17.3**

Opportunity Loss Table for the Organic Salad Dressings Marketing Example (in Millions of Dollars)

| Event | Optimum Action | Profit of Optimum Action | Alternative Course of Action | |
|---|---|---|---|---|
| | | | Gradual | Concentrated |
| Low demand | Gradual | 1 | 1 − 1 = 0 | 1 − (−5) = 6 |
| High demand | Concentrated | 10 | 10 − 4 = 6 | 10 − 10 = 0 |

Figure 17.3 represents the Microsoft Excel opportunity loss table.

**FIGURE 17.3**

Microsoft Excel opportunity loss table worksheet

*See Section E17.1 or P17.1 to create this.*

| | A | B | C | D | E |
|---|---|---|---|---|---|
| 1 | Organic Salad Dressing Marketing Opportunity Loss Table | | | | |
| 2 | | | | | |
| 3 | Payoff Table: | | | | |
| 4 | | Gradual | Concentrated | | |
| 5 | Low demand | 1 | -5 | | |
| 6 | High demand | 4 | 10 | | |
| 7 | | | | | |
| 8 | | | | | |
| 9 | Opportunity Loss Table: | | | | |
| 10 | | Optimum | Optimum | Alternatives | |
| 11 | | Action | Profit | Gradual | Concentrated |
| 12 | Low demand | Gradual | 1 | 0 | 6 |
| 13 | High demand | Concentrated | 10 | 6 | 0 |

You can also develop an opportunity loss table for the stock selection problem in the Using Statistics scenario. Here, there are four possible events or economic conditions that will affect the one-year return for each of the two stocks. In a recession, stock $A$ is best, providing a return of $30 as compared to a loss of $50 from stock $B$. In a stable economy, stock $A$ again is better than stock $B$ because it provides a return of $70 compared to $30 for stock $B$. However, under conditions of moderate growth or boom, stock $B$ is superior to stock $A$. In a moderate growth period, stock $B$ provides a return of $250 as compared to $100 from stock $A$, while in boom conditions, the difference between stocks is even greater, with stock $B$ providing a return of $400 as compared to $150 for stock $A$. Table 17.4 summarizes the complete set of opportunity losses.

**TABLE 17.4**

Opportunity Loss Table ($) for Two Stocks Under Four Economic Conditions

| Event | Optimum Action | Profit of Optimum Action | Alternative Course of Action | |
|---|---|---|---|---|
| | | | A | B |
| Recession | A | 30 | 30 − 30 = 0 | 30 − (−50) = 80 |
| Stable economy | A | 70 | 70 − 70 = 0 | 70 − 30 = 40 |
| Moderate growth | B | 250 | 250 − 100 = 150 | 250 − 250 = 0 |
| Boom | B | 400 | 400 − 150 = 250 | 400 − 400 = 0 |

# PROBLEMS FOR SECTION 17.1

## Learning the Basics

**17.1** For this problem, use the following payoff table:

| | ACTION | |
|---|---|---|
| EVENT | A ($) | B ($) |
| 1 | 50 | 100 |
| 2 | 200 | 125 |

a. Construct an opportunity loss table.
b. Construct a decision tree.

**17.2** For this problem, use the following payoff table:

| | ACTION | |
|---|---|---|
| EVENT | A ($) | B ($) |
| 1 | 50 | 10 |
| 2 | 300 | 100 |
| 3 | 500 | 200 |

a. Construct an opportunity loss table.
b. Construct a decision tree.

## Applying the Concepts

**17.3** A manufacturer of designer jeans must decide whether to build a large factory or a small factory in a particular location. The profit per pair of jeans manufactured is estimated as $10. A small factory will incur an annual cost of $200,000, with a production capacity of 50,000 pairs of jeans per year. A large factory will incur an annual cost of $400,000, with a production capacity of 100,000 pairs of jeans per year. Four levels of manufacturing demand are considered likely: 10,000, 20,000, 50,000, and 100,000 pairs of jeans per year.

a. Determine the payoffs for the possible levels of production for a small factory.
b. Determine the payoffs for the possible levels of production for a large factory.
c. Based on the results of (a) and (b), construct a payoff table, indicating the events and alternative courses of action.
d. Construct a decision tree.
e. Construct an opportunity loss table.

**✓SELF Test** **17.4** An author is trying to choose between two publishing companies that are competing for the marketing rights to her new novel. Company A has offered the author $10,000 plus $2 per book sold. Company B has offered the author $2,000 plus $4 per book sold. The author believes that five levels of demand for the book are possible: 1,000, 2,000, 5,000, 10,000, and 50,000 books sold.

a. Compute the payoffs for each level of demand for company A and company B.
b. Construct a payoff table, indicating the events and alternative courses of action.
c. Construct a decision tree.
d. Construct an opportunity loss table.

**17.5** The DellaVecchia Garden Center purchases and sells Christmas trees during the holiday season. It purchases the trees for $10 each and sells them for $20 each. Any trees not sold by Christmas day are sold for $2 each to a company that makes wood chips. The garden center estimates that four levels of demand are possible: 100, 200, 500, and 1,000 trees.

a. Compute the payoffs for purchasing 100, 200, 500, or 1,000 trees for each of the four levels of demand.
b. Construct a payoff table, indicating the events and alternative courses of action.
c. Construct a decision tree.
d. Construct an opportunity loss table.

## 17.2 CRITERIA FOR DECISION MAKING

After you compute the profit and opportunity loss for each event under each alternative course of action, you need to determine the criteria for selecting the most desirable course of action. Some criteria involve the assignment of probabilities to each event but others do not. This section introduces two criteria that do not use probabilities, the maximax payoff and the maximin payoff.

This section presents three decision criteria involving probabilities. They are expected monetary value, expected opportunity loss, and the return-to-risk ratio. For criteria in which a probability is assigned to each event, the probability is based on information available from past data, from the opinions of the decision maker, or from knowledge about the probability distribution that the event may follow. Using these probabilities, along with the payoffs or opportunity losses of each event–action combination, you select the best course of action according to a particular criterion.

## Maximax Payoff

The **maximax payoff criterion** is an optimistic payoff criterion. Using this criterion, you do the following:

1. Find the maximum payoff for each action.
2. Choose the action that has the highest of these maximum payoffs.

Example 17.4 illustrates the application of the maximax criterion to the organic salad dressings marketing example.

**EXAMPLE 17.4**    FINDING THE BEST COURSE OF ACTION ACCORDING TO THE MAXIMAX CRITERION FOR THE ORGANIC SALAD DRESSINGS MARKETING EXAMPLE

Return to Table 17.1 on page 795, the payoff table for deciding how to market organic salad dressings. Determine the best course of action according to the maximax criterion.

**SOLUTION** First you find the maximum profit for each action. For a gradual introduction to the market, the maximum profit is $4 million. For a concentrated introduction to the market, the maximum profit is $10 million. Because the maximum of the maximum profits is $10 million, you choose the action that involves a concentrated introduction to the market. Table 17.5 summarizes the use of this criterion.

**TABLE 17.5**

Using the Maximax Criterion for the Organic Salad Dressings Marketing Example (in Millions of Dollars)

| EVENT, $E_i$ | ALTERNATIVE COURSE OF ACTION | |
|---|---|---|
| | Gradual, $A_1$ | Concentrated, $A_2$ |
| Low demand, $E_1$ | 1 | −5 |
| High demand, $E_2$ | 4 | 10 |
| Maximum Profit for each action | 4 | 10* |

As a second application of the maximax payoff criterion, return to the Using Statistics scenario and the payoff table presented in Table 17.2 on page 796. Table 17.6 summarizes the maximax payoff criterion for this example.

**TABLE 17.6**

Using the Maximax Criterion for the Predicted One-Year Return ($) on $1,000 Investment in Each of Two Stocks, Under Four Economic Conditions

| ECONOMIC CONDITION | STOCK | |
|---|---|---|
| | A | B |
| Recession | 30 | −50 |
| Stable economy | 70 | 30 |
| Moderate growth | 100 | 250 |
| Boom | 150 | 400 |
| Maximum Profit for each action | 150 | 400* |

Because the maximum of the maximum profits is $400, you choose stock B.

## Maximin Payoff

The **maximin payoff criterion** is a pessimistic payoff criterion. Using this criterion, you do the following:

1. Find the minimum payoff for each action.
2. Choose the action that has the highest of these minimum payoffs.

Example 17.5 illustrates the application of the maximin criterion to the organic salad dressing marketing example.

---

**EXAMPLE 17.5**
FINDING THE BEST COURSE OF ACTION ACCORDING TO THE MAXIMIN CRITERION FOR THE ORGANIC SALAD DRESSINGS MARKETING EXAMPLE

Return to Table 17.1 on page 795, the payoff table for deciding how to market organic salad dressings. Determine the best course of action according to the maximin criterion.

**SOLUTION** First you find the minimum profit for each action. For a gradual introduction to the market, the minimum profit is $1 million. For a concentrated introduction to the market, the minimum profit is −$5 million. Because the maximum of the minimum profits is $1 million, you choose the action that involves a gradual introduction to the market. Table 17.7 summarizes the use of this criterion.

**TABLE 17.7**

Using the Maximin Criterion for the Organic Salad Dressings Marketing Example (in Millions of Dollars)

| | ALTERNATIVE COURSE OF ACTION | |
|---|---|---|
| EVENT, $E_i$ | Gradual, $A_1$ | Concentrated, $A_2$ |
| Low demand, $E_1$ | 1 | −5 |
| High demand, $E_2$ | 4 | 10 |
| Minimum Profit for each action | 1* | −5 |

As a second application of the maximin payoff criterion, return to the Using Statistics scenario and the payoff table presented in Table 17.2 on page 796. Table 17.8 summarizes the maximin payoff criterion for this example.

**TABLE 17.8**

Using the Maximin Criterion for the Predicted One-Year Return ($) on $1,000 Investment in Each of Two Stocks, Under Four Economic Conditions

| | STOCK | |
|---|---|---|
| ECONOMIC CONDITION | A | B |
| Recession | 30 | −50 |
| Stable economy | 70 | 30 |
| Moderate growth | 100 | 250 |
| Boom | 150 | 400 |
| Minimum Profit for each action | 30* | −50 |

Because the maximum of the minimum profits is $30, you choose stock A.

## Expected Monetary Value

The expected value of a probability distribution was computed in Equation (5.1) on page 181. Now you use this equation to compute the expected monetary value for each alternative course of action. The **expected monetary value (*EMV*)** for a course of action $j$ is the payoff ($X_{ij}$) for each combination of event $i$ and action $j$ multiplied by $P_i$, the probability of occurrence of event $i$, summed over all events [see Equation (17.1)].

Expected Monetary Value

$$EMV(j) = \sum_{i=1}^{N} X_{ij} P_i \qquad \text{(17.1)}$$

where

$EMV(j)$ = expected monetary value of action $j$

$X_{ij}$ = payoff that occurs when course of action $j$ is selected and event $i$ occurs

$P_i$ = probability of occurrence of event $i$

$N$ = number of events

Criterion: Select the course of action with the largest $EMV$.

Example 17.6 illustrates the application of expected monetary value to the organic salad dressings marketing example.

**EXAMPLE 17.6**

COMPUTING THE *EMV* IN THE ORGANIC SALAD DRESSINGS MARKETING EXAMPLE

Returning to the payoff table for deciding how to market organic salad dressings (Example 17.1 on page 794), suppose that the probability is 0.60 that there will be low demand (so that the probability is 0.40 that there will be high demand). Compute the expected monetary value for each alternative course of action and determine how to market organic salad dressings.

**SOLUTION** You use Equation (17.1) to determine the expected monetary value for each alternative course of action. Table 17.9 summarizes these computations.

**TABLE 17.9**

Expected Monetary Value (in Millions of Dollars) for Each Alternative for the Organic Salad Dressings Marketing Example

| Event | $P_i$ | Gradual, $A_1$ | $X_{ij}P_i$ | Concentrated, $A_2$ | $X_{ij}P_i$ |
|---|---|---|---|---|---|
| | | \multicolumn{4}{c}{**Alternative Course of Action**} | | |
| **Low demand, $E_1$** | 0.60 | 1 | $1(0.6) = 0.6$ | −5 | $-5(0.6) = -3.0$ |
| **High demand, $E_2$** | 0.40 | 4 | $4(0.4) = \underline{1.6}$ | 10 | $10(0.4) = \underline{4.0}$ |
| | | | $EMV(A_1) = 2.2$ | | $EMV(A_2) = 1.0$ |

The expected monetary value for a gradual introduction to the market is $2.2 million, and the expected monetary value for a concentrated introduction to the market is $1 million. Thus, if your objective is to choose the action that maximizes the expected monetary value, you would choose the action of a gradual introduction to the market because its *EMV* is highest.

As a second application of expected monetary value, return to the Using Statistics scenario and the payoff table presented in Table 17.2 on page 796. Suppose the company economist assigns the following probabilities to the different economic conditions:

$P(\text{Recession}) = 0.10$
$P(\text{Stable economy}) = 0.40$
$P(\text{Moderate growth}) = 0.30$
$P(\text{Boom}) = 0.20$

Table 17.10 shows the computations of the expected monetary value for each of the two stocks.

**TABLE 17.10**

Expected Monetary Value ($) for Each of Two Stocks Under Four Economic Conditions

| Event | $P_i$ | A | $X_{ij}P_i$ | B | $X_{ij}P_i$ |
|---|---|---|---|---|---|
| | | | **Alternative Course of Action** | | |
| **Recession** | 0.10 | 30 | $30(0.1) = 3$ | −50 | $-50(0.1) = -5$ |
| **Stable economy** | 0.40 | 70 | $70(0.4) = 28$ | 30 | $30(0.4) = 12$ |
| **Moderate growth** | 0.30 | 100 | $100(0.3) = 30$ | 250 | $250(0.3) = 75$ |
| **Boom** | 0.20 | 150 | $150(0.2) = \underline{30}$ | 400 | $400(0.2) = \underline{80}$ |
| | | | $EMV(A) = 91$ | | $EMV(B) = 162$ |

Thus, the expected monetary value, or profit, for stock A is $91, and the expected monetary value, or profit, for stock B is $162. Using these results, you should choose stock B because the expected monetary value for stock B is almost twice that for stock A. In terms of expected rate of return on the $1,000 investment, stock B is 16.2% compared to 9.1% for stock A.

## Expected Opportunity Loss

In the examples on page 801 and above, you learned how to use the expected monetary value criterion when making a decision. An equivalent criterion, based on opportunity losses, is introduced next. Payoffs and opportunity losses can be viewed as two sides of the same coin depending on whether you wish to view the problem in terms of *maximizing* expected monetary value or *minimizing* expected opportunity loss. The **expected opportunity loss (EOL)** of action $j$ is the loss, $L_{ij}$, for each combination of event $i$ and action $j$ multiplied by $P_i$, the probability of occurrence of the event $i$, summed over all events [see Equation (17.2)].

Expected Opportunity Loss

$$EOL(j) = \sum_{i=1}^{N} L_{ij}P_i \qquad (17.2)$$

where

$L_{ij}$ = opportunity loss that occurs when course of action $j$ is selected and event $i$ occurs

$P_i$ = probability of occurrence of event $i$

Criterion: Select the course of action with the smallest *EOL*. Selecting the course of action with the smallest *EOL* is equivalent to selecting the course of action with the largest *EMV*. See Equation (17.1) on page 801.

Example 17.7 illustrates the application of expected opportunity loss for the organic salad dressings marketing example.

---

**EXAMPLE 17.7**

COMPUTING THE *EOL* FOR THE ORGANIC SALAD DRESSINGS MARKETING EXAMPLE

Referring to the opportunity loss table given in Table 17.3 on page 797, and assuming that the probability is 0.60 that there will be low demand, compute the expected opportunity loss for each alternative course of action (see Table 17.11 on page 803). Determine how to market the organic salad dressings.

**TABLE 17.11**

Expected Opportunity Loss (in Millions of Dollars) for Each Alternative for the Organic Salad Dressings Marketing Example

| | | Alternative Course of Action | | | | |
|---|---|---|---|---|---|---|
| Event, $E_i$ | $P_i$ | Gradual, $A_1$ | $L_{ij}P_i$ | Concentrated, $A_2$ | $L_{ij}P_i$ |
| Low demand, $E_1$ | 0.60 | 0 | $0(0.6) = 0$ | 6 | $6(0.6) = 3.6$ |
| High demand, $E_2$ | 0.40 | 6 | $6(0.4) = 2.4$ | 0 | $0(0.4) = 0$ |
| | | | $EOL(A_1) = \overline{2.4}$ | | $EOL(A_2) = \overline{3.6}$ |

**SOLUTION** The expected opportunity loss is lower for a gradual introduction to the market ($2.4 million) than for a concentrated introduction to the market ($3.6 million). Therefore, using the *EOL* criterion, the optimal decision is for a gradual introduction to the market. This outcome is expected because the equivalent *EMV* criterion produced the same optimal strategy.

The expected opportunity loss from the best decision is called the **expected value of perfect information (*EVPI*)**. Equation (17.3) defines the *EVPI*.

Expected Value of Perfect Information

$$EVPI = \text{Expected profit under certainty} - \text{Expected monetary value of the best alternative} \qquad \textbf{(17.3)}$$

The **expected profit under certainty** represents the expected profit that you could make if you had perfect information about which event will occur.

Example 17.8 illustrates the expected value of perfect information.

**EXAMPLE 17.8**    COMPUTING THE *EVPI* IN THE ORGANIC SALAD DRESSINGS MARKETING EXAMPLE

Referring to the data in Example 17.6, compute the expected profit under certainty and the expected value of perfect information.

**SOLUTION** As the marketing manager of the food products company, if you could always predict the future, a profit of $1 million would be made for the 60% of the time there is low demand and a profit of $10 million would be made for the 40% of the time there is high demand. Thus,

$$\text{Expected profit under certainty} = 0.60(\$1) + 0.40(\$10)$$
$$= \$0.60 + \$4.00$$
$$= \$4.60$$

The $4.60 million represents the profit you could make if you knew with *certainty* what the demand would be for the organic salad dressings. You use the *EMV* calculations in Table 17.9 on page 801 and Equation (17.3) to compute the expected value of perfect information:

$$EVPI = \text{Expected profit under certainty} - \text{Expected monetary value of the best alternative}$$
$$= \$4.6 - (\$2.2) = \$2.4$$

This *EVPI* value of $2.4 million represents the maximum amount that you should be willing to pay for perfect information. Of course, you can never have perfect information, and you should never pay the entire *EVPI* for more information. Rather, the *EVPI* provides a guideline for an upper bound on how much you might consider paying for better information. The *EVPI* is also the expected opportunity loss for a gradual introduction to the market, the best action according to the *EMV* criterion.

Return to the Using Statistics scenario and the opportunity loss table presented in Table 17.4 on page 797. Table 17.12 presents the computations to determine the expected opportunity loss for stock *A* and stock *B*.

**TABLE 17.12**

Expected Opportunity Loss for Each Alternative ($) for the Stock Selection Example

|  |  |  | Alternative Course of Action |  |  |
|---|---|---|---|---|---|
| Event | $P_i$ | A | $L_{ij}P_i$ | B | $L_{ij}P_i$ |
| **Recession** | 0.10 | 0 | $0(0.1) = 0$ | 80 | $80(0.1) = 8$ |
| **Stable economy** | 0.40 | 0 | $0(0.4) = 0$ | 40 | $40(0.4) = 16$ |
| **Moderate growth** | 0.30 | 150 | $150(0.3) = 45$ | 0 | $0(0.3) = 0$ |
| **Boom** | 0.20 | 250 | $250(0.2) = \underline{50}$ | 0 | $0(0.2) = \underline{0}$ |
|  |  |  | $EOL(A) = 95$ |  | $EOL(B) = EVPI = 24$ |

The expected opportunity loss is lower for stock *B* than for stock *A*. Your optimal decision is to choose stock *B*, which is consistent with the decision made using expected monetary value. The expected value of perfect information is $24 (per $1,000 invested), meaning that you should be willing to pay up to $24 for perfect information.

## Return-to-Risk Ratio

Unfortunately, neither the expected monetary value nor the expected opportunity loss criterion takes into account the *variability* of the payoffs for the alternative courses of action under different events. From Table 17.2 on page 796, you see that the return for stock *A* varies from $30 in a recession to $150 in an economic boom, whereas the return for stock *B* (the one chosen according to the expected monetary value and expected opportunity loss criteria) varies from a loss of $50 in a recession to a profit of $400 in an economic boom.

To take into account the variability of the events (in this case, the different economic conditions), you can compute the variance and standard deviation of each stock, using Equations (5.2) and (5.3) on page 182. Using the information presented in Table 17.10 on page 802, for stock *A*, $EMV(A) = \mu_A = \$91$, the variance is

$$\sigma_A^2 = \sum_{i=1}^{N}(X_i - \mu)^2 P(X_i)$$

$$= (30-91)^2(0.1)+(70-91)^2(0.4)+(100-91)^2(0.3)+(150-91)^2(0.2)$$

$$= 1,269$$

and $\sigma_A = \sqrt{1,269} = \$35.62$.

For stock *B*, $EMV(B) = \mu_B = \$162$, the variance is

$$\sigma_B^2 = \sum_{i=1}^{N}(X_i - \mu)^2 P(X_i)$$

$$= (-50-162)^2(0.1)+(30-162)^2(0.4)+(250-162)^2(0.3)+(400-162)^2(0.2)$$

$$= 25,116$$

and $\sigma_B = \sqrt{25,116} = \$158.48$.

Because you are comparing two stocks with different means, you should evaluate the relative risk associated with each stock. Once you compute the standard deviation of the return from each stock, you compute the coefficient of variation discussed in Section 3.2. Substituting $\sigma$ for $S$ and $EMV$ for $\bar{X}$ in Equation (3.8) on page 101, you find that the coefficient of variation for stock $A$ is equal to

$$CV_A = \left( \frac{\sigma_A}{EMV_A} \right) 100\%$$

$$= \left( \frac{35.62}{91} \right) 100\% = 39.1\%$$

whereas the coefficient of variation for stock $B$ is equal to

$$CV_B = \left( \frac{\sigma_B}{EMV_B} \right) 100\%$$

$$= \left( \frac{158.48}{162} \right) 100\% = 97.8\%$$

Thus, there is much more variation in the return for stock $B$ than for stock $A$.

When there are large differences in the amount of variability in the different events, a criterion other than $EMV$ or $EOL$ is needed to express the relationship between the return (as expressed by the $EMV$) and the risk (as expressed by the standard deviation). Equation (17.4) defines the **return-to-risk ratio (RTRR)** as the expected monetary value of action $j$ divided by the standard deviation of action $j$.

**Return-to-Risk Ratio**

$$RTRR(j) = \frac{EMV(j)}{\sigma_j} \qquad\qquad \textbf{(17.4)}$$

where

$EMV(j) =$ expected monetary value for alternative course of action $j$

$\sigma_j =$ standard deviation for alternative course of action $j$

Criterion: Select the course of action with the largest $RTRR$.

For each of the two stocks discussed previously, you compute the return-to-risk ratios as follows. For stock $A$, the return-to-risk ratio is equal to

$$RTRR(A) = \frac{91}{35.62} = 2.55$$

For stock $B$, the return-to-risk ratio is equal to

$$RTRR(B) = \frac{162}{158.48} = 1.02$$

Thus, relative to the risk as expressed by the standard deviation, the expected return is much higher for stock $A$ than for stock $B$. Stock $A$ has a smaller expected monetary value than stock $B$, but also has a much smaller risk than stock $B$. The return-to-risk ratio shows $A$ to be preferable to $B$. Figure 17.4 represents Microsoft Excel results.

**FIGURE 17.4**

Microsoft Excel expected monetary value and standard deviation worksheet

*See Section E17.2 or P17.2 to create this.*

| | A | B | C | D | E |
|---|---|---|---|---|---|
| 1 | Stock Selection Analysis | | | | |
| 2 | | | | | |
| 3 | Probabilities & Payoffs Table: | | | | |
| 4 | | P | Stock A | Stock B | |
| 5 | Recession | 0.1 | 30 | -50 | |
| 6 | Stable economy | 0.4 | 70 | 30 | |
| 7 | Moderate growth | 0.3 | 100 | 250 | |
| 8 | Boom | 0.2 | 150 | 400 | |
| 9 | | | | | |
| 10 | Statistics for: | Stock A | Stock B | | |
| 11 | Expected Monetary Value | 91 | 162 | | |
| 12 | Variance | 1269 | 25116 | | |
| 13 | Standard Deviation | 35.6230 | 158.4803 | | |
| 14 | Coefficient of Variation | 0.3915 | 0.9783 | | |
| 15 | Return to Risk Ratio | 2.5545 | 1.0222 | | |
| 16 | | | | | |
| 17 | Opportunity Loss Table: | | | | |
| 18 | | Optimum | Optimum | | Alternatives |
| 19 | | Action | Profit | Stock A | Stock B |
| 20 | Recession | Stock A | 30 | 0 | 80 |
| 21 | Stable economy | Stock A | 70 | 0 | 40 |
| 22 | Moderate growth | Stock B | 250 | 150 | 0 |
| 23 | Boom | Stock B | 400 | 250 | 0 |
| 24 | | | | Stock A | Stock B |
| 25 | Expected Opportunity Loss | | | 95 | 24 |
| 26 | | | | | EVPI |

# PROBLEMS FOR SECTION 17.2

## Learning the Basics

**17.6** For the following payoff table:

| | ACTION | |
|---|---|---|
| EVENT | A ($) | B ($) |
| 1 | 50 | 100 |
| 2 | 200 | 125 |

The probability of event 1 is 0.5, and the probability of event 2 is also 0.5.

**a.** Determine the optimal action based on the maximax criterion.

**b.** Determine the optimal action based on the maximin criterion.

**c.** Compute the expected monetary value (*EMV*) for actions $A$ and $B$.

**d.** Compute the expected opportunity loss (*EOL*) for actions $A$ and $B$.

**e.** Explain the meaning of the expected value of perfect information (*EVPI*) in this problem.

**f.** Based on the results of (c) or (d), which action would you choose? Why?

**g.** Compute the coefficient of variation for each action.

**h.** Compute the return-to-risk ratio (*RTRR*) for each action.

**i.** Based on (g) and (h), what action would you choose? Why?

**j.** Compare the results of (f) and (i) and explain any differences.

**17.7** For the following payoff table:

| | ACTION | |
|---|---|---|
| EVENT | A ($) | B ($) |
| 1 | 50 | 10 |
| 2 | 300 | 100 |
| 3 | 500 | 200 |

The probability of event 1 is 0.8, the probability of event 2 is 0.1, and the probability of event 3 is 0.1.

**a.** Determine the optimal action based on the maximax criterion.

**b.** Determine the optimal action based on the maximin criterion.

**c.** Compute the expected monetary value (*EMV*) for actions $A$ and $B$.

**d.** Compute the expected opportunity loss (*EOL*) for actions *A* and *B*.

**e.** Explain the meaning of the expected value of perfect information (*EVPI*) in this problem.

**f.** Based on the results of (c) or (d), which action would you choose? Why?

**g.** Compute the coefficient of variation for each action.

**h.** Compute the return-to-risk ratio (*RTRR*) for each action.

**i.** Based on (g) and (h), what action would you choose? Why?

**j.** Compare the results of (f) and (i) and explain any differences.

**k.** Would your answers to (f) and (i) be different if the probabilities for the three events were 0.1, 0.1, and 0.8, respectively? Discuss.

**17.8** For a potential investment of $1,000, if a stock has an *EMV* of $100 and a standard deviation of $25, what is the
**a.** rate of return?
**b.** coefficient of variation?
**c.** return-to-risk ratio?

**17.9** A stock has the following predicted returns under the following economic conditions:

| Economic Condition | Probability | Return ($) |
| --- | --- | --- |
| Recession | 0.30 | 50 |
| Stable economy | 0.30 | 100 |
| Moderate growth | 0.30 | 120 |
| Boom | 0.10 | 200 |

Compute the
**a.** expected monetary value.
**b.** standard deviation.
**c.** coefficient of variation.
**d.** return-to-risk ratio.

**17.10** The following are the returns ($) for two stocks:

| | A | B |
| --- | --- | --- |
| Expected monetary value | 90 | 60 |
| Standard deviation | 10 | 10 |

Which stock would you choose and why?

**17.11** The following are the returns ($) for two stocks:

| | A | B |
| --- | --- | --- |
| Expected monetary value | 60 | 60 |
| Standard deviation | 20 | 10 |

Which stock would you choose and why?

## Applying the Concepts

**SELF Test** **17.12** A vendor at a local baseball stadium must determine whether to sell ice cream or soft drinks at today's game. The vendor believes that the profit made will depend on the weather. The payoff table (in $) is as follows:

| | ACTION | |
| --- | --- | --- |
| EVENT | Sell Soft Drinks | Sell Ice Cream |
| Cool weather | 50 | 30 |
| Warm weather | 60 | 90 |

Based on her past experience at this time of year, the vendor estimates the probability of warm weather as 0.60.

**a.** Determine the optimal action based on the maximax criterion.

**b.** Determine the optimal action based on the maximin criterion.

**c.** Compute the expected monetary value (*EMV*) for selling soft drinks and selling ice cream.

**d.** Compute the expected opportunity loss (*EOL*) for selling soft drinks and selling ice cream.

**e.** Explain the meaning of the expected value of perfect information (*EVPI*) in this problem.

**f.** Based on the results of (c) or (d), which would you choose to sell, soft drinks or ice cream? Why?

**g.** Compute the coefficient of variation for selling soft drinks and selling ice cream.

**h.** Compute the return-to-risk ratio (*RTRR*) for selling soft drinks and selling ice cream.

**i.** Based on (g) and (h), what would you choose to sell, soft drinks or ice cream? Why?

**j.** Compare the results of (f) and (i) and explain any differences.

**17.13** The Islander Fishing Company purchases clams for $1.50 per pound from fishermen and sells them to various restaurants for $2.50 per pound. Any clams not sold to the restaurants by the end of the week can be sold to a local soup company for $0.50 per pound. The company can purchase 500, 1,000, or 2,000 pounds. The probabilities of various levels of demand are as follows:

| Demand (Pounds) | Probability |
| --- | --- |
| 500 | 0.2 |
| 1,000 | 0.4 |
| 2,000 | 0.4 |

**a.** For each possible purchase level (500, 1,000, or 2,000 pounds), compute the profit (or loss) for each level of demand.

**b.** Determine the optimal action based on the maximax criterion.

**c.** Determine the optimal action based on the maximin criterion.

**d.** Using the expected monetary value (*EMV*) criterion, determine the optimal number of pounds of clams the company should purchase from the fishermen. Discuss.

e. Compute the standard deviation for each possible purchase level.

f. Compute the expected opportunity loss (*EOL*) for purchasing 500, 1,000, and 2,000 pounds of clams.

g. Explain the meaning of the expected value of perfect information (*EVPI*) in this problem.

h. Compute the coefficient of variation for purchasing 500, 1,000, and 2,000 pounds of clams. Discuss.

i. Compute the return-to-risk ratio (*RTRR*) for purchasing 500, 1,000, and 2,000 pounds of clams. Discuss.

j. Based on (d) and (f), would you choose to purchase 500, 1,000, or 2,000 pounds of clams? Why?

k. Compare the results of (d), (f), (h), and (i) and explain any differences.

l. Suppose that clams can be sold to restaurants for $3 per pound. Repeat (a) through (j) with this selling price for clams and compare the results with those in (k).

m. What would be the effect on the results in (a) through (k) if the probability of the demand for 500, 1,000, and 2,000 clams were 0.4, 0.4, and 0.2, respectively?

**17.14** An investor has a certain amount of money available to invest now. Three alternative investments are available. The estimated profits ($) of each investment under each economic condition are indicated in the following payoff table:

| | INVESTMENT SELECTION | | |
| --- | --- | --- | --- |
| EVENT | *A* | *B* | *C* |
| Economy declines | 500 | −2,000 | −7,000 |
| No change | 1,000 | 2,000 | −1,000 |
| Economy expands | 2,000 | 5,000 | 20,000 |

Based on his own past experience, the investor assigns the following probabilities to each economic condition:

$P$ (Economy declines) = 0.30
$P$ (No change) = 0.50
$P$ (Economy expands) = 0.20

a. Determine the optimal action based on the maximax criterion.

b. Determine the optimal action based on the maximin criterion.

c. Compute the expected monetary value (*EMV*) for each investment.

d. Compute the expected opportunity loss (*EOL*) for each investment.

e. Explain the meaning of the expected value of perfect information (*EVPI*) in this problem.

f. Based on the results of (c) or (d), which investment would you choose? Why?

g. Compute the coefficient of variation for each investment.

h. Compute the return-to-risk ratio (*RTRR*) for each investment.

i. Based on (g) and (h), what investment would you choose? Why?

j. Compare the results of (f) and (i) and explain any differences.

k. Suppose the probabilities of the different economic conditions are as follows:

1. 0.1, 0.6, and 0.3
2. 0.1, 0.3, and 0.6
3. 0.4, 0.4, and 0.2
4. 0.6, 0.3, and 0.1

Repeat (c) through (j) with each of these sets of probabilities and compare the results with those originally computed in (c)–(j). Discuss.

**17.15** In Problem 17.3 on page 798, you developed a payoff table for building a small factory or a large factory for manufacturing designer jeans. Given the results of that problem, suppose that the probabilities of the demand are as follows:

| Demand | Probability |
| --- | --- |
| 10,000 | 0.1 |
| 20,000 | 0.4 |
| 50,000 | 0.2 |
| 100,000 | 0.3 |

a. Determine the optimal action based on the maximax criterion.

b. Determine the optimal action based on the maximin criterion.

c. Compute the expected monetary value (*EMV*) for building a small factory and building a large factory.

d. Compute the expected opportunity loss (*EOL*) for building a small factory and building a large factory.

e. Explain the meaning of the expected value of perfect information (*EVPI*) in this problem.

f. Based on the results of (c) or (d), would you choose to build a small factory or a large factory? Why?

g. Compute the coefficient of variation for building a small factory and building a large factory.

h. Compute the return-to-risk ratio (*RTRR*) for building a small factory and building a large factory.

i. Based on (g) and (h), would you choose to build a small factory or a large factory? Why?

j. Compare the results of (f) and (i) and explain any differences.

k. Suppose that the probabilities of demand are 0.4, 0.2, 0.2, and 0.2, respectively. Repeat (c) through (j) with these probabilities and compare the results with those of (c) through (j).

**17.16** In Problem 17.4 on page 798, you developed a payoff table to assist an author in choosing between signing with company *A* or with company *B*. Given the results computed in that problem, suppose that the probabilities of the levels of demand for the novel are as follows:

| Demand | Probability |
|---|---|
| 1,000 | 0.45 |
| 2,000 | 0.20 |
| 5,000 | 0.15 |
| 10,000 | 0.10 |
| 50,000 | 0.10 |

**a.** Determine the optimal action based on the maximax criterion.

**b.** Determine the optimal action based on the maximin criterion.

**c.** Compute the expected monetary value (*EMV*) for signing with company *A* and with company *B*.

**d.** Compute the expected opportunity loss (*EOL*) for signing with company *A* and with company *B*.

**e.** Explain the meaning of the expected value of perfect information (*EVPI*) in this problem.

**f.** Based on the results of (c) or (d), if you were the author, which company would you choose to sign with, company *A* or company *B*? Why?

**g.** Compute the coefficient of variation for signing with company *A* and signing with company *B*.

**h.** Compute the return-to-risk ratio (*RTRR*) for signing with company *A* and signing with company *B*.

**i.** Based on (g) and (h), which company would you choose to sign with, company *A* or company *B*? Why?

**j.** Compare the results of (f) and (i) and explain any differences.

**k.** Suppose that the probabilities of demand are 0.3, 0.2, 0.2, 0.1, and 0.2, respectively. Repeat (c) through (j) with these probabilities and compare the results with those for (c) through (j).

**17.17** In Problem 17.5 on page 798, you developed a payoff table for whether to purchase 100, 200, 500, or 1,000 Christmas trees. Given the results of that problem, suppose that the probabilities of the demand for the different number of trees are as follows:

| Demand (Number of Trees) | Probability |
|---|---|
| 100 | 0.20 |
| 200 | 0.50 |
| 500 | 0.20 |
| 1,000 | 0.10 |

**a.** Determine the optimal action based on the maximax criterion.

**b.** Determine the optimal action based on the maximin criterion.

**c.** Compute the expected monetary value (*EMV*) for purchasing 100, 200, 500, and 1,000 trees.

**d.** Compute the expected opportunity loss (*EOL*) for purchasing 100, 200, 500, and 1,000 trees.

**e.** Explain the meaning of the expected value of perfect information (*EVPI*) in this problem.

**f.** Based on the results of (c) or (d), would you choose to purchase 100, 200, 500, or 1,000 trees? Why?

**g.** Compute the coefficient of variation for purchasing 100, 200, 500, and 1,000 trees.

**h.** Compute the return-to-risk ratio (*RTRR*) for purchasing 100, 200, 500, and 1,000 trees.

**i.** Based on (g) and (h), would you choose to purchase 100, 200, 500, or 1,000 trees? Why?

**j.** Compare the results of (f) and (i) and explain any differences.

**k.** Suppose that the probabilities of demand are 0.4, 0.2, 0.2, and 0.2, respectively. Repeat (c) through (j) with these probabilities and compare the results with those for (c) through (j).

## 17.3   DECISION MAKING WITH SAMPLE INFORMATION

In Sections 17.1 and 17.2 you learned the framework for making decisions when there are several alternative courses of action. You then studied five different criteria for choosing between alternatives. For three of the criteria, you assigned the probabilities of the various events, using the past experience and/or the subjective judgment of the decision maker. This section introduces decision making when sample information is available to estimate probabilities. Example 17.9 illustrates decision making with sample information.

**EXAMPLE 17.9**     DECISION MAKING USING SAMPLE INFORMATION FOR THE ORGANIC SALAD DRESSINGS MARKETING EXAMPLE

Before determining whether to have a gradual or concentrated introduction to the market, the marketing research department conducts an extensive study and releases a report, either that there will be low demand or high demand. In the past, when there was low demand, 30% of the time the market research department stated there would be high demand. When there was high demand, 80% of the time the market research department stated there would be high demand. For the organic salad dressings, the marketing research department has stated that there will be high demand. Compute the expected monetary value of each alternative course of action given this information.

**SOLUTION**　You need to use Bayes' theorem (see Section 4.3) to revise the probabilities. To use Equation (4.9) on page 163 for the organic salad dressings marketing example, let

event $D =$ low demand　　　event $M =$ market research predicts low demand
event $D' =$ high demand　　event $M' =$ market research predicts high demand

and

$$P(D) = 0.60 \quad P(M'|D) = 0.30$$
$$P(D') = 0.40 \quad P(M'|D') = 0.80$$

Then, using Equation (4.9),

$$P(D'|M') = \frac{P(M'|D')P(D')}{P(M'|D)P(D) + P(M'|D')P(D')}$$

$$= \frac{(0.80)(0.40)}{(0.30)(0.60) + (0.80)(0.40)}$$

$$= \frac{0.32}{0.18 + 0.32} = \frac{0.32}{0.50}$$

$$= 0.64$$

The probability of high demand, given that the market research department predicted high demand, is 0.64. Thus, the probability of low demand, given that the market research department predicted high demand, is $1 - 0.64 = 0.36$. Table 17.13 summarizes the computation of the probabilities.

**TABLE 17.13**

Bayes' Theorem Calculations for the Organic Salad Dressings Marketing Example

| Event $S_i$ | Prior Probability $P(D_i)$ | Conditional Probability $P(M'\|D_i)$ | Joint Probability $P(M'\|D_i)P(D_i)$ | Revised Probability $P(D_i\|M')$ |
|---|---|---|---|---|
| $D =$ low demand | 0.60 | 0.30 | 0.18 | $P(D\|M') = 0.18/0.50 = 0.36$ |
| $D' =$ high demand | 0.40 | 0.80 | 0.32 | $P(D'\|M') = 0.32/0.50 = 0.64$ |
| | | | 0.50 | |

You need to use the revised probabilities, not the original subjective probabilities, to compute the expected monetary value of each alternative. Table 17.14 illustrates the computations.

**TABLE 17.14**

Expected Monetary Value (in Millions of Dollars) Using Revised Probabilities for Each Alternative in the Organic Salad Dressings Marketing Example

| Event | $P_i$ | Gradual, $A_1$ | $X_{ij}P_i$ | Concentrated, $A_2$ | $X_{ij}P_i$ |
|---|---|---|---|---|---|
| Low demand | 0.36 | 1 | $1(0.36) = 0.36$ | $-5$ | $-5(0.36) = -1.8$ |
| High demand | 0.64 | 4 | $4(0.64) = 2.56$ | 10 | $10(0.64) = 6.4$ |
| | | | $EMV(A_1) = 2.92$ | | $EMV(A_2) = 4.6$ |

*See Section E17.2 or P17.2 to create this.*

In this case, the optimal decision is to have a concentrated introduction to the market because a profit of $4.6 million is expected as compared to a profit of $2.92 million if the organic salad dressings have a gradual introduction to the market. This decision is different from the one considered optimal prior to the collection of the sample information in the form of the market research report (see Example 17.6 on page 801). The favorable recommendation contained in the report greatly increases the probability that there will be high demand for the organic salad dressings.

---

Because the relative desirability of the two stocks under consideration in the Using Statistics scenario is directly affected by economic conditions, you should use a forecast of the economic conditions in the upcoming year. You can then use Bayes' theorem, introduced in Section 4.3, to revise the probabilities associated with the different economic conditions. Suppose that such a forecast can predict either an expanding economy ($F_1$) or a declining or stagnant economy ($F_2$). Past experience indicates that, when there is a recession, prior forecasts predicted an expanding economy 20% of the time. When there is a stable economy, prior forecasts predicted an expanding economy 40% of the time. When there is moderate growth, prior forecasts predicted an expanding economy 70% of the time. Finally, when there is a boom economy, prior forecasts predicted an expanding economy 90% of the time.

If the forecast is for an expanding economy, you can revise the probabilities of economic conditions by using Bayes' theorem, Equation (4.9) on page 163. Let

event $E_1$ = recession          event $F_1$ = expanding economy is predicted

event $E_2$ = stable economy     event $F_2$ = declining or stagnant economy is predicted

event $E_3$ = moderate growth

event $E_4$ = boom economy

and

$$P(E_1) = 0.10 \quad P(F_1|E_1) = 0.20$$
$$P(E_2) = 0.40 \quad P(F_1|E_2) = 0.40$$
$$P(E_3) = 0.30 \quad P(F_1|E_3) = 0.70$$
$$P(E_4) = 0.20 \quad P(F_1|E_4) = 0.90$$

Then, using Bayes' theorem

$$P(E_1|F_1) = \frac{P(F_1|E_1)P(E_1)}{P(F_1|E_1)P(E_1) + P(F_1|E_2)P(E_2) + P(F_1|E_3)P(E_3) + P(F_1|E_4)P(E_4)}$$

$$= \frac{(0.20)(0.10)}{(0.20)(0.10) + (0.40)(0.40) + (0.70)(0.30) + (0.90)(0.20)}$$

$$= \frac{0.02}{0.57} = 0.035$$

$$P(E_2|F_1) = \frac{P(F_1|E_2)P(E_2)}{P(F_1|E_1)P(E_1) + P(F_1|E_2)P(E_2) + P(F_1|E_3)P(E_3) + P(F_1|E_4)P(E_4)}$$

$$= \frac{(0.40)(0.40)}{(0.20)(0.10) + (0.40)(0.40) + (0.70)(0.30) + (0.90)(0.20)}$$

$$= \frac{0.16}{0.57} = 0.281$$

$$P(E_3|F_1) = \frac{P(F_1|E_3)P(E_3)}{P(F_1|E_1)P(E_1) + P(F_1|E_2)P(E_2) + P(F_1|E_3)P(E_3) + P(F_1|E_4)P(E_4)}$$

$$= \frac{(0.70)(0.30)}{(0.20)(0.10) + (0.40)(0.40) + (0.70)(0.30) + (0.90)(0.20)}$$

$$= \frac{0.21}{0.57} = 0.368$$

$$P(E_4|F_1) = \frac{P(F_1|E_4)P(E_4)}{P(F_1|E_1)P(E_1) + P(F_1|E_2)P(E_2) + P(F_1|E_3)P(E_3) + P(F_1|E_4)P(E_4)}$$

$$= \frac{(0.90)(0.20)}{(0.20)(0.10) + (0.40)(0.40) + (0.70)(0.30) + (0.90)(0.20)}$$

$$= \frac{0.18}{0.57} = 0.316$$

Table 17.15 summarizes the computation of these probabilities. Figure 17.5 displays the joint probabilities in a decision tree. You need to use the revised probabilities, not the original subjective probabilities, to compute the expected monetary value. Table 17.16 shows these computations.

**TABLE 17.15**

Bayes' Theorem Calculations for the Stock Selection Example

| Event, $E_i$ | Prior Probability, $P(E_i)$ | Conditional Probability, $P(F_1|E_i)$ | Joint Probability $P(F_1|E_i)P(E_i)$ | Revised Probability, $P(E_i|F_1)$ |
|---|---|---|---|---|
| Recession, $E_1$ | 0.10 | 0.20 | 0.02 | 0.02/0.57 = 0.035 |
| Stable economy, $E_2$ | 0.40 | 0.40 | 0.16 | 0.16/0.57 = 0.281 |
| Moderate growth, $E_3$ | 0.30 | 0.70 | 0.21 | 0.21/0.57 = 0.368 |
| Boom, $E_4$ | 0.20 | 0.90 | 0.18 | 0.18/0.57 = 0.316 |
| | | | 0.57 | |

**FIGURE 17.5**

Decision tree with joint probabilities for stock selection example

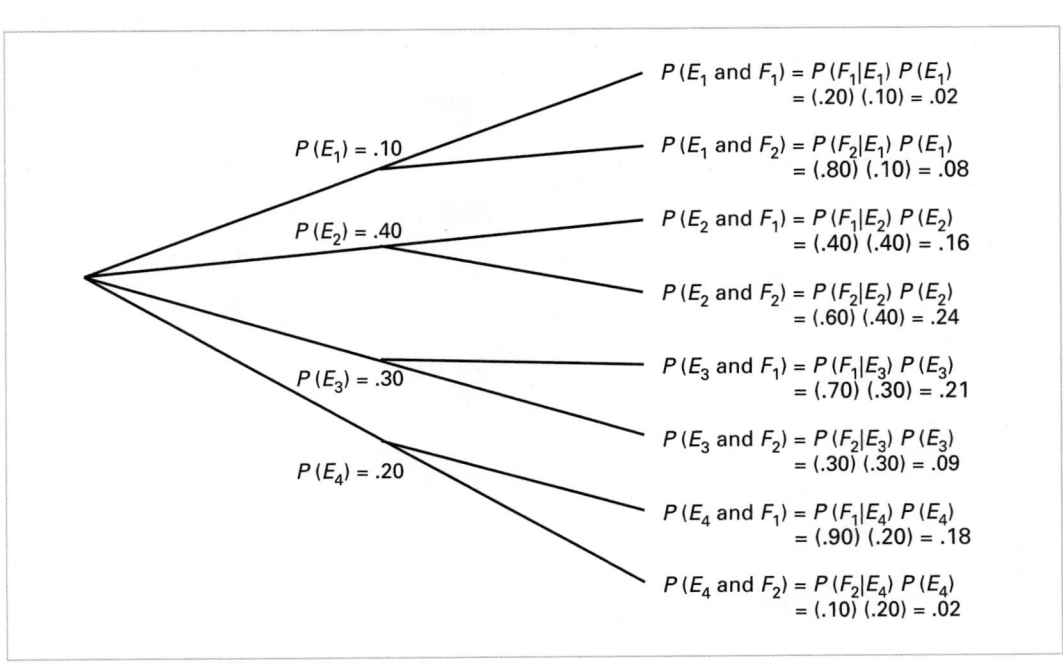

$P(E_1 \text{ and } F_1) = P(F_1|E_1) \, P(E_1)$
$= (.20)(.10) = .02$

$P(E_1 \text{ and } F_2) = P(F_2|E_1) \, P(E_1)$
$= (.80)(.10) = .08$

$P(E_2 \text{ and } F_1) = P(F_1|E_2) \, P(E_2)$
$= (.40)(.40) = .16$

$P(E_2 \text{ and } F_2) = P(F_2|E_2) \, P(E_2)$
$= (.60)(.40) = .24$

$P(E_3 \text{ and } F_1) = P(F_1|E_3) \, P(E_3)$
$= (.70)(.30) = .21$

$P(E_3 \text{ and } F_2) = P(F_2|E_3) \, P(E_3)$
$= (.30)(.30) = .09$

$P(E_4 \text{ and } F_1) = P(F_1|E_4) \, P(E_4)$
$= (.90)(.20) = .18$

$P(E_4 \text{ and } F_2) = P(F_2|E_4) \, P(E_4)$
$= (.10)(.20) = .02$

$P(E_1) = .10$

$P(E_2) = .40$

$P(E_3) = .30$

$P(E_4) = .20$

**TABLE 17.16**

Expected Monetary Value, Using Revised Probabilities, for Each of Two Stocks under Four Economic Conditions

| Event | $P_i$ | A | $X_{ij}P_i$ | B | $X_{ij}P_i$ |
|---|---|---|---|---|---|
| | | | **Alternative Courses of Action** | | |
| **Recession** | 0.035 | 30 | 30(0.035) = 1.05 | −50 | −50(0.035) = −1.75 |
| **Stable economy** | 0.281 | 70 | 70(0.281) = 19.67 | 30 | 30(0.281) = 8.43 |
| **Moderate growth** | 0.368 | 100 | 100(0.368) = 36.80 | 250 | 250(0.368) = 92.00 |
| **Boom** | 0.316 | 150 | 150(0.316) = 47.40 | 400 | 400(0.316) = 126.40 |
| | | | $EMV(A) = 104.92$ | | $EMV(B) = 225.08$ |

Thus, the expected monetary value, or profit, for stock $A$ is \$104.92, and the expected monetary value, or profit, for stock $B$ is \$225.08. Using this criterion, you should once again choose stock $B$ because the expected monetary value is much higher for this stock. However, you should reexamine the return-to-risk ratios in light of these revised probabilities. Using Equations (5.2) and (5.3) on page 182, for stock $A$ because $EMV(A) = \mu_A = \$104.92$,

$$\sigma_A^2 = \sum_{i=1}^{N}(X_i - \mu)^2 P(X_i)$$

$$= (30 - 104.92)^2(0.035) + (70 - 104.92)^2(0.281)$$

$$+ (100 - 104.92)^2(0.368) + (150 - 104.92)^2(0.316)$$

$$= 1{,}190.194$$

$$\sigma_A = \sqrt{1{,}190.194} = \$34.50.$$

For stock $B$, because $EMV(B) = \mu_B = \$225.08$,

$$\sigma_B^2 = \sum_{i=1}^{N}(X_i - \mu)^2 P(X_i)$$

$$= (-50 - 225.08)^2(0.035) + (30 - 225.08)^2(0.281)$$

$$+ (250 - 225.08)^2(0.368) + (400 - 225.08)^2(0.316)$$

$$= 23{,}239.39$$

$$\sigma_B = \sqrt{23{,}239.39} = \$152.445.$$

To compute the coefficient of variation, substitute $\sigma$ for $S$ and $EMV$ for $\bar{X}$ in Equation (3.8) on page 101,

$$CV_A = \left(\frac{\sigma_A}{EMV_A}\right)100\%$$

$$= \left(\frac{34.50}{104.92}\right)100\% = 32.88\%$$

and

$$CV_B = \left(\frac{\sigma_B}{EMV_B}\right)100\%$$

$$= \left(\frac{152.445}{225.08}\right)100\% = 67.73\%$$

Thus, there is still much more variation in the returns from stock $B$ than from stock $A$. For each of these two stocks, you calculate the return-to-risk ratios as follows. For stock $A$, the return-to-risk ratio is equal to

$$RTRR(A) = \frac{104.92}{34.50} = 3.041$$

For stock $B$, the return-to-risk ratio is equal to

$$RTRR(B) = \frac{225.08}{152.445} = 1.476$$

Thus, using the return-to-risk ratio, you should select stock $A$. This decision is different from the one you reached when using expected monetary value (or the equivalent expected opportunity loss). What stock should you buy? Your final decision will depend on whether you believe it is more important to maximize the expected return on investment (select stock $B$) or to control the relative risk (select stock $A$).

## PROBLEMS FOR SECTION 17.3

### Learning the Basics

**17.18** Consider the following payoff table:

| | ACTION | |
|---|---|---|
| EVENT | A ($) | B ($) |
| 1 | 50 | 100 |
| 2 | 200 | 125 |

For this problem, $P(E_1) = 0.5$, $P(E_2) = 0.5$, $P(F|E_1) = 0.6$, and $P(F|E_2) = 0.4$. Suppose that you are informed that event $F$ occurs.

a. Revise the probabilities $P(E_1)$ and $P(E_2)$ now that you know that event $F$ has occurred. Based on these revised probabilities, answer (b) through (i).
b. Compute the expected monetary value of action $A$ and action $B$.
c. Compute the expected opportunity loss of action $A$ and action $B$.
d. Explain the meaning of the expected value of perfect information (*EVPI*) in this problem.
e. On the basis of (b) or (c), which action should you choose? Why?
f. Compute the coefficient of variation for each action.
g. Compute the return-to-risk ratio (*RTRR*) for each action.
h. On the basis of (f) and (g), which action should you choose? Why?
i. Compare the results of (e) and (h), and explain any differences.

**17.19** Consider the following payoff table:

| | ACTION | |
|---|---|---|
| EVENT | A ($) | B ($) |
| 1 | 50 | 10 |
| 2 | 300 | 100 |
| 3 | 500 | 200 |

For this problem, $P(E_1) = 0.8$, $P(E_2) = 0.1$, $P(E_3) = 0.1$, $P(F|E_1) = 0.2$, $P(F|E_2) = 0.4$, and $P(F|E_3) = 0.4$. Suppose you are informed that event $F$ occurs.

a. Revise the probabilities $P(E_1)$, $P(E_2)$, and $P(E_3)$ now that you know that event $F$ has occurred. Based on these revised probabilities, answer (b) through (i).
b. Compute the expected monetary value of action $A$ and action $B$.
c. Compute the expected opportunity loss of action $A$ and action $B$.
d. Explain the meaning of the expected value of perfect information (*EVPI*) in this problem.
e. On the basis of (b) and (c), which action should you choose? Why?
f. Compute the coefficient of variation for each action.
g. Compute the return-to-risk ratio (*RTRR*) for each action.
h. On the basis of (f) and (g), which action should you choose? Why?
i. Compare the results of (e) and (h) and explain any differences.

## Applying the Concepts

**✓SELF** **17.20** In Problem 17.12 on page 807, a vendor
**Test** at a baseball stadium was deciding whether to sell
ice cream or soft drinks at today's game. Prior to making her
decision, she decides to listen to the local weather forecast.
In the past, when it has been cool, the weather reporter has
forecast cool weather 80% of the time. When it has been
warm, the weather reporter has forecast warm weather 70%
of the time. The local weather forecast is for cool weather.

**a.** Revise the prior probabilities now that you know that the
weather forecast is for cool weather.
**b.** Use these revised probabilities to do Problem 17.12.
**c.** Compare the results in (b) to those of Problem 17.12.

**17.21** In Problem 17.14 on page 808, an investor is trying
to determine the optimal investment decision among three
investment opportunities. Prior to making his investment
decision, the investor decides to consult with his financial
adviser. In the past, when the economy has declined, the
financial adviser has given a rosy forecast 20% of the time
(with a gloomy forecast 80% of the time). When there has
been no change in the economy, the financial adviser has
given a rosy forecast 40% of the time. When there has been
an expanding economy, the financial adviser has given a
rosy forecast 70% of the time. The financial adviser in this
case gives a gloomy forecast for the economy.

**a.** Revise the probabilities of the investor based on this
economic forecast by the financial adviser.
**b.** Use these revised probabilities to do Problem 17.14.
**c.** Compare the results in (b) to those of Problem 17.14.

**17.22** In Problem 17.16 on page 808, an author is deciding which of two competing publishing companies to select
to publish her new novel. Prior to making a final decision,
the author decides to have an experienced reviewer examine her novel. This reviewer has an outstanding reputation
for predicting the success of a novel. In the past, for novels
that sold 1,000 copies, only 1% received favorable reviews.
Of novels that sold 5,000 copies, 25% received favorable
reviews. Of novels that sold 10,000 copies, 60% received
favorable reviews. Of novels that sold 50,000 copies, 99%
received favorable reviews. After examining the author's
novel, the reviewer gives it an unfavorable review.

**a.** Revise the probabilities of the number of books sold in
light of the reviewer's unfavorable review.
**b.** Use these revised probabilities to do Problem 17.16.
**c.** Compare the results in (b) to those of Problem 17.16.

## 17.4 UTILITY

The methods used in Sections 17.1 through 17.3 assume that each *incremental* amount of profit or
loss has the same value as the previous amounts of profits attained or losses incurred. In fact, under
many circumstances in the business world, this assumption of incremental changes is not valid.
Most companies, as well as most individuals, make special efforts to avoid large losses. At the
same time, many companies, as well as most individuals, place less value on extremely large profits as compared to initial profits. Such differential evaluation of incremental profits or losses is
referred to as **utility**, a concept first discussed by Daniel Bernoulli in the eighteenth century (see
reference 1). To illustrate this concept, suppose that you are faced with the following two choices:

Choice 1: A fair coin is to be tossed. If it lands on heads, you will receive $0.60; if it lands
on tails, you will pay $0.40.
Choice 2: Do not play the game.

What decision should you choose? The expected value of playing this game is $(0.60)(0.50) +
(-0.40)(0.50) = +\$0.10$, and the expected value of not playing the game is 0.

Most people will decide to play the game because the expected value is positive and only
small amounts of money are involved. Suppose, however, that the game is formulated with a
payoff of $600,000 when the coin lands on heads and a loss of $400,000 when the coin lands on
tails. The expected value of playing the game is now +$100,000. With these payoffs, even though
the expected value is positive, most individuals will not play the game because of the severe negative consequences of losing $400,000. Each additional dollar amount of either profit or loss
does not have the same utility as the previous amount. Large negative amounts for most individuals have severely negative utility. Conversely, the extra value of each incremental dollar of
profit decreases when high enough profit levels are reached. (In other words, the difference
between 0 and $100,000 is much more than the difference between $1,000,000 and $1,100,000.)

An important part of the decision-making process, which is beyond the scope of this text
(see references 2 and 4), is to develop a utility curve for the decision maker that represents the
utility of each specified dollar amount. Figure 17.6 illustrates three types of utility curves:
those of the risk averter, the risk seeker, and the risk-neutral person.

**FIGURE 17.6**

Three types of utility curves

Panel A: Risk Averter's Curve
Panel B: Risk Seeker's Curve
Panel C: Risk-Neutral Curve

The **risk averter's curve** shows a rapid increase in utility for initial amounts of money followed by a gradual leveling off for increasing dollar amounts. This curve is appropriate for most individuals or businesses because the value of each additional dollar is not as great after large amounts of money have already been earned.

The **risk seeker's curve** represents the utility of someone who enjoys taking risks. The utility is greater for large dollar amounts. This curve represents an individual who is interested only in "striking it rich" and is willing to take large risks for the opportunity of making large profits.

The **risk-neutral curve** represents the expected monetary value approach. Each additional dollar of profit has the same value as the previous dollar.

After a utility curve is developed in a specific situation, you convert the dollar amounts to utilities. Then you compute the utility of each alternative course of action and apply the decision criteria of expected utility value, expected opportunity loss, and return-to-risk ratio to make a decision.

## PROBLEMS FOR SECTION 17.4

### Applying the Concepts

**17.23** Do you consider yourself a risk seeker, a risk averter, or a risk-neutral person? Explain.

**17.24** Refer to Problems 17.3–17.5 and 17.12–17.14 on pages 798 and 807–808, respectively. In which problems do you think the expected monetary value (risk-neutral) criterion is inappropriate? Why?

## Risky Business

*From the Authors' Desktop*

When you make investment decisions, you need to think about your own personal tolerance for risk. When given the chance to make large sums of money, some people can shrug off a 20% loss, while others feel ruined when they lose even a small amount such as $20. What about you? Are you willing to risk losing a lot of money for a chance to strike it rich? Or are you more comfortable with a less risky scenario, even though your chance to strike it rich will be smaller?

How can you identify stocks, mutual funds, or other types of investments that fit your own personal tolerance for risk? One way to begin is to examine the standard deviation of the investments you are considering during recent periods of time. You will also want to assess your own willingness to tolerate different losses. What would you do if you lost 10%, 30%, 50%, 90% of your investment? Would you sell? Would you buy more in the hope that the investment would go back up? Also, think about what you would

do if your investment went up 10%, 50%, 100%, 200%. Would you sell the entire investment? Part of the investment? Or would you buy more? And you may want to think about the volatility of your investments, that is, any patterns of extreme increases and decreases in the value over short periods of time, that can add to the risk.

Everyone is different, but knowing how you would answer these questions before you are faced with a decision will help you make better investment decisions.

# SUMMARY

In this chapter, you learned how to develop payoff tables and decision trees, to use various criteria to choose between alternative courses of action, and to revise probabilities in light of sample information using Bayes' theorem. In the Using Statistics scenario, you learned how the manager of The Reliable Fund could use these tools to decide whether to purchase stock *A* or stock *B*. You found that stock *B* had a higher expected monetary value, a lower expected opportunity loss, but a lower return-to-risk ratio.

# KEY EQUATIONS

**Expected Monetary Value**

$$EMV(j) = \sum_{i=1}^{N} X_{ij} P_i \qquad (17.1)$$

**Expected Opportunity Loss**

$$EOL(j) = \sum_{i=1}^{N} L_{ij} P_i \qquad (17.2)$$

**Expected Value of Perfect Information**

$$EVPI = \text{Expected profit under certainty} \\ - \text{Expected monetary value of} \\ \text{the best alternative} \qquad (17.3)$$

**Return-to-Risk Ratio**

$$RTRR(j) = \frac{EMV(j)}{\sigma_j} \qquad (17.4)$$

# KEY TERMS

alternative courses of action    794
decision criteria    794
decision tree    795
events or states of the world    794
expected monetary value (*EMV*)    800
expected opportunity loss (*EOL*)    802
expected profit under certainty    803

expected value of perfect information
   (*EVPI*)    803
maximax payoff criterion    799
maximin payoff criterion    799
opportunity loss    796
payoffs    794
payoff table    794

return-to-risk ratio (*RTRR*)    805
risk averter's curve    816
risk-neutral curve    816
risk seeker's curve    816
utility    815

# CHAPTER REVIEW PROBLEMS

## Checking Your Understanding

**17.25** What is the difference between an event and an alternative course of action?

**17.26** What are the advantages and disadvantages of a payoff table as compared to a decision tree?

**17.27** How are opportunity losses computed from payoffs?

**17.28** Why can't an opportunity loss be negative?

**17.29** How does expected monetary value (*EMV*) differ from expected opportunity loss (*EOL*)?

**17.30** What is the meaning of the expected value of perfect information (*EVPI*)?

**17.31** How does the expected value of perfect information differ from the expected profit under certainty?

**17.32** What are the advantages and disadvantages of using expected monetary value (*EMV*) as compared to the return-to-risk ratio (*RTRR*)?

**17.33** How is Bayes' theorem used to revise probabilities in light of sample information?

**17.34** What is the difference between a risk averter and a risk seeker?

**17.35** Why should you use utilities instead of payoffs in certain circumstances?

## Applying the Concepts

**17.36** A supermarket chain purchases large quantities of white bread for sale during a week. The stores purchase the bread for $0.75 per loaf and sell it for $1.10 per loaf. Any loaves not sold by the end of the week can be sold to a local thrift shop for $0.40. Based on past demand, the probability of various levels of demand is as follows:

| Demand (Loaves) | Probability |
|---|---|
| 6,000 | 0.10 |
| 8,000 | 0.50 |
| 10,000 | 0.30 |
| 12,000 | 0.10 |

a. Construct the payoff table, indicating the events and alternative courses of action.
b. Construct the decision tree.
c. Compute the expected monetary value (EMV) for purchasing 6,000, 8,000, 10,000, and 12,000 loaves.
d. Compute the expected opportunity loss (EOL) for purchasing 6,000, 8,000, 10,000, and 12,000 loaves.
e. Explain the meaning of the expected value of perfect information (EVPI) in this problem.
f. Based on the results of (c) or (d), how many loaves would you purchase? Why?
g. Compute the coefficient of variation for each purchase level.
h. Compute the return-to-risk ratio (RTRR) for each purchase level.
i. Based on (g) and (h), what action would you choose? Why?
j. Compare the results of (f) and (i) and explain any differences.
k. Suppose that new information changes the probabilities associated with the demand level. Use the following probabilities to repeat (c) through (j).

| Demand (Loaves) | Probability |
|---|---|
| 6,000 | 0.30 |
| 8,000 | 0.40 |
| 10,000 | 0.20 |
| 12,000 | 0.10 |

**17.37** The owner of a company that supplies home heating oil would like to determine whether to offer a solar heating installation service to its customers. The owner of the company has determined that a startup cost of $150,000

would be necessary, but a profit of $2,000 can be made on each solar heating system installed. The owner estimates the probability of various demand levels as follows:

| Number of Units Installed | Probability |
|---|---|
| 50 | 0.40 |
| 100 | 0.30 |
| 200 | 0.30 |

a. Construct the payoff table, indicating the events and alternative courses of action.
b. Construct the decision tree.
c. Construct the opportunity loss table.
d. Compute the expected monetary value (EMV) for offering this solar heating system installation service.
e. Compute the expected opportunity loss (EOL) for offering this solar heating system installation service.
f. Explain the meaning of the expected value of perfect information (EVPI) in this problem.
g. Compute the return-to-risk ratio (RTRR) for offering this solar heating system installation service.
h. Based on the results of (d), (e) and (g), should the company offer this solar heating system installation service? Why?
i. How would your answers to (a) through (h) be affected if the startup cost were $200,000?

**17.38** The manufacturer of a nationally distributed brand of potato chips wants to determine the feasibility of changing the product package from a cellophane bag to an unbreakable container. The product manager believes that there are three possible national market responses to a change in product package: weak, moderate, and strong. The projected payoffs, in millions of dollars, in increased or decreased profit compared to the current package are as follows:

| | STRATEGY | |
|---|---|---|
| EVENT | Use New Package | Keep Old Package |
| **Weak national response** | −4 | 0 |
| **Moderate national response** | 1 | 0 |
| **Strong national response** | 5 | 0 |

Based on past experience, the product manager assigns the following probabilities to the different levels of national response:

P (Weak national response) = 0.30
P (Moderate national response) = 0.60
P (Strong national response) = 0.10

a. Construct the decision tree.
b. Construct the opportunity loss table.
c. Compute the expected monetary value (EMV) for offering this new product package.

**d.** Compute the expected opportunity loss (*EOL*) for offering this new product package.

**e.** Explain the meaning of the expected value of perfect information (*EVPI*) in this problem.

**f.** Compute the return-to-risk ratio (*RTRR*) for offering this new product package.

**g.** Based on the results of (c), (d) and (f), should the company offer this new product package? Why?

**h.** What are your answers to parts (c) through (g) if the probabilities are 0.6, 0.3, and 0.1, respectively?

**i.** What are your answers to parts (c) through (g) if the probabilities are 0.1, 0.3, and 0.6, respectively?

Before making a final decision, the product manager would like to test market the new package in a selected city by substituting the new package for the old package. A determination is then made about whether sales have increased, decreased, or stayed the same. In previous test marketing of other products, when there was a subsequent weak national response, sales in the test city decreased 60% of the time, stayed the same 30% of the time, and increased 10% of the time. Where there was a moderate national response, sales in the test city decreased 20% of the time, stayed the same 40% of the time, and increased 40% of the time. When there was a strong national response, sales in the test city decreased 5% of the time, stayed the same 35% of the time, and increased 60% of the time.

**j.** If sales in the test city stayed the same, revise the original probabilities in light of this new information.

**k.** Use the revised probabilities in (j) to repeat (c) through (g).

**l.** If sales in the test city decreased, revise the original probabilities in light of this new information.

**m.** Use the revised probabilities in (l) to repeat (c) through (g).

**17.39** An entrepreneur wants to determine whether it would be profitable to establish a gardening service in a local suburb. The entrepreneur believes that there are four possible levels of demand for this gardening service:

Very low demand—1% of the households would use the service.

Low demand—5% of the households would use the service.

Moderate demand—10% of the households would use the service.

High demand—25% of the households would use the service.

Based on past experiences in other suburbs, the entrepreneur assigns the following probabilities to the various demand levels:

$P$(Very low demand) = 0.20
$P$(Low demand) = 0.50
$P$(Moderate demand) = 0.20
$P$(High demand) = 0.10

The entrepreneur has calculated the following profits or losses ($) of this garden service for each demand level (over a period of 1 year):

|  | ACTION | |
|---|---|---|
| DEMAND | Provide Garden Service | Do Not Provide Garden Service |
| Very low | − 50,000 | 0 |
| Low | 60,000 | 0 |
| Moderate | 130,000 | 0 |
| High | 300,000 | 0 |

**a.** Construct a decision tree.

**b.** Construct an opportunity loss table.

**c.** Compute the expected monetary value (*EMV*) for offering this garden service.

**d.** Compute the expected opportunity loss (*EOL*) for offering this garden service.

**e.** Explain the meaning of the expected value of perfect information (*EVPI*) in this problem.

**f.** Compute the return-to-risk ratio (*RTRR*) for offering this garden service.

**g.** Based on the results of (c), (d), and (f), should the entrepreneur offer this garden service? Why?

Before making a final decision, the entrepreneur conducts a survey to determine demand for the gardening service. A random sample of 20 households is selected, and 3 indicate that they would use this gardening service.

**h.** Revise the prior probabilities in light of this sample information. (*Hint:* Use the binomial distribution to determine the probability of the outcome that occurred, given a particular level of demand.)

**i.** Use the revised probabilities in (h) to repeat (c) through (g).

**17.40** A manufacturer of a brand of inexpensive felt-tip pens maintains a production process that produces 10,000 pens per day. In order to maintain the highest quality of this product, the manufacturer guarantees free replacement of any defective pen sold. Each defective pen produced costs 20 cents for the manufacturer to replace. Based on past experience, four rates of producing defective pens are possible:

Very low—1% of the pens manufactured will be defective.

Low—5% of the pens manufactured will be defective.

Moderate—10% of the pens manufactured will be defective.

High—20% of the pens manufactured will be defective.

The manufacturer can reduce the rate of defective pens produced by having a mechanic fix the machines at the end of each day. This mechanic can reduce the rate to 1%, but his services will cost $80.

A payoff table based on the daily production of 10,000 pens, indicating the replacement costs ($) for each of the two alternatives (calling in the mechanic and not calling in the mechanic), is as follows:

| | ACTION | |
| DEFECTIVE RATE | Do Not Call Mechanic | Call Mechanic |
| --- | --- | --- |
| Very low (1%) | 20 | 100 |
| Low (5%) | 100 | 100 |
| Moderate (10%) | 200 | 100 |
| High (20%) | 400 | 100 |

Based on past experience, each defective rate is assumed to be equally likely to occur.

**a.** Construct a decision tree.

**b.** Construct an opportunity loss table.

**c.** Compute the expected monetary value (*EMV*) for calling and for not calling the mechanic.

**d.** Compute the expected opportunity loss (*EOL*) for calling and for not calling the mechanic.

**e.** Explain the meaning of the expected value of perfect information (*EVPI*) in this problem.

**f.** Compute the return-to-risk ratio (*RTRR*) for calling and not calling the mechanic.

**g.** Based on the results of (c), (d), and (f), should the company call the mechanic? Why?

**h.** At the end of a day's production, a sample of 15 pens is selected, and 2 are defective. Revise the prior probabilities in light of this sample information. (*Hint:* Use the binomial distribution to determine the probability of the outcome that occurred, given a particular defective rate.)

**i.** Use the revised probabilities in (h) to repeat (c) through (g).

# WEB CASE

*Apply your knowledge of decision-making techniques in this Web Case, which extends the EndRun Web Case from earlier chapters.*

StraightArrow Banking & Investments is a Tri-Cities competitor of EndRun that is currently advertising its StraightArrow StraightDeal fund.

Visit the StraightArrow Web page at **www.prenhall. com/Springville/SA_Home.htm** (or open the `SA_Home.htm` file from the Student CD-ROM Web Case Folder), and examine the claims and supporting data for the fund. Compare those claims and data to the supporting data found on the EndRun Happy Bull and Worried Bear Funds Web page, **www.prenhall.com/Springville/ER_BullsandBears.htm** (or open the `ER_BullsandBears.htm` file from the Student CD-ROM Web Case folder) first discussed in the Web Case for Chapter 5. Then answer the following:

**1.** Is the StraightArrow StraightDeal fund a better investment than either of the EndRun funds? Support your answer by performing an appropriate analysis and summarizing your results.

**2.** Before making a decision about which fund makes a better investment, you decide that you need a reliable forecast for the direction of the economy in the next year. After further investigation, you find that the consensus of leading economists is that the economy will be expanding in the next year. You also find out that in the past, when there has been a recession, leading economists predicted an expanding economy 10% of the time. When there was a stable economy, they predicted an expanding economy 50% of the time, and when there was an expanding economy, they predicted an expanding economy 75% of the time. When there was a rapidly expanding economy, they predicted an expanding economy 90% of the time. Does this information change your answer to Question 1? Why or why not?

# REFERENCES

1. Bernstein, P. L., *Against the Gods: The Remarkable Story of Risk* (New York: Wiley, 1996).
2. *Microsoft Excel 2007* (Redmond, WA: Microsoft Corp., 2007).
3. Render, B., R. M. Stair, and M. Hanna, *Quantitative Analysis for Management*, 9th ed. (Upper Saddle River, NJ: Prentice Hall, 2006).
4. Tversky, A., and D. Kahneman, "Rationale Choice and the Framing of Decisions," *Journal of Business*, 59 (1986): pp. 251–278.

# Appendix E17
## Using Microsoft Excel for Decision Making

### E17.1 Computing Opportunity Loss

You compute opportunity loss by making entries in the **OLT2x2** worksheet of the `Opportunity Loss.xls` workbook. This worksheet (shown in Figure 17.3 on page 797) uses the **INDEX(*cell range*, 1, *column number*)**, and **MATCH(*cell to be matched, cell range in which to look for a match*, 0)** functions together to display the correct alternative course of action labels for the cells in the Optimum Action column.

Figure E17.1 shows the formulas for columns B through E of the opportunity loss table. The MATCH function in the column B formulas matches the optimum profit found in column C with one of two payoff values and returns either the value 1 or 2 depending on whether the first or second payoff value matched the optimum profit. The returned value (1 or 2) is, in turn, used by INDEX as the *column number* to decide which of the two alternative courses of action labels will be displayed in the column B cell.

To adapt this worksheet for other problems involving 2 events and 2 alternative courses of action, enter new payoff data and labels in the Payoff Table area in rows 4 through 6. Although modifying the worksheet for other numbers of events and alternative courses of action is beyond the scope of this text, advanced Excel users may benefit from studying the formulas displayed in the **OLT2x2Formulas** worksheet.

|    | B | C | D | E |
|----|---|---|---|---|
| 10 | Optimum | Optimum | Alternatives | |
| 11 | Action | Profit | =B4 | =C4 |
| 12 | =INDEX($B$4:$C$4, 1, MATCH(C12, B5:C5, 0)) | =MAX(B5:C5) | =$C12 - B5 | =$C12 - C5 |
| 13 | =INDEX($B$4:$C$4, 1, MATCH(C13, B6:C6, 0)) | =MAX(B6:C6) | =$C13 - B6 | =$C13 - C6 |

**FIGURE E17.1** Opportunity Loss Table columns B though E formulas

### E17.2 Computing Expected Monetary Value

You compute the expected monetary value by making entries in the **EMV4Ex2A** worksheet of the `Expected Monetary Value.xls` workbook. The worksheet, shown in Figure 17.4 on page 806, uses the **SUMPRODUCT(*multiplier cell range, multiplicand cell range*)** function to compute the expected monetary value, the standard deviation, and the expected opportunity loss. In the opportunity loss table area, the worksheet uses the INDEX and MATCH functions to determine the optimum action (see related discussion in Section E17.1).

To adapt this worksheet for other problems involving 4 events and 2 alternative courses of action, make new entries in the Probabilities & Payoff Table area. Although modifying the worksheet for other numbers of events and alternative courses of action is beyond the scope of this text, advanced Excel users may benefit from studying the formulas displayed in the **EMV4Ex2AFormulas** worksheet.

# Appendix P17
## Using PHStat2 for Decision Making

### P17.1 Computing Opportunity Loss

To compute opportunity loss, use **PHStat → Decision-Making → Opportunity Loss**. This procedure creates an opportunity loss analysis worksheet based on the number of events and alternative actions that you specify. To complete the worksheet, enter payoff data and labels in the tinted table cells that begin in row 4. (The #DIV/0! messages that may appear in several cells will disappear after you enter your data. This is not an error.)

### P17.2 Computing Expected Monetary Value

To compute expected monetary value, use **PHStat → Decision-Making → Expected Monetary Value**. The procedure creates an expected monetary value worksheet based on the number of events and alternative actions that you specify. To complete the worksheet, enter probabilities and payoff data and labels in the tinted table cells that begin in row 4. (The #DIV/0! messages that may appear in several cells will disappear after you enter your data. This is not an error.)

# CHAPTER
# EIGHTEEN
## STATISTICAL APPLICATIONS IN QUALITY MANAGEMENT

# LEARNING OBJECTIVES

## In this chapter, you learn:

- How to construct various control charts
- Which control chart to use for a particular type of data
- How to measure the capability of a process
- The basic themes of total quality management and Deming's 14 points
- The basic aspects of Six Sigma

# USING STATISTICS @ Beachcomber Hotel

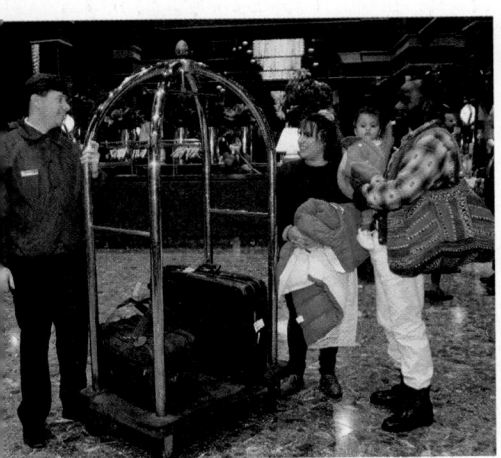

You find yourself managing the Beachcomber Hotel, one of the resorts owned by T.C. Resort Properties (see Chapter 12). You want to continually improve the quality of service that your guests receive so that overall guest satisfaction increases. To help you achieve this improvement, T.C. Resort Properties has provided its managers with training in Six Sigma. In order to meet the business objective of increasing the return rate of guests at your hotel, you have decided to focus on the critical first impressions of the service that your hotel provides. Is the assigned hotel room ready when a guest checks in? Are all expected amenities, such as extra towels and a complimentary guest basket, in the room when the guest first walks in? Are the video-entertainment center and high-speed Internet access working properly? And do guests receive their luggage in a reasonable amount of time?

To study these guest satisfaction issues, you have embarked on an improvement project that measures two critical-to-quality (CTQ) measurements: the readiness of the room and the time it takes to deliver luggage. You would like to learn the following:

- Are the proportion of rooms ready and the time required to deliver luggage to the rooms acceptable?
- Are the proportion of rooms ready and the luggage delivery time consistent from day to day, or are they increasing or decreasing?
- On the days when the proportion of rooms that are not ready or the time to deliver luggage is greater than normal, are these due to a chance occurrence, or are there fundamental flaws in the processes used to make rooms ready and to deliver luggage?

Companies manufacturing products, as well as those providing services, such as the Beachcomber Hotel in the "Using Statistics" scenario, realize that quality is essential for survival in the global economy. Among the areas in which quality has an impact on our everyday work and personal lives are the design, production, and reliability of our automobiles; the services provided by hotels, banks, schools, retailing operations, and mail-order companies; the continuous improvement in computer chips that makes for faster and more powerful computers; and the availability of new technology and equipment that has led to improved diagnosis of illnesses and the improved delivery of health care services.

This chapter will first cover control charts, a statistical tool that is widely used for quality improvement. Then, two important quality improvement approaches, total quality management and Six Sigma management, will be discussed.

## 18.1   THE THEORY OF CONTROL CHARTS

One widely used statistical tool, developed by Walter Shewhart (see reference 16), used for monitoring and improving a process is the control chart. A process is defined as follows:

A **process** is the value-added transformation of inputs to outputs.

The inputs and outputs of a process can involve machines, materials, methods, measurement, people, and the environment. Each of the inputs is a source of variability. Variability in the output can result in poor service and poor product quality, both of which often decrease customer satisfaction.

The **control chart** is used to analyze a process in which data are collected sequentially over time. You can use a control chart to study past performance, to evaluate present conditions, or to predict future outcomes. Control charts are used at the beginning of quality improvement efforts to study an existing process (called Phase 1 control charts). Information gained from analyzing Phase I control charts forms the basis for process improvement. After improvements to the process are implemented, control charts are then used to monitor the processes to ensure that the improvements continue (called Phase 2 control charts).

Different types of control charts allow you to analyze different types of critical-to-quality (CTQ in Six Sigma lingo—see Section 18.8) variables—for categorical variables, such as the proportion of hotel rooms that are nonconforming in terms of the availability of amenities and the working order of all appliances in the room; for discrete variables such as the number of hotel guests registering a complaint in a week; and for continuous variables, such as the length of time required for delivering luggage to the room.

In addition to providing a visual display of data representing a process, a principal focus of a control chart is the attempt to separate special causes of variation from common causes of variation.

**Special causes of variation** represent large fluctuations or patterns in the data that are not part of a process. These fluctuations are often caused by changes in the process that represent either problems to correct or opportunities to exploit. Some organizations refer to special causes of variation as **assignable causes of variation**.

**Common causes of variation** represent the inherent variability that exists in a process. These fluctuations consist of the numerous small causes of variability that operate randomly or by chance. Some organizations refer to common causes of variation as **chance causes of variation**.

One experiment that is useful to help you appreciate the distinction between common and special causes of variation was developed by Walter Shewhart (see reference 16) more than 80 years ago. The experiment requires that you repeatedly write the letter A over and over again in a horizontal line across a piece of paper:

AAAAAAAAAAAAAAAAA

When you do this, you immediately notice that the A's are all similar but not exactly the same. In addition, you may notice some difference in the size of the A's from letter to letter. This difference is due to common cause variation. Nothing special happened that caused the differences in the size of the A's. You probably would have a hard time trying to explain why the largest A is bigger than the smallest A. These types of differences almost certainly represent common cause variation.

However, if you did the experiment over again, but wrote half of the A's with your right hand and the other half of the A's with your left hand, you would almost certainly see a very big difference in the A's written with each hand. In this case, which hand was used to write the A's is the source of the special cause variation.

The distinction between the two causes of variation is crucial because special causes of variation are not part of a process and are correctable or exploitable without changing the system. Common causes of variation, however, can be reduced only by changing the system. Such systemic changes are the responsibility of management.

Control charts allow you to monitor a process and identify the presence or absence of special causes. By doing so, control charts help prevent two types of errors. The first type of error involves the belief that an observed value represents special cause variation when it is due to the common cause variation of the system. Treating common cause variation as special cause variation often results in overadjusting a process. This overadjustment, known as **tampering**, increases the variation in the process. The second type of error involves treating special cause variation as common cause variation. This error results in not taking immediate corrective action when necessary. Although both of these types of errors can occur even when using a control chart, they are far less likely.

To construct a control chart, you collect samples from the output of a process over time. The samples used for constructing control charts are known as **subgroups**. For each subgroup (i.e., sample), you calculate the value of a statistic associated with a CTQ variable. Commonly used statistics include the sample proportion for categorical variables (see Section 18.2), the number of nonconformities (see Section 18.4), and the mean and range of a numerical variable (see Section 18.5). You then plot the values over time and add control limits to the chart. The most typical form of a control chart sets control limits that are within ±3 standard deviations[1] of the statistical measure of interest. Equation (18.1) defines, in general, the upper and lower control limits for control charts.

[1]*Recall from Section 6.2 that in the normal distribution, $\mu \pm 3\sigma$ includes almost all (99.73%) of the values in the population.*

Constructing Control Limits

$$\text{Process mean} \pm 3 \text{ standard deviations} \qquad\qquad \textbf{(18.1)}$$

so that

**Upper control limit (UCL)** = process mean +3 standard deviations

**Lower control limit (LCL)** = process mean −3 standard deviations

When these control limits are set, you evaluate the control chart by trying to find any pattern that might exist in the values over time and by determining whether any points fall outside the control limits. Figure 18.1 illustrates three different patterns.

**FIGURE 18.1**

Three control chart patterns

In Panel A of Figure 18.1, there is no apparent pattern in the values over time, and there are no points that fall outside the 3 standard deviation control limits. The process appears stable and contains only common cause variation. Panel B, on the contrary, contains two points that fall outside the 3 standard deviation control limits. You should investigate these points to try to determine the special causes that led to their occurrence. Although Panel C does not have any points outside the control limits, it has a series of consecutive points above the mean value (the center line) as well as a series of consecutive points below the mean value. In addition, a long-term overall downward trend is clearly visible. You should investigate the situation to try to determine what may have caused this pattern.

Detecting a pattern is not always so easy. The following simple rule (see references 9, 13, and 18) can help you to detect a trend or a shift in the mean level of a process:

- Eight or more *consecutive* points that lie above the center line or eight or more *consecutive* points that lie below the center line[2]

A process whose control chart indicates an out-of-control condition (i.e., a point outside the control limits or a series of points that exhibits a pattern) is said to be out of control. An **out-of-control process** contains both common causes of variation and special causes of variation. Because special causes of variation are not part of the process design, an out-of-control process is unpredictable. When you determine that a process is out of control, you must identify the special causes of variation that are producing the out-of-control conditions. If the special causes are detrimental to the quality of the product or service, you need to implement plans to eliminate this source of variation. When a special cause increases quality, you should change the process so that the special cause is incorporated into the process design. Thus, this beneficial special cause now becomes a common cause source of variation, and the process is improved.

A process whose control chart does not indicate any out-of-control conditions is said to be in control. An **in-control process** contains only common causes of variation. Because these sources of variation are inherent to the process itself, an in-control process is predictable. In-control processes are sometimes said to be in a **state of statistical control**. When a process is in control, you must determine whether the amount of common cause variation in the process is small enough to satisfy the customers of the products or services. (In Section 18.6, you will learn statistical methods that allow you to compare common cause variation to customer expectations.) If the common cause variation is small enough to consistently satisfy the customer, you then use control charts to monitor the process on a continuing basis to make sure the process remains in control. If the common cause variation is too large, you need to alter the process itself.

## 18.2   CONTROL CHART FOR THE PROPORTION: THE *p* CHART

Various types of control charts are used to monitor processes and determine whether special cause variation is present in a process. **Attribute charts** are used for categorical or discrete variables. This section introduces the ***p* chart**, which is used for categorical variables. The *p* chart gets its name from the fact that you plot the *proportion* of items in a sample that are in a category of interest. For example, sampled items are often classified according to whether they conform or do not conform to operationally defined requirements. Thus, the *p* chart is frequently used to monitor and analyze the proportion of nonconforming items in repeated samples (i.e., subgroups) selected from a process.

To begin the discussion of *p* charts, recall that you studied proportions and the binomial distribution in Section 5.3. Then, in Section 7.5 on page 278, the sample proportion is defined as $p = X/n$, and the standard deviation of the sample proportion is defined as

$$\sigma_p = \sqrt{\frac{\pi(1-\pi)}{n}}$$

Using Equation (18.1) on page 826, control limits for the proportion of nonconforming[3] items from the sample data are established in Equation (18.2).

---

[2]This rule is often referred to as the runs rule. A similar rule used by some companies is called the trend rule: Eight or more consecutive points that increase in value or eight or more consecutive points that decrease in value. Some statisticians (see reference 5) have criticized the trend rule. It should only be used with extreme caution.

[3]In this chapter, and in quality management, the phrase "proportion of nonconforming items" is often used, although the p chart can be used to monitor any proportion of interest. Recall that in the earlier discussions of the binomial distribution, the phrase "proportion of items of interest" was used.

Control Limits for the $p$ Chart

$$\bar{p} \pm 3\sqrt{\frac{\bar{p}(1-\bar{p})}{\bar{n}}}$$

$$\text{UCL} = \bar{p} + 3\sqrt{\frac{\bar{p}(1-\bar{p})}{\bar{n}}}$$  (18.2)

$$\text{LCL} = \bar{p} - 3\sqrt{\frac{\bar{p}(1-\bar{p})}{\bar{n}}}$$

For equal $n_i$,

$$\bar{n} = n_i \text{ and } \bar{p} = \frac{\sum_{i=1}^{k} p_i}{k}$$

or in general,

$$\bar{n} = \frac{\sum_{i=1}^{k} n_i}{k} \text{ and } \bar{p} = \frac{\sum_{i=1}^{k} X_i}{\sum_{i=1}^{k} n_i}$$

where   $X_i$ = number of nonconforming items in subgroup $i$

$n_i$ = sample (or subgroup) size for subgroup $i$

$p_i = \dfrac{X_i}{n_i}$ = proportion of nonconforming items in subgroup $i$

$k$ = number of subgroups selected

$\bar{n}$ = mean subgroup size

$\bar{p}$ = proportion of nonconforming items in the $k$ subgroups combined

Any negative value for the LCL means that the LCL does not exist.

To show the application of the $p$ chart, return to the Using Statistics scenario on page 824 concerning the Beachcomber Hotel. During the process improvement effort in the Measure phase of Six Sigma (see Section 18.8), a nonconforming room was operationally defined as the absence of an amenity or an appliance not in working order upon check-in. During the Analyze phase of Six Sigma (see Section 18.8), data on the nonconformances were collected daily from a sample of 200 rooms (see the file Hotel1). Table 18.1 lists the number and proportion of nonconforming rooms for each day in the four-week period.

For these data, $k = 28$, $\sum_{i=1}^{k} p_i = 2.315$ and, because the $n_i$ are equal, $n_i = \bar{n} = 200$. Thus,

$$\bar{p} = \frac{\sum_{i=1}^{k} p_i}{k} = \frac{2.315}{28} = 0.0827$$

**TABLE 18.1**

Nonconforming Hotel Rooms at Check-in over a 28-Day Period

| Day (i) | Rooms Studied ($n_i$) | Rooms Not Ready ($X_i$) | Proportion ($p_i$) | Day (i) | Rooms Studied ($n_i$) | Rooms Not Ready ($X_i$) | Proportion ($p_i$) |
|---|---|---|---|---|---|---|---|
| 1 | 200 | 16 | 0.080 | 15 | 200 | 18 | 0.090 |
| 2 | 200 | 7 | 0.035 | 16 | 200 | 13 | 0.065 |
| 3 | 200 | 21 | 0.105 | 17 | 200 | 15 | 0.075 |
| 4 | 200 | 17 | 0.085 | 18 | 200 | 10 | 0.050 |
| 5 | 200 | 25 | 0.125 | 19 | 200 | 14 | 0.070 |
| 6 | 200 | 19 | 0.095 | 20 | 200 | 25 | 0.125 |
| 7 | 200 | 16 | 0.080 | 21 | 200 | 19 | 0.095 |
| 8 | 200 | 15 | 0.075 | 22 | 200 | 12 | 0.060 |
| 9 | 200 | 11 | 0.055 | 23 | 200 | 6 | 0.030 |
| 10 | 200 | 12 | 0.060 | 24 | 200 | 12 | 0.060 |
| 11 | 200 | 22 | 0.110 | 25 | 200 | 18 | 0.090 |
| 12 | 200 | 20 | 0.100 | 26 | 200 | 15 | 0.075 |
| 13 | 200 | 17 | 0.085 | 27 | 200 | 20 | 0.100 |
| 14 | 200 | 26 | 0.130 | 28 | 200 | 22 | 0.110 |

Using Equation (18.2),

$$0.0827 \pm 3\sqrt{\frac{(0.0827)(0.9173)}{200}}$$

so that

$$UCL = 0.0827 + 0.0584 = 0.1411$$

and

$$LCL = 0.0827 - 0.0584 = 0.0243$$

Figure 18.2 on page 830 displays the Microsoft Excel $p$ chart for the data of Table 18.1. Figure 18.3 illustrates Minitab results. Figure 18.2 and Figure 18.3 show a process in a state of statistical control, with the individual points distributed around $\bar{p}$ without any pattern and all the points within the control limits. Thus, any improvement in the process of making rooms ready for guests must come from the reduction of common cause variation. Such reductions require changes in the process. These changes are the responsibility of management. Remember that improvements in quality cannot occur until changes to the process itself are successfully implemented.

This example illustrates a situation in which the subgroup size does not vary. As a general rule, as long as none of the subgroup sizes, $n_i$, differ from the mean subgroup size, $\bar{n}$, by more than ±25% of $\bar{n}$ (see reference 9), you can use Equation (18.2) on page 828 to compute the control limits for the $p$ chart. If any subgroup size differs by more than ±25% of $\bar{n}$, you use alternative formulas for calculating the control limits (see references 9 and 13). To illustrate the use of the $p$ chart when the subgroup sizes are unequal, Example 18.1 studies the production of medical sponges.

**FIGURE 18.2**

Microsoft Excel *p* chart for the nonconforming hotel rooms

*See Sections E18.1 and E18.2 or Section P18.1 to create this.*

**FIGURE 18.3**

Minitab *p* chart for the nonconforming hotel rooms

*See Section M18.1 to create this.*

**EXAMPLE 18.1**    USING THE *p* CHART FOR UNEQUAL SUBGROUP SIZES

Table 18.2 indicates the number of medical sponges produced daily and the number that are nonconforming for a period of 32 days (see the file **Sponge**). Construct a control chart for these data.

**TABLE 18.2**

Medical Sponges
Produced and Number
Nonconforming over a
32-Day Period

| Day $(i)$ | Sponges Produced $(n_i)$ | Nonconforming Sponges $(X_i)$ | Proportion $(p_i)$ | Day $(i)$ | Sponges Produced $(n_i)$ | Nonconforming Sponges $(X_i)$ | Proportion $(p_i)$ |
|---|---|---|---|---|---|---|---|
| 1  | 690 | 21 | 0.030 | 17 | 575 | 20 | 0.035 |
| 2  | 580 | 22 | 0.038 | 18 | 610 | 16 | 0.026 |
| 3  | 685 | 20 | 0.029 | 19 | 596 | 15 | 0.025 |
| 4  | 595 | 21 | 0.035 | 20 | 630 | 24 | 0.038 |
| 5  | 665 | 23 | 0.035 | 21 | 625 | 25 | 0.040 |
| 6  | 596 | 19 | 0.032 | 22 | 615 | 21 | 0.034 |
| 7  | 600 | 18 | 0.030 | 23 | 575 | 23 | 0.040 |
| 8  | 620 | 24 | 0.039 | 24 | 572 | 20 | 0.035 |
| 9  | 610 | 20 | 0.033 | 25 | 645 | 24 | 0.037 |
| 10 | 595 | 22 | 0.037 | 26 | 651 | 39 | 0.060 |
| 11 | 645 | 19 | 0.029 | 27 | 660 | 21 | 0.032 |
| 12 | 675 | 23 | 0.034 | 28 | 685 | 19 | 0.028 |
| 13 | 670 | 22 | 0.033 | 29 | 671 | 17 | 0.025 |
| 14 | 590 | 26 | 0.044 | 30 | 660 | 22 | 0.033 |
| 15 | 585 | 17 | 0.029 | 31 | 595 | 24 | 0.040 |
| 16 | 560 | 16 | 0.029 | 32 | 600 | 16 | 0.027 |

**SOLUTION**  For these data,

$$k = 32, \quad \sum_{i=1}^{k} n_i = 19{,}926$$

$$\sum_{i=1}^{k} X_i = 679$$

Thus, using Equation (18.2) on page 828,

$$\bar{n} = \frac{19{,}926}{32} = 622.69$$

$$\bar{p} = \frac{679}{19{,}926} = 0.034$$

so that

$$0.034 \pm 3 \sqrt{\frac{(0.034)(1 - 0.034)}{622.69}}$$

$$= 0.034 \pm 0.022$$

Thus,

$$\text{UCL} = 0.034 + 0.022 = 0.056$$

$$\text{LCL} = 0.034 - 0.022 = 0.012$$

Figure 18.4 displays the Microsoft Excel control chart for the sponge data. In Figure 18.5, however, Minitab calculates separate control limits for each day, depending on the subgroup size for that day and therefore the UCL and LCL are represented by jagged lines. From Figure 18.4 or Figure 18.5, you can see that day 26, on which there were 39 nonconforming sponges produced out of 651 sampled, is above the UCL. Management needs to determine the reason (i.e., root cause) for this special cause variation and take corrective action. Once actions are taken, you can remove the data from day 26 and then construct and analyze a new control chart.

**FIGURE 18.4**

Microsoft Excel *p* chart for the proportion of nonconforming medical sponges

*See Sections E18.1 and E18.2 or Section P18.1 to create this.*

**FIGURE 18.5**

Microsoft Excel *p* chart for the proportion of nonconforming medical sponges

*See Section M18.1 to create this.*

# PROBLEMS FOR SECTION 18.2

## Learning the Basics

**18.1** The following data were collected on nonconformances for a period of 10 days:

| Day | Sample Size | Nonconformances |
|-----|-------------|-----------------|
| 1   | 100         | 12              |
| 2   | 100         | 14              |
| 3   | 100         | 10              |
| 4   | 100         | 18              |
| 5   | 100         | 22              |
| 6   | 100         | 14              |
| 7   | 100         | 15              |
| 8   | 100         | 13              |
| 9   | 100         | 14              |
| 10  | 100         | 16              |

**a.** On what day is the proportion of nonconformances largest? smallest?
**b.** What are the LCL and UCL?
**c.** Are there any special causes of variation?

**18.2** The following data were collected on nonconformances for a period of 10 days:

| Day | Sample Size | Nonconformances |
|-----|-------------|-----------------|
| 1   | 111         | 12              |
| 2   | 93          | 14              |
| 3   | 105         | 10              |
| 4   | 92          | 18              |
| 5   | 117         | 22              |
| 6   | 88          | 14              |
| 7   | 117         | 15              |
| 8   | 87          | 13              |
| 9   | 119         | 14              |
| 10  | 107         | 16              |

**a.** On what day is the proportion of nonconformances largest? smallest?
**b.** What are the LCL and UCL?
**c.** Are there any special causes of variation?

## Applying the Concepts

**18.3** A medical transcription service enters medical data on patient files for hospitals. The service studied ways to improve the turnaround time (defined as the time between sending data and the time the client receives completed files). After studying the process, it was determined that turnaround time was increased by transmission errors. A transmission error was defined as data transmitted that did not go through as planned and needed to be retransmitted. Each day, a sample of 125 transmissions were randomly selected and evaluated for errors (see the file **Transmit**). The following table presents the number and proportion of transmissions with errors:

| Day (i) | Number of Errors ($X_i$) | Proportion of Errors ($p_i$) | Day (i) | Number of Errors ($X_i$) | Proportion of Errors ($p_i$) |
|---------|-----|-------|----|-----|-------|
| 1  | 6  | 0.048 | 17 | 4  | 0.032 |
| 2  | 3  | 0.024 | 18 | 6  | 0.048 |
| 3  | 4  | 0.032 | 19 | 3  | 0.024 |
| 4  | 4  | 0.032 | 20 | 5  | 0.040 |
| 5  | 9  | 0.072 | 21 | 1  | 0.008 |
| 6  | 0  | 0.000 | 22 | 3  | 0.024 |
| 7  | 0  | 0.000 | 23 | 14 | 0.112 |
| 8  | 8  | 0.064 | 24 | 6  | 0.048 |
| 9  | 4  | 0.032 | 25 | 7  | 0.056 |
| 10 | 3  | 0.024 | 26 | 3  | 0.024 |
| 11 | 4  | 0.032 | 27 | 10 | 0.080 |
| 12 | 1  | 0.008 | 28 | 7  | 0.056 |
| 13 | 10 | 0.080 | 29 | 5  | 0.040 |
| 14 | 9  | 0.072 | 30 | 0  | 0.000 |
| 15 | 3  | 0.024 | 31 | 3  | 0.024 |
| 16 | 1  | 0.008 |    |    |       |

**a.** Construct a *p* chart.
**b.** Is the process in a state of statistical control? Why?

**SELF Test** **18.4** The following data represent the findings from a study conducted at a factory that manufactures film canisters. For 32 days, 500 film canisters were sampled and inspected (see the file **Canister**). The following table lists the number of defective film canisters (i.e., nonconforming items) for each day (i.e., subgroup):

| Day | Number Nonconforming | Day | Number Nonconforming |
|-----|----------------------|-----|----------------------|
| 1  | 26 | 17 | 23 |
| 2  | 25 | 18 | 19 |
| 3  | 23 | 19 | 18 |
| 4  | 24 | 20 | 27 |
| 5  | 26 | 21 | 28 |
| 6  | 20 | 22 | 24 |
| 7  | 21 | 23 | 26 |
| 8  | 27 | 24 | 23 |
| 9  | 23 | 25 | 27 |
| 10 | 25 | 26 | 28 |
| 11 | 22 | 27 | 24 |
| 12 | 26 | 28 | 22 |
| 13 | 25 | 29 | 20 |
| 14 | 29 | 30 | 25 |
| 15 | 20 | 31 | 27 |
| 16 | 19 | 32 | 19 |

**a.** Construct a *p* chart.
**b.** Is the process in a state of statistical control? Why?

**18.5** A hospital administrator is concerned with the time to process patients' medical records after discharge. She determined that all records should be processed within 5 days of discharge. Thus, any record not processed within 5 days of a patient's discharge is nonconforming. The administrator recorded the number of patients discharged and the number of records not processed within the 5-day standard for a 30-day period in the file Medrec.

**a.** Construct a $p$ chart for these data.

**b.** Does the process give an out-of-control signal? Explain.

**c.** If the process is out of control, assume that special causes were subsequently identified and corrective action was taken to keep them from happening again. Then eliminate the data causing the out-of-control signals and recalculate the control limits.

**18.6** The bottling division of Sweet Suzy's Sugarless Cola maintains daily records of the occurrences of unacceptable cans flowing from the filling and sealing machine. The following table (whose data are stored in the file Colaspc) lists the number of cans filled and the number of nonconforming cans for one month (based on a 5-day workweek):

| Day | Cans Filled | Unacceptable Cans | Day | Cans Filled | Unacceptable Cans |
|-----|-------------|-------------------|-----|-------------|-------------------|
| 1 | 5,043 | 47 | 12 | 5,314 | 70 |
| 2 | 4,852 | 51 | 13 | 5,097 | 64 |
| 3 | 4,908 | 43 | 14 | 4,932 | 59 |
| 4 | 4,756 | 37 | 15 | 5,023 | 75 |
| 5 | 4,901 | 78 | 16 | 5,117 | 71 |
| 6 | 4,892 | 66 | 17 | 5,099 | 68 |
| 7 | 5,354 | 51 | 18 | 5,345 | 78 |
| 8 | 5,321 | 66 | 19 | 5,456 | 88 |
| 9 | 5,045 | 61 | 20 | 5,554 | 83 |
| 10 | 5,113 | 72 | 21 | 5,421 | 82 |
| 11 | 5,247 | 63 | 22 | 5,555 | 87 |

**a.** Construct a $p$ chart for the proportion of unacceptable cans for the month. Does the process give an out-of-control signal?

**b.** If you want to develop a process for reducing the proportion of unacceptable cans, how should you proceed?

**18.7** The manager of the accounting office of a large hospital is studying the problem of entering incorrect account numbers into the computer system. A subgroup of 200 account numbers is selected from each day's output, and each account number is inspected to determine whether it is a nonconforming item. The results for a period of 39 days are in the file Errorspc.

**a.** Construct a $p$ chart for the proportion of nonconforming items. Does the process give an out-of-control signal?

**b.** Based on your answer to (a), if you were the manager of the accounting office, what would you do to improve the process of account number entry?

**18.8** A regional manager of a telephone company is responsible for processing requests concerning additions, changes, or deletions of telephone service. She forms a service improvement team to look at the corrections in terms of central office equipment and facilities required to process the orders that are issued to service requests. Data collected over a period of 30 days are in the file Telespc.

**a.** Construct a $p$ chart for the proportion of corrections. Does the process give an out-of-control signal?

**b.** What should the regional manager do to improve the processing of requests for changes in telephone service?

## 18.3 THE RED BEAD EXPERIMENT: UNDERSTANDING PROCESS VARIABILITY

[4]For information on how to obtain such a bowl, contact Lightning Calculator at **www.qualitytng.com** or call 248-641-7030.

This chapter began with a discussion of common cause variation and special cause variation. Now that you have studied the $p$ chart, this section presents a famous parable, the **red bead experiment**, to enhance your understanding of common cause and special cause variation. The red bead experiment involves the selection of beads from a bowl that contains 4,000 beads.[4] Unknown to the participants in the experiment, 3,200 (80%) of the beads are white and 800

(20%) are red. You can use several different scenarios for conducting the experiment. The one used here begins with a facilitator (who will play the role of company supervisor) asking members of the audience to volunteer for the jobs of workers (at least four are needed), inspectors (two are needed), chief inspector (one is needed), and recorder (one is needed). A worker's job consists of using a paddle that has five rows of 10 bead-size holes to select 50 beads from the bowl of beads.

When the participants have been selected, the supervisor explains the jobs to them. The job of the workers is to produce white beads because red beads are unacceptable to the customers. Strict procedures are to be followed. Work standards call for the daily production of exactly 50 beads by each worker (a strict quota system). Management has established a standard that no more than 2 red beads (4%) per worker are to be produced on any given day.

Each worker dips the paddle into the box of beads so that when it is removed, each of the 50 holes contains a bead. The worker carries the paddle to the two inspectors, who independently record the count of red beads. The chief inspector compares their counts and announces the results to the audience. The recorder writes down the number and percentage of red beads next to the name of the worker.

When all the people know their jobs, "production" can begin. Suppose that on the first "day," the number of red beads "produced" by the four workers (call them Alyson, David, Peter, and Sharyn) was 9, 12, 13, and 7, respectively. How should management react to the day's production when the standard says that no more than 2 red beads per worker should be produced? Should all the workers be reprimanded, or should only David and Peter be given a stern warning that they will be fired if they don't improve?

Suppose that production continues for an additional two days. Table 18.3 summarizes the results for all three days.

**TABLE 18.3**

Red Bead Experiment Results for Four Workers over Three Days

| NAME | DAY 1 | DAY 2 | DAY 3 | All Three Days |
|------|-------|-------|-------|----------------|
| **Alyson** | 9 (18%) | 11 (22%) | 6 (12%) | 26 (17.33%) |
| **David** | 12 (24%) | 12 (24%) | 8 (16%) | 32 (21.33%) |
| **Peter** | 13 (26%) | 6 (12%) | 12 (24%) | 31 (20.67%) |
| **Sharyn** | 7 (14%) | 9 (18%) | 8 (16%) | 24 (16.0%) |
| *All four workers* | 41 | 38 | 34 | 113 |
| *Mean* | 10.25 | 9.5 | 8.5 | 9.42 |
| *Percentage* | 20.5% | 19% | 17% | 18.83% |

From Table 18.3, on each day, some of the workers were above the mean and some below the mean. On day 1, Sharyn did best, but on day 2, Peter (who had the worst record on day 1) was best, and on day 3, Alyson was best. How can you explain all this variation? Using Equation (18.2) on page 828 to develop a $p$ chart for these data,

$$k = 4 \text{ workers} \times 3 \text{ days} = 12, \; n = 50, \; \sum_{i=1}^{k} X_i = 113, \text{ and } \sum_{i=1}^{k} n_i = 600$$

Thus,

$$\bar{p} = \frac{113}{600} = 0.1883$$

so that

$$\bar{p} \pm 3\sqrt{\frac{\bar{p}(1-\bar{p})}{\bar{n}}}$$

$$= 0.1883 \pm 3\sqrt{\frac{0.1883(1-0.1883)}{50}}$$

$$= 0.1883 \pm 0.1659$$

Thus,

$$\text{UCL} = 0.1883 + 0.1659 = 0.3542$$

$$\text{LCL} = 0.1883 - 0.1659 = 0.0224$$

Figure 18.6 represents the $p$ chart for the data of Table 18.3. In Figure 18.6, all the points are within the control limits, and there are no patterns in the results. The differences between the workers merely represent common cause variation inherent in an in-control process.

**FIGURE 18.6**

$p$ Chart for the Red Bead Experiment

*See Sections E18.1 and E18.2, or Sections P18.1 or M18.1, to create an equivalent chart.*

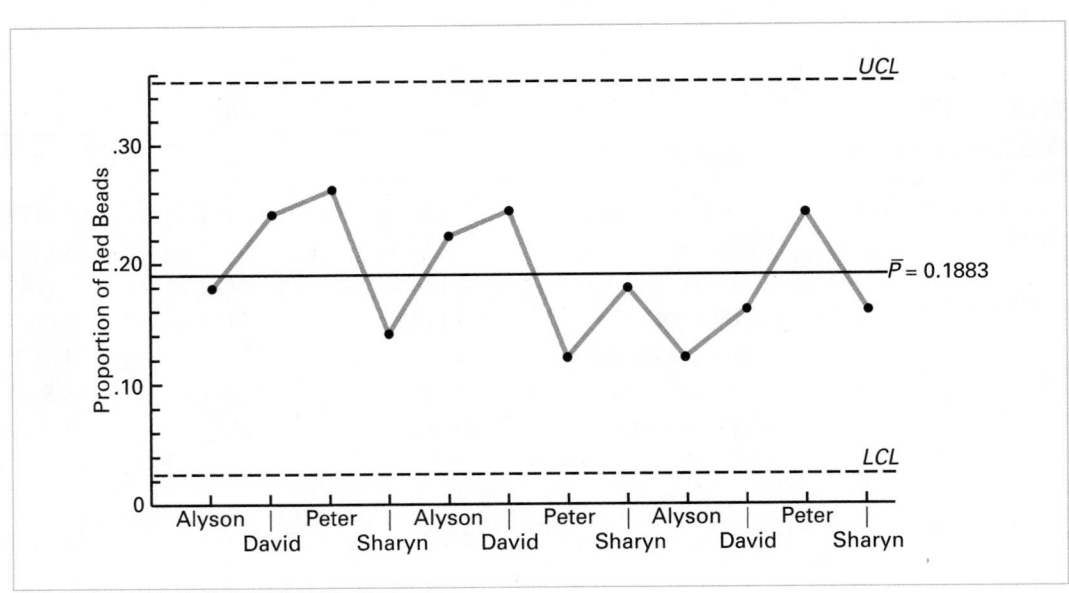

Four morals to the parable of the red beads are

- Variation is an inherent part of any process.
- Workers work within a process over which they have little control. It is the process that primarily determines their performance.
- Only management can change the process.
- There will always be some workers above the mean and some workers below the mean.

## PROBLEMS FOR SECTION 18.3

### Applying the Concepts

**18.9** In the red bead experiment, how do you think many managers would have reacted after day 1? day 2? day 3?

**18.10 (Class Project)** Obtain a version of the red bead experiment for your class.

a. Conduct the experiment in the same way as described in this section.

b. Remove 400 red beads from the bead bowl before beginning the experiment. How do your results differ from those in (a)? What does this tell you about the effect of the system on the workers?

## 18.4 CONTROL CHART FOR AN AREA OF OPPORTUNITY: THE *c* CHART

This section introduces you to the *c* chart. Recall that you use the *p* chart for monitoring and analyzing the proportion of nonconforming items. You use the **c chart** for monitoring and analyzing the number of nonconformities in an area of opportunity. **Areas of opportunity** can be individual units of products or services, or units of time, space, or area. Nonconformities are sometimes referred to as defects or flaws. Examples of the number of nonconformities in areas of opportunity are the number of flaws in a square foot of carpet, the number of typographical errors on a printed page, and the number of hotel customers filing a complaint in a given week. This situation differs from the one in which you used the *p* chart. Instead of classifying each unit as conforming or nonconforming, you count the number of nonconformities in each area of opportunity.

The above situation fits the assumptions of a Poisson distribution (see Section 5.4). For the Poisson distribution, the standard deviation of the number of nonconformities is the square root of the mean number of nonconformities ($\lambda$). Assuming that the size of each area of opportunity remains constant,[5] you can compute the control limits for the number of nonconformities per area of opportunity using the observed mean number of nonconformities as an estimate of $\lambda$. Equation (18.3) defines the control limits for the *c* chart, which you use to monitor and analyze the number of nonconformities per area of opportunity.

[5] If the size of the unit varies, you should use the *u* chart instead of the *c* chart (see references 9, 13, and 18).

---

**Control Limits for the *c* Chart**

$$\bar{c} \pm 3\sqrt{\bar{c}} \qquad\qquad (18.3)$$

$$UCL = \bar{c} + 3\sqrt{\bar{c}}$$

$$LCL = \bar{c} - 3\sqrt{\bar{c}}$$

where

$$\bar{c} = \frac{\sum_{i=1}^{k} c_i}{k},$$

$k$ = number of areas of opportunity

$c_i$ = number of nonconformities in unit $i$

---

To help study the hotel service quality in the Using Statistics scenario on page 824, you can use a *c* chart to monitor the number of customer complaints filed with the hotel. If guests of the hotel are dissatisfied with any part of their stay, they are asked to file a customer complaint form. At the end of each week, the number of complaints filed is recorded. In this example, a complaint is a nonconformity and the area of opportunity is one week. Table 18.4 lists the number of complaints from the last 50 weeks (which are in the file **Complaints**).

**TABLE 18.4**

Number of Complaints in the Last 50 Weeks

| Week | Number of Complaints | Week | Number of Complaints | Week | Number of Complaints |
|------|----------------------|------|----------------------|------|----------------------|
| 1 | 8 | 18 | 7 | 35 | 3 |
| 2 | 10 | 19 | 10 | 36 | 5 |
| 3 | 6 | 20 | 11 | 37 | 2 |
| 4 | 7 | 21 | 8 | 38 | 4 |
| 5 | 5 | 22 | 7 | 39 | 3 |
| 6 | 7 | 23 | 8 | 40 | 3 |
| 7 | 9 | 24 | 6 | 41 | 4 |
| 8 | 8 | 25 | 7 | 42 | 2 |
| 9 | 7 | 26 | 7 | 43 | 4 |
| 10 | 9 | 27 | 5 | 44 | 5 |
| 11 | 10 | 28 | 8 | 45 | 5 |
| 12 | 7 | 29 | 6 | 46 | 3 |
| 13 | 8 | 30 | 7 | 47 | 2 |
| 14 | 11 | 31 | 5 | 48 | 5 |
| 15 | 10 | 32 | 5 | 49 | 4 |
| 16 | 9 | 33 | 4 | 50 | 4 |
| 17 | 8 | 34 | 4 | | |

For these data,

$$k = 50 \text{ and } \sum_{i=1}^{k} c_i = 312$$

Thus,

$$\bar{c} = \frac{312}{50} = 6.24$$

so that using Equation (18.3) on page 837,

$$\bar{c} \pm 3\sqrt{\bar{c}}$$

$$= 6.24 \pm 3\sqrt{6.24}$$

$$= 6.24 \pm 7.494$$

Thus,

$$\text{UCL} = 6.24 + 7.494 = 13.734$$

$$\text{LCL} = 6.24 - 7.494 < 0$$

Therefore, the LCL does not exist.

Figure 18.7 displays the Minitab control chart for the complaint data of Table 18.4. The $c$ chart does not indicate any points outside the control limits. However, because there are eight or more consecutive points that lie above the center line and there are also eight or more consecutive points that lie below the center line, the process is out-of control. There is a clear pattern to the number of customer complaints over time. During the first half of the sequence almost all the weeks had more than the mean number of complaints, and almost all the weeks in the second half had less than the mean. This change, which is an improvement, is due to a special cause of variation. The next step is to investigate the process and determine the special cause that produced this pattern. When identified, you then need to ensure that this becomes a permanent improvement, not a temporary phenomenon. In other words, the source of the special cause of variation must become part of the permanent ongoing process in order for the number of customer complaints not to slip back to the high levels experienced in the first half of the data.

**FIGURE 18.7**

Minitab *c* Chart for
Hotel Complaints

*See Section M18.1 to create
this. (Microsoft Excel users,
see Sections E18.3 and
E18.4 to create an
equivalent chart. PHstat2
users, see Section P18.2.)*

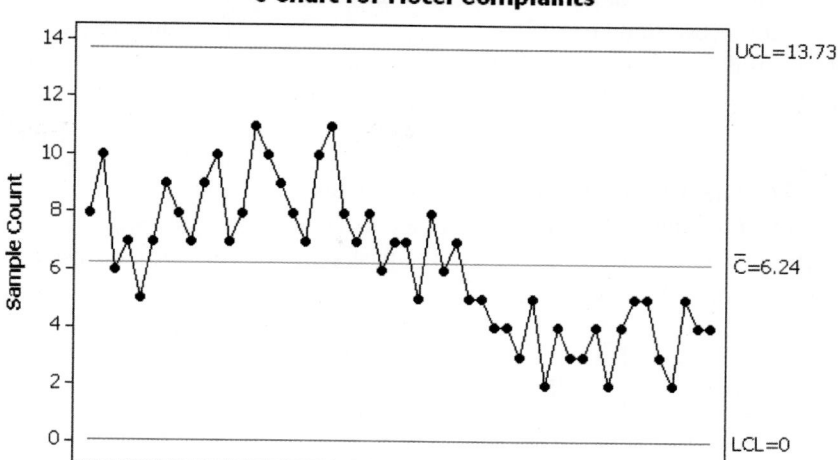

---

## PROBLEMS FOR SECTION 18.4

### Learning the Basics

**18.11** The following data were collected on the number of nonconformities per unit for 10 time periods:

| Time | Nonconformities Per Unit | Time | Nonconformities Per Unit |
|------|--------------------------|------|--------------------------|
| 1 | 7 | 6 | 5 |
| 2 | 3 | 7 | 3 |
| 3 | 6 | 8 | 5 |
| 4 | 3 | 9 | 2 |
| 5 | 4 | 10 | 0 |

**a.** Construct the appropriate control chart and determine the LCL and UCL.
**b.** Are there any special causes of variation?

**18.12** The following data were collected on the number of nonconformities per unit for 10 time periods:

| Time | Nonconformities Per Unit | Time | Nonconformities Per Unit |
|------|--------------------------|------|--------------------------|
| 1 | 25 | 6 | 15 |
| 2 | 11 | 7 | 12 |
| 3 | 10 | 8 | 10 |
| 4 | 11 | 9 | 9 |
| 5 | 6 | 10 | 6 |

**a.** Construct the appropriate control chart and determine the LCL and UCL.
**b.** Are there any special causes of variation?

### Applying the Concepts

**18.13** To improve service quality, the owner of a dry-cleaning business wants to study the number of dry-cleaned items that are returned for rework per day. Records were kept for a 4-week period (the store is open Monday through Saturday) with the results given below and in the file **Dryclean**.

| Day | Items Returned For Rework | Day | Items Returned For Rework |
|-----|---------------------------|-----|---------------------------|
| 1 | 4 | 13 | 5 |
| 2 | 6 | 14 | 8 |
| 3 | 3 | 15 | 3 |
| 4 | 7 | 16 | 4 |
| 5 | 6 | 17 | 10 |
| 6 | 8 | 18 | 9 |
| 7 | 6 | 19 | 6 |
| 8 | 4 | 20 | 5 |
| 9 | 8 | 21 | 8 |
| 10 | 6 | 22 | 6 |
| 11 | 5 | 23 | 7 |
| 12 | 12 | 24 | 9 |

**a.** Construct a *c* chart for the number of items per day that are returned for rework. Do you think that the process is in a state of statistical control?
**b.** Should the owner of the dry-cleaning store take action to investigate why 12 items were returned for rework on

day 12? Explain. Would your answer change if 20 items were returned for rework on day 12?

c. On the basis of the results in (a), what should the owner of the dry-cleaning store do to reduce the number of items per day that are returned for rework?

**✓SELF Test 18.14** The branch manager of a savings bank has recorded the number of errors of a particular type that each of 12 tellers has made during the past year. The results were as follows (see the Teller file):

| Teller | Number of Errors | Teller | Number of Errors |
|--------|------------------|--------|------------------|
| Alice  | 4                | Mitchell | 6              |
| Carl   | 7                | Nora   | 3                |
| Gina   | 12               | Paul   | 5                |
| Jane   | 6                | Susan  | 4                |
| Linda  | 2                | Thomas | 7                |
| Marla  | 5                | Vera   | 5                |

a. Do you think the bank manager will single out Gina for any disciplinary action regarding her performance in the last year?

b. Construct a c chart for the number of errors committed by the 12 tellers. Is the number of errors in a state of statistical control?

c. Based on the c chart developed in (b), do you now think that Gina should be singled out for disciplinary action regarding her performance? Does your conclusion now agree with what you expected the manager to do?

d. On the basis of the results in (b), what should the branch manager do to reduce the number of errors?

**18.15** Falls are one source of preventable hospital injury. Although most patients who fall are not hurt, a risk of serious injury is involved. The data in the file Ptfalls represent the number of patient falls per month over a 28-month period in a 19-bed AIDS unit at a major metropolitan hospital.

a. Construct a c chart for the number of patient falls per month. Is the process of patient falls per month in a state of statistical control?

b. What effect would it have on your conclusions if you knew that the AIDS unit was started only one month prior to the beginning of data collection?

c. Compile a list of factors that might produce special cause variation in this problem?

**18.16** A member of the volunteer fire department for Trenton, Ohio, decided to apply the control chart methodology he learned in his business statistics class to data collected by the fire department. He was interested in determining whether weeks containing more than the mean number of fire runs were due to inherent, chance-cause variation, or if there were special causes of variation such as increased arson, severe drought, or holiday-related activities. The data in the file Fireruns contain the number of fire runs made per week (Sunday through Saturday) during a recent year.

Source: *Extracted from* The City of Trenton 2001 Annual Report, Trenton, Ohio, February 21, 2002.

a. What is the mean number of fire runs made per week?

b. Construct a c chart for the number of fire runs per week.

c. Is the process in a state of statistical control?

d. Weeks 15 and 41 experienced seven fire runs each. Are these large values explainable by common causes, or does it appear that special causes of variation occurred in these weeks?

e. Explain how the fire department can use these data to chart and monitor future weeks in real time (i.e., on a week-to-week basis)?

**18.17** Rochester-Electro-Medical Inc. is a manufacturing company based in Tampa, Florida, that produces medical products. Recently, management felt the need to improve the safety of the workplace and began a safety sampling study. The following data (stored in the file Safety) represent the number of unsafe acts observed by the company safety director over an initial time period in which he made 20 tours of the plant.

| Tour | Number of Unsafe Acts | Tour | Number of Unsafe Acts |
|------|----------------------|------|----------------------|
| 1    | 10                   | 11   | 2                    |
| 2    | 6                    | 12   | 8                    |
| 3    | 6                    | 13   | 7                    |
| 4    | 10                   | 14   | 6                    |
| 5    | 8                    | 15   | 6                    |
| 6    | 12                   | 16   | 11                   |
| 7    | 2                    | 17   | 13                   |
| 8    | 1                    | 18   | 9                    |
| 9    | 23                   | 19   | 6                    |
| 10   | 3                    | 20   | 9                    |

Source: *Extracted from* H. Gitlow, A. R. Berkins, and M. He, "Safety Sampling: A Case Study," Quality Engineering, *14, 2002, pp. 405–419.*

a. Construct a c chart for the number of unsafe acts.

b. Based on the results of (a), is the process in a state of statistical control?

c. What should management do next to improve the process?

## 18.5    CONTROL CHARTS FOR THE RANGE AND THE MEAN

You use **variables control charts** to monitor and analyze a process when you have numerically measured data. Common numerical variables include time, money, and weight. Because numerical variables provide more information than categorical data, such as the proportion of nonconforming items, variables control charts are more sensitive in detecting special cause variation than the $p$ chart. Variables charts are typically used in pairs. One chart monitors the variability in a process, and the other monitors the process mean. You must examine the chart that monitors variability first because if it indicates the presence of out-of-control conditions, the interpretation of the chart for the mean will be misleading. Although businesses currently use several alternative pairs of charts (see references 9, 13, and 18), this book considers only the control charts for the range and the mean.

### The $R$ Chart

You can use several different types of control charts to monitor the variability in a numerically measured characteristic of interest. The simplest and most common is the control chart for the range, the **$R$ chart**. You use the range chart only when the sample size is 10 or less. If the sample size is greater than 10, a standard deviation chart is preferable (see references 9, 13, and 18). Because sample sizes of five or less are typically used in many applications, the standard deviation chart is not illustrated in this book. The $R$ chart enables you to determine whether the variability in a process is in control or whether changes in the amount of variability are occurring over time. If the process range is in control, then the amount of variation in the process is consistent over time, and you can use the results of the $R$ chart to develop the control limits for the mean.

To develop control limits for the range, you need an estimate of the mean range and the standard deviation of the range. As shown in Equation (18.4), these control limits depend on two constants, the **$d_2$ factor**, which represents the relationship between the standard deviation and the range for varying sample sizes, and the **$d_3$ factor**, which represents the relationship between the standard deviation and the standard error of the range for varying sample sizes. Table E.13 contains values for these factors. Equation (18.4) defines the control limits for the $R$ chart.

---

Control Limits for the Range

$$\bar{R} \pm 3\bar{R}\frac{d_3}{d_2}$$

$$\text{UCL} = \bar{R} + 3\bar{R}\frac{d_3}{d_2} \tag{18.4}$$

$$\text{LCL} = \bar{R} - 3\bar{R}\frac{d_3}{d_2}$$

where

$$\bar{R} = \frac{\sum_{i=1}^{k} R_i}{k}$$

---

You can simplify the calculations in Equation (18.4) by using the **$D_3$ factor**, equal to $1 - 3(d_3/d_2)$, and the **$D_4$ factor**, equal to $1 + 3(d_3/d_2)$, to express the control limits (see Table E.13), as shown in Equations (18.5a) and (18.5b).

Calculating Control Limits for the Range

$$UCL = D_4 \bar{R} \qquad \text{(18.5a)}$$

$$LCL = D_3 \bar{R} \qquad \text{(18.5b)}$$

To illustrate the $R$ chart, return to the Using Statistics scenario concerning hotel service quality on page 824. As part of the *Measure* phase of a Six Sigma project (see Section 18.8), the amount of time to deliver luggage was operationally defined as the time from when the guest completes check-in procedures to the time the luggage arrives in the guest's room. During the *Analyze* phase of the Six Sigma project, data were recorded over a four-week period (see the file Hotel2). Subgroups of five deliveries were selected from the evening shift on each day. Table 18.5 summarizes the results for all 28 days.

For the data in Table 18.5,

$$k = 28, \sum_{i=1}^{k} R_i = 97.5, \bar{R} = \frac{\sum_{i=1}^{k} R_i}{k} = \frac{97.5}{28} = 3.482$$

**TABLE 18.5**

Luggage Delivery Times and Subgroup Mean and Range for 28 Days

| Day | Luggage Delivery Times (in minutes) | | | | | Mean | Range |
|-----|------|------|------|------|------|-------|-------|
| 1 | 6.7 | 11.7 | 9.7 | 7.5 | 7.8 | 8.68 | 5.0 |
| 2 | 7.6 | 11.4 | 9.0 | 8.4 | 9.2 | 9.12 | 3.8 |
| 3 | 9.5 | 8.9 | 9.9 | 8.7 | 10.7 | 9.54 | 2.0 |
| 4 | 9.8 | 13.2 | 6.9 | 9.3 | 9.4 | 9.72 | 6.3 |
| 5 | 11.0 | 9.9 | 11.3 | 11.6 | 8.5 | 10.46 | 3.1 |
| 6 | 8.3 | 8.4 | 9.7 | 9.8 | 7.1 | 8.66 | 2.7 |
| 7 | 9.4 | 9.3 | 8.2 | 7.1 | 6.1 | 8.02 | 3.3 |
| 8 | 11.2 | 9.8 | 10.5 | 9.0 | 9.7 | 10.04 | 2.2 |
| 9 | 10.0 | 10.7 | 9.0 | 8.2 | 11.0 | 9.78 | 2.8 |
| 10 | 8.6 | 5.8 | 8.7 | 9.5 | 11.4 | 8.80 | 5.6 |
| 11 | 10.7 | 8.6 | 9.1 | 10.9 | 8.6 | 9.58 | 2.3 |
| 12 | 10.8 | 8.3 | 10.6 | 10.3 | 10.0 | 10.00 | 2.5 |
| 13 | 9.5 | 10.5 | 7.0 | 8.6 | 10.1 | 9.14 | 3.5 |
| 14 | 12.9 | 8.9 | 8.1 | 9.0 | 7.6 | 9.30 | 5.3 |
| 15 | 7.8 | 9.0 | 12.2 | 9.1 | 11.7 | 9.96 | 4.4 |
| 16 | 11.1 | 9.9 | 8.8 | 5.5 | 9.5 | 8.96 | 5.6 |
| 17 | 9.2 | 9.7 | 12.3 | 8.1 | 8.5 | 9.56 | 4.2 |
| 18 | 9.0 | 8.1 | 10.2 | 9.7 | 8.4 | 9.08 | 2.1 |
| 19 | 9.9 | 10.1 | 8.9 | 9.6 | 7.1 | 9.12 | 3.0 |
| 20 | 10.7 | 9.8 | 10.2 | 8.0 | 10.2 | 9.78 | 2.7 |
| 21 | 9.0 | 10.0 | 9.6 | 10.6 | 9.0 | 9.64 | 1.6 |
| 22 | 10.7 | 9.8 | 9.4 | 7.0 | 8.9 | 9.16 | 3.7 |
| 23 | 10.2 | 10.5 | 9.5 | 12.2 | 9.1 | 10.30 | 3.1 |
| 24 | 10.0 | 11.1 | 9.5 | 8.8 | 9.9 | 9.86 | 2.3 |
| 25 | 9.6 | 8.8 | 11.4 | 12.2 | 9.3 | 10.26 | 3.4 |
| 26 | 8.2 | 7.9 | 8.4 | 9.5 | 9.2 | 8.64 | 1.6 |
| 27 | 7.1 | 11.1 | 10.8 | 11.0 | 10.2 | 10.04 | 4.0 |
| 28 | 11.1 | 6.6 | 12.0 | 11.5 | 9.7 | 10.18 | 5.4 |
| | | | | | Sums: | 265.38 | 97.5 |

For $n = 5$, from Table E.13, $D_3 = 0$ and $D_4 = 2.114$. Then, using Equation (18.5),

$$\text{UCL} = D_4 \bar{R} = (2.114)(3.482) = 7.36$$

and the LCL does not exist.

Figure 18.8 displays the Microsoft Excel $R$ chart for the luggage delivery times. Figure 18.8 does not indicate any individual ranges outside the control limits or any obvious patterns.

**FIGURE 18.8**

Microsoft Excel $R$ chart for the luggage delivery times

*See Sections E18.5 and E18.6 or Section P18.3 to create this. (Minitab users, see Section M18.3 to create an equivalent chart.)*

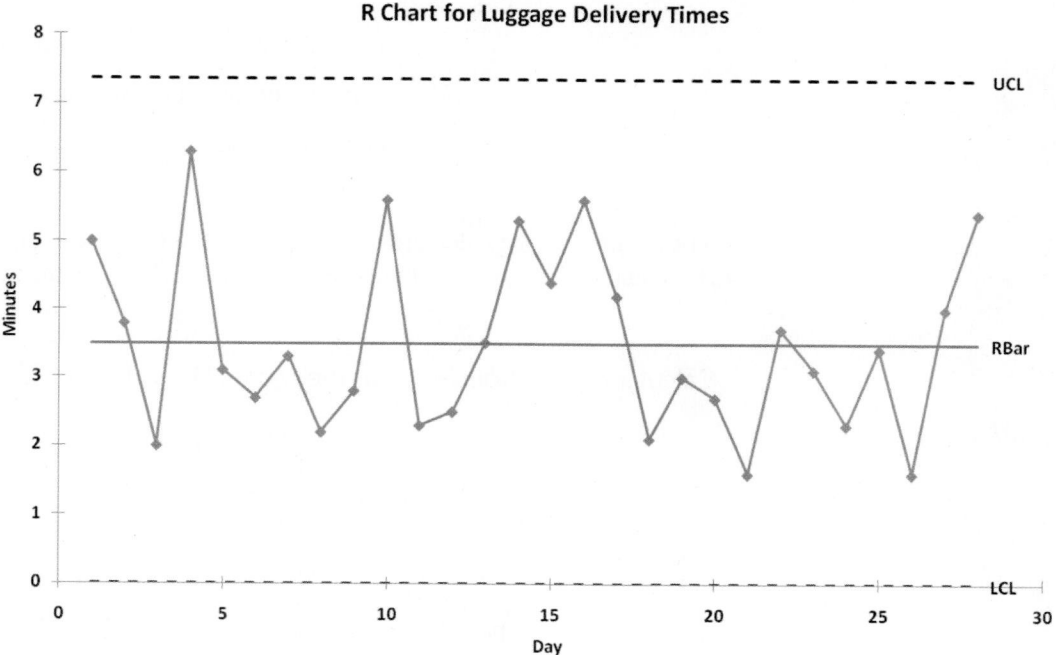

## The $\bar{X}$ Chart

Now that you have determined from the control chart that the range is in control, you continue by examining the control chart for the process mean, the $\bar{X}$ **chart**.

The control chart for $\bar{X}$ uses $k$ subgroups collected in $k$ consecutive periods of time. Each subgroup contains $n$ items. You calculate an $\bar{X}$ for each subgroup and plot these $\bar{X}$ values on the control chart. To compute control limits for the mean, you need to compute the mean of the subgroup means (called $X$ double bar, and denoted $\bar{\bar{X}}$) and the estimate of the standard error of the mean (denoted $\bar{R}/(d_2\sqrt{n})$). The estimate of the standard error of the mean is a function of the $d_2$ factor, which represents the relationship between the standard deviation and the range for varying sample sizes.[6] Equations (18.6) and (18.7) define the control limits for the $\bar{X}$ chart.

[6] $\bar{R}/d_2$ *is used to estimate the standard error of the individual items in the population, and* $\bar{R}/d_2\sqrt{n}$ *is used to estimate the standard deviation of the mean.*

## Control Limits for the $\bar{X}$ Chart

$$\bar{\bar{X}} \pm 3 \frac{\bar{R}}{d_2 \sqrt{n}}$$

$$\text{UCL} = \bar{\bar{X}} + 3 \frac{\bar{R}}{d_2 \sqrt{n}} \qquad \qquad \textbf{(18.6)}$$

where

$$\text{LCL} = \bar{\bar{X}} - 3 \frac{\bar{R}}{d_2 \sqrt{n}}$$

$$\bar{\bar{X}} = \frac{\sum_{i=1}^{k} \bar{X}_i}{k} \qquad \bar{R} = \frac{\sum_{i=1}^{k} R_i}{k}$$

$\bar{X}_i$ = sample mean of $n$ observations at time $i$

$R_i$ = range of $n$ observations at time $i$

$k$ = number of subgroups

You can simplify the calculations in Equation (18.6) by utilizing the $A_2$ **factor** given in Table E.13, equal to $3/d_2 \sqrt{n}$. Equations (18.7a) and (18.7b) show the simplified control limits.

## Calculating Control Limits for the Mean, Using the $A_2$ Factor

$$\text{UCL} = \bar{\bar{X}} + A_2 \bar{R} \qquad \qquad \textbf{(18.7a)}$$

$$\text{LCL} = \bar{\bar{X}} - A_2 \bar{R} \qquad \qquad \textbf{(18.7b)}$$

From Table 18.5 on page 842,

$$k = 28, \sum_{i=1}^{k} \bar{X}_i = 265.38, \sum_{i=1}^{k} R_i = 97.5$$

so that

$$\bar{\bar{X}} = \frac{\sum_{i=1}^{k} \bar{X}_i}{k} = \frac{265.38}{28} = 9.478$$

$$\bar{R} = \frac{\sum_{i=1}^{k} R_i}{k} = \frac{97.5}{28} = 3.482$$

Using Equations (18.7a) and (18.7b), and $A_2 = 0.577$, for $n = 5$, from Table E.13,

$$\text{UCL} = 9.478 + (0.577)(3.482) = 9.478 + 2.009 = 11.487$$

$$\text{LCL} = 9.478 - (0.577)(3.482) = 9.478 - 2.009 = 7.469$$

Figure 18.9 displays the Microsoft Excel $\bar{X}$ chart for the luggage delivery time data. Figure 18.10 presents Minitab $R$ and $\bar{X}$ charts.

**FIGURE 18.9**

Microsoft Excel $\bar{X}$ chart for the luggage delivery times

*See Sections E18.5 and E18.6 or Section P18.3 to create this.*

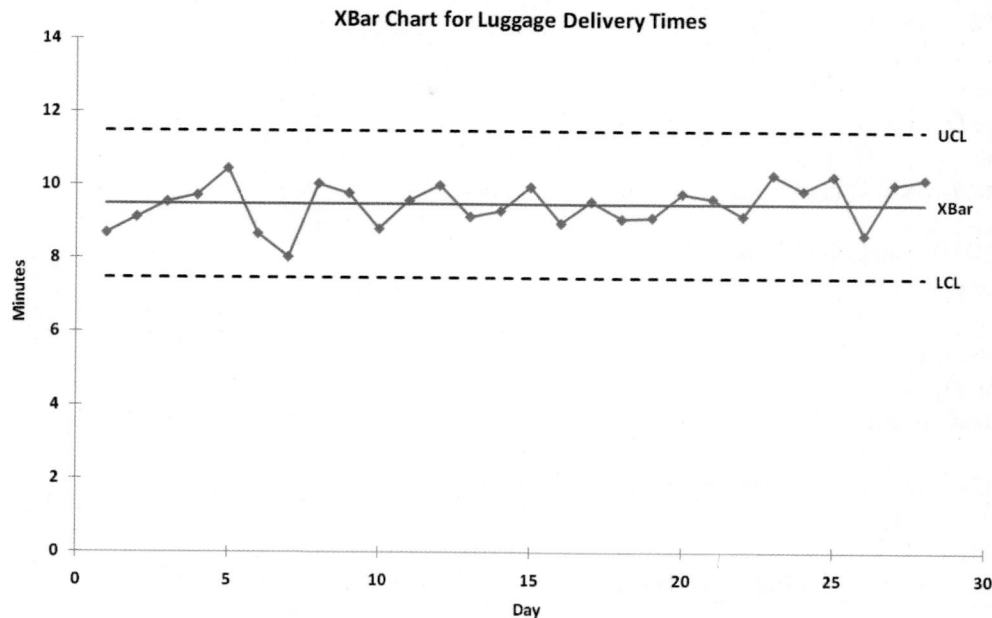

**FIGURE 18.10**

Minitab $R$ and $\bar{X}$ charts for the luggage delivery times

*See Section M18.3 to create this.*

Figures 18.9 or 18.10 do not reveal any points outside the control limits, and there are no obvious patterns in either chart. Although there is a considerable amount of variability among the 28 subgroup means, because both the $R$ chart and the $\bar{X}$ chart are in control, the luggage delivery process is in a state of statistical control. If you want to reduce the variation or lower the mean delivery time, you need to change the process.

# PROBLEMS FOR SECTION 18.5

## Learning the Basics

**18.18** For subgroups of $n = 4$, what is the value of
a. the $d_2$ factor?
b. the $d_3$ factor?
c. the $D_3$ factor?
d. the $D_4$ factor?
e. the $A_2$ factor?

**18.19** For subgroups of $n = 3$, what is the value of
a. the $d_2$ factor?
b. the $d_3$ factor?
c. the $D_3$ factor?
d. the $D_4$ factor?
e. the $A_2$ factor?

**18.20** The following summary of data is for subgroups of $n = 3$ for a 10-day period:

| Day | Mean | Range | Day | Mean | Range |
|-----|-------|-------|-----|-------|-------|
| 1 | 48.03 | 0.29 | 6 | 48.07 | 0.22 |
| 2 | 48.08 | 0.43 | 7 | 47.99 | 0.16 |
| 3 | 47.90 | 0.16 | 8 | 48.04 | 0.15 |
| 4 | 48.03 | 0.13 | 9 | 47.99 | 0.46 |
| 5 | 47.81 | 0.32 | 10 | 48.04 | 0.15 |

a. Compute control limits for the range.
b. Is there evidence of special cause variation in (a)?
c. Compute control limits for the mean.
d. Is there evidence of special cause variation in (c)?

**18.21** The following summary of data is for subgroups of $n = 4$ for a 10-day period:

| Day | Mean | Range | Day | Mean | Range |
|-----|------|-------|-----|------|-------|
| 1 | 13.6 | 3.5 | 6 | 12.9 | 4.8 |
| 2 | 14.3 | 4.1 | 7 | 17.3 | 4.5 |
| 3 | 15.3 | 5.0 | 8 | 13.9 | 2.9 |
| 4 | 12.6 | 2.8 | 9 | 12.6 | 3.8 |
| 5 | 11.8 | 3.7 | 10 | 15.2 | 4.6 |

a. Compute control limits for the range.
b. Is there evidence of special cause variation in (a)?
c. Compute control limits for the mean.
d. Is there evidence of special cause variation in (c)?

## Applying the Concepts

**SELF Test** **18.22** The manager of a branch of a local bank wants to study waiting times of customers for teller service during the 12:00 noon-to-1:00 p.m. lunch hour. A subgroup of four customers is selected (one at each 15-minute interval during the hour), and the time, in minutes, is measured from the point each customer enters the line to when he or she reaches the teller window. The results over a four-week period are in the data file **Banktime** and are as follows:

| Day | | Time in Minutes | | |
|-----|-----|-----|-----|-----|
| 1 | 7.2 | 8.4 | 7.9 | 4.9 |
| 2 | 5.6 | 8.7 | 3.3 | 4.2 |
| 3 | 5.5 | 7.3 | 3.2 | 6.0 |
| 4 | 4.4 | 8.0 | 5.4 | 7.4 |
| 5 | 9.7 | 4.6 | 4.8 | 5.8 |
| 6 | 8.3 | 8.9 | 9.1 | 6.2 |
| 7 | 4.7 | 6.6 | 5.3 | 5.8 |
| 8 | 8.8 | 5.5 | 8.4 | 6.9 |
| 9 | 5.7 | 4.7 | 4.1 | 4.6 |
| 10 | 3.7 | 4.0 | 3.0 | 5.2 |
| 11 | 2.6 | 3.9 | 5.2 | 4.8 |
| 12 | 4.6 | 2.7 | 6.3 | 3.4 |
| 13 | 4.9 | 6.2 | 7.8 | 8.7 |
| 14 | 7.1 | 6.3 | 8.2 | 5.5 |
| 15 | 7.1 | 5.8 | 6.9 | 7.0 |
| 16 | 6.7 | 6.9 | 7.0 | 9.4 |
| 17 | 5.5 | 6.3 | 3.2 | 4.9 |
| 18 | 4.9 | 5.1 | 3.2 | 7.6 |
| 19 | 7.2 | 8.0 | 4.1 | 5.9 |
| 20 | 6.1 | 3.4 | 7.2 | 5.9 |

a. Construct control charts for the range and the mean.
b. Is the process in control?

**18.23** The manager of a warehouse for a telephone company is involved in a process that receives expensive circuit boards and returns them to central stock so that they can be reused at a later date. Speedy processing of these circuit boards is critical in providing good service to customers and reducing capital expenditures. The data in the file **Warehse** represent the number of circuit boards processed per day by a subgroup of five employees over a 30-day period.
a. Construct control charts for the range and the mean.
b. Is the process in control?

**18.24** An article in the *Mid-American Journal of Business* presents an analysis for a spring water bottling operation. One of the characteristics of interest is the amount of magnesium, measured in parts per million (ppm), in the water. The data in the following table (stored in the file **SPwater**) represent the magnesium levels from 30 subgroups of four bottles collected over a 30-hour period:

| Hour | 1 | 2 | 3 | 4 |
|------|-------|-------|-------|-------|
| 1 | 19.91 | 19.62 | 19.15 | 19.85 |
| 2 | 20.46 | 20.44 | 20.34 | 19.61 |
| 3 | 20.25 | 19.73 | 19.98 | 20.32 |
| 4 | 20.39 | 19.43 | 20.36 | 19.85 |
| 5 | 20.02 | 20.02 | 20.13 | 20.34 |
| 6 | 19.89 | 19.77 | 20.92 | 20.09 |
| 7 | 19.89 | 20.45 | 19.44 | 19.95 |
| 8 | 20.08 | 20.13 | 20.11 | 19.32 |
| 9 | 20.30 | 20.42 | 20.68 | 19.60 |
| 10 | 20.19 | 20.00 | 20.23 | 20.59 |
| 11 | 19.66 | 21.24 | 20.35 | 20.34 |
| 12 | 20.30 | 20.11 | 19.64 | 20.29 |
| 13 | 19.83 | 19.75 | 20.62 | 20.60 |
| 14 | 20.27 | 20.88 | 20.62 | 20.40 |
| 15 | 19.98 | 19.02 | 20.34 | 20.34 |
| 16 | 20.46 | 19.97 | 20.32 | 20.83 |
| 17 | 19.74 | 21.02 | 19.62 | 19.90 |
| 18 | 19.85 | 19.26 | 19.88 | 20.20 |
| 19 | 20.77 | 20.58 | 19.73 | 19.48 |
| 20 | 20.21 | 20.82 | 20.01 | 19.93 |
| 21 | 20.30 | 20.09 | 20.03 | 20.13 |
| 22 | 20.48 | 21.06 | 20.13 | 20.42 |
| 23 | 20.60 | 19.74 | 20.52 | 19.42 |
| 24 | 20.20 | 20.08 | 20.32 | 19.51 |
| 25 | 19.66 | 19.67 | 20.26 | 20.41 |
| 26 | 20.72 | 20.58 | 20.71 | 19.99 |
| 27 | 19.77 | 19.40 | 20.49 | 19.83 |
| 28 | 19.99 | 19.65 | 19.41 | 19.58 |
| 29 | 19.44 | 20.15 | 20.14 | 20.76 |
| 30 | 20.03 | 19.96 | 19.86 | 19.91 |

Source: *Extracted from Susan K. Humphrey and Timothy C. Krehbiel, "Managing Process Capability,"* The Mid-American Journal of Business, 14, Fall 1999, pp. 7–12.

a. Construct a control chart for the range.
b. Construct a control chart for the mean.
c. Is the process in control?

**18.25** The data in the following table (stored in the file Tensile) are the tensile strengths of bolts of cloth. The data were collected in subgroups of three bolts of cloth over a 25-hour period:

| Hour | 1 | 2 | 3 | Hour | 1 | 2 | 3 |
|------|-------|-------|-------|------|-------|-------|-------|
| 1 | 15.06 | 14.62 | 15.10 | 11 | 15.20 | 14.61 | 18.45 |
| 2 | 17.58 | 15.75 | 16.72 | 12 | 14.49 | 16.15 | 17.80 |
| 3 | 13.83 | 14.83 | 15.61 | 13 | 15.89 | 15.04 | 16.67 |
| 4 | 17.19 | 15.75 | 15.42 | 14 | 16.29 | 14.61 | 15.67 |
| 5 | 14.56 | 15.37 | 15.67 | 15 | 15.84 | 12.16 | 15.40 |
| 6 | 14.82 | 17.25 | 15.73 | 16 | 15.12 | 15.60 | 13.83 |
| 7 | 17.92 | 14.76 | 14.40 | 17 | 18.48 | 16.07 | 16.31 |
| 8 | 16.53 | 14.52 | 17.31 | 18 | 17.55 | 14.73 | 16.95 |
| 9 | 13.83 | 14.53 | 15.32 | 19 | 13.57 | 17.55 | 15.81 |
| 10 | 16.45 | 13.85 | 16.32 | 20 | 16.23 | 16.92 | 16.45 |
| | | | | 21 | 14.60 | 16.83 | 15.34 |
| | | | | 22 | 16.73 | 18.60 | 16.76 |
| | | | | 23 | 18.03 | 14.55 | 13.87 |
| | | | | 24 | 16.61 | 16.45 | 16.95 |
| | | | | 25 | 15.86 | 17.00 | 18.28 |

a. Construct a control chart for the range.
b. Construct a control chart for the mean.
c. Is the process in control?

**18.26** The director of radiology at a large metropolitan hospital is concerned about scheduling in the radiology facilities. On a typical day, 250 patients are transported to the radiology department for treatment or diagnostic procedures. If patients do not reach the radiology unit at their scheduled times, back-ups occur, and other patients experience delays. The time it takes to transport patients to the radiology unit is operationally defined as the time between when the transporter is assigned to the patient and when the patient arrives at the radiology unit. A sample of $n = 4$ patients was selected each day for 20 days, and the time to transport each patient (in minutes) was determined, with the results in the data file Transport.
a. Construct control charts for the range and the mean.
b. Is the process in control?

**18.27** A filling machine for a tea bag manufacturer produces approximately 170 tea bags per minute. The process manager monitors the weight of the tea placed in individual bags. A subgroup of $n = 4$ tea bags is taken every 15 minutes for 25 consecutive time periods. The results are given below and stored in the file Tea3:

| Sample | Weight (in Grams) | | | |
|--------|------|------|------|------|
| 1 | 5.32 | 5.77 | 5.50 | 5.61 |
| 2 | 5.63 | 5.44 | 5.54 | 5.40 |
| 3 | 5.56 | 5.40 | 5.67 | 5.57 |
| 4 | 5.32 | 5.45 | 5.50 | 5.42 |
| 5 | 5.45 | 5.53 | 5.46 | 5.47 |
| 6 | 5.29 | 5.42 | 5.50 | 5.44 |
| 7 | 5.57 | 5.40 | 5.52 | 5.54 |
| 8 | 5.44 | 5.61 | 5.49 | 5.58 |
| 9 | 5.53 | 5.25 | 5.67 | 5.53 |
| 10 | 5.41 | 5.55 | 5.51 | 5.53 |
| 11 | 5.55 | 5.58 | 5.58 | 5.56 |
| 12 | 5.58 | 5.36 | 5.45 | 5.53 |
| 13 | 5.63 | 5.75 | 5.46 | 5.54 |
| 14 | 5.48 | 5.44 | 5.45 | 5.60 |
| 15 | 5.49 | 5.57 | 5.43 | 5.36 |
| 16 | 5.54 | 5.62 | 5.66 | 5.59 |
| 17 | 5.46 | 5.46 | 5.38 | 5.49 |
| 18 | 5.72 | 5.36 | 5.59 | 5.25 |
| 19 | 5.58 | 5.50 | 5.36 | 5.40 |
| 20 | 5.43 | 5.51 | 5.37 | 5.32 |
| 21 | 5.59 | 5.58 | 5.60 | 5.46 |
| 22 | 5.42 | 5.41 | 5.40 | 5.69 |
| 23 | 5.64 | 5.59 | 5.42 | 5.56 |
| 24 | 5.62 | 5.38 | 5.75 | 5.47 |
| 25 | 5.51 | 5.54 | 5.73 | 5.77 |

a. What are some of the sources of common cause variation that might be present in this process?
b. What problems might occur that would result in special causes of variation?
c. Construct control charts for the range and the mean.
d. Is the process in control?

**18.28** A manufacturing company makes brackets for bookshelves. The brackets provide critical structural support and must have a 90-degree bend ±1 degree. Measurements of the bend of the brackets were taken at 18 different times. Five brackets were sampled at each time. The data are in the file `Angle`.

a. Construct control charts for the range and the mean.
b. Is the process in control?

## 18.6 PROCESS CAPABILITY

Often, it is necessary to analyze the amount of common cause variation present in an in-control process. Is the common cause variation small enough to satisfy customers with the product or service? Or is the common cause variation so large that there are too many dissatisfied customers, and a process change is needed?

Analyzing the capability of a process is a way to answer these questions. There are many methods available to analyze and report process capability (see reference 3). This section begins with a method to estimate the percentage of products or services that will satisfy the customer. Later in the section, capability indices are introduced.

### Customer Satisfaction and Specification Limits

Quality is defined by the customer. A customer who believes that a product or service has met or exceeded his or her expectations will be satisfied. The management of a company must listen to the customer and translate the customer's needs and expectations into easily measured **critical-to-quality (CTQ)** variables. Management then sets specification limits for these CTQ variables.

**Specification limits** are technical requirements set by management in response to customers' needs and expectations. The **upper specification limit (USL)** is the largest value a CTQ can have and still conform to customer expectations. Likewise, the **lower specification limit (LSL)** is the smallest value a CTQ can have and still conform to customer expectations.

For example, a soap manufacturer understands that customers expect their soap to produce a certain amount of lather. The customer can become dissatisfied if the soap produces too much or too little lather. Product engineers know that the level of free fatty acids in the soap controls the amount of lather. Thus, the process manager, with input from the product engineers, sets both a USL and a LSL for the amount of free fatty acids in the soap.

As an example of a case in which only a single specification limit is involved, consider the Using Statistics scenario concerning hotel service quality on page 824. Because customers want their bags delivered as quickly as possible, hotel management sets a USL for the time required for delivery. In this case, there is no LSL. As you can see in both the luggage delivery time and soap examples, specification limits are customer-driven requirements placed on a product or a service. If a process consistently meets these requirements, the process is capable of satisfying the customer. **Process capability** is the ability of a process to consistently meet specified customer-driven requirements.

One way to analyze the capability of a process is to estimate the percentage of products or services that are within specifications. To do this, you must have an in-control process because an out-of-control process does not allow you to predict its capability. If you are dealing with an out-of-control process, you must first identify and eliminate the special causes of variation before performing a capability analysis. Out-of-control processes are unpredictable, and, therefore, you cannot conclude that such processes are capable of meeting specifications or satisfying customer expectations in the future. To estimate the percentage of product or service within specifications in an in-control process, first you must estimate the mean and standard deviation of the population of all $X$

values, the CTQ variable of interest for the product or service. The estimate for the mean of the population is $\bar{\bar{X}}$, the mean of all the sample means [see Equation (18.7) on page 844]. The estimate of the standard deviation of the population is $\bar{R}$ divided by $d_2$. You can use the $\bar{\bar{X}}$ and $\bar{R}$ from in-control $\bar{X}$ and $R$ charts, respectively. You need to find the appropriate $d_2$ value in Table E.13.

In this book, the population of $X$ values is assumed to be approximately normally distributed. (If your data are not approximately normally distributed, see reference 3 for an alternative approach.) Assuming that the process is in control and $X$ is approximately normal, you can use Equation (18.8) to estimate the probability that a process outcome is within specifications.

---

**Estimating the Capability of a Process**

For a CTQ variable with an LSL and a USL:

$$P(\text{An outcome will be within specifications}) = P(\text{LSL} < X < \text{USL})$$

$$= P\left( \frac{\text{LSL} - \bar{\bar{X}}}{\bar{R}/d_2} < Z < \frac{\text{USL} - \bar{\bar{X}}}{\bar{R}/d_2} \right) \quad \textbf{(18.8a)}$$

For a CTQ variable with only a USL:

$$P(\text{An outcome will be within specifications}) = P(X < \text{USL})$$

$$= P\left( Z < \frac{\text{USL} - \bar{\bar{X}}}{\bar{R}/d_2} \right) \quad \textbf{(18.8b)}$$

For a CTQ variable with only an LSL:

$$P(\text{An outcome will be within specifications}) = P(\text{LSL} < X)$$

$$= P\left( \frac{\text{LSL} - \bar{\bar{X}}}{\bar{R}/d_2} < Z \right) \quad \textbf{(18.8c)}$$

where $Z$ is a standardized normal random variable

---

In Section 18.5, you determined that the luggage delivery process was in control. Suppose that the hotel management has instituted a policy that 99% of all luggage deliveries must be completed in 14 minutes or less. From the summary computations on page 842:

$$n = 5 \quad \bar{\bar{X}} = 9.478 \quad \bar{R} = 3.482$$

and from Table E.13,

$$d_2 = 2.326$$

Using Equation (18.8b),

$$P(\text{Delivery is made within specifications}) = P(X < 14)$$

$$= P\left( Z < \frac{14 - 9.478}{3.482/2.326} \right)$$

$$= P(Z < 3.02)$$

Using Table E.2,

$$P(Z < 3.02) = 0.99874$$

Thus, you estimate that 99.874% of the luggage deliveries will be made within the specified time. The process is capable of meeting the 99% goal set forth by the hotel management.

## Capability Indices

A common approach in business is to use capability indices to report the capability of a process. A **capability index** is an aggregate measure of a process's ability to meet specification limits. The larger the value of a capability index, the more capable the process is of meeting customer requirements. Equation (18.9) defines $C_p$, the most commonly used index.

$C_p$

$$C_p = \frac{\text{USL} - \text{LSL}}{6(\bar{R}/d_2)} \qquad\qquad (18.9)$$

$$= \frac{\text{Specification spread}}{\text{Process spread}}$$

The numerator in Equation (18.9) represents the distance between the upper and lower specification limits, referred to as the specification spread. The denominator, $6(\bar{R}/d_2)$, represents a 6 standard deviation spread in the data (the mean $\pm 3$ standard deviations), referred to as the process spread. (Recall from Chapter 6 that approximately 99.73% of the values from a normal distribution fall in the interval from the mean $\pm 3$ standard deviations.) You want the process spread to be small in comparison to the specification spread in order for the vast majority of the process output to fall within the specification limits. Therefore, the larger the value of $C_p$, the better the capability of the process.

$C_p$ is a measure of process potential, not of actual performance, because it does not consider the current process mean. A $C_p$ value of 1 indicates that if the process mean could be centered (i.e., equal to the halfway point between the USL and LSL), approximately 99.73% of the values would be inside the specification limits. A $C_p$ value greater than 1 indicates that a process has the potential of having more than 99.73% of its outcomes within specifications. A $C_p$ value less than 1 indicates that the process is not very capable of meeting customer requirements, for even if the process is perfectly centered, fewer than 99.73% of the process outcomes will be within specifications. Historically, many companies required a $C_p$ greater than or equal to 1. Now that the global economy has become more quality conscious, many companies are requiring a $C_p$ as large as 1.33, 1.5, and for companies adopting Six Sigma, 2.0.

To illustrate the calculation and interpretation of the $C_p$ index, suppose a soft-drink producer bottles its beverage into 12-ounce bottles. The LSL is 11.82 ounces, and the USL is 12.18 ounces. Each hour, four bottles are selected, and the range and the mean are plotted on control charts. At the end of 24 hours, the capability of the process is studied. Suppose that the control charts indicate that the process is in control and the following summary calculations were recorded on the control charts:

$$n = 4 \qquad \bar{\bar{X}} = 12.02 \qquad \bar{R} = 0.10$$

To calculate the $C_p$ index, assuming that the data are normally distributed, from Table E.13, $d_2 = 2.059$ for $n = 4$. Using Equation (18.9),

$$C_p = \frac{USL - LSL}{6(\bar{\bar{R}}/d_2)}$$

$$= \frac{12.18 - 11.82}{6(0.10/2.059)} = 1.24$$

Because the $C_p$ index is greater than 1, the bottling process has the potential to fill more than 99.73% of the bottles within the specification limits.

In summary, the $C_p$ index is an aggregate measure of process potential. The larger the value of $C_p$, the more potential the process has of satisfying the customer. In other words, a large $C_p$ indicates that the current amount of common cause variation is small enough to consistently produce items within specifications. For a process to reach its full potential, the process mean needs to be at or near the center of the specification limits. Capability indices that measure actual process performance are considered next.

### CPL, CPU, and $C_{pk}$

To measure the capability of a process in terms of actual process performance, the most common indices are CPL, CPU, and $C_{pk}$. Equation (18.10) defines CPL and CPU.

CPL and CPU

$$CPL = \frac{\bar{\bar{X}} - LSL}{3(\bar{\bar{R}}/d_2)} \qquad \textbf{(18.10a)}$$

$$CPU = \frac{USL - \bar{\bar{X}}}{3(\bar{\bar{R}}/d_2)} \qquad \textbf{(18.10b)}$$

Because the process mean is used in the calculation of CPL and CPU, these indices measure process performance—unlike $C_p$, which measures only potential. A value of CPL (or CPU) equal to 1.0 indicates that the process mean is 3 standard deviations away from the LSL (or USL). For CTQ variables with only an LSL, the CPL measures the process performance. For CTQ variables with only a USL, the CPU measures the process performance. In either case, the larger the value of the index, the greater the capability of the process.

In the Using Statistics scenario, the Beachcomber Hotel has a policy that luggage deliveries are to be made in 14 minutes or less. Thus, the CTQ variable delivery time has a USL of 14, and there is no LSL. Because you previously determined that the luggage delivery process was in control, you can now calculate the CPU. From the summary computations on page 844,

$$\bar{\bar{X}} = 9.478 \quad \bar{R} = 3.482$$

And, from Table E.13, $d_2 = 2.326$. Then, using Equation (18.10b),

$$CPU = \frac{USL - \bar{\bar{X}}}{3(\bar{R}/d_2)} = \frac{14 - 9.478}{3(3.482/2.326)} = 1.01$$

The capability index for the luggage delivery CTQ variable is 1.01. Because this value is slightly more than 1, the USL is slightly more than 3 standard deviations above the mean. To increase *CPU* even farther above 1.00 and therefore increase customer satisfaction, you need to investigate changes in the luggage delivery process. To study a process that has a *CPL* and a *CPU*, see the bottling process scenario in Example 18.2.

---

**EXAMPLE 18.2**       CALCULATING *CPL* AND *CPU* FOR THE BOTTLING PROCESS

In the soft-drink bottle filling process described on page 850, the following information was provided:

$$n = 4 \quad \bar{\bar{X}} = 12.02 \quad \bar{R} = 0.10 \quad \text{LSL} = 11.82 \quad \text{USL} = 12.18 \quad d_2 = 2.059$$

Calculate the *CPL* and *CPU* for these data.

**SOLUTION**   You compute the capability indices *CPL* and *CPU* by using Equations (18.10a) and (18.10b):

$$CPL = \frac{\bar{\bar{X}} - \text{LSL}}{3(\bar{R}/d_2)}$$

$$= \frac{12.02 - 11.82}{3(0.10/2.059)} = 1.37$$

$$CPU = \frac{\text{USL} - \bar{\bar{X}}}{3(\bar{R}/d_2)}$$

$$= \frac{12.18 - 12.02}{3(0.10/2.059)} = 1.10$$

Both the *CPL* and *CPU* are greater than 1, indicating that the process mean is more than 3 standard deviations away from both the LSL and USL. Because the *CPU* is less than the *CPL*, you know that the mean is closer to the USL than the LSL.

---

The capability index, $C_{pk}$ [shown in Equation (18.11)], measures actual process performance for CTQ variables with two-sided specification limits. $C_{pk}$ is equal to the value of either the *CPL* or *CPU*, whichever is smallest.

$C_{pk}$

$$C_{pk} = MIN[CPL, CPU] \tag{18.11}$$

A value of 1 for $C_{pk}$ indicates that the process mean is 3 standard deviations away from the closest specification limit. If the characteristic is normally distributed, then a value of 1 indicates that at least 99.73% of the current output is within specifications. As with all other capability indices, the larger the value of $C_{pk}$, the better. Example 18.3 illustrates the use of the $C_{pk}$ index.

**EXAMPLE 18.3**   CALCULATING $C_{pk}$ FOR THE BOTTLING PROCESS

The soft-drink producer in Example 18.2 requires the bottle filling process to have a $C_{pk}$ greater than or equal to 1. Calculate the $C_{pk}$ index.

**SOLUTION**  In Example 18.2, $CPL = 1.37$ and $CPU = 1.10$. Using Equation (18.11):

$$C_{pk} = MIN[CPL, CPU]$$

$$= MIN[1.37, 1.10] = 1.10$$

The $C_{pk}$ index is greater than 1, indicating that the actual process performance exceeds the company's requirement. More than 99.73% of the bottles contain between 11.82 and 12.18 ounces.

# PROBLEMS FOR SECTION 18.6

## Learning the Basics

**18.29**  For an in-control process with subgroup data $n = 4$, $\bar{\bar{X}} = 20$, and $\bar{R} = 2$, find the estimate of
a. the population mean of all $X$ values.
b. the population standard deviation of all $X$ values.

**18.30**  For an in-control process with subgroup data $n = 3$, $\bar{\bar{X}} = 100$, and $\bar{R} = 3.386$, calculate the percentage of outcomes within specifications if
a. LSL = 98 and USL = 102.
b. LSL = 93 and USL = 107.5.
c. LSL = 93.8 and there is no USL.
d. USL = 110 and there is no LSL.

**18.31**  For an in-control process with subgroup data $n = 3$, $\bar{\bar{X}} = 100$, and $\bar{R} = 3.386$, calculate the $C_p$, CPL, CPU, and $C_{pk}$ if
a. LSL = 98 and USL = 102.
b. LSL = 93 and USL = 107.5.

## Applying the Concepts

**✓ SELF Test**  **18.32**  Referring to the data of Problem 18.24 on page 846, and the data file **Spwater**, the researchers stated, "Some of the benefits of a capable process are increased customer satisfaction, increased operating efficiencies, and reduced costs." To illustrate this point, the authors presented a capability analysis for a spring water bottling operation. One of the CTQ variables is the amount of magnesium, measured in parts per million (ppm), in the water. The LSL and USL for the level of magnesium in a bottle are 18 ppm and 22 ppm, respectively.
a. Estimate the percentage of bottles that are within specifications.
b. Calculate the $C_p$, CPL, CPU, and $C_{pk}$.

**18.33**  Refer to the data in Problem 18.25 on page 847 concerning the tensile strengths of bolts of cloth (see the file **Tensile**). There is no USL for tensile strength, and the LSL is 13.
a. Estimate the percentage of bolts that are within specifications.
b. Calculate the $C_p$ and CPL.

**18.34**  Refer to Problem 18.27 on page 847 concerning a filling machine for a tea bag manufacturer (see the file **Tea3**). In that problem, you should have concluded that the process is in control. The label weight for this product is 5.5 grams, the LSL is 5.2 grams, and the USL is 5.8 grams. Company policy states that at least 99% of the tea bags produced must be inside the specifications in order for the process to be considered capable.
a. Estimate the percentage of the tea bags that are inside the specification limits. Is the process capable of meeting the company policy?
b. If management implemented a new policy stating that 99.7% of all tea bags are required to be within the specifications, is this process capable of reaching that goal? Explain.

**18.35**  Refer to Problem 18.22 on page 846 concerning waiting time for customers at a bank (see the file **Banktime**). Suppose management has set a USL of 5 minutes on waiting time and specified that at least 99% of the waiting times must be less than 5 minutes in order for the process to be considered capable.
a. Estimate the percentage of the waiting times that are inside the specification limits. Is the process capable of meeting the company policy?
b. If management implemented a new policy, stating that 99.7% of all waiting times are required to be within specifications, is this process capable of reaching that goal? Explain.

## 18.7 TOTAL QUALITY MANAGEMENT

An increased interest in improving the quality of products and services in the United States occurred as a reaction to improvements of Japanese industry that began as early as 1950. Individuals such as W. Edwards Deming, Joseph Juran, and Kaoru Ishikawa developed an approach that focuses on continuous improvement of products and services through an increased emphasis on statistics, process improvement, and optimization of the total system. This approach, widely known as **total quality management (TQM)**, is characterized by these themes:

- The primary focus is on process improvement.
- Most of the variation in a process is due to the system and not the individual.
- Teamwork is an integral part of a quality management organization.
- Customer satisfaction is a primary organizational goal.
- Organizational transformation must occur in order to implement quality management.
- Fear must be removed from organizations.
- Higher quality costs less, not more, but requires an investment in training.

In the 1980s, the federal government of the United States increased its efforts to encourage the improvement of quality in American business. Congress passed the Malcolm Baldrige National Improvement Act of 1987 and began awarding the Malcolm Baldrige Award to companies making the greatest strides in improving quality and customer satisfaction. Deming became a prominent consultant to many Fortune 500 companies, including Ford, General Motors, and Procter & Gamble. Many companies adopted some or all the basic themes of TQM.

Today, many quality improvement systems are in place in organizations worldwide. Although most organizations no longer use the name TQM, the underlying philosophy and statistical methods used in today's quality improvement systems are consistent with TQM and the work of Deming. This holistic approach to quality is captured in **Deming's 14 points for management** listed here:

1. Create constancy of purpose for improvement of product and service.
2. Adopt the new philosophy.
3. Cease dependence on inspection to achieve quality.
4. End the practice of awarding business on the basis of price tag alone. Instead, minimize total cost by working with a single supplier.
5. Improve constantly and forever every process for planning, production, and service.
6. Institute training on the job.
7. Adopt and institute leadership.
8. Drive out fear.
9. Break down barriers between staff areas.
10. Eliminate slogans, exhortations, and targets for the workforce.
11. Eliminate numerical quotas for the workforce and numerical goals for management.
12. Remove barriers that rob people of pride of workmanship. Eliminate the annual rating or merit system.
13. Institute a vigorous program of education and self-improvement for everyone.
14. Put everyone in the company to work to accomplish the transformation.

Points 1, 2, 5, 7, and 14 focus on the need for organizational transformation and the responsibility of top management to assert leadership in committing to the transformation. Without this commitment, any improvements obtained will be limited.

One aspect of the improvement process is illustrated by the **Shewhart-Deming cycle**, shown in Figure 18.11. The Shewhart-Deming cycle represents a continuous cycle of "plan, do, study, and act." The first step, planning, represents the initial design phase for planning a change in a manufacturing or service process. This step involves teamwork among individuals from different areas within an organization. The second step, doing, involves implementing the change, preferably on a small scale. The third step, studying, involves analyzing the results, using statistical methods to determine what was learned. The fourth step, acting, involves the acceptance of the change, its abandonment, or further study of the change under different conditions.

**FIGURE 18.11**

Shewhart-Deming cycle

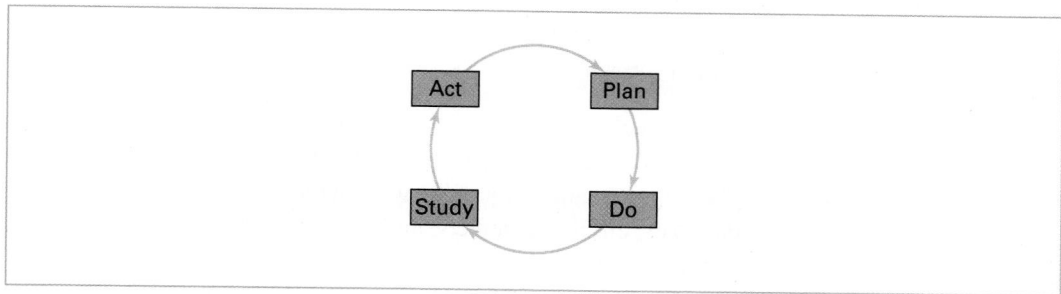

Point 3, cease dependence on inspection to achieve quality, implies that any inspection whose purpose is to improve quality is too late because the quality is already built into the product. It is better to focus on making it right the first time. Among the difficulties involved in inspection (besides high costs) are the failure of inspectors to agree on the operational definitions for nonconforming items and the problem of separating good and bad items. The following example illustrates the difficulties inspectors face.

Suppose your job involves proofreading the sentence in Figure 18.12, with the objective of counting the number of occurrences of the letter F. Perform this task and record the number of occurrences of the letter F that you discover.

**FIGURE 18.12**

An example of a proofreading process

Source: *Adapted from W. W. Scherkenbach, The Deming Route to Quality and Productivity: Road Maps and Roadblocks (Washington, DC: Ceep Press, 1986).*

> FINISHED FILES ARE THE RESULT
> OF YEARS OF SCIENTIFIC
> STUDY COMBINED WITH THE
> EXPERIENCE OF MANY YEARS

People usually see either three F's or six F's. The correct number is six F's. The number you see depends on the method you use to examine the sentence. You are likely to find three F's if you read the sentence phonetically and six F's if you count the number of F's carefully. The point of the exercise is to show that, if such a simple process as counting F's leads to inconsistency of inspectors' results, what will happen when a much more complicated process fails to provide clear operational definitions?

Point 4, end the practice of awarding business on the basis of price tag alone, focus on the idea that there is no real long-term meaning to price without knowledge of the quality of the product. In addition, minimizing the number of entities in the supply chain will reduce the variation involved.

Points 6 and 13 refer to training and reflect the needs of all employees. Continuous learning is critical for quality improvement within an organization. In particular, management needs to understand the differences between special causes and common causes of variation so that proper action is taken in each circumstance.

Points 8 through 12 relate to the evaluation of employee performance. Deming believed that an emphasis on targets and exhortations places an improper burden on the workforce. Workers cannot produce beyond what the system allows (as illustrated in the red bead experiment in

Section 18.3). It is management's job to *improve* the system, not to raise the expectations on workers beyond the system's capability.

Although Deming's points are thought provoking, some have criticized his approach for lacking a formal, objective accountability (see reference 12). Many managers of large organizations, used to seeing financial analyses of policy changes, need a more prescriptive approach.

## 18.8   SIX SIGMA

**Six Sigma** is a quality improvement system originally developed by Motorola in the mid-1980s. After seeing the huge financial successes at Motorola, GE, and other early adopters of Six Sigma, many companies worldwide have now instituted Six Sigma to improve efficiency, cut costs, eliminate defects, and reduce product variation (see references 1, 4, 11, and 17). Six Sigma offers a more prescriptive and systematic approach to process improvement than TQM. It is also distinguished from other quality improvement systems by its clear focus on achieving bottom-line results in a relatively short three- to six-month period of time.

The name Six Sigma comes from the fact that it is a managerial approach designed to create processes that result in no more than 3.4 defects per million. The Six Sigma approach assumes that processes are designed so that the upper and lower specification limits are six standard deviations away from the mean. Then, if the processes are monitored correctly with control charts, the worst possible scenario is for the mean to shift to within 4.5 standard deviations from the nearest specification limit. The area under the normal curve less than 4.5 standard deviations below the mean is approximately 3.4 out of a million. (Table E.1 reports this probability as 0.000003398.)

### The DMAIC Model

To guide managers in their task of improving short- and long-term results, Six Sigma uses a five-step process known as the **DMAIC model**—named for the five steps in the process:

- *Define* The problem is defined, along with the costs, the benefits, and the impact on the customer.
- *Measure* Operational definitions for each critical-to-quality (CTQ) variable are developed. In addition, the measurement procedure is verified so that it is consistent over repeated measurements.
- *Analyze* The root causes of *why* defects occur are determined, and variables in the process causing the defects are identified. Data are collected to determine benchmark values for each process variable. This analysis often uses control charts (discussed in Sections 18.2–18.5).
- *Improve* The importance of each process variable on the CTQ variable is studied using designed experiments (see Chapter 11 and references 9, 10, and 13). The objective is to determine the best level for each variable.
- *Control* The objective is to maintain the benefits for the long term by avoiding potential problems that can occur when a process is changed.

The Define phase of a Six Sigma project consists of the development of a project charter, performing a SIPOC analysis, and identifying the customers for the output of the process. The development of a project charter involves forming a table of business objectives and indicators for all potential Six Sigma projects. Importance ratings are assigned by top management, projects are prioritized, and the most important project is selected. A SIPOC analysis is used to identify the **S**uppliers to the process, list the **I**nput provided to the suppliers, flowchart the **P**rocess, list the process **O**utputs, and identify the **C**ustomers of the process. This is followed by a Voice of the Customer analysis that involves market segmentation in which different types of users of the process are identified and the circumstances of their use of the process are identified. Statistical methods used in the Define phase include tables and charts, descriptive statistics, and control charts.

In the Measure phase of a Six Sigma project, members of a team first develop operational definitions (see Section 1.3) of each CTQ variable. This is done so that everyone will have a firm understanding of the CTQ. Then studies are undertaken to ensure that there is a valid measurement system for the CTQ that is consistent across measurements. Finally, baseline data are collected to determine the capability and stability of the current process. Statistical methods used in the Measure phase include tables and charts, descriptive statistics, the normal distribution, the Analysis of Variance, and control charts.

The Analyze phase of a Six Sigma project focuses on the factors that affect the central tendency, variation, and shape of each CTQ variable. Factors are identified, related to each CTQ, have operational definitions developed, and have measurement systems established. Statistical methods used in the Analyze phase include tables and charts, descriptive statistics, the Analysis of Variance, regression analysis, and control charts.

In the Improve phase of a Six Sigma project, team members carry out designed experiments to actively intervene in a process. The objective of the experimental design is to determine the settings of the factors that will optimize the central tendency, variation, and shape of each CTQ variable. Statistical methods used in the Improve phase include tables and charts, descriptive statistics, regression analysis, hypothesis testing, the Analysis of Variance, and designed experiments.

The Control phase of a Six Sigma project focuses on the maintenance of improvements that have been made in the Improve phase. A risk abatement plan is developed to identify elements that can cause damage to a process. Statistical methods used in the Control phase include tables and charts, descriptive statistics, and control charts.

## Roles in a Six Sigma Organization

Six Sigma requires that the employees of an organization have well-defined roles. The roles of senior executive (C.E.O. or president), executive committee, champion, process owner, master black belt, black belt, and green belt are critical to Six Sigma. More importantly, everyone must be properly trained in order to successfully fulfill their roles' tasks and responsibilities.

The role of the **senior executive** is critical for Six Sigma's ultimate success. The most successful, highly publicized Six Sigma efforts have all had unwavering, clear, and committed leadership from top management. Although Six Sigma concepts and processes can be initiated at lower levels, high-level success cannot be achieved without the leadership of the senior executive.

The members of the **executive committee** consist of the top management of an organization. They need to operate at the same level of commitment to Six Sigma as the senior executive.

**Champions** take a strong sponsorship and leadership role in conducting and implementing Six Sigma projects. They work closely with the executive committee, the black belt assigned to their project, and the master black belt overseeing their project. A champion should be a member of the executive committee, or at least someone who reports directly to a member of the executive committee. He or she should have enough influence to remove obstacles or provide resources without having to go higher in the organization.

A **process owner** is the manager of a process. He or she has responsibility for the process and has the authority to change the process on her or his signature. The process owner should be identified and involved immediately in all Six Sigma projects relating to his or her own area.

A **master black belt** takes on a leadership role in the implementation of the Six Sigma process and as an advisor to senior executives. The master black belt must use his/her skills while working on projects that are led by black belts and green belts. A master black belt has successfully led many teams through complex Six Sigma projects. He or she is a proven change agent, leader, facilitator, and technical expert in Six Sigma.

A **black belt** works full-time on Six Sigma projects. A black belt is mentored by a master black belt, but may report to a manager for his or her tour of duty as a black belt. Ideally, a black belt works well in a team format, can manage meetings, is familiar with statistics and systems theory, and has a focus on the customer.

A **green belt** is an individual who works on Six Sigma projects part-time (approximately 25%), either as a team member for complex projects or as a project leader for simpler projects. Most managers in a mature Six Sigma organization are green belts. Green belt certification is a critical prerequisite for advancement into upper management in a Six Sigma organization.

Recent research (see reference 4) indicates that more than 80% of the top 100 publicly traded companies in the United States use Six Sigma. So, you do need to be aware of the distinction between master black belt, black belt, and green belt if you are to function effectively in a Six Sigma organization.

In a Six Sigma organization, 25% to 50% of the organization will be green belts, only 6% to 12% of the organization need to be black belts, and only 1% of the organization need to be master black belts (reference 9). Individual companies, professional organizations such as the American Society for Quality, and universities such as the University of Miami offer certification programs for green belt, black belt, and master black belt. For more information on certification and other aspects of Six Sigma, see references 9, 10, and 13.

# Name That . . . Quality Improvement Approach

*From the Authors' Desktop*

Although many organizations use Six Sigma, other companies may use different quality improvement systems. In addition to TQM, other names that you may be exposed to include Baldrige, ISO, Lean Six Sigma, and Lean Management Systems. Try not to get confused by all the quality improvement terminology you may encounter. What all of these quality approaches have in common is much more important than how they differ. They all focus on process improvement, have customer satisfaction as a primary organizational goal, believe that teamwork is essential for organizational success, require commitment from top management, and place a high value on training.

# SUMMARY

In this chapter you have learned how to use several different types of control charts to distinguish between common causes and special causes of variation. You have learned how to measure the capability of a process by estimating the percentage of items within specifications and by calculating capability indices. By applying these concepts to the services provided by the Beachcomber Hotel, you have learned how a manager can identify problems and continually improve service quality. The chapter also introduced you to managerial approaches used to improve the quality of products and services, including TQM and Six Sigma.

# KEY EQUATIONS

## Constructing Control Limits

Process mean $\pm 3$ standard deviations   **(18.1)**

Upper control limit (UCL) = process mean
$\qquad\qquad\qquad\qquad + 3$ standard deviations

Lower control limit (LCL) = process mean
$\qquad\qquad\qquad\qquad - 3$ standard deviations

## Control Limits for the $p$ Chart

$$\bar{p} \pm 3\sqrt{\frac{\bar{p}(1-\bar{p})}{\bar{n}}}$$

$$\text{UCL} = \bar{p} + 3\sqrt{\frac{\bar{p}(1-\bar{p})}{\bar{n}}}$$   **(18.2)**

$$\text{LCL} = \bar{p} - 3\sqrt{\frac{\bar{p}(1-\bar{p})}{\bar{n}}}$$

## Control Limits for the $c$ Chart

$$\bar{c} \pm 3\sqrt{\bar{c}}$$   **(18.3)**

$$\text{UCL} = \bar{c} + 3\sqrt{\bar{c}}$$

$$\text{LCL} = \bar{c} - 3\sqrt{\bar{c}}$$

## Control Limits for the Range

$$\bar{R} \pm 3\bar{R}\frac{d_3}{d_2}$$

$$\text{UCL} = \bar{R} + 3\bar{R}\frac{d_3}{d_2}$$   **(18.4)**

$$\text{LCL} = \bar{R} - 3\bar{R}\frac{d_3}{d_2}$$

## Calculating Control Limits for the Range

$$\text{UCL} = D_4\bar{R}$$   **(18.5a)**

$$\text{LCL} = D_3\bar{R}$$   **(18.5b)**

## Control Limits for the $\bar{X}$ Chart

$$\bar{\bar{X}} \pm 3\frac{\bar{R}}{d_2\sqrt{n}}$$

$$\text{UCL} = \bar{\bar{X}} + 3\frac{\bar{R}}{d_2\sqrt{n}}$$   **(18.6)**

$$\text{LCL} = \bar{\bar{X}} - 3\frac{\bar{R}}{d_2\sqrt{n}}$$

## Calculating Control Limits for the Mean, Using the $A_2$ Factor

$$\text{UCL} = \bar{\bar{X}} + A_2\bar{R}$$   **(18.7a)**

$$\text{LCL} = \bar{\bar{X}} - A_2\bar{R}$$   **(18.7b)**

## Estimating the Capability of a Process

For a CTQ variable with an LSL and a USL:

$P(\text{An outcome will be within specifications})$
$= P(\text{LSL} < X < \text{USL})$
$$= P\left(\frac{\text{LSL} - \bar{\bar{X}}}{\bar{R}/d_2} < Z < \frac{\text{USL} - \bar{\bar{X}}}{\bar{R}/d_2}\right)$$   **(18.8a)**

For a CTQ variable with only a USL:

$P(\text{An outcome will be within specifications})$
$= P(X < \text{USL})$
$$= P\left(Z < \frac{\text{USL} - \bar{\bar{X}}}{\bar{R}/d_2}\right)$$   **(18.8b)**

For a CTQ variable with only an LSL:

$P(\text{An outcome will be within specifications})$
$= P(\text{LSL} < X)$
$$= P\left(\frac{\text{LSL} - \bar{\bar{X}}}{\bar{R}/d_2} < Z\right)$$   **(18.8c)**

**$C_p$**

$$C_p = \frac{USL - LSL}{6(\bar{R}/d_2)}$$

$$= \frac{\text{Specification spread}}{\text{Process spread}}$$

(18.9)

**CPL and CPU**

$$CPL = \frac{\bar{\bar{X}} - LSL}{3(\bar{R}/d_2)}$$

(18.10a)

$$CPU = \frac{USL - \bar{\bar{X}}}{3(\bar{R}/d_2)}$$

(18.10b)

**$C_{pk}$**

$$C_{pk} = MIN[CPL, CPU]$$

(18.11)

# KEY TERMS

$A_2$ factor   844
areas of opportunity   837
assignable causes of variation   825
attribute charts   827
black belt   857
c chart   837
capability index   850
champion   857
chance causes of variation   825
common causes of variation   825
control chart   825
critical-to-quality (CTQ)   848
$d_2$ factor   841
$d_3$ factor   841
$D_3$ factor   841
$D_4$ factor   841

Deming's 14 points for management   854
DMAIC model   856
executive committee   857
green belt   858
in-control process   827
lower control limit (LCL)   826
lower specification limit (LSL)   848
master black belt   857
out-of-control process   827
p chart   827
process   824
process capability   848
process owner   857
R chart   841
red bead experiment   834

senior executive   857
Shewhart-Deming cycle   854
Six Sigma   856
special causes of variation   825
specification limits   848
state of statistical control   827
subgroups   826
tampering   826
total quality management (TQM)   854
upper control limit (UCL)   826
upper specification limit (USL)   848
variables control charts   841
$\bar{X}$ chart   843

# CHAPTER REVIEW PROBLEMS

## Checking Your Understanding

**18.36** What is the difference between common cause variation and special cause variation?

**18.37** What should you do to improve a process when special causes of variation are present?

**18.38** What should you do to improve a process when only common causes of variation are present?

**18.39** Under what circumstances do you use a p chart?

**18.40** What is the difference between attribute control charts and variables control charts?

**18.41** Why are $\bar{X}$ and R charts used together?

**18.42** What principles did you learn from the red bead experiment?

**18.43** What is the difference between process potential and process performance?

**18.44** A company requires a $C_{pk}$ value of 1 or larger. If a process has $C_p = 1.5$ and $C_{pk} = 0.8$, what changes should you make to the process?

**18.45** Why is a capability analysis *not* performed on out-of-control processes?

## Applying the Concepts

**18.46** According to the American Society for Quality, customers in the United States consistently rate service quality lower than product quality (American Society for Quality, *The Quarterly Quality Report*, **www.asq.org**, May 16, 2006). For example, products in the beverage, personal care and cleaning industries, and major appliance sectors all received very high customer satisfaction ratings. At the other extreme, services provided by airlines, banks, and insurance companies all received low customer satisfaction ratings.

a. Why do you think service quality consistently rates lower than product quality?

b. What are the similarities and differences between measuring service quality and product quality?

c. Do Deming's 14 points apply to both products and services?

d. Can Six Sigma be used for both products and services?

**18.47** Six Flags Amusement Parks lost $133 million on revenue of $1.09 billion in 2005. To turn things around, Six Flags CEO Mark Shapiro is focusing on big problems (such as cutting long-term debt) and small details (such as cleaner restrooms and grounds). His attention to providing clean parks is part of his overall strategy to get entire families to enjoy their day in the park so much that they want to return (extracted from L. Petrecca, "Six Flags CEO Waves the Signal Flag for Families," **usatoday.com**, June 13, 2006). Suppose that you have been hired as a summer intern at a large amusement park. Every day, your task is to conduct 200 exit interviews in the parking lot when customers leave. You need to construct questions to address the cleanliness of the park and the customers' intent to return again. When you begin to construct a short questionnaire, you remember the control chart material you learned in a statistics course, and you decide to write questions that will provide you with data to graph on control charts. After collecting data for 30 days, you plan to construct the control charts.

a. Write a question that will allow you to develop a control chart of customers' perceptions of cleanliness of the park.

b. Give examples of common cause variation and special cause variation for the control chart.

c. If the control chart is in control, what does that indicate and what do you do next?

d. If the control chart is out of control, what does that indicate and what do you do next?

e. Repeat (a) through (d), this time addressing the customers' intent to return to the park.

f. After the initial 30 days, assuming that the charts indicate in-control processes or that the root sources of special cause variation have been corrected, explain how the charts can be used on a daily basis to monitor and improve the quality in the park.

**18.48** Researchers at Miami University in Oxford, Ohio, investigated the use of *p* charts to monitor the market share of a product and to document the effectiveness of marketing promotions. Market share is defined as the company's

proportion of the total number of products sold in a category. If a *p* chart based on a company's market share indicates an in-control process, then the company's share in the marketplace is deemed to be stable and consistent over time. In the example given in the article, the RudyBird Diskette Company collected daily sales data from a nationwide retail audit service. The first 30 days of data in the accompanying table (see the file **Rudybird**) indicate the total number of cases of computer disks sold and the number of RudyBird diskettes sold. The final 7 days of data were taken after RudyBird launched a major in-store promotion. A control chart was used to see if the in-store promotion would result in special cause variation in the marketplace.

### Cases Sold Before the Promotion

| Day | Total | RudyBird | Day | Total | RudyBird |
|---|---|---|---|---|---|
| 1 | 154 | 35 | 16 | 177 | 56 |
| 2 | 153 | 43 | 17 | 143 | 43 |
| 3 | 200 | 44 | 18 | 200 | 69 |
| 4 | 197 | 56 | 19 | 134 | 38 |
| 5 | 194 | 54 | 20 | 192 | 47 |
| 6 | 172 | 38 | 21 | 155 | 45 |
| 7 | 190 | 43 | 22 | 135 | 36 |
| 8 | 209 | 62 | 23 | 189 | 55 |
| 9 | 173 | 53 | 24 | 184 | 44 |
| 10 | 171 | 39 | 25 | 170 | 47 |
| 11 | 173 | 44 | 26 | 178 | 48 |
| 12 | 168 | 37 | 27 | 167 | 42 |
| 13 | 184 | 45 | 28 | 204 | 71 |
| 14 | 211 | 58 | 29 | 183 | 64 |
| 15 | 179 | 35 | 30 | 169 | 43 |

### Cases Sold After the Promotion

| Day | Total | RudyBird |
|---|---|---|
| 31 | 201 | 92 |
| 32 | 177 | 76 |
| 33 | 205 | 85 |
| 34 | 199 | 90 |
| 35 | 187 | 77 |
| 36 | 168 | 79 |
| 37 | 198 | 97 |

Source: *Extracted from C. T. Crespy, T. C. Krehbiel, and J. M. Stearns, "Integrating Analytic Methods into Marketing Research Education: Statistical Control Charts as an Example,"* Marketing Education Review, *5, Spring 1995, pp. 11–23.*

a. Construct a *p* chart using data from the first 30 days (prior to the promotion) to monitor the market share for RudyBird Diskettes.

**b.** Is the market share for RudyBird in control before the start of the in-store promotion?

**c.** On your control chart, extend the control limits generated in (b) and plot the proportions for days 31 through 37. What effect, if any, did the in-store promotion have on RudyBird's market share?

**18.49** The manufacturer of Boston and Vermont asphalt shingles constructed control charts and analyzed several quality characteristics. One characteristic of interest is the strength of the sealant on the shingle. During each day of production, three shingles are tested for their sealant strength. (Thus, a subgroup is operationally defined as one day of production, and the sample size for each subgroup is 3.) Separate pieces are cut from the upper and lower portions of a shingle and then reassembled to simulate shingles on a roof. A timed heating process is used to simulate the sealing process. The sealed shingle pieces are pulled apart, and the amount of force (in pounds) required to break the sealant bond is measured and recorded. This variable is called the *sealant strength*. The LSL and USL for sealant strength are 1.0 and 1.5 pounds, respectively. The data file `Sealant` contains sealant strength measurements on 25 days of production for Boston shingles and 19 days for Vermont shingles.

For the Boston shingles,

**a.** construct a control chart for the range.
**b.** construct a control chart for the mean.
**c.** is the process in control?
**d.** if the process is in control, estimate the percentage of the shingles whose sealant strength is inside the specification limits.
**e.** if the process is in control, calculate the $C_p$, CPL, CPU, and $C_{pk}$.
**f.** if the manufacturer requires that 99.73% of all shingles be within the specification limits, comment on the capability of the process, based on your calculations in (d) and (e).
**g.** Repeat (a) through (f), using the 19 production days for Vermont shingles.

**18.50** A professional basketball player has embarked on a program to study his ability to shoot foul shots. On each day in which a game is not scheduled, he intends to shoot 100 foul shots. He maintains records over a period of 40 days of practice, with the following results stored in the file `Foulspc`:

**a.** Construct a *p* chart for the proportion of successful foul shots. Do you think that the player's foul-shooting process is in statistical control? If not, why not?
**b.** What if you were told that the player used a different method of shooting foul shots for the last 20 days? How might this information change your conclusions in (a)?
**c.** If you knew the information in (b) prior to doing (a), how might you do the analysis differently?

| Day | Foul Shots Made | Day | Foul Shots Made | Day | Foul Shots Made |
|-----|-----|-----|-----|-----|-----|
| 1 | 73 | 15 | 73 | 29 | 76 |
| 2 | 75 | 16 | 76 | 30 | 80 |
| 3 | 69 | 17 | 69 | 31 | 78 |
| 4 | 72 | 18 | 68 | 32 | 83 |
| 5 | 77 | 19 | 72 | 33 | 84 |
| 6 | 71 | 20 | 70 | 34 | 81 |
| 7 | 68 | 21 | 64 | 35 | 86 |
| 8 | 70 | 22 | 67 | 36 | 85 |
| 9 | 67 | 23 | 72 | 37 | 86 |
| 10 | 74 | 24 | 70 | 38 | 87 |
| 11 | 75 | 25 | 74 | 39 | 85 |
| 12 | 72 | 26 | 76 | 40 | 85 |
| 13 | 70 | 27 | 75 | | |
| 14 | 74 | 28 | 78 | | |

**18.51** The funds-transfer department of a bank is concerned with turnaround time for investigations of funds-transfer payments. A payment may involve the bank as a remitter of funds, a beneficiary of funds, or an intermediary in the payment. An investigation is initiated by a payment inquiry or a query by a party involved in the payment or any department affected by the flow of funds. When a query is received, an investigator reconstructs the transaction trail of the payment and verifies that the information is correct and that the proper payment is transmitted. The investigator then reports the results of the investigation, and the transaction is considered closed. It is important that investigations are closed rapidly, preferably within the same day. The number of new investigations and the number and proportion closed on the same day that the inquiry was made are in the file `Fundtran`.

**a.** Construct a control chart for these data.
**b.** Is the process in a state of statistical control? Explain.
**c.** Based on the results of (a) and (b), what should management do next to improve the process?

**18.52** A branch manager of a brokerage company is concerned with the number of undesirable trades made by her sales staff. A trade is considered undesirable if there is an error on the trade ticket. Trades with errors are canceled and resubmitted. The cost of correcting errors is billed to the brokerage company. The branch manager wants to know whether the proportion of undesirable trades is in a state of statistical control so she can plan the next step in a quality improvement process. Data were collected for a 30-day period, with the following results (stored in the file `Trade`):

| Day | Undesirable Trades | Total Trades | Day | Undesirable Trades | Total Trades |
|-----|-----|-----|-----|-----|-----|
| 1 | 2 | 74 | 16 | 3 | 54 |
| 2 | 12 | 85 | 17 | 12 | 74 |
| 3 | 13 | 114 | 18 | 11 | 103 |
| 4 | 33 | 136 | 19 | 11 | 100 |
| 5 | 5 | 97 | 20 | 14 | 88 |
| 6 | 20 | 115 | 21 | 4 | 58 |
| 7 | 17 | 108 | 22 | 10 | 69 |
| 8 | 10 | 76 | 23 | 19 | 135 |
| 9 | 8 | 69 | 24 | 1 | 67 |
| 10 | 18 | 98 | 25 | 11 | 77 |
| 11 | 3 | 104 | 26 | 12 | 88 |
| 12 | 12 | 98 | 27 | 4 | 66 |
| 13 | 15 | 105 | 28 | 11 | 72 |
| 14 | 6 | 98 | 29 | 13 | 118 |
| 15 | 21 | 204 | 30 | 15 | 138 |

**a.** Construct a control chart for these data.

**b.** Is the process in control? Explain.

**c.** Based on the results of (a) and (b), what should the manager do next to improve the process?

**18.53** As chief operating officer of a local community hospital, you have just returned from a three-day seminar on quality and productivity. It is your intention to implement many of the ideas that you learned at the seminar. You have decided to construct control charts for the upcoming month for the following variables: number of daily admissions, proportion of rework in the laboratory (based on 1,000 daily samples), and time (in hours) between receipt of a specimen at the laboratory and completion of the work (based on a subgroup of 10 specimens per day). The data collected are summarized in the file **Hospadm**. You are to make a presentation to the chief executive officer of the hospital and the board of directors. Prepare a report that summarizes the conclusions drawn from analyzing control charts for these variables. In addition, recommend additional variables to measure and monitor by using control charts.

**18.54** For a period of four weeks, record your pulse rate (in beats per minute) just after you get out of bed in the morning and also before you go to sleep at night. Construct $\bar{X}$ and $R$ charts and determine whether your pulse rate is in a state of statistical control. Discuss.

**18.55** (**Class Project**) Use the table of random numbers (Table E.1) to simulate the selection of different-colored balls from an urn, as follows:

1. Start in the row corresponding to the day of the month in which you were born plus the last two digits of the year in which you were born. For example, if you were born October 3, 1986, you would start in row 3 + 86 = 89. If your total exceeds 100, subtract 100 from the total.
2. Select two-digit random numbers.
3. If you select a random number from 00 to 94, consider the ball to be white; if the random number is from 95 to 99, consider the ball to be red.

Each student is to select 100 such two-digit random numbers and report the number of "red balls" in the sample. Construct a control chart for the proportion of red balls. What conclusions can you draw about the system of selecting red balls? Are all the students part of the system? Is anyone outside the system? If so, what explanation can you give for someone who has too many red balls? If a bonus were paid to the top 10% of the students (the 10% with the fewest red balls), what effect would that have on the rest of the students? Discuss.

# THE HARNSWELL SEWING MACHINE COMPANY CASE

## Phase 1

For almost 50 years, the Harnswell Sewing Machine Company has manufactured industrial sewing machines. The company specializes in automated machines called pattern tackers that sew repetitive patterns on such mass-produced products as shoes, garments, and seat belts. Aside from the sales of machines, the company sells machine parts. Because the company's products have a reputation for being superior, Harnswell is able to command a price premium for its product line.

Recently, the operations manager, Natalie York, purchased several books relating to quality at a local bookstore. After reading them, she considered the feasibility of beginning a quality program at the company. At the current time, the company has no formal quality program. Parts are 100% inspected at the time of shipping to a customer or installation in a machine, yet Natalie has always wondered why inventory of certain parts (in particular, the half-inch cam rollers) invariably falls short before a full year lapses, even though 7,000 pieces have been produced for a demand of 5,000 pieces per year.

After a great deal of reflection and with some apprehension, Natalie has decided that she will approach John Harnswell, the owner of the company, about the possibility of beginning a program to improve quality in the company, starting with a trial project in the machine parts area. As she is walking to Mr. Harnswell's office for the meeting, she has second thoughts about whether this is such a good idea. After all, just last month, Mr. Harnswell told her, "Why do you need to go to graduate school for your master's degree in business? That is a waste of your time and will not be of any value to the Harnswell Company. All those professors are just up in their ivory towers and don't know a thing about running a business, like I do."

As she enters his office, Mr. Harnswell, ever courteous to her, invites Natalie to sit down across from him. "Well, what do you have on your mind this morning?" Mr. Harnswell asks her in an inquisitive tone. She begins by starting to talk about the books that she has just completed reading and about how she has some interesting ideas for making production even better than it is now and improving profits. Before she can finish, Mr. Harnswell has started to answer. "Look, everything has been fine since I started this company in 1968. I have built this company up from nothing to one that employs more than 100 people. Why do you want to make waves? Remember, if it ain't broke, don't fix it." With that he ushers her from his office with the admonishment of, "What am I going to do with you if you keep coming up with these ridiculous ideas?"

## EXERCISES

HS18.1  Based on what you have read, which of Deming's 14 points of management are most lacking in the Harnswell Sewing Machine Company? Explain.

HS18.2  What changes, if any, do you think that Natalie York might be able to institute in the company? Explain.

DO NOT CONTINUE UNTIL YOU HAVE COMPLETED THE PHASE 1 EXERCISES.

### Phase 2

Natalie slowly walks down the hall after leaving Mr. Harnswell's office, feeling rather downcast. He just won't listen to anyone, she thinks. As she walks, Jim Murante, the shop foreman, comes up beside her. "So," he says, "did you really think that he would listen to you? I've been here more than 25 years. The only way he listens is if he is shown something that worked after it has already been done. Let's see what we can plan together."

Natalie and Jim decide to begin by investigating the production of the cam rollers, which are precision-ground parts. The last part of the production process involves the grinding of the outer diameter. After grinding, the part mates with the cam groove of the particular sewing pattern. The half-inch rollers technically have an engineering specification for the outer diameter of the roller of 0.5075 inch (the specifications are actually metric, but in factory floor jargon, they are referred to as half-inch), plus a tolerable error of 0.0003 inch on the lower side. Thus, the outer diameter is allowed to be

between 0.5072 and 0.5075 inch. Anything larger is reclassified into a different and less costly category, and anything smaller is unusable for anything other than scrap.

The grinding of the cam roller is done on a single machine with a single tool setup and no change in the grinding wheel after initial setup. The operation is done by Dave Martin, the head machinist, who has 30 years of experience in the trade and specific experience producing the cam roller part. Because production occurs in batches, Natalie and Jim sample five parts produced from each batch. Table HS18.1 presents data collected over 30 batches (stored in the file **Harnswell**).

## TABLE HS18.1
Diameter of Cam Rollers (in Inches)

| | Cam Roller | | | | |
|---|---|---|---|---|---|
| **Batch** | **1** | **2** | **3** | **4** | **5** |
| 1 | .5076 | .5076 | .5075 | .5077 | .5075 |
| 2 | .5075 | .5077 | .5076 | .5076 | .5075 |
| 3 | .5075 | .5075 | .5075 | .5075 | .5076 |
| 4 | .5075 | .5076 | .5074 | .5076 | .5073 |
| 5 | .5075 | .5074 | .5076 | .5073 | .5076 |
| 6 | .5076 | .5075 | .5076 | .5075 | .5075 |
| 7 | .5076 | .5076 | .5076 | .5075 | .5075 |
| 8 | .5075 | .5076 | .5076 | .5075 | .5074 |
| 9 | .5074 | .5076 | .5075 | .5075 | .5076 |
| 10 | .5076 | .5077 | .5075 | .5075 | .5075 |
| 11 | .5075 | .5075 | .5075 | .5076 | .5075 |
| 12 | .5075 | .5076 | .5075 | .5077 | .5075 |
| 13 | .5076 | .5076 | .5073 | .5076 | .5074 |
| 14 | .5075 | .5076 | .5074 | .5076 | .5075 |
| 15 | .5075 | .5075 | .5076 | .5074 | .5073 |
| 16 | .5075 | .5074 | .5076 | .5075 | .5075 |
| 17 | .5075 | .5074 | .5075 | .5074 | .5072 |
| 18 | .5075 | .5075 | .5076 | .5075 | .5076 |
| 19 | .5076 | .5076 | .5075 | .5075 | .5076 |
| 20 | .5075 | .5074 | .5077 | .5076 | .5074 |
| 21 | .5075 | .5074 | .5075 | .5075 | .5075 |
| 22 | .5076 | .5076 | .5075 | .5076 | .5074 |
| 23 | .5076 | .5076 | .5075 | .5075 | .5076 |
| 24 | .5075 | .5076 | .5075 | .5076 | .5075 |
| 25 | .5075 | .5075 | .5075 | .5075 | .5074 |
| 26 | .5077 | .5076 | .5076 | .5074 | .5075 |
| 27 | .5075 | .5075 | .5074 | .5076 | .5075 |
| 28 | .5077 | .5076 | .5075 | .5075 | .5076 |
| 29 | .5075 | .5075 | .5074 | .5075 | .5075 |
| 30 | .5076 | .5075 | .5075 | .5076 | .5075 |

## EXERCISE

HS18.3  **a.** Is the process in control? Why?

**b.** What recommendations do you have for improving the process?

DO NOT CONTINUE UNTIL YOU HAVE COMPLETED THE PHASE 2 EXERCISE.

## Phase 3

Natalie examines the $\bar{X}$ and $R$ charts developed from the data presented in Table HS18.1. The $R$ chart indicates that the process is in control, but the $\bar{X}$ chart reveals that the mean for batch 17 is outside the LCL. This immediately gives her cause for concern because low values for the roller diameter could mean that parts have to be scrapped. Natalie goes to see Jim Murante, the shop foreman, to try to find out what had happened to batch 17. Jim looks up the production records to determine when this batch was produced. "Aha!" he exclaims. "I think I've got the answer! This batch was produced on that really cold morning we had last month. I've been after Mr. Harnswell for a long time to let us install an automatic thermostat here in the shop so that the place doesn't feel so cold when we get here in the morning. All he ever tells me is that people aren't as tough as they used to be."

Natalie stands there almost in shock. She realizes that what happened is that, rather than standing idle until the environment and the equipment warmed to acceptable temperatures, the machinist opted to manufacture parts that might have to be scrapped. In fact, Natalie recalls that a major problem occurred on that same day, when several other expensive parts had to be scrapped. Natalie says to Jim, "We just have to do something. We can't let this go on now that we know what problems it is potentially causing." Natalie and Jim decide to take enough money out of petty cash to get the thermostat without having to fill out a requisition requiring Mr. Harnswell's signature. They install the thermostat and set the heating control so that the heat turns on a half hour before the shop opens each morning.

## EXERCISES

HS18.4 What should Natalie now do concerning the cam roller data? Explain.

HS18.5 Explain how the actions of Natalie and Jim to avoid this particular problem in the future have resulted in quality improvement.

DO NOT CONTINUE UNTIL YOU HAVE COMPLETED THE PHASE 3 EXERCISES.

## Phase 4

Because corrective action was taken to eliminate the special cause of variation, Natalie removes the data for batch 17 from the analysis. The control charts for the remaining days indicate a stable system, with only common causes of variation operating on the system. Then, Natalie and Jim sit down with Dave Martin and several other machinists to try to determine all the possible causes for the existence of oversized and scrapped rollers. Natalie is still troubled by the data. After all, she wants to find out whether the process is giving oversizes (which are downgraded) and undersizes (which are scrapped). She thinks about which tables and charts might be most helpful.

## EXERCISE

HS18.6 **a.** Construct a frequency distribution and a stem-and-leaf display of the cam roller diameters. Which one do you prefer?

**b.** Based on your results in (a), construct all appropriate graphs of the cam roller diameters.

**c.** Write a report, expressing your conclusions concerning the cam roller diameters. Be sure to discuss the diameters as they relate to the specifications.

DO NOT CONTINUE UNTIL YOU HAVE COMPLETED THE PHASE 4 EXERCISE.

## Phase 5

Natalie notices immediately that the overall mean diameter with batch 17 eliminated is 0.507527, which is higher than the specification value. Thus, the mean diameter of the rollers produced is so high that they will be downgraded in value. In fact, 55 of the 150 rollers sampled (36.67%) are above the specification value. If this percentage is extrapolated to the full year's production, 36.67% of the 7,000 pieces manufactured, or 2,567, could not be sold as half-inch rollers, leaving only 4,433 available for sale. "No wonder we often have shortages that require costly emergency runs," she thinks. She also notes that not one diameter is below the lower specification of 0.5072, so not one of the rollers had to be scrapped.

Natalie realizes that there has to be a reason for all this. Along with Jim Murante, she decides to show the results to Dave Martin, the head machinist. Dave says that the results don't surprise him that much. "You know," he says, "there is only 0.0003 inch in diameter that I'm allowed in variation. If I aim for exactly halfway between 0.5072 and 0.5075, I'm afraid that I'll make a lot of short pieces that will have to be scrapped. I know from way back when I first started here that Mr. Harnswell and everybody else will come down on my head if they start seeing too many of those scraps. I figure that if I aim at 0.5075, the worst thing that will happen will be a bunch of downgrades, but I won't make any pieces that have to be scrapped."

## EXERCISES

HS18.7 What approach do you think the machinist should take in terms of the diameter he should aim for? Explain.

HS18.8 What do you think that Natalie should do next? Explain.

# MANAGING THE *SPRINGVILLE HERALD*

## Phase 1

An advertising production team is charged with reducing the number and dollar amount of the advertising errors, with initial focus on the ran-in-error category. The team collects data, including the number of ads with errors, on a Monday-to-Saturday basis. Table SH18.1 includes the total number of ads and the number containing errors for a period of one month (see the file SH18-1). (Sundays are excluded because a special type of production is used for that day.)

### TABLE SH18.1

Number of Ads with Errors and Daily Number of Display Ads

| Day | Number of Ads with Errors | Total Number of Ads | Day | Number of Ads with Errors | Total Number of Ads |
|-----|---------------------------|---------------------|-----|---------------------------|---------------------|
| 1 | 4 | 228 | 14 | 5 | 245 |
| 2 | 6 | 273 | 15 | 7 | 266 |
| 3 | 5 | 239 | 16 | 2 | 197 |
| 4 | 3 | 197 | 17 | 4 | 228 |
| 5 | 6 | 259 | 18 | 5 | 236 |
| 6 | 7 | 203 | 19 | 4 | 208 |
| 7 | 8 | 289 | 20 | 3 | 214 |
| 8 | 14 | 241 | 21 | 8 | 258 |
| 9 | 9 | 263 | 22 | 10 | 267 |
| 10 | 5 | 199 | 23 | 4 | 217 |
| 11 | 6 | 275 | 24 | 9 | 277 |
| 12 | 4 | 212 | 25 | 7 | 258 |
| 13 | 3 | 207 | | | |

### EXERCISES

SH18.1  What is the first thing that the team from the advertising production department should do to reduce the number of errors? Explain.

SH18.2  **a.** Construct the appropriate control chart for these data.
   **b.** Is the process in a state of statistical control? Explain.
   **c.** What should the team recommend as the next step to improve the process?

DO NOT CONTINUE UNTIL YOU HAVE COMPLETED THE PHASE 1 EXERCISES.

## Phase 2

The advertising production team examines the *p* chart developed from the data of Table SH18.1. Using the rules for determining out-of-control points, they observe that day 8 is above the UCL. Upon investigation, they determine that on that day, there was an employee from another work area assigned to the processing of the ads because several employees were out ill. The group brainstorms ways of avoiding the problem in the future and recommends that a team of people from other work areas receive training on the work done by this area. Members of this team can then cover the processing of the ads by rotating in one- or two-hour shifts.

### EXERCISES

SH18.3  What should the advertising production team now do concerning the data of Table SH18.1? Explain.

SH18.4  Explain how the actions of the team to avoid this particular problem in the future have resulted in quality improvement.

SH18.5  In addition to the number of ads with errors, what other information concerning errors on a daily basis should the team collect?

DO NOT CONTINUE UNTIL YOU HAVE COMPLETED THE PHASE 2 EXERCISES.

## Phase 3

A print production team also is charged with improving the quality of the *Herald*. The team has chosen the blackness of the print of the newspaper as its first project. Blackness is measured on a device that records the results on a standard scale, where the blacker the spot, the higher the blackness measure. The blackness of the print should be approximately 1.0. The lower and upper specifications for blackness are 0.8 and 1.2, respectively. Five spots on the first newspaper printed each day are randomly selected, and the blackness of each spot is measured. Table SH18.2 presents the results for 25 days (stored in the file SH18-2).

### EXERCISE

SH18.6  **a.** Construct the appropriate control charts for these data.
   **b.** Is the process in a state of statistical control? Explain.
   **c.** Perform a capability analysis. Is the process capable of meeting the blackness specifications?
   **d.** What should the team recommend as the next step to improve the process?

## TABLE SH18.2
Newsprint Blackness for 25 Consecutive Days

| Day | Spot 1 | 2 | 3 | 4 | 5 | Day | Spot 1 | 2 | 3 | 4 | 5 |
|---|---|---|---|---|---|---|---|---|---|---|---|
| 1 | 0.96 | 1.01 | 1.12 | 1.07 | 0.97 | 14 | 1.03 | 0.89 | 1.03 | 1.12 | 1.03 |
| 2 | 1.06 | 1.00 | 1.02 | 1.16 | 0.96 | 15 | 0.96 | 1.12 | 0.95 | 0.88 | 0.99 |
| 3 | 1.00 | 0.90 | 0.98 | 1.18 | 0.96 | 16 | 1.01 | 0.87 | 0.99 | 1.04 | 1.16 |
| 4 | 0.92 | 0.89 | 1.01 | 1.16 | 0.90 | 17 | 0.98 | 0.85 | 0.99 | 1.04 | 1.16 |
| 5 | 1.02 | 1.16 | 1.03 | 0.89 | 1.00 | 18 | 1.03 | 0.82 | 1.21 | 0.98 | 1.08 |
| 6 | 0.88 | 0.92 | 1.03 | 1.16 | 0.91 | 19 | 1.02 | 0.84 | 1.15 | 0.94 | 1.08 |
| 7 | 1.05 | 1.13 | 1.01 | 0.93 | 1.03 | 20 | 0.90 | 1.02 | 1.10 | 1.04 | 1.08 |
| 8 | 0.95 | 0.86 | 1.14 | 0.90 | 0.95 | 21 | 0.96 | 1.05 | 1.01 | 0.93 | 1.01 |
| 9 | 0.99 | 0.89 | 1.00 | 1.15 | 0.92 | 22 | 0.89 | 1.04 | 0.97 | 0.99 | 0.95 |
| 10 | 0.89 | 1.18 | 1.03 | 0.96 | 1.04 | 23 | 0.96 | 1.00 | 0.97 | 1.04 | 0.95 |
| 11 | 0.97 | 1.13 | 0.95 | 0.86 | 1.06 | 24 | 1.01 | 0.98 | 1.04 | 1.01 | 0.92 |
| 12 | 1.00 | 0.87 | 1.02 | 0.98 | 1.13 | 25 | 1.01 | 1.00 | 0.92 | 0.90 | 1.11 |
| 13 | 0.96 | 0.79 | 1.17 | 0.97 | 0.95 | | | | | | |

# REFERENCES

1. Arndt, M., "Quality Isn't Just for Widgets," *BusinessWeek*, July 22, 2002, pp. 72–73.
2. Automotive Industry Action Group (AIAG), *Statistical Process Control Reference Manual* (Chrysler, Ford, and General Motors Quality and Supplier Assessment Staff, 1995).
3. Bothe, D. R., *Measuring Process Capability* (New York: McGraw-Hill, 1997).
4. Cyger, M. "The Last Word—Riding the Bandwagon," *iSixSigma Magazine*, November/December 2006.
5. Davis, R. B., and T. C. Krehbiel, "Shewhart and Zone Control Charts under Linear Trend," *Communications in Statistics: Simulation and Computation*, 2002, 31(1), pp. 91–96.
6. Deming, W. E., *The New Economics for Business, Industry, and Government* (Cambridge, MA: MIT Center for Advanced Engineering Study, 1993).
7. Deming, W. E., *Out of the Crisis* (Cambridge, MA: MIT Center for Advanced Engineering Study, 1986).
8. Gabor, A., *The Man Who Discovered Quality* (New York: Time Books, 1990).
9. Gitlow, H., and D. Levine, *Six Sigma for Green Belts and Champions* (Upper Saddle River, NJ: Financial Times/Prentice Hall, 2005).
10. Gitlow, H., D. Levine, and E. Popovich, *Design for Six Sigma for Green Belts and Champions* (Upper Saddle River, NJ: Financial Times/Prentice Hall, 2006).
11. Hahn, G. J., N. Doganaksoy, and R. Hoerl, "The Evolution of Six Sigma," *Quality Engineering*, 12 (2000): 317–326.
12. Lemak, D. L. , N. P. Mero, and R. Reed, " When Quality Works: A Premature Post-Mortem on TQM," *Journal of Business and Management*, 8 (2002): 391–407.
13. Levine, D. M., *Statistics for Six Sigma for Green Belts with Minitab and JMP* (Upper Saddle River, NJ: Financial Times/Prentice Hall, 2006).
14. *Microsoft Excel 2007* (Redmond, WA: Microsoft Corp., 2007).
15. Scherkenbach, W. W., *The Deming Route to Quality and Productivity: Road Maps and Roadblocks* (Washington, DC: CEEP Press, 1987).
16. Shewhart, W. A., *Economic Control of the Quality of Manufactured Product* (New York: Van Nostrand-Reinhard, 1931, reprinted by the American Society for Quality Control, Milwaukee, 1980).
17. Snee, R. D., "Impact of Six Sigma on Quality," *Quality Engineering*, 12 (2000): ix–xiv.
18. Vardeman, S. B., and J. M. Jobe, *Statistical Methods for Quality Assurance: Basics, Measurement, Control, Capability and Improvement* (New York: Springer-Verlag, 2009).
19. Walton, M., *The Deming Management Method* (New York: Perigee Books, 1986).

# Appendix E18
## Using Microsoft Excel for Control Charts

### E18.1 Computing Control Limits for p Charts

You compute control limits for *p* charts by making entries in the **pChartData** worksheet of the p Chart.xls workbook.

Open to that worksheet and enter time period data into column A, the sample/subgroup size for each time period in column B, and the number of nonconforming items for each time period in column C. Then select the preexisting formulas in the cell range D2:G2 and copy them down through all data rows. (Before you enter your data, these cells will display the message #DIV/0!. This is not an error.)

The formulas that you copy are shown in Figure E18.1. The cell D2 formula computes a point to be plotted on the *p* chart. The cell E2 formula displays the lower control limit value, the cell F2 formula displays the center values, and the G2 formula displays the upper control limit. As you copy the formulas in these last three columns, the same set of three values appears in every row to facilitate creating a *p* chart as explained in Section E18.2.

| | D | E | F | G |
|---|---|---|---|---|
| 1 | p | LCL | Center | UCL |
| 2 | =C2/B2 | = pCalcs!$B$12 | =pCalcs!$B$13 | =pCalcs!$B$14 |

**FIGURE E18.1** pChartData worksheet formulas

As you complete this worksheet by copying formulas, you also complete the **pCalcs** worksheet that summarizes the control limits formulas. You make no entries into the pCalcs worksheet; its data come from summarizing your entries in the pChartData worksheet. Figure E18.2 shows a completed pCalcs worksheet for the *p* chart shown in Figure 18.2 on page 830.

| | A | B | |
|---|---|---|---|
| 1 | p Chart Summary | | |
| 2 | | | |
| 3 | Intermediate Calculations | | |
| 4 | Sum of Subgroup Sizes | 5600 | =SUM(pChartData!B:B) |
| 5 | Number of Subgroups Taken | 28 | =COUNT(pChartData!B:B) |
| 6 | Average Sample/Subgroup Size | 200 | =B4/B5 |
| 7 | Average Proportion of Nonconforming Items | 0.0827 | =SUM(pChartData!C:C)/B4 |
| 8 | Three Standard Deviations | 0.0584 | =3 * SQRT(B7 * (1 - B7)/B6) |
| 9 | Preliminary Lower Control Limit | 0.0243 | =B7 - B8 |
| 10 | | | |
| 11 | p Chart Control Limits | | |
| 12 | Lower Control Limit | 0.0243 | =IF(B9 > 0, B9, 0) |
| 13 | Center | 0.0827 | =B7 |
| 14 | Upper Control Limit | 0.1411 | =B7 + B8 |

**FIGURE E18.2** pCalcs worksheet

### E18.2 Creating p Charts: Overview

You create *p* charts by using Excel charting features with your completed **pChartData** and **pCalcs** worksheets (discussed in the previous section).

### E18.2A Creating p charts (Excel 97–2003)

Open to your completed **pChartData** worksheet. Select **Insert → Chart** and make the following entries in the Wizard Step dialog boxes:

**Wizard Step 1** Click **XY (Scatter)** from the Standard Types Chart type box and then select the first choice in the bottom row of Chart sub-type choices, labeled as Scatter with data points connected by lines.

**Wizard Step 2** Click the **Data Range** tab. Enter the column A cell range of your time period data followed by the columns D through G cell range that contain the formulas as the **Data Range**. Because you are entering a data range composed of two nonadjacent areas, you must separate the two cell ranges with a comma. For example, if your pChartData worksheet contained entries in rows 2 through 29, you would enter **A1:A29,D1:G29** as the Data Range. Click the **Columns** option after you have entered your Data Range.

**Wizard Step 3** Click the **Titles** tab. Enter a title as the **Chart title** and enter appropriate values for the **Value (X) axis** and **Value (Y) axis** titles. Click, in turn, the **Axes**, **Gridlines**, **Legend**, and **Data Labels** tabs and use the formatting settings that are given in Section E2.3A on page 72.

At this point, the UCL, Center, and LCL lines of your *p* chart will be missing labels and be incorrectly formatted. You can correct these errors using the following instructions.

**To add labels for the control chart and center lines.** Display the Drawing toolbar by selecting **View → Toolbars → Drawing**. For each line, click the **Text Box icon** and drag the mouse to draw a box to hold a label. (Figure E18.3 shows the Excel 2003 Text Box icon selected; the icons in other Excel versions are similar.) Type the label (UCL, pBar, or LCL). If necessary, you can adjust the size of the box by clicking and dragging one of the corner circle handles. If necessary, you can adjust the position of the box by clicking and dragging the halo around the text box.

**FIGURE E18.3** Text Box icon of the Drawing toolbar (Excel 2003)

**To eliminate data point markers from the control chart and center lines.**   For each line, right-click the line and select **Format Data Series** from the shortcut menu. In the **Marker Options** panel, select the **None** option and then click **Close**.

**To reformat the UCL and LCL lines.**   For each line, right-click the line and select **Format Data Series** from the shortcut menu. In the **Patterns** tab of the Format Data Series Data dialog box, select the first dashed line choice from the **Style drop-down** list box in the **Line** group, select the **None** option in the **Marker** group and click **OK**.

**To reformat the center line.**   Right-click the line and select **Format Data Series** from the shortcut menu. In the **Patterns** tab of the Format Data Series Data dialog box, select a red color from the **Color** drop-down list in the **Line** group, select the **None** option in the **Marker** group, and click **OK**.

## E18.2B Creating p charts (Excel 2007)

Open to your completed **pChartData** worksheet and select the column A and columns D through G data. To select these nonadjacent areas together, hold down the **Ctrl** key while selecting the ranges. Then select **Insert → Scatter → Scatter with Straight Lines and Markers**. Finish by relocating your chart to a chart sheet and customizing your chart using the instructions in Section E.2.3B on page 73. At this point, the UCL, Center, and LCL lines of your p chart will be missing labels and be incorrectly formatted. You can correct these errors using the following instructions.

**To add labels for the control chart and center lines.**   For each line, click **Insert → Text Box** and drag the mouse to draw a box to hold a label. Right-click in the box and select **Edit Test** from the shortcut menu. Type the label (UCL, pBar, or LCL) and click outside the text box. If necessary, you can adjust the size of the box by clicking and dragging one of the corner circle handles. If necessary, you can adjust the position of the box by clicking and dragging the box.

**To reformat the UCL and LCL lines.**   For each line, right-click the line and select **Format Data Series** from the shortcut menu. In the **Line Style** panel, select one of the choices from the **Dash type** drop-down list. In the **Marker Options** panel, select the **None** option and then click **Close**.

**To reformat the center line.**   Right-click the line and select **Format Data Series** from the shortcut menu. In the **Line** panel, select one of the red choices from the **Color** drop-down list. In the **Marker Options** panel, select the **None** option and then click **Close**.

## E18.3 Computing Control Limits for c Charts

You compute control limits for c charts by making entries in the **cChartData** worksheet of the `c Chart.xls` workbook.

Open to that worksheet and enter time period data into column A and the number of nonconforming items for each time period in column B. Then select the preexisting formulas in the cell range C2:E2 and copy them down through all data rows. (Before you enter your data, these cells will display the message #DIV/0!. This is not an error.)

The formulas that you copy are shown in Figure E18.4. The cell C2 formula displays the lower control limit, the cell D2 formula displays the center values, and the E2 formula displays the upper control limit. As you copy the formulas in these last three columns, the same set of three values appears in every row to facilitate creating a c chart as explained in Section E18.4.

| | C | D | E |
|---|---|---|---|
| 1 | LCL | Center Line | UCL |
| 2 | =cCalcs!$B$10 | =cCalcs!$B$11 | =cCalcs!$B$12 |

**FIGURE E18.4** cChartData worksheet formulas

As you complete this worksheet by copying formulas, you also complete the **cCalcs** worksheet that summarizes the control limits formulas. You make no entries into the cCalcs worksheet its values come from summarizing your entries in the cChartData worksheet. Figure E18.5 shows a completed cCalcs worksheet for the c chart similar to the one shown in Figure 18.7 on page 839.

| | A | B | |
|---|---|---|---|
| 1 | c Chart Summary | | |
| 2 | | | |
| 3 | Intermediate Calculations | | |
| 4 | Sum of NonConformities | 312 | =SUM(cChartData!B:B) |
| 5 | Number of Units Sampled | 50 | =COUNT(cChartData!B:B) |
| 6 | CBar | 6.24 | =B4/B5 |
| 7 | Preliminary Lower Control Limit | -1.2540 | =B6 - 3 * SQRT(B6) |
| 8 | | | |
| 9 | c Chart Control Limits | | |
| 10 | Lower Control Limit | 0.0000 | =IF(B7 > 0, B7, 0) |
| 11 | Center | 6.2400 | =B6 |
| 12 | Upper Control Limit | 13.7340 | =B6 + 3 * SQRT(B6) |

**FIGURE E18.5** cCalcs worksheet

## E18.4 Creating c Charts: Overview

You create c charts by using Excel charting features with your completed **cChartData** and **cCalcs** worksheets discussed in the previous section. The process of creating a

$c$ chart is nearly identical to the process of creating a $p$ chart.

## E18.4A Creating $c$ charts (Excel 97–2003)

Follow the Section E18.2A instructions with these exceptions: Open to your completed **cChartData** worksheet in the `c Chart.xls` workbook and in Wizard Step 2, enter the columns A through E cell range that contains your time period data, number of nonconformances, and the formulas to compute the LCL, center line, and UCL, as the **Data Range**.

## E18.4B Creating $c$ charts (Excel 2007)

Follow the Section E18.2B instructions with these exceptions: Open to your completed **cChartData** worksheet of the `c Chart.xls` workbook and select the columns A through E cell range that contains your time period data, number of nonconformances, and the formulas to compute the LCL, center line, and UCL.

## E18.5 Computing Control Limits for $R$ and $\bar{X}$ Charts

You compute control limits for $R$ and $\bar{X}$ charts by making entries in the **RXChartData** and **RXCalcs** worksheets in the `RandXBarChart.xls` workbook.

Open to the **RXChartData** worksheet of the `RandXBarChart.xls` workbook. Enter the time period, $\bar{X}$, and range data into columns A, B, and C, respectively. If you have only the raw data for each time period, you first need to compute the mean and range for each time period. If necessary, use the AVERAGE function to compute the mean. Use the MAX and MIN functions to determine the largest and smallest value and then subtract the smallest value from the largest value to compute the range.

With columns A through C completed, select the preexisting formulas in the cell range D2:I2 and copy them down through all data rows. (Before you enter your data, these cells will display the message #DIV/0!. This is not an error.) The formulas that you copy compute the control limit and center lines for both the $R$ and $\bar{X}$ chart. These formulas are similar to the pChartData worksheet formulas discussed in Section E18.1.

After copying these formulas, open to the **RXCalcs** worksheet (to which the formulas refer). Enter the sample/subgroup size in cell B4. Use Table E.13 to look up the proper values for the $D_3$, $D_4$, and $A_2$ factors and enter those values in cells B8, B9, and B18, respectively, to complete the worksheet. Figure E18.6 shows a completed RXCalcs worksheet for the R and $\bar{X}$ charts shown in Figures 18.8 and 18.9 on pages 843 and 845.

| | A | B | |
|---|---|---|---|
| 1 | R and XBar Chart Summary | | |
| 2 | | | |
| 3 | **Data** | | |
| 4 | **Sample/Subgroup Size** | 5 | |
| 5 | | | |
| 6 | R Chart Intermediate Calculations | | |
| 7 | RBar | 3.4821 | =AVERAGE(RXChartData!C:C) |
| 8 | D3 Factor | 0 | |
| 9 | D4 Factor | 2.114 | |
| 10 | | | |
| 11 | **R Chart Control Limits** | | |
| 12 | **Lower Control Limit** | 0.0000 | =B8 * B7 |
| 13 | **Center** | 3.4821 | =B7 |
| 14 | **Upper Control Limit** | 7.3613 | =B9 * B7 |
| 15 | | | |
| 16 | XBar Chart Intemediate Calculations | | |
| 17 | Average of Subgroup Averages | 9.4779 | =AVERAGE(RXChartData!B:B) |
| 18 | A2 Factor | 0.577 | |
| 19 | A2 Factor * RBar | 2.0092 | =B18 * B7 |
| 20 | | | |
| 21 | **XBar Chart Control Limits** | | |
| 22 | **Lower Control Limit** | 7.4687 | =B17- B19 |
| 23 | **Center** | 9.4779 | =B17 |
| 24 | **Upper Control Limit** | 11.4871 | =B17 + B19 |

**FIGURE E18.6** RXCalcs worksheet

## E18.6 Creating $R$ and $\bar{X}$ Charts: Overview

You create $R$ or $\bar{X}$ charts by using Excel charting features with your completed RXChartData and RXCalcs worksheets (see previous section).

## E18.6A Creating $R$ and $\bar{X}$ Charts (Excel 97–2003)

Open to your completed **RXChartData** worksheet. Select **Insert → Chart** and make the following entries in the Wizard Step dialog boxes:

**Wizard Step 1**   Click **XY (Scatter)** from the **Standard Types Chart type** box and then select the first choice in the bottom row of **Chart sub-type** choices, labeled as **Scatter with data points connected by lines**.

**Wizard Step 2**   Click the **Data Range** tab. To create an $R$ chart, enter the column A cell range of your time period data followed by the columns C through F cell range that contain the formulas as the **Data Range**. To create an $\bar{X}$ chart, enter the column A and B cell range followed by the columns G through I cell range that contain the formulas as the **Data Range**. Because you are entering a data range composed of two nonadjacent areas, you must separate the two cell ranges with a comma. For example, if your RXChartData worksheet contained entries in rows 2 through 29, you would enter **A1:A29,C1:F29** if creating an $R$ chart or **A1:B29,G1:I29** if creating an $\bar{X}$ chart. Click the **Columns** option after you have entered your Data Range.

**Wizard Step 3**   Click the **Titles** tab. Enter a title as the **Chart title** and enter appropriate values for the **Value (X) axis** and **Value (Y) axis** titles. Click, in turn, the **Axes**, **Gridlines**, **Legend**, and **Data Labels** tabs and use the formatting settings that are given in Section E2.3A on page 72.

At this point, the UCL, Center, and LCL lines of your $R$ or $\bar{X}$ chart will be missing labels and be incorrectly formatted. Use the Section E18.2A instructions for correcting $p$ chart format errors to correct your $R$ or $\bar{X}$ chart.

### E18.6B Creating $R$ and $\bar{X}$ Charts (Excel 2007)

Open to your completed **RXChartData** worksheet. To create an $R$ chart, select the column A and columns C through F data. To create an $\bar{X}$ chart, select the columns A and B and columns G through I data. To select these nonadjacent areas together, hold down the **Ctrl** key while selecting the ranges. Then select **Insert → Scatter → Scatter with Straight Lines and Markers**. Finish by relocating your chart to a chart sheet and customizing your chart, using the instructions in Section E.2.3B on page 73.

At this point, the UCL, Center, and LCL lines of your $R$ or $\bar{X}$ chart will be missing labels and be incorrectly formatted. Use the Section E18.2B instructions for correcting $p$ chart format errors to correct your $R$ or $\bar{X}$ chart.

# Appendix P18
## Using PHStat2 for Control Charts

## P18.1 Creating $p$ Charts

To create a $p$ chart, including computing the control limits for the chart, use **PHStat → Control Charts → p Chart**. This procedure creates a $p$ chart, and two supporting worksheets, from the data that you specify. If your sample/subgroup sizes do not vary, click **Size does not vary** and enter the sample/subgroup size in its box. If sample/subgroup sizes do vary, click **Size varies** and enter the cell range that lists the sample/subgroup sizes for each time period. The two supporting worksheets created are similar to the pChartData and pCalcs worksheets described in Section E18.1 on page 868.

## P18.2 Creating $c$ Charts

To create a $c$ chart, including computing the control limits for the chart, use **PHStat → Control Charts → c Chart**. This procedure creates a $c$ chart, and two supporting worksheets, from the data that you specify. The two supporting worksheets created are similar to the cChartData and cCalcs worksheets described in Section E18.3 on page 869.

## P18.3 Creating $R$ and $\bar{X}$ Charts

To create an $R$ or $\bar{X}$ chart, use **PHStat → Control Charts → R & XBar Charts**. This procedure creates an $R$ chart or an $\bar{X}$ chart and an $R$ chart, and two supporting worksheets, from the data that you specify. The two supporting worksheets created are similar to the RXChartData and RXCalcs worksheets described in Section E18.5 on page 870.

The procedure requires that your data include the range and mean for each time period. If you have only the raw data for each time period, you first need to compute the mean and range for each time period. If necessary, use the AVERAGE function to compute the mean. Use the MAX and MIN functions to determine the largest and smallest value and then subtract the smallest value from the largest value to compute the range.

# Appendix M18
## Using Minitab for Control Charts

### M18.1 Creating *p* Charts

To illustrate creating a *p* chart:

1. Open the **Hotel1.mtw** worksheet that contains the number of rooms not ready data of Table 18.1 on page 829.
2. Select **Stat → Control Charts → Attribute Charts → P**.

In the P Chart dialog box (see Figure M18.1):

3. Enter **'Not ready'** in the **Variables** box.

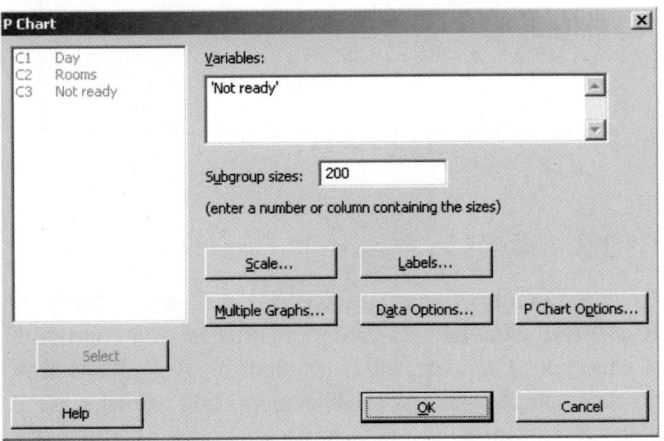

**FIGURE M18.1** Minitab P Chart dialog box

4. Enter **200** in the **Subgroup sizes** box (the subgroup sizes are equal).
5. Click **P Chart Options**.

In the P Chart - Options dialog box (see Figure M18.2):

6. Click the **Tests** tab.
7. Select **Perform selected tests for special causes** from the drop-down list.
8. Select **1 point > K standard deviations from the center line** and enter **3** in the **K** box.
9. Select **K points in a row on same side of center line** and enter **8** in the **K** box.
10. If there are points you want to omit when estimating the center line and control limits, click the **Estimate** tab and enter the points to omit. (There are no points to omit in this example so this box should be blank.)
11. Click **OK**.
12. Back in the P Chart dialog box, click **OK**.

During a single Minitab session, Minitab remembers certain control chart settings, such as points to omit. If you create more than one control chart during a single session, you may have to clear the contents of boxes such as the one that holds points to omit.

**FIGURE M18.2** Minitab P Chart - Options dialog box

## M18.2 Creating *c* Charts

To illustrate how to create a *c* chart:

1. Open the **Complaints.mtw** worksheet that contains the number of hotel complaints data of Table 18.4 on page 838.
2. Select **Stat → Control Charts → Attribute Charts → C**.

In the C Chart dialog box (see Figure M18.3):

3. Enter **Complaints** in the **Variables** box.
4. Click **C Chart Options**.

**FIGURE M18.3** Minitab C Chart dialog box

In the C Chart - Options dialog box (not shown, but similar to the P Chart - Options dialog box shown in Figure M18.2):

5. Click the **Tests** tab.
6. Select **Perform selected tests for special causes** from the drop-down list.

7. Select **1 point > K standard deviations from the center line** and enter **3** in the **K** box.
8. Select **K points in a row on same side of center line** and enter **8** in the **K** box.
9. If there are points you want to omit when estimating the center line and control limits, click the **Estimate** tab and enter the points to omit. (There are no points to omit in this example so this box should be blank.)
10. Click **OK**.
11. Back in the C Chart dialog box, click **OK**.

During a single Minitab session, Minitab remembers certain control chart settings, such as points to omit. If you create more than one control chart during a single session, you may have to clear or change the contents of certain boxes, such as the one that holds points to omit, as you create your chart.

## M18.3 Creating *R* and $\bar{X}$ Charts

To illustrate how to create *R* and $\bar{X}$ charts:

1. Open the **Hotel2.mtw** worksheet that contains the luggage delivery times data of Table 18.5 on page 842 in unstacked order.
2. Select **Stat → Control Charts → Variable Charts for Subgroups → Xbar-R**.

In the Xbar-R Chart dialog box (see Figure M18.4):

3. Select **Observations for a subgroup are in one row of columns** from the drop-down list because the data are unstacked. (If you were using stacked data, you would select **All observations for a chart are in one column** from the drop-down list.)
4. Enter **'Time 1'-'Time 5'** in the box below the drop-down list. (If you were using stacked data, enter the column that contains the stacked data.)
5. Click **Xbar-R Options**.

**FIGURE M18.4** Minitab Xbar-R Chart dialog box

In the Xbar-R Chart - Options dialog box (see Figure M18.5):

6.  Click the **Tests** tab.
7.  Select **Perform selected tests for special causes** from the drop-down list.
8.  Select **1 point > K standard deviations from the center line** and enter **3** in the **K** box.
9.  Select **K points in a row on same side of center line** and enter **8** in the **K** box.
10. Click the **Estimate** tab.
11. Click **Rbar**.
12. If there are points you want to omit when estimating the center line and control limits, enter the points to omit in the box below the drop-down list. (There are no points to omit in this example so this box should be blank.)
13. Click **OK**.
14. Back in the Xbar-R Chart dialog box, click **OK**.

During a single Minitab session, Minitab remembers certain control chart settings, such as points to omit. If you create more than one control chart during a single session, you may have to clear or change the contents of certain boxes, such as the one that holds points to omit, as you create your chart.

**FIGURE M18.5** Minitab Xbar-R Chart - Options dialog box

# CHAPTER
# NINETEEN

## DATA ANALYSIS OVERVIEW

**USING STATISTICS *IN* YOUR LIFE**

### 19.1 ANALYZING NUMERICAL VARIABLES

How to Describe the Characteristics of the
Numerical Variable

How to Draw Conclusions about the Population
Mean or Standard Deviation

How to Determine Whether the Mean or Standard
Deviation Differs Depending on the Group

How to Determine Which Factors Affect the Value
of a Variable

How to Predict the Value of a Variable Based on the
Value of Other Variables

How To Determine Whether the Values of a
Variable are Stable over Time

### 19.2 ANALYZING CATEGORICAL VARIABLES

How to Describe the Proportion of Items of Interest
in Each Category

How to Draw Conclusions about the Proportion of
Items of Interest

How to Determine Whether the Proportion of Items
of Interest Differs Depending on the Group

How to Predict the Proportion of Items of Interest
Based on the Value of Other Variables

How to Determine Whether the Proportion of Items
of Interest Is Stable over Time

## LEARNING OBJECTIVES

### In this chapter, you learn:

- The steps involved in choosing what statistical methods
  to use to conduct a data analysis

# USING STATISTICS *in* Your Life

You are a student who is completing an introductory business statistics course, that is, you are *you*. As you go on to other courses and new business situations, you find yourself needing to analyze data. What seemed straightforward when doing homework problems in statistics is now much harder—after all, when doing a problem in the multiple regression chapter, you "knew" that methods of multiple regression would be used somewhere in your answer. In your new context, you wonder if you should use multiple regression—or whether using simple linear regression would be better—or even if any type of regression would be appropriate. You also wonder if you should use several methods from more than one chapter to complete your analysis. The question for you becomes how can you apply the statistics you've learned to future situations that require data analysis?

A logical starting point is to review and summarize what you have learned from this book. Table 19.1 presents a summary of the contents of this book, arranged by data analysis task. This table adds specifics to the broad and general summary presented in "Coming Attractions" on page 5.

**TABLE 19.1**

Commonly Used Data Analysis Tasks Discussed in this Book

DESCRIBING A GROUP OR SEVERAL GROUPS

**For Numerical Variables:**
Ordered array, stem-and-leaf display, frequency distribution, relative frequency distribution, percentage distribution, cumulative percentage distribution, histogram, polygon, cumulative percentage polygon **(Sections 2.2 and 2.3)**
Boxplot **(Section 3.5)**
Normal probability plot **(Section 6.3)**
Mean, median, mode, quartiles, geometric mean, range, interquartile range, standard deviation, variance, coefficient of variation **(Sections 3.1, 3.2, and 3.5)**
Index numbers **(Section 16.8)**
**For Categorical Variables:**
Summary table, bar chart, pie chart, Pareto chart **(Section 2.1)**

MAKING INFERENCES ABOUT ONE GROUP

**For Numerical Variables:**
Confidence interval estimate of the mean **(Sections 8.1 and 8.2)**
*t* test for the mean **(Section 9.2)**
Chi-square test for a variance or standard deviation **(Section 12.5)**
**For Categorical Variables:**
Confidence interval estimate of the proportion **(Section 8.3)**
*Z* test of hypothesis for the proportion **(Section 9.4)**

COMPARING TWO GROUPS

**For Numerical Variables:**
Tests for the difference in the means of two independent populations **(Section 10.1)**
Wilcoxon rank sum test **(Section 12.6)**
*F* test for the difference between two variances **(Section 10.4)**
Paired *t* test **(Section 10.2)**
Wilcoxon signed ranks test **(Section 12.7)**
**For Categorical Variables:**
*Z* test for the difference between two proportions **(Section 10.3)**
Chi-square test for the difference between two proportions **(Section 12.1)**
McNemar test for two related samples **(Section 12.4)**

**TABLE 19.1**
(continued)

COMPARING MORE THAN TWO GROUPS

**For Numerical Variables:**
One-way analysis of variance **(Section 11.1)**
Kruskal-Wallis test **(Section 12.8)**
Randomized block design **(Section 11.2)**
Friedman test **(Section 12.9)**
Two-way analysis of variance **(Section 11.3)**

**For Categorical Variables:**
Chi-square test for differences among more than two proportions **(Section 12.2)**

ANALYZING THE RELATIONSHIP BETWEEN TWO VARIABLES

**For Numerical Variables:**
Scatter plot, time-series plot **(Section 2.5)**
Covariance, coefficient of correlation, $t$ test of correlation **(Sections 3.6 and 13.7)**
Simple linear regression **(Chapter 13)**
Time-series forecasting **(Chapter 16)**

**For Categorical Variables:**
Contingency table, side-by-side bar chart **(Section 2.4)**
Chi-Square Test of Independence **(Section 12.3)**

ANALYZING THE RELATIONSHIP BETWEEN TWO OR MORE VARIABLES

**For Numerical Dependent Variables:**
Multiple regression **(Chapters 14 and 15)**
**For Categorical Dependent Variables:**
Logistic regression **(Section 14.7)**

ANALYZING PROCESS DATA

**For Numerical Variables:**
$\bar{X}$ and $R$ control charts **(Section 18.5)**
**For Categorical Variables:**
$p$ chart **(Section 18.2)**

As Table 19.1 reflects, the first step in applying statistics is to determine the type of variable, numerical or categorical, you are analyzing. Remember that *numerical variables* have values that represent quantities. *Categorical variables* have values that can only be placed into categories, such as yes and no.

Once you know the variable type, you can select the statistical methods that are appropriate for that variable type. Doing so helps you avoid some serious errors such as taking the arithmetic mean of a categorical variable.

Even though knowing which methods belong with which type of variable is helpful, a list such as Table 19.1 does not help you get started in applying your statistical knowledge to a specific data analysis task. Use the rest of this chapter to learn the questions that will help guide you and allow you to constructively apply what you have learned in this book. Not surprisingly, the chapter contains separate sections for numerical and categorical variables.

## 19.1 ANALYZING NUMERICAL VARIABLES

When you analyze numerical variables, there are a number of data analysis tasks you can undertake. These tasks can be summarized by the list of questions in Exhibit 19.1. Each question is independent of the others and you can ask as many or as few questions as is appropriate for your analysis. How to go about answering these questions follows Exhibit 19.1.

EXHIBIT 19.1 QUESTIONS TO ASK WHEN ANALYZING NUMERICAL VARIABLES

When analyzing numerical variables, ask yourself, do you seek to:

- describe the characteristics of the variable (possibly broken down into several groups)?
- draw conclusions about the mean and standard deviation of the variable in a population?
- determine whether the mean and standard deviation of the variable differs depending on the group?
- determine which factors affect the value of a variable?
- predict the value of the variable based on the value of other variables?
- determine whether the values of the variable are stable over time?

## How to Describe the Characteristics of the Numerical Variable

You develop tables and charts and compute descriptive statistics to describe characteristics. Specifically, you can create a stem-and-leaf display, percentage distribution, histogram, polygon, boxplot, and normal probability plot (see Sections 2.2, 2.3, 3.5, and 6.3), and compute statistics such as the mean, median, mode, quartiles, range, interquartile range, standard deviation, variance, and coefficient of variation (see Sections 3.1, 3.2, and 3.5).

## How to Draw Conclusions about the Population Mean or Standard Deviation

You have several different choices and you can use any combination of these choices. To estimate the mean value of the variable in a population, you construct a confidence interval estimate of the mean (see Section 8.2). To determine whether the population mean is equal to a specific value, you conduct a $t$ test of hypothesis for the mean (see Section 9.2). To determine whether the population standard deviation or variance is equal to a specific value, you conduct a $\chi^2$ test of hypothesis for the standard deviation or variance (see Section 12.5).

## How to Determine Whether the Mean or Standard Deviation Differs Depending on the Group

When examining differences between groups, you first need to establish which categorical variable divides your data into groups. You then need to know whether this grouping variable divides your data in two groups, as a gender variable would divide your data into male and female groups, or whether the variable divides your data into more than two groups (such as the four parachute suppliers discussed in Section 11.1). Finally, you must ask if your data set contains independent groups or if your data set contains matched or repeated measurements.

### *If the Grouping Variable Defines Two Independent Groups and You Are Interested in Central Tendency*  Which hypothesis tests you use depends on the assumptions you make about your data.

If you assume that your numerical variable is normally distributed and that the variances are equal, you conduct a pooled $t$ test for the difference between the means (see Section 10.1). To evaluate the assumption of normality that this test includes, you can construct boxplots and normal probability plots for each group.

If you cannot assume that the variances are equal, you conduct a separate-variance $t$ test for the difference between the means (see Section 10.1). To test whether the variances are equal, assuming that the populations are normally distributed, you can conduct an $F$ test for the differences between the variances.

In either case, if you believe that your numerical variables are not normally distributed, you can do a Wilcoxon rank sum test (see Section 12.6) and compare these results to those of the $t$ test.

***If the Grouping Variable Defines Two Groups of Matched Samples or Repeated Measurements***   If you can assume that the paired differences are normally distributed, you conduct a paired $t$ test (see Section 10.2); otherwise you conduct a Wilcoxon signed ranks test (see Section 12.7).

***If the Grouping Variable Defines Two Independent Groups and You Are Interested in Variability***   If you can assume that your numerical variable is normally distributed, you conduct an $F$ test for the difference between two variances (see Section 10.4).

***If the Grouping Variable Defines More Than Two Independent Groups***   If you can assume that the values of the numerical variable are normally distributed, you conduct a one-way analysis of variance (see Section 11.1); otherwise you conduct a Kruskal-Wallis test (see Section 12.8).

***If the Grouping Variable Defines More Than Two Groups of Matched Samples or Repeated Measurements***   You have a design where the rows represent the blocks and the columns represent the levels of a factor. If you can assume that the values of the numerical variable are normally distributed, you conduct a randomized block design $F$-test (see Section 11.2); otherwise, you conduct a Friedman test (see Section 12.9).

### How to Determine Which Factors Affect the Value of a Variable

If there are two factors to be examined to determine their effect on the values of a variable, you develop a two-factor factorial design (see Section 11.3).

### How to Predict the Value of a Variable Based on the Value of Other Variables

You conduct least-squares regression analysis. If you have values over a period of time and you want to forecast the variable for future time periods, you can use moving averages, exponential smoothing, least-squares forecasting, and autoregressive modeling (see Chapter 16).

When predicting the values of a numerical dependent variable, which least-squares regression model you develop depends on the number of independent variables in your model. If there is only one independent variable being used to predict the numerical dependent variable of interest, you develop a simple linear regression model (see Chapter 13); otherwise, you develop a multiple regression model (see Chapters 14 and 15).

### How to Determine Whether the Values of a Variable Are Stable over Time

If you are studying a process and have collected data on the values of a numerical variable over a time period, you construct $R$ and $\overline{X}$ charts (see Section 18.5).

## 19.2   ANALYZING CATEGORICAL VARIABLES

As is the case with numerical variables, when you analyze categorical variables, there are several data analysis tasks you can undertake. These tasks can be summarized by the list of questions in Exhibit 19.2. Each question is independent of the others and you can ask as many or as few questions as is appropriate for your analysis. How to go about answering these questions follows Exhibit 19.2.

---

**EXHIBIT 19.2 QUESTIONS TO ASK WHEN ANALYZING CATEGORICAL VARIABLES**

When analyzing categorical variables, ask yourself, do you seek to:

- describe the proportion of items of interest in each category (possibly broken down into several groups)?
- draw conclusions about the proportion of items of interest in a population?
- determine whether the proportion of items of interest differs depending on the group?
- predict the proportion of items of interest based on the value of other variables?
- determine whether the proportion of items of interest is stable over time?

---

## How to Describe the Proportion of Items of Interest in Each Category

You create summary tables and use these charts: bar chart, pie chart, Pareto chart, or side-by-side bar chart (see Sections 2.1 and 2.4).

## How to Draw Conclusions about the Proportion of Items of Interest

You can do two different things. You can estimate the proportion of items of interest in a population by constructing a confidence interval estimate of the proportion (see Section 8.3). You can determine whether the population proportion is equal to a specific value by conducting a $Z$ test of hypothesis for the proportion (see Section 9.4).

## How to Determine Whether the Proportion of Items of Interest Differs Depending on the Group

When examining this difference, you first need to establish the number of categories associated with your categorical variable and the number of groups in your analysis. If your data contain two groups, you must also ask if your data contain independent groups or if your data contain matched samples or repeated measurements.

***For Two Categories and Two Independent Groups***    You conduct either the $Z$ test for the difference between two proportions (see Section 10.3) or the $\chi^2$ test for the difference between two proportions (see Section 12.1).

***For Two Categories and Two Groups of Matched or Repeated Measurements***
You conduct the McNemar test (see Section 12.4).

***For Two Categories and More Than Two Independent Groups***    You conduct a $\chi^2$ test for the difference among several proportions (see Section 12.2).

***For More Than Two Categories and More Than Two Groups***    You conduct a $\chi^2$ test of independence (see Section 12.3).

## How to Predict the Proportion of Items of Interest Based on the Value of Other Variables

You develop a logistic regression model (see Section 14.7).

## How to Determine Whether the Proportion of Items of Interest Is Stable over Time

If you are studying a process and have collected data over a time period, you can create the appropriate control chart. If you have collected the proportion of items of interest over a time period, you develop a $p$ chart (see Section 18.2).

# CHAPTER REVIEW PROBLEMS

**19.1** Problems with a telephone line that prevent a customer from receiving or making calls are upsetting to both the customer and the telephone company. The data contained in the file **Phone** represent samples of 20 problems reported to two different offices of a telephone company and the time to clear these problems, in minutes, from the customers' lines:

Central Office I Time to Clear Problems (minutes)

| | | | | | | | | | |
|---|---|---|---|---|---|---|---|---|---|
| 1.48 | 1.75 | 0.78 | 2.85 | 0.52 | 1.60 | 4.15 | 3.97 | 1.48 | 3.10 |
| 1.02 | 0.53 | 0.93 | 1.60 | 0.80 | 1.05 | 6.32 | 3.93 | 5.45 | 0.97 |

Central Office II Time to Clear Problems (minutes)

| | | | | | | | | | |
|---|---|---|---|---|---|---|---|---|---|
| 7.55 | 3.75 | 0.10 | 1.10 | 0.60 | 0.52 | 3.30 | 2.10 | 0.58 | 4.02 |
| 3.75 | 0.65 | 1.92 | 0.60 | 1.53 | 4.23 | 0.08 | 1.48 | 1.65 | 0.72 |

You want to reach conclusions about differences in the time to clear problems between the two central offices. Completely analyze the data.

**19.2** In many manufacturing processes, the term *work-in-process* (often abbreviated WIP) is used. At the BLK Publishing book manufacturing plants, WIP represents the time it takes for sheets from a press to be folded, gathered, sewn, tipped on end sheets, and bound together to form a book, and the book placed in a packing carton. The operational definition of the variable of interest, processing time, is the number of days (measured in hundredths) from when the sheets come off the press to when the book is placed in a packing carton. The data contained in the file **Wip** represent samples of 20 books at each of two production plants.

Plant A

| | | | | | | | | | |
|---|---|---|---|---|---|---|---|---|---|
| 5.62 | 5.29 | 16.25 | 10.92 | 11.46 | 21.62 | 8.45 | 8.58 | 5.41 | 11.42 |
| 11.62 | 7.29 | 7.50 | 7.96 | 4.42 | 10.50 | 7.58 | 9.29 | 7.54 | 8.92 |

Plant B

| | | | | | | | | | |
|---|---|---|---|---|---|---|---|---|---|
| 9.54 | 11.46 | 16.62 | 12.62 | 25.75 | 15.41 | 14.29 | 13.13 | 13.71 | 10.04 |
| 5.75 | 12.46 | 9.17 | 13.21 | 6.00 | 2.33 | 14.25 | 5.37 | 6.25 | 9.71 |

You want to reach conclusions about differences in the processing time between the two plants. Completely analyze the data.

**19.3** Many factors determine the attendance at Major League Baseball games. These factors can include when the game is played, the weather, the opponent, whether the team is having a good season, and whether a marketing promotion is held. Popular promotions during a recent season included the traditional hat days and poster days and the new craze, bobble-heads of star players (extracted from T. C. Boyd and T. C. Krehbiel, "An Analysis of the Effects of Specific Promotion Types on Attendance at Major League Baseball Games," *Mid-American Journal of*

*Business*, 2006, 21, pp. 21–32). The data file **Baseball** includes the following variables for a recent Major League Baseball season:

TEAM—Kansas City Royals, Philadelphia Phillies, Chicago Cubs, or Cincinnati Reds
ATTENDANCE—Paid attendance for the game
TEMP—High temperature for the day
WIN%—Team's winning percentage at the time of the game
OPWIN%—Opponent team's winning percentage at the time of the game
WEEKEND—1 if game played on Friday, Saturday, or Sunday; 0 otherwise
PROMOTION—1 if a promotion was held; 0 if no promotion was held

You want to predict attendance and determine the factors that influence attendance. Completely analyze the data for the Kansas City Royals.

**19.4** Repeat Problem 19.3 for the Philadelphia Phillies.

**19.5** Repeat Problem 19.3 for the Chicago Cubs.

**19.6** Repeat Problem 19.3 for the Cincinnati Reds.

**19.7** The economics of baseball has caused a great deal of controversy, with owners arguing that they are losing money, players arguing that owners are making money, and fans complaining about how expensive it is to attend a game and watch games on cable television. In addition to data related to team statistics for a recent season, the file **BB2001** contains team-by-team statistics on ticket prices; the fan cost index; regular-season gate receipts; local television, radio, and cable receipts; all other operating revenue; player compensation and benefits; national and other local expenses; and income from baseball operations along with team performance statistics including the number of wins.

You want to examine each of the non-team performance statistics and also be able to predict the number of wins. Write a report that summarizes your results.

**19.8** The data file **Homes** contains information on all the single-family houses sold in a small city in the Midwestern United States for one year. The variables included are:

Price—Selling price of home, in dollars
Location—Rating of the location from 1 to 5, with 1 the worst and 5 the best
Condition—Rating of the condition of the home from 1 to 5, with 1 the worst and 5 the best
Bedrooms—Number of bedrooms in the home
Bathrooms—Number of bathrooms in the home
Other Rooms—Number of rooms in the home other than bedrooms and bathrooms

You want to be able to predict the selling price of the homes. Completely analyze the data.

**19.9** Zagat's publishes restaurant ratings for various locations in the United States. The data file `Restaurants2` contains the Zagat rating for food, decor, service, and the price per person for a sample of 50 restaurants located in an urban area and 50 restaurants located in a suburban area.

Source: *Extracted from* Zagat Survey 2007 New York City Restaurants *and* Zagat Survey 2007–2008, Long Island Restaurants.

You want to study differences in the cost of a meal between the urban and suburban areas and be able to predict the cost of a meal. Completely analyze the data.

*Problems 19.10–19.19 pertain to the Whitney Gourmet Cat Food Company, a fictitious cat food manufacturing company.*

## Background

It has been estimated by research organizations that there are more than 70 million cats kept as pets in homes in the United States. The market for pet food is an extremely large and lucrative one (more than $15 billion) that has attracted corporations such as Heinz, Nestle, Mars, and Ralston Purina, along with a multitude of small companies that attempt to occupy a market niche with specialty products. Often these specialty products are sold only in pet food stores and veterinarian's offices, not in supermarkets. In recent years changing lifestyles and attitudes has led to an increasing demand for a higher quality food product that will be eaten with greater regularity and interest by the family cat who often is the only companion for the individual with whom it lives.

Several years ago, the founder of the Whitney Gourmet Cat Food Company, Livia Joy, began experimenting with the preparation of homemade cat food for her cat, Whitney (for whom the company is named). Her idea was based on the belief that alternate types of meat and seafood, along with a chunkier formulation with less fillers, would lead to a higher level of satisfaction (and less finicky behavior) by cats, without sacrificing nutritional standards. Within a short period of time, her cottage industry was ready to become commercial, and a processing plant was built and used for producing canned cat food. Currently, two varieties of food are manufactured, one that contains kidney parts, and the other that contains shrimp. In the five years that the company has been operating commercially, sales have risen rapidly, particularly in the past three years, when the number of sales outlets has been greatly expanded. However, with the rapid expansion of the company came the realization that it is now too large to be managed as a cottage industry. Senior management of the company under the leadership of Ms. Joy is increasingly conscious of the need to increase the efficiency of operations and strive for ever-improving quality levels.

**19.10** A task force consisting of corporate-level officers and department heads was formed to consider how to go about the quality improvement effort. There was agreement that the first step was the development of a mission statement for the company that could succinctly communicate its mission to both customers and employees.

Once the mission statement was developed, the task force turned to a discussion of which areas of operations should be examined for improvement opportunities. After much brainstorming and discussion, the task force decided that one critical area for improvement was the number of cans that were deemed to be nonconforming for any one of a variety of reasons.

As Al Brenner, the production manager, and a team of other managers brainstormed about how to go about the quality improvement process, the group came to the realization that, in the rapid expansion that had taken place in the past three years, perhaps not enough attention had been paid to properly training workers for their jobs. The company was running two shifts of workers for the past year in an effort to keep up with demand for the product and had several hundred people working on various aspects of the production and canning process. One of the aspects that concerned the group was whether or not the three inspectors who worked on each shift were consistently applying the current definition for what was to be considered as a nonconforming can of cat food. The team decided that an evaluation of the final process of inspection of cans needed to be carried out.

Al Brenner, the production manager, selected twelve cans that, in his opinion, ranged from clearly conforming, to marginal, to nonconforming for one of several reasons. The cans were tagged with an identification number and placed on tables set up in a conference room. The three inspectors from each of the two shifts were instructed to evaluate the cans in the same way that they did on their job every day. Inspection test results are summarized in the following table.

*Inspection Test Results for Twelve Cans of Cat Food*

| | Inspector | | | | | |
| | Shift 1 | | | Shift 2 | | |
| Classification | 1 | 2 | 3 | 4 | 5 | 6 |
|---|---|---|---|---|---|---|
| **Nonconforming** | 4 | 4 | 4 | 4 | 4 | 4 |
| **Conforming** | 8 | 8 | 8 | 8 | 8 | 8 |

**a.** What conclusions about the consistency of the inspectors can you reach?

**b.** What other information concerning the inspection test results would be useful to obtain?

**19.11** The following table represents a summary of the inspection decisions for the twelve cans made by each of the six inspectors.

### Inspection Test Results for 12 Cans of Cat Food

| Can | Inspector | Conforming | Non-conforming | Reason |
|-----|-----------|------------|----------------|--------|
| 1 | 1 | x | | |
| | 2 | x | | |
| | 3 | x | | |
| | 4 | | x | Blemish on top of can |
| | 5 | | x | Blemish on top of can |
| | 6 | x | | |
| 2 | Accepted by all | | | |
| 3* | 1 | | x | Pull tab missing |
| | 2 | | x | Pull tab missing |
| | 3 | | x | Pull tab missing |
| | 4 | | x | Pull tab missing |
| | 5 | | x | Pull tab missing |
| | 6 | | x | Pull tab missing |
| 4* | Accepted by all | | | |
| 5* | 1 | x | | |
| | 2 | | x | Crack in top of can |
| | 3 | | x | Crack in top of can |
| | 4 | x | | |
| | 5 | x | | |
| | 6 | | x | Improper pull tab location |
| 6* | 1 | | x | Surface defect on side of can |
| | 2 | x | | |
| | 3 | | x | Surface defect on side of can |
| | 4 | | x | Surface defect on side of can |
| | 5 | x | | |
| | 6 | x | | |
| 7 | Accepted by all | | | |
| 8 | Accepted by all | | | |
| 9* | 1 | | x | Crack in side of can |
| | 2 | | x | Crack in side of can |
| | 3 | x | | |
| | 4 | x | | |
| | 5 | x | | |
| | 6 | | x | Crack in side of can |

| Can | Inspector | Conforming | Non-conforming | Reason |
|-----|-----------|------------|----------------|--------|
| 10 | 1 | x | | |
| | 2 | | x | Improper pull tab location |
| | 3 | x | | |
| | 4 | x | | |
| | 5 | | x | Surface defect on side of can |
| | 6 | x | | |
| 11* | 1 | | x | Crack in top of can |
| | 2 | x | | |
| | 3 | | x | Crack in top of can |
| | 4 | | x | Blemish on top of can |
| | 5 | | x | Crack in top of can |
| | 6 | | x | Crack in top of can |
| 12 | Accepted by all | | | |

* Classified as nonconforming by production manager

What conclusions about the inspection process can you reach after analyzing the data in the table?

**19.12** One of the concerns of the production team relates to the weight of the cans of cat food. Research indicates that there will be increasing competition in the gourmet cat food market as larger companies begin to attack the segment of the market that smaller companies, such as Whitney, have gained in the past several years. There is also evidence that consumers seem to make purchasing decisions on the basis of price, quality, and consistency of the product. One of the aspects of consistency appears to be the perception of the fill level of the can when it is opened. This is primarily a function of the amount of food that the extruding machine places in the can and is measured by the weight of the filled can. Legal requirements for a can labeled as 3 ounces allow for a fill of no less than 2.95 ounces, whereas a fill of more than 3.10 ounces may result in overpacking of the can and spillage when the can is opened.

Each week 100 cans of each of the two products, kidney and shrimp, are randomly selected for evaluation by the State Department of Weights and Measures. The company traditionally has selected 50 cans of each type from each of the two shifts of workers. The results for the latest week are summarized in the following table and stored in the file Whitney1.

### Weight (in ounces) of Canned Cat Food

**Kidney**

**Shift 1**

| | | | | | | | | | |
|---|---|---|---|---|---|---|---|---|---|
| 3.0298 | 2.9912 | 2.9867 | 3.0558 | 3.0220 | 2.9708 | 2.9989 | 3.0120 | 3.0147 | 3.0057 |
| 3.0064 | 3.0118 | 3.0022 | 2.9882 | 3.0230 | 3.0159 | 3.0259 | 3.0054 | 3.0108 | 2.9930 |
| 3.0418 | 3.0353 | 3.0099 | 3.0398 | 3.0193 | 3.0094 | 3.0019 | 3.0322 | 3.0277 | 2.9953 |
| 3.0199 | 3.0256 | 2.9956 | 2.9940 | 2.9929 | 3.0127 | 3.0197 | 2.9911 | 2.9974 | 3.0196 |
| 3.0057 | 3.0514 | 3.0233 | 3.0262 | 3.0264 | 2.9920 | 3.0393 | 3.0075 | 2.9968 | 2.9914 |

**Shift 2**

| | | | | | | | | | |
|---|---|---|---|---|---|---|---|---|---|
| 3.0457 | 3.0620 | 2.9888 | 3.0665 | 3.0156 | 3.0385 | 3.0458 | 3.0778 | 3.0652 | 3.0038 |
| 3.0160 | 3.0175 | 3.1002 | 3.0335 | 3.0535 | 3.0469 | 3.0586 | 3.0380 | 3.0378 | 3.0328 |
| 2.9792 | 3.0468 | 3.0396 | 3.0460 | 3.0590 | 3.0608 | 3.0180 | 3.0174 | 3.0231 | 3.0399 |
| 3.0428 | 3.0556 | 3.0045 | 3.0475 | 3.0280 | 3.0667 | 3.0308 | 3.0732 | 3.0497 | 3.0121 |
| 3.0690 | 3.0175 | 3.0353 | 3.0176 | 3.0530 | 3.0641 | 3.0628 | 3.0431 | 3.0283 | 3.0412 |

**Shrimp**

**Shift 1**

| | | | | | | | | | |
|---|---|---|---|---|---|---|---|---|---|
| 3.0189 | 2.9663 | 3.0120 | 2.9931 | 3.0394 | 3.0268 | 2.9932 | 2.9608 | 3.0258 | 3.0409 |
| 2.9900 | 3.0189 | 3.0282 | 3.0369 | 2.9816 | 3.0395 | 2.9723 | 2.9970 | 3.0826 | 3.0070 |
| 2.9571 | 2.9745 | 3.0167 | 3.0099 | 3.0386 | 2.9338 | 3.0053 | 3.0359 | 2.9682 | 3.0023 |
| 3.0447 | 3.0799 | 2.9774 | 2.9998 | 3.0147 | 3.0430 | 2.9918 | 3.0057 | 2.9861 | 2.9851 |
| 2.9970 | 2.9645 | 3.0336 | 3.0221 | 2.9234 | 3.0345 | 3.0509 | 2.9809 | 3.0345 | 2.9641 |

**Shift 2**

| | | | | | | | | | |
|---|---|---|---|---|---|---|---|---|---|
| 2.9800 | 3.0092 | 2.9781 | 3.0547 | 3.0384 | 3.0193 | 3.0718 | 2.9220 | 3.0487 | 3.0228 |
| 2.9999 | 3.0438 | 3.0122 | 3.0934 | 2.9865 | 3.0171 | 3.0315 | 3.0086 | 2.9743 | 3.0403 |
| 3.0186 | 2.9799 | 3.0264 | 3.0129 | 3.0060 | 3.0075 | 2.9357 | 3.0260 | 3.0409 | 2.9782 |
| 3.0207 | 3.0204 | 3.0119 | 3.0495 | 3.0624 | 3.0333 | 3.0329 | 3.0212 | 2.9497 | 2.9710 |
| 3.0743 | 3.0474 | 3.0878 | 3.0346 | 2.9864 | 2.9916 | 3.0696 | 2.9933 | 3.0224 | 2.9840 |

You want to study any differences between shifts and between kidney and shrimp cat food. Completely analyze the data.

**19.13** Once the team focusing on the nonconforming cans of cat food realized that different inspectors were operationally defining nonconformance in ways that were not consistent with each other or with the criteria used by the production manager, additional training had to be provided to develop operational definitions that were understood and could be followed by all the inspectors. Data collected for the first month after the training was conducted indicated the percentage of the nonconformances that were due to various reasons. The results are summarized as follows:

### Summary Table of Reasons for Nonconformance in Canned Cat Food

| Reason | Percentage of Nonconformances |
|---|---|
| Blemish on top of can | 16 |
| Crack in side of can | 9 |
| Crack in top of can | 35 |
| Improper pull tab location | 14 |
| Pull tab missing | 15 |
| Surface defect on side of can | 8 |
| Others | 3 |

a. Write a report to management concerning the percentage of different types of nonconformances in canned cat food.

b. At this stage of the analysis, what other information concerning the different types of nonconformances would be useful to obtain?

**19.14** As the team studying the nonconforming cans examined the data of the table in Problem 19.13, they realized that the data did not allow them to compare the types of nonconformances produced by each of the two shifts. The group decided that it would be useful to obtain separate data concerning nonconformances for each of the two shifts. These data are summarized in the following table.

### Summary Table of Reasons for Nonconformance in Canned Cat Food for the Two Shifts

| Reason | Shift 1 Percentage of Nonconformances | Shift 2 Percentage of Nonconformances |
|---|---|---|
| Blemish on top of can | 14 | 18 |
| Crack in side of can | 11 | 6 |
| Crack in top of can | 42 | 30 |
| Improper pull tab location | 10 | 16 |
| Pull tab missing | 8 | 20 |
| Surface defect on side of can | 10 | 7 |
| Others | 5 | 3 |

Write a report to management concerning the percentage of different types of nonconformances in canned cat food for the two shifts.

**19.15** As the team studying ways of improving the nonconformance in the canned cat food began to investigate the current process, they found that, in some instances, production needed expensive overtime costs to meet the requirements requested by the market forecasting team. They also realized that although data had been collected concerning the level of production and the rate of nonconformance for an entire day, no data were available about the stability and magnitude of the rate of nonconformance and the production volume throughout the day. Their previous study of the process indicated that output could be nonconforming for a variety of reasons. The reasons broke down into two categories, those quality characteristics due to the can, and those characteristics concerning the fill weight of the container. Because these nonconformities stem from different sets of underlying causes, they decided to study them separately. The group assigned to study and reduce the nonconformities due to the can decided that at 15-minute intervals during each shift, a sample of 100 cans would be selected and the total number cans would be determined. In addition, the number of nonconforming cans produced during this time period would be recorded. The results for a single day's production of kidney cat food and a single day's production of shrimp cat food are provided in the following table and are stored in the file `Whitney2`.

*Number of Nonconforming Cans Obtained from Subgroups of 100 Cans of Kidney and Shrimp Cat Food and Production Volume for 15-Minute Time Periods*

**Shift 1—Kidney**

| Time Interval | Number of Nonconforming Cans | Production Volume |
|---|---|---|
| 1 | 4 | 852 |
| 2 | 3 | 826 |
| 3 | 6 | 828 |
| 4 | 5 | 838 |
| 5 | 6 | 844 |
| 6 | 7 | 804 |
| 7 | 6 | 830 |
| 8 | 8 | 782 |
| 9 | 8 | 774 |
| 10 | 7 | 796 |
| 11 | 9 | 768 |
| 12 | 10 | 744 |
| 13 | 10 | 750 |
| 14 | 11 | 732 |
| 15 | 9 | 766 |
| 16 | 12 | 724 |
| 17 | 11 | 716 |
| 18 | 11 | 736 |
| 19 | 13 | 718 |
| 20 | 13 | 714 |

**Shift 1—Kidney**

| Time Interval | Number of Nonconforming Cans | Production Volume |
|---|---|---|
| 21 | 14 | 698 |
| 22 | 12 | 720 |
| 23 | 13 | 714 |
| 24 | 15 | 688 |
| 25 | 14 | 690 |
| 26 | 17 | 672 |
| 27 | 16 | 680 |
| 28 | 15 | 700 |
| 29 | 15 | 706 |
| 30 | 14 | 698 |

**Shift 2—Kidney**

| Time Interval | Number of Nonconforming Cans | Production Volume |
|---|---|---|
| 1 | 6 | 830 |
| 2 | 6 | 836 |
| 3 | 8 | 794 |
| 4 | 6 | 820 |
| 5 | 9 | 776 |
| 6 | 10 | 758 |
| 7 | 9 | 774 |
| 8 | 11 | 742 |
| 9 | 12 | 732 |
| 10 | 11 | 746 |
| 11 | 11 | 728 |
| 12 | 13 | 714 |
| 13 | 14 | 700 |
| 14 | 13 | 702 |
| 15 | 12 | 726 |
| 16 | 15 | 684 |
| 17 | 14 | 696 |
| 18 | 13 | 716 |
| 19 | 16 | 678 |
| 20 | 16 | 674 |
| 21 | 18 | 662 |
| 22 | 15 | 680 |
| 23 | 16 | 684 |
| 24 | 17 | 668 |
| 25 | 17 | 660 |
| 26 | 19 | 652 |
| 27 | 18 | 650 |
| 28 | 17 | 650 |
| 29 | 16 | 676 |
| 30 | 15 | 678 |

*(continued)*

## Shift 1—Shrimp

| Time Interval | Number of Nonconforming Cans | Production Volume |
|---|---|---|
| 1 | 4 | 882 |
| 2 | 3 | 900 |
| 3 | 6 | 848 |
| 4 | 5 | 868 |
| 5 | 6 | 844 |
| 6 | 7 | 824 |
| 7 | 6 | 830 |
| 8 | 8 | 782 |
| 9 | 6 | 834 |
| 10 | 7 | 816 |
| 11 | 6 | 818 |
| 12 | 5 | 844 |
| 13 | 6 | 810 |
| 14 | 4 | 862 |
| 15 | 7 | 806 |
| 16 | 8 | 784 |
| 17 | 6 | 816 |
| 18 | 7 | 796 |
| 19 | 7 | 818 |
| 20 | 5 | 834 |
| 21 | 6 | 798 |
| 22 | 4 | 840 |
| 23 | 3 | 854 |
| 24 | 6 | 788 |
| 25 | 5 | 790 |
| 26 | 7 | 792 |
| 27 | 7 | 780 |
| 28 | 6 | 820 |
| 29 | 5 | 826 |
| 30 | 5 | 828 |

## Shift 2—Shrimp

| Time Interval | Number of Nonconforming Cans | Production Volume |
|---|---|---|
| 1 | 6 | 820 |
| 2 | 5 | 846 |
| 3 | 7 | 808 |
| 4 | 8 | 798 |
| 5 | 9 | 794 |
| 6 | 9 | 804 |
| 7 | 7 | 790 |
| 8 | 10 | 742 |
| 9 | 9 | 774 |
| 10 | 10 | 756 |
| 11 | 8 | 778 |
| 12 | 7 | 794 |
| 13 | 7 | 790 |
| 14 | 8 | 762 |

## Shift 2—Shrimp

| Time Interval | Number of Nonconforming Cans | Production Volume |
|---|---|---|
| 15 | 6 | 826 |
| 16 | 8 | 774 |
| 17 | 6 | 816 |
| 18 | 7 | 776 |
| 19 | 8 | 758 |
| 20 | 10 | 714 |
| 21 | 9 | 758 |
| 22 | 8 | 770 |
| 23 | 8 | 764 |
| 24 | 10 | 708 |
| 25 | 9 | 750 |
| 26 | 6 | 822 |
| 27 | 8 | 780 |
| 28 | 9 | 760 |
| 29 | 7 | 786 |
| 30 | 10 | 748 |

You want to study the process of producing cans of cat food for the two shifts and the two types of food. Completely analyze the data.

**19.16** The production team investigating nonconformities due to the weight of the cans determined that as was the case with the group studying nonconformance due to the cans, data had been collected over a daily and weekly time period, but no data were available about the stability of the canned weight throughout a specific time period, such as a day. After a thorough discussion, the group determined that at 15-minute intervals during each shift, a subgroup of five cans would be selected, and the contents of the selected cans would be weighed. The results for a single day's production of kidney cat food and a single day's production of shrimp cat food are provided in the following table and stored in the file Whitney3.

*Weight (in ounces) of Kidney and Shrimp Canned Cat Food Obtained from Subgroups of Size 5 Selected at Consecutive 15-Minute Intervals*

### Shift 1—Kidney

| Time | Weight | | | | |
|---|---|---|---|---|---|
| 1 | 3.0469 | 3.0555 | 3.0627 | 3.0412 | 3.0473 |
| 2 | 2.9739 | 3.0609 | 3.0023 | 2.9813 | 3.0430 |
| 3 | 3.0467 | 3.0465 | 3.0296 | 3.0701 | 2.9850 |
| 4 | 3.0135 | 3.0308 | 2.9942 | 2.9724 | 3.0398 |
| 5 | 3.0532 | 3.0098 | 2.9927 | 3.0323 | 2.9549 |
| 6 | 3.0109 | 3.0142 | 3.0069 | 3.0436 | 3.0196 |
| 7 | 3.0232 | 3.0334 | 3.0352 | 3.0476 | 3.0140 |

## Shift 1—Kidney

| Time | Weight | | | | |
|------|--------|--------|--------|--------|--------|
| 8  | 3.0077 | 2.9686 | 3.0354 | 2.9890 | 3.0119 |
| 9  | 3.0370 | 3.0111 | 3.0316 | 3.0774 | 3.0161 |
| 10 | 3.0188 | 3.0339 | 2.9885 | 3.0423 | 3.0182 |
| 11 | 3.0234 | 3.0749 | 3.0451 | 3.0165 | 3.0283 |
| 12 | 3.0432 | 3.0652 | 3.0331 | 3.0412 | 3.0218 |
| 13 | 3.0568 | 3.0373 | 3.0580 | 3.0918 | 3.0156 |
| 14 | 3.0572 | 3.0795 | 3.0104 | 2.9942 | 3.0604 |
| 15 | 3.0703 | 3.0506 | 3.0102 | 3.0335 | 3.0248 |
| 16 | 3.0753 | 3.0023 | 3.0193 | 3.0680 | 3.0674 |
| 17 | 3.0113 | 3.0469 | 3.0592 | 3.0604 | 3.0258 |
| 18 | 3.0646 | 3.0459 | 3.0532 | 3.0347 | 2.9950 |
| 19 | 3.0322 | 3.0289 | 3.0165 | 3.0494 | 3.0399 |
| 20 | 3.0240 | 3.0216 | 3.0480 | 3.0590 | 3.0135 |
| 21 | 3.0469 | 3.0558 | 3.0627 | 3.0412 | 3.0473 |
| 22 | 3.0545 | 3.0627 | 3.0231 | 3.0503 | 3.0498 |
| 23 | 3.0844 | 3.0368 | 3.0512 | 3.0263 | 3.0687 |
| 24 | 3.0726 | 3.0919 | 3.0237 | 3.0381 | 3.0495 |
| 25 | 3.0423 | 3.0515 | 3.0548 | 3.0437 | 3.0890 |
| 26 | 3.0562 | 3.0544 | 3.0579 | 3.0127 | 3.0768 |
| 27 | 3.0162 | 3.0411 | 3.0971 | 3.0682 | 3.0555 |
| 28 | 3.0327 | 3.0430 | 3.0372 | 3.0701 | 3.0371 |
| 29 | 3.0497 | 3.0746 | 3.0541 | 3.0664 | 3.0781 |
| 30 | 3.0881 | 3.0459 | 3.0524 | 3.0143 | 3.0713 |

## Shift 2—Kidney

| Time | Weight | | | | |
|------|--------|--------|--------|--------|--------|
| 24 | 3.0090 | 3.1295 | 3.1638 | 3.0875 | 3.0243 |
| 25 | 3.1273 | 3.1491 | 2.9957 | 3.0528 | 2.9669 |
| 26 | 3.0800 | 3.0920 | 3.0297 | 3.1517 | 3.0362 |
| 27 | 3.0091 | 3.0089 | 3.0452 | 3.1076 | 2.9953 |
| 28 | 3.1298 | 3.0405 | 3.1641 | 3.0937 | 3.0430 |
| 29 | 3.0209 | 3.0163 | 3.0362 | 3.0524 | 3.0794 |
| 30 | 3.1185 | 3.0889 | 3.1126 | 3.0671 | 3.0249 |

## Shift 1—Shrimp

| Time | Weight | | | | |
|------|--------|--------|--------|--------|--------|
| 1  | 2.9878 | 3.0296 | 3.0113 | 3.0207 | 3.0112 |
| 2  | 3.0199 | 3.0242 | 3.0238 | 3.0032 | 3.0573 |
| 3  | 2.9754 | 3.0407 | 2.9537 | 2.9664 | 2.9834 |
| 4  | 2.9952 | 2.9972 | 3.0407 | 3.0277 | 3.0082 |
| 5  | 3.0543 | 3.0307 | 2.9892 | 2.9997 | 3.0231 |
| 6  | 3.0680 | 2.9925 | 3.0420 | 2.9838 | 3.0567 |
| 7  | 2.9901 | 3.0162 | 3.0126 | 3.0115 | 2.9716 |
| 8  | 2.9917 | 2.9687 | 3.0240 | 3.0046 | 3.0267 |
| 9  | 2.9757 | 3.0162 | 3.0066 | 2.9963 | 2.9894 |
| 10 | 3.0246 | 2.9813 | 3.0061 | 3.0145 | 3.0023 |
| 11 | 3.0448 | 2.9462 | 3.0230 | 3.0219 | 2.9974 |
| 12 | 2.9951 | 3.0144 | 3.0259 | 2.9543 | 2.9777 |
| 13 | 3.0193 | 3.0429 | 3.0016 | 3.0927 | 3.0185 |
| 14 | 2.9809 | 2.9886 | 2.9869 | 3.0047 | 3.0296 |
| 15 | 3.0546 | 3.0202 | 2.9776 | 3.0399 | 2.9801 |
| 16 | 3.0273 | 3.0342 | 2.9936 | 3.0402 | 3.0017 |
| 17 | 3.0385 | 3.0144 | 3.0171 | 3.0089 | 3.0021 |
| 18 | 2.9975 | 3.0550 | 2.9953 | 2.9857 | 3.0092 |
| 19 | 3.0317 | 3.0368 | 3.0033 | 3.0347 | 3.0228 |
| 20 | 3.0455 | 3.0035 | 3.0139 | 2.9934 | 3.0000 |
| 21 | 3.0081 | 2.9607 | 3.0578 | 3.0015 | 3.0489 |
| 22 | 2.9984 | 3.0017 | 3.0224 | 2.9441 | 3.0002 |
| 23 | 3.0418 | 2.9935 | 2.9875 | 3.0376 | 3.0186 |
| 24 | 2.9712 | 2.9818 | 2.9967 | 2.9791 | 2.9870 |
| 25 | 3.0345 | 2.9846 | 3.0298 | 3.0160 | 3.0485 |
| 26 | 3.0536 | 3.0497 | 2.9997 | 3.0583 | 3.0445 |
| 27 | 3.0193 | 3.0102 | 3.0338 | 3.1054 | 3.0382 |
| 28 | 2.9675 | 3.0002 | 3.0000 | 3.0267 | 2.9990 |
| 29 | 3.0516 | 2.9836 | 3.0057 | 3.0442 | 2.9892 |
| 30 | 3.0014 | 3.0425 | 3.0371 | 3.0441 | 3.0013 |

## Shift 2—Kidney

| Time | Weight | | | | |
|------|--------|--------|--------|--------|--------|
| 1  | 3.0375 | 2.9948 | 3.0579 | 3.0681 | 3.0066 |
| 2  | 3.0171 | 3.0543 | 3.0276 | 3.0407 | 3.0658 |
| 3  | 3.0396 | 3.0166 | 3.0494 | 3.0223 | 3.0599 |
| 4  | 3.0382 | 3.0553 | 3.0537 | 3.0464 | 3.0257 |
| 5  | 3.0133 | 3.0105 | 3.0284 | 3.0313 | 3.0434 |
| 6  | 2.9633 | 3.0168 | 3.0251 | 3.0299 | 3.0163 |
| 7  | 3.0307 | 3.0535 | 3.0420 | 3.0626 | 3.0681 |
| 8  | 3.0121 | 2.9772 | 3.0587 | 3.0332 | 2.9906 |
| 9  | 3.0064 | 3.0190 | 3.0049 | 3.0744 | 3.0433 |
| 10 | 3.0095 | 2.9479 | 3.0197 | 3.0117 | 3.0388 |
| 11 | 3.0323 | 3.1076 | 3.0630 | 3.0472 | 3.0545 |
| 12 | 3.0666 | 3.0303 | 3.0239 | 2.9633 | 3.0056 |
| 13 | 3.0286 | 3.0994 | 3.0471 | 3.0256 | 3.1019 |
| 14 | 2.9962 | 3.0417 | 3.0570 | 3.0883 | 3.0763 |
| 15 | 2.9988 | 3.0273 | 3.0319 | 3.0853 | 3.0871 |
| 16 | 3.0525 | 3.0772 | 3.0880 | 3.0404 | 3.0547 |
| 17 | 3.0278 | 3.1090 | 3.0493 | 2.9609 | 3.0592 |
| 18 | 3.0443 | 3.0117 | 3.0575 | 3.0198 | 3.0799 |
| 19 | 3.0711 | 3.1070 | 3.0213 | 3.0457 | 3.0626 |
| 20 | 3.0778 | 3.0573 | 3.0861 | 3.0738 | 3.0611 |
| 21 | 3.0494 | 2.9637 | 3.0941 | 3.0877 | 3.0800 |
| 22 | 2.9855 | 3.0611 | 3.0227 | 3.0981 | 3.0479 |
| 23 | 3.0908 | 3.0716 | 3.1603 | 3.0862 | 3.1155 |

## Shift 2—Shrimp

| Time | Weight | | | | |
|------|--------|--------|--------|--------|--------|
| 1 | 3.0252 | 2.9964 | 3.0046 | 3.0341 | 3.0118 |
| 2 | 3.0276 | 3.0486 | 3.0267 | 3.0241 | 3.0485 |
| 3 | 3.0426 | 3.0110 | 2.9867 | 2.9866 | 2.9962 |
| 4 | 3.0478 | 2.9996 | 3.0388 | 3.0619 | 3.0524 |
| 5 | 3.0337 | 3.0199 | 2.9919 | 3.0126 | 3.0528 |

### Shift 2—Shrimp

| Time | Weight | | | | |
|------|--------|--------|--------|--------|--------|
| 6  | 3.0242 | 3.0858 | 3.0236 | 3.0545 | 3.0466 |
| 7  | 3.0062 | 2.9936 | 3.0508 | 3.0502 | 3.0160 |
| 8  | 3.0125 | 3.0367 | 3.0086 | 3.0227 | 3.0531 |
| 9  | 3.0307 | 3.0621 | 3.0114 | 3.0181 | 3.0080 |
| 10 | 3.0199 | 3.0273 | 3.0194 | 3.0080 | 2.9785 |
| 11 | 3.0837 | 3.0074 | 2.9401 | 3.0058 | 3.0568 |
| 12 | 2.9749 | 3.0086 | 3.0347 | 3.0316 | 3.0769 |
| 13 | 3.0136 | 3.0319 | 3.0238 | 2.9691 | 3.0530 |
| 14 | 3.0313 | 2.9979 | 3.0482 | 3.0168 | 3.0081 |
| 15 | 2.9661 | 3.0583 | 3.0020 | 3.0580 | 3.0127 |
| 16 | 2.9884 | 3.0071 | 2.9732 | 3.0670 | 3.1069 |
| 17 | 3.0564 | 3.0531 | 2.9720 | 3.0179 | 3.0326 |
| 18 | 3.0332 | 3.0263 | 3.0088 | 3.0557 | 3.0382 |
| 19 | 3.0341 | 3.0200 | 3.0298 | 3.0987 | 3.0345 |
| 20 | 2.9899 | 3.0843 | 2.9976 | 2.0585 | 2.9181 |
| 21 | 2.9312 | 3.0082 | 3.0182 | 3.0032 | 3.0255 |
| 22 | 3.1153 | 3.0723 | 3.0131 | 3.0920 | 3.0504 |
| 23 | 2.0386 | 3.0153 | 3.0902 | 3.0176 | 3.0525 |
| 24 | 3.0354 | 2.9645 | 2.9756 | 3.0379 | 3.0894 |
| 25 | 3.0532 | 2.9473 | 3.0441 | 2.9786 | 3.0337 |
| 26 | 3.0047 | 2.9941 | 3.0733 | 3.0473 | 3.0246 |
| 27 | 3.0559 | 3.0066 | 2.9601 | 3.0739 | 3.0229 |
| 28 | 2.0304 | 3.0612 | 3.0354 | 3.0476 | 3.0576 |
| 29 | 2.9958 | 3.0052 | 2.9911 | 3.0737 | 2.9849 |
| 30 | 3.0605 | 3.0391 | 2.9679 | 2.9848 | 3.0836 |

You want to study the process of producing cans of cat food for the two shifts and the two types of food. Completely analyze the data.

**19.17** The team involved in the study of the weight of the canned kidney cat food was very concerned about the effect of the size of the pieces of food on the can weight. The opinion of the team clearly indicated that any change in the formulation of the food had to be considered very carefully because the chunkier formulation might be one of the reasons that the cats liked the food. The team decided that before any final decision was made concerning the formulation, an experiment should be conducted. A local animal shelter was contacted and agreed to participate in the study. A random sample of 20 cats from the population at the shelter was selected. Ten cats were randomly assigned to each of the two size formulations (fine and chunky) of kidney cat food being tested. Each of the cats was then presented with 3 ounces of the selected formulation in their dish at feeding time. The response variable of interest was operationally defined as the amount of food (in ounces) that the cat consumed within a 10-minute time interval that began when the filled dish was presented. This definition was selected in an attempt to distinguish between what the cat seemed to really be attracted to and what would be eaten because nothing else

was available. The results for this experiment are presented in the following table (and stored in the file Whitney4).

### Ounces of Food Eaten for Two Formulations of Kidney Canned Cat Food

| Fine | | Chunky | |
|------|------|--------|------|
| 2.31 | 2.01 | 2.76 | 2.22 |
| 2.07 | 1.75 | 2.32 | 1.88 |
| 1.45 | 2.11 | 1.98 | 2.09 |
| 1.93 | 2.27 | 1.64 | 2.65 |
| 2.04 | 2.38 | 2.54 | 2.51 |

You want to reach conclusions about differences in the amount of food eaten between the two formulations. Completely analyze the data.

**19.18** The Whitney Gourmet Cat Food Company was interested in exploring ways of expanding its market share by offering new cat food products in addition to the existing kidney and shrimp foods. Experimental formulations were developed for two new products, one based on chicken livers, and the other based on salmon. The team agreed that an experiment should be conducted to compare the two new foods with the two existing products, and in addition, with a supermarket brand of a beef-based product. A local animal shelter was contacted and agreed to participate in the study. A random sample of 50 cats from the population at the shelter was selected. Ten cats were randomly assigned to each of the five products being tested. Each of the cats was then presented with 3 ounces of the selected food in a dish at feeding time. The response variable of interest was operationally defined as the amount of food (in ounces) that the cat consumed within a 10-minute time interval that began when the filled dish was presented. This definition was selected in an attempt to distinguish between what the cat seemed to really be attracted to and what would be eaten because nothing else was available. The results for this experiment are presented in the following table and stored in the file Whitney5.

### Ounces Eaten for Five Cat Food Products

| Kidney | Shrimp | Chicken Liver | Salmon | Beef |
|--------|--------|---------------|--------|------|
| 2.37 | 2.26 | 2.29 | 1.79 | 2.09 |
| 2.62 | 2.69 | 2.23 | 2.33 | 1.87 |
| 2.31 | 2.25 | 2.41 | 1.96 | 1.67 |
| 2.47 | 2.45 | 2.68 | 2.05 | 1.64 |
| 2.59 | 2.34 | 2.25 | 2.26 | 2.16 |
| 2.62 | 2.37 | 2.17 | 2.24 | 1.75 |
| 2.34 | 2.22 | 2.37 | 1.96 | 1.18 |
| 2.47 | 2.56 | 2.26 | 1.58 | 1.92 |
| 2.45 | 2.36 | 2.45 | 2.18 | 1.32 |
| 2.32 | 2.59 | 2.57 | 1.93 | 1.94 |

You want to reach conclusions about differences in the amount of food eaten among the five types of food. Completely analyze the data.

**19.19** When the team studying the canned weight of the cat food and production volume examined the results of a single day's production, the group came to the realization that the size of the pieces of meat that were contained in the can and the can fill height could impact the weight of the can. The team wondered whether the current larger chunk size produced higher can weight and more variability, so a finer cutting size was studied along with the current size. In addition, the target for the sensing mechanism that determines the fill height was lowered slightly to determine the effect on can weight. Twenty cans were filled for each of the four combinations of piece size and fill height. The contents of each can was weighed and the amount above or below the label weight of 3 ounces recorded as the variable Coded Weight. For example, a can containing 2.90 ounces is given a Coded Weight of − 0.10. The results are presented in the following table and stored in the file Whitney6.

| Piece Size | Fill Height | Coded Weight | | | | |
|---|---|---|---|---|---|---|
| Fine | Low | −0.10 | +0.06 | +0.13 | +0.05 | −0.04 |
| | | +0.20 | +0.08 | +0.10 | +0.02 | −0.10 |
| | | +0.32 | +0.21 | +0.17 | +0.28 | +0.26 |
| | | +0.22 | +0.26 | +0.19 | +0.16 | +0.24 |
| Current | Low | +1.90 | +2.13 | +2.22 | +1.96 | +1.87 |
| | | +2.17 | +2.05 | +2.11 | +2.19 | +2.03 |
| | | +2.81 | +2.90 | +2.69 | +2.72 | +2.80 |
| | | +2.71 | +2.76 | +2.83 | +2.68 | +2.77 |
| Fine | Current | +1.12 | +1.06 | +0.94 | +1.11 | +1.08 |
| | | +1.02 | +1.04 | +0.98 | +1.10 | +1.05 |
| | | +1.57 | +1.48 | +1.63 | +1.59 | +1.60 |
| | | +1.51 | +1.60 | +1.62 | +1.58 | +1.53 |
| Current | Current | +3.05 | +2.94 | +2.98 | +3.10 | +3.09 |
| | | +3.02 | +2.97 | +3.11 | +3.06 | +3.04 |
| | | +3.96 | +3.89 | +4.07 | +4.02 | +4.06 |
| | | +3.95 | +4.07 | +4.11 | +3.92 | +3.95 |

Analyze these data and write a report for presentation to the team. Indicate the importance of the piece size and the fill height on the weight of the canned cat food. Be sure to include a recommendation for the level of each factor that will come closest to meeting the target weight, and the limitations of this experiment, along with recommendations for future experiments that might be undertaken.

# APPENDICES

## A.  REVIEW OF ARITHMETIC, ALGEBRA, AND LOGARITHMS

### A.1    RULES FOR ARITHMETIC OPERATIONS

| RULE | EXAMPLE |
|---|---|
| 1. $a + b = c$ and $b + a = c$ | $2 + 1 = 3$ and $1 + 2 = 3$ |
| 2. $a + (b + c) = (a + b) + c$ | $5 + (7 + 4) = (5 + 7) + 4 = 16$ |
| 3. $a - b = c$ but $b - a \neq c$ | $9 - 7 = 2$ but $7 - 9 \neq 2$ |
| 4. $(a)(b) = (b)(a)$ | $(7)(6) = (6)(7) = 42$ |
| 5. $(a)(b + c) = ab + ac$ | $(2)(3 + 5) = (2)(3) + (2)(5) = 16$ |
| 6. $a \div b \neq b \div a$ | $12 \div 3 \neq 3 \div 12$ |
| 7. $\dfrac{a + b}{c} = \dfrac{a}{c} + \dfrac{b}{c}$ | $\dfrac{7 + 3}{2} = \dfrac{7}{2} + \dfrac{3}{2} = 5$ |
| 8. $\dfrac{a}{b + c} \neq \dfrac{a}{b} + \dfrac{a}{c}$ | $\dfrac{3}{4 + 5} \neq \dfrac{3}{4} + \dfrac{3}{5}$ |
| 9. $\dfrac{1}{a} + \dfrac{1}{b} = \dfrac{b + a}{ab}$ | $\dfrac{1}{3} + \dfrac{1}{5} = \dfrac{5 + 3}{(3)(5)} = \dfrac{8}{15}$ |
| 10. $\left(\dfrac{a}{b}\right)\left(\dfrac{c}{d}\right) = \left(\dfrac{ac}{bd}\right)$ | $\left(\dfrac{2}{3}\right)\left(\dfrac{6}{7}\right) = \left(\dfrac{(2)(6)}{(3)(7)}\right) = \dfrac{12}{21}$ |
| 11. $\dfrac{a}{b} \div \dfrac{c}{d} = \dfrac{ad}{bc}$ | $\dfrac{5}{8} \div \dfrac{3}{7} = \left(\dfrac{(5)(7)}{(8)(3)}\right) = \dfrac{35}{24}$ |

### A.2    RULES FOR ALGEBRA: EXPONENTS AND SQUARE ROOTS

| RULE | EXAMPLE |
|---|---|
| 1. $(X^a)(X^b) = X^{a+b}$ | $(4^2)(4^3) = 4^5$ |
| 2. $(X^a)^b = X^{ab}$ | $(2^2)^3 = 2^6$ |
| 3. $(X^a / X^b) = X^{a-b}$ | $\dfrac{3^5}{3^3} = 3^2$ |
| 4. $\dfrac{X^a}{X^a} = X^0 = 1$ | $\dfrac{3^4}{3^4} = 3^0 = 1$ |
| 5. $\sqrt{XY} = \sqrt{X}\sqrt{Y}$ | $\sqrt{(25)(4)} = \sqrt{25}\sqrt{4} = 10$ |
| 6. $\sqrt{\dfrac{X}{Y}} = \dfrac{\sqrt{X}}{\sqrt{Y}}$ | $\sqrt{\dfrac{16}{100}} = \dfrac{\sqrt{16}}{\sqrt{100}} = 0.40$ |

## A.3    RULES FOR LOGARITHMS

### Base 10

Log is the symbol used for base-10 logarithms:

| RULE | EXAMPLE |
|---|---|
| 1. $\log(10^a) = a$ | $\log(100) = \log(10^2) = 2$ |
| 2. If $\log(a) = b$, then $a = 10^b$ | If $\log(a) = 2$, then $a = 10^2 = 100$ |
| 3. $\log(ab) = \log(a) + \log(b)$ | $\log(100) = \log[(10)(10)] = \log(10) + \log(10) = 1 + 1 = 2$ |
| 4. $\log(a^b) = (b)\log(a)$ | $\log(1{,}000) = \log(10^3) = (3)\log(10) = (3)(1) = 3$ |
| 5. $\log(a/b) = \log(a) - \log(b)$ | $\log(100) = \log(1{,}000/10)$ |
| | $\qquad = \log(1{,}000) - \log(10) = 3 - 1 = 2$ |

**EXAMPLE**

Take the base-10 logarithm of each side of the following equation:

$$Y = \beta_0 \beta_1^X \varepsilon$$

**SOLUTION:** Apply rules 3 and 4:

$$\log(Y) = \log(\beta_0 \beta_1^X \varepsilon)$$
$$= \log(\beta_0) + \log(\beta_1^X) + \log(\varepsilon)$$
$$= \log(\beta_0) + (X)\log(\beta_1) + \log(\varepsilon)$$

### Base e

ln is the symbol used for base $e$ logarithms, commonly referred to as natural logarithms. $e$ is Euler's number, and $e \cong 2.718282$:

| RULE | EXAMPLE |
|---|---|
| 1. $\ln(e^a) = a$ | $\ln(7.389056) = \ln(e^2) = 2$ |
| 2. If $\ln(a) = b$, then $a = e^b$ | If $\ln(a) = 2$, then $a = e^2 = 7.389056$ |
| 3. $\ln(ab) = \ln(a) + \ln(b)$ | $\ln(100) = \ln[(10)(10)]$ |
| | $\ln(10) + \ln(10) = 2.302585 + 2.302585 = 4.605170$ |
| 4. $\ln(a^b) = (b)\ln(a)$ | $\ln(1{,}000) = \ln(10^3) = 3\ln(10) = 3(2.302585) = 6.907755$ |
| 5. $\ln(a/b) = \ln(a) - \ln(b)$ | $\ln(100) = \ln(1{,}000/10) = \ln(1{,}000) - \ln(10)$ |
| | $\qquad = 6.907755 - 2.302585 = 4.605170$ |

**EXAMPLE**

Take the base $e$ logarithm of each side of the following equation:

$$Y = \beta_0 \beta_1^X \varepsilon$$

**SOLUTION:** Apply rules 3 and 4:

$$\ln(Y) = \ln(\beta_0 \beta_1^X \varepsilon)$$
$$= \ln(\beta_0) + \ln(\beta_1^X) + \ln(\varepsilon)$$
$$= \ln(\beta_0) + (X)\ln(\beta_1) + \ln(\varepsilon)$$

## B.  SUMMATION NOTATION, STATISTICAL SYMBOLS, AND GREEK ALPHABET

### B.1    SUMMATION NOTATION

The symbol $\Sigma$, the Greek capital letter sigma, is used to denote "taking the sum of." Consider a set of $n$ values for variable $X$. The expression $\sum_{i=1}^{n} X_i$ means that these $n$ values are to be added together. Thus:

$$\sum_{i=1}^{n} X_i = X_1 + X_2 + X_3 + \cdots + X_n$$

The following problem illustrates the use of summation notation. Consider five values of a variable $X$: $X_1 = 2, X_2 = 0, X_3 = -1, X_4 = 5$, and $X_5 = 7$. Thus:

$$\sum_{i=1}^{5} X_i = X_1 + X_2 + X_3 + X_4 + X_5 = 2 + 0 + (-1) + 5 + 7 = 13$$

In statistics, the squared values of a variable are often summed. Thus:

$$\sum_{i=1}^{n} X_i^2 = X_1^2 + X_2^2 + X_3^2 + \cdots + X_n^2$$

and, in the example above:

$$\sum_{i=1}^{5} X_i^2 = X_1^2 + X_2^2 + X_3^2 + X_4^2 + X_5^2$$
$$= 2^2 + 0^2 + (-1)^2 + 5^2 + 7^2$$
$$= 4 + 0 + 1 + 25 + 49$$
$$= 79$$

$\sum_{i=1}^{n} X_i^2$, the summation of the squares, is *not* the same as $\left(\sum_{i=1}^{n} X_i\right)^2$, the square of the sum:

$$\sum_{i=1}^{n} X_i^2 \neq \left(\sum_{i=1}^{n} X_i\right)^2$$

In the example given earlier, the summation of squares is equal to 79. This is not equal to the square of the sum, which is $13^2 = 169$.

Another frequently used operation involves the summation of the product. Consider two variables, $X$ and $Y$, each having $n$ values. Then:

$$\sum_{i=1}^{n} X_i Y_i = X_1 Y_1 + X_2 Y_2 + X_3 Y_3 + \cdots + X_n Y_n$$

Continuing with the previous example, suppose there is a second variable, $Y$, whose five values are $Y_1 = 1$, $Y_2 = 3$, $Y_3 = -2$, $Y_4 = 4$, and $Y_5 = 3$. Then,

$$\sum_{i=1}^{n} X_i Y_i = X_1 Y_1 + X_2 Y_2 + X_3 Y_3 + X_4 Y_4 + X_5 Y_5$$

$$= (2)(1) + (0)(3) + (-1)(-2) + (5)(4) + (7)(3)$$

$$= 2 + 0 + 2 + 20 + 21$$

$$= 45$$

In computing $\displaystyle\sum_{i=1}^{n} X_i Y_i$, realize that the first value of $X$ is multiplied by the first value of $Y$, the second value of $X$ is multiplied by the second value of $Y$, and so on. These products are then summed in order to compute the desired result. However, the summation of products is *not* equal to the product of the individual sums:

$$\sum_{i=1}^{n} X_i Y_i \neq \left( \sum_{i=1}^{n} X_i \right) \left( \sum_{i=1}^{n} Y_i \right)$$

In this example,

$$\sum_{i=1}^{5} X_i = 13$$

and

$$\sum_{i=1}^{5} Y_i = 1 + 3 + (-2) + 4 + 3 = 9$$

so that

$$\left( \sum_{i=1}^{5} X_i \right) \left( \sum_{i=1}^{5} Y_i \right) = (13)(9) = 117$$

However,

$$\sum_{i=1}^{5} X_i Y_i = 45$$

The following table summarizes these results:

| VALUE | $X_i$ | $Y_i$ | $X_i Y_i$ |
|-------|-------|-------|-----------|
| 1 | 2 | 1 | 2 |
| 2 | 0 | 3 | 0 |
| 3 | -1 | -2 | 2 |
| 4 | 5 | 4 | 20 |
| 5 | 7 | 3 | 21 |
| | $\displaystyle\sum_{i=1}^{5} X_i = 13$ | $\displaystyle\sum_{i=1}^{5} Y_i = 9$ | $\displaystyle\sum_{i=1}^{5} X_i Y_i = 45$ |

RULE 1 The summation of the values of two variables is equal to the sum of the values of each summed variable:

$$\sum_{i=1}^{n}(X_i + Y_i) = \sum_{i=1}^{n}X_i + \sum_{i=1}^{n}Y_i$$

Thus,

$$\sum_{i=1}^{5}(X_i + Y_i) = (2+1)+(0+3)+(-1+(-2))+(5+4)+(7+3)$$

$$= 3+3+(-3)+9+10$$

$$= 22$$

$$\sum_{i=1}^{5}X_i + \sum_{i=1}^{5}Y_i = 13+9 = 22$$

RULE 2 The summation of a difference between the values of two variables is equal to the difference between the summed values of the variables:

$$\sum_{i=1}^{n}(X_i - Y_i) = \sum_{i=1}^{n}X_i - \sum_{i=1}^{n}Y_i$$

Thus,

$$\sum_{i=1}^{5}(X_i - Y_i) = (2-1)+(0-3)+(-1-(-2))+(5-4)+(7-3)$$

$$= 1+(-3)+1+1+4$$

$$= 4$$

$$\sum_{i=1}^{5}X_i - \sum_{i=1}^{5}Y_i = 13-9 = 4$$

RULE 3 The sum of a constant times a variable is equal to that constant times the sum of the values of the variable:

$$\sum_{i=1}^{n}cX_i = c\sum_{i=1}^{n}X_i$$

where $c$ is a constant. Thus, if $c = 2$,

$$\sum_{i=1}^{5}cX_i = \sum_{i=1}^{5}2X_i = (2)(2)+(2)(0)+(2)(-1)+(2)(5)+(2)(7)$$

$$= 4+0+(-2)+10+14$$

$$= 26$$

$$c\sum_{i=1}^{5}X_i = 2\sum_{i=1}^{5}X_i = (2)(13) = 26$$

RULE 4 A constant summed $n$ times will be equal to $n$ times the value of the constant.

$$\sum_{i=1}^{n} c = nc$$

where $c$ is a constant. Thus, if the constant $c = 2$ is summed 5 times,

$$\sum_{i=1}^{5} c = 2 + 2 + 2 + 2 + 2 = 10$$

$$nc = (5)(2) = 10$$

## EXAMPLE

Suppose there are six values for the variables $X$ and $Y$, such that $X_1 = 2$, $X_2 = 1$, $X_3 = 5$, $X_4 = -3$, $X_5 = 1$, $X_6 = -2$, and $Y_1 = 4$, $Y_2 = 0$, $Y_3 = -1$, $Y_4 = 2$, $Y_5 = 7$, and $Y_6 = -3$. Compute each of the following:

(a) $\displaystyle\sum_{i=1}^{6} X_i$

(f) $\displaystyle\sum_{i=1}^{6} (X_i + Y_i)$

(b) $\displaystyle\sum_{i=1}^{6} Y_i$

(g) $\displaystyle\sum_{i=1}^{6} (X_i - Y_i)$

(c) $\displaystyle\sum_{i=1}^{6} X_i^2$

(h) $\displaystyle\sum_{i=1}^{6} (X_i - 3Y_i + 2X_i^2)$

(d) $\displaystyle\sum_{i=1}^{6} Y_i^2$

(i) $\displaystyle\sum_{i=1}^{6} (cX_i)$, where $c = -1$

(e) $\displaystyle\sum_{i=1}^{6} X_i Y_i$

(j) $\displaystyle\sum_{i=1}^{6} (X_i - 3Y_i + c)$, where $c = +3$

ANSWERS
(a) 4   (b) 9   (c) 44   (d) 79   (e) 10   (f) 13   (g) −5   (h) 65   (i) −4   (j) −5

## References

1. Bashaw, W. L., *Mathematics for Statistics* (New York: Wiley, 1969).
2. Lanzer, P., *Basic Math: Fractions, Decimals, Percents* (Hicksville, NY: Video Aided Instruction, 2006).
3. Levine, D., *The MBA Primer: Business Statistics* (Cincinnati, OH: Southwestern Publishing, 2000).
4. Levine, D., *Statistics* (Hicksville, NY: Video Aided Instruction, 2006).
5. Shane, H., *Algebra 1* (Hicksville, NY: Video Aided Instruction, 2006).

## B.2 STATISTICAL SYMBOLS

+ add                                   × multiply

− subtract                              ÷ divide

= equal to                              ≠ not equal to

≅ approximately equal to

> greater than                          < less than

≥ greater than or equal to              ≤ less than or equal to

## B.3 GREEK ALPHABET

| GREEK LETTER | | LETTER NAME | ENGLISH EQUIVALENT | GREEK LETTER | | LETTER NAME | ENGLISH EQUIVALENT |
|---|---|---|---|---|---|---|---|
| A | α | Alpha | a | N | ν | Nu | n |
| B | β | Beta | b | Ξ | ξ | Xi | x |
| Γ | γ | Gamma | g | O | o | Omicron | ŏ |
| Δ | δ | Delta | d | Π | π | Pi | p |
| E | ε | Epsilon | ĕ | P | ρ | Rho | r |
| Z | ζ | Zeta | z | Σ | σ | Sigma | s |
| H | η | Eta | ē | T | τ | Tau | t |
| Θ | θ | Theta | th | Y | υ | Upsilon | u |
| I | ι | Iota | i | Φ | φ | Phi | ph |
| K | κ | Kappa | k | X | χ | Chi | ch |
| Λ | λ | Lambda | l | Ψ | ψ | Psi | ps |
| M | μ | Mu | m | Ω | ω | Omega | ō |

# C. BASIC COMPUTING SKILLS

## C.1 INTRODUCTION

Using Microsoft Excel or Minitab with this book requires certain basic computing skills. If you have ever sent an instant message, surfed the Web, played music or games through a computer, or written word-processed assignments, you probably have already mastered these skills required to use the end-of-chapter appendices. If you already have the basic computing skills that this book requires, this appendix will introduce you to the vocabulary and conventions used in this book to present computer-related operations.

## C.2 MOUSING OPERATIONS

You make extensive use of your mouse (or equivalent pointing device) to move an onscreen mouse pointer as you operate Excel or Minitab. Microsoft Windows expects your mouse to have one mouse button designated as the primary button (this is typically the left button) and another button designated as the secondary button (typically the right button). Throughout the appendices, you will need to distinguish among the following seven mousing verbs that involve moving the mouse and one of these two buttons:

**Click, Select,** and **Clear** These verbs tell you to move the mouse pointer over the object of the instruction and press the primary button. Click suggests that an action is completed when you press the primary button, as in "click the **OK** button." Select suggests that you will be choosing or highlighting a choice from an onscreen list *or* opening a new onscreen list or submenu. Selecting something is typically followed by clicking something else, as in "select the file name and then click **OK**." Clear is the click operation that clears the checkmark in an onscreen check box (see Figure C.2 on page 900).

**Double-click** This verb tells you to move the **mouse pointer** over an object and click the primary button twice in rapid succession. You double-click program icons on the Windows Desktop to open programs, and you double-click onscreen objects such as parts of a chart to further edit or format them.

**Right-click** This verb tells you to move the mouse pointer over an object and click the secondary button. You right-click onscreen objects to display a **shortcut menu** of commands from which you click or select an action.

**Drag** and **Drag-and-drop** These verbs represent a two-step process. In the first step, you move the mouse pointer over an object and press and hold down the primary button while you move the mouse pointer somewhere else. In the second step, you move the mouse pointer somewhere else and release the primary button. Drag suggests that you are selecting part of a whole; drag-and-drop suggests that you are moving an entire whole. You drag the mouse to select contiguous parts of a worksheet or to move or resize the borders of onscreen windows, but you drag-and-drop a Windows Desktop icon to move it from one part of the screen to another.

## C.3  WINDOW ELEMENTS

The "windows" in Microsoft Windows are onscreen rectangular frames that divide the screen. When you open a program, Microsoft Windows displays a program window, the typical elements of which are shown in Figures C.1 and C.2 and explained in Table C.1. As you use a program, the program will display **dialog boxes**, specialized windows that contain messages or ask you to make entries and selections. Figure C.3 shows two examples of dialog boxes and the elements commonly found in all dialog boxes and explained in Table C.2.

**FIGURE C.1** Microsoft Excel 2003 and Microsoft Excel 2007 Program Windows

**TABLE C.1**

Program Window Elements

| Element | Function |
|---|---|
| **Title bar** | Displays the name of the program and contains the Minimize, Resize, and Close buttons for the program window. You drag and drop the title bar to reposition a program window on your screen. |
| **Minimize, Resize, and Close buttons** | Change the display of the program window. **Minimize** hides the window without closing the program, **Resize** permits you to change the size of the window, and **Close** removes the window from the screen and closes the program. A second set of these buttons that appear in Microsoft Excel perform the three actions for the currently active worksheet. (Similar buttons, obscured in Figure C.2, perform the same functions for the Minitab Session and Worksheet area.) |
| **Menu Bar** | The horizontal list of words at the top of the window that represent sets of commands. You select a menu bar word and typically reveal another list of command choices that either lead to some direct action, the display of a dialog box, or the display of another list of choices. |
| **Toolbars** | An array of clickable buttons that serve as shortcuts to program commands. |
| **Task Pane** | A closable window that lists clickable links that represent shortcuts to menu and toolbar operations (seen only in Excel 2002 and 2003). |
| **Ribbon** | Distinctive of Excel 2007, the Ribbon with its **Tabs** and **Tab Groups** performs the combined functions of a menu bar, task pane, and toolbars. Some tab groups contain **Launcher Buttons** that display dialog boxes, task panes, or **galleries**, illustrated sets of choices. |
| **Office Button and Quick Access Toolbar** | Other distinctive features of Excel 2007. The **Office Button** displays a menu of commonly issued commands similar to the File menu in other programs and gives you access to many Excel options settings. The **Quick Access Toolbar** (to the immediate right of the Office Button) displays shortcuts to commonly used commands. |
| **Worksheet area** | Displays the currently opened workbooks (Excel) or worksheets (Minitab). In Excel, this area also contains **Sheet tabs** on which you can double-click to go a specific sheet in a workbook. (Although you can open more than one Excel workbook or more than one Minitab worksheet at one time in a worksheet area, no instructions in this book will ever ask you to do so.) |
| **Scroll bars** | Allow you to travel horizontally or vertically through a worksheet to reveal parts that cannot otherwise be seen, for example, row 100. |

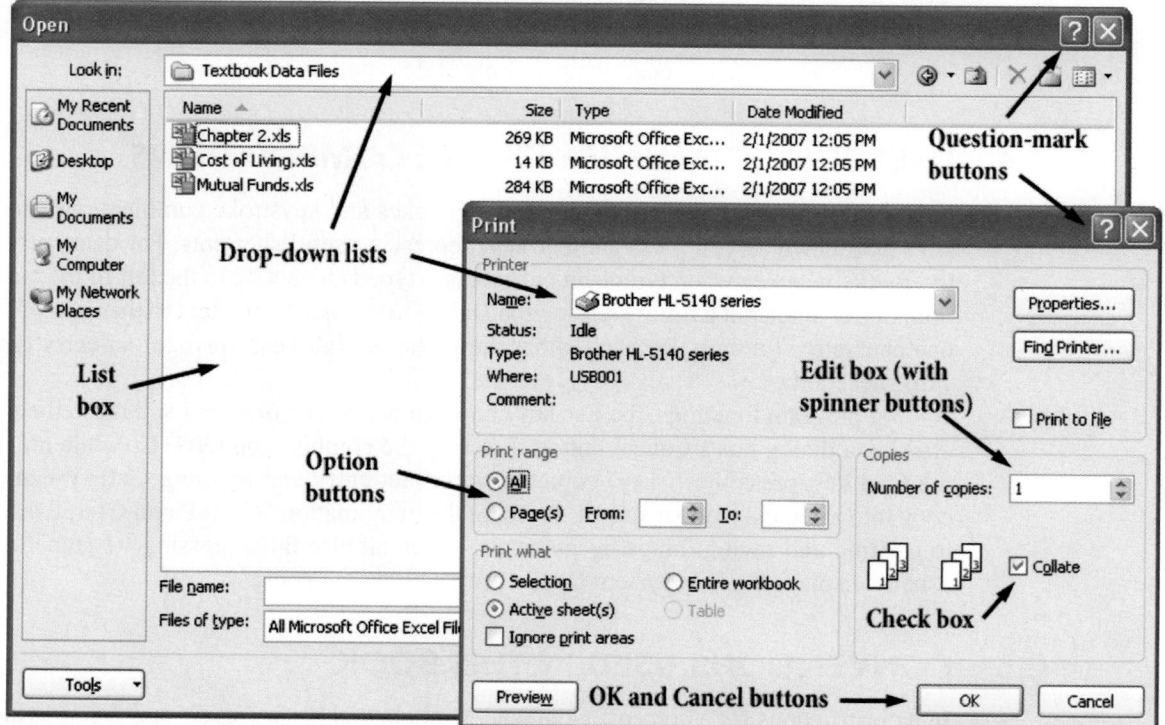

**FIGURE C.2** Minitab 15 Program Windows

**FIGURE C.3** Dialog box elements

**TABLE C.2**

Dialog Box Elements

| Element | Function |
|---|---|
| **Command buttons** | Clickable areas that cause a program to take some action. Many dialog boxes contain an **OK button** that causes a program to take an action using the current entries and selections in the dialog box as well as a **Cancel button** that closes a dialog box and cancels the pending operation associated with the dialog box. |
| **List boxes** | Display lists of choices available to you. Should a list exceed the dimensions of a list box, you will see **scroll buttons** or **sliders** (not shown in Figure C.3) that you can click to reveal choices not currently displayed. In Minitab, you will frequently select an item from a list box and then press a command button to perform some action. |
| **Drop-down lists** | Display lists of choices when you click over them. |
| **Edit boxes** | Areas into which you type entries. Some edit boxes contain drop-down lists or **spinner buttons** that you can use to complete the entry. Excel edit boxes for cell ranges typically contain a button that allows you to drag the mouse over a cell range as an alternative to typing the cell range. |
| **Option buttons** | Present you with a set of mutually exclusive choices. When you click one option button, all the other option buttons in the set are cleared. |
| **Check boxes** | Present you with optional actions that are not mutually exclusive choices. Unlike with option buttons, clicking a check box does not affect the status of other check boxes, and more than one check box can be checked at a time. Clicking a check box that contains a checkmark **clears** the check box as discussed in Section C.2. |
| **Question-mark buttons** | Display help messages related to a dialog box. Dialog boxes that do not contain a question-mark button typically contain a command button labeled **Help** that performs this function. (Minitab dialog boxes contain only Help command buttons.) |

## C.4　USEFUL KEYS AND KEYSTROKE COMBINATIONS

In Microsoft Excel and Minitab, certain keystrokes and keystroke combinations (one or more keys held down as you press another key) represent useful shortcuts. For data entry, pressing the **Backspace** key when typing an entry erases typed characters to the left of the current position, one character at a time. Pressing the **Delete** key erases characters to the right of the cursor, one character at a time. Pressing either the **Enter** or **Tab** keys finalizes an entry typed into a worksheet cell.

For program functions, the **Esc** key cancels a dialog box or action and is often equivalent to clicking a dialog box's Cancel button. Pressing the combination **Ctrl+C** (while holding down the **Ctrl** key, press the **C** key) copies a worksheet entry and pressing **Crtl+V** can paste that copy into a second worksheet cell. Pressing the combinations **Ctrl+P** and **Ctrl+S** are shortcuts to printing and saving things, respectively. When all else fails, pressing **F1** (function key #1) usually displays the help system for the program you are using.

## C.5　CONVENTIONS USED IN THIS BOOK

In its instructions for Microsoft Excel and Minitab, this book uses several typographic conventions. In the previous section, you have already been introduced to the convention used for a keystroke combination (e.g., **Ctrl+C**). Throughout this book, the targets of mousing operations are boldfaced, as in "Click **Labels**" or "Click **OK**." For dialog boxes that are divided into subtitled areas or tabs, the book identifies the area or tab as in "click **All** in the **Page range** section" or "in the **Context** tab of the Help dialog box, click the first entry." When object names or labels can vary due to context, the book uses italics as a placeholder for a specific object, as in "Select *variable column*."

To describe a sequence of menu bar or ribbon selections, the book uses an arrow symbol to link selections. For example, when the book says, "**File → New**", first select File and then from the list of choices that appears, select New. ("**File → New**" would be a valid sequence in Excel 97–2003 and in Minitab; the equivalent Excel 2007 sequence would be "**Office Button → New**".) In the PHStat2 appendices, selection sequences are given relative to the PHStat menu, for example, as **PHStat → Descriptive Statistics → Boxplot**. If you use Excel 2007, you will need to click the **Add-Ins** ribbon tab first in order to use these selection sequences.

# D.  STUDENT CD-ROM CONTENTS

## D.1  STUDENT CD-ROM OVERVIEW

The Student CD-ROM packaged with this book contains various resources to support your learning of statistics. You can use the small Windows "start" program included on the CD-ROM to copy and install the contents of the CD-ROM to your computer system or manually explore the CD-ROM contents.

The following CD-ROM folders contain learning resources used in this book.

### Excel Data Files

Located in the **Browse** folder, the **Excel Data Files** folder contains the Microsoft Excel workbook files (with the extension .xls) used in the examples and problems in this text. A detailed list of the files appears in Section D.2.

### Minitab Data Files

Located in the **Browse** folder, the **Minitab Data Files** folder contains the Minitab worksheet files (with the extension .mtw) used in the examples and problems in this text. A detailed list of the files appears in Section D.2.

### Herald Case

Located in the **Browse** folder, the **Herald Case** folder contains the files for the "Managing the *Springville Herald*" case. (These files are also available online at the URLs listed in the case.)

### Web Case

Located in the **Browse** folder, the **Web Case** folder contains the files for all the Web Cases that appear at the end of chapters. (These files are also available online at the URLs listed in each case.)

### PHStat2

Located in the **Install** folder, the **PHStat2** folder contains the PHStat2 version 2.8 setup program. Run this program to install PHStat2 on a Windows PC. (For more information, see Appendix F and the **PHStat2 readme file** in the CD_ROM PHStat2 folder.)

### Excel Workbooks

Located in the **Browse** folder, the Microsoft Excel workbooks folder contains the workbooks described and used in the Excel appendices sections. Copies of these files also appear in the Excel Data Files folder.

### Visual Explorations in Statistics

Located in the **Browse** folder, Visual Explorations contains the files necessary to use the Visual Explorations in Statistics add-in workbook (`Visual Explorations.xla`). Before using this workbook, you should review the "Macro Security Issues" part of Section E1.8 on pages 20–21 and you may also want to consult the Appendix F FAQs. You can open and use the `Visual Explorations.xla` file directly from the CD in Microsoft Excel. If you prefer to use Visual Explorations without the CD present, copy the files `Visual Explorations.xla` and `Veshelp.chm` to the folder of your choice. (The `Veshelp.chm` file contains the orientation and help files for this add-in.)

### Student CD-ROM Topics

Located in the **Browse** folder, the Student CD-ROM Topics folder contains supplemental textbook sections as electronic Adobe Reader files with the extension .pdf. You will need the Adobe Acrobat reader program installed on your system in order to read these sections. (In the Install folder is a version of the Adobe Reader that you can install on your system, if necessary.)

## D.2 DATA FILE DESCRIPTIONS

The following presents in alphabetical order, a listing of the data files that can be found in both the **Excel Data Files** and **Minitab Data Files** folder. Elsewhere in this book, these file names appear in a special typeface, for example as `Mutual Funds`.

**AAAMILEAGE** Gasoline mileage from AAA members and combined city-highway driving gasoline mileage according to current government standards (Chapters 10, 12)

**ACCESS** Coded access read times (in msec), file size, programmer group, and buffer size (Chapter 11)

**ACT** ACT scores for type of course (rows) and length of course (columns) (Chapter 11)

**ACT-ONEWAY** ACT scores by groups (Chapter 11)

**ADVERTISE** Sales (in thousands of dollars), radio ads (in thousands of dollars), and newspaper ads (in thousands of dollars) for 22 cities (Chapters 14, 15)

**ADVERTISING** Sales (in millions of dollars) and newspaper ads (in thousands of dollars) (Chapter 15)

**AMPHRS** Capacity of batteries (Chapter 12)

**ANGLE** Subgroup number and angle (Chapter 18)

**ANSCOMBE** Data sets A, B, C, and D—each with 11 pairs of $X$ and $Y$ values (Chapter 13)

**AUTO** Miles per gallon, horsepower, and weight for a sample of 50 car models (Chapters 14, 15)

**BANK1** Waiting time (in minutes) spent by a sample of 15 customers at a bank located in a commercial district (Chapters 3, 9, 10, 12)

**BANK2** Waiting time (in minutes) spent by a sample of 15 customers at a bank located in a residential area (Chapters 3, 10, 12)

**BANKING** Banking preference and percentage (Chapter 2)

**BANKTIME** Waiting times of bank customers (Chapter 18)

**BANKYIELD** Yield for money market account and yield for five-year CD (Chapters 3, 10)

**BASEBALL** Team, attendance, high temperature on game day, winning percentage of home team, opponent's winning percentage, game played on Friday, Saturday, or Sunday (0 = no, 1 = yes), promotion held (0 = no, 1 = yes) (Chapter 19)

**BASKET** Year, price of bread, beef, eggs, and lettuce (Chapter 16)

**BATTERYLIFE** Life of a camera battery, in number of shots (Chapters 2, 3, 8)

**BB2001** Team; league (0 = American, 1 = National); wins; earned run average; runs scored; hits allowed; walks allowed; saves; errors; average ticket prices; fan cost index; regular season gate receipts; local television, radio, and cable revenues; other local operating revenues; player compensation and benefits; national and other local expenses; and income from baseball operations (Chapter 19)

**BB2006** Team, league (0 = American, 1 = National), wins, earned run average, runs scored, hits allowed, walks allowed, saves, errors, and cost of attending a game (Chapters 2, 6, 13, 14, 15)

**BBREVENUE** Team, value, and revenue (Chapter 13)

**BEDBATH** Year, coded year, and number of stores opened (Chapter 16)

**BESTREST** State, city, restaurant, hotel, cost (estimated price of dinner, including one drink and tip), and rating (1 to 100, with 1 the top-rated restaurant) (Chapter 3)

**BREAKFAST** Menu choice and delivery time difference for early and late (Chapter 11)

**BREAKFAST2** Menu choice and delivery time difference for early and late (Chapter 11)

**BREAKSTW** Breaking strength for operators (rows) and machines (columns) (Chapter 11)

**BULBS** Length of life of 40 lightbulbs from manufacturer A (=1) and 40 lightbulbs from manufacturer B (=2) (Chapters 2, 10)

**CABERNET** California and Washington ratings (Chapter 12)

**CABOT** Year and revenue for Cabot Corporation (Chapter 16)

**CANISTER** Day and number of nonconforming film canisters (Chapter 18)

**CDYIELD** Yield of money market account, 6-month CD, 1-year CD, 2.5-year CD, and 5-year CD (Chapters 11, 12)

**CEO** Company and total compensation of CEOs (Chapters 2, 3)

**CHICKEN** Sandwich, calories, fat (in grams), saturated fat (in grams), carbohydrates (in grams), and sodium (in milligrams) (Chapters 2, 3, 6, 8)

**CIRCUITS** Thickness of semiconductor wafers, by batch and position (Chapters 11, 12)

**CIRCULATION** Magazine, reported newsstand sales, and audited newsstand sales (Chapter 13)

**CLOSING** Rank, state, and closing costs (Chapter 6)

**COCACOLA** Year, coded year, and operating revenues (in billions of dollars) at Coca-Cola Company (Chapter 16)

**COFFEE** Rating of coffees, by expert and brand (Chapters 10, 11, 12)

**COFFEEDRINK** Product, calories, and fat in coffee drinks (Chapters 3, 13)

**COFFEEPRICE** Year and price per pound of coffee in the United States (Chapter 16)

**COLA** Sales for normal and end-aisle locations (Chapters 10, 12)

**COLASPC** Day, total number of cans filled, and number of unacceptable cans (over a 22-day period) (Chapter 18)

**COLLEGES-BASKETBALL** School, coach's salary for 2005–2006, expenses for 2004–2005, revenues for 2004–2005 (in millions of dollars), and winning percentage in 2005–2006 (Chapters 2, 3, 13)

**COLLEGETUITION** State, tuition, and change in tuition (Chapter 3)

**COMPLAINTS** Day and number of complaints (Chapter 18)

**COMPUTERS** Download time of three brands of computers (Chapter 11)

**COMPUTERS2** Download time, brand, and browser (Chapter 11)

**CONCRETE1** Compressive strength after two days and seven days (Chapters 10, 12)

**CONCRETE2** Compressive strength after 2 days, 7 days, and 28 days (Chapters 11, 12)

**CONTEST2001** Returns for experts, readers, and dart throwers (Chapters 11, 12)

**COST OF LIVING** City, overall cost rating, apartment rent, and costs of a cup of coffee, a hamburger, dry cleaning a men's suit, toothpaste, and movie tickets (Chapters 2, 3)

**CPI-U** Year, coded year, and value of CPI-U, the consumer price index (Chapter 16)

**CRACK** Type of crack and crack size (Chapters 10, 12)

**CREDIT** Month, coded month, credit charges (Chapter 16)

**CURRENCY** Year, coded year, and mean annual exchange rates (against the U.S. dollar) for the Canadian dollar, Japanese yen, and English pound (Chapter 16)

**CUSTSALE** Week number, number of customers, and sales (in thousands of dollars) over a period of 15 consecutive weeks (Chapter 13)

**DAILYNASDAQ** Date and NASDAQ value (Chapter 16)

**DATING** Year and number of subscribers (Chapter 2)

**DEALS** Year and number of mergers and acquisitions from January 1 to January 11 (Chapters 2, 16)

**DELIVERY** Customer number, number of cases, and delivery time (Chapter 13)

**DENTAL** Annual family dental expenses for 10 employees (Chapter 8)

**DIFFTEST** Differences in the sales invoices and actual amounts from a sample of 50 vouchers (Chapter 8)

**DIGITALCAMERAS** Battery life, camera type, life for subcompact cameras, life for compact cameras (Chapters 10, 12)

**DINNER** Time to prepare and cook dinner (Chapter 9)

**DISCOUNT** The amount of discount taken from 150 invoices (Chapter 8)

**DISPRAZ** Price, price squared, and sales of disposable razors in 15 stores (Chapter 15)

**DJIA** Year, coded year, and Dow Jones Industrial Average at the end of the year (Chapter 16)

**DOMESTICBEER** Brand, alcohol percentage, calories, and carbohydrates in U.S. domestic beers (Chapters 2, 3, 6, 15)

**DOWMARKETCAP** Company, ticker symbol, and market capitalization, in billions of dollars (Chapter 3)

**DRILL** Time to drill additional 5 feet, depth, and type of hole (Chapter 14)

**DRINK** Amount of soft drink filled in a subgroup of 50 consecutive 2-liter bottles (Chapters 2, 9)

**DRYCLEAN** Day, number of items returned (Chapter 18)

**ELECTRICITY** Year and cost of electricity (Chapter 16)

**ELECUSE** Electricity consumption (in kilowatts) and mean temperature (in degrees Fahrenheit) over a consecutive 24-month period (Chapter 13)

**ENERGY** State and per-capita kilowatt hour use (Chapter 3)

**ENERGY2** Year, price of electricity, natural gas, and fuel oil (Chapter 16)

**ERRORSPC** Number of nonconforming items and number of accounts processed over 39 days (Chapter 18)

**ERWAITING** Emergency room waiting time (in minutes) at the main facility and at satellite 1, satellite 2, and satellite 3 (Chapters 11, 12)

**ESPRESSO** Tamp (the distance in inches between the espresso grounds and the top of the portafilter) and time (the number of seconds the heart, body, and crema are separated) (Chapter 13)

**FEDRECEIPT** Year, coded year, and federal receipts (in billions of current dollars) (Chapter 16)

**FFCHAIN** Raters and restaurant ratings (Chapters 11, 12)

**FIFO** Historical cost (in dollars) and audited value (in dollars) for a sample of 120 inventory items (Chapter 8)

**FIRERUNS** Week and number of fire runs (Chapter 18)

**FLYASH** Fly ash percentage, fly ash percentage squared, and strength (Chapter 15)

**FORCE** Force required to break an insulator (Chapters 2, 3, 8, 9)

**FORD** Quarter, coded quarter, revenue, and three dummy variables for quarters (Chapter 16)

**FOULSPC** Number of foul shots made and number taken over 40 days (Chapter 18)

**FREEPORT** Address, appraised value, property size (acres), house size, age, number of rooms, number of bathrooms, and number of cars that can be parked in the garage located in Freeport, New York (Chapter 15)

**FRUIT** Fruit and year, price, and quantity (Chapter 16)

**FUNDTRAN** Day, number of new investigations, and number of investigations closed over a 30-day period (Chapter 18)

**FURNITURE** Days between receipt and resolution of a sample of 50 complaints regarding purchased furniture (Chapters 2, 3, 8, 9)

**GAS** Week and price per gallon, in cents (Chapter 2)

**GASOLINE** Year, gasoline price, 1980 price index, and 1995 price index (Chapter 16)

**GCFREEROSLYN** Address, appraised value, location, property size (acres), house size, age, number of rooms, number of bathrooms, and number of cars that can be parked in the garage in Glen Cove, Freeport, and Roslyn, New York (Chapter 15)

**GCROSLYN** Address, appraised value, location, property size (acres), house size, age, number of rooms, number of bathrooms, and number of cars that can be parked in the garage in Glen Cove and Roslyn, New York (Chapter 15)

**GDP** Year and real gross domestic product (Chapter 16)

**GE** Year, coded year, and stock price (Chapter 16)

**GEAR** Tooth size, part positioning, and gear distortion (Chapter 11)

**GLENCOVE** Address, appraised value, property size (acres), house size, age, number of rooms, number of bathrooms, and number of cars that can be parked in the garage in Glen Cove, New York (Chapters 14, 15)

**GOLFBALL** Distance for designs 1, 2, 3, and 4 (Chapters 11, 12)

**GPIGMAT** GMAT scores and GPI for 20 students (Chapter 13)

**GRADSURVEY** Gender, age (as of last birthday), height (in inches), major, current cumulative grade point average, undergraduate area of specialization, undergraduate cumulative grade point average, GMAT score, current employment status, number of different full-time jobs held in the past 10 years, expected salary upon completion of MBA (in thousands of dollars), anticipated salary after 5 years of experience after MBA (in thousands of dollars), satisfaction with student advisement services on campus, and amount spent for books and supplies this semester (Chapters 1, 2, 3, 4, 6, 8, 10, 11, 12)

**GRANULE** Granule loss in Boston and Vermont shingles (Chapters 3, 8, 9, 10)

**HARNSWELL** Day and diameter of cam rollers (in inches) for samples of five parts produced in each of 30 batches (Chapter 18)

**HEMLOCKFARMS** Asking price, hot tub, rooms, lake view, bathrooms, bedrooms, loft/den, finished basement, and number of acres (Chapter 15)

**HOMES** Price, location, condition, bedrooms, bathrooms, and other rooms (Chapter 19)

**HOSPADM** Day, number of admissions, mean processing time (in hours), range of processing times, and proportion of laboratory rework (over a 30-day period) (Chapter 18)

**HOTEL1** Day, number of rooms, number of nonconforming rooms per day over a 28-day period, and proportion of nonconforming items (Chapter 18)

**HOTEL2** Day and delivery time for subgroups of five luggage deliveries per day over a 28-day period (Chapter 18)

**HOUSE1** Selling price (in thousands of dollars), assessed value (in thousands of dollars), type (new = 0, old = 1), and time period of sale for 30 houses (Chapters 13, 14, 15)

**HOUSE2** Assessed value (in thousands of dollars), size (in thousands of square feet), and age (in years) for 15 houses (Chapters 13, 14)

**HOUSE3** Assessed value (in thousands of dollars), size (in thousands of square feet), and presence of a fireplace for 15 houses (Chapter 14)

**HOUSING** Quarter and units (Chapter 16)

**HTNGOIL** Monthly consumption of heating oil (in gallons), temperature (in degrees Fahrenheit), attic insulation (in inches), and style (0 = not ranch, 1 = ranch) (Chapters 14, 15)

**ICECREAM** Daily temperature (in degrees Fahrenheit) and sales (in thousands of dollars) for 21 days (Chapter 13)

**INDICES** Year and total rate of return (in percentage) for the Dow Jones Industrial Average (DJIA), the Standard & Poor's 500 (S&P 500), and the technology-heavy NASDAQ Composite (NASDAQ) (Chapter 3)

**INSURANCE** Processing time for insurance policies (Chapters 3, 8, 9)

**INTAGLIO** Surface hardness of untreated and treated steel plates (Chapters 10, 12)

**INVOICE** Number of invoices processed and amount of time (in hours) for 30 days (Chapter 13)

**INVOICES** Amount recorded (in dollars) from a sample of 12 sales invoices (Chapter 9)

**ITEMERR** Amount of error (in dollars) from a sample of 200 items (Chapter 8)

**KEYBOARD DEFECTS** Defect and frequency (Chapter 2)

**LARGEST BONDS** Five-year return of bond funds (Chapter 3)

**LAUNDRY** Dirt (in pounds) removed for detergent brands (rows) and cycle times (columns) (Chapter 11)

**LOGPURCH** Annual spending ($000) purchase (0 = no, 1 = yes), additional credit cards (0 = no, 1 = yes) (Chapter 14)

**LOCATE** Sales volume (in thousands of dollars) for front, middle, and rear locations (Chapters 11, 12)

**LUGGAGE** Delivery time, in minutes, for luggage in Wing A and Wing B of a hotel (Chapters 10, 12)

**MANAGERS** Sales (ratio of yearly sales divided by the target sales value for that region), score from the Wonderlic Personnel Test, score on the Strong-Campbell Interest Inventory Test, number of years of selling experience prior to becoming a sales manager, and whether the sales manager has a degree in electrical engineering (0 = no, 1 = yes) (Chapter 15)

**MBA** Success (0 = no, 1 = yes), GPA score, GMAT score (Chapter 14)

**MCDONALDS** Year, coded year, and annual total revenues (in billions of dollars) at McDonald's Corporation (Chapter 16)

**MEASUREMENT** Sample, in-line measurement, and analytical lab measurement (Chapters 10, 12)

**MEDICARE** Difference in amount reimbursed and amount that should have been reimbursed for office visits (Chapter 8)

**MEDREC** Day, number of discharged patients, and number of records not processed for a 30-day period (Chapter 18)

**METALS** Year and the total rate of return (in percentage) for platinum, gold, and silver (Chapter 3)

**MILEAGE** Mileage of autos calculated by owner, currently reported by the government, and forecasted according to government plans (Chapters 2, 3, 13)

**MOISTURE** Moisture content of Boston shingles and Vermont shingles (Chapter 9)

**MOVIE** Box office gross (in millions) and DVD sales (in thousands) (Chapter 13)

**MOVIEPRICES** Movie chain and prices (Chapters 2, 3, 8, 9)

**MOVIES** Year and movie attendance (Chapters 2, 16)

**MOVING** Labor hours, cubic feet, number of large pieces of furniture, and availability of an elevator (Chapters 13, 14)

**MUSICONLINE** Album/artist and prices at iTunes, Wal-Mart, MusicNow, Musicmatch, and Napster (Chapters 11, 12)

**MUTUALFUNDS** Category, objective, assets, fees, expense ratio, 2006 return, three-year return, five-year return, and risk (Chapters 2, 3, 4, 6, 8, 10, 11, 12, 15)

**MYELOMA** Patient, measurement before transplant, and measurement after transplant (Chapter 10)

**NATURALGAS** Coded quarter, price, and three dummy variables for quarters (Chapter 16)

**NBA2007** Team, number of wins, points per game (for team, opponent, and the difference between team and opponent), field goal (shots made) percentage (for team, opponent, and the difference between team and opponent), turnovers (losing the ball before a shot is taken) per game (for team, opponent, and the difference between team and opponent), offensive rebound percentage, and defensive rebound percentage (Chapters 14, 15)

**NEIGHBOR** Selling price (in thousands of dollars), number of rooms, and neighborhood location (east = 0, west = 1) for 20 houses (Chapter 14)

**OMNIPOWER** Bars sold, price (in cents), and promotion expenses (in dollars) (Chapter 14)

**ORDER** Time in a restaurant (Chapter 8)

**O-RING** Flight number, temperature, and O-ring damage index (Chapter 13)

**OYSTERS** Year, coded year, and number of bushels harvested (Chapter 16)

**PAIN-RELIEF** Temperature, brand of pain relief tablet, and time to dissolve (Chapter 11)

**PALLET** Weight of Boston and weight of Vermont shingles (Chapters 2, 8, 9, 10)

**PARACHUTE** Tensile strength of parachutes from suppliers 1, 2, 3, and 4 (Chapters 11, 12)

**PARACHUTE2** Tensile strength for looms and suppliers (Chapter 11)

**PASTA** Weight for type of pasta (rows) and cooking time (columns) (Chapter 11)

**PEN** Gender, ad, and product rating (Chapters 11, 12)

**PERFORM** Performance rating before and after motivational training (Chapters 10, 12)

**PETFOOD** Shelf space (in feet), weekly sales (in dollars), and aisle location (back = 0, front = 1) (Chapters 13, 14)

**PHONE** Time (in minutes) to clear telephone line problems and location (I and II) for samples of 20 customer problems reported to each of the two office locations (Chapter 19)

**PHOTO** Density for developer strength (rows) and development time (columns) (Chapter 11)

**PIZZAHUT** Gender (0 = female, 1 = male), price, and purchase behavior (0 = no, 1 = yes) (Chapter 14)

**PIZZATIME** Time period, delivery time for local restaurant, delivery time for national chain (Chapter 10)

**PLUMBINV** Difference in dollars between actual amounts recorded on sales invoices and the amounts entered into the accounting system (Chapter 8)

**POLIO** Year and incidence rates per 100,000 persons of reported poliomyelitis (Chapter 16)

**POTATO** Percentage of solids content in filter cake, acidity (in pH), lower pressure, upper pressure, cake thickness, varidrive speed, and drum speed setting for 54 measurements (Chapter 15)

**PROPERTYTAXES** State and property taxes per capita (Chapters 2, 6)

**PROTEIN** Calories (in grams), protein, percentage of calories from fat, percentage of calories from saturated fat, and cholesterol (in mg) for 25 popular protein foods (Chapter 2)

**PTFALLS** Month and patient falls (Chapter 18)

**PUMPKIN** Circumference and weight of pumpkins (Chapter 13)

**RADON** Solar radiation, soil temperature, vapor pressure, wind speed, relative humidity, dew point, ambient temperature, and radon concentration (Chapter 15)

**RAISINS** Weight of packages of raisins (Chapter 12)

**REDWOOD** Height, diameter, and bark thickness (Chapter 14)

**RENT** Monthly rental cost (in dollars) and apartment size (in square footage) for a sample of 25 apartments (Chapter 13)

**RESTAURANTS** Location, food rating, decor rating, service rating, summated rating, coded location (0 = urban, 1 = suburban), and price of restaurants (Chapters 2, 10, 13, 14)

**RESTAURANTS2** Location, food rating, decor rating, service rating, summated rating, coded location (0 = urban, 1 = suburban), and price of restaurants (Chapter 19)

**ROSLYN** Address, appraised value, property size (acres), house size, age, number of rooms, number of bathrooms, and number of cars that can be parked in the garage in Roslyn, New York (Chapter 15)

**RUDYBIRD** Day, total cases sold, and cases of Rudybird sold (Chapter 18)

**RXDRUGS** Name of drug, price at two U.S. online drug stores and at Aptecha (Chapter 11)

**S&PINDEX** Coded quarters, end-of-quarter values of the quarterly Standard & Poor's Composite Stock Price Index, and three quarterly dummy variables (Chapter 16)

**SAFETY** Tour, number of unsafe acts (Chapter 18)

**SATISFACTION** Satisfaction (0 = no, 1 = yes), delivery time difference, previous stay at hotel (0 = no, 1 = yes) (Chapter 14)

**SAVINGS** Bank, money market rate, one-year CD rate, and five-year CD rate (Chapters 2, 3, 6)

**SCRUBBER** Airflow, water flow, recirculating water flow, orifice diameter, and NTU (Chapter 15)

**SEALANT** Sample number, sealant strength for Boston shingles, and sealant strength for Vermont shingles (Chapter 18)

**SEDANS** Model and miles per gallon (Chapters 3, 8)

**SH2** Day and number of calls received at the help desk (Chapters 2, 3)

**SH8** Rate ($) willing to pay for the newspaper (Chapter 8)

**SH9** Blackness of newsprint (Chapter 9)

**SH10** Length of early calls (in seconds), length of late calls (in seconds), and difference (in seconds) (Chapter 10)

**SH11-1** Call, presentation plan (structured = 1, semistructured = 2, unstructured = 3), and length of call (in seconds) (Chapter 11)

**SH11-2** Gender of caller, type of greeting, and length of call (Chapter 11)

**SH13** Hours per month spent telemarketing and number of new subscriptions per month over a 24-month period (Chapter 13)

**SH14** Hours per week spent telemarketing, number of new subscriptions, and type of presentation (Chapter 14)

**SH16** Month and number of home-delivery subscriptions over the most recent 24-month period (Chapter 16)

**SH18-1** Day, number of ads with errors, number of ads, and number of errors over a 25-day period (Chapter 18)

**SH18-2** Day and newsprint blackness measures for each of five spots made over 25 consecutive weekdays (Chapter 18)

**SITE** Store number, square footage (in thousands of square feet), and sales (in millions of dollars) in 14 Sunflowers Apparel stores (Chapter 13)

**SPENDING** State and per-capita federal spending ($000) in 2004 (Chapters 2, 3, 6)

**SPONGE** Day, number of sponges produced, number of nonconforming sponges, proportion of nonconforming sponges (Chapter 18)

**SPORTING** Sales, age, annual population growth, income, percentage with high school diploma, and percentage with college diploma (Chapters 13, 15)

**SPWATER** Sample number and amount of magnesium (Chapter 18)

**STANDBY** Standby hours, staff, remote hours, Dubner hours, and labor hours for 26 weeks (Chapters 14, 15)

**STATES** State, commuting time, percentage of homes with more than eight rooms, median income, and percentage of housing that costs more than 30% of family income (Chapter 2)

**STEEL** Error in actual length and specified length (Chapters 2, 6, 8, 9)

**STOCKS & BONDS** Date, closing price of the Dow Jones Industrial Average, and closing price of Vanguard Long-Term Bond Index Fund (Chapter 13)

**STOCKS2006** Week and closing weekly stock price for S&P, Target, Sara Lee, and GE (Chapters 2, 13)

**STRATEGIC** Year and billions of barrels in U.S. strategic oil reserve (Chapter 16)

**STUDYTIME** Gender and study time (Chapter 10)

**SUPERMARKET** Day, number of customers, and check-out time (Chapter 13)

**SUV** Model, miles per gallon (Chapters 3, 8)

**TAX** Quarterly sales tax receipts (in thousands of dollars) for 50 business establishments (Chapter 3)

**TAXES** County taxes (in dollars) and age of house (in years) for 19 single-family houses (Chapter 15)

**TEA3** Sample number and weight of tea bags (Chapter 18)

**TEABAGS** Weight of tea bags (Chapters 3, 8, 9)

**TELESPC** Number of orders and number of corrections over 30 days (Chapter 18)

**TELLER** Number of errors by tellers (Chapter 18)

**TENSILE** Sample number and strength (Chapter 18)

**TESTRANK** Rank scores for 10 people trained using a "traditional" method (Method = 0) and 10 people trained using an "experimental" method (Method = 1) (Chapter 12)

**TEXTBOOK** Textbook, book store price, and Amazon price (Chapters 10, 12)

**THEMEPARKS** Name of location and admission price for one-day tickets (Chapter 3)

**TIMES** Times to get ready (Chapter 3)

**TOMATO** Fertilizer and yield (Chapter 15)

**TOMATOES** Year and price per pound in the United States (Chapter 16)

**TOYSRUS** Quarter, coded quarter, revenue, and three dummy variables for quarters (Chapter 16)

**TRADE** Day, number of undesirable trades, and number of total trades made over a 30-day period (Chapter 18)

**TRADES** Day, number of incoming calls, and number of trade executions per day over a 35-day period (Chapter 13)

**TRAINING** Assembly time and training program (team-based = 0, individual-based = 1) (Chapters 10, 12)

**TRANSMIT** Day and number of errors in transmission (Chapter 18)

**TRANSPORT** Days and patient transport times (in minutes) for samples of four patients per day over a 30-day period (Chapter 18)

**TRASHBAGS** Weight required to break four brands of trash bags (Chapters 11, 12)

**TREASURY** Year and interest rate (Chapter 16)

**TROUGH** Width of trough (Chapters 2, 3, 8, 9)

**TRSNYC** Year, unit value of variable A, and unit value of variable B (Chapter 16)

**TSMODEL1** Years, coded years, and three time series (I, II, III) (Chapter 16)

**TSMODEL2** Years, coded years, and two time series (I, II) (Chapter 16)

**TUITION2006** School, in-state tuition and fees, and out-of-state tuition and fees (Chapter 3)

**TVCHANNELS** Year and the number of TV channels received (Chapter 2)

**UNDERGRADSURVEY** Gender, age (*as of last birthday*), height (*in inches*), class designation, major, graduate school intention, cumulative grade point average, expected starting salary (in thousands of dollars), anticipated salary after five years of experience (in thousands of dollars), current employment status, number of campus club/group/organization/team affiliations, satisfaction with student advisement services on campus, and amount spent on books and supplies this semester (Chapters 1, 2, 3, 4, 6, 8, 10, 11, 12)

**UNDERWRITING** Score on proficiency exam, score on end of training exam, and training method (Chapter 14)

**UNEMPLOY** Year, month, and monthly unemployment rates (Chapters 2, 16)

**UNLEADED** Year, month, and price (Chapter 16)

**UTILITY** Utilities charges for 50 one-bedroom apartments (Chapters 2, 6)

**VB** Time (in minutes) for nine students to write and run a Visual Basic program (Chapter 10)

**WAIT** Waiting times and seating times, in minutes (Chapter 6)

**WALMART** Quarter and quarterly revenues (Chapter 16)

**WARECOST** Distribution cost (in thousands of dollars), sales (in thousands of dollars), and number of orders for 24 months (Chapters 13, 14, 15)

**WAREHSE** Number of units handled per day and employee number (Chapter 18)

**WHITNEY1** Type (1 = kidney, 2 = shrimp), shift, and weight in ounces (Chapter 19)

**WHITNEY2** Type (1 = kidney, 2 = shrimp), shift, time, nonconformances, and volume (Chapter 19)

**WHITNEY3** Type (1 = kidney, 2 = shrimp), shift, time, and weight in ounces (Chapter 19)

**WHITNEY4** Type (1 = fine, 2 = chunky) and weight in ounces (Chapter 19)

**WHITNEY5** Type (1 = kidney, 2 = shrimp, 3 = chicken liver, 4 = salmon, 5 = beef) and ounces eaten (Chapter 19)

**WHITNEY6** Piece size (F = fine, C = chunky), fill height (L = low, C = current), and coded weight in ounces (Chapter 19)

**WHOLEFOODS1** Item, price at Whole Foods, and price at Fairway (Chapters 10, 12)

**WHOLEFOODS2** Item, price at Whole Foods, price at Gristede's, price at Fairway, and price at Stop & Shop (Chapters 11, 12)

**WINE** Summated ratings of different wines by experts (Chapter 11)

**WIP** Processing times at each of two plants (A = 1, B = 2) (Chapter 19)

**WONDERLIC** School, average Wonderlic score of football players trying out for the NFL, and graduation rate (Chapters 2, 3, 13)

**WORKFORCE** Year, population, and size of the workforce (Chapter 16)

**WRIGLEY** Year, coded year, actual revenue, consumer price index, and real revenue (Chapter 16)

**YARN** Breaking strength, pressure, yarn sample, and side-by-side aspect (nozzle = 1, opposite = 2) (Chapter 11)

**YIELD** Cleansing step, etching step, and yield (Chapter 11)

# E. TABLES

# E. TABLES

**TABLE E.1**

Table of Random Numbers

| Row | Column | | | | | | | |
|---|---|---|---|---|---|---|---|---|
| | 00000 12345 | 00001 67890 | 11111 12345 | 11112 67890 | 22222 12345 | 22223 67890 | 33333 12345 | 33334 67890 |
| 01 | 49280 | 88924 | 35779 | 00283 | 81163 | 07275 | 89863 | 02348 |
| 02 | 61870 | 41657 | 07468 | 08612 | 98083 | 97349 | 20775 | 45091 |
| 03 | 43898 | 65923 | 25078 | 86129 | 78496 | 97653 | 91550 | 08078 |
| 04 | 62993 | 93912 | 30454 | 84598 | 56095 | 20664 | 12872 | 64647 |
| 05 | 33850 | 58555 | 51438 | 85507 | 71865 | 79488 | 76783 | 31708 |
| 06 | 97340 | 03364 | 88472 | 04334 | 63919 | 36394 | 11095 | 92470 |
| 07 | 70543 | 29776 | 10087 | 10072 | 55980 | 64688 | 68239 | 20461 |
| 08 | 89382 | 93809 | 00796 | 95945 | 34101 | 81277 | 66090 | 88872 |
| 09 | 37818 | 72142 | 67140 | 50785 | 22380 | 16703 | 53362 | 44940 |
| 10 | 60430 | 22834 | 14130 | 96593 | 23298 | 56203 | 92671 | 15925 |
| 11 | 82975 | 66158 | 84731 | 19436 | 55790 | 69229 | 28661 | 13675 |
| 12 | 30987 | 71938 | 40355 | 54324 | 08401 | 26299 | 49420 | 59208 |
| 13 | 55700 | 24586 | 93247 | 32596 | 11865 | 63397 | 44251 | 43189 |
| 14 | 14756 | 23997 | 78643 | 75912 | 83832 | 32768 | 18928 | 57070 |
| 15 | 32166 | 53251 | 70654 | 92827 | 63491 | 04233 | 33825 | 69662 |
| 16 | 23236 | 73751 | 31888 | 81718 | 06546 | 83246 | 47651 | 04877 |
| 17 | 45794 | 26926 | 15130 | 82455 | 78305 | 55058 | 52551 | 47182 |
| 18 | 09893 | 20505 | 14225 | 68514 | 47427 | 56788 | 96297 | 78822 |
| 19 | 54382 | 74598 | 91499 | 14523 | 68479 | 27686 | 46162 | 83554 |
| 20 | 94750 | 89923 | 37089 | 20048 | 80336 | 94598 | 26940 | 36858 |
| 21 | 70297 | 34135 | 53140 | 33340 | 42050 | 82341 | 44104 | 82949 |
| 22 | 85157 | 47954 | 32979 | 26575 | 57600 | 40881 | 12250 | 73742 |
| 23 | 11100 | 02340 | 12860 | 74697 | 96644 | 89439 | 28707 | 25815 |
| 24 | 36871 | 50775 | 30592 | 57143 | 17381 | 68856 | 25853 | 35041 |
| 25 | 23913 | 48357 | 63308 | 16090 | 51690 | 54607 | 72407 | 55538 |
| 26 | 79348 | 36085 | 27973 | 65157 | 07456 | 22255 | 25626 | 57054 |
| 27 | 92074 | 54641 | 53673 | 54421 | 18130 | 60103 | 69593 | 49464 |
| 28 | 06873 | 21440 | 75593 | 41373 | 49502 | 17972 | 82578 | 16364 |
| 29 | 12478 | 37622 | 99659 | 31065 | 83613 | 69889 | 58869 | 29571 |
| 30 | 57175 | 55564 | 65411 | 42547 | 70457 | 03426 | 72937 | 83792 |
| 31 | 91616 | 11075 | 80103 | 07831 | 59309 | 13276 | 26710 | 73000 |
| 32 | 78025 | 73539 | 14621 | 39044 | 47450 | 03197 | 12787 | 47709 |
| 33 | 27587 | 67228 | 80145 | 10175 | 12822 | 86687 | 65530 | 49325 |
| 34 | 16690 | 20427 | 04251 | 64477 | 73709 | 73945 | 92396 | 68263 |
| 35 | 70183 | 58065 | 65489 | 31833 | 82093 | 16747 | 10386 | 59293 |
| 36 | 90730 | 35385 | 15679 | 99742 | 50866 | 78028 | 75573 | 67257 |
| 37 | 10934 | 93242 | 13431 | 24590 | 02770 | 48582 | 00906 | 58595 |
| 38 | 82462 | 30166 | 79613 | 47416 | 13389 | 80268 | 05085 | 96666 |
| 39 | 27463 | 10433 | 07606 | 16285 | 93699 | 60912 | 94532 | 95632 |
| 40 | 02979 | 52997 | 09079 | 92709 | 90110 | 47506 | 53693 | 49892 |
| 41 | 46888 | 69929 | 75233 | 52507 | 32097 | 37594 | 10067 | 67327 |
| 42 | 53638 | 83161 | 08289 | 12639 | 08141 | 12640 | 28437 | 09268 |
| 43 | 82433 | 61427 | 17239 | 89160 | 19666 | 08814 | 37841 | 12847 |
| 44 | 35766 | 31672 | 50082 | 22795 | 66948 | 65581 | 84393 | 15890 |
| 45 | 10853 | 42581 | 08792 | 13257 | 61973 | 24450 | 52351 | 16602 |
| 46 | 20341 | 27398 | 72906 | 63955 | 17276 | 10646 | 74692 | 48438 |
| 47 | 54458 | 90542 | 77563 | 51839 | 52901 | 53355 | 83281 | 19177 |
| 48 | 26337 | 66530 | 16687 | 35179 | 46560 | 00123 | 44546 | 79896 |
| 49 | 34314 | 23729 | 85264 | 05575 | 96855 | 23820 | 11091 | 79821 |
| 50 | 28603 | 10708 | 68933 | 34189 | 92166 | 15181 | 66628 | 58599 |

*continued*

**TABLE E.1**

Table of Random Numbers (*Continued*)

| Row | Column 00000 12345 | 00001 67890 | 11111 12345 | 11112 67890 | 22222 12345 | 22223 67890 | 33333 12345 | 33334 67890 |
|-----|-------|-------|-------|-------|-------|-------|-------|-------|
| 51 | 66194 | 28926 | 99547 | 16625 | 45515 | 67953 | 12108 | 57846 |
| 52 | 78240 | 43195 | 24837 | 32511 | 70880 | 22070 | 52622 | 61881 |
| 53 | 00833 | 88000 | 67299 | 68215 | 11274 | 55624 | 32991 | 17436 |
| 54 | 12111 | 86683 | 61270 | 58036 | 64192 | 90611 | 15145 | 01748 |
| 55 | 47189 | 99951 | 05755 | 03834 | 43782 | 90599 | 40282 | 51417 |
| 56 | 76396 | 72486 | 62423 | 27618 | 84184 | 78922 | 73561 | 52818 |
| 57 | 46409 | 17469 | 32483 | 09083 | 76175 | 19985 | 26309 | 91536 |
| 58 | 74626 | 22111 | 87286 | 46772 | 42243 | 68046 | 44250 | 42439 |
| 59 | 34450 | 81974 | 93723 | 49023 | 58432 | 67083 | 36876 | 93391 |
| 60 | 36327 | 72135 | 33005 | 28701 | 34710 | 49359 | 50693 | 89311 |
| 61 | 74185 | 77536 | 84825 | 09934 | 99103 | 09325 | 67389 | 45869 |
| 62 | 12296 | 41623 | 62873 | 37943 | 25584 | 09609 | 63360 | 47270 |
| 63 | 90822 | 60280 | 88925 | 99610 | 42772 | 60561 | 76873 | 04117 |
| 64 | 72121 | 79152 | 96591 | 90305 | 10189 | 79778 | 68016 | 13747 |
| 65 | 95268 | 41377 | 25684 | 08151 | 61816 | 58555 | 54305 | 86189 |
| 66 | 92603 | 09091 | 75884 | 93424 | 72586 | 88903 | 30061 | 14457 |
| 67 | 18813 | 90291 | 05275 | 01223 | 79607 | 95426 | 34900 | 09778 |
| 68 | 38840 | 26903 | 28624 | 67157 | 51986 | 42865 | 14508 | 49315 |
| 69 | 05959 | 33836 | 53758 | 16562 | 41081 | 38012 | 41230 | 20528 |
| 70 | 85141 | 21155 | 99212 | 32685 | 51403 | 31926 | 69813 | 58781 |
| 71 | 75047 | 59643 | 31074 | 38172 | 03718 | 32119 | 69506 | 67143 |
| 72 | 30752 | 95260 | 68032 | 62871 | 58781 | 34143 | 68790 | 69766 |
| 73 | 22986 | 82575 | 42187 | 62295 | 84295 | 30634 | 66562 | 31442 |
| 74 | 99439 | 86692 | 90348 | 66036 | 48399 | 73451 | 26698 | 39437 |
| 75 | 20389 | 93029 | 11881 | 71685 | 65452 | 89047 | 63669 | 02656 |
| 76 | 39249 | 05173 | 68256 | 36359 | 20250 | 68686 | 05947 | 09335 |
| 77 | 96777 | 33605 | 29481 | 20063 | 09398 | 01843 | 35139 | 61344 |
| 78 | 04860 | 32918 | 10798 | 50492 | 52655 | 33359 | 94713 | 28393 |
| 79 | 41613 | 42375 | 00403 | 03656 | 77580 | 87772 | 86877 | 57085 |
| 80 | 17930 | 00794 | 53836 | 53692 | 67135 | 98102 | 61912 | 11246 |
| 81 | 24649 | 31845 | 25736 | 75231 | 83808 | 98917 | 93829 | 99430 |
| 82 | 79899 | 34061 | 54308 | 59358 | 56462 | 58166 | 97302 | 86828 |
| 83 | 76801 | 49594 | 81002 | 30397 | 52728 | 15101 | 72070 | 33706 |
| 84 | 36239 | 63636 | 38140 | 65731 | 39788 | 06872 | 38971 | 53363 |
| 85 | 07392 | 64449 | 17886 | 63632 | 53995 | 17574 | 22247 | 62607 |
| 86 | 67133 | 04181 | 33874 | 98835 | 67453 | 59734 | 76381 | 63455 |
| 87 | 77759 | 31504 | 32832 | 70861 | 15152 | 29733 | 75371 | 39174 |
| 88 | 85992 | 72268 | 42920 | 20810 | 29361 | 51423 | 90306 | 73574 |
| 89 | 79553 | 75952 | 54116 | 65553 | 47139 | 60579 | 09165 | 85490 |
| 90 | 41101 | 17336 | 48951 | 53674 | 17880 | 45260 | 08575 | 49321 |
| 91 | 36191 | 17095 | 32123 | 91576 | 84221 | 78902 | 82010 | 30847 |
| 92 | 62329 | 63898 | 23268 | 74283 | 26091 | 68409 | 69704 | 82267 |
| 93 | 14751 | 13151 | 93115 | 01437 | 56945 | 89661 | 67680 | 79790 |
| 94 | 48462 | 59278 | 44185 | 29616 | 76537 | 19589 | 83139 | 28454 |
| 95 | 29435 | 88105 | 59651 | 44391 | 74588 | 55114 | 80834 | 85686 |
| 96 | 28340 | 29285 | 12965 | 14821 | 80425 | 16602 | 44653 | 70467 |
| 97 | 02167 | 58940 | 27149 | 80242 | 10587 | 79786 | 34959 | 75339 |
| 98 | 17864 | 00991 | 39557 | 54981 | 23588 | 81914 | 37609 | 13128 |
| 99 | 79675 | 80605 | 60059 | 35862 | 00254 | 36546 | 21545 | 78179 |
| 00 | 72335 | 82037 | 92003 | 34100 | 29879 | 46613 | 89720 | 13274 |

Source: *Partially extracted from the Rand Corporation,* A Million Random Digits with 100,000 Normal Deviates *(Glencoe, IL, The Free Press, 1955).*

## TABLE E.2

The Cumulative Standardized Normal Distribution

Entry represents area under the cumulative standardized normal distribution from $-\infty$ to $Z$

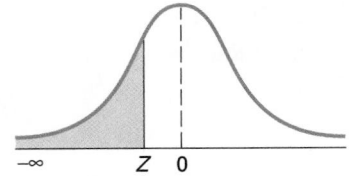

| | | | | | Cumulative Probabilities | | | | | |
|---|---|---|---|---|---|---|---|---|---|---|
| Z | 0.00 | 0.01 | 0.02 | 0.03 | 0.04 | 0.05 | 0.06 | 0.07 | 0.08 | 0.09 |
| −6.0 | 0.000000001 | | | | | | | | | |
| −5.5 | 0.000000019 | | | | | | | | | |
| −5.0 | 0.000000287 | | | | | | | | | |
| −4.5 | 0.000003398 | | | | | | | | | |
| −4.0 | 0.000031671 | | | | | | | | | |
| −3.9 | 0.00005 | 0.00005 | 0.00004 | 0.00004 | 0.00004 | 0.00004 | 0.00004 | 0.00004 | 0.00003 | 0.00003 |
| −3.8 | 0.00007 | 0.00007 | 0.00007 | 0.00006 | 0.00006 | 0.00006 | 0.00006 | 0.00005 | 0.00005 | 0.00005 |
| −3.7 | 0.00011 | 0.00010 | 0.00010 | 0.00010 | 0.00009 | 0.00009 | 0.00008 | 0.00008 | 0.00008 | 0.00008 |
| −3.6 | 0.00016 | 0.00015 | 0.00015 | 0.00014 | 0.00014 | 0.00013 | 0.00013 | 0.00012 | 0.00012 | 0.00011 |
| −3.5 | 0.00023 | 0.00022 | 0.00022 | 0.00021 | 0.00020 | 0.00019 | 0.00019 | 0.00018 | 0.00017 | 0.00017 |
| −3.4 | 0.00034 | 0.00032 | 0.00031 | 0.00030 | 0.00029 | 0.00028 | 0.00027 | 0.00026 | 0.00025 | 0.00024 |
| −3.3 | 0.00048 | 0.00047 | 0.00045 | 0.00043 | 0.00042 | 0.00040 | 0.00039 | 0.00038 | 0.00036 | 0.00035 |
| −3.2 | 0.00069 | 0.00066 | 0.00064 | 0.00062 | 0.00060 | 0.00058 | 0.00056 | 0.00054 | 0.00052 | 0.00050 |
| −3.1 | 0.00097 | 0.00094 | 0.00090 | 0.00087 | 0.00084 | 0.00082 | 0.00079 | 0.00076 | 0.00074 | 0.00071 |
| −3.0 | 0.00135 | 0.00131 | 0.00126 | 0.00122 | 0.00118 | 0.00114 | 0.00111 | 0.00107 | 0.00103 | 0.00100 |
| −2.9 | 0.0019 | 0.0018 | 0.0018 | 0.0017 | 0.0016 | 0.0016 | 0.0015 | 0.0015 | 0.0014 | 0.0014 |
| −2.8 | 0.0026 | 0.0025 | 0.0024 | 0.0023 | 0.0023 | 0.0022 | 0.0021 | 0.0021 | 0.0020 | 0.0019 |
| −2.7 | 0.0035 | 0.0034 | 0.0033 | 0.0032 | 0.0031 | 0.0030 | 0.0029 | 0.0028 | 0.0027 | 0.0026 |
| −2.6 | 0.0047 | 0.0045 | 0.0044 | 0.0043 | 0.0041 | 0.0040 | 0.0039 | 0.0038 | 0.0037 | 0.0036 |
| −2.5 | 0.0062 | 0.0060 | 0.0059 | 0.0057 | 0.0055 | 0.0054 | 0.0052 | 0.0051 | 0.0049 | 0.0048 |
| −2.4 | 0.0082 | 0.0080 | 0.0078 | 0.0075 | 0.0073 | 0.0071 | 0.0069 | 0.0068 | 0.0066 | 0.0064 |
| −2.3 | 0.0107 | 0.0104 | 0.0102 | 0.0099 | 0.0096 | 0.0094 | 0.0091 | 0.0089 | 0.0087 | 0.0084 |
| −2.2 | 0.0139 | 0.0136 | 0.0132 | 0.0129 | 0.0125 | 0.0122 | 0.0119 | 0.0116 | 0.0113 | 0.0110 |
| −2.1 | 0.0179 | 0.0174 | 0.0170 | 0.0166 | 0.0162 | 0.0158 | 0.0154 | 0.0150 | 0.0146 | 0.0143 |
| −2.0 | 0.0228 | 0.0222 | 0.0217 | 0.0212 | 0.0207 | 0.0202 | 0.0197 | 0.0192 | 0.0188 | 0.0183 |
| −1.9 | 0.0287 | 0.0281 | 0.0274 | 0.0268 | 0.0262 | 0.0256 | 0.0250 | 0.0244 | 0.0239 | 0.0233 |
| −1.8 | 0.0359 | 0.0351 | 0.0344 | 0.0336 | 0.0329 | 0.0322 | 0.0314 | 0.0307 | 0.0301 | 0.0294 |
| −1.7 | 0.0446 | 0.0436 | 0.0427 | 0.0418 | 0.0409 | 0.0401 | 0.0392 | 0.0384 | 0.0375 | 0.0367 |
| −1.6 | 0.0548 | 0.0537 | 0.0526 | 0.0516 | 0.0505 | 0.0495 | 0.0485 | 0.0475 | 0.0465 | 0.0455 |
| −1.5 | 0.0668 | 0.0655 | 0.0643 | 0.0630 | 0.0618 | 0.0606 | 0.0594 | 0.0582 | 0.0571 | 0.0559 |
| −1.4 | 0.0808 | 0.0793 | 0.0778 | 0.0764 | 0.0749 | 0.0735 | 0.0721 | 0.0708 | 0.0694 | 0.0681 |
| −1.3 | 0.0968 | 0.0951 | 0.0934 | 0.0918 | 0.0901 | 0.0885 | 0.0869 | 0.0853 | 0.0838 | 0.0823 |
| −1.2 | 0.1151 | 0.1131 | 0.1112 | 0.1093 | 0.1075 | 0.1056 | 0.1038 | 0.1020 | 0.1003 | 0.0985 |
| −1.1 | 0.1357 | 0.1335 | 0.1314 | 0.1292 | 0.1271 | 0.1251 | 0.1230 | 0.1210 | 0.1190 | 0.1170 |
| −1.0 | 0.1587 | 0.1562 | 0.1539 | 0.1515 | 0.1492 | 0.1469 | 0.1446 | 0.1423 | 0.1401 | 0.1379 |
| −0.9 | 0.1841 | 0.1814 | 0.1788 | 0.1762 | 0.1736 | 0.1711 | 0.1685 | 0.1660 | 0.1635 | 0.1611 |
| −0.8 | 0.2119 | 0.2090 | 0.2061 | 0.2033 | 0.2005 | 0.1977 | 0.1949 | 0.1922 | 0.1894 | 0.1867 |
| −0.7 | 0.2420 | 0.2388 | 0.2358 | 0.2327 | 0.2296 | 0.2266 | 0.2236 | 0.2206 | 0.2177 | 0.2148 |
| −0.6 | 0.2743 | 0.2709 | 0.2676 | 0.2643 | 0.2611 | 0.2578 | 0.2546 | 0.2514 | 0.2482 | 0.2451 |
| −0.5 | 0.3085 | 0.3050 | 0.3015 | 0.2981 | 0.2946 | 0.2912 | 0.2877 | 0.2843 | 0.2810 | 0.2776 |
| −0.4 | 0.3446 | 0.3409 | 0.3372 | 0.3336 | 0.3300 | 0.3264 | 0.3228 | 0.3192 | 0.3156 | 0.3121 |
| −0.3 | 0.3821 | 0.3783 | 0.3745 | 0.3707 | 0.3669 | 0.3632 | 0.3594 | 0.3557 | 0.3520 | 0.3483 |
| −0.2 | 0.4207 | 0.4168 | 0.4129 | 0.4090 | 0.4052 | 0.4013 | 0.3974 | 0.3936 | 0.3897 | 0.3859 |
| −0.1 | 0.4602 | 0.4562 | 0.4522 | 0.4483 | 0.4443 | 0.4404 | 0.4364 | 0.4325 | 0.4286 | 0.4247 |
| −0.0 | 0.5000 | 0.4960 | 0.4920 | 0.4880 | 0.4840 | 0.4801 | 0.4761 | 0.4721 | 0.4681 | 0.4641 |

*continued*

## TABLE E.2

The Cumulative Standardized Normal Distribution (*Continued*)

Entry represents area under the cumulative standardized normal distribution from $-\infty$ to Z

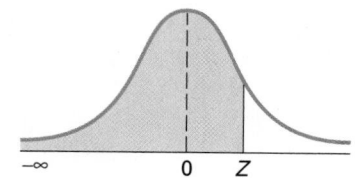

| | | | | | Cumulative Probabilities | | | | | |
|---|---|---|---|---|---|---|---|---|---|---|
| Z | 0.00 | 0.01 | 0.02 | 0.03 | 0.04 | 0.05 | 0.06 | 0.07 | 0.08 | 0.09 |
| 0.0 | 0.5000 | 0.5040 | 0.5080 | 0.5120 | 0.5160 | 0.5199 | 0.5239 | 0.5279 | 0.5319 | 0.5359 |
| 0.1 | 0.5398 | 0.5438 | 0.5478 | 0.5517 | 0.5557 | 0.5596 | 0.5636 | 0.5675 | 0.5714 | 0.5753 |
| 0.2 | 0.5793 | 0.5832 | 0.5871 | 0.5910 | 0.5948 | 0.5987 | 0.6026 | 0.6064 | 0.6103 | 0.6141 |
| 0.3 | 0.6179 | 0.6217 | 0.6255 | 0.6293 | 0.6331 | 0.6368 | 0.6406 | 0.6443 | 0.6480 | 0.6517 |
| 0.4 | 0.6554 | 0.6591 | 0.6628 | 0.6664 | 0.6700 | 0.6736 | 0.6772 | 0.6808 | 0.6844 | 0.6879 |
| 0.5 | 0.6915 | 0.6950 | 0.6985 | 0.7019 | 0.7054 | 0.7088 | 0.7123 | 0.7157 | 0.7190 | 0.7224 |
| 0.6 | 0.7257 | 0.7291 | 0.7324 | 0.7357 | 0.7389 | 0.7422 | 0.7454 | 0.7486 | 0.7518 | 0.7549 |
| 0.7 | 0.7580 | 0.7612 | 0.7642 | 0.7673 | 0.7704 | 0.7734 | 0.7764 | 0.7794 | 0.7823 | 0.7852 |
| 0.8 | 0.7881 | 0.7910 | 0.7939 | 0.7967 | 0.7995 | 0.8023 | 0.8051 | 0.8078 | 0.8106 | 0.8133 |
| 0.9 | 0.8159 | 0.8186 | 0.8212 | 0.8238 | 0.8264 | 0.8289 | 0.8315 | 0.8340 | 0.8365 | 0.8389 |
| 1.0 | 0.8413 | 0.8438 | 0.8461 | 0.8485 | 0.8508 | 0.8531 | 0.8554 | 0.8577 | 0.8599 | 0.8621 |
| 1.1 | 0.8643 | 0.8665 | 0.8686 | 0.8708 | 0.8729 | 0.8749 | 0.8770 | 0.8790 | 0.8810 | 0.8830 |
| 1.2 | 0.8849 | 0.8869 | 0.8888 | 0.8907 | 0.8925 | 0.8944 | 0.8962 | 0.8980 | 0.8997 | 0.9015 |
| 1.3 | 0.9032 | 0.9049 | 0.9066 | 0.9082 | 0.9099 | 0.9115 | 0.9131 | 0.9147 | 0.9162 | 0.9177 |
| 1.4 | 0.9192 | 0.9207 | 0.9222 | 0.9236 | 0.9251 | 0.9265 | 0.9279 | 0.9292 | 0.9306 | 0.9319 |
| 1.5 | 0.9332 | 0.9345 | 0.9357 | 0.9370 | 0.9382 | 0.9394 | 0.9406 | 0.9418 | 0.9429 | 0.9441 |
| 1.6 | 0.9452 | 0.9463 | 0.9474 | 0.9484 | 0.9495 | 0.9505 | 0.9515 | 0.9525 | 0.9535 | 0.9545 |
| 1.7 | 0.9554 | 0.9564 | 0.9573 | 0.9582 | 0.9591 | 0.9599 | 0.9608 | 0.9616 | 0.9625 | 0.9633 |
| 1.8 | 0.9641 | 0.9649 | 0.9656 | 0.9664 | 0.9671 | 0.9678 | 0.9686 | 0.9693 | 0.9699 | 0.9706 |
| 1.9 | 0.9713 | 0.9719 | 0.9726 | 0.9732 | 0.9738 | 0.9744 | 0.9750 | 0.9756 | 0.9761 | 0.9767 |
| 2.0 | 0.9772 | 0.9778 | 0.9783 | 0.9788 | 0.9793 | 0.9798 | 0.9803 | 0.9808 | 0.9812 | 0.9817 |
| 2.1 | 0.9821 | 0.9826 | 0.9830 | 0.9834 | 0.9838 | 0.9842 | 0.9846 | 0.9850 | 0.9854 | 0.9857 |
| 2.2 | 0.9861 | 0.9864 | 0.9868 | 0.9871 | 0.9875 | 0.9878 | 0.9881 | 0.9884 | 0.9887 | 0.9890 |
| 2.3 | 0.9893 | 0.9896 | 0.9898 | 0.9901 | 0.9904 | 0.9906 | 0.9909 | 0.9911 | 0.9913 | 0.9916 |
| 2.4 | 0.9918 | 0.9920 | 0.9922 | 0.9925 | 0.9927 | 0.9929 | 0.9931 | 0.9932 | 0.9934 | 0.9936 |
| 2.5 | 0.9938 | 0.9940 | 0.9941 | 0.9943 | 0.9945 | 0.9946 | 0.9948 | 0.9949 | 0.9951 | 0.9952 |
| 2.6 | 0.9953 | 0.9955 | 0.9956 | 0.9957 | 0.9959 | 0.9960 | 0.9961 | 0.9962 | 0.9963 | 0.9964 |
| 2.7 | 0.9965 | 0.9966 | 0.9967 | 0.9968 | 0.9969 | 0.9970 | 0.9971 | 0.9972 | 0.9973 | 0.9974 |
| 2.8 | 0.9974 | 0.9975 | 0.9976 | 0.9977 | 0.9977 | 0.9978 | 0.9979 | 0.9979 | 0.9980 | 0.9981 |
| 2.9 | 0.9981 | 0.9982 | 0.9982 | 0.9983 | 0.9984 | 0.9984 | 0.9985 | 0.9985 | 0.9986 | 0.9986 |
| 3.0 | 0.99865 | 0.99869 | 0.99874 | 0.99878 | 0.99882 | 0.99886 | 0.99889 | 0.99893 | 0.99897 | 0.99900 |
| 3.1 | 0.99903 | 0.99906 | 0.99910 | 0.99913 | 0.99916 | 0.99918 | 0.99921 | 0.99924 | 0.99926 | 0.99929 |
| 3.2 | 0.99931 | 0.99934 | 0.99936 | 0.99938 | 0.99940 | 0.99942 | 0.99944 | 0.99946 | 0.99948 | 0.99950 |
| 3.3 | 0.99952 | 0.99953 | 0.99955 | 0.99957 | 0.99958 | 0.99960 | 0.99961 | 0.99962 | 0.99964 | 0.99965 |
| 3.4 | 0.99966 | 0.99968 | 0.99969 | 0.99970 | 0.99971 | 0.99972 | 0.99973 | 0.99974 | 0.99975 | 0.99976 |
| 3.5 | 0.99977 | 0.99978 | 0.99978 | 0.99979 | 0.99980 | 0.99981 | 0.99981 | 0.99982 | 0.99983 | 0.99983 |
| 3.6 | 0.99984 | 0.99985 | 0.99985 | 0.99986 | 0.99986 | 0.99987 | 0.99987 | 0.99988 | 0.99988 | 0.99989 |
| 3.7 | 0.99989 | 0.99990 | 0.99990 | 0.99990 | 0.99991 | 0.99991 | 0.99992 | 0.99992 | 0.99992 | 0.99992 |
| 3.8 | 0.99993 | 0.99993 | 0.99993 | 0.99994 | 0.99994 | 0.99994 | 0.99994 | 0.99995 | 0.99995 | 0.99995 |
| 3.9 | 0.99995 | 0.99995 | 0.99996 | 0.99996 | 0.99996 | 0.99996 | 0.99996 | 0.99996 | 0.99997 | 0.99997 |
| 4.0 | 0.999968329 | | | | | | | | | |
| 4.5 | 0.999996602 | | | | | | | | | |
| 5.0 | 0.999999713 | | | | | | | | | |
| 5.5 | 0.999999981 | | | | | | | | | |
| 6.0 | 0.999999999 | | | | | | | | | |

## TABLE E.3

Critical Values of $t$

For a particular number of degrees of freedom, entry represents the critical value of $t$ corresponding to a specified upper-tail area ($\alpha$).

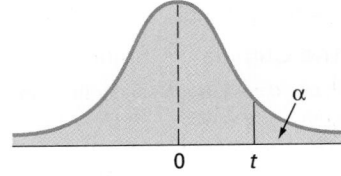

| Degrees of Freedom | Cumulative Probabilities | | | | | |
|---|---|---|---|---|---|---|
| | 0.75 | 0.90 | 0.95 | 0.975 | 0.99 | 0.995 |
| | Upper-Tail Areas | | | | | |
| | 0.25 | 0.10 | 0.05 | 0.025 | 0.01 | 0.005 |
| 1 | 1.0000 | 3.0777 | 6.3138 | 12.7062 | 31.8207 | 63.6574 |
| 2 | 0.8165 | 1.8856 | 2.9200 | 4.3027 | 6.9646 | 9.9248 |
| 3 | 0.7649 | 1.6377 | 2.3534 | 3.1824 | 4.5407 | 5.8409 |
| 4 | 0.7407 | 1.5332 | 2.1318 | 2.7764 | 3.7469 | 4.6041 |
| 5 | 0.7267 | 1.4759 | 2.0150 | 2.5706 | 3.3649 | 4.0322 |
| 6 | 0.7176 | 1.4398 | 1.9432 | 2.4469 | 3.1427 | 3.7074 |
| 7 | 0.7111 | 1.4149 | 1.8946 | 2.3646 | 2.9980 | 3.4995 |
| 8 | 0.7064 | 1.3968 | 1.8595 | 2.3060 | 2.8965 | 3.3554 |
| 9 | 0.7027 | 1.3830 | 1.8331 | 2.2622 | 2.8214 | 3.2498 |
| 10 | 0.6998 | 1.3722 | 1.8125 | 2.2281 | 2.7638 | 3.1693 |
| 11 | 0.6974 | 1.3634 | 1.7959 | 2.2010 | 2.7181 | 3.1058 |
| 12 | 0.6955 | 1.3562 | 1.7823 | 2.1788 | 2.6810 | 3.0545 |
| 13 | 0.6938 | 1.3502 | 1.7709 | 2.1604 | 2.6503 | 3.0123 |
| 14 | 0.6924 | 1.3450 | 1.7613 | 2.1448 | 2.6245 | 2.9768 |
| 15 | 0.6912 | 1.3406 | 1.7531 | 2.1315 | 2.6025 | 2.9467 |
| 16 | 0.6901 | 1.3368 | 1.7459 | 2.1199 | 2.5835 | 2.9208 |
| 17 | 0.6892 | 1.3334 | 1.7396 | 2.1098 | 2.5669 | 2.8982 |
| 18 | 0.6884 | 1.3304 | 1.7341 | 2.1009 | 2.5524 | 2.8784 |
| 19 | 0.6876 | 1.3277 | 1.7291 | 2.0930 | 2.5395 | 2.8609 |
| 20 | 0.6870 | 1.3253 | 1.7247 | 2.0860 | 2.5280 | 2.8453 |
| 21 | 0.6864 | 1.3232 | 1.7207 | 2.0796 | 2.5177 | 2.8314 |
| 22 | 0.6858 | 1.3212 | 1.7171 | 2.0739 | 2.5083 | 2.8188 |
| 23 | 0.6853 | 1.3195 | 1.7139 | 2.0687 | 2.4999 | 2.8073 |
| 24 | 0.6848 | 1.3178 | 1.7109 | 2.0639 | 2.4922 | 2.7969 |
| 25 | 0.6844 | 1.3163 | 1.7081 | 2.0595 | 2.4851 | 2.7874 |
| 26 | 0.6840 | 1.3150 | 1.7056 | 2.0555 | 2.4786 | 2.7787 |
| 27 | 0.6837 | 1.3137 | 1.7033 | 2.0518 | 2.4727 | 2.7707 |
| 28 | 0.6834 | 1.3125 | 1.7011 | 2.0484 | 2.4671 | 2.7633 |
| 29 | 0.6830 | 1.3114 | 1.6991 | 2.0452 | 2.4620 | 2.7564 |
| 30 | 0.6828 | 1.3104 | 1.6973 | 2.0423 | 2.4573 | 2.7500 |
| 31 | 0.6825 | 1.3095 | 1.6955 | 2.0395 | 2.4528 | 2.7440 |
| 32 | 0.6822 | 1.3086 | 1.6939 | 2.0369 | 2.4487 | 2.7385 |
| 33 | 0.6820 | 1.3077 | 1.6924 | 2.0345 | 2.4448 | 2.7333 |
| 34 | 0.6818 | 1.3070 | 1.6909 | 2.0322 | 2.4411 | 2.7284 |
| 35 | 0.6816 | 1.3062 | 1.6896 | 2.0301 | 2.4377 | 2.7238 |
| 36 | 0.6814 | 1.3055 | 1.6883 | 2.0281 | 2.4345 | 2.7195 |
| 37 | 0.6812 | 1.3049 | 1.6871 | 2.0262 | 2.4314 | 2.7154 |
| 38 | 0.6810 | 1.3042 | 1.6860 | 2.0244 | 2.4286 | 2.7116 |
| 39 | 0.6808 | 1.3036 | 1.6849 | 2.0227 | 2.4258 | 2.7079 |
| 40 | 0.6807 | 1.3031 | 1.6839 | 2.0211 | 2.4233 | 2.7045 |
| 41 | 0.6805 | 1.3025 | 1.6829 | 2.0195 | 2.4208 | 2.7012 |
| 42 | 0.6804 | 1.3020 | 1.6820 | 2.0181 | 2.4185 | 2.6981 |
| 43 | 0.6802 | 1.3016 | 1.6811 | 2.0167 | 2.4163 | 2.6951 |
| 44 | 0.6801 | 1.3011 | 1.6802 | 2.0154 | 2.4141 | 2.6923 |
| 45 | 0.6800 | 1.3006 | 1.6794 | 2.0141 | 2.4121 | 2.6896 |
| 46 | 0.6799 | 1.3002 | 1.6787 | 2.0129 | 2.4102 | 2.6870 |
| 47 | 0.6797 | 1.2998 | 1.6779 | 2.0117 | 2.4083 | 2.6846 |
| 48 | 0.6796 | 1.2994 | 1.6772 | 2.0106 | 2.4066 | 2.6822 |

continued

**TABLE E.3**

Critical Values of *t*
(*Continued*)

| | Cumulative Probabilities | | | | | |
|---|---|---|---|---|---|---|
| | 0.75 | 0.90 | 0.95 | 0.975 | 0.99 | 0.995 |
| Degrees of Freedom | Upper-Tail Areas | | | | | |
| | 0.25 | 0.10 | 0.05 | 0.025 | 0.01 | 0.005 |
| 49 | 0.6795 | 1.2991 | 1.6766 | 2.0096 | 2.4049 | 2.6800 |
| 50 | 0.6794 | 1.2987 | 1.6759 | 2.0086 | 2.4033 | 2.6778 |
| 51 | 0.6793 | 1.2984 | 1.6753 | 2.0076 | 2.4017 | 2.6757 |
| 52 | 0.6792 | 1.2980 | 1.6747 | 2.0066 | 2.4002 | 2.6737 |
| 53 | 0.6791 | 1.2977 | 1.6741 | 2.0057 | 2.3988 | 2.6718 |
| 54 | 0.6791 | 1.2974 | 1.6736 | 2.0049 | 2.3974 | 2.6700 |
| 55 | 0.6790 | 1.2971 | 1.6730 | 2.0040 | 2.3961 | 2.6682 |
| 56 | 0.6789 | 1.2969 | 1.6725 | 2.0032 | 2.3948 | 2.6665 |
| 57 | 0.6788 | 1.2966 | 1.6720 | 2.0025 | 2.3936 | 2.6649 |
| 58 | 0.6787 | 1.2963 | 1.6716 | 2.0017 | 2.3924 | 2.6633 |
| 59 | 0.6787 | 1.2961 | 1.6711 | 2.0010 | 2.3912 | 2.6618 |
| 60 | 0.6786 | 1.2958 | 1.6706 | 2.0003 | 2.3901 | 2.6603 |
| 61 | 0.6785 | 1.2956 | 1.6702 | 1.9996 | 2.3890 | 2.6589 |
| 62 | 0.6785 | 1.2954 | 1.6698 | 1.9990 | 2.3880 | 2.6575 |
| 63 | 0.6784 | 1.2951 | 1.6694 | 1.9983 | 2.3870 | 2.6561 |
| 64 | 0.6783 | 1.2949 | 1.6690 | 1.9977 | 2.3860 | 2.6549 |
| 65 | 0.6783 | 1.2947 | 1.6686 | 1.9971 | 2.3851 | 2.6536 |
| 66 | 0.6782 | 1.2945 | 1.6683 | 1.9966 | 2.3842 | 2.6524 |
| 67 | 0.6782 | 1.2943 | 1.6679 | 1.9960 | 2.3833 | 2.6512 |
| 68 | 0.6781 | 1.2941 | 1.6676 | 1.9955 | 2.3824 | 2.6501 |
| 69 | 0.6781 | 1.2939 | 1.6672 | 1.9949 | 2.3816 | 2.6490 |
| 70 | 0.6780 | 1.2938 | 1.6669 | 1.9944 | 2.3808 | 2.6479 |
| 71 | 0.6780 | 1.2936 | 1.6666 | 1.9939 | 2.3800 | 2.6469 |
| 72 | 0.6779 | 1.2934 | 1.6663 | 1.9935 | 2.3793 | 2.6459 |
| 73 | 0.6779 | 1.2933 | 1.6660 | 1.9930 | 2.3785 | 2.6449 |
| 74 | 0.6778 | 1.2931 | 1.6657 | 1.9925 | 2.3778 | 2.6439 |
| 75 | 0.6778 | 1.2929 | 1.6654 | 1.9921 | 2.3771 | 2.6430 |
| 76 | 0.6777 | 1.2928 | 1.6652 | 1.9917 | 2.3764 | 2.6421 |
| 77 | 0.6777 | 1.2926 | 1.6649 | 1.9913 | 2.3758 | 2.6412 |
| 78 | 0.6776 | 1.2925 | 1.6646 | 1.9908 | 2.3751 | 2.6403 |
| 79 | 0.6776 | 1.2924 | 1.6644 | 1.9905 | 2.3745 | 2.6395 |
| 80 | 0.6776 | 1.2922 | 1.6641 | 1.9901 | 2.3739 | 2.6387 |
| 81 | 0.6775 | 1.2921 | 1.6639 | 1.9897 | 2.3733 | 2.6379 |
| 82 | 0.6775 | 1.2920 | 1.6636 | 1.9893 | 2.3727 | 2.6371 |
| 83 | 0.6775 | 1.2918 | 1.6634 | 1.9890 | 2.3721 | 2.6364 |
| 84 | 0.6774 | 1.2917 | 1.6632 | 1.9886 | 2.3716 | 2.6356 |
| 85 | 0.6774 | 1.2916 | 1.6630 | 1.9883 | 2.3710 | 2.6349 |
| 86 | 0.6774 | 1.2915 | 1.6628 | 1.9879 | 2.3705 | 2.6342 |
| 87 | 0.6773 | 1.2914 | 1.6626 | 1.9876 | 2.3700 | 2.6335 |
| 88 | 0.6773 | 1.2912 | 1.6624 | 1.9873 | 2.3695 | 2.6329 |
| 89 | 0.6773 | 1.2911 | 1.6622 | 1.9870 | 2.3690 | 2.6322 |
| 90 | 0.6772 | 1.2910 | 1.6620 | 1.9867 | 2.3685 | 2.6316 |
| 91 | 0.6772 | 1.2909 | 1.6618 | 1.9864 | 2.3680 | 2.6309 |
| 92 | 0.6772 | 1.2908 | 1.6616 | 1.9861 | 2.3676 | 2.6303 |
| 93 | 0.6771 | 1.2907 | 1.6614 | 1.9858 | 2.3671 | 2.6297 |
| 94 | 0.6771 | 1.2906 | 1.6612 | 1.9855 | 2.3667 | 2.6291 |
| 95 | 0.6771 | 1.2905 | 1.6611 | 1.9853 | 2.3662 | 2.6286 |
| 96 | 0.6771 | 1.2904 | 1.6609 | 1.9850 | 2.3658 | 2.6280 |
| 97 | 0.6770 | 1.2903 | 1.6607 | 1.9847 | 2.3654 | 2.6275 |
| 98 | 0.6770 | 1.2902 | 1.6606 | 1.9845 | 2.3650 | 2.6269 |
| 99 | 0.6770 | 1.2902 | 1.6604 | 1.9842 | 2.3646 | 2.6264 |
| 100 | 0.6770 | 1.2901 | 1.6602 | 1.9840 | 2.3642 | 2.6259 |
| 110 | 0.6767 | 1.2893 | 1.6588 | 1.9818 | 2.3607 | 2.6213 |
| 120 | 0.6765 | 1.2886 | 1.6577 | 1.9799 | 2.3578 | 2.6174 |
| ∞ | 0.6745 | 1.2816 | 1.6449 | 1.9600 | 2.3263 | 2.5758 |

## TABLE E.4

Critical Values of $\chi^2$

For a particular number of degrees of freedom, entry represents the critical value of $\chi^2$ corresponding to a specified upper-tail area ($\alpha$).

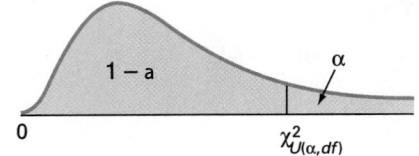

| Degrees of Freedom | Cumulative Probabilities | | | | | | | | | | | |
|---|---|---|---|---|---|---|---|---|---|---|---|---|
| | 0.005 | 0.01 | 0.025 | 0.05 | 0.10 | 0.25 | 0.75 | 0.90 | 0.95 | 0.975 | 0.99 | 0.995 |
| | Upper Tail Areas ($\alpha$) | | | | | | | | | | | |
| | 0.995 | 0.99 | 0.975 | 0.95 | 0.90 | 0.75 | 0.25 | 0.10 | 0.05 | 0.025 | 0.01 | 0.005 |
| 1 | | | 0.001 | 0.004 | 0.016 | 0.102 | 1.323 | 2.706 | 3.841 | 5.024 | 6.635 | 7.879 |
| 2 | 0.010 | 0.020 | 0.051 | 0.103 | 0.211 | 0.575 | 2.773 | 4.605 | 5.991 | 7.378 | 9.210 | 10.597 |
| 3 | 0.072 | 0.115 | 0.216 | 0.352 | 0.584 | 1.213 | 4.108 | 6.251 | 7.815 | 9.348 | 11.345 | 12.838 |
| 4 | 0.207 | 0.297 | 0.484 | 0.711 | 1.064 | 1.923 | 5.385 | 7.779 | 9.488 | 11.143 | 13.277 | 14.860 |
| 5 | 0.412 | 0.554 | 0.831 | 1.145 | 1.610 | 2.675 | 6.626 | 9.236 | 11.071 | 12.833 | 15.086 | 16.750 |
| 6 | 0.676 | 0.872 | 1.237 | 1.635 | 2.204 | 3.455 | 7.841 | 10.645 | 12.592 | 14.449 | 16.812 | 18.458 |
| 7 | 0.989 | 1.239 | 1.690 | 2.167 | 2.833 | 4.255 | 9.037 | 12.017 | 14.067 | 16.013 | 18.475 | 20.278 |
| 8 | 1.344 | 1.646 | 2.180 | 2.733 | 3.490 | 5.071 | 10.219 | 13.362 | 15.507 | 17.535 | 20.090 | 21.955 |
| 9 | 1.735 | 2.088 | 2.700 | 3.325 | 4.168 | 5.899 | 11.389 | 14.684 | 16.919 | 19.023 | 21.666 | 23.589 |
| 10 | 2.156 | 2.558 | 3.247 | 3.940 | 4.865 | 6.737 | 12.549 | 15.987 | 18.307 | 20.483 | 23.209 | 25.188 |
| 11 | 2.603 | 3.053 | 3.816 | 4.575 | 5.578 | 7.584 | 13.701 | 17.275 | 19.675 | 21.920 | 24.725 | 26.757 |
| 12 | 3.074 | 3.571 | 4.404 | 5.226 | 6.304 | 8.438 | 14.845 | 18.549 | 21.026 | 23.337 | 26.217 | 28.299 |
| 13 | 3.565 | 4.107 | 5.009 | 5.892 | 7.042 | 9.299 | 15.984 | 19.812 | 22.362 | 24.736 | 27.688 | 29.819 |
| 14 | 4.075 | 4.660 | 5.629 | 6.571 | 7.790 | 10.165 | 17.117 | 21.064 | 23.685 | 26.119 | 29.141 | 31.319 |
| 15 | 4.601 | 5.229 | 6.262 | 7.261 | 8.547 | 11.037 | 18.245 | 22.307 | 24.996 | 27.488 | 30.578 | 32.801 |
| 16 | 5.142 | 5.812 | 6.908 | 7.962 | 9.312 | 11.912 | 19.369 | 23.542 | 26.296 | 28.845 | 32.000 | 34.267 |
| 17 | 5.697 | 6.408 | 7.564 | 8.672 | 10.085 | 12.792 | 20.489 | 24.769 | 27.587 | 30.191 | 33.409 | 35.718 |
| 18 | 6.265 | 7.015 | 8.231 | 9.390 | 10.865 | 13.675 | 21.605 | 25.989 | 28.869 | 31.526 | 34.805 | 37.156 |
| 19 | 6.844 | 7.633 | 8.907 | 10.117 | 11.651 | 14.562 | 22.718 | 27.204 | 30.144 | 32.852 | 36.191 | 38.582 |
| 20 | 7.434 | 8.260 | 9.591 | 10.851 | 12.443 | 15.452 | 23.828 | 28.412 | 31.410 | 34.170 | 37.566 | 39.997 |
| 21 | 8.034 | 8.897 | 10.283 | 11.591 | 13.240 | 16.344 | 24.935 | 29.615 | 32.671 | 35.479 | 38.932 | 41.401 |
| 22 | 8.643 | 9.542 | 10.982 | 12.338 | 14.042 | 17.240 | 26.039 | 30.813 | 33.924 | 36.781 | 40.289 | 42.796 |
| 23 | 9.260 | 10.196 | 11.689 | 13.091 | 14.848 | 18.137 | 27.141 | 32.007 | 35.172 | 38.076 | 41.638 | 44.181 |
| 24 | 9.886 | 10.856 | 12.401 | 13.848 | 15.659 | 19.037 | 28.241 | 33.196 | 36.415 | 39.364 | 42.980 | 45.559 |
| 25 | 10.520 | 11.524 | 13.120 | 14.611 | 16.473 | 19.939 | 29.339 | 34.382 | 37.652 | 40.646 | 44.314 | 46.928 |
| 26 | 11.160 | 12.198 | 13.844 | 15.379 | 17.292 | 20.843 | 30.435 | 35.563 | 38.885 | 41.923 | 45.642 | 48.290 |
| 27 | 11.808 | 12.879 | 14.573 | 16.151 | 18.114 | 21.749 | 31.528 | 36.741 | 40.113 | 43.194 | 46.963 | 49.645 |
| 28 | 12.461 | 13.565 | 15.308 | 16.928 | 18.939 | 22.657 | 32.620 | 37.916 | 41.337 | 44.461 | 48.278 | 50.993 |
| 29 | 13.121 | 14.257 | 16.047 | 17.708 | 19.768 | 23.567 | 33.711 | 39.087 | 42.557 | 45.722 | 49.588 | 52.336 |
| 30 | 13.787 | 14.954 | 16.791 | 18.493 | 20.599 | 24.478 | 34.800 | 40.256 | 43.773 | 46.979 | 50.892 | 53.672 |

For larger values of degrees of freedom ($df$) the expression $Z = \sqrt{2\chi^2} - \sqrt{2(df)-1}$ may be used and the resulting upper-tail area can be found from the cumulative standardized normal distribution (Table E.2).

## TABLE E.5
### Critical Values of F

For a particular combination of numerator and denominator degrees of freedom, entry represents the critical values of $F$ corresponding to the cumulative probability $(1 - \alpha)$ and a specified upper-tail area $(\alpha)$.

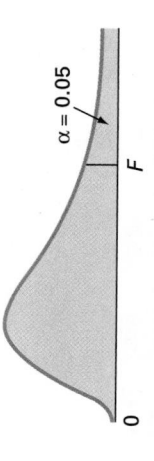

$\alpha = 0.05$

**Cumulative Probabilities = 0.95**

**Upper Tail Areas = 0.05**

**Numerator, $df_1$**

| Denominator, $df_2$ | 1 | 2 | 3 | 4 | 5 | 6 | 7 | 8 | 9 | 10 | 12 | 15 | 20 | 24 | 30 | 40 | 60 | 120 | ∞ |
|---|---|---|---|---|---|---|---|---|---|---|---|---|---|---|---|---|---|---|---|
| 1 | 161.40 | 199.50 | 215.70 | 224.60 | 230.20 | 234.00 | 236.80 | 238.90 | 240.50 | 241.90 | 243.90 | 245.90 | 248.00 | 249.10 | 250.10 | 251.10 | 252.20 | 253.30 | 254.30 |
| 2 | 18.51 | 19.00 | 19.16 | 19.25 | 19.30 | 19.33 | 19.35 | 19.37 | 19.38 | 19.40 | 19.41 | 19.43 | 19.45 | 19.45 | 19.46 | 19.47 | 19.48 | 19.49 | 19.50 |
| 3 | 10.13 | 9.55 | 9.28 | 9.12 | 9.01 | 8.94 | 8.89 | 8.85 | 8.81 | 8.79 | 8.74 | 8.70 | 8.66 | 8.64 | 8.62 | 8.59 | 8.57 | 8.55 | 8.53 |
| 4 | 7.71 | 6.94 | 6.59 | 6.39 | 6.26 | 6.16 | 6.09 | 6.04 | 6.00 | 5.96 | 5.91 | 5.86 | 5.80 | 5.77 | 5.75 | 5.72 | 5.69 | 5.66 | 5.63 |
| 5 | 6.61 | 5.79 | 5.41 | 5.19 | 5.05 | 4.95 | 4.88 | 4.82 | 4.77 | 4.74 | 4.68 | 4.62 | 4.56 | 4.53 | 4.50 | 4.46 | 4.43 | 4.40 | 4.36 |
| 6 | 5.99 | 5.14 | 4.76 | 4.53 | 4.39 | 4.28 | 4.21 | 4.15 | 4.10 | 4.06 | 4.00 | 3.94 | 3.87 | 3.84 | 3.81 | 3.77 | 3.74 | 3.70 | 3.67 |
| 7 | 5.59 | 4.74 | 4.35 | 4.12 | 3.97 | 3.87 | 3.79 | 3.73 | 3.68 | 3.64 | 3.57 | 3.51 | 3.44 | 3.41 | 3.38 | 3.34 | 3.30 | 3.27 | 3.23 |
| 8 | 5.32 | 4.46 | 4.07 | 3.84 | 3.69 | 3.58 | 3.50 | 3.44 | 3.39 | 3.35 | 3.28 | 3.22 | 3.15 | 3.12 | 3.08 | 3.04 | 3.01 | 2.97 | 2.93 |
| 9 | 5.12 | 4.26 | 3.86 | 3.63 | 3.48 | 3.37 | 3.29 | 3.23 | 3.18 | 3.14 | 3.07 | 3.01 | 2.94 | 2.90 | 2.86 | 2.83 | 2.79 | 2.75 | 2.71 |
| 10 | 4.96 | 4.10 | 3.71 | 3.48 | 3.33 | 3.22 | 3.14 | 3.07 | 3.02 | 2.98 | 2.91 | 2.85 | 2.77 | 2.74 | 2.70 | 2.66 | 2.62 | 2.58 | 2.54 |
| 11 | 4.84 | 3.98 | 3.59 | 3.36 | 3.20 | 3.09 | 3.01 | 2.95 | 2.90 | 2.85 | 2.79 | 2.72 | 2.65 | 2.61 | 2.57 | 2.53 | 2.49 | 2.45 | 2.40 |
| 12 | 4.75 | 3.89 | 3.49 | 3.26 | 3.11 | 3.00 | 2.91 | 2.85 | 2.80 | 2.75 | 2.69 | 2.62 | 2.54 | 2.51 | 2.47 | 2.43 | 2.38 | 2.34 | 2.30 |
| 13 | 4.67 | 3.81 | 3.41 | 3.18 | 3.03 | 2.92 | 2.83 | 2.77 | 2.71 | 2.67 | 2.60 | 2.53 | 2.46 | 2.42 | 2.38 | 2.34 | 2.30 | 2.25 | 2.21 |
| 14 | 4.60 | 3.74 | 3.34 | 3.11 | 2.96 | 2.85 | 2.76 | 2.70 | 2.65 | 2.60 | 2.53 | 2.46 | 2.39 | 2.35 | 2.31 | 2.27 | 2.22 | 2.18 | 2.13 |
| 15 | 4.54 | 3.68 | 3.29 | 3.06 | 2.90 | 2.79 | 2.71 | 2.64 | 2.59 | 2.54 | 2.48 | 2.40 | 2.33 | 2.29 | 2.25 | 2.20 | 2.16 | 2.11 | 2.07 |
| 16 | 4.49 | 3.63 | 3.24 | 3.01 | 2.85 | 2.74 | 2.66 | 2.59 | 2.54 | 2.49 | 2.42 | 2.35 | 2.28 | 2.24 | 2.19 | 2.15 | 2.11 | 2.06 | 2.01 |
| 17 | 4.45 | 3.59 | 3.20 | 2.96 | 2.81 | 2.70 | 2.61 | 2.55 | 2.49 | 2.45 | 2.38 | 2.31 | 2.23 | 2.19 | 2.15 | 2.10 | 2.06 | 2.01 | 1.96 |
| 18 | 4.41 | 3.55 | 3.16 | 2.93 | 2.77 | 2.66 | 2.58 | 2.51 | 2.46 | 2.41 | 2.34 | 2.27 | 2.19 | 2.15 | 2.11 | 2.06 | 2.02 | 1.97 | 1.92 |
| 19 | 4.38 | 3.52 | 3.13 | 2.90 | 2.74 | 2.63 | 2.54 | 2.48 | 2.42 | 2.38 | 2.31 | 2.23 | 2.16 | 2.11 | 2.07 | 2.03 | 1.98 | 1.93 | 1.88 |
| 20 | 4.35 | 3.49 | 3.10 | 2.87 | 2.71 | 2.60 | 2.51 | 2.45 | 2.39 | 2.35 | 2.28 | 2.20 | 2.12 | 2.08 | 2.04 | 1.99 | 1.95 | 1.90 | 1.84 |
| 21 | 4.32 | 3.47 | 3.07 | 2.84 | 2.68 | 2.57 | 2.49 | 2.42 | 2.37 | 2.32 | 2.25 | 2.18 | 2.10 | 2.05 | 2.01 | 1.96 | 1.92 | 1.87 | 1.81 |
| 22 | 4.30 | 3.44 | 3.05 | 2.82 | 2.66 | 2.55 | 2.46 | 2.40 | 2.34 | 2.30 | 2.23 | 2.15 | 2.07 | 2.03 | 1.98 | 1.94 | 1.89 | 1.84 | 1.78 |
| 23 | 4.28 | 3.42 | 3.03 | 2.80 | 2.64 | 2.53 | 2.44 | 2.37 | 2.32 | 2.27 | 2.20 | 2.13 | 2.05 | 2.01 | 1.96 | 1.91 | 1.86 | 1.81 | 1.76 |
| 24 | 4.26 | 3.40 | 3.01 | 2.78 | 2.62 | 2.51 | 2.42 | 2.36 | 2.30 | 2.25 | 2.18 | 2.11 | 2.03 | 1.98 | 1.94 | 1.89 | 1.84 | 1.79 | 1.73 |
| 25 | 4.24 | 3.39 | 2.99 | 2.76 | 2.60 | 2.49 | 2.40 | 2.34 | 2.28 | 2.24 | 2.16 | 2.09 | 2.01 | 1.96 | 1.92 | 1.87 | 1.82 | 1.77 | 1.71 |
| 26 | 4.23 | 3.37 | 2.98 | 2.74 | 2.59 | 2.47 | 2.39 | 2.32 | 2.27 | 2.22 | 2.15 | 2.07 | 1.99 | 1.95 | 1.90 | 1.85 | 1.80 | 1.75 | 1.69 |
| 27 | 4.21 | 3.35 | 2.96 | 2.73 | 2.57 | 2.46 | 2.37 | 2.31 | 2.25 | 2.20 | 2.13 | 2.06 | 1.97 | 1.93 | 1.88 | 1.84 | 1.79 | 1.73 | 1.67 |
| 28 | 4.20 | 3.34 | 2.95 | 2.71 | 2.56 | 2.45 | 2.36 | 2.29 | 2.24 | 2.19 | 2.12 | 2.04 | 1.96 | 1.91 | 1.87 | 1.82 | 1.77 | 1.71 | 1.65 |
| 29 | 4.18 | 3.33 | 2.93 | 2.70 | 2.55 | 2.43 | 2.35 | 2.28 | 2.22 | 2.18 | 2.10 | 2.03 | 1.94 | 1.90 | 1.85 | 1.81 | 1.75 | 1.70 | 1.64 |
| 30 | 4.17 | 3.32 | 2.92 | 2.69 | 2.53 | 2.42 | 2.33 | 2.27 | 2.21 | 2.16 | 2.09 | 2.01 | 1.93 | 1.89 | 1.84 | 1.79 | 1.74 | 1.68 | 1.62 |
| 40 | 4.08 | 3.23 | 2.84 | 2.61 | 2.45 | 2.34 | 2.25 | 2.18 | 2.12 | 2.08 | 2.00 | 1.92 | 1.84 | 1.79 | 1.74 | 1.69 | 1.64 | 1.58 | 1.51 |
| 60 | 4.00 | 3.15 | 2.76 | 2.53 | 2.37 | 2.25 | 2.17 | 2.10 | 2.04 | 1.99 | 1.92 | 1.84 | 1.75 | 1.70 | 1.65 | 1.53 | 1.53 | 1.47 | 1.39 |
| 120 | 3.92 | 3.07 | 2.68 | 2.45 | 2.29 | 2.17 | 2.09 | 2.02 | 1.96 | 1.91 | 1.83 | 1.75 | 1.66 | 1.61 | 1.55 | 1.50 | 1.43 | 1.35 | 1.25 |
| ∞ | 3.84 | 3.00 | 2.60 | 2.37 | 2.21 | 2.10 | 2.01 | 1.94 | 1.88 | 1.83 | 1.75 | 1.67 | 1.57 | 1.52 | 1.46 | 1.39 | 1.32 | 1.22 | 1.00 |

*continued*

## TABLE E.5
Critical Values of $F$ (Continued)

$\alpha = 0.025$

Cumulative Probabilities = 0.975

Upper Tail Areas = 0.025

Numerator, $df_1$

| Denominator, $df_2$ | 1 | 2 | 3 | 4 | 5 | 6 | 7 | 8 | 9 | 10 | 12 | 15 | 20 | 24 | 30 | 40 | 60 | 120 | ∞ |
|---|---|---|---|---|---|---|---|---|---|---|---|---|---|---|---|---|---|---|---|
| 1 | 647.80 | 799.50 | 864.20 | 899.60 | 921.80 | 937.10 | 948.20 | 956.70 | 963.30 | 968.60 | 976.70 | 984.90 | 993.10 | 997.20 | 1,001.00 | 1,006.00 | 1,010.00 | 1,014.00 | 1,018.00 |
| 2 | 38.51 | 39.00 | 39.17 | 39.25 | 39.30 | 39.33 | 39.36 | 39.39 | 39.39 | 39.40 | 39.41 | 39.43 | 39.45 | 39.46 | 39.46 | 39.47 | 39.48 | 39.49 | 39.50 |
| 3 | 17.44 | 16.04 | 15.44 | 15.10 | 14.88 | 14.73 | 14.62 | 14.54 | 14.47 | 14.42 | 14.34 | 14.25 | 14.17 | 14.12 | 14.08 | 14.04 | 13.99 | 13.95 | 13.90 |
| 4 | 12.22 | 10.65 | 9.98 | 9.60 | 9.36 | 9.20 | 9.07 | 8.98 | 8.90 | 8.84 | 8.75 | 8.66 | 8.56 | 8.51 | 8.46 | 8.41 | 8.36 | 8.31 | 8.26 |
| 5 | 10.01 | 8.43 | 7.76 | 7.39 | 7.15 | 6.98 | 6.85 | 6.76 | 6.68 | 6.62 | 6.52 | 6.43 | 6.33 | 6.28 | 6.23 | 6.18 | 6.12 | 6.07 | 6.02 |
| 6 | 8.81 | 7.26 | 6.60 | 6.23 | 5.99 | 5.82 | 5.70 | 5.60 | 5.52 | 5.46 | 5.37 | 5.27 | 5.17 | 5.12 | 5.07 | 5.01 | 4.96 | 4.90 | 4.85 |
| 7 | 8.07 | 6.54 | 5.89 | 5.52 | 5.29 | 5.12 | 4.99 | 4.90 | 4.82 | 4.76 | 4.67 | 4.57 | 4.47 | 4.42 | 4.36 | 4.31 | 4.25 | 4.20 | 4.14 |
| 8 | 7.57 | 6.06 | 5.42 | 5.05 | 4.82 | 4.65 | 4.53 | 4.43 | 4.36 | 4.30 | 4.20 | 4.10 | 4.00 | 3.95 | 3.89 | 3.84 | 3.78 | 3.73 | 3.67 |
| 9 | 7.21 | 5.71 | 5.08 | 4.72 | 4.48 | 4.32 | 4.20 | 4.10 | 4.03 | 3.96 | 3.87 | 3.77 | 3.67 | 3.61 | 3.56 | 3.51 | 3.45 | 3.39 | 3.33 |
| 10 | 6.94 | 5.46 | 4.83 | 4.47 | 4.24 | 4.07 | 3.95 | 3.85 | 3.78 | 3.72 | 3.62 | 3.52 | 3.42 | 3.37 | 3.31 | 3.26 | 3.20 | 3.14 | 3.08 |
| 11 | 6.72 | 5.26 | 4.63 | 4.28 | 4.04 | 3.88 | 3.76 | 3.66 | 3.59 | 3.53 | 3.43 | 3.33 | 3.23 | 3.17 | 3.12 | 3.06 | 3.00 | 2.94 | 2.88 |
| 12 | 6.55 | 5.10 | 4.47 | 4.12 | 3.89 | 3.73 | 3.61 | 3.51 | 3.44 | 3.37 | 3.28 | 3.18 | 3.07 | 3.02 | 2.96 | 2.91 | 2.85 | 2.79 | 2.72 |
| 13 | 6.41 | 4.97 | 4.35 | 4.00 | 3.77 | 3.60 | 3.48 | 3.39 | 3.31 | 3.25 | 3.15 | 3.05 | 2.95 | 2.89 | 2.84 | 2.78 | 2.72 | 2.66 | 2.60 |
| 14 | 6.30 | 4.86 | 4.24 | 3.89 | 3.66 | 3.50 | 3.38 | 3.29 | 3.21 | 3.15 | 3.05 | 2.95 | 2.84 | 2.79 | 2.73 | 2.67 | 2.61 | 2.55 | 2.49 |
| 15 | 6.20 | 4.77 | 4.15 | 3.80 | 3.58 | 3.41 | 3.29 | 3.20 | 3.12 | 3.06 | 2.96 | 2.86 | 2.76 | 2.70 | 2.64 | 2.59 | 2.52 | 2.46 | 2.40 |
| 16 | 6.12 | 4.69 | 4.08 | 3.73 | 3.50 | 3.34 | 3.22 | 3.12 | 3.05 | 2.99 | 2.89 | 2.79 | 2.68 | 2.63 | 2.57 | 2.51 | 2.45 | 2.38 | 2.32 |
| 17 | 6.04 | 4.62 | 4.01 | 3.66 | 3.44 | 3.28 | 3.16 | 3.06 | 2.98 | 2.92 | 2.82 | 2.72 | 2.62 | 2.56 | 2.50 | 2.44 | 2.38 | 2.32 | 2.25 |
| 18 | 5.98 | 4.56 | 3.95 | 3.61 | 3.38 | 3.22 | 3.10 | 3.01 | 2.93 | 2.87 | 2.77 | 2.67 | 2.56 | 2.50 | 2.44 | 2.38 | 2.32 | 2.26 | 2.19 |
| 19 | 5.92 | 4.51 | 3.90 | 3.56 | 3.33 | 3.17 | 3.05 | 2.96 | 2.88 | 2.82 | 2.72 | 2.62 | 2.51 | 2.45 | 2.39 | 2.33 | 2.27 | 2.20 | 2.13 |
| 20 | 5.87 | 4.46 | 3.86 | 3.51 | 3.29 | 3.13 | 3.01 | 2.91 | 2.84 | 2.77 | 2.68 | 2.57 | 2.46 | 2.41 | 2.35 | 2.29 | 2.22 | 2.16 | 2.09 |
| 21 | 5.83 | 4.42 | 3.82 | 3.48 | 3.25 | 3.09 | 2.97 | 2.87 | 2.80 | 2.73 | 2.64 | 2.53 | 2.42 | 2.37 | 2.31 | 2.25 | 2.18 | 2.11 | 2.04 |
| 22 | 5.79 | 4.38 | 3.78 | 3.44 | 3.22 | 3.05 | 2.93 | 2.84 | 2.76 | 2.70 | 2.60 | 2.50 | 2.39 | 2.33 | 2.27 | 2.21 | 2.14 | 2.08 | 2.00 |
| 23 | 5.75 | 4.35 | 3.75 | 3.41 | 3.18 | 3.02 | 2.90 | 2.81 | 2.73 | 2.67 | 2.57 | 2.47 | 2.36 | 2.30 | 2.24 | 2.18 | 2.11 | 2.04 | 1.97 |
| 24 | 5.72 | 4.32 | 3.72 | 3.38 | 3.15 | 2.99 | 2.87 | 2.78 | 2.70 | 2.64 | 2.54 | 2.44 | 2.33 | 2.27 | 2.21 | 2.15 | 2.08 | 2.01 | 1.94 |
| 25 | 5.69 | 4.29 | 3.69 | 3.35 | 3.13 | 2.97 | 2.85 | 2.75 | 2.68 | 2.61 | 2.51 | 2.41 | 2.30 | 2.24 | 2.18 | 2.12 | 2.05 | 1.98 | 1.91 |
| 26 | 5.66 | 4.27 | 3.67 | 3.33 | 3.10 | 2.94 | 2.82 | 2.73 | 2.65 | 2.59 | 2.49 | 2.39 | 2.28 | 2.22 | 2.16 | 2.09 | 2.03 | 1.95 | 1.88 |
| 27 | 5.63 | 4.24 | 3.65 | 3.31 | 3.08 | 2.92 | 2.80 | 2.71 | 2.63 | 2.57 | 2.47 | 2.36 | 2.25 | 2.19 | 2.13 | 2.07 | 2.00 | 1.93 | 1.85 |
| 28 | 5.61 | 4.22 | 3.63 | 3.29 | 3.06 | 2.90 | 2.78 | 2.69 | 2.61 | 2.55 | 2.45 | 2.34 | 2.23 | 2.17 | 2.11 | 2.05 | 1.98 | 1.91 | 1.83 |
| 29 | 5.59 | 4.20 | 3.61 | 3.27 | 3.04 | 2.88 | 2.76 | 2.67 | 2.59 | 2.53 | 2.43 | 2.32 | 2.21 | 2.15 | 2.09 | 2.03 | 1.96 | 1.89 | 1.81 |
| 30 | 5.57 | 4.18 | 3.59 | 3.25 | 3.03 | 2.87 | 2.75 | 2.65 | 2.57 | 2.51 | 2.41 | 2.31 | 2.20 | 2.14 | 2.07 | 2.01 | 1.94 | 1.87 | 1.79 |
| 40 | 5.42 | 4.05 | 3.46 | 3.13 | 2.90 | 2.74 | 2.62 | 2.53 | 2.45 | 2.39 | 2.29 | 2.18 | 2.07 | 2.01 | 1.94 | 1.88 | 1.80 | 1.72 | 1.64 |
| 60 | 5.29 | 3.93 | 3.34 | 3.01 | 2.79 | 2.63 | 2.51 | 2.41 | 2.33 | 2.27 | 2.17 | 2.06 | 1.94 | 1.88 | 1.82 | 1.74 | 1.67 | 1.58 | 1.48 |
| 120 | 5.15 | 3.80 | 3.23 | 2.89 | 2.67 | 2.52 | 2.39 | 2.30 | 2.22 | 2.16 | 2.05 | 1.94 | 1.82 | 1.76 | 1.69 | 1.61 | 1.53 | 1.43 | 1.31 |
| ∞ | 5.02 | 3.69 | 3.12 | 2.79 | 2.57 | 2.41 | 2.29 | 2.19 | 2.11 | 2.05 | 1.94 | 1.83 | 1.71 | 1.64 | 1.57 | 1.48 | 1.39 | 1.27 | 1.00 |

*continued*

# TABLE E.5

Critical Values of F (Continued)

$\alpha = 0.01$

Cumulative Probabilities = 0.99

Upper Tail Areas = 0.01

Numerator, $df_1$

| Denominator, $df_2$ | 1 | 2 | 3 | 4 | 5 | 6 | 7 | 8 | 9 | 10 | 12 | 15 | 20 | 24 | 30 | 40 | 60 | 120 | ∞ |
|---|---|---|---|---|---|---|---|---|---|---|---|---|---|---|---|---|---|---|---|
| 1 | 4,052.00 | 4,999.50 | 5,403.00 | 5,625.00 | 5,764.00 | 5,859.00 | 5,928.00 | 5,982.00 | 6,022.00 | 6,056.00 | 6,106.00 | 6,157.00 | 6,209.00 | 6,235.00 | 6,261.00 | 6,287.00 | 6,313.00 | 6,339.00 | 6,366.00 |
| 2 | 98.50 | 99.00 | 99.17 | 99.25 | 99.30 | 99.33 | 99.36 | 99.37 | 99.39 | 99.40 | 99.42 | 99.43 | 44.45 | 99.46 | 99.47 | 99.47 | 99.48 | 99.49 | 99.50 |
| 3 | 34.12 | 30.82 | 29.46 | 28.71 | 28.24 | 27.91 | 27.67 | 27.49 | 27.35 | 27.23 | 27.05 | 26.87 | 26.69 | 26.60 | 26.50 | 26.41 | 26.32 | 26.22 | 26.13 |
| 4 | 21.20 | 18.00 | 16.69 | 15.98 | 15.52 | 15.21 | 14.98 | 14.80 | 14.66 | 14.55 | 14.37 | 14.20 | 14.02 | 13.93 | 13.84 | 13.75 | 13.65 | 13.56 | 13.46 |
| 5 | 16.26 | 13.27 | 12.06 | 11.39 | 10.97 | 10.67 | 10.46 | 10.29 | 10.16 | 10.05 | 9.89 | 9.72 | 9.55 | 9.47 | 9.38 | 9.29 | 9.20 | 9.11 | 9.02 |
| 6 | 13.75 | 10.92 | 9.78 | 9.15 | 8.75 | 8.47 | 8.26 | 8.10 | 7.98 | 7.87 | 7.72 | 7.56 | 7.40 | 7.31 | 7.23 | 7.14 | 7.06 | 6.97 | 6.88 |
| 7 | 12.25 | 9.55 | 8.45 | 7.85 | 7.46 | 7.19 | 6.99 | 6.84 | 6.72 | 6.62 | 6.47 | 6.31 | 6.16 | 6.07 | 5.99 | 5.91 | 5.82 | 5.74 | 5.65 |
| 8 | 11.26 | 8.65 | 7.59 | 7.01 | 6.63 | 6.37 | 6.18 | 6.03 | 5.91 | 5.81 | 5.67 | 5.52 | 5.36 | 5.28 | 5.20 | 5.12 | 5.03 | 4.95 | 4.86 |
| 9 | 10.56 | 8.02 | 6.99 | 6.42 | 6.06 | 5.80 | 5.61 | 5.47 | 5.35 | 5.26 | 5.11 | 4.96 | 4.81 | 4.73 | 4.65 | 4.57 | 4.48 | 4.40 | 4.31 |
| 10 | 10.04 | 7.56 | 6.55 | 5.99 | 5.64 | 5.39 | 5.20 | 5.06 | 4.94 | 4.85 | 4.71 | 4.56 | 4.41 | 4.33 | 4.25 | 4.17 | 4.08 | 4.00 | 3.91 |
| 11 | 9.65 | 7.21 | 6.22 | 5.67 | 5.32 | 5.07 | 4.89 | 4.74 | 4.63 | 4.54 | 4.40 | 4.25 | 4.10 | 4.02 | 3.94 | 3.86 | 3.78 | 3.69 | 3.60 |
| 12 | 9.33 | 6.93 | 5.95 | 5.41 | 5.06 | 4.82 | 4.64 | 4.50 | 4.39 | 4.30 | 4.16 | 4.01 | 3.86 | 3.78 | 3.70 | 3.62 | 3.54 | 3.45 | 3.36 |
| 13 | 9.07 | 6.70 | 5.74 | 5.21 | 4.86 | 4.62 | 4.44 | 4.30 | 4.19 | 4.10 | 3.96 | 3.82 | 3.66 | 3.59 | 3.51 | 3.43 | 3.34 | 3.25 | 3.17 |
| 14 | 8.86 | 6.51 | 5.56 | 5.04 | 4.69 | 4.46 | 4.28 | 4.14 | 4.03 | 3.94 | 3.80 | 3.66 | 3.51 | 3.43 | 3.35 | 3.27 | 3.18 | 3.09 | 3.00 |
| 15 | 8.68 | 6.36 | 5.42 | 4.89 | 4.56 | 4.32 | 4.14 | 4.00 | 3.89 | 3.80 | 3.67 | 3.52 | 3.37 | 3.29 | 3.21 | 3.13 | 3.05 | 2.96 | 2.87 |
| 16 | 8.53 | 6.23 | 5.29 | 4.77 | 4.44 | 4.20 | 4.03 | 3.89 | 3.78 | 3.69 | 3.55 | 3.41 | 3.26 | 3.18 | 3.10 | 3.02 | 2.93 | 2.81 | 2.75 |
| 17 | 8.40 | 6.11 | 5.18 | 4.67 | 4.34 | 4.10 | 3.93 | 3.79 | 3.68 | 3.59 | 3.46 | 3.31 | 3.16 | 3.08 | 3.00 | 2.92 | 2.83 | 2.75 | 2.65 |
| 18 | 8.29 | 6.01 | 5.09 | 4.58 | 4.25 | 4.01 | 3.84 | 3.71 | 3.60 | 3.51 | 3.37 | 3.23 | 3.08 | 3.00 | 2.92 | 2.84 | 2.75 | 2.66 | 2.57 |
| 19 | 8.18 | 5.93 | 5.01 | 4.50 | 4.17 | 3.94 | 3.77 | 3.63 | 3.52 | 3.43 | 3.30 | 3.15 | 3.00 | 2.92 | 2.84 | 2.76 | 2.67 | 2.58 | 2.49 |
| 20 | 8.10 | 5.85 | 4.94 | 4.43 | 4.10 | 3.87 | 3.70 | 3.56 | 3.46 | 3.37 | 3.23 | 3.09 | 2.94 | 2.86 | 2.78 | 2.69 | 2.61 | 2.52 | 2.42 |
| 21 | 8.02 | 5.78 | 4.87 | 4.37 | 4.04 | 3.81 | 3.64 | 3.51 | 3.40 | 3.31 | 3.17 | 3.03 | 2.88 | 2.80 | 2.72 | 2.64 | 2.55 | 2.46 | 2.36 |
| 22 | 7.95 | 5.72 | 4.82 | 4.31 | 3.99 | 3.76 | 3.59 | 3.45 | 3.35 | 3.26 | 3.12 | 2.98 | 2.83 | 2.75 | 2.67 | 2.58 | 2.50 | 2.40 | 2.31 |
| 23 | 7.88 | 5.66 | 4.76 | 4.26 | 3.94 | 3.71 | 3.54 | 3.41 | 3.30 | 3.21 | 3.07 | 2.93 | 2.78 | 2.70 | 2.62 | 2.54 | 2.45 | 2.35 | 2.26 |
| 24 | 7.82 | 5.61 | 4.72 | 4.22 | 3.90 | 3.67 | 3.50 | 3.36 | 3.26 | 3.17 | 3.03 | 2.89 | 2.74 | 2.66 | 2.58 | 2.49 | 2.40 | 2.31 | 2.21 |
| 25 | 7.77 | 5.57 | 4.68 | 4.18 | 3.85 | 3.63 | 3.46 | 3.32 | 3.22 | 3.13 | 2.99 | 2.85 | 2.70 | 2.62 | 2.54 | 2.45 | 2.36 | 2.27 | 2.17 |
| 26 | 7.72 | 5.53 | 4.64 | 4.14 | 3.82 | 3.59 | 3.42 | 3.29 | 3.18 | 3.09 | 2.96 | 2.81 | 2.66 | 2.58 | 2.50 | 2.42 | 2.33 | 2.23 | 2.13 |
| 27 | 7.68 | 5.49 | 4.60 | 4.11 | 3.78 | 3.56 | 3.39 | 3.26 | 3.15 | 3.06 | 2.93 | 2.78 | 2.63 | 2.55 | 2.47 | 2.38 | 2.29 | 2.20 | 2.10 |
| 28 | 7.64 | 5.45 | 4.57 | 4.07 | 3.75 | 3.53 | 3.36 | 3.23 | 3.12 | 3.03 | 2.90 | 2.75 | 2.60 | 2.52 | 2.44 | 2.35 | 2.26 | 2.17 | 2.06 |
| 29 | 7.60 | 5.42 | 4.54 | 4.04 | 3.73 | 3.50 | 3.33 | 3.20 | 3.09 | 3.00 | 2.87 | 2.73 | 2.57 | 2.49 | 2.41 | 2.33 | 2.23 | 2.14 | 2.03 |
| 30 | 7.56 | 5.39 | 4.51 | 4.02 | 3.70 | 3.47 | 3.30 | 3.17 | 3.07 | 2.98 | 2.84 | 2.70 | 2.55 | 2.47 | 2.39 | 2.30 | 2.21 | 2.11 | 2.01 |
| 40 | 7.31 | 5.18 | 4.31 | 3.83 | 3.51 | 3.29 | 3.12 | 2.99 | 2.89 | 2.80 | 2.66 | 2.52 | 2.37 | 2.29 | 2.20 | 2.11 | 2.02 | 1.92 | 1.80 |
| 60 | 7.08 | 4.98 | 4.13 | 3.65 | 3.34 | 3.12 | 2.95 | 2.82 | 2.72 | 2.63 | 2.50 | 2.35 | 2.20 | 2.12 | 2.03 | 1.94 | 1.84 | 1.73 | 1.60 |
| 120 | 6.85 | 4.79 | 3.95 | 3.48 | 3.17 | 2.96 | 2.79 | 2.66 | 2.56 | 2.47 | 2.34 | 2.19 | 2.03 | 1.95 | 1.86 | 1.76 | 1.66 | 1.53 | 1.38 |
| ∞ | 6.63 | 4.61 | 3.78 | 3.32 | 3.02 | 2.80 | 2.64 | 2.51 | 2.41 | 2.32 | 2.18 | 2.04 | 1.88 | 1.79 | 1.70 | 1.59 | 1.47 | 1.32 | 1.00 |

continued

# TABLE E.5
Critical Values of F (Continued)

$\alpha = 0.005$

Cumulative Probabilities = 0.995

Upper Tail Areas = 0.005

Numerator, $df_1$

| Denominator, $df_2$ | 1 | 2 | 3 | 4 | 5 | 6 | 7 | 8 | 9 | 10 | 12 | 15 | 20 | 24 | 30 | 40 | 60 | 120 | ∞ |
|---|---|---|---|---|---|---|---|---|---|---|---|---|---|---|---|---|---|---|---|
| 1 | 16,211.00 | 20,000.00 | 21,615.00 | 22,500.00 | 23,056.00 | 23,437.00 | 23,715.00 | 23,925.00 | 24,091.00 | 24,224.00 | 24,426.00 | 24,630.00 | 24,836.00 | 24,910.00 | 25,044.00 | 25,148.00 | 25,253.00 | 25,359.00 | 25,465.00 |
| 2 | 198.50 | 199.00 | 199.20 | 199.20 | 199.30 | 199.30 | 199.40 | 199.40 | 199.40 | 199.40 | 199.40 | 199.40 | 199.40 | 199.50 | 199.50 | 199.50 | 199.50 | 199.50 | 199.50 |
| 3 | 55.55 | 49.80 | 47.47 | 46.19 | 45.39 | 44.84 | 44.43 | 44.13 | 43.88 | 43.69 | 43.39 | 43.08 | 42.78 | 42.62 | 42.47 | 42.31 | 42.15 | 41.99 | 41.83 |
| 4 | 31.33 | 26.28 | 24.26 | 23.15 | 22.46 | 21.97 | 21.62 | 21.35 | 21.14 | 20.97 | 20.70 | 20.44 | 20.17 | 20.03 | 19.89 | 19.75 | 19.61 | 19.47 | 19.32 |
| 5 | 22.78 | 18.31 | 16.53 | 15.56 | 14.94 | 14.51 | 14.20 | 13.96 | 13.77 | 13.62 | 13.38 | 13.15 | 12.90 | 12.78 | 12.66 | 12.53 | 12.40 | 12.27 | 12.11 |
| 6 | 18.63 | 14.54 | 12.92 | 12.03 | 11.46 | 11.07 | 10.79 | 10.57 | 10.39 | 10.25 | 10.03 | 9.81 | 9.59 | 9.47 | 9.36 | 9.24 | 9.12 | 9.00 | 8.88 |
| 7 | 16.24 | 12.40 | 10.88 | 10.05 | 9.52 | 9.16 | 8.89 | 8.68 | 8.51 | 8.38 | 8.18 | 7.97 | 7.75 | 7.65 | 7.53 | 7.42 | 7.31 | 7.19 | 7.08 |
| 8 | 14.69 | 11.04 | 9.60 | 8.81 | 8.30 | 7.95 | 7.69 | 7.50 | 7.34 | 7.21 | 7.01 | 6.81 | 6.61 | 6.50 | 6.40 | 6.29 | 6.18 | 6.06 | 5.95 |
| 9 | 13.61 | 10.11 | 8.72 | 7.96 | 7.47 | 7.13 | 6.88 | 6.69 | 6.54 | 6.42 | 6.23 | 6.03 | 5.83 | 5.73 | 5.62 | 5.52 | 5.41 | 5.30 | 5.19 |
| 10 | 12.83 | 9.43 | 8.08 | 7.34 | 6.87 | 6.54 | 6.30 | 6.12 | 5.97 | 5.85 | 5.66 | 5.47 | 5.27 | 5.17 | 5.07 | 4.97 | 4.86 | 4.75 | 4.61 |
| 11 | 12.23 | 8.91 | 7.60 | 6.88 | 6.42 | 6.10 | 5.86 | 5.68 | 5.54 | 5.42 | 5.24 | 5.05 | 4.86 | 4.75 | 4.65 | 4.55 | 4.44 | 4.34 | 4.23 |
| 12 | 11.75 | 8.51 | 7.23 | 6.52 | 6.07 | 5.76 | 5.52 | 5.35 | 5.20 | 5.09 | 4.91 | 4.72 | 4.53 | 4.43 | 4.33 | 4.23 | 4.12 | 4.01 | 3.90 |
| 13 | 11.37 | 8.19 | 6.93 | 6.23 | 5.79 | 5.48 | 5.25 | 5.08 | 4.94 | 4.82 | 4.64 | 4.46 | 4.27 | 4.17 | 4.07 | 3.97 | 3.87 | 3.76 | 3.65 |
| 14 | 11.06 | 7.92 | 6.68 | 6.00 | 5.56 | 5.26 | 5.03 | 4.86 | 4.72 | 4.60 | 4.43 | 4.25 | 4.06 | 3.96 | 3.86 | 3.76 | 3.66 | 3.55 | 3.41 |
| 15 | 10.80 | 7.70 | 6.48 | 5.80 | 5.37 | 5.07 | 4.85 | 4.67 | 4.54 | 4.42 | 4.25 | 4.07 | 3.88 | 3.79 | 3.69 | 3.58 | 3.48 | 3.37 | 3.26 |
| 16 | 10.58 | 7.51 | 6.30 | 5.64 | 5.21 | 4.91 | 4.69 | 4.52 | 4.38 | 4.27 | 4.10 | 3.92 | 3.73 | 3.64 | 3.54 | 3.44 | 3.33 | 3.22 | 3.11 |
| 17 | 10.38 | 7.35 | 6.16 | 5.50 | 5.07 | 4.78 | 4.56 | 4.39 | 4.25 | 4.14 | 3.97 | 3.79 | 3.61 | 3.51 | 3.41 | 3.31 | 3.21 | 3.10 | 2.98 |
| 18 | 10.22 | 7.21 | 6.03 | 5.37 | 4.96 | 4.66 | 4.44 | 4.28 | 4.14 | 4.03 | 3.86 | 3.68 | 3.50 | 3.40 | 3.30 | 3.20 | 3.10 | 2.99 | 2.87 |
| 19 | 10.07 | 7.09 | 5.92 | 5.27 | 4.85 | 4.56 | 4.34 | 4.18 | 4.04 | 3.93 | 3.76 | 3.59 | 3.40 | 3.31 | 3.21 | 3.11 | 3.00 | 2.89 | 2.78 |
| 20 | 9.94 | 6.99 | 5.82 | 5.17 | 4.76 | 4.47 | 4.26 | 4.09 | 3.96 | 3.85 | 3.68 | 3.50 | 3.32 | 3.22 | 3.12 | 3.02 | 2.92 | 2.81 | 2.69 |
| 21 | 9.83 | 6.89 | 5.73 | 5.09 | 4.68 | 4.39 | 4.18 | 4.02 | 3.88 | 3.77 | 3.60 | 3.43 | 3.24 | 3.15 | 3.05 | 2.95 | 2.84 | 2.73 | 2.61 |
| 22 | 9.73 | 6.81 | 5.65 | 5.02 | 4.61 | 4.32 | 4.11 | 3.94 | 3.81 | 3.70 | 3.54 | 3.36 | 3.18 | 3.08 | 2.98 | 2.88 | 2.77 | 2.66 | 2.55 |
| 23 | 9.63 | 6.73 | 5.58 | 4.95 | 4.54 | 4.26 | 4.05 | 3.88 | 3.75 | 3.64 | 3.47 | 3.30 | 3.12 | 3.02 | 2.92 | 2.82 | 2.71 | 2.60 | 2.48 |
| 24 | 9.55 | 6.66 | 5.52 | 4.89 | 4.49 | 4.20 | 3.99 | 3.83 | 3.69 | 3.59 | 3.42 | 3.25 | 3.06 | 2.97 | 2.87 | 2.77 | 2.66 | 2.55 | 2.43 |
| 25 | 9.48 | 6.60 | 5.46 | 4.84 | 4.43 | 4.15 | 3.94 | 3.78 | 3.64 | 3.54 | 3.37 | 3.20 | 3.01 | 2.92 | 2.82 | 2.72 | 2.61 | 2.50 | 2.38 |
| 26 | 9.41 | 6.54 | 5.41 | 4.79 | 4.38 | 4.10 | 3.89 | 3.73 | 3.60 | 3.49 | 3.33 | 3.15 | 2.97 | 2.87 | 2.77 | 2.67 | 2.56 | 2.45 | 2.33 |
| 27 | 9.34 | 6.49 | 5.36 | 4.74 | 4.34 | 4.06 | 3.85 | 3.69 | 3.56 | 3.45 | 3.28 | 3.11 | 2.93 | 2.83 | 2.73 | 2.63 | 2.52 | 2.41 | 2.29 |
| 28 | 9.28 | 6.44 | 5.32 | 4.70 | 4.30 | 4.02 | 3.81 | 3.65 | 3.52 | 3.41 | 3.25 | 3.07 | 2.89 | 2.79 | 2.69 | 2.59 | 2.48 | 2.37 | 2.25 |
| 29 | 9.23 | 6.40 | 5.28 | 4.66 | 4.26 | 3.98 | 3.77 | 3.61 | 3.48 | 3.38 | 3.21 | 3.04 | 2.86 | 2.76 | 2.66 | 2.56 | 2.45 | 2.33 | 2.21 |
| 30 | 9.18 | 6.35 | 5.24 | 4.62 | 4.23 | 3.95 | 3.74 | 3.58 | 3.45 | 3.34 | 3.18 | 3.01 | 2.82 | 2.73 | 2.63 | 2.52 | 2.42 | 2.30 | 2.18 |
| 40 | 8.83 | 6.07 | 4.98 | 4.37 | 3.99 | 3.71 | 3.51 | 3.35 | 3.22 | 3.12 | 2.95 | 2.78 | 2.60 | 2.50 | 2.40 | 2.30 | 2.18 | 2.06 | 1.93 |
| 60 | 8.49 | 5.79 | 4.73 | 4.14 | 3.76 | 3.49 | 3.29 | 3.13 | 3.01 | 2.90 | 2.74 | 2.57 | 2.39 | 2.29 | 2.19 | 2.08 | 1.96 | 1.83 | 1.69 |
| 120 | 8.18 | 5.54 | 4.50 | 3.92 | 3.55 | 3.28 | 3.09 | 2.93 | 2.81 | 2.71 | 2.54 | 2.37 | 2.19 | 2.09 | 1.98 | 1.87 | 1.75 | 1.61 | 1.43 |
| ∞ | 7.88 | 5.30 | 4.28 | 3.72 | 3.35 | 3.09 | 2.90 | 2.74 | 2.62 | 2.52 | 2.36 | 2.19 | 2.00 | 1.90 | 1.79 | 1.67 | 1.53 | 1.36 | 1.00 |

Source: Reprinted from E. S. Pearson and H. O. Hartley, eds., Biometrika Tables for Statisticians, 3rd ed., 1966, by permission of the Biometrika Trustees.

# Table E.6

## Table of Binomial Probabilities
### (begins on the following page)

## TABLE E.6

### Table of Binomial Probabilities

For a given combination of $n$ and $p$, entry indicates the probability of obtaining a specified value of $X$. To locate entry, **when $p \le .50$**, read $p$ across the top heading and both $n$ and $X$ down the left margin; **when $p \ge .50$**, read $p$ across the bottom heading and both $n$ and $X$ up the right margin.

| $n$ | $X$ | 0.01 | 0.02 | 0.03 | 0.04 | 0.05 | 0.06 | 0.07 | 0.08 | 0.09 | 0.10 | 0.15 | 0.20 | 0.25 | 0.30 | 0.35 | 0.40 | 0.45 | 0.50 | $X$ | $n$ |
|---|---|---|---|---|---|---|---|---|---|---|---|---|---|---|---|---|---|---|---|---|---|
| 2 | 0 | 0.9801 | 0.9604 | 0.9409 | 0.9216 | 0.9025 | 0.8836 | 0.8649 | 0.8464 | 0.8281 | 0.8100 | 0.7225 | 0.6400 | 0.5625 | 0.4900 | 0.4225 | 0.3600 | 0.3025 | 0.2500 | 2 | 2 |
|  | 1 | 0.0198 | 0.0392 | 0.0582 | 0.0768 | 0.0950 | 0.1128 | 0.1302 | 0.1472 | 0.1638 | 0.1800 | 0.2550 | 0.3200 | 0.3750 | 0.4200 | 0.4550 | 0.4800 | 0.4950 | 0.5000 | 1 |  |
|  | 2 | 0.0001 | 0.0004 | 0.0009 | 0.0016 | 0.0025 | 0.0036 | 0.0049 | 0.0064 | 0.0081 | 0.0100 | 0.0225 | 0.0400 | 0.0625 | 0.0900 | 0.1225 | 0.1600 | 0.2025 | 0.2500 | 0 | 2 |
| 3 | 0 | 0.9703 | 0.9412 | 0.9127 | 0.8847 | 0.8574 | 0.8306 | 0.8044 | 0.7787 | 0.7536 | 0.7290 | 0.6141 | 0.5120 | 0.4219 | 0.3430 | 0.2746 | 0.2160 | 0.1664 | 0.1250 | 3 | 3 |
|  | 1 | 0.0294 | 0.0576 | 0.0847 | 0.1106 | 0.1354 | 0.1590 | 0.1816 | 0.2031 | 0.2236 | 0.2430 | 0.3251 | 0.3840 | 0.4219 | 0.4410 | 0.4436 | 0.4320 | 0.4084 | 0.3750 | 2 |  |
|  | 2 | 0.0003 | 0.0012 | 0.0026 | 0.0046 | 0.0071 | 0.0102 | 0.0137 | 0.0177 | 0.0221 | 0.0270 | 0.0574 | 0.0960 | 0.1406 | 0.1890 | 0.2389 | 0.2880 | 0.3341 | 0.3750 | 1 |  |
|  | 3 | 0.0000 | 0.0000 | 0.0000 | 0.0001 | 0.0001 | 0.0002 | 0.0003 | 0.0005 | 0.0007 | 0.0010 | 0.0034 | 0.0080 | 0.0156 | 0.0270 | 0.0429 | 0.0640 | 0.0911 | 0.1250 | 0 | 3 |
| 4 | 0 | 0.9606 | 0.9224 | 0.8853 | 0.8493 | 0.8145 | 0.7807 | 0.7481 | 0.7164 | 0.6857 | 0.6561 | 0.5220 | 0.4096 | 0.3164 | 0.2401 | 0.1785 | 0.1296 | 0.0915 | 0.0625 | 4 | 4 |
|  | 1 | 0.0388 | 0.0753 | 0.1095 | 0.1416 | 0.1715 | 0.1993 | 0.2252 | 0.2492 | 0.2713 | 0.2916 | 0.3685 | 0.4096 | 0.4219 | 0.4116 | 0.3845 | 0.3456 | 0.2995 | 0.2500 | 3 |  |
|  | 2 | 0.0006 | 0.0023 | 0.0051 | 0.0088 | 0.0135 | 0.0191 | 0.0254 | 0.0325 | 0.0402 | 0.0486 | 0.0975 | 0.1536 | 0.2109 | 0.2646 | 0.3105 | 0.3456 | 0.3675 | 0.3750 | 2 |  |
|  | 3 | 0.0000 | 0.0001 | 0.0001 | 0.0002 | 0.0005 | 0.0008 | 0.0013 | 0.0019 | 0.0027 | 0.0036 | 0.0115 | 0.0256 | 0.0469 | 0.0756 | 0.1115 | 0.1536 | 0.2005 | 0.2500 | 1 |  |
|  | 4 | — | 0.0000 | 0.0000 | 0.0000 | 0.0000 | 0.0000 | 0.0000 | 0.0000 | 0.0001 | 0.0001 | 0.0005 | 0.0016 | 0.0039 | 0.0081 | 0.0150 | 0.0256 | 0.0410 | 0.0625 | 0 | 4 |
| 5 | 0 | 0.9510 | 0.9039 | 0.8587 | 0.8154 | 0.7738 | 0.7339 | 0.6957 | 0.6591 | 0.6240 | 0.5905 | 0.4437 | 0.3277 | 0.2373 | 0.1681 | 0.1160 | 0.0778 | 0.0503 | 0.0312 | 5 | 5 |
|  | 1 | 0.0480 | 0.0922 | 0.1328 | 0.1699 | 0.2036 | 0.2342 | 0.2618 | 0.2866 | 0.3086 | 0.3280 | 0.3915 | 0.4096 | 0.3955 | 0.3601 | 0.3124 | 0.2592 | 0.2059 | 0.1562 | 4 |  |
|  | 2 | 0.0010 | 0.0038 | 0.0082 | 0.0142 | 0.0214 | 0.0299 | 0.0394 | 0.0498 | 0.0610 | 0.0729 | 0.1382 | 0.2048 | 0.2637 | 0.3087 | 0.3364 | 0.3456 | 0.3369 | 0.3125 | 3 |  |
|  | 3 | 0.0000 | 0.0001 | 0.0003 | 0.0006 | 0.0011 | 0.0019 | 0.0030 | 0.0043 | 0.0060 | 0.0081 | 0.0244 | 0.0512 | 0.0879 | 0.1323 | 0.1811 | 0.2304 | 0.2757 | 0.3125 | 2 |  |
|  | 4 | 0.0000 | 0.0000 | 0.0000 | 0.0000 | 0.0000 | 0.0001 | 0.0001 | 0.0002 | 0.0003 | 0.0004 | 0.0022 | 0.0064 | 0.0146 | 0.0283 | 0.0488 | 0.0768 | 0.1128 | 0.1562 | 1 |  |
|  | 5 | — | 0.0000 | 0.0000 | 0.0000 | 0.0000 | 0.0000 | 0.0000 | 0.0000 | 0.0000 | 0.0000 | 0.0001 | 0.0003 | 0.0010 | 0.0024 | 0.0053 | 0.0102 | 0.0185 | 0.0312 | 0 | 5 |
| 6 | 0 | 0.9415 | 0.8858 | 0.8330 | 0.7828 | 0.7351 | 0.6899 | 0.6470 | 0.6064 | 0.5679 | 0.5314 | 0.3771 | 0.2621 | 0.1780 | 0.1176 | 0.0754 | 0.0467 | 0.0277 | 0.0156 | 6 | 6 |
|  | 1 | 0.0571 | 0.1085 | 0.1546 | 0.1957 | 0.2321 | 0.2642 | 0.2922 | 0.3164 | 0.3370 | 0.3543 | 0.3993 | 0.3932 | 0.3560 | 0.3025 | 0.2437 | 0.1866 | 0.1359 | 0.0937 | 5 |  |
|  | 2 | 0.0014 | 0.0055 | 0.0120 | 0.0204 | 0.0305 | 0.0422 | 0.0550 | 0.0688 | 0.0833 | 0.0984 | 0.1762 | 0.2458 | 0.2966 | 0.3241 | 0.3280 | 0.3110 | 0.2780 | 0.2344 | 4 |  |
|  | 3 | 0.0000 | 0.0002 | 0.0005 | 0.0011 | 0.0021 | 0.0036 | 0.0055 | 0.0080 | 0.0110 | 0.0146 | 0.0415 | 0.0819 | 0.1318 | 0.1852 | 0.2355 | 0.2765 | 0.3032 | 0.3125 | 3 |  |
|  | 4 | 0.0000 | 0.0000 | 0.0000 | 0.0000 | 0.0001 | 0.0002 | 0.0003 | 0.0005 | 0.0008 | 0.0012 | 0.0055 | 0.0154 | 0.0330 | 0.0595 | 0.0951 | 0.1372 | 0.1861 | 0.2344 | 2 |  |
|  | 5 | — | 0.0000 | 0.0000 | 0.0000 | 0.0000 | 0.0000 | 0.0000 | 0.0000 | 0.0000 | 0.0001 | 0.0004 | 0.0015 | 0.0044 | 0.0102 | 0.0205 | 0.0369 | 0.0609 | 0.0937 | 1 |  |
|  | 6 | — | — | — | — | 0.0000 | 0.0000 | 0.0000 | 0.0000 | 0.0000 | 0.0000 | 0.0000 | 0.0001 | 0.0002 | 0.0007 | 0.0018 | 0.0041 | 0.0083 | 0.0156 | 0 | 6 |

| n | X | 0.50 | 0.55 | 0.60 | 0.65 | 0.70 | 0.75 | 0.80 | 0.85 | 0.90 | 0.91 | 0.92 | 0.93 | 0.94 | 0.95 | 0.96 | 0.97 | 0.98 | 0.99 | X |
|---|---|------|------|------|------|------|------|------|------|------|------|------|------|------|------|------|------|------|------|---|
| 7 | 7 | 0.0078 | 0.0152 | 0.0280 | 0.0490 | 0.0824 | 0.1335 | 0.2097 | 0.3206 | 0.4783 | 0.5168 | 0.5578 | 0.6017 | 0.6485 | 0.6983 | 0.7514 | 0.8080 | 0.8681 | 0.9321 | 0 |
|   | 6 | 0.0547 | 0.0872 | 0.1306 | 0.1848 | 0.2471 | 0.3115 | 0.3670 | 0.3960 | 0.3720 | 0.3578 | 0.3396 | 0.3170 | 0.2897 | 0.2573 | 0.2192 | 0.1749 | 0.1240 | 0.0659 | 1 |
|   | 5 | 0.1641 | 0.2140 | 0.2613 | 0.2985 | 0.3177 | 0.3115 | 0.2753 | 0.2097 | 0.1240 | 0.1061 | 0.0886 | 0.0716 | 0.0555 | 0.0406 | 0.0274 | 0.0162 | 0.0076 | 0.0020 | 2 |
|   | 4 | 0.2734 | 0.2918 | 0.2903 | 0.2679 | 0.2269 | 0.1730 | 0.1147 | 0.0617 | 0.0230 | 0.0175 | 0.0128 | 0.0090 | 0.0059 | 0.0036 | 0.0019 | 0.0008 | 0.0003 | 0.0000 | 3 |
|   | 3 | 0.2734 | 0.2388 | 0.1935 | 0.1442 | 0.0972 | 0.0577 | 0.0287 | 0.0109 | 0.0026 | 0.0017 | 0.0011 | 0.0007 | 0.0004 | 0.0002 | 0.0001 | 0.0000 | — | — | 4 |
|   | 2 | 0.1641 | 0.1172 | 0.0774 | 0.0466 | 0.0250 | 0.0115 | 0.0043 | 0.0012 | 0.0002 | 0.0001 | 0.0001 | 0.0000 | 0.0000 | 0.0000 | — | — | — | — | 5 |
|   | 1 | 0.0547 | 0.0320 | 0.0172 | 0.0084 | 0.0036 | 0.0013 | 0.0004 | 0.0001 | 0.0000 | 0.0000 | 0.0000 | — | — | — | — | — | — | — | 6 |
|   | 0 | 0.0078 | 0.0037 | 0.0016 | 0.0006 | 0.0002 | 0.0001 | 0.0000 | 0.0000 | 0.0000 | 0.0000 | 0.0000 | — | — | — | — | — | — | — | 7 |
| 8 | 8 | 0.0039 | 0.0084 | 0.0168 | 0.0319 | 0.0576 | 0.1001 | 0.1678 | 0.2725 | 0.4305 | 0.4703 | 0.5132 | 0.5596 | 0.6096 | 0.6634 | 0.7214 | 0.7837 | 0.8508 | 0.9227 | 0 |
|   | 7 | 0.0312 | 0.0548 | 0.0896 | 0.1373 | 0.1977 | 0.2670 | 0.3355 | 0.3847 | 0.3826 | 0.3721 | 0.3570 | 0.3370 | 0.3113 | 0.2793 | 0.2405 | 0.1939 | 0.1389 | 0.0746 | 1 |
|   | 6 | 0.1094 | 0.1569 | 0.2090 | 0.2587 | 0.2965 | 0.3115 | 0.2936 | 0.2376 | 0.1488 | 0.1288 | 0.1087 | 0.0888 | 0.0695 | 0.0515 | 0.0351 | 0.0210 | 0.0099 | 0.0026 | 2 |
|   | 5 | 0.2187 | 0.2568 | 0.2787 | 0.2786 | 0.2541 | 0.2076 | 0.1468 | 0.0839 | 0.0331 | 0.0255 | 0.0189 | 0.0134 | 0.0089 | 0.0054 | 0.0029 | 0.0013 | 0.0004 | 0.0001 | 3 |
|   | 4 | 0.2734 | 0.2627 | 0.2322 | 0.1875 | 0.1361 | 0.0865 | 0.0459 | 0.0185 | 0.0046 | 0.0031 | 0.0021 | 0.0013 | 0.0007 | 0.0004 | 0.0002 | 0.0001 | 0.0000 | 0.0000 | 4 |
|   | 3 | 0.2187 | 0.1719 | 0.1239 | 0.0808 | 0.0467 | 0.0231 | 0.0092 | 0.0026 | 0.0004 | 0.0002 | 0.0001 | 0.0001 | 0.0000 | 0.0000 | 0.0000 | 0.0000 | — | — | 5 |
|   | 2 | 0.1094 | 0.0703 | 0.0413 | 0.0217 | 0.0100 | 0.0038 | 0.0011 | 0.0002 | 0.0000 | 0.0000 | 0.0000 | 0.0000 | — | — | — | — | — | — | 6 |
|   | 1 | 0.0312 | 0.0164 | 0.0079 | 0.0033 | 0.0012 | 0.0004 | 0.0001 | 0.0000 | — | — | — | — | — | — | — | — | — | — | 7 |
|   | 0 | 0.0039 | 0.0017 | 0.0007 | 0.0002 | 0.0001 | 0.0000 | 0.0000 | — | — | — | — | — | — | — | — | — | — | — | 8 |
| 9 | 9 | 0.0020 | 0.0046 | 0.0101 | 0.0207 | 0.0404 | 0.0751 | 0.1342 | 0.2316 | 0.3874 | 0.4279 | 0.4722 | 0.5204 | 0.5730 | 0.6302 | 0.6925 | 0.7602 | 0.8337 | 0.9135 | 0 |
|   | 8 | 0.0176 | 0.0339 | 0.0605 | 0.1004 | 0.1556 | 0.2253 | 0.3020 | 0.3679 | 0.3874 | 0.3809 | 0.3695 | 0.3525 | 0.3292 | 0.2985 | 0.2597 | 0.2116 | 0.1531 | 0.0830 | 1 |
|   | 7 | 0.0703 | 0.1110 | 0.1612 | 0.2162 | 0.2668 | 0.3003 | 0.3020 | 0.2597 | 0.1722 | 0.1507 | 0.1285 | 0.1061 | 0.0840 | 0.0629 | 0.0433 | 0.0262 | 0.0125 | 0.0034 | 2 |
|   | 6 | 0.1641 | 0.2119 | 0.2508 | 0.2716 | 0.2668 | 0.2336 | 0.1762 | 0.1069 | 0.0446 | 0.0348 | 0.0261 | 0.0186 | 0.0125 | 0.0077 | 0.0042 | 0.0019 | 0.0006 | 0.0001 | 3 |
|   | 5 | 0.2461 | 0.2600 | 0.2508 | 0.2194 | 0.1715 | 0.1168 | 0.0661 | 0.0283 | 0.0074 | 0.0052 | 0.0034 | 0.0021 | 0.0012 | 0.0006 | 0.0003 | 0.0001 | 0.0000 | 0.0000 | 4 |
|   | 4 | 0.2461 | 0.2128 | 0.1672 | 0.1181 | 0.0735 | 0.0390 | 0.0165 | 0.0050 | 0.0008 | 0.0005 | 0.0003 | 0.0002 | 0.0001 | 0.0000 | 0.0000 | 0.0000 | — | — | 5 |
|   | 3 | 0.1641 | 0.1160 | 0.0743 | 0.0424 | 0.0210 | 0.0087 | 0.0028 | 0.0006 | 0.0001 | 0.0000 | 0.0000 | 0.0000 | 0.0000 | — | — | — | — | — | 6 |
|   | 2 | 0.0703 | 0.0407 | 0.0212 | 0.0098 | 0.0039 | 0.0012 | 0.0003 | 0.0000 | 0.0000 | — | — | — | — | — | — | — | — | — | 7 |
|   | 1 | 0.0176 | 0.0083 | 0.0035 | 0.0013 | 0.0004 | 0.0001 | 0.0000 | — | — | — | — | — | — | — | — | — | — | — | 8 |
|   | 0 | 0.0020 | 0.0008 | 0.0003 | 0.0001 | 0.0000 | 0.0000 | 0.0000 | — | — | — | — | — | — | — | — | — | — | — | 9 |
| 10 | 10 | 0.0010 | 0.0025 | 0.0060 | 0.0135 | 0.0282 | 0.0563 | 0.1074 | 0.1969 | 0.3487 | 0.3894 | 0.4344 | 0.4840 | 0.5386 | 0.5987 | 0.6648 | 0.7374 | 0.8171 | 0.9044 | 0 |
|   | 9 | 0.0098 | 0.0207 | 0.0403 | 0.0725 | 0.1211 | 0.1877 | 0.2684 | 0.3474 | 0.3874 | 0.3851 | 0.3777 | 0.3643 | 0.3438 | 0.3151 | 0.2770 | 0.2281 | 0.1667 | 0.0914 | 1 |
|   | 8 | 0.0439 | 0.0763 | 0.1209 | 0.1757 | 0.2335 | 0.2816 | 0.3020 | 0.2759 | 0.1937 | 0.1714 | 0.1478 | 0.1234 | 0.0988 | 0.0746 | 0.0519 | 0.0317 | 0.0153 | 0.0042 | 2 |
|   | 7 | 0.1172 | 0.1665 | 0.2150 | 0.2522 | 0.2668 | 0.2503 | 0.2013 | 0.1298 | 0.0574 | 0.0452 | 0.0343 | 0.0248 | 0.0168 | 0.0105 | 0.0058 | 0.0026 | 0.0008 | 0.0001 | 3 |
|   | 6 | 0.2051 | 0.2384 | 0.2508 | 0.2377 | 0.2001 | 0.1460 | 0.0881 | 0.0401 | 0.0112 | 0.0078 | 0.0052 | 0.0033 | 0.0019 | 0.0010 | 0.0004 | 0.0001 | 0.0000 | 0.0000 | 4 |
|   | 5 | 0.2461 | 0.2340 | 0.2007 | 0.1536 | 0.1029 | 0.0584 | 0.0264 | 0.0085 | 0.0015 | 0.0009 | 0.0005 | 0.0003 | 0.0001 | 0.0001 | 0.0000 | 0.0000 | — | — | 5 |
|   | 4 | 0.2051 | 0.1596 | 0.1115 | 0.0689 | 0.0368 | 0.0162 | 0.0055 | 0.0012 | 0.0001 | 0.0001 | 0.0000 | 0.0000 | 0.0000 | 0.0000 | — | — | — | — | 6 |
|   | 3 | 0.1172 | 0.0746 | 0.0425 | 0.0212 | 0.0090 | 0.0031 | 0.0008 | 0.0001 | 0.0000 | 0.0000 | — | — | — | — | — | — | — | — | 7 |
|   | 2 | 0.0439 | 0.0229 | 0.0106 | 0.0043 | 0.0014 | 0.0004 | 0.0001 | 0.0000 | — | — | — | — | — | — | — | — | — | — | 8 |
|   | 1 | 0.0098 | 0.0042 | 0.0016 | 0.0005 | 0.0001 | 0.0000 | 0.0000 | — | — | — | — | — | — | — | — | — | — | — | 9 |
|   | 0 | 0.0010 | 0.0003 | 0.0001 | 0.0000 | 0.0000 | 0.0000 | 0.0000 | — | — | — | — | — | — | — | — | — | — | — | 10 |
| n | X | 0.50 | 0.55 | 0.60 | 0.65 | 0.70 | 0.75 | 0.80 | 0.85 | 0.90 | 0.91 | 0.92 | 0.93 | 0.94 | 0.95 | 0.96 | 0.97 | 0.98 | 0.99 | X |

continued

**TABLE E.6**

Table of Binomial Probabilities (Continued)

| n | X | 0.01 | 0.02 | 0.03 | 0.04 | 0.05 | 0.06 | 0.07 | 0.08 | 0.09 | 0.10 | 0.15 | 0.20 | 0.25 | 0.30 | 0.35 | 0.40 | 0.45 | 0.50 | X | n |
|---|---|------|------|------|------|------|------|------|------|------|------|------|------|------|------|------|------|------|------|---|---|
| 20 | 0 | 0.8179 | 0.6676 | 0.5438 | 0.4420 | 0.3585 | 0.2901 | 0.2342 | 0.1887 | 0.1516 | 0.1216 | 0.0388 | 0.0115 | 0.0032 | 0.0008 | 0.0002 | 0.0000 | 0.0000 | — | 20 | |
| | 1 | 0.1652 | 0.2725 | 0.3364 | 0.3683 | 0.3774 | 0.3703 | 0.3526 | 0.3282 | 0.3000 | 0.2702 | 0.1368 | 0.0576 | 0.0211 | 0.0068 | 0.0020 | 0.0005 | 0.0001 | 0.0000 | 19 | |
| | 2 | 0.0159 | 0.0528 | 0.0988 | 0.1458 | 0.1887 | 0.2246 | 0.2521 | 0.2711 | 0.2818 | 0.2852 | 0.2293 | 0.1369 | 0.0699 | 0.0278 | 0.0100 | 0.0031 | 0.0008 | 0.0002 | 18 | |
| | 3 | 0.0010 | 0.0065 | 0.0183 | 0.0364 | 0.0596 | 0.0860 | 0.1139 | 0.1414 | 0.1672 | 0.1901 | 0.2428 | 0.2054 | 0.1339 | 0.0716 | 0.0323 | 0.0123 | 0.0040 | 0.0011 | 17 | |
| | 4 | 0.0000 | 0.0006 | 0.0024 | 0.0065 | 0.0133 | 0.0233 | 0.0364 | 0.0523 | 0.0703 | 0.0898 | 0.1821 | 0.2182 | 0.1897 | 0.1304 | 0.0738 | 0.0350 | 0.0139 | 0.0046 | 16 | |
| | 5 | — | 0.0000 | 0.0002 | 0.0009 | 0.0022 | 0.0048 | 0.0088 | 0.0145 | 0.0222 | 0.0319 | 0.1028 | 0.1746 | 0.2023 | 0.1789 | 0.1272 | 0.0746 | 0.0365 | 0.0148 | 15 | |
| | 6 | — | — | 0.0000 | 0.0001 | 0.0003 | 0.0008 | 0.0017 | 0.0032 | 0.0055 | 0.0089 | 0.0454 | 0.1091 | 0.1686 | 0.1916 | 0.1712 | 0.1244 | 0.0746 | 0.0370 | 14 | |
| | 7 | — | — | — | 0.0000 | 0.0000 | 0.0001 | 0.0002 | 0.0005 | 0.0011 | 0.0020 | 0.0160 | 0.0545 | 0.1124 | 0.1643 | 0.1844 | 0.1659 | 0.1221 | 0.0739 | 13 | |
| | 8 | — | — | — | — | — | 0.0000 | 0.0000 | 0.0001 | 0.0002 | 0.0004 | 0.0046 | 0.0222 | 0.0609 | 0.1144 | 0.1614 | 0.1797 | 0.1623 | 0.1201 | 12 | |
| | 9 | — | — | — | — | — | — | 0.0000 | 0.0000 | 0.0000 | 0.0001 | 0.0011 | 0.0074 | 0.0271 | 0.0654 | 0.1158 | 0.1597 | 0.1771 | 0.1602 | 11 | |
| | 10 | — | — | — | — | — | — | — | 0.0000 | — | 0.0000 | 0.0002 | 0.0020 | 0.0099 | 0.0308 | 0.0686 | 0.1171 | 0.1593 | 0.1762 | 10 | |
| | 11 | — | — | — | — | — | — | — | — | — | — | 0.0000 | 0.0005 | 0.0030 | 0.0120 | 0.0336 | 0.0710 | 0.1185 | 0.1602 | 9 | |
| | 12 | — | — | — | — | — | — | — | — | — | — | — | 0.0001 | 0.0008 | 0.0039 | 0.0136 | 0.0355 | 0.0727 | 0.1201 | 8 | |
| | 13 | — | — | — | — | — | — | — | — | — | — | — | 0.0000 | 0.0002 | 0.0010 | 0.0045 | 0.0146 | 0.0366 | 0.0739 | 7 | |
| | 14 | — | — | — | — | — | — | — | — | — | — | — | — | 0.0000 | 0.0002 | 0.0012 | 0.0049 | 0.0150 | 0.0370 | 6 | |
| | 15 | — | — | — | — | — | — | — | — | — | — | — | — | — | 0.0000 | 0.0003 | 0.0013 | 0.0049 | 0.0148 | 5 | |
| | 16 | — | — | — | — | — | — | — | — | — | — | — | — | — | — | 0.0000 | 0.0003 | 0.0013 | 0.0046 | 4 | |
| | 17 | — | — | — | — | — | — | — | — | — | — | — | — | — | — | — | 0.0000 | 0.0002 | 0.0011 | 3 | |
| | 18 | — | — | — | — | — | — | — | — | — | — | — | — | — | — | — | — | 0.0000 | 0.0002 | 2 | |
| | 19 | — | — | — | — | — | — | — | — | — | — | — | — | — | — | — | — | — | 0.0000 | 1 | |
| | 20 | — | — | — | — | — | — | — | — | — | — | — | — | — | — | — | — | — | — | 0 | 20 |
| n | X | 0.99 | 0.98 | 0.97 | 0.96 | 0.95 | 0.94 | 0.93 | 0.92 | 0.91 | 0.90 | 0.85 | 0.80 | 0.75 | 0.70 | 0.65 | 0.60 | 0.55 | 0.50 | X | n |

**TABLE E.7**

Table of Poisson
Probabilities

For a given value of λ, entry
indicates the probability of a
specified value of X.

λ

| X | 0.1 | 0.2 | 0.3 | 0.4 | 0.5 | 0.6 | 0.7 | 0.8 | 0.9 | 1.0 |
|---|-----|-----|-----|-----|-----|-----|-----|-----|-----|-----|
| 0 | 0.9048 | 0.8187 | 0.7408 | 0.6703 | 0.6065 | 0.5488 | 0.4966 | 0.4493 | 0.4066 | 0.3679 |
| 1 | 0.0905 | 0.1637 | 0.2222 | 0.2681 | 0.3033 | 0.3293 | 0.3476 | 0.3595 | 0.3659 | 0.3679 |
| 2 | 0.0045 | 0.0164 | 0.0333 | 0.0536 | 0.0758 | 0.0988 | 0.1217 | 0.1438 | 0.1647 | 0.1839 |
| 3 | 0.0002 | 0.0011 | 0.0033 | 0.0072 | 0.0126 | 0.0198 | 0.0284 | 0.0383 | 0.0494 | 0.0613 |
| 4 | 0.0000 | 0.0001 | 0.0003 | 0.0007 | 0.0016 | 0.0030 | 0.0050 | 0.0077 | 0.0111 | 0.0153 |
| 5 | 0.0000 | 0.0000 | 0.0000 | 0.0001 | 0.0002 | 0.0004 | 0.0007 | 0.0012 | 0.0020 | 0.0031 |
| 6 | 0.0000 | 0.0000 | 0.0000 | 0.0000 | 0.0000 | 0.0000 | 0.0001 | 0.0002 | 0.0003 | 0.0005 |
| 7 | 0.0000 | 0.0000 | 0.0000 | 0.0000 | 0.0000 | 0.0000 | 0.0000 | 0.0000 | 0.0000 | 0.0001 |

λ

| X | 1.1 | 1.2 | 1.3 | 1.4 | 1.5 | 1.6 | 1.7 | 1.8 | 1.9 | 2.0 |
|---|-----|-----|-----|-----|-----|-----|-----|-----|-----|-----|
| 0 | 0.3329 | 0.3012 | 0.2725 | 0.2466 | 0.2231 | 0.2019 | 0.1827 | 0.1653 | 0.1496 | 0.1353 |
| 1 | 0.3662 | 0.3614 | 0.3543 | 0.3452 | 0.3347 | 0.3230 | 0.3106 | 0.2975 | 0.2842 | 0.2707 |
| 2 | 0.2014 | 0.2169 | 0.2303 | 0.2417 | 0.2510 | 0.2584 | 0.2640 | 0.2678 | 0.2700 | 0.2707 |
| 3 | 0.0738 | 0.0867 | 0.0998 | 0.1128 | 0.1255 | 0.1378 | 0.1496 | 0.1607 | 0.1710 | 0.1804 |
| 4 | 0.0203 | 0.0260 | 0.0324 | 0.0395 | 0.0471 | 0.0551 | 0.0636 | 0.0723 | 0.0812 | 0.0902 |
| 5 | 0.0045 | 0.0062 | 0.0084 | 0.0111 | 0.0141 | 0.0176 | 0.0216 | 0.0260 | 0.0309 | 0.0361 |
| 6 | 0.0008 | 0.0012 | 0.0018 | 0.0026 | 0.0035 | 0.0047 | 0.0061 | 0.0078 | 0.0098 | 0.0120 |
| 7 | 0.0001 | 0.0002 | 0.0003 | 0.0005 | 0.0008 | 0.0011 | 0.0015 | 0.0020 | 0.0027 | 0.0034 |
| 8 | 0.0000 | 0.0000 | 0.0001 | 0.0001 | 0.0001 | 0.0002 | 0.0003 | 0.0005 | 0.0006 | 0.0009 |
| 9 | 0.0000 | 0.0000 | 0.0000 | 0.0000 | 0.0000 | 0.0000 | 0.0001 | 0.0001 | 0.0001 | 0.0002 |

λ

| X | 2.1 | 2.2 | 2.3 | 2.4 | 2.5 | 2.6 | 2.7 | 2.8 | 2.9 | 3.0 |
|---|-----|-----|-----|-----|-----|-----|-----|-----|-----|-----|
| 0 | 0.1225 | 0.1108 | 0.1003 | 0.0907 | 0.0821 | 0.0743 | 0.0672 | 0.0608 | 0.0550 | 0.0498 |
| 1 | 0.2572 | 0.2438 | 0.2306 | 0.2177 | 0.2052 | 0.1931 | 0.1815 | 0.1703 | 0.1596 | 0.1494 |
| 2 | 0.2700 | 0.2681 | 0.2652 | 0.2613 | 0.2565 | 0.2510 | 0.2450 | 0.2384 | 0.2314 | 0.2240 |
| 3 | 0.1890 | 0.1966 | 0.2033 | 0.2090 | 0.2138 | 0.2176 | 0.2205 | 0.2225 | 0.2237 | 0.2240 |
| 4 | 0.0992 | 0.1082 | 0.1169 | 0.1254 | 0.1336 | 0.1414 | 0.1488 | 0.1557 | 0.1622 | 0.1680 |
| 5 | 0.0417 | 0.0476 | 0.0538 | 0.0602 | 0.0668 | 0.0735 | 0.0804 | 0.0872 | 0.0940 | 0.1008 |
| 6 | 0.0146 | 0.0174 | 0.0206 | 0.0241 | 0.0278 | 0.0319 | 0.0362 | 0.0407 | 0.0455 | 0.0504 |
| 7 | 0.0044 | 0.0055 | 0.0068 | 0.0083 | 0.0099 | 0.0118 | 0.0139 | 0.0163 | 0.0188 | 0.0216 |
| 8 | 0.0011 | 0.0015 | 0.0019 | 0.0025 | 0.0031 | 0.0038 | 0.0047 | 0.0057 | 0.0068 | 0.0081 |
| 9 | 0.0003 | 0.0004 | 0.0005 | 0.0007 | 0.0009 | 0.0011 | 0.0014 | 0.0018 | 0.0022 | 0.0027 |
| 10 | 0.0001 | 0.0001 | 0.0001 | 0.0002 | 0.0002 | 0.0003 | 0.0004 | 0.0005 | 0.0006 | 0.0008 |
| 11 | 0.0000 | 0.0000 | 0.0000 | 0.0000 | 0.0000 | 0.0001 | 0.0001 | 0.0001 | 0.0002 | 0.0002 |
| 12 | 0.0000 | 0.0000 | 0.0000 | 0.0000 | 0.0000 | 0.0000 | 0.0000 | 0.0000 | 0.0000 | 0.0001 |

λ

| X | 3.1 | 3.2 | 3.3 | 3.4 | 3.5 | 3.6 | 3.7 | 3.8 | 3.9 | 4.0 |
|---|-----|-----|-----|-----|-----|-----|-----|-----|-----|-----|
| 0 | 0.0450 | 0.0408 | 0.0369 | 0.0334 | 0.0302 | 0.0273 | 0.0247 | 0.0224 | 0.0202 | 0.0183 |
| 1 | 0.1397 | 0.1340 | 0.1217 | 0.1135 | 0.1057 | 0.0984 | 0.0915 | 0.0850 | 0.0789 | 0.0733 |
| 2 | 0.2165 | 0.2087 | 0.2008 | 0.1929 | 0.1850 | 0.1771 | 0.1692 | 0.1615 | 0.1539 | 0.1465 |
| 3 | 0.2237 | 0.2226 | 0.2209 | 0.2186 | 0.2158 | 0.2125 | 0.2087 | 0.2046 | 0.2001 | 0.1954 |
| 4 | 0.1734 | 0.1781 | 0.1823 | 0.1858 | 0.1888 | 0.1912 | 0.1931 | 0.1944 | 0.1951 | 0.1954 |
| 5 | 0.1075 | 0.1140 | 0.1203 | 0.1264 | 0.1322 | 0.1377 | 0.1429 | 0.1477 | 0.1522 | 0.1563 |
| 6 | 0.0555 | 0.0608 | 0.0662 | 0.0716 | 0.0771 | 0.0826 | 0.0881 | 0.0936 | 0.0989 | 0.1042 |
| 7 | 0.0246 | 0.0278 | 0.0312 | 0.0348 | 0.0385 | 0.0425 | 0.0466 | 0.0508 | 0.0551 | 0.0595 |
| 8 | 0.0095 | 0.0111 | 0.0129 | 0.0148 | 0.0169 | 0.0191 | 0.0215 | 0.0241 | 0.0269 | 0.0298 |
| 9 | 0.0033 | 0.0040 | 0.0047 | 0.0056 | 0.0066 | 0.0076 | 0.0089 | 0.0102 | 0.0116 | 0.0132 |
| 10 | 0.0010 | 0.0013 | 0.0016 | 0.0019 | 0.0023 | 0.0028 | 0.0033 | 0.0039 | 0.0045 | 0.0053 |
| 11 | 0.0003 | 0.0004 | 0.0005 | 0.0006 | 0.0007 | 0.0009 | 0.0011 | 0.0013 | 0.0016 | 0.0019 |
| 12 | 0.0001 | 0.0001 | 0.0001 | 0.0002 | 0.0002 | 0.0003 | 0.0003 | 0.0004 | 0.0005 | 0.0006 |
| 13 | 0.0000 | 0.0000 | 0.0000 | 0.0000 | 0.0001 | 0.0001 | 0.0001 | 0.0001 | 0.0002 | 0.0002 |
| 14 | 0.0000 | 0.0000 | 0.0000 | 0.0000 | 0.0000 | 0.0000 | 0.0000 | 0.0000 | 0.0000 | 0.0001 |

*continued*

**TABLE E.7**

Table of Poisson
Probabilities
(*Continued*)

|  | | | | | | λ | | | | |
|---|---|---|---|---|---|---|---|---|---|---|
| X | 4.1 | 4.2 | 4.3 | 4.4 | 4.5 | 4.6 | 4.7 | 4.8 | 4.9 | 5.0 |
| 0 | 0.0166 | 0.0150 | 0.0136 | 0.0123 | 0.0111 | 0.0101 | 0.0091 | 0.0082 | 0.0074 | 0.0067 |
| 1 | 0.0679 | 0.0630 | 0.0583 | 0.0540 | 0.0500 | 0.0462 | 0.0427 | 0.0395 | 0.0365 | 0.0337 |
| 2 | 0.1393 | 0.1323 | 0.1254 | 0.1188 | 0.1125 | 0.1063 | 0.1005 | 0.0948 | 0.0894 | 0.0842 |
| 3 | 0.1904 | 0.1852 | 0.1798 | 0.1743 | 0.1687 | 0.1631 | 0.1574 | 0.1517 | 0.1460 | 0.1404 |
| 4 | 0.1951 | 0.1944 | 0.1933 | 0.1917 | 0.1898 | 0.1875 | 0.1849 | 0.1820 | 0.1789 | 0.1755 |
| 5 | 0.1600 | 0.1633 | 0.1662 | 0.1687 | 0.1708 | 0.1725 | 0.1738 | 0.1747 | 0.1753 | 0.1755 |
| 6 | 0.1093 | 0.1143 | 0.1191 | 0.1237 | 0.1281 | 0.1323 | 0.1362 | 0.1398 | 0.1432 | 0.1462 |
| 7 | 0.0640 | 0.0686 | 0.0732 | 0.0778 | 0.0824 | 0.0869 | 0.0914 | 0.0959 | 0.1002 | 0.1044 |
| 8 | 0.0328 | 0.0360 | 0.0393 | 0.0428 | 0.0463 | 0.0500 | 0.0537 | 0.0575 | 0.0614 | 0.0653 |
| 9 | 0.0150 | 0.0168 | 0.0188 | 0.0209 | 0.0232 | 0.0255 | 0.0280 | 0.0307 | 0.0334 | 0.0363 |
| 10 | 0.0061 | 0.0071 | 0.0081 | 0.0092 | 0.0104 | 0.0118 | 0.0132 | 0.0147 | 0.0164 | 0.0181 |
| 11 | 0.0023 | 0.0027 | 0.0032 | 0.0037 | 0.0043 | 0.0049 | 0.0056 | 0.0064 | 0.0073 | 0.0082 |
| 12 | 0.0008 | 0.0009 | 0.0011 | 0.0014 | 0.0016 | 0.0019 | 0.0022 | 0.0026 | 0.0030 | 0.0034 |
| 13 | 0.0002 | 0.0003 | 0.0004 | 0.0005 | 0.0006 | 0.0007 | 0.0008 | 0.0009 | 0.0011 | 0.0013 |
| 14 | 0.0001 | 0.0001 | 0.0001 | 0.0001 | 0.0002 | 0.0002 | 0.0003 | 0.0003 | 0.0004 | 0.0005 |
| 15 | 0.0000 | 0.0000 | 0.0000 | 0.0000 | 0.0001 | 0.0001 | 0.0001 | 0.0001 | 0.0001 | 0.0002 |

|  | | | | | | λ | | | | |
|---|---|---|---|---|---|---|---|---|---|---|
| X | 5.1 | 5.2 | 5.3 | 5.4 | 5.5 | 5.6 | 5.7 | 5.8 | 5.9 | 6.0 |
| 0 | 0.0061 | 0.0055 | 0.0050 | 0.0045 | 0.0041 | 0.0037 | 0.0033 | 0.0030 | 0.0027 | 0.0025 |
| 1 | 0.0311 | 0.0287 | 0.0265 | 0.0244 | 0.0225 | 0.0207 | 0.0191 | 0.0176 | 0.0162 | 0.0149 |
| 2 | 0.0793 | 0.0746 | 0.0701 | 0.0659 | 0.0618 | 0.0580 | 0.0544 | 0.0509 | 0.0477 | 0.0446 |
| 3 | 0.1348 | 0.1293 | 0.1239 | 0.1185 | 0.1133 | 0.1082 | 0.1033 | 0.0985 | 0.0938 | 0.0892 |
| 4 | 0.1719 | 0.1681 | 0.1641 | 0.1600 | 0.1558 | 0.1515 | 0.1472 | 0.1428 | 0.1383 | 0.1339 |
| 5 | 0.1753 | 0.1748 | 0.1740 | 0.1728 | 0.1714 | 0.1697 | 0.1678 | 0.1656 | 0.1632 | 0.1606 |
| 6 | 0.1490 | 0.1515 | 0.1537 | 0.1555 | 0.1571 | 0.1584 | 0.1594 | 0.1601 | 0.1605 | 0.1606 |
| 7 | 0.1086 | 0.1125 | 0.1163 | 0.1200 | 0.1234 | 0.1267 | 0.1298 | 0.1326 | 0.1353 | 0.1377 |
| 8 | 0.0692 | 0.0731 | 0.0771 | 0.0810 | 0.0849 | 0.0887 | 0.0925 | 0.0962 | 0.0998 | 0.1033 |
| 9 | 0.0392 | 0.0423 | 0.0454 | 0.0486 | 0.0519 | 0.0552 | 0.0586 | 0.0620 | 0.0654 | 0.0688 |
| 10 | 0.0200 | 0.0220 | 0.0241 | 0.0262 | 0.0285 | 0.0309 | 0.0334 | 0.0359 | 0.0386 | 0.0413 |
| 11 | 0.0093 | 0.0104 | 0.0116 | 0.0129 | 0.0143 | 0.0157 | 0.0173 | 0.0190 | 0.0207 | 0.0225 |
| 12 | 0.0039 | 0.0045 | 0.0051 | 0.0058 | 0.0065 | 0.0073 | 0.0082 | 0.0092 | 0.0102 | 0.0113 |
| 13 | 0.0015 | 0.0018 | 0.0021 | 0.0024 | 0.0028 | 0.0032 | 0.0036 | 0.0041 | 0.0046 | 0.0052 |
| 14 | 0.0006 | 0.0007 | 0.0008 | 0.0009 | 0.0011 | 0.0013 | 0.0015 | 0.0017 | 0.0019 | 0.0022 |
| 15 | 0.0002 | 0.0002 | 0.0003 | 0.0003 | 0.0004 | 0.0005 | 0.0006 | 0.0007 | 0.0008 | 0.0009 |
| 16 | 0.0001 | 0.0001 | 0.0001 | 0.0001 | 0.0001 | 0.0002 | 0.0002 | 0.0002 | 0.0003 | 0.0003 |
| 17 | 0.0000 | 0.0000 | 0.0000 | 0.0000 | 0.0000 | 0.0000 | 0.0001 | 0.0001 | 0.0001 | 0.0001 |

|  | | | | | | λ | | | | |
|---|---|---|---|---|---|---|---|---|---|---|
| X | 6.1 | 6.2 | 6.3 | 6.4 | 6.5 | 6.6 | 6.7 | 6.8 | 6.9 | 7.0 |
| 0 | 0.0022 | 0.0020 | 0.0018 | 0.0017 | 0.0015 | 0.0014 | 0.0012 | 0.0011 | 0.0010 | 0.0009 |
| 1 | 0.0137 | 0.0126 | 0.0116 | 0.0106 | 0.0098 | 0.0090 | 0.0082 | 0.0076 | 0.0070 | 0.0064 |
| 2 | 0.0417 | 0.0390 | 0.0364 | 0.0340 | 0.0318 | 0.0296 | 0.0276 | 0.0258 | 0.0240 | 0.0223 |
| 3 | 0.0848 | 0.0806 | 0.0765 | 0.0726 | 0.0688 | 0.0652 | 0.0617 | 0.0584 | 0.0552 | 0.0521 |
| 4 | 0.1294 | 0.1249 | 0.1205 | 0.1162 | 0.1118 | 0.1076 | 0.1034 | 0.0992 | 0.0952 | 0.0912 |
| 5 | 0.1579 | 0.1549 | 0.1519 | 0.1487 | 0.1454 | 0.1420 | 0.1385 | 0.1349 | 0.1314 | 0.1277 |
| 6 | 0.1605 | 0.1601 | 0.1595 | 0.1586 | 0.1575 | 0.1562 | 0.1546 | 0.1529 | 0.1511 | 0.1490 |
| 7 | 0.1399 | 0.1418 | 0.1435 | 0.1450 | 0.1462 | 0.1472 | 0.1480 | 0.1486 | 0.1489 | 0.1490 |
| 8 | 0.1066 | 0.1099 | 0.1130 | 0.1160 | 0.1188 | 0.1215 | 0.1240 | 0.1263 | 0.1284 | 0.1304 |
| 9 | 0.0723 | 0.0757 | 0.0791 | 0.0825 | 0.0858 | 0.0891 | 0.0923 | 0.0954 | 0.0985 | 0.1014 |
| 10 | 0.0441 | 0.0469 | 0.0498 | 0.0528 | 0.0558 | 0.0588 | 0.0618 | 0.0649 | 0.0679 | 0.0710 |
| 11 | 0.0245 | 0.0265 | 0.0285 | 0.0307 | 0.0330 | 0.0353 | 0.0377 | 0.0401 | 0.0426 | 0.0452 |
| 12 | 0.0124 | 0.0137 | 0.0150 | 0.0164 | 0.0179 | 0.0194 | 0.0210 | 0.0277 | 0.0245 | 0.0264 |
| 13 | 0.0058 | 0.0065 | 0.0073 | 0.0081 | 0.0089 | 0.0098 | 0.0108 | 0.0119 | 0.0130 | 0.0142 |
| 14 | 0.0025 | 0.0029 | 0.0033 | 0.0037 | 0.0041 | 0.0046 | 0.0052 | 0.0058 | 0.0064 | 0.0071 |

*continued*

**TABLE E.7**

Table of Poisson
Probabilities
(*Continued*)

|  | | | | | | λ | | | | |
|---|---|---|---|---|---|---|---|---|---|---|
| X | 6.1 | 6.2 | 6.3 | 6.4 | 6.5 | 6.6 | 6.7 | 6.8 | 6.9 | 7.0 |
| 15 | 0.0010 | 0.0012 | 0.0014 | 0.0016 | 0.0018 | 0.0020 | 0.0023 | 0.0026 | 0.0029 | 0.0033 |
| 16 | 0.0004 | 0.0005 | 0.0005 | 0.0006 | 0.0007 | 0.0008 | 0.0010 | 0.0011 | 0.0013 | 0.0014 |
| 17 | 0.0001 | 0.0002 | 0.0002 | 0.0002 | 0.0003 | 0.0003 | 0.0004 | 0.0004 | 0.0005 | 0.0006 |
| 18 | 0.0000 | 0.0001 | 0.0001 | 0.0001 | 0.0001 | 0.0001 | 0.0001 | 0.0002 | 0.0002 | 0.0002 |
| 19 | 0.0000 | 0.0000 | 0.0000 | 0.0000 | 0.0000 | 0.0000 | 0.0000 | 0.0001 | 0.0001 | 0.0001 |

|  | | | | | | λ | | | | |
|---|---|---|---|---|---|---|---|---|---|---|
| X | 7.1 | 7.2 | 7.3 | 7.4 | 7.5 | 7.6 | 7.7 | 7.8 | 7.9 | 8.0 |
| 0 | 0.0008 | 0.0007 | 0.0007 | 0.0006 | 0.0006 | 0.0005 | 0.0005 | 0.0004 | 0.0004 | 0.0003 |
| 1 | 0.0059 | 0.0054 | 0.0049 | 0.0045 | 0.0041 | 0.0038 | 0.0035 | 0.0032 | 0.0029 | 0.0027 |
| 2 | 0.0208 | 0.0194 | 0.0180 | 0.0167 | 0.0156 | 0.0145 | 0.0134 | 0.0125 | 0.0116 | 0.0107 |
| 3 | 0.0492 | 0.0464 | 0.0438 | 0.0413 | 0.0389 | 0.0366 | 0.0345 | 0.0324 | 0.0305 | 0.0286 |
| 4 | 0.0874 | 0.0836 | 0.0799 | 0.0764 | 0.0729 | 0.0696 | 0.0663 | 0.0632 | 0.0602 | 0.0573 |
| 5 | 0.1241 | 0.1204 | 0.1167 | 0.1130 | 0.1094 | 0.1057 | 0.1021 | 0.0986 | 0.0951 | 0.0916 |
| 6 | 0.1468 | 0.1445 | 0.1420 | 0.1394 | 0.1367 | 0.1339 | 0.1311 | 0.1282 | 0.1252 | 0.1221 |
| 7 | 0.1489 | 0.1486 | 0.1481 | 0.1474 | 0.1465 | 0.1454 | 0.1442 | 0.1428 | 0.1413 | 0.1396 |
| 8 | 0.1321 | 0.1337 | 0.1351 | 0.1363 | 0.1373 | 0.1382 | 0.1388 | 0.1392 | 0.1395 | 0.1396 |
| 9 | 0.1042 | 0.1070 | 0.1096 | 0.1121 | 0.1144 | 0.1167 | 0.1187 | 0.1207 | 0.1224 | 0.1241 |
| 10 | 0.0740 | 0.0770 | 0.0800 | 0.0829 | 0.0858 | 0.0887 | 0.0914 | 0.0941 | 0.0967 | 0.0993 |
| 11 | 0.0478 | 0.0504 | 0.0531 | 0.0558 | 0.0585 | 0.0613 | 0.0640 | 0.0667 | 0.0695 | 0.0722 |
| 12 | 0.0283 | 0.0303 | 0.0323 | 0.0344 | 0.0366 | 0.0388 | 0.0411 | 0.0434 | 0.0457 | 0.0481 |
| 13 | 0.0154 | 0.0168 | 0.0181 | 0.0196 | 0.0211 | 0.0227 | 0.0243 | 0.0260 | 0.0278 | 0.0296 |
| 14 | 0.0078 | 0.0086 | 0.0095 | 0.0104 | 0.0113 | 0.0123 | 0.0134 | 0.0145 | 0.0157 | 0.0169 |
| 15 | 0.0037 | 0.0041 | 0.0046 | 0.0051 | 0.0057 | 0.0062 | 0.0069 | 0.0075 | 0.0083 | 0.0090 |
| 16 | 0.0016 | 0.0019 | 0.0021 | 0.0024 | 0.0026 | 0.0030 | 0.0033 | 0.0037 | 0.0041 | 0.0045 |
| 17 | 0.0007 | 0.0008 | 0.0009 | 0.0010 | 0.0012 | 0.0013 | 0.0015 | 0.0017 | 0.0019 | 0.0021 |
| 18 | 0.0003 | 0.0003 | 0.0004 | 0.0004 | 0.0005 | 0.0006 | 0.0006 | 0.0007 | 0.0008 | 0.0009 |
| 19 | 0.0001 | 0.0001 | 0.0001 | 0.0002 | 0.0002 | 0.0002 | 0.0003 | 0.0003 | 0.0003 | 0.0004 |
| 20 | 0.0000 | 0.0000 | 0.0001 | 0.0001 | 0.0001 | 0.0001 | 0.0001 | 0.0001 | 0.0001 | 0.0002 |
| 21 | 0.0000 | 0.0000 | 0.0000 | 0.0000 | 0.0000 | 0.0000 | 0.0000 | 0.0000 | 0.0001 | 0.0001 |

|  | | | | | | λ | | | | |
|---|---|---|---|---|---|---|---|---|---|---|
| X | 8.1 | 8.2 | 8.3 | 8.4 | 8.5 | 8.6 | 8.7 | 8.8 | 8.9 | 9.0 |
| 0 | 0.0003 | 0.0003 | 0.0002 | 0.0002 | 0.0002 | 0.0002 | 0.0002 | 0.0002 | 0.0001 | 0.0001 |
| 1 | 0.0025 | 0.0023 | 0.0021 | 0.0019 | 0.0017 | 0.0016 | 0.0014 | 0.0013 | 0.0012 | 0.0011 |
| 2 | 0.0100 | 0.0092 | 0.0086 | 0.0079 | 0.0074 | 0.0068 | 0.0063 | 0.0058 | 0.0054 | 0.0050 |
| 3 | 0.0269 | 0.0252 | 0.0237 | 0.0222 | 0.0208 | 0.0195 | 0.0183 | 0.0171 | 0.0160 | 0.0150 |
| 4 | 0.0544 | 0.0517 | 0.0491 | 0.0466 | 0.0443 | 0.0420 | 0.0398 | 0.0377 | 0.0357 | 0.0337 |
| 5 | 0.0882 | 0.0849 | 0.0816 | 0.0784 | 0.0752 | 0.0722 | 0.0692 | 0.0663 | 0.0635 | 0.0607 |
| 6 | 0.1191 | 0.1160 | 0.1128 | 0.1097 | 0.1066 | 0.1034 | 0.1003 | 0.0972 | 0.0941 | 0.0911 |
| 7 | 0.1378 | 0.1358 | 0.1338 | 0.1317 | 0.1294 | 0.1271 | 0.1247 | 0.1222 | 0.1197 | 0.1171 |
| 8 | 0.1395 | 0.1392 | 0.1388 | 0.1382 | 0.1375 | 0.1366 | 0.1356 | 0.1344 | 0.1332 | 0.1318 |
| 9 | 0.1256 | 0.1269 | 0.1280 | 0.1290 | 0.1299 | 0.1306 | 0.1311 | 0.1315 | 0.1317 | 0.1318 |
| 10 | 0.1017 | 0.1040 | 0.1063 | 0.1084 | 0.1104 | 0.1123 | 0.1140 | 0.1157 | 0.1172 | 0.1186 |
| 11 | 0.0749 | 0.0776 | 0.0802 | 0.0828 | 0.0853 | 0.0878 | 0.0902 | 0.0925 | 0.0948 | 0.0970 |
| 12 | 0.0505 | 0.0530 | 0.0555 | 0.0579 | 0.0604 | 0.0629 | 0.0654 | 0.0679 | 0.0703 | 0.0728 |
| 13 | 0.0315 | 0.0334 | 0.0354 | 0.0374 | 0.0395 | 0.0416 | 0.0438 | 0.0459 | 0.0481 | 0.0504 |
| 14 | 0.0182 | 0.0196 | 0.0210 | 0.0225 | 0.0240 | 0.0256 | 0.0272 | 0.0289 | 0.0306 | 0.0324 |
| 15 | 0.0098 | 0.0107 | 0.0116 | 0.0126 | 0.0136 | 0.0147 | 0.0158 | 0.0169 | 0.0182 | 0.0194 |
| 16 | 0.0050 | 0.0055 | 0.0060 | 0.0066 | 0.0072 | 0.0079 | 0.0086 | 0.0093 | 0.0101 | 0.0109 |
| 17 | 0.0024 | 0.0026 | 0.0029 | 0.0033 | 0.0036 | 0.0040 | 0.0044 | 0.0048 | 0.0053 | 0.0058 |
| 18 | 0.0011 | 0.0012 | 0.0014 | 0.0015 | 0.0017 | 0.0019 | 0.0021 | 0.0024 | 0.0026 | 0.0029 |
| 19 | 0.0005 | 0.0005 | 0.0006 | 0.0007 | 0.0008 | 0.0009 | 0.0010 | 0.0011 | 0.0012 | 0.0014 |
| 20 | 0.0002 | 0.0002 | 0.0002 | 0.0003 | 0.0003 | 0.0004 | 0.0004 | 0.0005 | 0.0005 | 0.0006 |
| 21 | 0.0001 | 0.0001 | 0.0001 | 0.0001 | 0.0001 | 0.0002 | 0.0002 | 0.0002 | 0.0002 | 0.0003 |
| 22 | 0.0000 | 0.0000 | 0.0000 | 0.0000 | 0.0001 | 0.0001 | 0.0001 | 0.0001 | 0.0001 | 0.0001 |

*continued*

**TABLE E.7**

Table of Poisson
Probabilities
(*Continued*)

| | | | | | $\lambda$ | | | | | |
|---|---|---|---|---|---|---|---|---|---|---|
| $X$ | 9.1 | 9.2 | 9.3 | 9.4 | 9.5 | 9.6 | 9.7 | 9.8 | 9.9 | 10 |
| 0 | 0.0001 | 0.0001 | 0.0001 | 0.0001 | 0.0001 | 0.0001 | 0.0001 | 0.0001 | 0.0001 | 0.0000 |
| 1 | 0.0010 | 0.0009 | 0.0009 | 0.0008 | 0.0007 | 0.0007 | 0.0006 | 0.0005 | 0.0005 | 0.0005 |
| 2 | 0.0046 | 0.0043 | 0.0040 | 0.0037 | 0.0034 | 0.0031 | 0.0029 | 0.0027 | 0.0025 | 0.0023 |
| 3 | 0.0140 | 0.0131 | 0.0123 | 0.0115 | 0.0107 | 0.0100 | 0.0093 | 0.0087 | 0.0081 | 0.0076 |
| 4 | 0.0319 | 0.0302 | 0.0285 | 0.0269 | 0.0254 | 0.0240 | 0.0226 | 0.0213 | 0.0201 | 0.0189 |
| 5 | 0.0581 | 0.0555 | 0.0530 | 0.0506 | 0.0483 | 0.0460 | 0.0439 | 0.0418 | 0.0398 | 0.0378 |
| 6 | 0.0881 | 0.0851 | 0.0822 | 0.0793 | 0.0764 | 0.0736 | 0.0709 | 0.0682 | 0.0656 | 0.0631 |
| 7 | 0.1145 | 0.1118 | 0.1091 | 0.1064 | 0.1037 | 0.1010 | 0.0982 | 0.0955 | 0.0928 | 0.0901 |
| 8 | 0.1302 | 0.1286 | 0.1269 | 0.1251 | 0.1232 | 0.1212 | 0.1191 | 0.1170 | 0.1148 | 0.1126 |
| 9 | 0.1317 | 0.1315 | 0.1311 | 0.1306 | 0.1300 | 0.1293 | 0.1284 | 0.1274 | 0.1263 | 0.1251 |
| 10 | 0.1198 | 0.1210 | 0.1219 | 0.1228 | 0.1235 | 0.1241 | 0.1245 | 0.1249 | 0.1250 | 0.1251 |
| 11 | 0.0991 | 0.1012 | 0.1031 | 0.1049 | 0.1067 | 0.1083 | 0.1098 | 0.1112 | 0.1125 | 0.1137 |
| 12 | 0.0752 | 0.0776 | 0.0799 | 0.0822 | 0.0844 | 0.0866 | 0.0888 | 0.0908 | 0.0928 | 0.0948 |
| 13 | 0.0526 | 0.0549 | 0.0572 | 0.0594 | 0.0617 | 0.0640 | 0.0662 | 0.0685 | 0.0707 | 0.0729 |
| 14 | 0.0342 | 0.0361 | 0.0380 | 0.0399 | 0.0419 | 0.0439 | 0.0459 | 0.0479 | 0.0500 | 0.0521 |
| 15 | 0.0208 | 0.0221 | 0.0235 | 0.0250 | 0.0265 | 0.0281 | 0.0297 | 0.0313 | 0.0330 | 0.0347 |
| 16 | 0.0118 | 0.0127 | 0.0137 | 0.0147 | 0.0157 | 0.0168 | 0.0180 | 0.0192 | 0.0204 | 0.0217 |
| 17 | 0.0063 | 0.0069 | 0.0075 | 0.0081 | 0.0088 | 0.0095 | 0.0103 | 0.0111 | 0.0119 | 0.0128 |
| 18 | 0.0032 | 0.0035 | 0.0039 | 0.0042 | 0.0046 | 0.0051 | 0.0055 | 0.0060 | 0.0065 | 0.0071 |
| 19 | 0.0015 | 0.0017 | 0.0019 | 0.0021 | 0.0023 | 0.0026 | 0.0028 | 0.0031 | 0.0034 | 0.0037 |
| 20 | 0.0007 | 0.0008 | 0.0009 | 0.0010 | 0.0011 | 0.0012 | 0.0014 | 0.0015 | 0.0017 | 0.0019 |
| 21 | 0.0003 | 0.0003 | 0.0004 | 0.0004 | 0.0005 | 0.0006 | 0.0006 | 0.0007 | 0.0008 | 0.0009 |
| 22 | 0.0001 | 0.0001 | 0.0002 | 0.0002 | 0.0002 | 0.0002 | 0.0003 | 0.0003 | 0.0004 | 0.0004 |
| 23 | 0.0000 | 0.0001 | 0.0001 | 0.0001 | 0.0001 | 0.0001 | 0.0001 | 0.0001 | 0.0002 | 0.0002 |
| 24 | 0.0000 | 0.0000 | 0.0000 | 0.0000 | 0.0000 | 0.0000 | 0.0000 | 0.0001 | 0.0001 | 0.0001 |

| $X$ | $\lambda = 20$ | $X$ | $\lambda = 20$ | $X$ | $\lambda = 20$ | $X$ | $\lambda = 20$ |
|---|---|---|---|---|---|---|---|
| 0 | 0.0000 | 10 | 0.0058 | 20 | 0.0888 | 30 | 0.0083 |
| 1 | 0.0000 | 11 | 0.0106 | 21 | 0.0846 | 31 | 0.0054 |
| 2 | 0.0000 | 12 | 0.0176 | 22 | 0.0769 | 32 | 0.0034 |
| 3 | 0.0000 | 13 | 0.0271 | 23 | 0.0669 | 33 | 0.0020 |
| 4 | 0.0000 | 14 | 0.0387 | 24 | 0.0557 | 34 | 0.0012 |
| 5 | 0.0001 | 15 | 0.0516 | 25 | 0.0446 | 35 | 0.0007 |
| 6 | 0.0002 | 16 | 0.0646 | 26 | 0.0343 | 36 | 0.0004 |
| 7 | 0.0005 | 17 | 0.0760 | 27 | 0.0254 | 37 | 0.0002 |
| 8 | 0.0013 | 18 | 0.0844 | 28 | 0.0181 | 38 | 0.0001 |
| 9 | 0.0029 | 19 | 0.0888 | 29 | 0.0125 | 39 | 0.0001 |

**TABLE E.8**

Lower and Upper Critical Values $T_1$ of Wilcoxon Rank Sum Test

| $n_2$ | $\alpha$ One-tail | Two-tail | $n_1$ 4 | 5 | 6 | 7 | 8 | 9 | 10 |
|---|---|---|---|---|---|---|---|---|---|
| 4 | 0.05 | 0.10 | 11,25 | | | | | | |
| | 0.025 | 0.05 | 10,26 | | | | | | |
| | 0.01 | 0.02 | —,— | | | | | | |
| | 0.005 | 0.01 | —,— | | | | | | |
| 5 | 0.05 | 0.10 | 12,28 | 19,36 | | | | | |
| | 0.025 | 0.05 | 11,29 | 17,38 | | | | | |
| | 0.01 | 0.02 | 10,30 | 16,39 | | | | | |
| | 0.005 | 0.01 | —,— | 15,40 | | | | | |
| 6 | 0.05 | 0.10 | 13,31 | 20,40 | 28,50 | | | | |
| | 0.025 | 0.05 | 12,32 | 18,42 | 26,52 | | | | |
| | 0.01 | 0.02 | 11,33 | 17,43 | 24,54 | | | | |
| | 0.005 | 0.01 | 10,34 | 16,44 | 23,55 | | | | |
| 7 | 0.05 | 0.10 | 14,34 | 21,44 | 29,55 | 39,66 | | | |
| | 0.025 | 0.05 | 13,35 | 20,45 | 27,57 | 36,69 | | | |
| | 0.01 | 0.02 | 11,37 | 18,47 | 25,59 | 34,71 | | | |
| | 0.005 | 0.01 | 10,38 | 16,49 | 24,60 | 32,73 | | | |
| 8 | 0.05 | 0.10 | 15,37 | 23,47 | 31,59 | 41,71 | 51,85 | | |
| | 0.025 | 0.05 | 14,38 | 21,49 | 29,61 | 38,74 | 49,87 | | |
| | 0.01 | 0.02 | 12,40 | 19,51 | 27,63 | 35,77 | 45,91 | | |
| | 0.005 | 0.01 | 11,41 | 17,53 | 25,65 | 34,78 | 43,93 | | |
| 9 | 0.05 | 0.10 | 16,40 | 24,51 | 33,63 | 43,76 | 54,90 | 66,105 | |
| | 0.025 | 0.05 | 14,42 | 22,53 | 31,65 | 40,79 | 51,93 | 62,109 | |
| | 0.01 | 0.02 | 13,43 | 20,55 | 28,68 | 37,82 | 47,97 | 59,112 | |
| | 0.005 | 0.01 | 11,45 | 18,57 | 26,70 | 35,84 | 45,99 | 56,115 | |
| 10 | 0.05 | 0.10 | 17,43 | 26,54 | 35,67 | 45,81 | 56,96 | 69,111 | 82,128 |
| | 0.025 | 0.05 | 15,45 | 23,57 | 32,70 | 42,84 | 53,99 | 65,115 | 78,132 |
| | 0.01 | 0.02 | 13,47 | 21,59 | 29,73 | 39,87 | 49,103 | 61,119 | 74,136 |
| | 0.005 | 0.01 | 12,48 | 19,61 | 27,75 | 37,89 | 47,105 | 58,122 | 71,139 |

Source: *Adapted from Table 1 of F. Wilcoxon and R. A. Wilcox,* Some Rapid Approximate Statistical Procedures *(Pearl River, NY: Lederle Laboratories, 1964), with permission of the American Cyanamid Company.*

**TABLE E.9**

Lower and Upper Critical Values $W$ of Wilcoxon Signed Ranks Test

| One-Tail | $\alpha = .05$ | $\alpha = .025$ | $\alpha = .01$ | $\alpha = .005$ |
|---|---|---|---|---|
| Two-Tail | $\alpha = .10$ | $\alpha = .05$ | $\alpha = .02$ | $\alpha = .01$ |
| $n$ | (Lower, Upper) | | | |
| 5 | 0,15 | —,— | —,— | —,— |
| 6 | 2,19 | 0,21 | —,— | —,— |
| 7 | 3,25 | 2,26 | 0,28 | —,— |
| 8 | 5,31 | 3,33 | 1,35 | 0,36 |
| 9 | 8,37 | 5,40 | 3,42 | 1,44 |
| 10 | 10,45 | 8,47 | 5,50 | 3,52 |
| 11 | 13,53 | 10,56 | 7,59 | 5,61 |
| 12 | 17,61 | 13,65 | 10,68 | 7,71 |
| 13 | 21,70 | 17,74 | 12,79 | 10,81 |
| 14 | 25,80 | 21,84 | 16,89 | 13,92 |
| 15 | 30,90 | 25,95 | 19,101 | 16,104 |
| 16 | 35,101 | 29,107 | 23,113 | 19,117 |
| 17 | 41,112 | 34,119 | 27,126 | 23,130 |
| 18 | 47,124 | 40,131 | 32,139 | 27,144 |
| 19 | 53,137 | 46,144 | 37,153 | 32,158 |
| 20 | 60,150 | 52,158 | 43,167 | 37,173 |

Source: *Adapted from Table 2 of F. Wilcoxon and R. A. Wilcox,* Some Rapid Approximate Statistical Procedures *(Pearl River, NY: Lederle Laboratories, 1964), with permission of the American Cyanamid Company.*

# TABLE E.10

Critical Values of the Studentized Range, Q

**Upper 5% Points ($\alpha = 0.05$)**

| Denominator, df | Numerator, df | | | | | | | | | | | | | | | | | | |
|---|---|---|---|---|---|---|---|---|---|---|---|---|---|---|---|---|---|---|---|
| | 2 | 3 | 4 | 5 | 6 | 7 | 8 | 9 | 10 | 11 | 12 | 13 | 14 | 15 | 16 | 17 | 18 | 19 | 20 |
| 1 | 18.00 | 27.00 | 32.80 | 37.10 | 40.40 | 43.10 | 45.40 | 47.40 | 49.10 | 50.60 | 52.00 | 53.20 | 54.30 | 55.40 | 56.30 | 57.20 | 58.00 | 58.80 | 59.60 |
| 2 | 6.09 | 8.30 | 9.80 | 10.90 | 11.70 | 12.40 | 13.00 | 13.50 | 14.00 | 14.40 | 14.70 | 15.10 | 15.40 | 15.70 | 15.90 | 16.10 | 16.40 | 16.60 | 16.80 |
| 3 | 4.50 | 5.91 | 6.82 | 7.50 | 8.04 | 8.48 | 8.85 | 9.18 | 9.46 | 9.72 | 9.95 | 10.15 | 10.35 | 10.52 | 10.69 | 10.84 | 10.98 | 11.11 | 11.24 |
| 4 | 3.93 | 5.04 | 5.76 | 6.29 | 6.71 | 7.05 | 7.35 | 7.60 | 7.83 | 8.03 | 8.21 | 8.37 | 8.52 | 8.66 | 8.79 | 8.91 | 9.03 | 9.13 | 9.23 |
| 5 | 3.64 | 4.60 | 5.22 | 5.67 | 6.03 | 6.33 | 6.58 | 6.80 | 6.99 | 7.17 | 7.32 | 7.47 | 7.60 | 7.72 | 7.83 | 7.93 | 8.03 | 8.12 | 8.21 |
| 6 | 3.46 | 4.34 | 4.90 | 5.31 | 5.63 | 5.89 | 6.12 | 6.32 | 6.49 | 6.65 | 6.79 | 6.92 | 7.03 | 7.14 | 7.24 | 7.34 | 7.43 | 7.51 | 7.59 |
| 7 | 3.34 | 4.16 | 4.68 | 5.06 | 5.36 | 5.61 | 5.82 | 6.00 | 6.16 | 6.30 | 6.43 | 6.55 | 6.66 | 6.76 | 6.85 | 6.94 | 7.02 | 7.09 | 7.17 |
| 8 | 3.26 | 4.04 | 4.53 | 4.89 | 5.17 | 5.40 | 5.60 | 5.77 | 5.92 | 6.05 | 6.18 | 6.29 | 6.39 | 6.48 | 6.57 | 6.65 | 6.73 | 6.80 | 6.87 |
| 9 | 3.20 | 3.95 | 4.42 | 4.76 | 5.02 | 5.24 | 5.43 | 5.60 | 5.74 | 5.87 | 5.98 | 6.09 | 6.19 | 6.28 | 6.36 | 6.44 | 6.51 | 6.58 | 6.64 |
| 10 | 3.15 | 3.88 | 4.33 | 4.65 | 4.91 | 5.12 | 5.30 | 5.46 | 5.60 | 5.72 | 5.83 | 5.93 | 6.03 | 6.11 | 6.20 | 6.27 | 6.34 | 6.40 | 6.47 |
| 11 | 3.11 | 3.82 | 4.26 | 4.57 | 4.82 | 5.03 | 5.20 | 5.35 | 5.49 | 5.61 | 5.71 | 5.81 | 5.90 | 5.99 | 6.06 | 6.14 | 6.20 | 6.26 | 6.33 |
| 12 | 3.08 | 3.77 | 4.20 | 4.51 | 4.75 | 4.95 | 5.12 | 5.27 | 5.40 | 5.51 | 5.62 | 5.71 | 5.80 | 5.88 | 5.95 | 6.03 | 6.09 | 6.15 | 6.21 |
| 13 | 3.06 | 3.73 | 4.15 | 4.45 | 4.69 | 4.88 | 5.05 | 5.19 | 5.32 | 5.43 | 5.53 | 5.63 | 5.71 | 5.79 | 5.86 | 5.93 | 6.00 | 6.05 | 6.11 |
| 14 | 3.03 | 3.70 | 4.11 | 4.41 | 4.64 | 4.83 | 4.99 | 5.13 | 5.25 | 5.36 | 5.46 | 5.55 | 5.64 | 5.72 | 5.79 | 5.85 | 5.92 | 5.97 | 6.03 |
| 15 | 3.01 | 3.67 | 4.08 | 4.37 | 4.60 | 4.78 | 4.94 | 5.08 | 5.20 | 5.31 | 5.40 | 5.49 | 5.58 | 5.65 | 5.72 | 5.79 | 5.85 | 5.90 | 5.96 |
| 16 | 3.00 | 3.65 | 4.05 | 4.33 | 4.56 | 4.74 | 4.90 | 5.03 | 5.15 | 5.26 | 5.35 | 5.44 | 5.52 | 5.59 | 5.66 | 5.72 | 5.79 | 5.84 | 5.90 |
| 17 | 2.98 | 3.63 | 4.02 | 4.30 | 4.52 | 4.71 | 4.86 | 4.99 | 5.11 | 5.21 | 5.31 | 5.39 | 5.47 | 5.55 | 5.61 | 5.68 | 5.74 | 5.79 | 5.84 |
| 18 | 2.97 | 3.61 | 4.00 | 4.28 | 4.49 | 4.67 | 4.82 | 4.96 | 5.07 | 5.17 | 5.27 | 5.35 | 5.43 | 5.50 | 5.57 | 5.63 | 5.69 | 5.74 | 5.79 |
| 19 | 2.96 | 3.59 | 3.98 | 4.25 | 4.47 | 4.65 | 4.79 | 4.92 | 5.04 | 5.14 | 5.23 | 5.32 | 5.39 | 5.46 | 5.53 | 5.59 | 5.65 | 5.70 | 5.75 |
| 20 | 2.95 | 3.58 | 3.96 | 4.23 | 4.45 | 4.62 | 4.77 | 4.90 | 5.01 | 5.11 | 5.20 | 5.28 | 5.36 | 5.43 | 5.49 | 5.55 | 5.61 | 5.66 | 5.71 |
| 24 | 2.92 | 3.53 | 3.90 | 4.17 | 4.37 | 4.54 | 4.68 | 4.81 | 4.92 | 5.01 | 5.10 | 5.18 | 5.25 | 5.32 | 5.38 | 5.44 | 5.50 | 5.54 | 5.59 |
| 30 | 2.89 | 3.49 | 3.84 | 4.10 | 4.30 | 4.46 | 4.60 | 4.72 | 4.83 | 4.92 | 5.00 | 5.08 | 5.15 | 5.21 | 5.27 | 5.33 | 5.38 | 5.43 | 5.48 |
| 40 | 2.86 | 3.44 | 3.79 | 4.04 | 4.23 | 4.39 | 4.52 | 4.63 | 4.74 | 4.82 | 4.91 | 4.98 | 5.05 | 5.11 | 5.16 | 5.22 | 5.27 | 5.31 | 5.36 |
| 60 | 2.83 | 3.40 | 3.74 | 3.98 | 4.16 | 4.31 | 4.44 | 4.55 | 4.65 | 4.73 | 4.81 | 4.88 | 4.94 | 5.00 | 5.06 | 5.11 | 5.16 | 5.20 | 5.24 |
| 120 | 2.80 | 3.36 | 3.69 | 3.92 | 4.10 | 4.24 | 4.36 | 4.48 | 4.56 | 4.64 | 4.72 | 4.78 | 4.84 | 4.90 | 4.95 | 5.00 | 5.05 | 5.09 | 5.13 |
| ∞ | 2.77 | 3.31 | 3.63 | 3.86 | 4.03 | 4.17 | 4.29 | 4.39 | 4.47 | 4.55 | 4.62 | 4.68 | 4.74 | 4.80 | 4.85 | 4.89 | 4.93 | 4.97 | 5.01 |

*continued*

# TABLE E.10
Critical Values of the Studentized Range, Q (Continued)

**Upper 1% Points (α = 0.01)**

| Denominator, $df$ | \multicolumn{19}{c}{Numerator, $df$} |
|---|

| Denominator, $df$ | 2 | 3 | 4 | 5 | 6 | 7 | 8 | 9 | 10 | 11 | 12 | 13 | 14 | 15 | 16 | 17 | 18 | 19 | 20 |
|---|---|---|---|---|---|---|---|---|---|---|---|---|---|---|---|---|---|---|---|
| 1 | 90.00 | 135.00 | 164.00 | 186.00 | 202.00 | 216.00 | 227.00 | 237.00 | 246.00 | 253.00 | 260.00 | 266.00 | 272.00 | 277.00 | 282.00 | 286.00 | 290.00 | 294.00 | 298.00 |
| 2 | 14.00 | 19.00 | 22.30 | 24.70 | 26.60 | 28.20 | 29.50 | 30.70 | 31.70 | 32.60 | 33.40 | 34.10 | 34.80 | 35.40 | 36.00 | 36.50 | 37.00 | 37.50 | 37.90 |
| 3 | 8.26 | 10.60 | 12.20 | 13.30 | 14.20 | 15.00 | 15.60 | 16.20 | 16.70 | 17.10 | 17.50 | 17.90 | 18.20 | 18.50 | 18.80 | 19.10 | 19.30 | 19.50 | 19.80 |
| 4 | 6.51 | 8.12 | 9.17 | 9.96 | 10.60 | 11.10 | 11.50 | 11.90 | 12.30 | 12.60 | 12.80 | 13.10 | 13.30 | 13.50 | 13.70 | 13.90 | 14.10 | 14.20 | 14.40 |
| 5 | 5.70 | 6.97 | 7.80 | 8.42 | 8.91 | 9.32 | 9.67 | 9.97 | 10.24 | 10.48 | 10.70 | 10.89 | 11.08 | 11.24 | 11.40 | 11.55 | 11.68 | 11.81 | 11.93 |
| 6 | 5.24 | 6.33 | 7.03 | 7.56 | 7.97 | 8.32 | 8.61 | 8.87 | 9.10 | 9.30 | 9.49 | 9.65 | 9.81 | 9.95 | 10.08 | 10.21 | 10.32 | 10.43 | 10.54 |
| 7 | 4.95 | 5.92 | 6.54 | 7.01 | 7.37 | 7.68 | 7.94 | 8.17 | 8.37 | 8.55 | 8.71 | 8.86 | 9.00 | 9.12 | 9.24 | 9.35 | 9.46 | 9.55 | 9.65 |
| 8 | 4.74 | 5.63 | 6.20 | 6.63 | 6.96 | 7.24 | 7.47 | 7.68 | 7.87 | 8.03 | 8.18 | 8.31 | 8.44 | 8.55 | 8.66 | 8.76 | 8.85 | 8.94 | 9.03 |
| 9 | 4.60 | 5.43 | 5.96 | 6.35 | 6.66 | 6.91 | 7.13 | 7.32 | 7.49 | 7.65 | 7.78 | 7.91 | 8.03 | 8.13 | 8.23 | 8.32 | 8.41 | 8.49 | 8.57 |
| 10 | 4.48 | 5.27 | 5.77 | 6.14 | 6.43 | 6.67 | 6.87 | 7.05 | 7.21 | 7.36 | 7.48 | 7.60 | 7.71 | 7.81 | 7.91 | 7.99 | 8.07 | 8.15 | 8.22 |
| 11 | 4.39 | 5.14 | 5.62 | 5.97 | 6.26 | 6.48 | 6.67 | 6.84 | 6.99 | 7.13 | 7.25 | 7.36 | 7.46 | 7.56 | 7.65 | 7.73 | 7.81 | 7.88 | 7.95 |
| 12 | 4.32 | 5.04 | 5.50 | 5.84 | 6.10 | 6.32 | 6.51 | 6.67 | 6.81 | 6.94 | 7.06 | 7.17 | 7.26 | 7.36 | 7.44 | 7.52 | 7.59 | 7.66 | 7.73 |
| 13 | 4.26 | 4.96 | 5.40 | 5.73 | 5.98 | 6.19 | 6.37 | 6.53 | 6.67 | 6.79 | 6.90 | 7.01 | 7.10 | 7.19 | 7.27 | 7.34 | 7.42 | 7.48 | 7.55 |
| 14 | 4.21 | 4.89 | 5.32 | 5.63 | 5.88 | 6.08 | 6.26 | 6.41 | 6.54 | 6.66 | 6.77 | 6.87 | 6.96 | 7.05 | 7.12 | 7.20 | 7.27 | 7.33 | 7.39 |
| 15 | 4.17 | 4.83 | 5.25 | 5.56 | 5.80 | 5.99 | 6.16 | 6.31 | 6.44 | 6.55 | 6.66 | 6.76 | 6.84 | 6.93 | 7.00 | 7.07 | 7.14 | 7.20 | 7.26 |
| 16 | 4.13 | 4.78 | 5.19 | 5.49 | 5.72 | 5.92 | 6.08 | 6.22 | 6.35 | 6.46 | 6.56 | 6.66 | 6.74 | 6.82 | 6.90 | 6.97 | 7.03 | 7.09 | 7.15 |
| 17 | 4.10 | 4.74 | 5.14 | 5.43 | 5.66 | 5.85 | 6.01 | 6.15 | 6.27 | 6.38 | 6.48 | 6.57 | 6.66 | 6.73 | 6.80 | 6.87 | 6.94 | 7.00 | 7.05 |
| 18 | 4.07 | 4.70 | 5.09 | 5.38 | 5.60 | 5.79 | 5.94 | 6.08 | 6.20 | 6.31 | 6.41 | 6.50 | 6.58 | 6.65 | 6.72 | 6.79 | 6.85 | 6.91 | 6.96 |
| 19 | 4.05 | 4.67 | 5.05 | 5.33 | 5.55 | 5.73 | 5.89 | 6.02 | 6.14 | 6.25 | 6.34 | 6.43 | 6.51 | 6.58 | 6.65 | 6.72 | 6.78 | 6.84 | 6.89 |
| 20 | 4.02 | 4.64 | 5.02 | 5.29 | 5.51 | 5.69 | 5.84 | 5.97 | 6.09 | 6.19 | 6.29 | 6.37 | 6.45 | 6.52 | 6.59 | 6.65 | 6.71 | 6.76 | 6.82 |
| 24 | 3.96 | 4.54 | 4.91 | 5.17 | 5.37 | 5.54 | 5.69 | 5.81 | 5.92 | 6.02 | 6.11 | 6.19 | 6.26 | 6.33 | 6.39 | 6.45 | 6.51 | 6.56 | 6.61 |
| 30 | 3.89 | 4.45 | 4.80 | 5.05 | 5.24 | 5.40 | 5.54 | 5.65 | 5.76 | 5.85 | 5.93 | 6.01 | 6.08 | 6.14 | 6.20 | 6.26 | 6.31 | 6.36 | 6.41 |
| 40 | 3.82 | 4.37 | 4.70 | 4.93 | 5.11 | 5.27 | 5.39 | 5.50 | 5.60 | 5.69 | 5.77 | 5.84 | 5.90 | 5.96 | 6.02 | 6.07 | 6.12 | 6.17 | 6.21 |
| 60 | 3.76 | 4.28 | 4.60 | 4.82 | 4.99 | 5.13 | 5.25 | 5.36 | 5.45 | 5.53 | 5.60 | 5.67 | 5.73 | 5.79 | 5.84 | 5.89 | 5.93 | 5.98 | 6.02 |
| 120 | 3.70 | 4.20 | 4.50 | 4.71 | 4.87 | 5.01 | 5.12 | 5.21 | 5.30 | 5.38 | 5.44 | 5.51 | 5.56 | 5.61 | 5.66 | 5.71 | 5.75 | 5.79 | 5.83 |
| ∞ | 3.64 | 4.12 | 4.40 | 4.60 | 4.76 | 4.88 | 4.99 | 5.08 | 5.16 | 5.23 | 5.29 | 5.35 | 5.40 | 5.45 | 5.49 | 5.54 | 5.57 | 5.61 | 5.65 |

Source: Reprinted from E. S. Pearson and H. O. Hartley, eds., Table 29 of Biometrika Tables for Statisticians, Vol. 1, 3rd ed., 1966, by permission of the Biometrika Trustees, London.

# TABLE E.11

Critical Values $d_L$ and $d_U$ of the Durbin-Watson Statistic, $D$ (Critical Values Are One-Sided)[a]

## $\alpha = 0.05$

| | $k=1$ | | $k=2$ | | $k=3$ | | $k=4$ | | $k=5$ | |
|---|---|---|---|---|---|---|---|---|---|---|
| $n$ | $d_L$ | $d_U$ | $d_L$ | $d_U$ | $d_L$ | $d_U$ | $d_L$ | $d_U$ | $d_L$ | $d_U$ |
| 15 | 1.08 | 1.36 | .95 | 1.54 | .82 | 1.75 | .69 | 1.97 | .56 | 2.21 |
| 16 | 1.10 | 1.37 | .98 | 1.54 | .86 | 1.73 | .74 | 1.93 | .62 | 2.15 |
| 17 | 1.13 | 1.38 | 1.02 | 1.54 | .90 | 1.71 | .78 | 1.90 | .67 | 2.10 |
| 18 | 1.16 | 1.39 | 1.05 | 1.53 | .93 | 1.69 | .82 | 1.87 | .71 | 2.06 |
| 19 | 1.18 | 1.40 | 1.08 | 1.53 | .97 | 1.68 | .86 | 1.85 | .75 | 2.02 |
| 20 | 1.20 | 1.41 | 1.10 | 1.54 | 1.00 | 1.68 | .90 | 1.83 | .79 | 1.99 |
| 21 | 1.22 | 1.42 | 1.13 | 1.54 | 1.03 | 1.67 | .93 | 1.81 | .83 | 1.96 |
| 22 | 1.24 | 1.43 | 1.15 | 1.54 | 1.05 | 1.66 | .96 | 1.80 | .86 | 1.94 |
| 23 | 1.26 | 1.44 | 1.17 | 1.54 | 1.08 | 1.66 | .99 | 1.79 | .90 | 1.92 |
| 24 | 1.27 | 1.45 | 1.19 | 1.55 | 1.10 | 1.66 | 1.01 | 1.78 | .93 | 1.90 |
| 25 | 1.29 | 1.45 | 1.21 | 1.55 | 1.12 | 1.66 | 1.04 | 1.77 | .95 | 1.89 |
| 26 | 1.30 | 1.46 | 1.22 | 1.55 | 1.14 | 1.65 | 1.06 | 1.76 | .98 | 1.88 |
| 27 | 1.32 | 1.47 | 1.24 | 1.56 | 1.16 | 1.65 | 1.08 | 1.76 | 1.01 | 1.86 |
| 28 | 1.33 | 1.48 | 1.26 | 1.56 | 1.18 | 1.65 | 1.10 | 1.75 | 1.03 | 1.85 |
| 29 | 1.34 | 1.48 | 1.27 | 1.56 | 1.20 | 1.65 | 1.12 | 1.74 | 1.05 | 1.84 |
| 30 | 1.35 | 1.49 | 1.28 | 1.57 | 1.21 | 1.65 | 1.14 | 1.74 | 1.07 | 1.83 |
| 31 | 1.36 | 1.50 | 1.30 | 1.57 | 1.23 | 1.65 | 1.16 | 1.74 | 1.09 | 1.83 |
| 32 | 1.37 | 1.50 | 1.31 | 1.57 | 1.24 | 1.65 | 1.18 | 1.73 | 1.11 | 1.82 |
| 33 | 1.38 | 1.51 | 1.32 | 1.58 | 1.26 | 1.65 | 1.19 | 1.73 | 1.13 | 1.81 |
| 34 | 1.39 | 1.51 | 1.33 | 1.58 | 1.27 | 1.65 | 1.21 | 1.73 | 1.15 | 1.81 |
| 35 | 1.40 | 1.52 | 1.34 | 1.58 | 1.28 | 1.65 | 1.22 | 1.73 | 1.16 | 1.80 |
| 36 | 1.41 | 1.52 | 1.35 | 1.59 | 1.29 | 1.65 | 1.24 | 1.73 | 1.18 | 1.80 |
| 37 | 1.42 | 1.53 | 1.36 | 1.59 | 1.31 | 1.66 | 1.25 | 1.72 | 1.19 | 1.80 |
| 38 | 1.43 | 1.54 | 1.37 | 1.59 | 1.32 | 1.66 | 1.26 | 1.72 | 1.21 | 1.79 |
| 39 | 1.43 | 1.54 | 1.38 | 1.60 | 1.33 | 1.66 | 1.27 | 1.72 | 1.22 | 1.79 |
| 40 | 1.44 | 1.54 | 1.39 | 1.60 | 1.34 | 1.66 | 1.29 | 1.72 | 1.23 | 1.79 |
| 45 | 1.48 | 1.57 | 1.43 | 1.62 | 1.38 | 1.67 | 1.34 | 1.72 | 1.29 | 1.78 |
| 50 | 1.50 | 1.59 | 1.46 | 1.63 | 1.42 | 1.67 | 1.38 | 1.72 | 1.34 | 1.77 |
| 55 | 1.53 | 1.60 | 1.49 | 1.64 | 1.45 | 1.68 | 1.41 | 1.72 | 1.38 | 1.77 |
| 60 | 1.55 | 1.62 | 1.51 | 1.65 | 1.48 | 1.69 | 1.44 | 1.73 | 1.41 | 1.77 |
| 65 | 1.57 | 1.63 | 1.54 | 1.66 | 1.50 | 1.70 | 1.47 | 1.73 | 1.44 | 1.77 |
| 70 | 1.58 | 1.64 | 1.55 | 1.67 | 1.52 | 1.70 | 1.49 | 1.74 | 1.46 | 1.77 |
| 75 | 1.60 | 1.65 | 1.57 | 1.68 | 1.54 | 1.71 | 1.51 | 1.74 | 1.49 | 1.77 |
| 80 | 1.61 | 1.66 | 1.59 | 1.69 | 1.56 | 1.72 | 1.53 | 1.74 | 1.51 | 1.77 |
| 85 | 1.62 | 1.67 | 1.60 | 1.70 | 1.57 | 1.72 | 1.55 | 1.75 | 1.52 | 1.77 |
| 90 | 1.63 | 1.68 | 1.61 | 1.70 | 1.59 | 1.73 | 1.57 | 1.75 | 1.54 | 1.78 |
| 95 | 1.64 | 1.69 | 1.62 | 1.71 | 1.60 | 1.73 | 1.58 | 1.75 | 1.56 | 1.78 |
| 100 | 1.65 | 1.69 | 1.63 | 1.72 | 1.61 | 1.74 | 1.59 | 1.76 | 1.57 | 1.78 |

## $\alpha = 0.01$

| | $k=1$ | | $k=2$ | | $k=3$ | | $k=4$ | | $k=5$ | |
|---|---|---|---|---|---|---|---|---|---|---|
| $n$ | $d_L$ | $d_U$ | $d_L$ | $d_U$ | $d_L$ | $d_U$ | $d_L$ | $d_U$ | $d_L$ | $d_U$ |
| 15 | .81 | 1.07 | .70 | 1.25 | .59 | 1.46 | .49 | 1.70 | .39 | 1.96 |
| 16 | .84 | 1.09 | .74 | 1.25 | .63 | 1.44 | .53 | 1.66 | .44 | 1.90 |
| 17 | .87 | 1.10 | .77 | 1.25 | .67 | 1.43 | .57 | 1.63 | .48 | 1.85 |
| 18 | .90 | 1.12 | .80 | 1.26 | .71 | 1.42 | .61 | 1.60 | .52 | 1.80 |
| 19 | .93 | 1.13 | .83 | 1.26 | .74 | 1.41 | .65 | 1.58 | .56 | 1.77 |
| 20 | .95 | 1.15 | .86 | 1.27 | .77 | 1.41 | .68 | 1.57 | .60 | 1.74 |
| 21 | .97 | 1.16 | .89 | 1.27 | .80 | 1.41 | .72 | 1.55 | .63 | 1.71 |
| 22 | 1.00 | 1.17 | .91 | 1.28 | .83 | 1.40 | .75 | 1.54 | .66 | 1.69 |
| 23 | 1.02 | 1.19 | .94 | 1.29 | .86 | 1.40 | .77 | 1.53 | .70 | 1.67 |
| 24 | 1.04 | 1.20 | .96 | 1.30 | .88 | 1.41 | .80 | 1.53 | .72 | 1.66 |
| 25 | 1.05 | 1.21 | .98 | 1.30 | .90 | 1.41 | .83 | 1.52 | .75 | 1.65 |
| 26 | 1.07 | 1.22 | 1.00 | 1.31 | .93 | 1.41 | .85 | 1.52 | .78 | 1.64 |
| 27 | 1.09 | 1.23 | 1.02 | 1.32 | .95 | 1.41 | .88 | 1.51 | .81 | 1.63 |
| 28 | 1.10 | 1.24 | 1.04 | 1.32 | .97 | 1.41 | .90 | 1.51 | .83 | 1.62 |
| 29 | 1.12 | 1.25 | 1.05 | 1.33 | .99 | 1.42 | .92 | 1.51 | .85 | 1.61 |
| 30 | 1.13 | 1.26 | 1.07 | 1.34 | 1.01 | 1.42 | .94 | 1.51 | .88 | 1.61 |
| 31 | 1.15 | 1.27 | 1.08 | 1.34 | 1.02 | 1.42 | .96 | 1.51 | .90 | 1.60 |
| 32 | 1.16 | 1.28 | 1.10 | 1.35 | 1.04 | 1.43 | .98 | 1.51 | .92 | 1.60 |
| 33 | 1.17 | 1.29 | 1.11 | 1.36 | 1.05 | 1.43 | 1.00 | 1.51 | .94 | 1.59 |
| 34 | 1.18 | 1.30 | 1.13 | 1.36 | 1.07 | 1.43 | 1.01 | 1.51 | .95 | 1.59 |
| 35 | 1.19 | 1.31 | 1.14 | 1.37 | 1.08 | 1.44 | 1.03 | 1.51 | .97 | 1.59 |
| 36 | 1.21 | 1.32 | 1.15 | 1.38 | 1.10 | 1.44 | 1.04 | 1.51 | .99 | 1.59 |
| 37 | 1.22 | 1.32 | 1.16 | 1.38 | 1.11 | 1.45 | 1.06 | 1.51 | 1.00 | 1.59 |
| 38 | 1.23 | 1.33 | 1.18 | 1.39 | 1.12 | 1.45 | 1.07 | 1.52 | 1.02 | 1.58 |
| 39 | 1.24 | 1.34 | 1.19 | 1.39 | 1.14 | 1.45 | 1.09 | 1.52 | 1.03 | 1.58 |
| 40 | 1.25 | 1.34 | 1.20 | 1.40 | 1.15 | 1.46 | 1.10 | 1.52 | 1.05 | 1.58 |
| 45 | 1.29 | 1.38 | 1.24 | 1.42 | 1.20 | 1.48 | 1.16 | 1.53 | 1.11 | 1.58 |
| 50 | 1.32 | 1.40 | 1.28 | 1.45 | 1.24 | 1.49 | 1.20 | 1.54 | 1.16 | 1.59 |
| 55 | 1.36 | 1.43 | 1.32 | 1.47 | 1.28 | 1.51 | 1.25 | 1.55 | 1.21 | 1.59 |
| 60 | 1.38 | 1.45 | 1.35 | 1.48 | 1.32 | 1.52 | 1.28 | 1.56 | 1.25 | 1.60 |
| 65 | 1.41 | 1.47 | 1.38 | 1.50 | 1.35 | 1.53 | 1.31 | 1.57 | 1.28 | 1.61 |
| 70 | 1.43 | 1.49 | 1.40 | 1.52 | 1.37 | 1.55 | 1.34 | 1.58 | 1.31 | 1.61 |
| 75 | 1.45 | 1.50 | 1.42 | 1.53 | 1.39 | 1.56 | 1.37 | 1.59 | 1.34 | 1.62 |
| 80 | 1.47 | 1.52 | 1.44 | 1.54 | 1.42 | 1.57 | 1.39 | 1.60 | 1.36 | 1.62 |
| 85 | 1.48 | 1.53 | 1.46 | 1.55 | 1.43 | 1.58 | 1.41 | 1.60 | 1.39 | 1.63 |
| 90 | 1.50 | 1.54 | 1.47 | 1.56 | 1.45 | 1.59 | 1.43 | 1.61 | 1.41 | 1.64 |
| 95 | 1.51 | 1.55 | 1.49 | 1.57 | 1.47 | 1.60 | 1.45 | 1.62 | 1.42 | 1.64 |
| 100 | 1.52 | 1.56 | 1.50 | 1.58 | 1.48 | 1.60 | 1.46 | 1.63 | 1.44 | 1.65 |

[a] $n$ = number of observations; $k$ = number of independent variables.

Source: This table is reproduced from Biometrika, 41 (1951): pp. 173 and 175, with the permission of the Biometrika Trustees.

## TABLE E.12
Selected Critical Values of F for Cook's $D_i$ Statistic

| Denominator $df = n - k - 1$ | 2 | 3 | 4 | 5 | 6 | 7 | 8 | 9 | 10 | 12 | 15 | 20 |
|---|---|---|---|---|---|---|---|---|---|---|---|---|
| 10 | .743 | .845 | .899 | .932 | .954 | .971 | .983 | .992 | 1.00 | 1.01 | 1.02 | 1.03 |
| 11 | .739 | .840 | .893 | .926 | .948 | .964 | .977 | .986 | .994 | 1.01 | 1.02 | 1.03 |
| 12 | .735 | .835 | .888 | .921 | .943 | .959 | .972 | .981 | .989 | 1.00 | 1.01 | 1.02 |
| 15 | .726 | .826 | .878 | .911 | .933 | .949 | .960 | .970 | .977 | .989 | 1.00 | 1.01 |
| 20 | .718 | .816 | .868 | .900 | .922 | .938 | .950 | .959 | .966 | .977 | .989 | 1.00 |
| 24 | .714 | .812 | .863 | .895 | .917 | .932 | .944 | .953 | .961 | .972 | .983 | .994 |
| 30 | .709 | .807 | .858 | .890 | .912 | .927 | .939 | .948 | .955 | .966 | .978 | .989 |
| 40 | .705 | .802 | .854 | .885 | .907 | .922 | .934 | .943 | .950 | .961 | .972 | .983 |
| 60 | .701 | .798 | .849 | .880 | .901 | .917 | .928 | .937 | .945 | .956 | .967 | .978 |
| 120 | .697 | .793 | .844 | .875 | .896 | .912 | .923 | .932 | .939 | .950 | .961 | .972 |
| ∞ | .693 | .789 | .839 | .870 | .891 | .907 | .918 | .927 | .934 | .945 | .956 | .967 |

Header spanning: α = 0.50; Numerator $df = k + 1$

Source: Extracted from E. S. Pearson and H. O. Hartley, eds., Biometrika Tables for Statisticians, 3rd ed., 1966, by permission of the Biometrika Trustees.

## TABLE E.13
Control Chart Factors

| Number of Observations in Sample ($n$) | $d_2$ | $d_3$ | $D_3$ | $D_4$ | $A_2$ |
|---|---|---|---|---|---|
| 2 | 1.128 | 0.853 | 0 | 3.267 | 1.880 |
| 3 | 1.693 | 0.888 | 0 | 2.575 | 1.023 |
| 4 | 2.059 | 0.880 | 0 | 2.282 | 0.729 |
| 5 | 2.326 | 0.864 | 0 | 2.114 | 0.577 |
| 6 | 2.534 | 0.848 | 0 | 2.004 | 0.483 |
| 7 | 2.704 | 0.833 | 0.076 | 1.924 | 0.419 |
| 8 | 2.847 | 0.820 | 0.136 | 1.864 | 0.373 |
| 9 | 2.970 | 0.808 | 0.184 | 1.816 | 0.337 |
| 10 | 3.078 | 0.797 | 0.223 | 1.777 | 0.308 |
| 11 | 3.173 | 0.787 | 0.256 | 1.744 | 0.285 |
| 12 | 3.258 | 0.778 | 0.283 | 1.717 | 0.266 |
| 13 | 3.336 | 0.770 | 0.307 | 1.693 | 0.249 |
| 14 | 3.407 | 0.763 | 0.328 | 1.672 | 0.235 |
| 15 | 3.472 | 0.756 | 0.347 | 1.653 | 0.223 |
| 16 | 3.532 | 0.750 | 0.363 | 1.637 | 0.212 |
| 17 | 3.588 | 0.744 | 0.378 | 1.622 | 0.203 |
| 18 | 3.640 | 0.739 | 0.391 | 1.609 | 0.194 |
| 19 | 3.689 | 0.733 | 0.404 | 1.596 | 0.187 |
| 20 | 3.735 | 0.729 | 0.415 | 1.585 | 0.180 |
| 21 | 3.778 | 0.724 | 0.425 | 1.575 | 0.173 |
| 22 | 3.819 | 0.720 | 0.435 | 1.565 | 0.167 |
| 23 | 3.858 | 0.716 | 0.443 | 1.557 | 0.162 |
| 24 | 3.895 | 0.712 | 0.452 | 1.548 | 0.157 |
| 25 | 3.931 | 0.708 | 0.459 | 1.541 | 0.153 |

Source: Reprinted from ASTM-STP 15D by kind permission of the American Society for Testing and Materials.

# F.  STUDENT CD-ROM AND SOFTWARE FAQs

Use this appendix to find answers to the most frequently asked questions about using the resources on the Student CD-ROM and using Microsoft Excel and PHStat2.

## F.1  ABOUT THE STUDENT CD-ROM

**What does the Student CD-ROM contain?**
The Student CD-ROM contains six categories of files that support this book:

1. **Data files.** These files contain the data used in chapter examples or named in problems. They exist as both Excel workbook files (in the **.xls** format, compatible with all Excel versions) and Minitab worksheet (**.mtw**) files. See Appendix D.2 for a complete listing of data files included on the Student CD-ROM.
2. **Case files.** These files, a mix of data and document files as well as facsimiles of Web page files, support both the *Managing the Springville Herald* running case and the various Web Cases.
3. **Student CD-ROM topic files.** These files are bonus chapter sections included as Adobe Reader (**.pdf** format) files.
4. **Excel appendix workbooks.** These files are Microsoft Excel workbooks that contain model solutions for applying Microsoft Excel to various statistical analyses. Most are designed as fill-in-the-data templates that can be reused indefinitely.
5. **Visual Explorations files.** These files support Visual Explorations, the interactive Excel add-in that illustrates selected statistical concepts.
6. **Windows applications.** These files are specific to Microsoft Windows XP or Vista (any version) and include the PHStat2 setup program, the Adobe Reader setup program, and the Student CD-ROM's own "start" program that simplifies access to the contents of the Student CD-ROM.

**Can I use the Student CD-ROM with an Apple Mac running the Mac OS?**
Although the Student CD-ROM is marked "For Windows," most Mac users will be able to retrieve and use the first five categories of files listed in the previous answer.

**Does the Student CD-ROM contain Microsoft Excel or Minitab?**
No, these programs must be acquired separately. Specially priced student-oriented versions of Microsoft Office (containing Excel) are available at many retailers and select retailers, including **mypearsonstore.com**, sell the student version of Minitab.

**Can I copy the Excel workbook files to my local hard disk or other storage device?**
Yes, you can, and you are encouraged to do so. Windows users can use the CD-ROM's own "start" program to facilitate this task. Some files that you copy may be reported as being a "read-only" file. If you make changes to such files, you will need to save the file under a different name.

**Can I buy a replacement Student CD-ROM disk?**
No, Student CD-ROM disks are not sold separately. However, a PHStat2 version either identical or similar to the one included on the Student CD-ROM is available for separate purchase.

## F.2  ABOUT MICROSOFT EXCEL

**Will I need access to my original Microsoft Office/Excel CDs or DVD?**
Yes, if you are using PHStat2 you may need to use the original program disks if the Analysis ToolPak and Analysis ToolPak–VBA (referred to as the "ToolPak" in this book) has not been installed on your system.

**What Microsoft Office security settings should I use? How do I change Office security settings?**
See Section E1.8, "Using Add-ins" on page 20 for specific answers to these questions. If you plan to use the Prentice Hall PHStat2 Excel add-in, also read the PHStat2 readme file on the Student CD-ROM.

**How can I check to see if the ToolPak has been installed in Excel 97–2003?**
Open Excel and select **Tools → Add-Ins** and in the Add-Ins dialog box that appears, verify that **Analysis ToolPak** (and **Analysis ToolPak–VBA**, if using PHStat2) is checked in the **Add-Ins available** list. If **Analysis ToolPak** does not appear, you will need to install it separately.

**How can I check to see if the ToolPak has been installed in Excel 2007?**
Open Excel and click the **Office Button**. In the Office Button pane, click **Excel Options**. In the Excel options dialog box that appears, click **Add-Ins** in the left pane and look for **Analysis ToolPak** (and **Analysis ToolPak–VBA**, if using PHStat2) under **Active Application Add-ins**. If they do not appear, click **Go** and continue with the instructions for using the Add-Ins dialog box presented in the answer for Excel 97–2003.

**How can I install the ToolPak?**
Close Microsoft Excel and rerun the Microsoft Office or Microsoft Excel setup program. When the setup program runs, choose the option that allows you to add components. This option is variously described as the **modify**, **add**, or **custom** option. Then, select install **Analysis ToolPak** (and **Analysis ToolPak–VBA**, if using PHStat2). You may need access to the original Microsoft Office/Excel setup CD-ROMs or DVDs to complete this task.

**Do I need to run a setup program to use the Visual Explorations add-in workbook (Visual Explorations.xla)?**
No, you can copy the files and install the files from the Visual Exporations folder on the Student CD-ROM and use this add-in file as you would use any of the workbook data files. You will need to properly adjust your Microsoft Office security settings (see Section E1.8 on page 20) in order to use this add-in.

**In Excel 97–2003, how can I specify the custom settings that you recommend?**
First, select **Tools → Customize**. In the Customize dialog box, clear (uncheck) the **Menus show recently used commands first** check box if it is checked and click the **Close** button. Then select **Tools → Options**. In the Options dialog box, click the **Calculation** tab and verify that the **Automatic** option button of the Calculation group has been selected. Click the **Edit** tab and verify that all check boxes except the **Fixed decimal, Provide feedback with Animation,** and **Enable automatic percent entry** have been selected. (Excel 97 does not contain an Automatic percent entry check box.) Click the **General** tab and verify that the **R1C1 reference style** check box is cleared, and, if using Excel 97, check the **Macro virus protection** check box. Enter **3** as the number of **Sheets in new workbook**, select **Arial** from the **Standard font** list, and select **10** from the **Size** drop-down list. Then click **OK** to finish the customization.

**In Excel 2007, how can I specify the custom settings that you recommend?**
First, click the **Office Button** and then click **Excel Options**. In the Excel Options dialog box, click **Formulas** in the left panel. In the **Formulas** right pane, click **Automatic** under Workbook Calculation and verify that all check boxes are checked except **Enable iterative calculation, R1C1 reference style,** and **Formulas referring to empty cells**. For greater customization, click **Advanced** in the left panel and scroll through the **Advanced options for working with Excel** that appears in the right panel. Click **OK** when finished.

## F.3   ABOUT PHSTAT2

**What is PHStat2?**
PHStat2 is software that makes operating Microsoft Excel as distraction free as possible. As a student studying statistics,

you can focus mainly on learning statistics and not worry about having to fully master Excel first. When PHStat2 is combined with the ToolPak add-in supplied with Microsoft Excel, just about all statistical methods taught in an introductory statistics course can be illustrated using Microsoft Excel.

**I do not want to use an add-in that will not be available in my business environment. Any comments?**
Chapter 1 talks about these issues in detail. To summarize those pages, PHStat2 helps you learn Microsoft Excel, and using PHStat2 will not leave you any less equipped to work with Microsoft Excel in a setting where it is not available.

**What do I need to do in order to begin using PHStat2?**
You run the PHStat2 setup program (setup.exe) that is included on the Student CD-ROM. To use this program successfully, you must have logged in to Windows using an account that has administrator or software-installing privileges. (Student and faculty accounts to log in to networked computers in academic settings typically do not have this privilege. If you have such an account, ask your network or lab technician for assistance.) If you are using Windows Vista or certain firewall or security-suite programs, you may see messages asking you to permit or allow certain system operations as the PHStat2 setup runs. (If you decline permission, PHStat2 will not be successfully set up.)

**What are the technical requirements for setting up and adding PHStat2 to my system?**
If your system can run Microsoft Excel, it can also run PHStat2. You need approximately up to 10 MB hard disk free space during the setup process and up to 3 MB hard disk space after PHStat2 is installed. You must also ensure that the Microsoft Excel Analysis ToolPak and Analysis ToolPak–VBA add-ins have been installed. (See related question in Section F.2.)

**Are updates to PHStat2 available?**
Yes, free minor updates to resolve issues may be available for download from the PHStat2 Web site (**www.prenhall. com/phstat**). When you visit that Web site, note that the Student CD-ROM contains version 2.8 of PHStat2.

**How can I identify which version of PHStat2 I have?**
Open Microsoft Excel with PHStat2 and select **Help for PHStat** from the PHStat menu. A dialog box will display your current XLA and DLL version numbers. The XLA version number identifies the version of PHStat2 you have. Both of these numbers will initially be 2.8.0 after you set up PHStat2 from the Student CD-ROM.

**Where can I get help setting up PHStat2?**
First, carefully review the Student CD-ROM PHStat2 readme file. If your problem is unresolved, visit the PHStat2 Web site (**www. prenhall.com/phstat**) for further information. If your problem is still unresolved, contact Pearson Education technical support at **247pearsoned.custhelp.com**.

**Where can I find tips for using PHStat2?**
While your classmates and instructor can be the best source of tips, you can also visit the online PHStat2 community at **phstatcommunity.org**.

## F.4   ABOUT MINITAB

**Which versions of Minitab can I use with this book?**
You should use Minitab 14 or Minitab 15 when following the instructions in the Minitab appendices. There is a student version of Minitab that can be bundled with the book.

## F.5   ADDITIONAL INFORMATION FOR NEW MICROSOFT EXCEL 2007 USERS

**I do not see the menu for an add-in workbook that I opened. Where is it?**
Unlike earlier versions of Excel that allowed add-ins to add menus to the menu bar, Excel 2007 places all add-in menus under the Add-ins tab. If you click Add-ins, you find the menus of all properly loaded add-ins.

**What does "Compatibility Mode" mean?**
When you see "Compatibility Mode" in the title bar, Excel 2007 is telling you that you are using a workbook compatible with earlier Excel versions. When you save such a workbook, Excel 2007 will automatically use the .xls file format of earlier versions.

**How can I update an older (.xls) workbook to the Excel 2007 .xlsx workbook format?**
The simplest way is to open the workbook file and select **Office Button → Convert**. Then save your file (select **Office Button → Save**). You can also open the workbook file and select **Office Button → Save As** and in the Save As dialog box, select **Excel Workbook (*.xlsx)** from the **Save as type** list.

The following represent worked-out solutions to Self-Test Problems and brief answers to most of the even-numbered problems in the text. For more detailed solutions, including explanations, interpretations, and Excel and Minitab output, see the *Student Solutions Manual*.

# CHAPTER 1

**1.2** Small, medium, and large sizes imply order but do not specify how much more soft drink is added at increasing levels.

**1.4 (a)** The number of telephones is a numerical variable that is discrete because the outcome is a count. It is ratio scaled because it has a true zero point. **(b)** The length of the longest long-distance call is a numerical variable that is continuous because any value within a range of values can occur. It is ratio scaled because it has a true zero point. **(c)** Whether there is a cell phone in the household is a categorical variable because the answer can be only yes or no. This also makes it a nominal-scaled variable. **(d)** Same answer as in (c).

**1.6 (a)** Categorical, nominal scale. **(b)** Numerical, continuous, ratio scale. **(c)** Numerical, discrete, ratio scale. **(d)** Numerical, discrete, ratio scale.

**1.8 (a)** Numerical, continuous, ratio scale. **(b)** Numerical, discrete, ratio scale. **(c)** Numerical, continuous, ratio scale. **(d)** Categorical, nominal scale.

**1.10** The underlying variable, ability of the students, may be continuous, but the measuring device, the test, does not have enough precision to distinguish between the two students.

**1.24 (a)** A primary data source collected through a survey was used in this study. **(b)** Deciding what to make for dinner at home at the last minute. **(c)** The amount of time to prepare dinner.

**1.26 (a)** Cat owner households in the United States. **(b)** 1. Categorical. 2. Categorical. 3. Numerical, discrete. 4. Categorical.

# CHAPTER 2

**2.4 (b)** The Pareto chart is best for portraying these data because it not only sorts the frequencies in descending order, it also provides the cumulative polygon on the same scale. **(c)** You can conclude that friends/family account for the largest percentage of 45%. When other, news media, and online user reviews are added to friends/family, this accounts for 83%.

**2.6 (b)** 88%. **(d)** The Pareto chart allows you to see which sources account for most of the electricity.

**2.8 (b)** The bar chart is more suitable if the purpose is to compare the categories. The pie chart is more suitable if the main objective is to investigate the portion of the whole that is in a particular category.

**2.10 (b)** Rooms dirty, rooms not stocked, and rooms needing maintenance have the largest number of complaints, so focusing on these categories can reduce the number of complaints the most.

**2.12** Stem-and-leaf display of finance scores:

| | |
|---|---|
| 5 | 34 |
| 6 | 9 |
| 7 | 4 |
| 8 | 0 |
| 9 | 38 |

$n = 7$

**2.14** 50  74  74  76  81  89  92.

**2.16 (a)** Ordered array: Cost($) 120, 130, 132, 134, 134, 139, 141, 146, 148, 149, 154, 157, 158, 159, 163, 170, 170, 175, 180, 183, 186, 191, 192, 194, 202, 207, 209, 209, 219, 288
**(b)** Stem-and-leaf display:

Stem unit:      10

| | |
|---|---|
| 12 | 0 |
| 13 | 0 2 4 4 9 |
| 14 | 1 6 8 9 |
| 15 | 4 7 8 9 |
| 16 | 3 |
| 17 | 0 0 5 |
| 18 | 0 3 6 |
| 19 | 1 2 4 |
| 20 | 2 7 9 9 |
| 21 | 9 |
| 22 | |
| 23 | |
| 24 | |
| 25 | |
| 26 | |
| 27 | |
| 28 | 8 |

**(c)** The stem-and-leaf display provides more information because it not only orders values from the smallest to the largest into stems and leaves, it also conveys information on how the values distribute and cluster over the range of the data.
**(d)** The costs of attending a baseball game do not appear to be concentrating around any particular value. In fact, the costs appear to spread evenly between $130 and $210 with the exception of an outlier at $288 for Boston.

**2.18 (a)** Ordered array:

4  5  7  8  16  19  19  20  20  23  24  25  29  29  30  30  30  30  40  56

**(b)** Stem-and-leaf display for fat; stem, 10 unit:

| | |
|---|---|
| 0 | 4 5 7 8 |
| 1 | 6 9 9 |
| 2 | 0 0 3 4 5 9 9 |
| 3 | 0 0 0 0 |
| 4 | 0 |
| 5 | 6 |

**(c)** The stem-and-leaf display conveys more information than the ordered array. You can also obtain a sense of the distribution of the data from the stem-and-leaf display. **(d)** They are concentrated around 29 and 30.

**2.20 (a)** 10 but less than 20, 20 but less than 30, 30 but less than 40, 40 but less than 50, 50 but less than 60, 60 but less than 70, 70 but less than 80, 80 but less than 90, 90 but less than 100. **(b)** 10. **(c)** 15, 25, 35, 45, 55, 65, 75, 85, 95.

**2.22 (a)**

| Electricity Costs | Frequency | Percentage |
|---|---|---|
| $80 up to $99 | 4 | 8% |
| $100 up to $119 | 7 | 14 |
| $120 up to $139 | 9 | 18 |
| $140 up to $159 | 13 | 26 |
| $160 up to $179 | 9 | 18 |
| $180 up to $199 | 5 | 10 |
| $200 up to $219 | 3 | 6 |

**(c)**

| Electricity Costs | Frequency | Percentage | Cumulative % |
|---|---|---|---|
| $99 | 4 | 8.00% | 8.00% |
| $119 | 7 | 14.00 | 22.00 |
| $139 | 9 | 18.00 | 40.00 |
| $159 | 13 | 26.00 | 66.00 |
| $179 | 9 | 18.00 | 84.00 |
| $199 | 5 | 10.00 | 94.00 |
| $219 | 3 | 6.00 | 100.00 |

**(d)** The majority of utility charges are clustered between $120 and $180.

**2.24** The property taxes per capita appear to be right-skewed with approximately 90% falling between $399 and $1,700, and the remaining 10% falling between $1,700 and $2,100. The center is at about $1,000.

**2.26 (a)**

| Width | Frequency | Percentage |
|---|---|---|
| 8.310–8.329 | 3 | 6.12% |
| 8.330–8.349 | 2 | 4.08 |
| 8.350–8.369 | 1 | 2.04 |
| 8.370–8.389 | 4 | 8.16 |
| 8.390–8.409 | 5 | 10.20 |
| 8.410–8.429 | 16 | 31.65 |
| 8.430–8.449 | 5 | 10.20 |
| 8.450–8.469 | 5 | 10.20 |
| 8.470–8.489 | 6 | 12.24 |
| 8.490–8.509 | 2 | 4.08 |

**(d)** All the troughs will meet the company's requirements of between 8.31 and 8.61 inches wide.

**2.28 (a)**

| Bulb Life (hrs) | % Less Than | Percentage, Mfgr A | Percentage, Mfgr B |
|---|---|---|---|
| 650–749 | 750 | 7.5% | 0.0% |
| 750–849 | 850 | 12.5 | 5.0 |
| 850–949 | 950 | 50.0 | 20.0 |
| 950–1,049 | 1,050 | 22.5 | 40.0 |
| 1,050–1,149 | 1,150 | 7.5 | 22.5 |
| 1,150–1,249 | 1,250 | 0.0 | 12.5 |

**(c)**

| Bulb Life (hrs) | Percentage Less Than, Mfgr A | Percentage Less Than, Mfgr B |
|---|---|---|
| 650–749 | 7.5% | 0.0% |
| 750–849 | 20.0 | 5.0 |
| 850–949 | 70.0 | 25.0 |
| 950–1049 | 92.5 | 65.0 |
| 1050–1149 | 100.0 | 87.5 |
| 1150–1249 | 100.0 | 100.0 |

**(d)** Manufacturer B produces bulbs with longer lives than Manufacturer A. The cumulative percentage for Manufacturer B shows 65% of its bulbs lasted less than 1,050 hours, contrasted with 70% of Manufacturer A's bulbs, which lasted less than 950 hours. None of Manufacturer A's bulbs lasted more than 1,149 hours, but 12.5% of Manufacturer B's bulbs lasted between 1,150 and 1,249 hours. At the same time, 7.5% of Manufacturer A's bulbs lasted less than 750 hours, whereas all of Manufacturer B's bulbs lasted at least 750 hours.

**2.30 (a)** Table of frequencies for all student responses:

STUDENT MAJOR CATEGORIES

| GENDER | A | C | M | Totals |
|---|---|---|---|---|
| Male | 14 | 9 | 2 | 25 |
| Female | 6 | 6 | 3 | 15 |
| Totals | 20 | 15 | 5 | 40 |

**(b)** Table of percentages based on overall student responses:

STUDENT MAJOR CATEGORIES

| GENDER | A | C | M | Totals |
|---|---|---|---|---|
| Male | 35.0% | 22.5% | 5.0% | 62.5% |
| Female | 15.0 | 15.0 | 7.5 | 37.5 |
| Totals | 50.0 | 37.5 | 12.5 | 100.0 |

**(c)** Table based on row percentages:

STUDENT MAJOR CATEGORIES

| GENDER | A | C | M | Totals |
|---|---|---|---|---|
| Male | 56.0% | 36.0% | 8.0% | 100.0% |
| Female | 40.0 | 40.0 | 20.0 | 100.0 |
| Totals | 50.0 | 37.5 | 12.5 | 100.0 |

**(d)** Table based on column percentages:

STUDENT MAJOR CATEGORIES

| GENDER | A | C | M | Totals |
|---|---|---|---|---|
| Male | 70.0% | 60.0% | 40.0% | 62.5% |
| Female | 30.0 | 40.0 | 60.0 | 37.5 |
| Totals | 100.0 | 100.0 | 100.0 | 100.0 |

**2.32 (a)** Contingency table:

| QUALITY | CONDITION OF DIE | | |
| | No Particles | Particles | Totals |
|---|---|---|---|
| Good | 320 | 14 | 334 |
| Bad | 80 | 36 | 116 |
| Totals | 400 | 50 | 450 |

Table of total percentages:

| QUALITY | CONDITION OF DIE | | |
| | No Particles | Particles | Totals |
|---|---|---|---|
| Good | 71% | 3% | 74% |
| Bad | 18 | 8 | 26 |
| Totals | 89 | 11 | 100 |

Table of row percentages:

| QUALITY | CONDITION OF DIE | | |
| | No Particles | Particles | Totals |
|---|---|---|---|
| Good | 96% | 4% | 100% |
| Bad | 69 | 31 | 100 |
| Totals | 89 | 11 | 100 |

Table of column percentages:

| QUALITY | CONDITION OF DIE | | |
| | No Particles | Particles | Totals |
|---|---|---|---|
| Good | 80% | 28% | 74% |
| Bad | 20 | 72 | 26 |
| Totals | 100 | 100 | 100 |

**(c)** The data suggest that there is some association between condition of the die and the quality of wafer because more good wafers are produced when no particles are found in the die, and more bad wafers are produced when there are particles found in the die.

**2.34 (a)** Table of row percentages:

| ENJOY SHOPPING FOR CLOTHING | GENDER | | |
| | Male | Female | Total |
|---|---|---|---|
| Yes | 38% | 62% | 100% |
| No | 74 | 26 | 100 |
| Total | 48 | 52 | 100 |

Table of column percentages:

| ENJOY SHOPPING FOR CLOTHING | GENDER | | |
| | Male | Female | Total |
|---|---|---|---|
| Yes | 57% | 86% | 72% |
| No | 43 | 14 | 28 |
| Total | 100 | 100 | 100 |

Table of total percentages:

| ENJOY SHOPPING FOR CLOTHING | GENDER | | |
| | Male | Female | Total |
|---|---|---|---|
| Yes | 27% | 45% | 72% |
| No | 21 | 7 | 28 |
| Total | 48 | 52 | 100 |

**(c)** A higher percentage of females enjoy shopping for clothing.

**2.36 (b)** The number of MBA and undergraduate students who choose the lowest-cost fund and the second-lowest-cost fund is about the same. More MBA students chose the third-lowest cost fund whereas more undergraduate students chose the highest cost fund.

**2.38 (b)** Yes, there is a strong positive relationship between $X$ and $Y$. As $X$ increases, so does $Y$.

**2.40 (b)** There is a positive relationship between owner mileage and current government standard mileage.

**2.42 (b)** There appears to be a positive relationship between the coachs' salary and revenue. **(c)** Yes, this is borne out by the data.

**2.44 (b)** The unemployment rate was stable at around 4% from January 2000 to around January 2001. Then it trended upward and leveled off at around 6% by December 2001. Around October 2003, it started to trend downward and reached about 4.5% by December 2006.

**2.46 (b)** There is an obvious upward trend in the average number of TV channels that the U.S. home received from 1985 to 2005. **(c)** With extrapolation, you would predict the average number of TV channels that the U.S. home will receive in 2010 to be around 140.

**2.64 (c)** The publisher gets the largest portion (64.8%) of the revenue. About half (32.2%) of the revenue received by the publisher covers manufacturing costs. The publisher's marketing and promotion account for the next largest share of the revenue, at 15.4%. Author, bookstore employee salaries and benefits, and publisher administrative costs and taxes each account for around 10% of the revenue, whereas the publisher after-tax profit, bookstore operations, bookstore pretax profit, and freight constitute the "trivial few" allocations of the revenue. Yes, the bookstore gets twice the revenue of the authors.

**2.66 (b)** In 2005, the United States relied on petroleum heavily, followed by coal and natural gas as major sources of energy, whereas renewable fuels accounted for less than 4% of the total consumption. Wood accounted for more than half of the renewable energy consumption.

**2.68 (b)** The Pareto plot is most appropriate because it not only sorts the frequencies in descending order, it also provides the cumulative polygon on the same scale. **(d)** The Pareto plot is most appropriate because it not only sorts the frequencies in descending order, it also provides the cumulative polygon on the same scale. **(e)** "Paid search" constitutes the largest category on U.S. online ad spending at 43%. Excluding the generic keyword "sneakers," searches using the keywords "sneaker pimps" and "Jordan sneaker" make up the majority of the searches for sneakers on specific brands.

**2.70 (a)**

| DESSERT ORDERED | GENDER Male | Female | Total |
|---|---|---|---|
| Yes | 71% | 29% | 100% |
| No | 48 | 52 | 100 |
| Total | 53 | 47 | 100 |

| DESSERT ORDERED | GENDER Male | Female | Total |
|---|---|---|---|
| Yes | 30% | 14% | 23% |
| No | 70 | 86 | 77 |
| Total | 100 | 100 | 100 |

| DESSERT ORDERED | BEEF ENTRÉE Yes | No | Total |
|---|---|---|---|
| Yes | 52% | 48% | 100% |
| No | 25 | 75 | 100 |
| Total | 31 | 69 | 100 |

| DESSERT ORDERED | BEEF ENTRÉE Yes | No | Total |
|---|---|---|---|
| Yes | 38% | 16% | 23% |
| No | 62 | 84 | 77 |
| Total | 100 | 100 | 100 |

| DESSERT ORDERED | BEEF ENTRÉE Yes | No | Total |
|---|---|---|---|
| Yes | 12% | 11% | 23% |
| No | 19 | 58 | 77 |
| Total | 31 | 69 | 100 |

**(b)** If the owner is interested in finding out the percentage of males and females who order dessert or the percentage of those who order a beef entrée and a dessert among all patrons, the table of total percentages is most informative. If the owner is interested in the effect of gender on ordering of dessert or the effect of ordering a beef entrée on the ordering of dessert, the table of column percentages will be most informative. Because dessert is usually ordered after the main entrée, and the owner has no direct control over the gender of patrons, the table of row percentages is not very useful here. **(c)** 30% of the men ordered desserts, compared to 14% of the women; men are more than twice as likely to order desserts as women. Almost 38% of the patrons ordering a beef entrée ordered dessert, compared to 16% of patrons ordering all other entrees. Patrons ordering beef are more than 2.3 times as likely to order dessert as patrons ordering any other entrée.

**2.72 (a)** 23575R15 accounts for over 80% of the warranty claims. **(b)** 91.82% of the warranty claims are from the ATX model. **(c)** Tread separation accounts for 73.23% of the warranty claims among the ATX model. **(d)** The number of claims is evenly distributed among the three incidents; other/unknown incidents account for almost 40% of the claims, tread separation accounts for about 35% of the claims, and blowout accounts for about 25% of the claims.

**2.74 (c)** Majority (about 71%) of the beers have percentage alcohol between 4.1% and 5.1% with one beer (O'Doul's) containing only 0.4% alcohol. There are two clusters in the distribution of calories. About 60% of the beers have between 135 and 175 calories and another cluster of 25% has between 95 and 115 calories. The distribution of carbohydrates is slightly right-skewed with carbohydrates for Sam Adams Cream Stout having a value equal to 23.9. There appears to be a positive relationship between percentage alcohol in a beer and its calories content. There is also an obvious positive relationship between calories content and carbohydrates content. Percentage alcohol content and calories content do not appear to be related.

**2.76 (c)** The distribution of the yields of the money market accounts is right-skewed with almost 80% of them having a return of less than 1.2% whereas only about 16% of them have yields higher than 2.0%. The distribution of the yields of one-year CDs is uniform between 3.4% and 5.4% with only about 16% of them having a yield of less than 3.4%. About 65% of the five-year CDs have yields that fall between 3.4% and 4.6%. Only 5% of them have yields that are lower than 3.4% and about 19% of them have yields higher than 5.0%. There appear to be positive relationships between all pairs of yields with one-year CDs and five-year CDs demonstrating the strongest positive relationship.

**2.78 (a)**

| Frequencies (Boston) | | |
|---|---|---|
| Weight (Boston) | Frequency | Percentage |
| 3,015 but less than 3,050 | 2 | 0.54% |
| 3,050 but less than 3,085 | 44 | 11.96 |
| 3,085 but less than 3,120 | 122 | 33.15 |
| 3,120 but less than 3,155 | 131 | 35.60 |
| 3,155 but less than 3,190 | 58 | 15.76 |
| 3,190 but less than 3,225 | 7 | 1.90 |
| 3,225 but less than 3,260 | 3 | 0.82 |
| 3,260 but less than 3,295 | 1 | 0.27 |

**(b)**

| Frequencies (Vermont) | | |
|---|---|---|
| Weight (Vermont) | Frequency | Percentage |
| 3,550 but less than 3,600 | 4 | 1.21% |
| 3,600 but less than 3,650 | 31 | 9.39 |
| 3,650 but less than 3,700 | 115 | 34.85 |
| 3,700 but less than 3,750 | 131 | 39.70 |
| 3,750 but less than 3,800 | 36 | 10.91 |
| 3,800 but less than 3,850 | 12 | 3.64 |
| 3,850 but less than 3,900 | 1 | 0.30 |

**(d)** 0.54% of the Boston shingles pallets are underweight, whereas 0.27% are overweight. 1.21% of the Vermont shingles pallets are underweight, whereas 3.94% are overweight.

**2.80 (a), (c)**

| Calories | Frequency | Percentage | Limit | Percentage Less Than |
|---|---|---|---|---|
| 50 but less than 100 | 3 | 12% | 100 | 12% |
| 100 but less than 150 | 3 | 12 | 150 | 24 |
| 150 but less than 200 | 9 | 36 | 200 | 60 |
| 200 but less than 250 | 6 | 24 | 250 | 84 |
| 250 but less than 300 | 3 | 12 | 300 | 96 |
| 300 but less than 350 | 0 | 0 | 350 | 96 |
| 350 but less than 400 | 1 | 4 | 400 | 100 |

| Protein | Frequency | Percentage | Limit | Percentage Less Than |
|---|---|---|---|---|
| 16 but less than 20 | 1 | 4% | 20 | 4% |
| 20 but less than 24 | 5 | 20 | 24 | 24 |
| 24 but less than 28 | 8 | 32 | 28 | 56 |
| 28 but less than 32 | 9 | 36 | 32 | 92 |
| 32 but less than 36 | 2 | 8 | 36 | 100 |

| Calories from Fat | Frequency | Percentage | Limit | Percentage Less Than |
|---|---|---|---|---|
| 0% but less than 10% | 3 | 12% | 10 | 12% |
| 10% but less than 20% | 4 | 16 | 20 | 28 |
| 20% but less than 30% | 2 | 8 | 30 | 36 |
| 30% but less than 40% | 5 | 20 | 40 | 56 |
| 40% but less than 50% | 3 | 12 | 50 | 68 |
| 50% but less than 60% | 5 | 20 | 60 | 88 |
| 60% but less than 70% | 2 | 8 | 70 | 96 |
| 70% but less than 80% | 1 | 4 | 80 | 100 |

| Calories from Saturated Fat | Frequency | Percentage | Limit | Percentage Less Than |
|---|---|---|---|---|
| 0% but less than 5% | 6 | 24% | 5 | 24% |
| 5% but less than 10% | 2 | 8 | 10 | 32 |
| 10% but less than 15% | 5 | 20 | 15 | 52 |
| 15% but less than 20% | 5 | 20 | 20 | 72 |
| 20% but less than 25% | 5 | 20 | 25 | 92 |
| 25% but less than 30% | 2 | 8 | 30 | 100 |

| Cholesterol | Frequency | Percentage | Limit | Percentage Less Than |
|---|---|---|---|---|
| 0 but less than 50 | 2 | 8% | 50 | 8% |
| 50 but less than 100 | 17 | 68 | 100 | 76 |
| 100 but less than 150 | 4 | 16 | 150 | 92 |
| 150 but less than 200 | 1 | 4 | 200 | 96 |
| 200 but less than 250 | 0 | 0 | 250 | 96 |
| 250 but less than 300 | 0 | 0 | 300 | 96 |
| 300 but less than 350 | 0 | 0 | 350 | 96 |
| 350 but less than 400 | 0 | 0 | 400 | 96 |
| 400 but less than 450 | 0 | 0 | 450 | 96 |
| 450 but less than 500 | 1 | 4 | 500 | 100 |

**(d)** The sampled fresh red meats, poultry, and fish vary from 98 to 397 calories per serving, with the highest concentration between 150 to 200 calories. One protein source, spareribs, with 397 calories, is more than 100 calories above the next highest caloric food. The protein content of the sampled foods varies from 16 to 33 grams, with 68% of the data values falling between 24 and 32 grams. Spareribs and fried liver are both very different from other foods sampled—the former on calories and the latter on cholesterol content.

**2.82 (c)** Total fat seems to be most closely related to calories because the points in the scatter plot are closer to the imaginary line that passes through the data points.

**2.84 (b)** There is a downward trend in the amount filled. **(c)** The amount filled in the next bottle will most likely be below 1.894 liter. **(d)** The scatter plot of the amount of soft drink filled against time reveals the trend of the data, whereas a histogram only provides information on the distribution of the data.

# CHAPTER 3

**3.2 (a)** Mean = 7, median = 7, mode = 7. **(b)** Range = 9, interquartile range = 5, $S^2 = 10.8$, $S = 3.286$, $CV = 46.948\%$. **(c)** $Z$ scores: 0, −0.913, 0.609, 0, −1.217, 1.522. None of the $Z$ scores are larger than 3.0 or smaller than −3.0. There is no outlier. **(d)** Symmetric because mean = median.

**3.4 (a)** Mean = 2, median = 7, mode = 7. **(b)** Range = 17, interquartile range = 14.5, $S^2 = 62$, $S = 7.874$, $CV = 393.7\%$. **(d)** Left-skewed because mean < median.

**3.6 (a)**

| | Grade $X$ | Grade $Y$ |
|---|---|---|
| Mean | 575 | 575.4 |
| Median | 575 | 575 |
| Standard deviation | 6.40 | 2.07 |

**(b)** If quality is measured by central tendency, Grade $X$ tires provide slightly better quality because $X$'s mean and median are both equal to the expected value, 575 mm. If, however, quality is measured by consistency, Grade $Y$ provides better quality because, even though $Y$'s mean is only slightly larger than the mean for Grade $X$, $Y$'s standard deviation is much smaller. The range in values for Grade $Y$ is 5 mm compared to the range in values for Grade $X$, which is 16 mm.

**(c)**

| | Grade $X$ | Grade $Y$, Altered |
|---|---|---|
| Mean | 575 | 577.4 |
| Median | 575 | 575 |
| Standard deviation | 6.40 | 6.11 |

When the fifth $Y$ tire measures 588 mm rather than 578 mm, $Y$'s mean inner diameter becomes 577.4 mm, which is larger than $X$'s mean inner diameter, and $Y$'s standard deviation increases from 2.07 mm to 6.11 mm. In this case, $X$'s tires are providing better quality in terms of the mean inner diameter, with only slightly more variation among the tires than $Y$'s.

**3.8 (a)** Mean = 36.53, median = 35.6. **(b)** Variance = 19.27, standard deviation = 4.39, range = 12, coefficient of variation = 12.02%. **(c)** The mean is only slightly larger than the median, so the data is only slightly right-skewed. **(d)** The mean cost is $36.53 and the median cost is $35.60. The average scatter of cost around the mean is $4.39. The difference between the highest and the lowest cost is $12.

**3.10 (a)** Mean = 19.25, median = 18, mode = 18. **(b)** Variance = 9.3056, standard deviation = 3.0505, range = 11, coefficient of variation = 15.85%. **(c)** Because the mean is larger than the median, the data are right-skewed. **(d)** The distributions of MPG of both 4 cylinder family sedans and small SUVs are skewed to the right. The mean MPG of 4 cylinder sedans is 5.75 higher than that of small SUVs. The average scatter of the MPG of 4 cylinder sedans is higher than that for small SUVs. The difference between the highest and the lowest MPG of sedans is also higher than that of SUVs. There is an obvious outlier in the MPG in Toyota Prius among the 4 cylinder family sedans whereas there is not an obvious outlier in the MPG among the small SUVs.

**3.12 (a)** Mean = 226.67, median = 210, first quartile = 110, third quartile = 380. **(b)** Variance = 17,756.06, standard deviation = 133.25, range = 425, interquartile range = 270, $CV = 58.79\%$. There is no outlier because none of the $Z$ scores has an absolute value that is greater than 3.0. **(c)** The data appear to be skewed to the right because the mean is greater than the median.

**3.14 (a)** Mean = 46.8, median = 42.5. **(b)** Range = 34, variance = 123.29, standard deviation = 11.10. **(c)** The admission price for one-day tickets is slightly skewed to the right because the mean is slightly greater than the median. **(d)(a)** Mean = 50.8, median = 42.5, first quartile = 40, third quartile = 62. **(b)** Range = 69, variance = 382.84, standard deviation = 19.57. **(c)** The admission price for one-day tickets is skewed to the right because the mean is much greater than the median due to the much higher price of the first observation, at $98.

**3.16 (a)** Mean = 7.11, median = 6.68. **(b)** Variance = 4.336, standard deviation = 2.082, range = 6.67, interquartile range = 3.09, $CV$ = 29.27%. **(c)** Because the mean is greater than the median, the distribution is right-skewed. **(d)** The mean and median are both greater than 5 minutes. The distribution is right-skewed, meaning that there are some unusually high values. Further, 13 of the 15 bank customers sampled (or 86.7%) had waiting times greater than 5 minutes. So the customer is likely to experience a waiting time in excess of 5 minutes. The manager overstated the bank's service record in responding that the customer would "almost certainly" not wait longer than 5 minutes for service.

**3.18 (a)** $\bar{R}_G = [(1 + 3.614)(1 - 0.78)]^{\frac{1}{2}} - 1 = 0.7512\%$. **(b)** If you purchased $1,000 of TASER stock at the start of 2004, its value at the end of 2005 was $1,007.51. **(c)** If you purchased $1,000 of TASER stock at the start of 2004, its value at the end of 2005 was $82.95 lower than that of GE stock. **(d)** $\bar{R}_G = [(1 + 3.614)(1 - 0.78)(1 + 0.093)]^{\frac{1}{3}} - 1 = 3.5234\%$.

**3.20 (a)** Platinum = 18.45%, Gold = 17.98%, Silver = 23.32%. **(b)** All three metals achieved positive rates of return over the five-year period with silver yielding the highest rate of return at 23.32%, followed by platinum at 18.45% and gold at 17.98%. **(c)** In general, investments in the metal market achieved a higher rate of return than investments in the stock market from 2002 to 2006.

**3.22 (a)** Population mean, $\mu = 6$. **(b)** Population standard deviation, $\sigma = 1.673$, population variance, $\sigma^2 = 2.8$.

**3.24 (a)** 68%. **(b)** 95%. **(c)** Not calculable, 75%, 88.89%. **(d)** $\mu - 4\sigma$ to $\mu + 4\sigma$ or −2.8 to 19.2.

**3.26 (a)** Mean = 12,999.2158, variance = 14,959,700.52, standard deviation = 3,867.7772. **(b)** 64.71%, 98.04%, and 100% of these states have mean per-capita energy consumption within 1, 2, and 3 standard deviations of the mean, respectively. **(c)** This is consistent with 68%, 95%, and 99.7%, according to the empirical rule. **(d)(a)** Mean = 12,857.7402, variance = 14,238,110.67, standard deviation = 3,773.3421. **(b)** 66%, 98%, and 100% of these states have a mean per-capita energy consumption within 1, 2, and 3 standard deviations of the mean, respectively. **(c)** This is consistent with 68%, 95%, and 99.7% according to the empirical rule.

**3.28 (a)** 25. **(b)** 11.010.

**3.30 (a)** March mean = $4,720, April mean = $4,400. **(b)** March $S$ = $2,250.08, April $S$ = $2,657.30. **(c)** No, the means are close relative to the size of the standard deviations. The standard deviations are about $400 apart.

**3.32 (a)** $A$: mean = 40.435, $B$: mean = 36.831. **(b)** $A$: $S$ = 11.097, $B$: $S$ = 8.334. **(c)** Yes, division $B$ appears to have younger employees who are less variable in age than in division $A$.

**3.34 (a)** 4, 9, 5. **(b)** 3, 4, 7, 9, 12. **(c)** The distances between the median and the extremes are close, 4 and 5, but the differences in the tails are

different (1 on the left and 3 on the right), so this distribution is slightly right-skewed. **(d)** In 3.2 (d), because mean = median, the distribution was said to be symmetric. The box part of the graph is symmetric, but the tails show right-skewness.

**3.36 (a)** −6.5, 8, 14.5. **(b)** −8, −6.5, 7, 8, 9. **(c)** The shape is left-skewed. **(d)** This is consistent with the answer in 3.4 (d).

**3.38 (a), (b)** Five-number summary: 35 110 210 380 460. **(c)** The distribution is slightly skewed to the right.

**3.40 (a)** First Quartile = 17, Third Quartile = 22, Interquartile Range = 5. **(b)** Five-number summary: 15 17 18 22 26. **(c)** The MPG of small SUVs is right-skewed.

**3.42 (a)** Commercial district five-number summary: 0.38 3.2 4.5 5.55 6.46. Residential area five-number summary: 3.82 5.64 6.68 8.73 10.49. **(b)** Commercial district: The distribution is skewed to the left. Residential area: The distribution is skewed slightly to the right. **(c)** The central tendency of the waiting times for the bank branch located in the commercial district of a city is lower than that of the branch located in the residential area. There are a few longer than normal waiting times for the branch located in the residential area, whereas there are a few exceptionally short waiting times for the branch located in the commercial area.

**3.44** U.S. stocks are highly correlated with the German stock market, somewhat correlated with the Brazilian stock market, and not very correlated with the Japanese stock market.

**3.46 (a)** $\text{cov}(X, Y) = 591.667$. **(b)** $r = 0.7196$. **(c)** The correlation coefficient is more valuable for expressing the relationship between calories and fat because it does not depend on the units used to measure calories and fat. **(d)** There is a strong positive linear relationship between calories and fat.

**3.48 (a)** $\text{cov}(X, Y) = 1.2132$. **(b)** $S_X^2 = 0.1944, S_Y^2 = 20.4054$

$$r = \frac{\text{cov}(X,Y)}{S_X S_Y} = \frac{1.2132}{(0.4409)(4.5172)} = 0.6092$$

**(c)** There is a moderate positive linear relationship between the coachs' salary and revenue.

**3.62 (a)** Mean = 43.89, median = 45, 1st quartile = 18, 3rd quartile = 63. **(b)** Range = 76, interquartile range = 45, variance = 639.2564, standard deviation = 25.28, $CV$ = 57.61%. **(c)** The distribution is skewed to the right because there are a few policies that require an exceptionally long period to be approved. **(d)** The mean approval process takes 43.89 days, with 50% of the policies being approved in less than 45 days. 50% of the applications are approved between 18 and 63 days. About 67% of the applications are approved between 18.6 and 69.2 days.

**3.64 (a)** Mean = 8.421, median = 8.42, range = 0.186, $S$ = 0.0461. The mean and median width are both 8.42 inches. The range of the widths is 0.186 inch, and the average scatter around the mean is 0.0461 inch. **(b)** 8.312, 8.404, 8.42, 8.459, 8.498. **(c)** Even though mean = median, the left tail is slightly longer so the distribution is slightly left-skewed. **(d)** All the troughs in this sample meet the specifications.

**3.66 (a), (b)**
Excel output:

|  | In-State Tuition/Fees | Out-of-State Tuition/Fees |
|---|---|---|
| Mean | 6841.8155 | 17167.71 |
| Median | 6340 | 16340 |
| Mode | 7062 | 14901 |
| Standard Deviation | 2212.2215 | 4274.009 |
| Sample Variance | 4893924.034 | 18267150 |
| Kurtosis | 4.29574 | −0.33509 |
| Skewness | 1.3504 | 0.5244 |
| Range | 14466 | 20007 |
| Minimum | 3094 | 8965 |
| Maximum | 17560 | 28972 |
| Sum | 704707 | 1768274 |
| Count | 103 | 103 |
| First Quartile | 5378 | 13928 |
| Third Quartile | 8143 | 20134 |
| Interquartile Range | 2765 | 6206 |
| Coefficient of Variation | 32.33% | 24.90% |

**(c)** Both in-state and out-of-state tuition and fees are right-skewed.
**(d)** $r = \dfrac{\text{cov}(X,Y)}{S_X S_Y} = 0.4911$.

**(e)** Both in-state and out-of-state tuition and fees are right-skewed due to the outliers in the right tails. There is a moderate positive linear relationship between in-state and out-of-state tuition and fees. Those schools with high in-state tuition and fees tend to also have high out-of-state tuition and fees.

**3.68 (a)** Boston: 0.04, 0.17, 0.23, 0.32, 0.98; Vermont: 0.02, 0.13, 0.20, 0.28, 0.83. **(b)** Both distributions are right-skewed. **(c)** Both sets of shingles did quite well in achieving a granule loss of 0.8 gram or less. The Boston shingles had only two data points greater than 0.8 gram. The next highest to these was 0.6 gram. These two data points can be considered outliers. Only 1.176% of the shingles failed the specification. In the Vermont shingles, only one data point was greater than 0.8 gram. The next highest was 0.58 gram. Thus, only 0.714% of the shingles failed to meet the specification.

**3.70 (a)** 0.80. **(b)** 0.53. **(c)** 0.92. **(d)** Total fat seems to be most closely related to calories because it has the highest correlation coefficient with calories.

**3.72 (a)** Mean = 7.5273, median = 7.263, first quartile = 6.353, third quartile = 8.248. **(b)** Range = 7.416, interquartile range = 1.895, variance = 2.6609, standard deviation = 1.6312, $CV$ = 21.67%. **(c)** The data are skewed to the right. **(d)** The per-capita spending by the 50 states is right-skewed because a few states spend a lot more than the rest.

# CHAPTER 4

**4.2 (a)** Simple events include selecting a red ball. **(b)** Selecting a white ball.

**4.4 (a)** 60/100 = 3/5 = 0.6. **(b)** 10/100 = 1/10 = 0.1. **(c)** 35/100 = 7/20 = 0.35. **(d)** 9/10 = 0.9.

**4.6 (a)** Mutually exclusive, not collectively exhaustive. **(b)** Not mutually exclusive, not collectively exhaustive. **(c)** Mutually exclusive, not collectively exhaustive. **(d)** Mutually exclusive, collectively exhaustive.

**4.8 (a)** "Makes less than $50,000." **(b)** "Makes less than $50,000 and tax code is unfair." **(c)** The complement of "tax code is fair" is "tax code is

unfair." **(d)** "Tax code is fair and makes less than $50,000" is a joint event because it consists of two characteristics or attributes.

**4.10 (a)** "A wafer is good." **(b)** "A wafer is good and no particle was found on the die." **(c)** "Bad wafer." **(d)** A wafer that is a "good wafer" and was produced by a die "with particles" is a joint event because it consists of two characteristics.

**4.12 (a)** P(Selected the highest-cost fund) = (27+18)/200 = 0.225. **(b)** P(Selected the highest-cost fund and is an undergraduate) = 27/200 = 0.135. **(c)** P(Selected the highest-cost fund or is an undergraduate) = (45+100−27)/200 = 0.59. **(d)** The probability of "selected the highest-cost fund or is an undergraduate" includes the probability of "selected the highest-cost fund," plus the probability of "undergraduate minus the joint probability of highest-cost fund and undergraduate."

**4.14 (a)** 360/500 = 18/25 = 0.72. **(b)** 224/500 = 56/125 = 0.448. **(c)** 396/500 = 99/125 = 0.792. **(d)** 500/500 = 1.00.

**4.16 (a)** 10/30 = 1/3 = 0.33. **(b)** 20/60 = 1/3 = 0.33. **(c)** 40/60 = 2/3 = 0.67. **(d)** Because $P(A \mid B) = P(A) = 1/3$, events $A$ and $B$ are independent.

**4.18** $\frac{1}{2} = 0.5$.

**4.20** Because $P(A \text{ and } B) = 0.20$ and $P(A) \, P(B) = 0.12$, events $A$ and $B$ are not independent.

**4.22 (a)** 36/116 = 0.3103. **(b)** 14/334 = 0.0419. **(c)** 320/334 = 0.9581 $P$(No particles) = 400/450 = 0.8889. Because $P$(No particles | Good) ≠ $P$(No particles), "a good wafer" and "a die with no particle" are not independent.

**4.24 (a)** P(Selected the highest-cost fund | Is an undergraduate) = 27/100 = 0.27. **(b)** P(Is an undergraduate | Selected the highest-cost fund) = 27/(27+18) = 0.6. **(c)** The conditional events are reversed. **(d)** Because P(Selected the highest-cost fund | Is an undergraduate) = 0.27 is not equal to P(Selected the highest-cost fund) = 0.225, the two events "student group" and "fund selected" are not independent.

**4.26 (a)** 0.025/0.6 = 0.0417. **(b)** 0.015/0.4 = 0.0375. **(c)** Because P(Needs warranty repair | Manufacturer based in U.S.) = 0.0417 and P(Needs warranty repair) = 0.04, the two events are not independent.

**4.28 (a)** 0.0045. **(b)** 0.012. **(c)** 0.0059. **(d)** 0.0483.

**4.30** 0.095.

**4.32 (a)** 0.736. **(b)** 0.997.

**4.34 (a)** $P(B' \mid O) = \dfrac{(0.5)(0.3)}{(0.5)(0.3) + (0.25)(0.7)} = 0.4615$.
**(b)** $P(O) = 0.175 + 0.15 = 0.325$.

**4.36 (a)** P(Huge success | Favorable review) = 0.099/0.459 = 0.2157; P(Moderate success | Favorable review) = 0.14/0.459 = 0.3050; P(Break even | Favorable review) = 0.16/0.459 = 0.3486; P(Loser | Favorable review) = 0.06/0.459 = 0.1307. **(b)** P(Favorable review) = 0.459.

**4.38** $3^{10} = 59,049$.

**4.40 (a)** $2^7 = 128$. **(b)** $6^7 = 279,936$. **(c)** There are two mutually exclusive and collectively exhaustive outcomes in (a) and six in (b).

**4.42** (8)(4)(3)(3) = 288.

**4.44** 5! = (5)(4)(3)(2)(1) = 120. Not all these orders are equally likely because the teams have a different probability of finishing first through fifth.

**4.46** $n! = 6! = 720$.

**4.48** $\dfrac{8!}{2!6!} = 28.$

**4.50** 4,950.

**4.62 (a)** $P$(all three are Republican) $= (0.3)^3 = 0.027.$ **(b)** $P$(all three are Democrats) $= 0.34^3 = 0.0393.$ **(c)** $P$(all three are Independents) $= 0.36^3 = 0.0467.$ **(d)** $P$(one Republican, one Democrat, and one Independent) $= (0.3)(0.34)(0.36) = 0.0367.$ **(e)** The approach you used in (a) through (d) is an example of empirical probability because the probability of each type of voters was obtained using the relative frequency of that type of voters.

**4.64 (a)**

|  |  | Age | | |
|---|---|---|---|---|
|  |  | 18–25 | 26–40 | Total |
| Goals | Getting Rich | 405 | 310 | 715 |
|  | Other | 95 | 190 | 285 |
|  | Total | 500 | 500 | 1000 |

**(b)** Simple event: "Has a goal of getting rich." Joint event: "Has a goal of getting rich and is between 18–25 years old." **(c)** $P$(Has a goal of getting rich) $= 715/1000 = 0.715.$ **(d)** $P$(Has a goal of getting rich and is in the 26–40-year-old group) $= 310/1000 = 0.31.$

**4.66 (a)** 0.0225. **(b)** $3,937.5 \cong 3,938$ can be expected to read the advertisement and place an order. **(c)** 0.03. **(d)** 5,250 can be expected to read the advertisement and place an order.

**4.68 (a)** 0.4712. **(b)** Because the probability that a fatality involved a rollover, given that the fatality involved an SUV, a van, or a pickup is 0.4712, which is almost twice the probability that a fatality involved a rollover with any vehicle type, at 0.24, SUVs, vans, and pickups are generally more prone to rollover accidents.

# CHAPTER 5

**5.2 (a)** C: $\mu = 2$, D: $\mu = 2$. **(b)** C: $\sigma = 1.414$, D: $\sigma = 1.095$. **(c)** Distribution C is uniform and symmetric; Distribution D is symmetric and has a single mode.

**5.4 (a)** $\mu = 0(0.10) + 1(0.20) + 2(0.45) + 3(0.15) + 4(0.05) + 5(0.05) - 2.0.$

**(b)** $\sigma = \sqrt{\begin{array}{l}(0-2)^2(0.10)+(1-2)^2(0.20)+(2-2)^2(0.45)+(3-2)^2(0.15)\\ +(4-2)^2(0.05)+(5-2)^2(0.05)\end{array}}$

$= 1.183.$

**5.6 (a)**

| X | P(X) |
|---|---|
| $\$-1$ | 21/36 |
| $\$+1$ | 15/36 |

**(b)**

| X | P(X) |
|---|---|
| $\$-1$ | 21/36 |
| $\$+1$ | 15/36 |

**(c)**

| X | P(X) |
|---|---|
| $\$-1$ | 30/36 |
| $\$+4$ | 6/36 |

**(d)** $\$-0.167$ for each method of play.

**5.8 (a)** 2.105769. **(b)** 1.467063.

**5.10 (a)** 90; 30. **(b)** 126.10, 10.95. **(c)** $-1,300$. **(d)** 120.

**5.12 (a)** 9.5 minutes. **(b)** 1.9209 minutes.

**5.14**

| $X*P(X)$ | $Y*P(Y)$ | $(X-\mu_X)^2*P(X)$ | $(Y-\mu_Y)^2*P(Y)$ | $(X-\mu_X)(Y-\mu_Y)*P(XY)$ |
|---|---|---|---|---|
| $-10$ | 5 | 2,528.1 | 129.6 | $-572.4$ |
| 0 | 45 | 1,044.3 | 5,548.8 | $-2,407.2$ |
| 24 | $-6$ | 132.3 | 346.8 | $-214.2$ |
| 45 | $-30$ | 2,484.3 | 3,898.8 | $-3,112.2$ |

**(a)** $E(X) = \mu_X = \displaystyle\sum_{i=1}^{N} X_i P(X_i) = 59$, $E(Y) = \mu_Y = \displaystyle\sum_{i=1}^{N} Y_i P(Y_i) = 14$

$\sigma_X = \sqrt{\displaystyle\sum_{i=1}^{N}[X_i - E(X)]^2 P(X_i)} = 78.6702$

**(b)** $\sigma_Y = \sqrt{\displaystyle\sum_{i=1}^{N}[Y_i - E(Y)]^2 P(Y_i)} = 99.62$

**(c)** $\sigma_{XY} = \displaystyle\sum_{i=1}^{N}[X_i - E(X)][Y_i - E(Y)]P(X_iY_i) = -6,306$

**(d)** Stock $X$ gives the investor a lower standard deviation while yielding a higher expected return, so the investor should select stock $X$.

**5.16 (a)** $\$71$; $\$97$. **(b)** 61.88; 84.27. **(c)** 5,113. **(d)** Risk-averse investors would invest in stock $X$, whereas risk takers would invest in stock $Y$.

**5.18 (a)** $E(X) = \$77$; $E(Y) = \$97$. **(b)** $\sigma_X = 39.76$; $\sigma_Y = 108.95$. **(c)** $\sigma_{XY} = 4161$. **(d)** The common stock fund gives the investor a higher expected return than the corporate bond fund, but also has a standard deviation more than 2.5 times higher than that for the corporate bond fund. An investor should carefully weigh the increased risk.

**5.20 (a)** 0.5997. **(b)** 0.0016. **(c)** 0.0439. **(d)** 0.4018.

**5.22**

|  | Mean | Standard Deviation |
|---|---|---|
| **(a)** | 0.40 | 0.600 |
| **(b)** | 1.60 | 0.980 |
| **(c)** | 4.00 | 0.894 |
| **(d)** | 1.50 | 0.866 |

**5.24 (a)** $P(X = 0) = 0.7351.$ **(b)** If the probabilities of the six events are not all equal, then you would calculate the probability in (a) by multiplying together the probability of no failure in each of the six events.

**5.26** Given $\pi = 0.878$ and $n = 3$,

**(a)** $P(X = 3) = \dfrac{n!}{X!(n-x)!}\pi^X(1-\pi)^{n-X} = \dfrac{3!}{3!0!}(0.878)^3(0.122)^0 = 0.6768.$

**(b)** $P(X = 0) = \dfrac{n!}{X!(n-x)!}\pi^X(1-\pi)^{n-X} = \dfrac{3!}{0!3!}(0.878)^0(0.122)^3 = 0.0018.$

**(c)** $P(X \geq 2) = P(X = 2) + P(X = 3)$

$= \dfrac{3!}{2!1!}(0.878)^2(0.122)^1 + \dfrac{3!}{3!0!}(0.878)^3(0.122)^0 = 0.9590.$

**(d)** $E(X) = n\pi = 3(0.878) = 2.634$  $\sigma_X = \sqrt{n\pi(1-\pi)}$

$= \sqrt{3(0.878)(0.122)} = 0.5669.$

**5.28 (a)** 0.1804. **(b)** 0.00205. **(c)** 0.4511. **(d)** 0.4437, 0.00000, 0.1648. The probability of loans to second home owners or investors is lower, so the chance of no loans to these individuals is higher.

**5.30 (a)** $P(X \le 5) = .00009919$. **(b)** $P(X \le 10) = 0.0719$. **(c)** $P(X \le 15) = 0.8173$.

**5.32 (a)** 0.2565. **(b)** 0.1396. **(c)** 0.3033. **(d)** 0.0247.

**5.34 (a)** 0.0337. **(b)** 0.0067. **(c)** 0.9596. **(d)** 0.0404.

**5.36 (a)** $P(X < 5) = P(X = 0) + P(X = 1) + P(X = 2) + P(X = 3)$
$$+ P(X = 4)$$
$$= \frac{e^{-6}(6)^0}{0!} + \frac{e^{-6}(6)^1}{1!} + \frac{e^{-6}(6)^2}{2!} + \frac{e^{-6}(6)^3}{3!} + \frac{e^{-6}(6)^4}{4!}$$
$$= 0.002479 + 0.014873 + 0.044618 + 0.089235$$
$$+ 0.133853$$
$$= 0.2851.$$

**(b)** $P(X = 5) = \dfrac{e^{-6}(6)^5}{5!} = 0.1606$.

**(c)** $P(X \ge 5) = 1 - P(X < 5) = 1 - 0.2851 = 0.7149$.

**(d)** $P(X = 4 \text{ or } X = 5) = P(X = 4) + P(X = 5) = \dfrac{e^{-6}(6)^4}{4!} + \dfrac{e^{-6}(6)^5}{5!}$
$$= 0.2945.$$

**5.38** $\lambda = 4.06$. **(a)** $P(X = 0) = 0.0172$. **(b)** $P(X \ge 1) = 0.9828$. **(c)** $P(X \ge 2) = 0.9127$.

**5.40 (a)** 0.0176. **(b)** 0.9093. **(c)** 0.9220.

**5.42 (a)** 0.2671. **(b)** 0.8525. **(c)** Because Ford had a lower mean rate of problems per car in 2007 compared to Dodge, the probability of a randomly selected Ford having zero problems and the probability of no more than 2 problems are both higher than their values for Dodge.

**5.44 (a)** 0.2101. **(b)** 0.7936. **(c)** Because Dodge had a lower mean rate of problems per car in 2007 compared to 2006, the probability of a randomly selected Dodge having zero problems and the probability of no more than 2 problems are both higher in 2007 than their values in 2006.

**5.46 (a)** 0.238. **(b)** 0.2. **(c)** 0.1591. **(d)** 0.0083.

**5.48 (a)** If $n = 6$, $A = 25$, and $N = 100$,
$$P(X \ge 2) = 1 - [P(X = 0) + P(X = 1)]$$
$$= 1 - \left[ \frac{\binom{25}{0}\binom{100-25}{6-0}}{\binom{100}{6}} + \frac{\binom{25}{1}\binom{100-25}{6-1}}{\binom{100}{6}} \right]$$
$$= 1 - [0.1689 + 0.3620] = 0.4691.$$

**(b)** If $n = 6$, $A = 30$, and $N = 100$,
$$P(X \ge 2) = 1 - [P(X = 0) + P(X = 1)]$$
$$= 1 - \left[ \frac{\binom{30}{0}\binom{100-30}{6-0}}{\binom{100}{6}} + \frac{\binom{30}{1}\binom{100-30}{6-1}}{\binom{100}{6}} \right]$$
$$= 1 - [0.1100 + 0.3046] = 0.5854.$$

**(c)** If $n = 6$, $A = 5$, and $N = 100$,
$$P(X \ge 2) = 1 - [P(X = 0) + P(X = 1)]$$
$$= 1 - \left[ \frac{\binom{5}{0}\binom{100-5}{6-0}}{\binom{100}{6}} + \frac{\binom{5}{1}\binom{100-5}{6-1}}{\binom{100}{6}} \right]$$
$$= 1 - [0.7291 + 0.2430] = 0.0279.$$

**(d)** If $n = 6$, $A = 10$, and $N = 100$,
$$P(X \ge 2) = 1 - [P(X = 0) + P(X = 1)]$$
$$= 1 - \left[ \frac{\binom{10}{0}\binom{100-10}{6-0}}{\binom{100}{6}} + \frac{\binom{10}{1}\binom{100-10}{6-1}}{\binom{100}{6}} \right]$$
$$= 1 - [0.5223 + 0.3687] = 0.1090.$$

**(e)** The probability that the entire group will be audited is very sensitive to the true number of improper returns in the population. If the true number is very low ($A = 5$), the probability is very low (0.0279). When the true number is increased by a factor of 6 ($A = 30$), the probability the group will be audited increases by a factor of almost 21 (0.5854).

**5.50 (a)** $P(X = 4) = 0.00003649$. **(b)** $P(X = 0) = 0.5455$. **(c)** $P(X \ge 1) = 0.4545$. **(d)** $X = 6$. **(a)** $P(X = 4) = 0.0005$. **(b)** $P(X = 0) = 0.3877$. **(c)** $P(X \ge 1) = 0.6123$.

**5.52 (a)** $P(X = 1) = 0.4835$. **(b)** $P(X \ge 1) = 0.6374$. **(c)** $P(X \le 2) = 0.9912$. **(d)** $\mu = n \times (A/N) = 0.8$.

**5.58 (a)** 0.74. **(b)** 0.74. **(c)** 0.3898. **(d)** 0.0012. **(e)** The assumption of independence may not be true.

**5.60 (a)** If $\pi = 0.50$ and $n = 11$, $P(X \ge 9) = 0.0327$. **(b)** If $\pi = 0.74$ and $n = 11$, $P(X \ge 9) = 0.4247$.

**5.62 (a)** 0.018228. **(b)** 0.089782. **(c)** 0.89199. **(d)** Mean = 3.3, standard deviation = 1.486943.

**5.64 (a)** 0.0000. **(b)** 0.04924. **(c)** 0.909646. **(d)** 0.49578.

**5.66 (a)** 0.0012. **(b)** 0.2456. **(c)** 0.6474. **(d)** 0.3526. **(e)** $E(X) = n\pi = 5.1$. Google can expect that slightly more than half of the people use its search engine.

**5.68 (a)** $\mu = n\pi = 2.6$. **(b)** $\sigma = \sqrt{n\pi(1 - \pi)} = 1.5040$. **(c)** $P(X = 0) = 0.0617$. **(d)** $P(X \le 2) = 0.5080$. **(e)** $P(X \ge 3) = 0.4920$.

**5.70 (a)** If $\pi = 0.50$ and $n = 37$, $P(X \ge 31) = 0.0000$. **(b)** If $\pi = 0.70$ and $n = 37$, $P(X \ge 31) = 0.0216$. **(c)** If $\pi = 0.90$ and $n = 36$, $P(X \ge 37) = 0.8564$. **(d)** Based on the results in (a)–(c), the probability that the Standard & Poor's 500 index will increase if there is an early gain in the first five trading days of the year is very likely to be close to 0.90 because that yields a probability of 85.64% that at least 31 of the 37 years the Standard & Poor's 500 index will increase the entire year.

**5.72 (a)** The assumptions needed are (i) the probability that a golfer loses a golf ball in a given interval is constant, (ii) the probability that a golfer loses more than one golf ball approaches 0 as the interval gets smaller, and (iii) the probability that a golfer loses a golf ball is independent from interval to interval. **(b)** 0.0111. **(c)** 0.70293. **(d)** 0.29707.

**5.74 (a)** Virtually zero. **(b)** 0.00000037737. **(c)** 0.00000173886.
**(d)** 0.000168669. **(e)** 0.0011998. **(f)** 0.00407937. **(g)** 0.006598978.
**(h)** 0.0113502. **(i)** 0.976601.

# CHAPTER 6

**6.2 (a)** 0.9089. **(b)** 0.0911. **(c)** +1.96. **(d)** −1.00 and +1.00.

**6.4 (a)** 0.1401. **(b)** 0.4168. **(c)** 0.3918. **(d)** +1.00.

**6.6 (a)** 0.9599. **(b)** 0.0228. **(c)** 43.42. **(d)** 46.64 and 53.36.

**6.8 (a)** $P(34 < X < 50) = P(-1.33 < Z < 0) = 0.4082$. **(b)** $P(X < 30) +$
$P(X > 60) = P(Z < -1.67) + P(Z > 0.83) = 0.0475 + (1.0 - 0.7967) = 0.2508$.
**(c)** $P(Z < -0.84) \cong 0.20$, $Z = -0.84 = \dfrac{X - 50}{12}$. $X = 50 - 0.84(12) = 39.92$

thousand miles, or 39,920 miles. **(d)** The smaller standard deviation
makes the $Z$ values larger.

**(a)** $P(34 < X < 50) = P(-1.60 < Z < 0) = 0.4452$.
**(b)** $P(X < 30) + P(X > 60) = P(Z < -2.00) + P(Z > 1.00) = 0.0228 +$
$(1.0 - 0.8413) = 0.1815$.
**(c)** $X = 50 - 0.84(10) = 41.6$ thousand miles, or 41,600 miles.

**6.10 (a)** 0.9878. **(b)** 0.8185. **(c)** 86.16%. **(d)** Option 1: Because your score
of 81% on this exam represents a $Z$ score of 1.00, which is below the
minimum $Z$ score of 1.28, you will not earn an A grade on the exam
under this grading option. Option 2: Because your score of 68% on this
exam represents a $Z$ score of 2.00, which is well above the minimum $Z$
score of 1.28, you will earn an A grade on the exam under this grading
option. You should prefer Option 2.

**6.12 (a)** 0.0228. **(b)** 0.2525. **(c)** 0.0912. **(d)** 0.0004.

**6.14** With 39 values, the smallest of the standard normal quantile values
covers an area under the normal curve of 0.025. The corresponding $Z$
value is −1.96. The middle (20th) value has a cumulative area of 0.50 and
a corresponding $Z$ value of 0.0. The largest of the standard normal
quantile values covers an area under the normal curve of 0.975, and its
corresponding $Z$ value is +1.96.

**6.16 (a)** Mean = 23.2, median = 23.5, range = 52, standard deviation =
12.3868, $6(S_X) = 6(12.3868) = 74.3205$, interquartile range = 14, $1.33(S_X)$
= $1.33(12.3868) = 16.4744$. The mean is almost equal to the median; the
range is smaller than 6 times the standard deviation, and the interquartile
range is slightly smaller than 1.33 times the standard deviation. The data
appear to be approximately normally distributed but slightly skewed to
the right. **(b)** The normal probability plot suggests that the data are
skewed to the right.

**6.18 (a)** Mean = 1040.863, median = 981, range = 1732, $6(S_X) =$
2571.2310, interquartile range = 593, $1.33(S_X) = 569.9562$. There are
62.75%, 78.43%, and 94.12% of the observations that fall within 1, 1.28,
and 2 standard deviations of the mean, respectively, as compared to the
approximate theoretical 66.67%, 80%, and 95%. Because the mean is
slightly larger than the median, the interquartile range is slightly larger
than 1.33 times the standard deviation, and the range is much smaller than
6 times the standard deviation, the data appear to deviate slightly from the
normal distribution. **(b)** The normal probability plot suggests that the data
appear to be slightly right-skewed.

**6.20 (a)** Interquartile range = 0.0025, $S_X = 0.0017$, range = 0.008,
$1.33(S_X) = 0.0023$, $6(S_X) = 0.0102$. Because the interquartile range is
close to $1.33(S_X)$ and the range is also close to $6(S_X)$, the data appear to be
approximately normally distributed. **(b)** The normal probability plot
suggests that the data appear to be approximately normally distributed.

**6.22 (a)** Five-number summary: 82 127 148.5 168 213; mean = 147.06,
mode = 130, range = 131, interquartile range = 41, standard deviation =
31.69. The mean is very close to the median. The five-number summary
suggests that the distribution is approximately symmetrical around the
median. The interquartile range is very close to 1.33 times the standard
deviation. The range is about $50 below 6 times the standard deviation. In
general, the distribution of the data appears to closely resemble a normal
distribution. **(b)** The normal probability plot confirms that the data appear
to be approximately normally distributed.

**6.24 (a)** $(20 - 0)/120 = 0.1667$. **(b)** $(30 - 10)/120 = 0.1667$. **(c)**
$(120 - 35)/120 = 0.7083$. **(d)** Mean = 60, standard deviation = 34.641.

**6.26 (a)** 0.1. **(b)** 0.3333. **(c)** 0.3333. **(d)** Mean = 4.5, standard deviation =
0.8660.

**6.28 (a)** 0.6321. **(b)** 0.3679. **(c)** 0.2326. **(d)** 0.7674.

**6.30 (a)** 0.7769. **(b)** 0.2231. **(c)** 0.1410. **(d)** 0.8590.

**6.32 (a)** For $\lambda = 2$, $P(X \le 1) = 0.864665$. **(b)** For $\lambda = 2$, $P(X \le 5) =$
0.99996. **(c)** For $\lambda = 1$, $P(X \le 1) = 0.6321$, for $\lambda = 1$, $P(X \le 1) = 0.9933$.

**6.34 (a)** 0.6321. **(b)** 0.3935. **(c)** 0.0952.

**6.36 (a)** 0.8647. **(b)** 0.3297. **(c)(a)** 0.9765. **(b)** 0.5276.

**6.38 (a)** 0.0457. **(b)** 0.0846. **(c)** 0.9154. **(d)** 0.8697.

**6.40 (a)** 0.2051. **(b)** 0.8281. **(c)** 0.7734. **(d)(a)** 0.2045. **(b)** 0.8286.
**(c)** 0.7717.

**6.42** If the grant is equally likely to be given on any day of the month, the
probability of seeing the results or more extreme results is virtually 0.

**6.52 (a)** 0.4772. **(b)** 0.9544. **(c)** 0.0456. **(d)** 1.8835. **(e)** 1.8710 and
2.1290.

**6.54 (a)** 0.2734. **(b)** 0.2038. **(c)** 4.404 ounces. **(d)** 4.188 ounces and 5.212
ounces.

**6.56 (a)** Waiting time will more closely resemble an exponential
distribution. **(b)** Seating time will more closely resemble a normal
distribution. **(c)** Both the histogram and normal probability plot suggest
that waiting time more closely resembles an exponential distribution.
**(d)** Both the histogram and normal probability plot suggest that seating
time more closely resembles a normal distribution.

**6.58 (a)** 0.8413. **(b)** 0.9330. **(c)** 0.9332. **(d)** 0.3347. **(e)** 0.4080 and
1.1920.

**6.60 (a)** Mean = 3,019.7255, median = 2,972, range = 1174, $6(S_X) =$
1,393.4693, interquartile range = 284, $1.33(S_X) = 308.8857$. There are
70.59%, 86.27%, and 96.08% of the observations that fall within 1, 1.28,
and 2 standard deviations of the mean, respectively, as compared to the
approximate theoretical 66.67%, 80%, and 95%. Because the mean is
slightly larger than the median, the interquartile range is slightly smaller
than 1.33 times the standard deviation, and the range is much smaller than
6 times the standard deviation, the data appear to deviate slightly from the
normal distribution. The normal probability plot suggests that the data
appear to be slightly right-skewed. **(b)** The variable RANK 2006 has a
uniform distribution between 1 and 52.

# CHAPTER 7

**7.2** Sample without replacement: Read from left to right in three-digit
sequences and continue unfinished sequences from the end of the row to
the beginning of the next row:

**Row 05:** 338 505 855 551 438 855 077 186 579 488 767 833 170
**Rows 05–06:** 897
**Row 06:** 340 033 648 847 204 334 639 193 639 411 095 924
**Rows 06–07:** 707
**Row 07:** 054 329 776 100 871 007 255 980 646 886 823 920 461
**Row 08:** 893 829 380 900 796 959 453 410 181 277 660 908 887
**Rows 08–09:** 237
**Row 09:** 818 721 426 714 050 785 223 801 670 353 362 449
**Rows 09–10:** 406

*Note:* All sequences above 902 and duplicates are discarded.

**7.4** A simple random sample would be less practical for personal interviews because of travel costs (unless interviewees are paid to go to a central interviewing location).

**7.6** Here all members of the population are equally likely to be selected, and the sample selection mechanism is based on chance. But selection of two elements is not independent; for example, if $A$ is in the sample, we know that $B$ is also and that $C$ and $D$ are not.

**7.8 (a)**

**Row 16:** 2323 6737 5131 8888 1718 0654 6832 4647 6510 4877
**Row 17:** 4579 4269 2615 1308 2455 7830 5550 5852 5514 7182
**Row 18:** 0989 3205 0514 2256 8514 4642 7567 8896 2977 8822
**Row 19:** 5438 2745 9891 4991 4523 6847 9276 8646 1628 3554
**Row 20:** 9475 0899 2337 0892 0048 8033 6945 9826 9403 6858
**Row 21:** 7029 7341 3553 1403 3340 4205 0823 4144 1048 2949
**Row 22:** 8515 7479 5432 9792 6575 5760 0408 8112 2507 3742
**Row 23:** 1110 0023 4012 8607 4697 9664 4894 3928 7072 5815
**Row 24:** 3687 1507 7530 5925 7143 1738 1688 5625 8533 5041
**Row 25:** 2391 3483 5763 3081 6090 5169 0546

*Note:* All sequences above 5,000 are discarded. There were no repeating sequences.

**(b)**  089  189  289  389  489  589  689  789  889  989
1089 1189 1289 1389 1489 1589 1689 1789 1889 1989
2089 2189 2289 2389 2489 2589 2689 2789 2889 2989
3089 3189 3289 3389 3489 3589 3689 3789 3889 3989
4089 4189 4289 4389 4489 4589 4689 4789 4889 4989

**(c)** With the single exception of invoice #0989, the invoices selected in the simple random sample are not the same as those selected in the systematic sample. It would be highly unlikely that a simple random sample would select the same units as a systematic sample.

**7.10** Before accepting the results of a survey of college students, you might want to know, for example:

Who funded the survey? Why was it conducted? What was the population from which the sample was selected? What sampling design was used? What mode of response was used: a personal interview, a telephone interview, or a mail survey? Were interviewers trained? Were survey questions field-tested? What questions were asked? Were they clear, accurate, unbiased, and valid? What operational definition of "vast majority" was used? What was the response rate? What was the sample size?

**7.12 (a)** The four types of survey errors are: coverage error, nonresponse error, sampling error, and measurement error. **(b)** When people who answer the survey tell you what they think you want to hear, rather than what they really believe, it introduces the halo effect, which is a source of measurement error. Also, every survey will have sampling error that reflects the chance differences from sample to sample, based on the probability of particular individuals being selected in the particular sample.

**7.14** Before accepting the results of the survey, you might want to know, for example:

Who funded the study? Why was it conducted? What was the population from which the sample was selected? What sampling design was used? What mode of response was used: a personal interview, a telephone interview, or a mail survey? Were interviewers trained? Were survey questions field-tested? What other questions were asked? Were they clear, accurate, unbiased, and valid? What was the response rate? What was the margin of error? What was the sample size? What was the frame being used?

**7.16** Before accepting the results of the survey, you might want to know, for example:

Who funded the study? Why was it conducted? What was the population from which the sample was selected? What was the frame being used? What sampling design was used? What mode of response was used: a personal interview, a telephone interview, or a mail survey? Were interviewers trained? Were survey questions field-tested? What other questions were asked? Were they clear, accurate, unbiased, and valid? What was the response rate? What was the margin of error? What was the sample size?

**7.18 (a)** Virtually zero. **(b)** 0.1587. **(c)** 0.0139. **(d)** 50.195.

**7.20 (a)** Both means are equal to 6. This property is called unbiasedness. **(c)** The distribution for $n = 3$ has less variability. The larger sample size has resulted in sample means being closer to $\mu$.

**7.22 (a)** When $n = 2$, the shape of the sampling distribution of $\bar{X}$ should closely resemble the shape of the distribution of the population from which the sample is selected. Because the mean is larger than the median, the distribution of the sales price of new houses is skewed to the right, and so is the sampling distribution of $\bar{X}$. **(b)** If you select samples of $n = 100$, the shape of the sampling distribution of the sample mean will be very close to a normal distribution with a mean of \$299,100 and a standard deviation of \$9,000. **(c)** 0.5398. **(d)** 0.1523.

**7.24 (a)** $P(\bar{X} > 3) = P(Z > -1.00) = 1.0 - 0.1587 = 0.8413$.
**(b)** $P(Z < 1.04) = 0.85$; $\bar{X} = 3.10 + 1.04(0.1) = 3.204$.

**(c)** To be able to use the standardized normal distribution as an approximation for the area under the curve, you must assume that the population is approximately symmetrical. **(d)** $P(Z < 1.04) = 0.85$; $\bar{X} = 3.10 + 1.04(0.05) = 3.152$ .

**7.26 (a)** 0.9969. **(b)** 0.0142. **(c)** 2.3830 and 2.6170. **(d)** 2.6170.
*Note:* These answers are computed using Microsoft Excel. They may be slightly different when Table E.2 is used.

**7.28 (a)** 0.30. **(b)** 0.0693.

**7.30 (a)** $\pi = 0.501$, $\sigma_P = \sqrt{\dfrac{\pi(1-\pi)}{n}} = \sqrt{\dfrac{0.501(1-0.501)}{100}} = 0.05$
$P(p > 0.55) = P(Z > 0.98) = 1.0 - 0.8365 = 0.1635$.

**(b)** $\pi = 0.60$, $\sigma_P = \sqrt{\dfrac{\pi(1-\pi)}{n}} = \sqrt{\dfrac{0.6(1-0.6)}{100}} = 0.04899$
$P(p > 0.55) = P(Z > -1.021) = 1.0 - 0.1539 = 0.8461$.

**(c)** $\pi = 0.49$, $\sigma_P = \sqrt{\dfrac{\pi(1-\pi)}{n}} = \sqrt{\dfrac{0.49(1-0.49)}{100}} = 0.05$
$P(p > 0.55) = P(Z > 1.20) = 1.0 - 0.8849 = 0.1151$.

**(d)** Increasing the sample size by a factor of 4 decreases the standard error by a factor of 2.
**(a)** $P(p > 0.55) = P(Z > 1.96) = 1.0 - 0.9750 = 0.0250$.
**(b)** $P(p > 0.55) = P(Z > -2.04) = 1.0 - 0.0207 = 0.9793$.
**(c)** $P(p > 0.55) = P(Z > 2.40) = 1.0 - 0.9918 = 0.0082$.

**7.32 (a)** 0.9298. **(b)** 0.8596. **(c)** 0.9865. **(d)(a)** 0.7695. **(b)** 0.5390. **(c)** 0.8656.

**7.34 (a)** Because $n = 200$, which is quite large, you use the sample proportion to approximate the population proportion and, hence, $\pi = 0.50$.

$$\mu_P = \pi = 0.5, \sigma_P = \sqrt{\frac{\pi(1-\pi)}{n}} = \sqrt{\frac{0.5(0.5)}{200}} = 0.0354$$

$P(0.45 < \pi < 0.55) = P(-1.4142 < Z < 1.4142) = 0.8427.$
**(b)** $P(A < \pi < B) = P(-1.6449 < Z < 1.6449) = 0.90.$ $A = 0.50 - 1.6449(0.0354) = 0.4418.$ $B = 0.50 + 1.6449(0.0354) = 0.5582.$ The probability is 90% that the sample percentage will be contained within 5.8% symmetrically around the population percentage.
**(c)** $P(A < \pi < B) = P(-1.96 < Z < +1.96) = 0.95.$ $A = 0.50 - 1.96(0.0354) = 0.4306.$ $B = 0.50 + 1.96(0.0354) = 0.5694.$ The probability is 95% that the sample percentage will be contained within 6.94% symmetrically around the population percentage.

**7.36 (a)** 0.1134. **(b)** 0.0034. **(c)** Increasing the sample size by a factor of 5 decreases the standard error by a factor of $\sqrt{5}$. The sampling distribution of the proportion becomes more concentrated around the true proportion of 0.56 and, hence, the probability in (b) becomes smaller than that in (a).

**7.38 (a)** 0.3626. **(b)** 0.9816. **(c)** 0.0092.

*Note:* These answers are computed using Microsoft Excel. They may be slightly different when Table E.2 is used.

**7.50 (a)** 0.4999. **(b)** 0.00009. **(c)** 0. **(d)** 0. **(e)** 0.7518.

**7.52 (a)** 0.8944. **(b)** 4.617; 4.783. **(c)** 4.641.

**7.54 (a)** 0.0002. **(b)** 0.3461. **(c)** 0.9759.

**7.56** Even though Internet polling is less expensive and faster and offers higher response rates than telephone surveys, it is a self-selection response method. Because respondents who choose to participate in the survey may not represent the view of the public, the data collected may not be appropriate for making inferences about the general population.

**7.58 (a)** Before accepting the results of this survey, you would like to know (i) how big is the sample size, (ii) what is the purpose of the survey, (iii) what sampling method is being used, (iv) what is the frame being used, (v) what is the response rate, and (vi) how the questions are being phrased. **(b)** The population will be all the AOL users. The frame can be compiled from the list of the AOL subscribers. Because there are two natural strata in the population, adults and teens, a stratified sampling method should be used to better represent the population.

**7.60 (a)** Before accepting the results of this survey, you would like to know (i) how big is the sample size, (ii) what is the purpose of the survey, (iii) what sampling method is being used, (iv) what is the frame being used, (v) what is the response rate, and (vi) how the questions are being phrased. **(b)** The population will be all the working males in the geographic region. The frame can be compiled from the list of men who file income tax returns in the region. Because not all extreme workers have a spouse or partner, you might be interested in knowing whether there is any connection between being an extreme worker and maintaining a relationship. So a stratified sample could be used to ensure that those who have a spouse or partner and those who do not are equally represented. These two strata can be identified through their income tax filing status.

# CHAPTER 8

**8.2** $114.68 \le \mu \le 135.32.$

**8.4 (a)** You would compute the mean first because you need the mean to compute the standard deviation. If you had a sample, you would compute

the sample mean. If you had the population mean, you would compute the population standard deviation. **(b)** If you have a sample, you are computing the sample standard deviation, not the population standard deviation needed in Equation (8.1). If you have a population and have computed the population mean and population standard deviation, you don't need a confidence interval estimate of the population mean because you already know the mean.

**8.6** Equation (8.1) assumes that you know the population standard deviation. Because you are selecting a sample of 100 from the population, you are computing a sample standard deviation, not the population standard deviation.

**8.8 (a)** 2.2622. **(b)** 3.2498. **(c)** 2.0395. **(d)** 1.9977. **(e)** 1.7531.

**8.10** $-0.12 \le \mu \le 11.84, 2.00 \le \mu \le 6.00.$ The presence of the outlier increases the sample mean and greatly inflates the sample standard deviation.

**8.12 (a)** $32 \pm (2.0096)(9)/\sqrt{50}$; $29.44 \le \mu \le 34.56.$ **(b)** The quality improvement team can be 95% confident that the population mean turnaround time is between 29.44 hours and 34.56 hours. **(c)** The project was a success because the initial turnaround time of 68 hours does not fall into the interval.

**8.14 (a)** $31.9267 \le \mu \le 41.1399.$ **(b)** You can be 95% confident that the population mean price for two tickets with online service charges, large popcorn, and two medium soft drinks is somewhere between \$31.93 and \$41.14.

**8.16 (a)** $18.0671 \le \mu \le 20.4329.$ **(b)** You can be 95% confident that the population mean miles per gallon of 2007 small SUVs is somewhere between 18.0671 and 20.4329. **(c)** Because the 95% confidence interval for population mean miles per gallon of 2007 small SUVs does not overlap with that for the population mean miles per gallon of 2007 family sedans, you are 95% confident that the population mean miles per gallon of 2007 small SUVs is lower than that of 2007 family sedans.

**8.18 (a)** $31.12 \le \mu \le 54.96.$ **(b)** The number of days is approximately normally distributed. **(c)** No, the outliers skew the data. **(d)** Because the sample size is fairly large, at $n = 50$, the use of the $t$ distribution is appropriate.

**8.20 (a)** $142.00 \le \mu \le 311.33.$ **(b)** The population distribution needs to be normally distributed. **(c)** Both the normal probability plot and the boxplot show that the distribution for battery life is approximately normally distributed.

**8.22** $0.19 \le \pi \le 0.31.$

**8.24 (a)** $p = \dfrac{X}{n} = \dfrac{135}{500} = 0.27$

$p \pm Z\sqrt{\dfrac{p(1-p)}{n}} = 0.27 \pm 2.58\sqrt{\dfrac{0.27(0.73)}{500}}$   $0.2189 \le \pi \le 0.3211.$

**(b)** The manager in charge of promotional programs concerning residential customers can infer that the proportion of households that would purchase an additional telephone line if it were made available at a substantially reduced installation cost is somewhere between 0.22 and 0.32, with 99% confidence.

**8.26 (a)** $0.2311 \le \pi \le 0.3089.$ **(b)** $0.2425 \le \pi \le 0.2975.$ **(c)** The larger the sample size, the narrower is the confidence interval, holding everything else constant.

**8.28 (a)** $0.5638 \le \pi \le 0.6362$. **(b)** $0.2272 \le \pi \le 0.2920$.

**8.30 (a)** $0.3783 \le \pi \le 0.4427$. **(b)** You can be 95% confident that the population proportion of all workers whose primary reason for staying on their job is interesting job responsibilities is somewhere between 0.3783 and 0.4427.

**8.32** $n = 35$.

**8.34** $n = 1,041$.

**8.36 (a)** $n = \dfrac{Z^2 \sigma^2}{e^2} = \dfrac{(1.96)^2 (400)^2}{50^2} = 245.86$

Use $n = 246$.

**(b)** $n = \dfrac{Z^2 \sigma^2}{e^2} = \dfrac{(1.96)^2 (400)^2}{25^2} = 983.41$

Use $n = 984$.

**8.38** $n = 97$.

**8.40 (a)** $n = 167$. **(b)** $n = 97$.

**8.42 (a)** $n = 246$. **(b)** $n = 385$. **(c)** $n = 554$. **(d)** When there is more variability in the population, a larger sample is needed to accurately estimate the mean.

**8.44 (a)** $n = 2,156$. **(b)** $n = 2,239$. **(c)** The sample size is larger in (b) than in (a) because the estimate of the true proportion is closer to 0.5 in (b) than in (a). **(d)** If you were to design the follow-up study, you would use one sample and ask the respondents both questions rather than selecting two separate samples because it costs more to select two samples than one.

**8.46 (a)** $p = 0.5498$; $0.5226 \le \pi \le 0.5770$. **(b)** $p = 0.4697$; $0.4424 \le \pi \le 0.4970$. **(c)** $p = 0.2799$; $0.2554 \le \pi \le 0.3045$. **(d) (a)** $n = 2,378$. **(b)** $= 2,393$. **(c)** $= 1,936$.

**8.48 (a)** If you conduct a follow-up study to estimate the population proportion of individuals who view oil companies favorably, you would use a $\pi$ of 0.15 in the sample size formula because it provides the most conservative value based on past information on the proportion. **(b)** $n = 545$.

**8.50** $\$10,721.53 \le \text{Total} \le \$14,978.47$.

**8.52 (a)** 0.054. **(b)** 0.0586. **(c)** 0.066.

**8.54** $(3,000)(\$261.40) \pm (3,000)(1.8331) \dfrac{(138.8046)}{\sqrt{10}} \left( \sqrt{\dfrac{3,000 - 10}{3,000 - 1}} \right)$

$\$543,176.96 \le \text{Total} \le \$1,025,224.04$.

**8.56** $\$5,443 \le \text{Total difference} \le \$54,229$.

**8.58 (a)** 0.0542. **(b)** Because the upper bound is higher than the tolerable exception rate of 0.04, the auditor should request a larger sample.

**8.66** $940.50 \le \mu \le 1007.50$. Based on the evidence gathered from the sample of 34 stores, the 95% confidence interval for the mean per-store count in all of the franchise's stores is from 940.50 to 1,007.50. With a 95% level of confidence, the franchise can conclude that the mean per-store count in all its stores is somewhere between 940.50 and 1,007.50, which is larger than the original average of 900 mean per-store count before the price reduction. Hence, reducing coffee prices is a good strategy to increase the mean customer count.

**8.68 (a)** $p = 0.80$, $0.7765 \le \pi \le 0.8235$. **(b)** $p = 0.88$, $0.8609 \le \pi \le 0.8991$. **(c)** $p = 0.56$, $0.5309 \le \pi \le 0.5891$. **(d) (a)** $n = 1,537$. **(b)** $n = 1,015$. **(c)** $n = 2,367$.

**8.70 (a)** $14.085 \le \mu \le 16.515$. **(b)** $0.530 \le \pi \le 0.820$. **(c)** $n = 25$. **(d)** $n = 784$. **(e)** If a single sample were to be selected for both purposes, the larger of the two sample sizes ($n = 784$) should be used.

**8.72 (a)** $8.049 \le \mu \le 11.351$. **(b)** $0.284 \le \pi \le 0.676$. **(c)** $n = 35$. **(d)** $n = 121$. **(e)** If a single sample were to be selected for both purposes, the larger of the two sample sizes ($n = 121$) should be used.

**8.74 (a)** $\$25.80 \le \mu \le \$31.24$. **(b)** $0.3037 \le \pi \le 0.4963$. **(c)** $n = 97$. **(d)** $n = 423$. **(e)** If a single sample were to be selected for both purposes, the larger of the two sample sizes ($n = 423$) should be used.

**8.76 (a)** $\$36.66 \le \mu \le \$40.42$. **(b)** $0.2027 \le \pi \le 0.3973$. **(c)** $n = 110$. **(d)** $n = 423$. **(e)** If a single sample were to be selected for both purposes, the larger of the two sample sizes ($n = 423$) should be used.

**8.78 (a)** $\pi \le 0.2013$. **(b)** Because the upper bound is higher than the tolerable exception rate of 0.15, the auditor should request a larger sample.

**8.80 (a)** $n = 27$. **(b)** $\$402,652.53 \le \text{Population total} \le \$450,950.79$.

**8.82 (a)** $8.41 \le \mu \le 8.43$. **(b)** With 95% confidence, the population mean width of troughs is somewhere between 8.41 and 8.43 inches.

**8.84 (a)** $0.2425 \le \mu \le 0.2856$. **(b)** $0.1975 \le \mu \le 0.2385$. **(c)** The amounts of granule loss for both brands are skewed to the right, but the sample sizes are large enough. **(d)** Because the two confidence intervals do not overlap, you can conclude that the mean granule loss of Boston shingles is higher than that of Vermont shingles.

# CHAPTER 9

**9.2** Because $Z_{STAT} = +2.21 > 1.96$, reject $H_0$.

**9.4** Reject $H_0$ if $Z_{STAT} < -2.58$ or if $Z_{STAT} > 2.58$.

**9.6** $p$-value $= 0.0456$.

**9.8** $p$-value $= 0.1676$.

**9.10** $H_0$: Defendant is guilty; $H_1$: Defendant is innocent. A Type I error would be not convicting a guilty person. A Type II error would be convicting an innocent person.

**9.12** $H_0$: $\mu = 20$ minutes. 20 minutes is adequate travel time between classes. $H_1$: $\mu \ne 20$ minutes. 20 minutes is not adequate travel time between classes.

**9.14** $H_0$: $\mu = 1.00$. The mean amount of paint per one-gallon can is one gallon. $H_1$: $\mu \ne 1.00$. The mean amount of paint per one-gallon can differs from one gallon.

**9.16** $t_{STAT} = 2.00$

**9.18 (a)** $\pm 2.1315$.

**9.20** No, you should not use a $t$ test because the original population is left-skewed and the sample size is not large enough for the $t$ test to be valid.

**9.22 (a)** Because $t_{STAT} = -2.4324 < -1.9842$, reject $H_0$. There is enough evidence to conclude that the population mean has changed from 41.4 days. **(b)** Because $t_{STAT} = -2.4324 > -2.6264$, do not reject $H_0$. There is not enough evidence to conclude that the population mean has changed from 41.4 days. **(c)** Because $t_{STAT} = -2.9907 < -1.9842$, reject $H_0$. There is enough evidence to conclude that the population mean has changed from 41.4 days. **(d)** No, the large sample size ensures that the use of the $t$ test is appropriate.

**9.24 (a)** $t_{STAT} = (3.57 - 3.70)/\sqrt{64} = -1.30$; Because $-1.9983 < t_{STAT} = -1.30 < 1.9983$ and the $p$-value of $0.1984 > 0.05$ There is no evidence that the population mean waiting time is different from 3.7 minutes. **(b)** Since $n = 64$, the central limit theorem should ensure that the sampling distribution of the mean is approximately normal. In general, the $t$-test is appropriate for this sample size except for the case where the population is extremely skewed or bimodal.

**9.26 (a)** Because $-2.5706 < t_{STAT} = 0.8556 < 2.5706$, do not reject $H_0$. There is not enough evidence to conclude that the mean price for two tickets, with online service charges, large popcorn, and two medium soft drinks, is different from \$35. **(b)** The $p$-value is 0.4313. If the population mean is \$35, the probability of observing a sample of six theater chains that will result in a sample mean farther away from the hypothesized value than this sample is 0.4313. **(c)** That the distribution of prices is normally distributed. **(d)** With a small sample size, it is difficult to evaluate the assumption of normality. However, the distribution may be symmetric because the mean and the median are close in value.

**9.28 (a)** Because $-2.0096 < t_{STAT} = 0.114 < 2.0096$, do not reject $H_0$. There is no evidence that the mean amount is different from two liters. **(b)** $p$-value = 0.9095. **(c)** and **(d)** Yes, the data appear to have met the normality assumption. **(e)** The amount of fill is decreasing over time. Therefore, the $t$ test is invalid.

**9.30 (a)** Because $t_{STAT} = -5.9355 < -2.0106$, reject $H_0$. There is enough evidence to conclude that mean widths of the troughs is different from 8.46 inches. **(b)** That the population distribution is normal. **(c)** Although the distribution of the widths is left-skewed, the large sample size means that the validity of the $t$ test is not seriously affected.

**9.32 (a)** Because $-2.68 < t_{STAT} = 0.094 < 2.68$, do not reject $H_0$. **(b)** $5.462 \leq \mu \leq 5.542$. **(c)** The conclusions are the same.

**9.34** $p$-value = 0.0228.

**9.36** $p$-value = 0.0838.

**9.38** $p$-value = 0.9162.

**9.40** $t_{STAT} = 2.7638$.

**9.42** $t_{STAT} = -2.5280$.

**9.44 (a)** $t_{STAT} = (2.73 - 2.80)/0.2/\sqrt{25} = -1.75$; Because $t_{STAT} = -1.75 < -1.7109$, reject $H_0$. **(b)** $p$-value = $0.0464 < 0.05$, reject $H_0$. **(c)** The probability of getting a sample mean of 2.73 feet or less if the population mean is 2.8 feet is 0.0464. **(d)** They are the same.

**9.46 (a)** $H_0: \mu \leq 5$; $H_1: \mu > 5$. **(b)** A Type I error occurs when you conclude that children take a mean of more than five trips a week to the store when in fact they take a mean of no more than five trips a week to the store. A Type II error occurs when you conclude that children take a mean of no more than five trips a week to the store when in fact they take a mean of more than five trips a week to the store. **(c)** Because $t_{STAT} = 2.9375 > 2.3263$ or the $p$-value of 0.0021 is less than 0.01, reject $H_0$. There is enough evidence to conclude the population mean number of trips to the store is greater than five per week. **(d)** The probability that the sample mean is 5.47 trips or more when the null hypothesis is true is 0.0021.

**9.48** $p = 0.22$.

**9.50** Do not reject $H_0$.

**9.52** $Z_{STAT} = 1.2671$, $p$-value = 0.1026. Because $0.1026 > 0.05$, do not reject $H_0$. There is not enough evidence to show that more than half of *The Oxford Press* readers planned to cut back on driving.

**9.54 (a)** $H_0: \pi = 0.5$; $H_1: \pi \neq 0.5$. Decision rule: If $Z_{STAT} > 1.96$ or $Z_{STAT} < -1.96$, reject $H_0$.

$$p = \frac{552}{1,083} = 0.5097$$

Test statistic:

$$Z_{STAT} = \frac{p - \pi}{\sqrt{\dfrac{\pi(1-\pi)}{n}}} = \frac{0.5097 - 0.5}{\sqrt{\dfrac{0.5(1-0.5)}{1,083}}} = 0.6381$$

Because $-1.96 < Z_{STAT} = 0.6381 < 1.96$, do not reject $H_0$ and conclude that there is not enough evidence to show that the percentage of people who trust energy-efficiency ratings differs from 50%. **(b)** $p$-value = 0.5234. Because the $p$-value of $0.5234 > 0.05$, do not reject $H_0$.

**9.56 (a)** $H_0: \pi \leq 0.08$. No more than 8% of students at your school are Omnivores. $H_1: \pi > 0.08$. More than 8% of students at your school are Omnivores. **(b)** $Z_{STAT} = 3.6490$, $p$-value = 0.0001316. Because $Z_{STAT} = 3.6490 > 1.96$ or $p$-value = $0.0001316 < 0.05$, reject $H_0$. There is enough evidence to show that the percentage of Omnivores at your school is greater than 8%.

**9.58 (a)** power = 0.3721$\beta$ = 0.6279. **(b)** power = 0.9529$\beta$ = 0.0471. **(c)** Holding everything else constant, the greater the distance from the true mean to the hypothesized mean, the higher is the power of the test and the lower is the probability of committing a Type II error. Holding everything else constant, the smaller the level of significance, the lower is the power of the test and the higher is the probability of committing a Type II error.

**9.60 (a)** power = 0.8873$\beta$ = 0.1127. **(b)** power = 0.0871$\beta$ = 0.9129.

**9.62 (a)** power = 0.4144$\beta$ = 0.5856. **(b)** power = 0.0665$\beta$ = 0.9335. **(c)** Holding everything else constant, the larger the sample size, the higher is the power of the test and the lower is the probability of committing a Type II error.

**9.74 (a)** Buying a site that is not profitable. **(b)** Not buying a profitable site. **(c)** Type I. **(d)** If the executives adopt a less stringent rejection criterion by buying sites for which the computer model predicts moderate or large profit, the probability of committing a Type I error will increase. Many more of the sites the computer model predicts that will generate moderate profit may end up not being profitable at all. On the other hand, the less stringent rejection criterion will lower the probability of committing a Type II error since more potentially profitable sites will be purchased.

**9.76 (a)** Because $t_{STAT} = 3.248 > 2.0010$, reject $H_0$. **(b)** $p$-value = 0.0019. **(c)** Because $Z_{STAT} = -0.32 > -1.645$, do not reject $H_0$. **(d)** Because $-2.0010 < t_{STAT} = 0.75 < 2.0010$, do not reject $H_0$. **(e)** Because $t_{STAT} = -1.61 > -1.645$, do not reject $H_0$.

**9.78 (a)** Because $t_{STAT} = -1.69 > -1.7613$, do not reject $H_0$. **(b)** The data are from a population that is normally distributed. **(c)** and **(d)** With the exception of one extreme point, the data are approximately normally distributed. **(e)** There is insufficient evidence to state that the waiting time is less than five minutes.

**9.80 (a)** Because $t_{STAT} = -1.47 > -1.6896$, do not reject $H_0$. **(b)** $p$-value = 0.0748. If the null hypothesis is true, the probability of obtaining a $t_{STAT}$ of $-1.47$ or more extreme is 0.0748. **(c)** Because $t_{STAT} = -3.10 < -1.6973$, reject $H_0$. **(d)** $p$-value = 0.0021. If the null hypothesis is true, the probability of obtaining a $t_{STAT}$ of $-3.10$ or more extreme is 0.0021. **(e)** The data in the population are assumed to be normally distributed.

**(f)** Both boxplots suggest that the data are skewed slightly to the right, more so for the Boston shingles. However, the very large sample sizes mean that the results of the $t$-test are relatively insensitive to the departure from normality.

**9.82 (a)** $t_{STAT} = -21.61$, reject $H_0$. **(b)** $p$-value = 0.0000. **(c)** $t_{STAT} = -27.19$, reject $H_0$. **(d)** $p$-value = 0.0000. **(e)** Because of the large sample sizes, you do not need to be concerned with the normality assumption.

# CHAPTER 10

**10.2 (a)** $t = 3.8959$. **(b)** $df = 21$. **(c)** 2.5177. **(d)** Because $t_{STAT} = 3.8959 > 2.5177$, reject $H_0$.

**10.4** $3.73 \le \mu_1 - \mu_2 \le 12.27$.

**10.6** Because $t_{STAT} = 4.1779 > 2.8982$ or $p$-value = 0.0006 < 0.05, reject $H_0$. There is evidence of a difference in the means of the two populations.

**10.8 (a)** Because $t_{STAT} = 5.2031 > 2.33$ or $p$-value = 0.0000 < 0.01, reject $H_0$. There is enough evidence to conclude that the mean breaking strength of parts produced by the new machine is greater than the mean breaking strength of parts produced by the old machine. **(b)** Because $t_{STAT} = 5.2031 > 2.33$ or $p$-value = 0.0000 < 0.01, reject $H_0$. There is enough evidence to conclude that the mean breaking strength of parts produced by the new machine is greater than the mean breaking strength of parts produced by the old machine. (The answers to (a) and (b) are the same because of the large sample size and the minimal difference between the variances.)

**10.10 (a)** Because $-2.0117 < t_{STAT} = 0.1023 < 2.0117$, do not reject $H_0$. There is no evidence of a difference in the two means for the age 8 group. Because $t_{STAT} = 3.375 > 1.9908$, reject $H_0$. There is evidence of a difference in the two means for the age 12 group. Because $t_{STAT} = 3.3349 > 1.9966$, reject $H_0$. There is evidence of a difference in the two means for the age 16 group. **(b)** The test results show that children in the United States begin to develop preferences for brand-name products as early as age 12.

**10.12 (a)** $H_0: \mu_1 = \mu_2$, where Populations: 1 = Males, 2 = Females.
$H_1: \mu_1 \ne \mu_2$
Decision rule: $df = 170$. If $t_{STAT} < -1.974$ or $t_{STAT} > 1.974$, reject $H_0$.
Test statistic:

$$S_p^2 = \frac{(n_1 - 1)(S_1^2) + (n_2 - 1)(S_2^2)}{(n_1 - 1) + (n_2 - 1)}$$

$$= \frac{(99)(13.35^2) + (71)(9.42^2)}{99 + 71} = 140.8489$$

$$t_{STAT} = \frac{(\bar{X}_1 - \bar{X}_2) - (\mu_1 - \mu_2)}{\sqrt{S_p^2 \left( \frac{1}{n_1} + \frac{1}{n_2} \right)}}$$

$$= \frac{(40.26 - 36.85) - 0}{\sqrt{140.8489 \left( \frac{1}{100} + \frac{1}{72} \right)}} = 1.859$$

Decision: Because $-1.974 < t_{STAT} = 1.859 < 1.974$, do not reject $H_0$. There is not enough evidence to conclude that the mean computer anxiety experienced by males and females is different. **(b)** $p$-value = 0.0648. **(c)** In order to use the pooled-variance $t$ test, you need to assume that the populations are normally distributed with equal variances.

**10.14 (a)** Because $t_{STAT} = -4.1343 < -2.0484$, reject $H_0$. **(b)** $p$-value = 0.0003. **(c)** The original populations of waiting times are approximately normally distributed. **(d)** $-4.2292 \le \mu_1 - \mu_2 \le -1.4268$.

**10.16 (a)** Because $t_{STAT} = 4.10 > 2.024$, reject $H_0$. There is evidence of a difference in the mean surface hardness between untreated and treated steel plates. **(b)** $p$-value = 0.0002. The probability that two samples have a mean difference of 9.3634 or more is 0.02% if there is no difference in the mean surface hardness between untreated and treated steel plates. **(c)** You need to assume that the population distribution of hardness of both untreated and treated steel plates is normally distributed. **(d)** $4.7447 \le \mu_1 - \mu_2 \le 13.9821$.

**10.18 (a)** Because $t_{STAT} = -2.1522 < -2.0211$, reject $H_0$. There is enough evidence to conclude that the mean assembly times, in seconds, are different between employees trained in a computer-assisted, individual-based program and those trained in a team-based program. **(b)** You must assume that each of the two independent populations is normally distributed. **(c)** Because $t_{STAT} = -2.152 < -2.052$ or $p$-value = 0.041 < 0.05, reject $H_0$. **(d)** The results in (a) and (c) are the same. **(e)** $-4.52 \le \mu_1 - \mu_2 \le -0.14$. You are 95% confident that the difference between the population means of the two training methods is between $-4.52$ and $-0.14$.

**10.20** $df = 19$.

**10.22 (a)** $t_{STAT} = (-1.5566)/(1.424)/\sqrt{9} = -3.2772$; Because $t_{STAT} = -3.2772 < -2.306$ or $p$-value = 0.0112 < 0.05, reject $H_0$. There is enough evidence of a difference in the mean summated ratings between the two brands. **(b)** You must assume that the distribution of the differences between the two ratings is approximately normal. **(c)** $p$-value is 0.0112. The probability of obtaining a mean difference in ratings that gives rise to a test statistic that deviates from 0 by 3.2772 or more in either direction is 0.0112 if there is no difference in the mean summated ratings between the two brands. **(d)** $-2.6501 \le \mu_D \le -0.4610$. You are 95% confident that the mean difference in summated ratings between brand A and brand B is somewhere between $-2.6501$ and $-0.4610$.

**10.24 (a)** Because $t_{STAT} = 6.7876 > 2.9768$ or $p$-value = 0.0000 < 0.01, reject $H_0$. There is evidence to conclude that there is a difference between the mean price of textbooks at the local bookstore and Amazon.com. **(b)** You must assume that the distribution of the differences between the measurements is approximately normal. **(c)** $\$9.27 \le \mu_D \le \$23.25$. You are 99% confident that the mean difference between the price of textbooks at the local bookstore and Amazon.com is somewhere between \$9.27 and \$23.25. **(d)** The results in (a) and (c) are the same. The hypothesized value of 0 for the difference in the price of textbooks between the local bookstore and Amazon.com is outside the 99% confidence interval.

**10.26 (a)** Because $t_{STAT} = 1.8425 < 1.943$, do not reject $H_0$. There is not enough evidence to conclude that the mean bone marrow microvessel density is higher before the stem cell transplant than after the stem cell transplant. **(b)** $p$-value = 0.0575. The probability that the $t$ statistic for the mean difference in density is 1.8425 or more is 5.75% if the mean density is not higher before the stem cell transplant than after the stem cell transplant. **(c)** $-28.26 \le \mu_D \le 200.55$. You are 95% confident that the mean difference in bone marrow microvessel density before and after the stem cell transplant is somewhere between $-28.26$ and 200.55.

**10.28 (a)** Because $t_{STAT} = -9.3721 < -2.4258$, reject $H_0$. **(b)** The population of differences in strength is approximately normally distributed. **(c)** $p = 0.000$.

**10.30 (a)** Because $-2.58 \le Z_{STAT} = -0.58 \le 2.58$, do not reject $H_0$. **(b)** $-0.273 \le \pi_1 - \pi_2 \le 0.173$.

**10.32 (a)** $H_0: \pi_1 \le \pi_2$. $H_1: \pi_1 > \pi_2$. Populations: 1 = parents, 2 = teachers.

**(b)** Because $Z_{STAT} = 7.9918 > 1.6449$, reject $H_0$. There is sufficient evidence to conclude that the population proportion of parents that are very confident that their child's school will meet the standards by the deadline is greater than the population proportion of teachers that are very confident that the school where they work will meet standards by the deadline. **(c)** Yes, the result in (b) makes it appropriate for the article to claim that parents are more confident.

**10.34 (a)** $H_0: \pi_1 = \pi_2$. $H_1: \pi_1 \neq \pi_2$. Decision rule: If $|Z_{STAT}| > 1.96$, reject $H_0$.
Test statistic:

$$\bar{p} = \frac{X_1 + X_2}{n_1 + n_2} = \frac{280 + 320}{505 + 500} = 0.5970$$

$$Z_{STAT} = \frac{(p_1 - p_2) - (\pi_2 - \pi_2)}{\sqrt{\bar{p}(1-\bar{p})\left(\frac{1}{n_1} + \frac{1}{n_2}\right)}} = \frac{(0.5545 - 0.64) - 0}{\sqrt{0.5970(1 - 0.5970)\left(\frac{1}{505} + \frac{1}{500}\right)}}$$

$$= -2.7644.$$

Decision: Because $Z_{STAT} = -2.7644 < -1.96$, reject $H_0$. There is sufficient evidence to conclude that there is a difference in the proportion of adults who think the U.S. tax code is unfair between the two income groups. **(b)** $p$-value = 0.0057. The probability of obtaining a difference in proportions that gives rise to a test statistic that deviates from 0 by 2.7644 or more in either direction is 0.0057 if there is no difference in the proportion of adults who think the U.S. tax code is unfair between the two income groups.

**10.36 (a)** Because $-1.96 < Z_{STAT} = 1.5240 < 1.96$, do not reject $H_0$. There is insufficient evidence of a difference between undergraduate and MBA students in the proportion who selected the highest-cost fund. **(b)** $p$-value = 0.1275. The probability of obtaining a difference in proportions that gives rise to a test statistic that deviates from 0 by 1.5240 or more in either direction is 0.1275 if there is no difference between undergraduate and MBA students in the proportion who selected the highest-cost fund.

**10.38 (a)** 2.20. **(b)** 2.57. **(c)** 3.50.

**10.40 (a)** Population B. $S^2 = 25$. **(b)** 1.5625.

**10.42** $df_{numerator} = 24$, $df_{denominator} = 24$.

**10.44** Because $F_{STAT} = 1.2109 < 2.27$, do not reject $H_0$.

**10.46 (a)** Because $F_{STAT} = 1.2995 < 3.18$, do not reject $H_0$. **(b)** Because $F_{STAT} = 1.2995 < 2.62$, do not reject $H_0$.

**10.48 (a)** $H_0 : \sigma_1^2 = \sigma_2^2$. $H_1 : \sigma_1^2 \neq \sigma_2^2$.
Decision rule: If $F_{STAT} > 1.556$, reject $H_0$.

Test statistic: $F_{STAT} = \dfrac{S_1^2}{S_2^2} = \dfrac{(13.35)^2}{(9.42)^2} = 2.008$.

Decision: Because $F_{STAT} = 2.008 > 1.556$, reject $H_0$. There is enough evidence to conclude that the two population variances are different. **(b)** $p$-value = 0.0022. **(c)** The test assumes that each of the two populations is normally distributed. **(d)** Based on (a) and (b), a separate-variance $t$ test should be used.

**10.50 (a)** Because $F_{STAT} = 1.0389 < 2.7324$ or $p$-value = 0.9789 > 0.05, do not reject $H_0$. There is not enough evidence of a difference in the variability of the battery life between the two types of digital cameras.

**(b)** $p$-value = 0.9789. The probability of obtaining a sample that yields a test statistic more extreme than 1.0389 is 0.9789 if there is no difference in the two population variances. **(c)** The test assumes that the two populations are both normally distributed. **(d)** Based on (a) and (b), a pooled-variance $t$ test should be used.

**10.52** Because $F_{STAT} = 3.0866 < 6.3852$, do not reject $H_0$. There is not enough evidence of a difference in the variance of the yield between money market accounts and five-year CDs.

**10.60 (a)** $H_0 : \sigma_1^2 \geq \sigma_2^2$ and $H_0 : \sigma_1^2 < \sigma_2^2$. **(b)** Type I error: Rejecting the null hypothesis that the price variance on the Internet is no lower than the price variance in the brick-and-mortar market when the price variance on the Internet is no lower than the price variance in the brick-and-mortar market. Type II error: Failing to reject the null hypothesis that price variance on the Internet is no lower than the price variance in the brick-and-mortar market when the price variance on the Internet is lower than the price variance in the brick-and-mortar market. **(c)** An $F$ test for differences in two variances can be used. **(d)** You need to assume that each of the two populations is normally distributed.
**(e) (a)** $H_0: \mu_1 \geq \mu_2$ and $H_1: \mu_1 < \mu_2$. **(b)** Type I error: Rejecting the null hypothesis that the mean price in the electronic market is no lower than the mean price in the physical market when the mean price in the electronic market is no lower than the mean price in the physical market. Type II error: Failing to reject the null hypothesis that the mean price in the electronic market is no lower than the mean price in the physical market when the mean price in the electronic market is lower than the mean price in the physical market. **(c)** A pooled $t$ test or a separate-variance $t$ test for the difference in the means can be used. **(d)** You must assume that the distribution of the prices in the electronic market and in the physical market are approximately normally distributed.

**10.62 (a)** The researchers can ask the teenagers, after viewing each ad, to rate the dangers of smoking, using a scale from 0 to 10, with 10 representing the most dangerous. **(b)** $H_0: \mu_T \geq \mu_S$ and $H_1: \mu_T < \mu_S$. **(c)** Type I error is the error made by concluding that ads produced by the state are more effective than those produced by Philip Morris even though it is not true. The risk of Type I error here is that teenagers can miss the opportunity from the better ads produced by Philip Morris to recognize the true dangers of smoking and the additional expenses the state will have to incur to produce and run the ads. Type II error is the error made by concluding that ads produced by Philip Morris are no less effective than those produced by the state even though ads produced by the state are more effective. The risk of Type II error here is that more teenagers will miss the opportunity to recognize the true dangers of smoking from the ads produced by the state. **(d)** Because both ads are shown to the same group of teenagers, a paired $t$ test for the mean difference is most appropriate. **(e)** Statistically reliable here means the conclusions drawn from the test are reliable because all the assumptions needed for the test to be valid are fulfilled.

**10.64 (a)** Because $F_{STAT} = 22.7067 > F_{\alpha} = 1.6275$, reject $H_0$. There is enough evidence to conclude that there is a difference between the variances in age of students at the Western school and at the Eastern school. **(b)** Because there is a difference between the variances in the age of students at the Western school and at the Eastern school, schools should take that into account when designing their curriculum to accommodate the larger variance in age of students in the state university in the Western United States. **(c)** It is more appropriate to use a separate-variance $t$ test. **(d)** Because $F_{STAT} = 1.3061 < 1.6275$, do not reject $H_0$. There is not enough evidence to conclude that there is a difference between the variances in years of spreadsheet usage of students at the Western school and at the Eastern school. **(e)** Using the pooled-variance $t$ test, because

$t_{STAT} = -4.6650 < -2.5978$, reject $H_0$. There is enough evidence of a difference in the mean years of spreadsheet usage of students at the Western school and at the Eastern school.

**10.66 (a)** Because $t_{STAT} = 3.3282 > 1.8595$, reject $H_0$. There is enough evidence to conclude that the introductory computer students required more than a mean of 10 minutes to write and run a program in Visual Basic. **(b)** Because $t_{STAT} = 1.3636 < 1.8595$, do not reject $H_0$. There is not enough evidence to conclude that the introductory computer students required more than a mean of 10 minutes to write and run a program in Visual Basic. **(c)** Although the mean time necessary to complete the assignment increased from 12 to 16 minutes as a result of the increase in one data value, the standard deviation went from 1.8 to 13.2, which reduced the $t$ value. **(d)** Because $F_{STAT} = 1.2308 < 3.8549$, do not reject $H_0$. There is not enough evidence to conclude that the population variances are different for the Introduction to Computers students and computer majors. Hence, the pooled-variance $t$ test is a valid test to determine whether computer majors can write a Visual Basic program in less time than introductory students, assuming that the distributions of the time needed to write a Visual Basic program for both the Introduction to Computers students and the computer majors are approximately normally distributed. Because $t_{STAT} = 4.0666 > 1.7341$, reject $H_0$. There is enough evidence that the mean time is higher for Introduction to Computers students than for computer majors. **(e)** $p$-value $= 0.000362$. If the true population mean amount of time needed for Introduction to Computer students to write a Visual Basic program is no more than 10 minutes, the probability of observing a sample mean greater than the 12 minutes in the current sample is 0.0362%. Hence, at a 5% level of significance, you can conclude that the population mean amount of time needed for Introduction to Computer students to write a Visual Basic program is more than 10 minutes. As illustrated in part (d), in which there is not enough evidence to conclude that the population variances are different for the Introduction to Computers students and computer majors, the pooled-variance $t$ test performed is a valid test to determine whether computer majors can write a Visual Basic program in less time than introductory students, assuming that the distribution of the time needed to write a Visual Basic program for both the Introduction to Computers students and the computer majors are approximately normally distributed.

**10.68** From the boxplot and the summary statistics, both distributions are approximately normally distributed. $F_{STAT} = 1.056 < 1.89$. There is insufficient evidence to conclude that the two population variances are significantly different at the 5% level of significance. $t_{STAT} = -5.084 < -1.99$. At the 5% level of significance, there is sufficient evidence to reject the null hypothesis of no difference in the mean life of the bulbs between the two manufacturers. You can conclude that there is a significant difference in the mean life of the bulbs between the two manufacturers.

**10.70** Population 1 is men and population 2 is women. Auto-related: Because $Z_{STAT} = 3.1346 > 1.96$, reject $H_0$. There is sufficient evidence to conclude that there is a difference between men and women. Cash: Because $-1.96 < Z_{STAT} = -0.5053 < 1.96$, do not reject $H_0$. There is insufficient evidence to conclude that there is a difference between men and women. Clothes: Because $Z_{STAT} = -4.4642 < -1.96$, reject $H_0$. There is sufficient evidence to conclude that there is a difference between men and women. Electronics: Because $Z_{STAT} = 2.1284 > 1.96$, reject $H_0$. There is sufficient evidence to conclude that there is a difference between men and women. Entertainment: Because $-1.96 < Z_{STAT} = 1.6759 < 1.96$, do not reject $H_0$. There is insufficient evidence to conclude that there is a difference between men and women. Food: Because $-1.96 < Z_{STAT} = -1.6917 < 1.96$, do not reject $H_0$. There is insufficient evidence to conclude that there is a difference between men and women. Investments: Because

$Z_{STAT} = 2.2717 > 1.96$, reject $H_0$. There is sufficient evidence to conclude that there is a difference between men and women. Travel: Because $-1.96 < Z_{STAT} = 1.5318 < 1.96$, do not reject $H_0$. There is insufficient evidence to conclude that there is a difference between men and women.

**10.72** Customer Product Rating Reviews: $-1.96 < Z_{STAT} = -1.6557 < 1.96$ and $p$-value $= 0.0978 > 0.05$, do not reject $H_0$. There is not enough evidence that there is a difference between adults and youths in the proportion who use customer product ratings/reviews. For sale listings with seller ratings: $-1.96 < Z_{STAT} = -1.2742 < 1.96$ and $p$-value $= 0.2026 > 0.05$, do not reject $H_0$. There is not enough evidence that there is a difference between adults and youths in the proportion who use for sale listings with seller ratings. For sale listings without seller ratings: $-1.96 < Z_{STAT} = -1.0172 < 1.96$ and $p$-value $= 0.3090 > 0.05$, do not reject $H_0$. There is not enough evidence that there is a difference between adults and youths in the proportion who use for sale listings without seller ratings. Online classified ads: $-1.96 < Z_{STAT} = -1.3079 < 1.96$ and $p$-value $= 0.1909 > 0.05$, do not reject $H_0$. There is not enough evidence that there is a difference between adults and youths in the proportion who use online classified ads. Message-board posts: $Z_{STAT} = -2.0624 < -1.96$ and $p$-value $= 0.0392 < 0.05$, reject $H_0$. There is enough evidence that there is a difference between adults and youths in the proportion who use message-board posts. Web blogs: $-1.96 < Z_{STAT} = -1.7397 < 1.96$ and $p$-value $= 0.0819 > 0.05$, do not reject $H_0$. There is not enough evidence that there is a difference between adults and youths in the proportion who use Web blogs. Dating site profile/personals: $= -1.96 < Z_{STAT} = -1.4188 < 1.96$ and $p$-value $= 0.1560 > 0.05$, do not reject $H_0$. There is not enough evidence that there is a difference between adults and youths in the proportion who use dating site profiles/personals. Peer-generated and peer-referenced information: $Z_{STAT} = -2.7267 < -1.96$ and $p$-value $= 0.0064 < 0.05$, reject $H_0$. There is enough evidence that there is a difference between adults and youths in the proportion who use peer-generated and peer-referenced information. Peer-posted event listings: $Z_{STAT} = -3.5878 < -1.96$ and $p$-value $= 0.0003 < 0.05$, reject $H_0$. There is enough evidence that there is a difference between adults and youths in the proportion who use peer-posted event listings.

**10.74** The normal probability plots suggest that the two populations are not normally distributed. An $F$ test is inappropriate for testing the difference in two variances. The sample variances for Boston and Vermont shingles are 0.0203 and 0.015, respectively. Because $t_{STAT} = 3.015 > 1.967$ or the $p$-value $= 0.0028 < \alpha = 0.05$, reject $H_0$. There is sufficient evidence to conclude that there is a difference in the mean granule loss of Boston and Vermont shingles.

# CHAPTER 11

**11.2 (a)** $SSW = 150$. **(b)** $MSA = 15$. **(c)** $MSW = 5$. **(d)** $F_{STAT} = 3$.

**11.4 (a)** 2. **(b)** 18. **(c)** 20.

**11.6 (a)** Reject $H_0$ if $F_{STAT} > 2.95$; otherwise, do not reject $H_0$. **(b)** Because $F_{STAT} = 4 > 2.95$, reject $H_0$. **(c)** The table does not have 28 degrees of freedom in the denominator, so use the next larger critical value, $Q_\alpha = 3.90$. **(d)** Critical range $= 6.166$.

**11.8 (a)** Because $F_{STAT} = 10.99 > F_\alpha = 4.26$, reject $H_0$. **(b)** Critical range $= 40.39$. The experts and darts are not different from each other, but they are both different from the readers. **(c)** It is not valid to infer that the dartboard is better than the professionals because their means are not significantly different. **(d)** Because $F_{STAT} = 0.101 < 4.26$, do not reject $H_0$. There is no evidence of a significant difference in the variation in the return for the three categories.

**11.10 (a)** $H_0$: $\mu_A = \mu_B = \mu_C = \mu_D$ and $H_1$: At least one mean is different.

$$MSA = \frac{SSA}{c-1} = \frac{1986.475}{3} = 662.1583.$$

$$MSW = \frac{SSW}{n-c} = \frac{495.5}{36} = 13.76389.$$

$$F_{STAT} = \frac{MSA}{MSW} = \frac{662.1583}{13.76389} = 48.1084.$$

$$F_{0.05,3,36} = 2.8663.$$

Because the $p$-value is approximately zero and $F_{STAT} = 48.1084 > 2.8663$, reject $H_0$. There is sufficient evidence of a difference in the mean strength of the four brands of trash bags.

**(b)** Critical range $= Q_\alpha \sqrt{\dfrac{MSW}{2}\left(\dfrac{1}{n_j} + \dfrac{1}{n_{j'}}\right)} = 3.79 \sqrt{\dfrac{13.7639}{2}\left(\dfrac{1}{10} + \dfrac{1}{10}\right)}$

$$= 4.446.$$

From the Tukey-Kramer procedure, there is a difference in mean strength between Kroger and Tuffstuff, Glad and Tuffstuff, and Hefty and Tuffstuff. **(c)** ANOVA output for Levene's test for homogeneity of variance:

$$MSA = \frac{SSA}{c-1} = \frac{24.075}{3} = 8.025.$$

$$MSW = \frac{SSW}{n-c} = \frac{198.2}{36} = 5.5056.$$

$$F_{STAT} = \frac{MSA}{MSW} = \frac{8.025}{5.5056} = 1.4576.$$

$$F_{0.05,3,36} = 2.8663.$$

Because the $p$-value $= 0.2423 > 0.05$ and $F_{STAT} = 1.458 < 2.866$, do not reject $H_0$. There is insufficient evidence to conclude that the variances in strength among the four brands of trash bags are different. **(d)** From the results in (a) and (b), Tuffstuff has the lowest mean strength and should be avoided.

**11.12 (a)** Because $F_{STAT} = 12.56 > F_{0.05,4,25} = 2.76$, reject $H_0$. **(b)** Critical range $= 4.67$. Advertisements $A$ and $B$ are different from Advertisements $C$ and $D$. Advertisement $E$ is only different from Advertisement $D$. **(c)** Because $F_{STAT} = 1.927 < 2.76$, do not reject $H_0$. There is no evidence of a significant difference in the variation in the ratings among the five advertisements. **(d)** The advertisements underselling the pen's characteristics had the highest mean ratings, and the advertisements overselling the pen's characteristics had the lowest mean ratings. Therefore, use an advertisement that undersells the pen's characteristics and avoid advertisements that oversell the pen's characteristics.

**11.14 (a)** Because $F_{STAT} = 53.03 > F_{0.05,3,30} = 2.92$, reject $H_0$. **(b)** Critical range $= 5.27$ (using 30 degrees of freedom). Designs 3 and 4 are different from Designs 1 and 2. Designs 1 and 2 are different from each other. **(c)** The assumptions are that the samples are randomly and independently selected (or randomly assigned), the original populations of distances are approximately normally distributed, and the variances are equal. **(d)** Because $F_{STAT} = 2.093 < 2.92$, do not reject $H_0$. There is no evidence of a significant difference in the variation in the distance among the four designs. **(e)** The manager should choose Design 3 or 4.

**11.16 (a)** $SSE = 75$. **(b)** $MSA = 15$, $MSBL = 12.5$, $MSE = 3.125$. **(c)** $F_{STAT} = 4.8$. **(d)** $F_{STAT} = 4$.

**11.18 (a)** $df$ numerator $= 5$, $df$ denominator $= 24$. **(b)** $Q_\alpha = 4.17$. **(c)** Critical range $= 2.786$.

**11.20 (a)** $MSE = 3$, $SSE = 3$, Because $F_{STAT} = 4 < F_{0.01,6,12} = 4.82$, do not reject $H_0$.

**11.22 (a)** Because $F_{STAT} = 5.185 > 3.07$, reject $H_0$. **(b)** Because $F_{STAT} = 5 > 2.49$, reject $H_0$.

**11.24 (a)** $F_{STAT} = 49.6481 > 3.5545$; $p$-value is virtually 0, reject $H_0$. There is evidence of a difference in the mean prices of prescription drugs at the three online pharmacies. **(b)** Critical range $= 24.867$. The mean price of Aptecha is significantly lower than US#1 and US#2 whereas there is no significant difference in mean price between US#1 and US#2 at the 5% level of significance.

**11.26 (a)** $H_0$: $\mu_{.1} = \mu_{.2} = \mu_{.3} = \mu_{.4} = \mu_{.5}$ where 1 = Itunes, 2 = Wal-Mart, 3 = MusicNow, 4 = Musicmatch, 5 = Napster    $H_1$: Not all $\mu_j$ are equal where $j = 1, 2, 3, 4, 5$    $F_{STAT} = 0.2113 < 3.0069$, $p$-value $= 0.9284 > 0.05$, do not reject $H_0$. There is no evidence of a difference in the mean prices for albums at the five digital music services. **(b)** The assumptions needed are: (i) samples are randomly and independently drawn, (ii) populations are normally distributed, (iii) populations have equal variances, and (iv) no interaction effect between treatments and blocks. **(c)** Because there is not enough evidence of a difference in the mean prices for albums at the five digital music services, it is inappropriate to perform a Tukey-Kramer procedure to determine which digital music services differ. **(d)** $H_0$: $\mu_{1.} = \mu_{2.} = \cdots = \mu_{5.}$   $H_1$: Not all $\mu_{i.}$ are equal where $i = 1, 2, ..., 5$   $F_{STAT} = 0.2274 < 3.0069$ and $p$-value $= 0.9191 > 0.05$, do not reject $H_0$. There is not enough evidence of a significant block effect in this experiment. The blocking has not been advantageous in reducing the experimental error.

**11.28 (a)** Because $F_{STAT} = 268.26 > 3.114$, reject $H_0$. There is enough evidence to conclude that there is a difference in the mean compressive strength after 2, 7, and 28 days. **(b)** Critical range $= 0.1651$. At the 0.05 level of significance, all of the comparisons are significant. **(c)** $RE = 2.558$. **(e)** The compressive strength of the concrete increases over the 3 time periods.

**11.30 (a)** 40. **(b)** 60 and 55. **(c)** 10. **(d)** 10.

**11.32 (a)** Because $F_{STAT} = 6.00 > 3.35$, reject $H_0$. **(b)** Because $F_{STAT} = 5.50 > F = 3.35$, reject $H_0$. **(c)** Because $F_{STAT} = 1.00 < F = 2.73$, do not reject $H_0$.

**11.34** $df$ B $= 4$, $df$ total $= 44$, $SSA = 160$, $SSAB = 80$, $SSE = 150$, $SST = 610$, $MSB = 55$, $MSE = 5$. For $A$: $F_{STAT} = 16$. For $AB$: $F_{STAT} = 2$.

**11.36 (a)** Because $F_{STAT} = 1.37 < 4.75$, do not reject $H_0$. **(b)** Because $F_{STAT} = 23.58 > F_{0.05,1,12} = 4.75$, reject $H_0$. **(c)** Because $F_{STAT} = 0.70 < F_{0.05,1,12} = 4.75$, do not reject $H_0$. **(e)** Developer strength has a significant effect on density, but development time does not.

**11.38 (a)** $H_0$: There is no interaction between brand and water temperature. $H_1$: There is an interaction between brand and water temperature.

$$MSAB = \frac{SSAB}{(r-1)(c-1)} = \frac{506.3104}{(1)(2)} = 253.1552$$

$$F_{STAT} = \frac{MSAB}{MSE} = \frac{253.1552}{12.2199} = 20.7167$$

Because $F_{STAT} = 20.7167 > 3.555$ or the $p$-value $= 0.0000214 < 0.05$, reject $H_0$. There is evidence of interaction between brand of pain reliever and temperature of the water. **(b)** Because there is an interaction between brand and the temperature of the water, it is inappropriate to analyze the main effect due to brand. **(c)** Becuase there is an interaction between brand and the temperature of the water, it is an inappropriate to analyze the main effect due to water temperature. **(e)** The difference in the mean time a tablet took to dissolve in cold and hot water depends on the brand, with Alka-Seltzer having the largest difference and Equate with the smallest difference.

**11.40 (a)** Because $F_{STAT} = 0.43 < F_{0.05,1,28} = 4.20$, do not reject $H_0$. **(b)** Because $F_{STAT} = 0.02 < F_{0.05,1,28} = 4.20$, do not reject $H_0$. **(c)** Because $F_{STAT} = 45.47 > F_{0.05,1,28} = 4.20$, reject $H_0$. **(e)** Only part positioning has a significant effect on distortion.

**11.52 (a)** Because $F_{STAT} = 1.485 < F_{0.05,9,16} = 2.54$, do not reject $H_0$. **(b)** Because $F_{STAT} = 0.79 < F_{0.05,3,16} = 3.24$, do not reject $H_0$. **(c)** Because $F_{STAT} = 52.07 > F_{0.05,3,16} = 3.24$, reject $H_0$. **(e)** Critical range = 0.0189. Washing cycles for 22 and 24 minutes are not different with respect to dirt removal, but they are both different from 18- and 20-minute cycles. **(f)** 22 minutes. (24 minutes was not different, but 22 does just as well and would use less energy.) **(g)** The results are the same.

**11.54 (a)** Because $F_{STAT} = 0.075 < F_{0.05,2,15} = 3.68$, do not reject $H_0$. **(b)** Because $F_{STAT} = 4.09 > F_{0.05,2,15} = 3.68$, reject $H_0$. **(c)** Critical range = 1.489. Breaking strength is significantly different between 30 and 50 psi.

**11.56 (a)** Because $F_{STAT} = 1.97 < F_{0.05,2,12} = 3.89$, do not reject $H_0$. **(b)** Because $F_{STAT} = 4.87 > F_{0.05,1,12} = 4.75$, reject $H_0$. **(c)** Because $F_{STAT} = 5.67 > F_{0.05,2,12} = 3.89$, reject $H_0$. **(e)** Critical range = 1.30. Mean breaking strength under 30 psi is significantly different from 40 psi and 50 psi. **(f)** The mean breaking strength is highest under 30 psi. **(g)** The two-factor experiment gave a more complete set of results than the one-factor experiment. Not only was the side-to-side aspect factor significant, the application of the Tukey procedure on the air-jet pressure factor determined that breaking strength scores are highest under 30 psi.

**11.58 (a)** Because $F_{STAT} = 1.4611 < 4.1132$, do not reject $H_0$. There is insufficient evidence to conclude that there is any interaction between type of breakfast and desired time. **(b)** Because $F_{STAT} = 15.0000 > 4.1132$, reject $H_0$. There is sufficient evidence to conclude that there is an effect that is due to type of breakfast. **(c)** Because $F_{STAT} = 3.5458 < 4.1132$, do not reject $H_0$. There is insufficient evidence to conclude that there is an effect due to desired time. **(e)** At the 5% level of significance, only the type of breakfast ordered has an effect on delivery time difference. There is no interaction between the type of breakfast ordered and the desired time.

**11.60 (a)** Because $F_{STAT} = 4.0835 > 3.55$, reject $H_0$. There is sufficient evidence to conclude that there is an interaction between buffer size and data file size. **(b)** and **(c)** You cannot directly conclude that there is a significant difference in mean read times due to buffer size or file size (main effects) because the mean read times for different buffer sizes are different for different sizes of files. **(e)** Conclusions about the relative speed of the buffers or file sizes cannot be drawn because buffers and file sizes interact. **(f)** In the completely randomized design, there is not enough evidence of a difference between mean access read times for the three file sizes. In the two-factor factorial design, there is significant interaction between buffer size and data file size.

**11.62** Because the $p$-value for the interaction is virtually zero, reject $H_0$. There is sufficient evidence to conclude that there is an interaction between browser and the type of computer. The existence of an interaction effect complicates the interpretation of the main effects. You cannot directly conclude that there is a significant difference between the mean download times of different browsers because the difference is not the same over all the computers. Likewise, you cannot directly conclude

that there is a significant difference between the mean download times of different computers because the difference is not the same over the two browsers. It appears that the Dell performs the same, regardless of browser type, and that the Mac performs faster with Netscape than it does with Internet Explorer. Collapsing the two factors into two groups and doing the analysis as a one-way ANOVA, $F_{STAT} = 257.6505 > 2.9467$, $p$-value is virtually 0. Because the $p$-value is virtually 0, reject $H_0$. There is evidence of a difference in the mean download times across the 4 groups. Using Tukey-Kramer multiple comparisons, critical range = 19.016. With the exception of the mean download times between Dell using Netscape Communicator and Dell using Internet Explorer, the mean download times are all different between the remaining pairs of configurations with Mac using Netscape Communicator having the lowest mean download times, followed by Mac using Internet Explorer. Dell using Netscape Communicators and Dell using Internet Explorer both have the longest mean download times.

**11.64 (a)** $F_{STAT} = 4.81 > 2.95$, reject $H_0$. There is sufficient evidence to show a difference in the mean rating scores among the wines. **(b)** The "within wines" term in (a) is $SSW$. It consists of the among blocks ($SSBL$) and "error" term ($SSE$) in (a). **(c)** In this study, the mean rating scores among the eight wines are so significantly different that employing the wrong procedure did not affect the overall conclusion—there is evidence of a difference among the wines. However, by not taking advantage of the actual blocking, the experimental error was inflated in $SSW$ and this could have led to an erroneous decision. Here the conclusions from the pairwise comparisons are much weaker. Using the Tukey-Kramer procedure, Wine #2 and Wine #5 are no longer significantly preferred over Wine #8. In addition, Wine #5 now differs from Wine #4 only by chance.

# CHAPTER 12

**12.2 (a)** For $df = 1$ and $\alpha = 0.05$, $\chi^2_{\alpha} = 3.841$. **(b)** For $df = 1$ and $\alpha = 0.025$, $\chi^2 = 5.024$. **(c)** For $df = 1$ and $\alpha = 0.01$, $\chi^2_{\alpha} = 6.635$.

**12.4 (a)** All $f_e = 25$. **(b)** Because $\chi^2_{STAT} = 4.00 > 3.841$, reject $H_0$.

**12.6 (a)** Because $\chi^2_{STAT} = 63.8686 > 3.841$, reject $H_0$. There is enough evidence to conclude that there is significant difference between the proportion of parents and teachers who enjoy shopping for clothing at the 0.05 level of significance. **(b)** $p$-value is virtually 0. The probability of obtaining a test statistic of 63.8686 or larger when the null hypothesis is true is virtually zero. **(c)** You should not compare the results in (a) to those of Problem 10.32 part (b) because that was a one-tail test.

**12.8 (a)** $H_0$: $\pi_1 = \pi_2$. $H_1$: $\pi_1 \neq \pi_2$.

**Observed Frequencies**

| | Column Variable | | |
| Row Variable | Less Than $50,000 | More Than $50,000 | Total |
| --- | --- | --- | --- |
| Fair | 225 | 180 | 405 |
| Unfair | 280 | 320 | 600 |
| Total | 505 | 500 | 1,005 |

**Expected Frequencies**

| | Column Variable | | |
| Row Variable | Less Than $50,000 | More Than $50,000 | Total |
| --- | --- | --- | --- |
| Fair | 203.5075 | 201.4925 | 405 |
| Unfair | 301.4925 | 298.5075 | 600 |
| Total | 505 | 500 | 1,005 |

Level of Significance 0.05 Number of Rows 2 Number of Columns 2 Degrees of Freedom 1 Critical Value 3.841459 Chi-Square Test Statistic = $(225 - 203.5075)^2/203.5075 + (280 - 301.4925)^2/301.4925 + (180 - 201.4925)^2/201.4925 + (320 - 298.5075)^2/298.5075 = 7.64198$ $p$-Value 0.005703 Decision: Because $\chi^2_{STAT} = 7.642 > 3.841$, reject $H_0$. There is enough evidence to conclude that there is a significant difference in the proportion of adults who think the U.S. tax code is unfair between the two income groups. **(b)** The probability of obtaining a test statistic of 7.642 or larger when the null hypothesis is true is 0.0057. **(c)** The results of (a) and (b) are exactly the same as those of Problem 10.34. The $\chi^2$ in (a) and the $Z$ in Problem 10.34 (a) satisfy the relationship that $\chi^2 = 7.642 = Z^2 = (-2.7644)^2$, and the $p$-value in Problem 10.34 (b) is exactly the same as the $p$-value obtained in (b).

**12.10 (a)** Because $\chi^2_{STAT} = 2.3226 < 3.841$, do not reject $H_0$. There is not enough evidence to conclude that there is a significant difference between undergraduate and MBA students in the proportion who selected the highest-cost fund. **(b)** $p$-value = 0.1275. The probability of obtaining a test statistic of 2.3226 or larger when the null hypothesis is true is 0.1275. **(c)** The results of (a) and (b) are exactly the same as those of Problem 10.36. The $\chi^2$ in (a) and the $Z$ in Problem 10.36 (a) satisfy the relationship that $\chi^2_{STAT} = 2.3226 = (Z_{STAT})^2 = (1.5240)^2$, and the $p$-value in Problem 10.36 (b) is exactly the same as the $p$-value obtained in (b).

**12.12 (a)** The expected frequencies for the first row are 20, 30, and 40. The expected frequencies for the second row are 30, 45, and 60. **(b)** Because $\chi^2_{STAT} = 12.5 > 5.991$, reject $H_0$. **(c)** A vs. B: $0.20 > 0.196$; therefore, A and B are different. A vs. C: $0.30 > 0.185$; therefore, A and C are different. B vs. C: $0.10 < 0.185$; therefore, B and C are not different.

**12.14. (a)** Because the calculated test statistic $\chi^2_{STAT} = 742.3961 > 9.4877$, reject $H_0$ and conclude that there is a difference in the proportion of people who eat out at least once a week in the various countries. **(b)** $p$-value is virtually zero. The probability of a test statistic greater than 742.3961 or more is approximately zero if there is no difference in the proportion of people who eat out at least once a week in the various countries. **(c)** At the 5% level of significance, there is no significant difference between the proportions in Germany and France, whereas there is a significant difference between all the remaining pairs of countries.

**12.16 (a)** $H_0$: $\pi_1 = \pi_2 = \pi_3$. $H_1$: At least one proportion differs.

| $f_0$ | $f_e$ | $(f_0 - f_e)$ | $(f_0 - f_e)^2/f_e$ |
|---|---|---|---|
| 48 | 42.667 | 5.333 | 0.667 |
| 152 | 157.333 | −5.333 | 0.181 |
| 56 | 42.667 | 13.333 | 4.166 |
| 144 | 157.333 | −13.333 | 1.130 |
| 24 | 42.667 | −18.667 | 8.167 |
| 176 | 157.333 | 18.667 | 2.215 |
| | | | 16.5253 |

Decision rule: $df = (c - 1) = (3 - 1) = 2$. If $\chi^2_{STAT} > 5.9915$, reject $H_0$.

Test statistic: $\chi^2_{STAT} = \sum_{\text{all cells}} \dfrac{(f_0 - f_e)^2}{f_e} = 16.5253$

Decision: Because $\chi^2_{STAT} = 16.5253 > 5.9915$, reject $H_0$. There is a significant difference in the age groups with respect to major grocery shopping day. **(b)** $p$-value = 0.0003. The probability that the test statistic is greater than or equal to 16.5253 is 0.03%, if the null hypothesis is true.

**(c) Pairwise**

| Comparisons | Critical Range | $|p_j - p_{j'}|$ |
|---|---|---|
| 1 to 2 | 0.1073 | 0.04 |
| 2 to 3 | 0.0959 | 0.16* |
| 1 to 3 | 0.0929 | 0.12* |

There is a significant difference between the 35–54 and over 54 groups, and between the under 35 and over 54 groups. **(d)** The stores can use this information to target their marketing on the specific groups of shoppers on Saturday and the days other than Saturday.

**12.18 (a)** Because $\chi^2_{STAT} = 20.3383 > 7.815$, reject $H_0$. There is evidence of a difference in the percentage working among the groups. **(b)** $p$-value = 0.0001. **(c)** Men 62–64 vs. Women 62–64: $0.11 < 0.196$; No significant difference. Men 62–64 vs. Men 65–69: $0.21 > 0.1903$; There is a significant difference. Men 62–64 vs. Women 65–69: $0.29 > 0.1826$; There is a significant difference. Women 62–64 vs. Men 65–69: $0.10 < 0.1887$; There is no significant difference. Women 62–64 vs. Women 65–69: $0.18 < 0.181$; There is no significant difference. Men 65–69 vs. Women 65–69: $0.08 < 0.174$; There is no significant difference.

**12.20** $df = (r - 1)(c - 1) = (3 - 1)(4 - 1) = 6$.

**12.22 (b)** $\chi^2_{STAT} = 8.3536 < 9.2103$, do not reject $H_0$ and conclude that there is not enough evidence that men and women feel differently about executive pay. **(c)** $\chi^2_{STAT} = 16.7073 > 9.2103$, reject $H_0$ and conclude that there is enough evidence that men and women feel differently about executive pay. **(d)** As you can see from the results in (b) and (c), the same proportions will result in a different test statistic and, hence, potentially different decisions.

**12.24 (a)** $H_0$: There is no relationship between the commuting time of company employees and the level of stress-related problems observed on the job. $H_1$: There is a relationship between the commuting time of company employees and the level of stress-related problems observed on the job.

| $f_0$ | $f_e$ | $(f_0 - f_e)$ | $(f_0 - f_e)^2/f_e$ |
|---|---|---|---|
| 9 | 12.1379 | −3.1379 | 0.8112 |
| 17 | 20.1034 | −3.1034 | 0.4791 |
| 18 | 11.7586 | 6.2414 | 3.3129 |
| 5 | 5.2414 | −0.2414 | 0.0111 |
| 8 | 8.6810 | −0.6810 | 0.0534 |
| 6 | 5.0776 | 0.9224 | 0.1676 |
| 18 | 14.6207 | 3.3793 | 0.7811 |
| 28 | 24.2155 | 3.7845 | 0.5915 |
| 7 | 14.1638 | −7.1638 | 3.6233 |
| | | | 9.8311 |

Decision rule: If $\chi^2_{STAT} > 13.277$, reject $H_0$.

Test statistic: $\chi^2_{STAT} = \sum_{\text{all cells}} \dfrac{(f_0 - f_e)^2}{f_e} = 9.8311$.

Decision: Because the $\chi^2_{STAT} = 9.8311 < 13.277$, do not reject $H_0$. There is not enough evidence to conclude that there is a relationship between the commuting time of company employees and the level of stress-related problems observed on the job. **(b)** Because $\chi^2_{STAT} = 9.831 > 9.488$, reject $H_0$. There is enough evidence at the 0.05 level to conclude that there is a relationship.

**12.26** Because $\chi^2_{STAT} = 129.520 > 21.026$, reject $H_0$. There is a relationship between when the decision is made of what to have for dinner and the type of household.

**12.28 (a)** $H_0: \pi_1 \geq \pi_2$ and $H_1: \pi_1 < \pi_2$, where 1 = beginning, 2 = end. Decision rule: If $Z < -1.645$, reject $H_0$.
Test statistic:

$$Z_{STAT} = \frac{B - C}{\sqrt{B + C}} = \frac{9 - 22}{\sqrt{9 + 22}} = -2.3349.$$

Decision: Because $Z_{STAT} = -2.3349 < -1.645$, reject $H_0$. There is evidence that the proportion of coffee drinkers who prefer Brand $A$ is lower at the beginning of the advertising campaign than at the end of the advertising campaign. **(b)** $p$-value = 0.0098. The probability of a test statistic smaller than $-2.3349$ is 0.98% if the proportion of coffee drinkers who prefer Brand $A$ is not lower at the beginning of the advertising campaign than at the end of the advertising campaign.

**12.30 (a)** Because $Z_{STAT} = -2.2361 < -1.645$, reject $H_0$. There is evidence that the proportion who prefer Brand $A$ is lower before the advertising than after the advertising. **(b)** $p$-value = 0.0127. The probability of a test statistic less than $-2.2361$ is 1.27% if the proportion who prefer Brand $A$ is not lower before the advertising than after the advertising.

**12.32 (a)** Because $Z_{STAT} = -3.8996 < -1.645$, reject $H_0$. There is evidence that the proportion of employees absent fewer than five days was lower in Year 1 than in Year 2. **(b)** The $p$-value is virtually zero. The probability of a test statistic smaller than $-3.8996$ is essentially zero if the proportion of employees absent fewer than five days was not lower in Year 1 than in Year 2.

**12.34 (a)** 9.2604 and 44.1814. **(b)** 8.9065 and 32.8523. **(c)** 7.2609 and 24.9958.

**12.36** 10.417.

**12.38 (a)** 6.262 and 27.488. **(b)** 7.261.

**12.40** You must assume that the data in the population are normally distributed to be able to use the chi-square test of a population variance or standard deviation. If the data selected do not come from an approximately normally distributed population, the accuracy of the test can be seriously affected.

**12.42 (a)** $H_0: \sigma = \$200$. $H_1: \sigma \neq \$200$.

Decision rule: $df = 24$. If $\chi^2_{STAT} < 12.401$ or $\chi^2_{STAT} > 39.364$, reject $H_0$.

Test statistic: $\chi^2_{STAT} = \frac{(n-1) \cdot S^2}{\sigma^2} = \frac{24 \cdot 237.52^2}{200^2} = 33.849$.

Decision: Because $12.401 < \chi^2_{STAT} = 33.849 < 39.364$, do not reject $H_0$. There is insufficient evidence to conclude that the standard deviation of the amount of auto repairs is not equal to $200. **(b)** You must assume that the data in the population are normally distributed to be able to use the chi-square test of a population variance or standard deviation. **(c)** $p$-value = 0.1748. The $p$-value is the probability that a sample is farther away from the hypothesized value of $200 than this sample value of $237.52 when the null hypothesis is true is 0.1748.

**12.44 (a)** Because $\chi^2_{STAT} = 1.2245 < 13.848$, reject $H_0$. There is sufficient evidence to conclude that the standard deviation of the diameter of doorknobs is less than 0.035 inch in the redesigned production process. **(b)** You must assume that the data in the population are normally

distributed to be able to use the chi-square test of a population variance or standard deviation. **(c)** $p$-value = 0.0230. The probability of a test statistic equal to or more extreme than the result from this sample data is 0.0230 if the population standard deviation is no less than 0.035 inch.

**12.46 (a)** Because $\chi^2_{STAT} = 21.492 < 30.144$, do not reject $H_0$. There is insufficient evidence to conclude that the standard deviation in the capacity of a certain type of battery is greater than 2.5 ampere-hours. **(b)** You must assume that the data in the population are normally distributed to be able to use the chi-square test of a population variance or standard deviation. **(c)** $p$-value = 0.3103. The probability of a test statistic equal to or more extreme than the result from this sample data is 0.3103 if the population standard deviation is no greater than 2.5 ampere-hours.

**12.48 (a)** 31. **(b)** 29. **(c)** 27. **(d)** 25.

**12.50** 40 and 79.

**12.52 (a)** The ranks for Sample 1 are 1, 2, 4, 5, and 10. The ranks for Sample 2 are 3, 6.5, 6.5, 8, 9, and 11. **(b)** 22. **(c)** 44.

**12.54** Decision: Because $T_1 = 22 > 20$, do not reject $H_0$.

**12.56 (a)** The data are ordinal. **(b)** The two-sample $t$ test is inappropriate because the data can only be placed in ranked order. **(c)** Because $Z_{STAT} = -2.2054 < -1.96$, reject $H_0$. There is evidence of a significant difference in the median rating of California Cabernets and Washington Cabernets.

**12.58 (a)** $H_0: M_1 = M_2$ where Populations: 1 = Wing A, 2 = Wing B. $H_1: M_1 \neq M_2$.
**Population 1** Sample Size = 20    Sum of Ranks = 561    **Population 2** Sample Size = 20    Sum of Ranks = 259    Total Sample Size $n = 40$
$T_1$ Test Statistic 561    $T_1$ Mean = 410    Standard Error of $T_1$ = 36.96846
**Two-Tailed Test** Lower Critical Value $-1.95996$ Upper Critical Value 1.959964

$$\mu_{T_1} = \frac{n_1(n+1)}{2} = \frac{20(40+1)}{2} = 410$$

$$\sigma_{T_1} = \sqrt{\frac{n_1 n_2 (n+1)}{12}} = \sqrt{\frac{20(20)(40+1)}{12}} = 36.9685$$

$$Z_{STAT} = \frac{T_1 - \mu_{T_1}}{\sigma_{T_1}} = \frac{561 - 410}{36.9685} = 4.0846$$

Decision: Because $Z_{STAT} = 4.0846 > 1.96$, reject $H_0$. $p$-value 4.42E-05 = approximately 0. There is enough evidence of a difference in the median delivery time in the two wings of the hotel. **(b)** The results of (a) are consistent with the results of Problem 10.69.

**12.60 (a)** Because $Z_{STAT} = -4.118 < -1.645$, reject $H_0$. There is enough evidence to conclude that the median crack size is less for the unflawed sample than for the flawed sample. **(b)** You must assume approximately equal variability in the two populations. **(c)** Using both the pooled-variance $t$ test and the separate-variance $t$ test allowed you to reject the null hypothesis and conclude in Problem 10.19 that the mean crack size is less for the unflawed sample than for the flawed sample. In this test, using the Wilcoxon rank sum test with large-sample $Z$-approximation also allowed you to reject the null hypothesis and conclude that the median crack size is less for the unflawed sample than for the flawed sample.

**12.62 (a)** Because $-1.96 < Z_{STAT} = 1.1833 < 1.96$, do not reject $H_0$. There is not enough evidence to conclude that there is a difference in the median battery life between subcompact cameras and compact cameras. **(b)** You must assume approximately equal variability in the two populations. **(c)** Using the pooled-variance $t$ test, you fail to reject the null hypothesis and conclude that there is not enough evidence of a difference in the mean battery life between the two types of digital cameras in Problem 10.11(a). Using the Wilcoxon rank sum test with large-sample $Z$-approximation, you also fail to reject the null hypothesis and conclude that there is not enough evidence of a difference in the median battery life between subcompact cameras and compact cameras.

**12.64** (a) 53. (b) 56. (c) 59. (d) 61.

**12.66** $W = 50$.

**12.68** Because $W = 50 > 47$, reject $H_0$.

**12.70** 61.

**12.72** (a) Because $W = 2 < 3$, reject $H_0$. There is enough evidence of a difference in the median summated rating between Brand $A$ and Brand $B$. (b) The results are similar.

**12.74** (a) Because the $p$-value $= 0.784$ is greater than the 0.05 level of significance, do not reject $H_0$. There is insufficient evidence of a difference in the median measurements in line and from an analytical lab. (b) The results are the same.

**12.76** (a) Because the $p$-value $= 0.009$ is less than the 0.05 level of significance, reject $H_0$. There is sufficient evidence of a difference in the median performance ratings between the two programs. (b) The results are the same.

**12.78** 15.086.

**12.80** (a) $H = 11.7924 > 5.991$, $p$-value $= 0.00275 < 0.05$, reject $H_0$. There is enough evidence of a difference in the median sales for the three locations. (b) In (a), you conclude that there is enough evidence of a difference in the median sales for the three locations, whereas in Problem 11.13(a), you conclude that the mean sales are different across the three store aisle locations. (c) If you believe that the sales will not be normally distributed, the Kruskal-Wallis rank test is more appropriate.

**12.82** (a) $H = 13.517 > 7.815$, $p$-value $= 0.0036 < 0.05$, reject $H_0$. There is sufficient evidence of a difference in the median waiting time in the four locations. (b) The results are consistent with those of Problem 11.9.

**12.84** (a) $H = 19.3269 > 9.488$, reject $H_0$. There is evidence of a difference in the median ratings of the ads. (b) The results are consistent with those of Problem 11.12. (c) Because the combined scores are not true continuous variables, the nonparametric Kruskal-Wallis rank test is more appropriate since it does not require the scores to be normally distributed.

**12.86** (a) Because $H = 22.26 > 7.815$ or the $p$-value is approximately zero, reject $H_0$. There is sufficient evidence of a difference in the median strength of the four brands of trash bags. (b) The results are the same.

**12.88** (a) Reject $H_0$ if $F_R > 9.2363$. (b) Because $F_R = 11.56 > 9.2363$, reject $H_0$.

**12.90** (a) $F_R = 1.4 < 9.4877$; $p$-value $= 0.8442 > 0.05$, do not reject $H_0$. There is insufficient evidence of a difference in the median prices at the digital music services. (b) The results are similar.

**12.92** (a) $F_R = 97.97 > 9.488$; $p$-value $= 0.0000 < 0.05$, reject $H_0$. There is evidence of a difference in the median thickness of the wafers for the five positions. (b) The results are similar.

**12.102** (a) Because $\chi^2_{STAT} = 0.412 < 3.841$, do not reject $H_0$. There is not enough evidence to conclude that there is a relationship between a student's gender and pizzeria selection. (b) Because $\chi^2_{STAT} = 2.624 < 3.841$, do not reject $H_0$. There is not enough evidence to conclude that there is a relationship between a student's gender and pizzeria selection.

(c) Because $\chi^2_{STAT} = 4.956 < 5.991$, do not reject $H_0$. There is not enough evidence to conclude that there is a relationship between price and pizzeria selection. (d) $p$-value $= 0.0839$. The probability of a sample that gives a test statistic equal to or greater than 4.956 is 8.39% if the null hypothesis of no relationship between price and pizzeria selection is true. (e) Because there is no evidence that price and pizzeria selection are related, it is inappropriate to determine which prices are different in terms of pizzeria preference.

**12.104** (a) Because $\chi^2_{STAT} = 11.895 < 12.592$, do not reject $H_0$. There is not enough evidence to conclude that there is a relationship between the attitudes of employees toward the use of self-managed work teams and employee job classification. (b) Because $\chi^2_{STAT} = 3.294 < 12.592$, do not reject $H_0$. There is not enough evidence to conclude that there is a relationship between the attitudes of employees toward vacation time without pay and employee job classification.

**12.106** (a) Because $Z_{STAT} = -1.7889 < -1.645$, reject $H_0$. There is enough evidence of a difference in the proportion of respondents who prefer Coca-Cola before and after viewing the ads. (b) $p$-value $= 0.0736$. The probability of a test statistic that differs from 0 by 1.7889 or more in either direction is 7.36% if there is not a difference in the proportion of respondents who prefer Coca-Cola before and after viewing the ads. (c) The frequencies in the second table are computed from the row and column totals of the first table. (d) Because the calculated test statistic $\chi^2_{STAT} = 0.6528 < 3.8415$, do not reject $H_0$ and conclude that there is not a significant difference in preference for Coca-Cola before and after viewing the ads. (e) $p$-value $= 0.4191$. The probability of a test statistic larger than 0.6528 is 41.91% if there is not a significant difference in preference for Coca-Cola before and after viewing the ads. (f) The McNemar test performed using the information in the first table takes into consideration the fact that the same set of respondents are surveyed before and after viewing the ads but the chi-square test performed using the information in the second table ignores this fact. The McNemar test should be used because of the related samples (before-after comparison).

**12.108** (a) Because $\chi^2_{STAT} = 11.635 > 7.815$, reject $H_0$. There is enough evidence to conclude that there is a relationship between the presence of environmental goals and the type of manufacturing process. (b) $p$-value $= 0.00874$. The probability of obtaining a data set that gives rise to a test statistic of 11.635 or more is 0.00874 if there is no relationship between the presence of environmental goals and the type of manufacturing process. (c) Because $\chi^2_{STAT} = 10.94 > 3.841$, reject $H_0$. There is enough evidence to conclude that there is a difference in improved environmental performance for teams with a specified goal of cutting costs. (d) $p$-value $= 0.000941$. The probability of obtaining a data set that gives rise to a test statistic of 10.94 or more is 0.000941 if there is no difference in improved environmental performance for teams with a specified goal of cutting costs. (e) Because $\chi^2_{STAT} = 0.612 < 3.841$, do not reject $H_0$. There is not enough evidence to conclude that there is a difference in improved profitability for teams with a specified goal of cutting costs. (f) $p$-value $= 0.4341$. The probability of obtaining a data set that gives rise to a test statistic of 0.612 or more is 0.4341 if there is no difference in improved profitability for teams with a specified goal of cutting costs. (g) $\chi^2_{STAT} = 3.454 < 3.841$, do not reject $H_0$. There is not enough evidence to conclude that there is a difference in improved morale for teams with a specified goal of cutting costs. (h) $p$-value $= 0.063$. The probability of obtaining a data set that gives rise to a test statistic of 3.454 or more is 0.063 if there is no difference in improved morale for teams with a specified goal of cutting costs.

# CHAPTER 13

**13.2 (a)** Yes. **(b)** No. **(c)** No. **(d)** Yes.

**13.4 (b)**

$$b_1 = \frac{SSXY}{SSX} = \frac{2,775}{375} = 7.4$$

$$b_0 = \bar{Y} - b_1\bar{X} = 237.5 - 7.4(12.5) = 145$$

For each increase in shelf space of an additional foot, weekly sales are estimated to increase by $7.40.
**(c)** $\hat{Y} = 145 + 7.4X = 145 + 7.4(8) = 204.2$, or $204.20.

**13.6 (b)** $b_0 = -2.37$, $b_1 = 0.0501$. **(c)** For every cubic foot increase in the amount moved, mean labor hours are estimated to increase by 0.0501. **(d)** 22.67 labor hours.

**13.8 (b)** $b_0 = -368.2846$, $b_1 = 4.7306$. **(c)** For each additional million-dollar increase in revenue, the mean annual value will increase by an estimated $4.7306 million. Literal interpretation of $b_0$ is not meaningful because an operating franchise cannot have zero revenue. **(d)** $341.3027 million.

**13.10 (b)** $b_0 = -140.1203$, $b_1 = 4.3331$ $\hat{Y} = b_0 + b_1X = \hat{Y} = -140.1203 + 4.3331X$ **(c)** For each increase of one additional million dollars of box office gross, the estimated mean DVDs sold will increase by 4.3331 thousands. **(d)** $\hat{Y} = b_0 + b_1X = \hat{Y} = -140.1203 + 4.3331(75) = 184.86285$ thousands.

**13.12** $r^2 = 0.90$. 90% of the variation in the dependent variable can be explained by the variation in the independent variable.

**13.14** $r^2 = 0.75$. 75% of the variation in the dependent variable can be explained by the variation in the independent variable.

**13.16 (a)** $r^2 = \frac{SSR}{SST} = \frac{20,535}{30,025} = 0.684$. 68.4% of the variation in sales can be explained by the variation in shelf space.

**(b)** $S_{YX} = \sqrt{\frac{SSE}{n-2}} = \sqrt{\frac{\sum_{i=1}^{n}(Y_i - \hat{Y}_i)^2}{n-2}} = \sqrt{\frac{9,490}{10}} = 30.8058.$

**(c)** Based on (a) and (b), the model should be very useful for predicting sales.

**13.18 (a)** $r^2 = 0.8892$. 88.92% of the variation in labor hours can be explained by the variation in cubic feet moved. **(b)** $S_{YX} = 5.0314$. **(c)** Based on (a) and (b), the model should be very useful for predicting the labor hours.

**13.20 (a)** $r^2 = 0.9334$. 93.34% of the variation in the value of a baseball franchise can be explained by the variation in its annual revenue. **(b)** $S_{YX} = 42.4335$. **(c)** Based on (a) and (b), the model should be very useful for predicting the value of a baseball franchise.

**13.22 (a)** $r^2 = 0.7278$. 72.78% of the variation in DVDs sold can be explained by the variation in box office gross. **(b)** $S_{YX} = 47.8668$. The variation of DVDs sold around the prediction line is 47.8668 millions. The typical difference between actual DVDs sold and the predicted DVDs sold using the regression equation is approximately 47.8668 millions. **(c)** Based on (a) and (b), the model is useful for predicting DVDs sold. **(d)** Other variables that might explain the variation in DVDs sold could be the amount spent on advertising, the timing of the release of the DVDs, and the distribution channels of the DVDs.

**13.24** A residual analysis of the data indicates a pattern, with sizable clusters of consecutive residuals that are either all positive or all negative. This pattern indicates a violation of the assumption of linearity. A quadratic model should be investigated.

**13.26** There does not appear to be a pattern in the residual plot. The assumptions of regression do not appear to be seriously violated.

**13.28** Based on the residual plot, there appears to be a nonlinear pattern in the residuals. A quadratic model should be investigated. The assumptions of normality and equal variance do not appear to be seriously violated.

**13.30** Based on the residual plot, there appears to be a nonlinear pattern in the residuals. A quadratic model should be investigated. There is some right-skewness in the residuals and some violation of the equal-variance assumption.

**13.32 (a)** An increasing linear relationship exists. **(b)** There is evidence of a strong positive autocorrelation among the residuals.

**13.34 (a)** No, because the data were not collected over time. **(b)** If a single store had been selected, then studied over a period of time, you would compute the Durbin-Watson statistic.

**13.36 (a)** $b_1 = \frac{SSXY}{SSX} = \frac{201,399.05}{12,495,626} = 0.0161$

$$b_0 = \bar{Y} - b_1\bar{X} = 71.2621 - 0.0161(4393) = 0.458$$

**(b)** $\hat{Y} = 0.458 + 0.0161X = 0.458 + 0.0161(4500) = 72.908$, or $72,908.
**(c)** There is no evidence of a pattern in the residuals over time.

**(d)** $D = \dfrac{\sum_{i=2}^{n}(e_i - e_{i-1})^2}{\sum_{i=1}^{n}e_i^2} = \dfrac{1,243.2244}{599.0683} = 2.08 > 1.45.$ There is no

evidence of positive autocorrelation among the residuals. **(e)** Based on a residual analysis, the model appears to be adequate.

**13.38 (a)** $b_0 = -2.535$, $b_1 = .06073$. **(b)** $2,505.40. **(d)** $D = 1.64 > d_U = 1.42$, so there is no evidence of positive autocorrelation among the residuals. **(e)** The plot shows some nonlinear pattern, suggesting that a nonlinear model might be better. Otherwise, the model appears to be adequate.

**13.40 (a)** 3.00. **(b)** ±2.1199. **(c)** Reject $H_0$. There is evidence that the fitted linear regression model is useful. **(d)** $1.32 \le \beta_1 \le 7.68$.

**13.42 (a)** $t_{STAT} = \dfrac{b_1 - \beta_1}{S_{b_1}} = \dfrac{7.4}{1.59} = 4.65 > 2.2281$. Reject $H_0$. There is evidence that the fitted linear regression model is useful.
**(b)** $b_1 \pm t_{\alpha/2}S_{b_1} = 7.4 \pm 2.2281(1.59)$   $3.86 \le \beta_1 \le 10.94$

**13.44 (a)** $t_{STAT} = 16.52 > 2.0322$; reject $H_0$. **(b)** $0.0439 \le \beta_1 \le 0.0562$.

**13.46 (a)** Because the $p$-value is approximately zero, reject $H_0$ at the 5% level of significance. There is evidence of a linear relationship between annual revenue and franchise value. **(b)** $4.2416 \le \beta_1 \le 5.2196$.

**13.48 (a)** The $p$-value is virtually $0 < 0.05$; reject $H_0$. **(b)** $3.3072 \le \beta_1 \le 5.3590$.

**13.50 (b)** If the S&P gains 30% in a year, the UOPIX is expected to gain an estimated 60%. **(c)** If the S&P loses 35% in a year, the UOPIX is expected to lose an estimated 70%.

**13.52 (a)** $r = 0.8935$. There appears to be a strong positive linear relationship between the mileage as calculated by owners and by current government standards. **(b)** $t_{STAT} = 5.2639 > 2.3646$, $p$-value $= 0.0012 <$ 0.05. Reject $H_0$. At the 0.05 level of significance, there is a significant linear relationship between the mileage as calculated by owners and by current government standards.

**13.54 (a)** $r = 0.5497$. There appears to be a moderate positive linear relationship between the average Wonderlic score of football players trying out for the NFL and the graduation rate for football players at selected schools. **(b)** $t_{STAT} = 3.9485$, $p$-value $= 0.0004 < 0.05$. Reject $H_0$. At the 0.05 level of significance, there is a significant linear relationship between the average Wonderlic score of football players trying out for the NFL and the graduation rate for football players at selected schools. **(c)** There is a significant linear relationship between the average Wonderlic score of football players trying out for the NFL and the graduation rate for football players at selected schools, but the positive linear relationship is only moderate.

**13.56 (a)** $15.95 \le \mu_{Y|X=4} \le 18.05$. **(b)** $14.651 \le Y_{X=4} \le 19.349$.

**13.58 (a)** $\hat{Y} \pm t_{\alpha/2} S_{YX} \sqrt{h_i}$

$$= 204.2 \pm 2.2281 (30.81)\sqrt{0.1373}$$

$$178.76 \le \mu_{Y|X=8} \le 229.64$$

**(b)** $\hat{Y} \pm t_{\alpha/2} S_{YX} \sqrt{1+h_i}$

$$= 204.2 \pm 2.2281(30.81)\sqrt{1+0.1373}$$

$$131.00 \le Y_{X=8} \le 277.40$$

**(c)** Part (b) provides a prediction interval for the individual response given a specific value of the independent variable, and part (a) provides an interval estimate for the mean value, given a specific value of the independent variable. Because there is much more variation in predicting an individual value than in estimating a mean value, a prediction interval is wider than a confidence interval estimate.

**13.60 (a)** $20.799 \le \mu_{Y|X=500} \le 24.542$. **(b)** $12.276 \le Y_{X=500} \le 33.065$. **(c)** You can estimate a mean more precisely than you can predict a single observation.

**13.62 (a)** $325.0222 \le \mu_{Y|X=150} \le 357.5832$. **(b)** $252.87 \le Y_{X=150} \le 429.7353$. **(c)** Part (b) provides a prediction interval for an individual response given a specific value of $X$ and part (a) provides a confidence interval estimate for the mean value given a specific value of $X$. Since there is much more variation in predicting an individual value than in estimating a mean, the prediction interval is wider than the confidence interval.

**13.74 (a)** $b_0 = 24.84$, $b_1 = 0.14$. **(b)** For each additional case, the predicted mean delivery time is estimated to increase by 0.14 minutes. **(c)** 45.84. **(d)** No, 500 is outside the relevant range of the data used to fit the regression equation. **(e)** $r^2 = 0.972$. **(f)** There is no obvious pattern in the residuals, so the assumptions of regression are met. The model appears to be adequate. **(g)** $t_{STAT} = 24.88 > 2.1009$; reject $H_0$. **(h)** $44.88 \le \mu_{Y|X=150} \le 46.80$. **(i)** $41.56 \le Y_{X=150} \le 50.12$. **(j)** $0.128 \le \beta_1 \le 0.152$.

**13.76 (a)** $b_0 = -122.3439$, $b_1 = 1.7817$. **(b)** For each additional thousand dollars in assessed value, the estimated mean selling price of a house increases by $1.7817 thousand. The estimated mean selling price of a house with a 0 assessed value is $-122.3439 thousand. However, this interpretation is not meaningful in the current setting because the assessed value cannot be 0. **(c)** $\hat{Y} = -122.3439 + 1.78171X = -122.3439 + 1.78171(170) = 180.5475$ thousand dollars. **(d)** $r^2 = 0.9256$. So 92.56% of

the variation in selling price can be explained by the variation in assessed value. **(e)** Neither the residual plot nor the normal probability plot reveal any potential violation of the linearity, equal variance, and normality assumptions. **(f)** $t_{STAT} = 18.6648 > 2.0484$, $p$-value is virtually zero. Because $p$-value $< 0.05$, reject $H_0$. There is evidence of a linear relationship between selling price and assessed value. **(g)** $178.7066 \le \mu_{Y|X=170} \le 182.3884$. **(h)** $173.1953 \le Y_{X=170} \le 187.8998$. **(i)** $1.5862 \le \beta_1 \le 1.9773$.

**13.78 (a)** $b_0 = 0.30$, $b_1 = 0.00487$. **(b)** For each additional point on the GMAT score, the predicted mean GPA is estimated to increase by 0.00487. **(c)** 3.222. **(d)** $r^2 = 0.798$. **(e)** There is no obvious pattern in the residuals, so the assumptions of regression are met. The model appears to be adequate. **(f)** $t_{STAT} = 8.43 > 2.1009$; reject $H_0$. **(g)** $3.144 \le \mu_{Y|X=600} \le 3.301$. **(h)** $2.886 \le Y_{X=600} \le 3.559$. **(i)** $.00366 \le \beta_1 \le .00608$.

**13.80 (a)** There is no clear relationship shown on the scatterplot. **(c)** Looking at all 23 flights, when the temperature is lower, there is likely to be some O-ring damage, particularly if the temperature is below 60 degrees. **(d)** 31 degrees is outside the relevant range, so a prediction should not be made. **(e)** Predicted $Y = 18.036 - 0.240X$, where $X =$ temperature and $Y =$ O-ring damage. **(g)** A nonlinear model would be more appropriate. **(h)** The appearance on the residual plot of a nonlinear pattern indicates a nonlinear model would be better.

**13.82 (a)** $b_0 = 14.6816$, $b_1 = 0.1135$. **(b)** For each additional percentage increase in graduation rate, the estimated mean average Wonderlic score increases by 0.1135. The estimated mean average Wonderlic score is 14.6816 for a school that has a 0% graduation rate. However, this interpretation is not meaningful in the current setting because graduation rate is very unlikely to be 0% for any school. **(c)** $\hat{Y} = 14.6816 + 0.11347X = 14.6816 + 0.11347(50) = 20.4$. **(d)** $r^2 = 0.3022$. So, 30.22% of the variation in average Wonderlic score can be explained by the variation in graduation rate. **(e)** Neither the residual plot nor the normal probability plot reveal any potential violation of the linearity, equal variance, and normality assumptions. **(f)** $t_{STAT} = 3.9485 > 2.0281$, $p$-value $= 0.0004$. Because $p$-value $< 0.05$, reject $H_0$. There is evidence of a linear relationship between the average Wonderlic score for football players trying out for the NFL from a school and the graduation rate. **(g)** $19.6 \le \mu_{Y|X=50} \le 21.1$. **(h)** $15.9 \le Y_{X=50} \le 24.8$. **(i)** $0.0552 \le \beta_1 \le 0.1718$.

**13.84 (a)** $b_0 = -2,629.222$, $b_1 = 82.472$. **(b)** For each additional centimeter in circumference, the mean weight is estimated to increase by 82.472 grams. **(c)** 2,319.08 grams. **(e)** $r^2 = 0.937$. **(f)** There appears to be a nonlinear relationship between circumference and weight. **(g)** $p$-value is virtually $0 < 0.05$; reject $H_0$. **(h)** $72.7875 \le \beta_1 \le 92.156$. **(i)** $2,186.959 \le \mu_{Y|X=60} \le 2,451.202$. **(j)** $1,726.551 \le Y_{X=60} \le 2,911.610$.

**13.86 (b)** $\hat{Y} = 931,626.16 + 21,782.76X$. **(c)** $b_1 = 21,782.76$ means that as the median age of the customer base increases by one year, the latest one-month mean sales total is estimated to increase by $21,782.76. **(d)** $r^2 = 0.0017$. Only 0.17% of the total variation in the franchise's latest one-month sales total can be explained by using the median age of customer base. **(e)** The residuals are very evenly spread out across different range of median age. **(f)** Because $-2.4926 < t_{STAT} = 0.2482 < 2.4926$, do not reject $H_0$. There is not enough evidence to conclude that there is a linear relationship between the one-month sales total and the median age of the customer base. **(g)** $-156,181.50 \le \beta_1 \le 199,747.02$.

**13.88 (a)** There is a positive linear relationship between total sales and the percentage of customer base with a college diploma. **(b)** $\hat{Y} = 789,847.38 + 35,854.15X$. **(c)** $b_1 = 35,854.15$ means that for each increase of one percent of the customer base having received a college diploma, the latest one-month mean sales total is estimated to increase by $35,854.15.

**(d)** $r^2 = 0.1036$. So 10.36% of the total variation in the franchise's latest one-month sales total can be explained by the percentage of the customer base with a college diploma. **(e)** The residuals are evenly spread out around zero. **(f)** Because $t_{STAT} = 2.0392 > 2.0281$, reject $H_0$. There is enough evidence to conclude that there is a linear relationship between one-month sales total and percentage of customer base with a college diploma. **(g)** $b_1 \pm t_{\alpha/2} \ S_{b_1} = 35,854.15 \pm 2.028(17,582.269)$   $195.75 \leq \beta_1 \leq 71,512.60$.

**13.90 (a)** $b_0 = -39.0137$, $b_1 = 1.3878$. **(b)** For each additional unit increase in summated rating, the mean price per person is estimated to increase by $1.3878. Because no restaurant will receive a summated rating of 0, it is inappropriate to interpret the $Y$ intercept. **(c)** $30.38. **(d)** $r^2 = 0.6586$. So, 65.86% of the variation in price per person can be explained by the variation in the summated rating. **(e)** There is no obvious pattern in the residuals so the assumptions of regression are met. The model appears to be adequate. **(f)** $t_{STAT} = 13.7484$, the $p$-value is virtually $0 < 0.05$; reject $H_0$. There is enough evidence to conclude that there is a linear relationship between price per person and summated rating. **(g)** $28.21 \leq \mu_{Y|X = 50} \leq 32.55$. **(h)** $16.36 \leq Y_{X=50} \leq 44.39$. **(i)** $1.19 \leq \beta_1 \leq 1.59$. **(j)** The linear regression model appears to have provided an adequate fit and shown a significant linear relationship between price per person and summated rating. Because 65.86% of the variation in price per person can be explained by the variation in summated rating, summated rating is moderately useful in predicting the price per person.

**13.92 (a)** The correlation of Target and Sara Lee is 0.0364, Target and GM is 0.7275, and Sara Lee and GE is −0.0780. **(b)** There is a fairly strong positive linear relationship between the stock price of Target and GE, almost no linear relationship between the stock price of Sara Lee and Target, and almost no linear relationship between the stock price of GE and Sara Lee. **(c)** It is not a good idea to have all the stocks in an individual's portfolio be strongly, positively correlated among each other because the portfolio risk can be reduced when a pair of stock prices is negatively related in a two-stock portfolio.

# CHAPTER 14

**14.2 (a)** For each one-unit increase in $X_1$, you estimate that $Y$ will decrease 2 units, holding $X_2$ constant. For each one-unit increase in $X_2$, you estimate that $Y$ will increase 7 units, holding $X_1$ constant. **(b)** The $Y$-intercept equal to 50 estimates the predicted value of $Y$ when both $X_1$ and $X_2$ are zero.

**14.4 (a)** $\hat{Y} = -2.72825 + 0.047114X_1 + 0.011947X_2$. **(b)** For a given number of orders, for each increase of $1,000 in sales, mean distribution cost is estimated to increase by $47.114. For a given amount of sales, for each increase of one order, mean distribution cost is estimated to increase by $11.95. **(c)** The interpretation of $b_0$ has no practical meaning here because it would represent the estimated distribution cost when there were no sales and no orders. **(d)** $\hat{Y} = -2.72825 + 0.047114(400) + 0.011947(4500) = 69.878$ or $69,878. **(e)** $66,419.93 \leq \mu_{Y|X} \leq 73,337.01$. **(f)** $59,380.61 \leq Y_X \leq 80,376.33$. **(g)** The interval in (e) is narrower because it is estimating the mean value, not an individual value.

**14.6 (a)** $\hat{Y} = 156.4 + 13.081X_1 + 16.795X_2$. **(b)** For a given amount of newspaper advertising, each increase by $1,000 in radio advertising is estimated to result in a mean increase in sales of $13,081. For a given amount of radio advertising, each increase by $1,000 in newspaper advertising is estimated to result in a mean increase in sales of $16,795. **(c)** When there is no money spent on radio advertising and newspaper advertising, the estimated mean sales is $156,430.44. **(d)** Holding the other independent variable constant, newspaper advertising seems to be more effective because its slope is greater.

**14.8 (a)** $\hat{Y} = 400.8057 + 456.4485X_1 - 2.4708X_2$, where $X_1 = $ land, $X_2 = $ age. **(b)** For a given age, each increase by one acre in land area is estimated to result in a mean increase in appraised value by $456.45 thousands. For a given acreage, each increase of one year in age is estimated to result in the mean decrease in appraised value by $2.47 thousands. **(c)** The interpretation of $b_0$ has no practical meaning here because it would represent the estimated appraised value of a new house that has no land area. **(d)** $\hat{Y} = 400.8057 + 456.4485(0.25) - 2.4708(45) = $403.73$ thousands. **(e)** $372.7370 \leq \mu_{Y|X} \leq 434.7243$. **(f)** $235.1964 \leq Y_X \leq 572.2649$.

**14.10 (a)** $MSR = 15$, $MSE = 12$. **(b)** 1.25. **(c)** $F_{STAT} = 1.25 < 4.10$; do not reject $H_0$. **(d)** 0.20. **(e)** 0.04.

**14.12 (a)** $F_{STAT} = 97.69 > F_\alpha = 3.89$ with 2 and $15 - 2 - 1 = 12$ degrees of freedom. Reject $H_0$. There is evidence of a significant linear relationship with at least one of the independent variables. **(b)** The $p$-value is 0.0001. **(c)** $r^2 = 0.9421$. 94.21% of the variation in the long-term ability to absorb shock can be explained by variation in forefoot absorbing capability and variation in midsole impact. **(d)** $r^2_{adj} = 0.93245$.

**14.14 (a)** $F_{STAT} = 74.13 > 3.467$; reject $H_0$. **(b)** $p$-value = 0. **(c)** $r^2 = 0.8759$. 87.59% of the variation in distribution cost can be explained by variation in sales and variation in number of orders. **(d)** $r^2_{adj} = 0.8641$.

**14.16 (a)** $F_{STAT} = 40.16 > F_\alpha = 3.522$ with 2 and $22 - 2 - 1 = 19$ degrees of freedom. Reject $H_0$. There is evidence of a significant linear relationship. **(b)** The $p$-value is less than 0.001. **(c)** $r^2 = 0.8087$. 80.87% of the variation in sales can be explained by variation in radio advertising and variation in newspaper advertising. **(d)** $r^2_{adj} = 0.7886$.

**14.18 (a)–(e)** Based on a residual analysis, there is no evidence of a violation in the assumptions of regression. **(f)** $D = \dfrac{1,077.0956}{477.0430} = 2.26$. **(g)** $D = 2.26 > 1.55$. There is no evidence of positive autocorrelation in the residuals.

**14.20 (a)** There appears to be a quadratic relationship in the plot of the residuals against both radio and newspaper advertising. **(b)** The Durbin-Watson test is not appropriate since all the data was collected in the same month. **(c)** Quadratic terms for both of these explanatory variables should be considered for inclusion in the model.

**14.22 (a)** The residual analysis reveals no patterns. **(b)** The Durbin-Watson test is not appropriate since the data are not a time series. **(c)** There are no apparent violations in the assumptions.

**14.24 (a)** Variable $X_2$ has a larger slope in terms of the $t$ statistic of 3.75 than variable $X_1$, which has a smaller slope in terms of the $t$ statistic of 3.33. **(b)** $1.46824 \leq \beta_1 \leq 6.53176$. **(c)** For $X_1$: $t_{STAT} = 4/1.2 = 3.33 > 2.1098$, with 17 degrees of freedom for $\alpha = 0.05$. Reject $H_0$. There is evidence that $X_1$ contributes to a model already containing $X_2$. For $X_2$: $t_{STAT} = 3/0.8 = 3.75 > 2.1098$, with 17 degrees of freedom for $\alpha = 0.05$. Reject $H_0$. There is evidence that $X_2$ contributes to a model already containing $X_1$. Both $X_1$ and $X_2$ should be included in the model.

**14.26 (a)** 95% confidence interval on $\beta_1$: $b_1 \pm S_{b_1}$, $0.0471 \pm 2.0796(0.0203)$, $0.00488 \leq \beta_1 \leq 0.08932$. **(b)** For $X_1$: $t_{STAT} = b_1/S_{b_1} = 0.0471/0.0203 = 2.32 > 2.0796$. Reject $H_0$. There is evidence that $X_1$ contributes to a model already containing $X_2$. For $X_2$: $t_{STAT} = b_1/S_{b_1} = 0.01195/0.00225 = 5.31 > 2.0796$. Reject $H_0$. There is evidence that $X_2$ contributes to a model already containing $X_1$. Both $X_1$ (sales) and $X_2$ (orders) should be included in the model.

**14.28 (a)** $9.398 \leq \beta_1 \leq 16.763$. **(b)** For $X_1$: $t_{STAT} = 7.43 > 2.093$. Reject $H_0$. There is evidence that $X_1$ contributes to a model already containing

$X_2$. For $X_2$: $t_{STAT} = 5.67 > 2.093$. Reject $H_0$. There is evidence that $X_2$ contributes to a model already containing $X_1$. Both $X_1$ (radio advertising) and $X_2$ (newspaper advertising) should be included in the model.

**14.30 (a)** $227.5865 \leq \beta_1 \leq 685.3104$. **(b)** For $X_1$: $t_{STAT} = 4.0922$ and $p$-value $= 0.0003$. Because $p$-value $< 0.05$, reject $H_0$. There is evidence that $X_1$ contributes to a model already containing $X_2$. For $X_2$: $t_{STAT} = -3.6295$ and $p$-value $= 0.0012$. Because $p$-value $< 0.05$, reject $H_0$. There is evidence that $X_2$ contributes to a model already containing $X_1$. Both $X_1$ (land area) and $X_2$ (age) should be included in the model.

**14.32 (a)** For $X_1$: $F_{STAT} = 1.25 < 4.96$; do not reject $H_0$. For $X_2$: $F_{STAT} = 0.833 < 4.96$; do not reject $H_0$. **(b)** 0.01111, 0.0769.

**14.34 (a)** For $X_1$: $SSR(X_1|X_2) = SSR(X_1 \text{ and } X_2) - SSR(X_2) = 3{,}368.087 - 3{,}246.062 = 122.025$, $F_{STAT} = \dfrac{SSR(X_2 \mid X_1)}{MSE} = \dfrac{122.025}{477.043/21} = 5.37 > 4.325$. Reject $H_0$. There is evidence that $X_1$ contributes to a model already containing $X_2$. For $X_2$: $SSR(X_2|X_1) = SSR(X_1 \text{ and } X_2) - SSR(X_1) = 3{,}368.087 - 2{,}726.822 = 641.265$, $F_{STAT} = \dfrac{SSR(X_2 \mid X_1)}{MSE} = \dfrac{641.265}{477.043/21} = 28.23 > 4.325$ Reject $H_0$. There is evidence that $X_2$ contributes to a model already containing $X_1$. Because both $X_1$ and $X_2$ make a significant contribution to the model in the presence of the other variable, both variables should be included in the model.

**(b)** $r^2_{Y1.2} = \dfrac{SSR(X_1 \mid X_2)}{SST - SSR(X_1 \text{ and } X_2) + SSR(X_1 \mid X_2)}$

$= \dfrac{122.025}{3{,}845.13 - 3{,}368.087 + 122.025} = 0.2037$

Holding constant the effect of the number of orders, 20.37% of the variation in distribution cost can be explained by the variation in sales.

$r^2_{Y2.1} = \dfrac{SSR(X_2 \mid X_1)}{SST - SSR(X_1 \text{ and } X_2) + SSR(X_2 \mid X_1)}$

$= \dfrac{641.265}{3{,}845.13 - 3{,}368.087 + 641.265} = 0.5734$

Holding constant the effect of sales, 57.34% of the variation in distribution cost can be explained by the variation in the number of orders.

**14.36 (a)** For $X_1$: $F_{STAT} = 55.28 > 4.381$. Reject $H_0$. There is evidence that $X_1$ contributes to a model already containing $X_2$. For $X_2$: $F_{STAT} = 32.12 > 4.381$. Reject $H_0$. There is evidence that $X_2$ contributes to a model already containing $X_1$. Because both $X_1$ and $X_2$ make a significant contribution to the model in the presence of the other variable, both variables should be included in the model. **(b)** $r^2_{Y1.2} = 0.7442$. Holding constant the effect of newspaper advertising, 74.42% of the variation in sales can be explained by the variation in radio advertising. $r^2_{Y2.1} = 0.6283$. Holding constant the effect of radio advertising, 62.83% of the variation in sales can be explained by the variation in newspaper advertising.

**14.38 (a)** Holding constant the effect of $X_2$, for each increase of one unit of $X_1$, $Y$ increases by 4 units. **(b)** Holding constant the effect of $X_1$, for each increase of one unit of $X_2$, $Y$ increases by 2 units. **(c)** Because $t_{STAT} = 3.27 > 2.1098$, reject $H_0$. Variable $X_2$ makes a significant contribution to the model.

**14.40 (a)** $\hat{Y} = 243.7371 + 9.2189X_1 + 12.6967X_2$, where $X_1$ = number of rooms and $X_2$ = neighborhood (east = 0). **(b)** Holding constant the effect of neighborhood, for each additional room, the selling price is estimated to increase by a mean of 9.2189 thousands of dollars, or \$9218.9. For a given number of rooms, a west neighborhood is estimated to increase the mean selling price over an east neighborhood by 12.6967 thousands of dollars, or \$12,696.7. **(c)** $\hat{Y} = 243.7371 + 9.2189(9) + 12.6967(0) = 326.7076$, or \$326,707.6. $\$321{,}471.44 \leq \mu_{Y|X} \leq \$331{,}943.71$.

$\$309{,}560.04 \leq Y_X \leq \$343{,}855.1$. **(d)** Based on a residual analysis, the model appears to be adequate. **(e)** $F_{STAT} = 55.39$, the $p$-value is virtually 0. Because $p$-value $< 0.05$, reject $H_0$. There is evidence of a significant relationship between selling price and the two independent variables (rooms and neighborhood). **(f)** For $X_1$: $t_{STAT} = 8.9537$, the $p$-value is virtually 0. Reject $H_0$. Number of rooms makes a significant contribution and should be included in the model. For $X_2$: $t_{STAT} = 3.5913$, $p$-value $= 0.0023 < 0.05$. Reject $H_0$. Neighborhood makes a significant contribution and should be included in the model. Based on these results, the regression model with the two independent variables should be used. **(g)** $7.0466 \leq \beta_1 \leq 11.3913$. **(h)** $5.2378 \leq \beta_2 \leq 20.1557$. **(i)** $r^2_{adj} = 0.851$. **(j)** $r^2_{Y1.2} = 0.825$. Holding constant the effect of neighborhood, 82.5% of the variation in selling price can be explained by variation in number of rooms. $r^2_{Y2.1} = 0.431$. Holding constant the effect of number of rooms, 43.1% of the variation in selling price can be explained by variation in neighborhood. **(k)** The slope of selling price with number of rooms is the same, regardless of whether the house is located in an east or west neighborhood. **(l)** $\hat{Y} = 253.95 + 8.032X_1 - 5.90X_2 + 2.089X_1X_2$. For $X_1X_2$, $p$-value $= 0.330$. Do not reject $H_0$. There is no evidence that the interaction term makes a contribution to the model. **(m)** The model in (a) should be used.

**14.42 (a)** Predicted time $= 8.01 + 0.00523$ Depth $- 2.105$ Dry. **(b)** Holding constant the effect of type of drilling, for each foot increase in depth of the hole, the mean drilling time is estimated to increase by 0.0052 minutes. For a given depth, a dry drilling hole is estimated to reduce the mean drilling time over wet drilling by 2.1052 minutes. **(c)** 6.428 minutes, $6.210 \leq \mu_{Y|X} \leq 6.646$, $4.923 \leq Y_X \leq 7.932$. **(d)** The model appears to be adequate. **(e)** $F_{STAT} = 111.11 > 3.09$; reject $H_0$. **(f)** $t_{STAT} = 5.03 > 1.9847$; reject $H_0$. $t_{STAT} = -14.03 < -1.9847$; reject $H_0$. Include both variables. **(g)** $0.0032 \leq \beta_1 \leq 0.0073$. **(h)** $-2.403 \leq \beta_2 \leq -1.808$ **(i)** 69.0%. **(j)** 0.207, 0.670. **(k)** The slope of the additional drilling time with the depth of the hole is the same, regardless of the type of drilling method used. **(l)** The $p$-value of the interaction term $= 0.462 > 0.05$, so the term is not significant and should not be included in the model. **(m)** The model in part (a) should be used.

**14.44 (a)** $\hat{Y} = 31.5594 - 0.0296X_1 + 0.0041X_2 + 0.000017159X_1X_2$, where $X_1$ = sales, $X_2$ = orders, $p$-value $= 0.3249 > 0.05$. Do not reject $H_0$. There is not enough evidence that the interaction term makes a contribution to the model. **(b)** Because there is not enough evidence of any interaction effect between sales and orders, the model in Problem 14.4 should be used.

**14.46 (a)** The $p$-value of the interaction term $= 0.002 < .05$, so the term is significant and should be included in the model. **(b)** Use the model developed in this problem.

**14.48 (a)** For $X_1X_2$, $p$-value $= 0.2353 > 0.05$. Do not reject $H_0$. There is not enough evidence that the interaction term makes a contribution to the model. **(b)** Because there is not enough evidence of an interaction effect between total staff present and remote hours, the model in Problem 14.7 should be used.

**14.50** Holding constant the effect of other variables, the natural logarithm of the estimated odds ratio for the dependent categorical response will increase by 2.2 for each unit increase in the independent variable to which the coefficient corresponds.

**14.52** 0.4286.

**14.54 (a)** ln(estimated odds ratio) $= -6.94 + 0.13947X_1 + 2.774X_2 = -6.94 + 0.13947(36) + 2.774(0) = -1.91908$.

Estimated odds ratio $= e^{-1.91908} = 0.1467$.

Estimated Probability of Success = Odds Ratio/(1 + Odds Ratio) = $0.1467/(1 + 0.1467) = 0.1280$. **(b)** From the text discussion of the example, 70.16% of the individuals who charge $36,000 per annum and possess additional cards can be expected to purchase the premium card. Only 12.80% of the individuals who charge $36,000 per annum and do not possess additional cards can be expected to purchase the premium card. For a given amount of money charged per annum, the likelihood of purchasing a premium card is substantially higher among individuals who already possess additional cards than for those who do not possess additional cards. **(c)** ln(estimated odds ratio) = $-6.94 + 0.13947X_1 + 2.774X_2 = -6.94 + 0.13947(18) + 2.774(0) = -4.42954$.

Estimated odds ratio = $e^{-4.42954} = 0.0119$.

Estimated Probability of Success = Odds Ratio/(1 + Odds Ratio) = $0.0119/(1 + 0.0119) = 0.01178$. **(d)** Among individuals who do not purchase additional cards, the likelihood of purchasing a premium card diminishes dramatically with a substantial decrease in the amount charged per annum.

**14.56 (a)** ln(estimated odds) = $-121.95 + 8.053$ GPA + $0.157$ GMAT. **(b)** Holding constant the effects of GMAT score, for each increase of one point in GPA, ln(estimated odds) increases by an estimate of 8.053. Holding constant the effects of GPA, for each increase of one point in GMAT score, ln(estimated odds) increases by an estimate of 0.15729. **(c)** 0.197. **(d)** Deviance statistic = $8.122 < 40.133$, do not reject $H_0$, so model is adequate. **(e)** For GPA: $Z_{STAT} = 1.60 < 1.96$, do not reject $H_0$. For GMAT: $Z_{STAT} = 2.07 > 1.96$, reject $H_0$. **(f)** ln(estimated odds) = $-2.765 + 1.02$ GPA. **(g)** ln(estimated odds) = $-60.15 + 0.099$ GMAT. **(h)** Use model in (g).

**14.68 (a)** $\hat{Y} = -3.9152 + 0.0319X_1 + 4.2228X_2$, where $X_1$ = number of cubic feet moved and $X_2$ = number of pieces of large furniture. **(b)** Holding constant the number of pieces of large furniture, for each additional cubic foot moved, the mean labor hours are estimated to increase by 0.0319. Holding constant the amount of cubic feet moved, for each additional piece of large furniture, the mean labor hours are estimated to increase by 4.2228. **(c)** $\hat{Y} = -3.9152 + 0.0319(500) + 4.2228(2) = 20.4926$. **(d)** Based on a residual analysis, the errors appear to be normally distributed. The equal-variance assumption might be violated because the variances appear to be larger around the center region of both independent variables. There might also be violation of the linearity assumption. A model with quadratic terms for both independent variables might be fitted. **(e)** $F_{STAT} = 228.80$, $p$-value is virtually 0. Because $p$-value < 0.05, reject $H_0$. There is evidence of a significant relationship between labor hours and the two independent variables (the amount of cubic feet moved and the number of pieces of large furniture). **(f)** The $p$-value is virtually 0. The probability of obtaining a test statistic of 228.80 or greater is virtually 0 if there is no significant relationship between labor hours and the two independent variables (the amount of cubic feet moved and the number of pieces of large furniture). **(g)** $r^2 = 0.9327$. 93.27% of the variation in labor hours can be explained by variation in the amount of cubic feet moved and the number of pieces of large furniture. **(h)** $r^2_{adj} = 0.9287$. **(i)** For $X_1$: $t_{STAT} = 6.9339$, the $p$-value is virtually 0. Reject $H_0$. The amount of cubic feet moved makes a significant contribution and should be included in the model. For $X_2$: $t_{STAT} = 4.6192$, the $p$-value is virtually 0. Reject $H_0$. The number of pieces of large furniture makes a significant contribution and should be included in the model. Based on these results, the regression model with the two independent variables should be used. **(j)** For $X_1$: $t_{STAT} = 6.9339$, the $p$-value is virtually 0. The probability of obtaining a sample that will yield a test statistic farther away than 6.9339 is virtually 0 if the number of cubic feet moved does not make a significant contribution holding the effect of the number of pieces of large furniture constant. For $X_2$: $t_{STAT} = 4.6192$, the $p$-value is virtually 0. The probability of obtaining a sample that will yield a test statistic farther away than 4.6192 is virtually 0 if the number of pieces of large furniture does not make a significant contribution

holding the effect of the amount of cubic feet moved constant. **(k)** $0.0226 \leq \beta_1 \leq 0.0413$. You are 95% confident that the mean labor hours will increase by somewhere between 0.0226 and 0.0413 for each additional cubic foot moved, holding constant the number of pieces of large furniture. In Problem 13.44, you are 95% confident that the mean labor hours will increase by somewhere between 0.0439 and 0.0562 for each additional cubic foot moved regardless of the number of pieces of large furniture. **(l)** $r^2_{Y1.2} = 0.5930$. Holding constant the effect of the number of pieces of large furniture, 59.3% of the variation in labor hours can be explained by variation in the amount of cubic feet moved. $r^2_{Y2.1} = 0.3927$. Holding constant the effect of the amount of cubic feet moved, 39.27% of the variation in labor hours can be explained by variation in the number of pieces of large furniture.

**14.70 (a)** $\hat{Y} = -120.0483 + 1.7506X_1 + 0.3680X_2$, where $X_1$ = assessed value and $X_2$ = time period. **(b)** Holding constant the time period, for each additional thousand dollars of assessed value, the mean selling price is estimated to increase by 1.7507 thousand dollars. Holding constant the assessed value, for each additional month since assessment, the mean selling price is estimated to increase by 0.3680 thousand dollars. **(c)** $\hat{Y} = -120.0483 + 1.7506(170) + 0.3680(12) = 181.9692$ thousand dollars. **(d)** Based on a residual analysis, the model appears to be adequate. **(e)** $F_{STAT} = 223.46$, the $p$-value is virtually 0. Because $p$-value < 0.05, reject $H_0$. There is evidence of a significant relationship between selling price and the two independent variables (assessed value and time period). **(f)** The $p$-value is virtually 0. The probability of obtaining a test statistic of 223.46 or greater is virtually 0 if there is no significant relationship between selling price and the two independent variables (assessed value and time period). **(g)** $r^2 = 0.9430$. 94.30% of the variation in selling price can be explained by variation in assessed value and time period. **(h)** $r^2_{adj} = 0.9388$. **(i)** For $X_1$: $t_{STAT} = 20.4137$, the $p$-value is virtually 0. Reject $H_0$. The assessed value makes a significant contribution and should be included in the model. For $X_2$: $t_{STAT} = 2.8734$, $p$-value = 0.0078 < 0.05. Reject $H_0$. The time period makes a significant contribution and should be included in the model. Based on these results, the regression model with the two independent variables should be used. **(j)** For $X_1$: $t_{STAT} = 20.4137$, the $p$-value is virtually 0. The probability of obtaining a sample that will yield a test statistic farther away than 20.4137 is virtually 0 if the assessed value does not make a significant contribution holding time period constant. For $X_2$: $t_{STAT} = 2.8734$, the $p$-value is virtually 0. The probability of obtaining a sample that will yield a test statistic farther away than 2.8734 is virtually 0 if the time period does not make a significant contribution holding the effect of the assessed value constant. **(k)** $1.5746 \leq \beta_1 \leq 1.9266$. You are 95% confident that the mean selling price will increase by an amount somewhere between $1.5746 thousand and $1.9266 thousand for each additional thousand-dollar increase in assessed value, holding constant the time period. In Problem 13.76, you are 95% confident that the mean selling price will increase by an amount somewhere between $1.5862 thousand and $1.9773 thousand for each additional thousand-dollar increase in assessed value regardless of the time period. **(l)** $r^2_{Y1.2} = 0.9392$. Holding constant the effect of the time period, 93.92% of the variation in selling price can be explained by variation in the assessed value. $r^2_{Y2.1} = 0.2342$. Holding constant the effect of the assessed value, 23.42% of the variation in selling price can be explained by variation in the time period.

**14.72 (a)** $\hat{Y} = 163.7751 + 10.7252X_1 - 0.2843X_2$, where $X_1$ = size and $X_2$ = age. **(b)** Holding age constant, for each additional thousand square feet, the mean assessed value is estimated to increase by $10.7252 thousand. Holding size constant, for each additional year, the mean assessed value is estimated to decrease by $0.2843 thousand. **(c)** $\hat{Y} = 163.7751 + 10.7252(1.75) - 0.2843(10) = 179.7017$ thousand dollars. **(d)** Based on a residual analysis, the errors appear to be normally distributed. The equal-variance assumption appears to be valid. There might also be violation of the linearity assumption for age. You may want to include a quadratic term for age in the model. **(e)** $F_{STAT} = 28.58$, $p$-value = 0.0000272776. Because $p$-value = 0.0000 < 0.05, reject $H_0$. There is evidence of a significant relationship between assessed value and the two independent variables (size and age). **(f)** $p$-value = 0.0000272776. The probability of obtaining an $F_{STAT}$ test statistic of 28.58 or greater is virtually 0 if there is no significant relationship between assessed value and the two independent variables (size and age). **(g)** $r^2 = 0.8265$. 82.65% of the variation in assessed value can be explained by variation in size and age. **(h)** $r^2_{adj} = 0.7976$. **(i)** For $X_1$: $t_{STAT} = 3.5581$, $p$-value = 0.0039 < 0.05. Reject $H_0$. The size of a house makes a significant contribution and should be included in the model. For $X_2$: $t_{STAT} = -3.4002$, $p$-value = 0.0053 < 0.05. Reject $H_0$. The age of a house makes a significant contribution and should be included in the model. Based on these results, the regression model with the two independent variables should be used. **(j)** For $X_1$: $p$-value = 0.0039. The probability of obtaining a sample that will yield a test statistic farther away than 3.5581 is 0.0039 if the size of a house does not make a significant contribution holding age constant. For $X_2$: $p$-value = 0.0053. The probability of obtaining a sample that will yield a test statistic farther away than $-3.4002$ is 0.0053 if the age of a house does not make a significant contribution, holding the effect of the size constant. **(k)** $4.1575 \le \beta_1 \le 17.2928$. You are 95% confident that the mean assessed value will increase by an amount somewhere between \$4.1575 thousand and \$17.2928 thousand for each additional thousand-square-foot increase in the size of a house, holding constant the age. In Problem 13.77, you are 95% confident that the mean assessed value will increase by an amount somewhere between \$9.4695 thousand and \$23.7972 thousand for each additional thousand-square-foot increase in heating area regardless of the age. **(l)** $r^2_{Y1.2} = 0.5134$. Holding constant the effect of age, 51.34% of the variation in assessed value can be explained by variation in the size. $r^2_{Y2.1} = 0.4907$. Holding constant the effect of the size, 49.07% of the variation in assessed value can be explained by variation in age. **(m)** Based on your answers to (a) through (l), the age of a house does have an effect on its assessed value.

**14.74 (a)** $\hat{Y} = 171.0689 - 19.3164X_1 - 5.1750X_2$, where $X_1$ = ERA and $X_2$ = League (American = 0). **(b)** Holding constant the effect of the league, for each additional ERA, the number of wins is estimated to decrease by a mean of 19.3164. For a given ERA, a team in the National League is estimated to have a mean of 5.1750 fewer wins than a team in the American League. **(c)** 84.1452 wins. **(d)** Based on a residual analysis, there appears to be a relationship between the residuals and ERA. The equal-variance and linearity assumptions appear to be valid. **(e)** $F_{STAT} = 23.2826$, $p$-value is virtually 0. Because $p$-value < 0.05, reject $H_0$. There is evidence of a significant relationship between wins and the two independent variables (ERA and league). **(f)** For $X_1$: $t_{STAT} = -6.6225$, $p$-value is virtually 0. Reject $H_0$. ERA makes a significant contribution and should be included in the model. For $X_2$: $t_{STAT} = -2.2247$, $p$-value = 0.0347 < 0.05. Reject $H_0$. The league makes a significant contribution and should be included in the model. Based on these results, the regression model with the two independent variables should be used. **(g)** $-25.3011 \le \beta_1 \le -13.3317$. **(h)** $-9.9479 \le \beta_2 \le -0.4021$. **(i)** $r^2_{adj} = 0.6058$. **(j)** $r^2_{Y1.2} = 0.6190$. Holding constant the effect of league, 61.90% of the variation in the number of wins can be explained by variation in ERA. $r^2_{Y2.1} = 0.1549$. Holding constant the effect of ERA, 15.49% of the variation in the number of wins can be explained by the league team plays in. **(k)** The slope of the number of wins with ERA is the same regardless of whether the team belongs to the American or the National League. **(l)** For $X_1X_2$: the p-value is 0.9433. Do not reject $H_0$. There is no evidence that the interaction term makes a contribution to the model. **(m)** The model in (a) should be used.

**14.76 (a)** ln(estimated odds) = $1.243 - 0.250$ price, yes. **(b)** ln(estimated odds) = $1.220 - .250$ price + $0.0377$ gender, yes, no. **(c)** Model in part (a) is better. **(d)** 0.2675. **(e)** 0.163. **(f)** 0.0946.

# CHAPTER 15

**15.2 (a)** Predicted HOCS is 2.8600, 3.0342, 3.1948, 3.3418, 3.4752, 3.5950, 3.7012, 3.7938, 3.8728, 3.9382, 3.99, 4.0282, 4.0528, 4.0638, 4.0612, 4.045, 4.0152, 3.9718, 3.9148, 3.8442, and 3.76. **(c)** The curvilinear relationship suggests that HOCS increases at a decreasing rate. It reaches its maximum value of 4.0638 at GPA = 3.3 and declines after that as GPA continues to increase. **(d)** An $r^2$ of 0.07 and an adjusted $r^2$ of 0.06 tell you that GPA has very low explanatory power in explaining the variation in HOCS. You can tell that the individual HOCS scores are scattered widely around the curvilinear relationship.

**15.4 (a)** $\hat{Y} = 2.6715 + 19.3903X_1 + 4.0334X_2$, where $X_1$ = alcohol and $X_2$ = carbohydrates. **(b)** $\hat{Y} = 8.2065 + 15.4149X_1 + 4.5213X_2 + 0.4856X_1^2 - 0.0234X_2^2$, where $X_1$ = alcohol and $X_2$ = carbohydrates. **(c)** Carbohydrates: $t_{STAT} = -0.9578$; $p$-value = 0.3417 > 0.05. Alcohol: $t_{STAT} = 1.4147$; $p$-value = 0.1619 > 0.05. $F_{STAT} = 1.9397$. The $p$-value is 0.1317 > 0.05, do not reject $H_0$. At the 5% level of significance, the quadratic terms are insignificant together. Hence, the model in (a) is better. **(d)** The normal probability plot suggests that the errors are left-skewed. The residual plots of the alcohol percentage and carbohydrates do not reveal any nonlinearity. Both the residual plot of the alcohol percentage and carbohydrates suggest that there might be violation of the equal variance assumption.

**15.6 (b)** Predicted yield = $6.643 + 0.895$ AmtFert $- 0.00411$ AmtFert$^2$. **(c)** Predicted yield = $6.643 + 0.895(70) - 0.00411(70)^2 = 49.168$ pounds. **(d)** The model appears to be adequate. **(e)** $F_{STAT} = 157.32 > 4.26$; reject $H_0$. **(f)** $p$-value = $0 < .05$, so the model is significant. **(g)** $t_{STAT} = -4.27 < -2.2622$; reject $H_0$. There is a significant quadratic effect. **(h)** $p$-value = 0.002 < 0.05, so the quadratic term is significant. **(i)** 97.2% of the variation in yield can be explained by the quadratic model. **(j)** 96.6%.

**15.8 (a)** 211.84. **(b)** For each additional unit of the logarithm of $X_1$, the logarithm of $Y$ is estimated to increase by 0.9 units, holding all other variables constant. For each additional unit of the logarithm of $X_2$, the logarithm of $Y$ is estimated to increase by 1.41 units, holding all other variables constant.

**15.10 (a)** $\hat{Y} = -82.7423 + 62.4604\sqrt{X_1} + 26.7589\sqrt{X_2}$, where $X_1$ = Alcohol % and $X_2$ = Carbohydrates. **(b)** The residual plot suggests that the errors are normally distributed. The residual plots from the square-root transformation of carbohydrates and alcohol show no evidence of a pattern. **(c)** $F_{STAT} = 550.9181$, the $p$-value is virtually 0. Reject $H_0$. There is evidence of a relationship between calories and the square root of alcohol and/or the square root of carbohydrates. $t_{STAT} = 17.6705$, the $p$-value is virtually 0. Because the $p$-value < 0.05, reject $H_0$. There is a significant relationship between calories and the square root of percent alcohol. $t_{STAT} = 23.9172$, the $p$-value is virtually 0. Because the $p$-value < 0.05, reject $H_0$. There is a significant relationship between calories and the square root of the number of carbohydrates. Therefore, both independent variables should be included in the model. **(d)** $r^2_{Y.12} = 94.19\%$. 94.19% of the variation in the number of calories can be explained by variation in the percent alcohol and the variation in the number of carbohydrates. **(e)** $r^2_{adj} = 0.9402$. **(f)** The model in Problem 15.4 (a) is slightly better for prediction purpose because it has the higher adjusted $r^2$ of 0.9617.

**15.12 (a)** Predicted ln(Yield) = 2.475 + 0.0185 AmtFert. **(b)** 32.95 pounds. **(c)** A quadratic pattern exists, so the model is not adequate. **(d)** $t_{STAT}$ = 6.11 > 2.2281; reject $H_0$. **(e)** 78.9%. **(f)** 76.8%. **(g)** Choose the model from Problem 15.6. That model has a much higher adjusted $r^2$ of 96.6%.

**15.14** 1.25.

**15.16** $R_1^2 = 0.64$, $VIF_1 = \dfrac{1}{1-0.64} = 2.778$, $R_2^2 = 0.64$, $VIF_2 = \dfrac{1}{1-0.64} = 2.778$. There is no evidence of collinearity.

**15.18** $VIF$ = 1.0 < 5. There is no evidence of collinearity.

**15.20** $VIF$ = 1.0428. There is no evidence of collinearity.

**15.22 (a)** 35.04. **(b)** $C_p$ > 3. This does not meet the criterion for consideration of a good model.

**15.24** Let Y = selling price, $X_1$ = assessed value, $X_2$ = time period, and $X_3$ = whether house was new (0 = no, 1 = yes). Based on a full regression model involving all of the variables, all the VIF values (1.32, 1.04, and 1.31, respectively) are less than 5. There is no reason to suspect the existence of collinearity. Based on a best-subsets regression and examination of the resulting $C_p$ values, the best models appear to be a model with variables $X_1$ and $X_2$, which has $C_p$ = 2.84, and the full regression model, which has $C_p$ = 4.0. Based on a regression analysis with all the original variables, variable $X_3$ fails to make a significant contribution to the model at the 0.05 level. Thus, the best model is the model using the assessed value ($X_1$) and time ($X_2$) as the independent variables. A residual analysis shows no strong patterns. The final model is $\hat{Y}$ = −120.0483 + 1.7506$X_1$ + 0.3680$X_2$, $r^2$ = 0.9430, $r_{adj}^2$ = 0.9388. Overall significance of the model: $F_{STAT}$ = 223.4575, p < 0.001. Each independent variable is significant at the 0.05 level.

**15.30 (a)** An analysis of the linear regression model with all of the seven possible independent variables reveals that two of the variables, points scored and points allowed, have $VIF$ values in excess of 5.0. These values are 9.32 and 10.51, respectively. Because points allowed is the variable with the largest of the two values, based on the procedure recommended in the text, this variable should be deleted from the model. An analysis of the linear regression model with the remaining independent variables indicates none of the remaining variables have a $VIF$ value that is 5.0 or larger. A best-subsets regression produced two potential models that have $C_p$ values less than or equal to k + 1. The model with $X_2 X_3 X_4 X_5$ and $X_6$ has $C_p$ = 5.0 and the model with $X_1 X_2 X_3 X_4 X_5$ and $X_6$ has $C_p$ = 7.0 where $X_1$ = points scored, $X_2$ = field goal %, $X_3$ = field goal % allowed, $X_4$ = turnover difference, $X_5$ = offensive rebound %, and $X_6$ = defensive rebound %. Looking at the p-values of the t statistics for each slope coefficient of the model that includes $X_1$ through $X_6$ reveals that $X_1$ = points scored is not significant at the 5% level of significance. The multiple regression model with points scored deleted shows that all coefficients are significant individually at the 5% level of significance. The best linear model is determined to be: $\hat{Y}$ = −336.3836 + 4.8102$X_2$ − 1.5033$X_3$ − 5.17123$X_4$ + 0.9169$X_5$ + 2.7549$X_6$. The overall model has F = 26.7870 (5 and 24 degrees of freedom) with a p-value that is virtually 0. $r_{Y.23456}^2$ = 0.8480, $r_{adj}^2$ = 0.8164. A residual analysis does not reveal any strong patterns. **(b)** An analysis of the linear regression model with all of the five possible independent variables reveals that none of the variables have $VIF$ values in excess of 5.0. A best-subsets regression reveals the following regression models that have $C_p$ values less than or equal to k + 1. $X_1$: $C_p$ = 1.6362, $X_1 X_2$: $C_p$ = 1.9517, $X_1 X_2 X_3$: $C_p$ = 2.7649, $X_1 X_2 X_4$: $C_p$ = 3.896, $X_1 X_2 X_5$: $C_p$ = 3.9459, $X_1 X_2 X_3 X_4$: $C_p$ = 4.7397, $X_1 X_2 X_3 X_5$: $C_p$ = 4.0782, $X_1 X_2 X_3$

$X_4 X_5$: $C_p$ = 6.0 where $X_1$ = point difference, $X_2$ = field goal % difference, $X_3$ = turnover difference, $X_4$ = offensive rebound %, and $X_5$ = defensive rebound %. Analysis of the p-value of the slope coefficients for the model that include $X_1$ through $X_5$ indicates that only point difference is significant at the 5% level of significance. Dropping offensive rebound %, which has the highest p-value, the new regression again indicates that only point difference is significant at the 5% level of significance. Repeating the same exercise of dropping the variable that has the highest p-value and performing the new regression leads to the most parsimonious model with only point difference being the significant variable at the 5% level of significance. The best linear model is determined to be: $\hat{Y}$ = 40.6500 + 2.6251$X_1$. Point difference is significantly different than zero at the 0.05 level. $r^2$ = 0.8920, $r_{adj}^2$ = 0.8882. The residual plot does not reveal any strong patterns. **(c)** The model in (b) with a higher adjusted $r^2$ of 0.8920 is better than that in (a) in predicting the number of wins.

**15.32 (a)** Best model: predicted Appraised Value = 136.794 + 276.0876 Land + 0.1288 House Size (sq ft) − 1.3989 Age.

**15.34 (a)** Predicted Appraised Value = 110.27 + 0.0821 House Size (sq ft).

**15.36** Let Y = appraised value, $X_1$ = land area, $X_2$ = interior size, $X_3$ = age, $X_4$ = number of rooms, $X_5$ = number of bathrooms, $X_6$ = garage size, $X_7$ = 1 if Glen Cove and 0 otherwise, and $X_8$ = 1 if Roslyn and 0 otherwise. **(a)** All $VIF$s are less than 5 in a full regression model involving all of the variables: There is no reason to suspect collinearity between any pair of variables. The following is the multiple regression model that has the smallest $C_p$ (9.0) and the highest adjusted $r^2$ (0.891):

Appraised Value = 49.4 + 343 Land (acres) + 0.115 House Size (sq ft)

−0.585 Age − 8.24 Rooms + 26.9 Baths + 5.0 Garage + 56.4 Glen Cove

+210 Roslyn

The individual t test for the significance of each independent variable at the 5% level of significance concludes that only $X_1$, $X_2$, $X_5$, $X_7$, and $X_8$ are significant individually. This subset, however, is not chosen when the $C_p$ criterion is used. The following is the multiple regression output for the model chosen by stepwise regression:

Appraised Value = 23.4 + 347 Land (acres) + 0.106 House Size (sq ft)

−0.792 Age + 26.4 Baths + 57.7 Glen Cove + 213 Roslyn

This model has a $C_p$ value of 7.7 and an adjusted $r^2$ of 89.0. All the variables are significant individually at the 5% level of significance. Combining the stepwise regression and the best-subset regression results along with the individual t-test results, the most appropriate multiple regression model for predicting the appraised value is

$$\hat{Y} = 23.40 + 347.02X_1 + 0.10614X_2 - 0.7921X_3$$
$$+26.38X_5 + 57.74X_7 + 213.46X_8$$

**(b)** The estimated mean appraised value in Glen Cove is 57.74 thousand dollars above Freeport for two otherwise identical properties. The estimated mean appraised value in Roslyn is 213.46 thousand dollars above Freeport for two otherwise identical properties.

**15.38** Explanation: Remove vapor pressure, air temperature, soil radiation, and wind speed due to $VIF$ > 5. After removing insignificant variables, the model has the single independent variable, dew point, and a coefficient of determination of only 10%.

# CHAPTER 16

**16.2 (a)** 1959. **(b)** The first four years and the last four years.

**16.4 (b), (c), and (d)**

| Year | Attendance | MA(3) | ES (W=0.5) | ES (W=0.25) |
|------|-----------|-------|-----------|------------|
| 1999 | 1.47 |        | 1.4700 | 1.4700 |
| 2000 | 1.42 | 1.4600 | 1.4450 | 1.4575 |
| 2001 | 1.49 | 1.5133 | 1.4675 | 1.4656 |
| 2002 | 1.63 | 1.5633 | 1.5488 | 1.5067 |
| 2003 | 1.57 | 1.5767 | 1.5594 | 1.5225 |
| 2004 | 1.53 | 1.5033 | 1.5447 | 1.5244 |
| 2005 | 1.41 | 1.4633 | 1.4773 | 1.4958 |
| 2006 | 1.45 |        | 1.4637 | 1.4844 |

**(e)** A smoothing coefficient of $W = 0.25$ smoothes out the attendance more than $W = 0.50$. The exponential smoothing with $W = 0.5$ assigns more weight to the more recent values and is better for forecasting, whereas the exponential smoothing with $W = 0.25$, which assigns more weight to more distant values, is better suited for eliminating unwanted cyclical and irregular variations.

**16.6 (e)** There is no obvious trend during the first 70 trading days in 2007.

**16.8 (b), (c), and (e)**

| Year | Cost | MA(3) | ES (W=0.5) | ES (W=0.25) |
|------|------|-------|-----------|------------|
| 1994–1995 | 8.16 |      | 8.16 | 8.16 |
| 1995–1996 | 8.10 | 8.14 | 8.13 | 8.15 |
| 1996–1997 | 8.17 | 8.13 | 8.15 | 8.15 |
| 1997–1998 | 8.12 | 8.08 | 8.14 | 8.14 |
| 1998–1999 | 7.94 | 8.01 | 8.04 | 8.09 |
| 1999–2000 | 7.98 | 8.01 | 8.01 | 8.06 |
| 2000–2001 | 8.11 | 8.15 | 8.06 | 8.08 |
| 2001–2002 | 8.37 | 8.23 | 8.21 | 8.15 |
| 2002–2003 | 8.20 | 8.35 | 8.21 | 8.16 |
| 2003–2004 | 8.49 | 8.49 | 8.35 | 8.24 |
| 2004–2005 | 8.78 | 8.98 | 8.56 | 8.38 |
| 2005–2006 | 9.67 |      | 9.12 | 8.70 |

**(d)** $W = 0.5$: $\hat{Y}_{2006-2007} = E_{2005-2006} = 9.12$. **(e)** $W = 0.25$: $\hat{Y}_{2006-2007} = E_{2005-2006} = 8.70$. **(f)** The exponentially smoothed forecast for 2006–2007 with $W = 0.5$ is higher than that with $W = 0.25$. The exponential smoothing with $W = 0.5$ assigns more weight to the more recent values and is better for forecasting, whereas the exponential smoothing with $W = 0.25$, which assigns more weight to more distant values, is better suited for eliminating unwanted cyclical and irregular variations.

**16.10 (a)** The $Y$ intercept $b_0 = 4.0$ is the fitted trend value reflecting the real total revenues (in millions of dollars) during the origin or base year 1986. **(b)** The slope $b_1 = 1.5$ indicates that the real total revenues are increasing at an estimated rate of $1.5 million per year. **(c)** Year is 1990, $X = 1990 - 1986 = 4$, $\hat{Y}_5 = 4.0 + 1.5(4) = 10.0$ million dollars. **(d)** Year is 2007, $X = 2007 - 1986 = 21$, $\hat{Y}_{20} = 4.0 + 1.5(21) = 35.5$ million dollars. **(e)** Year is 2010, $X = 2010 - 1986 = 24$, $\hat{Y}_{23} = 4.0 + 1.5(24) = 40$ million dollars.

**16.12 (b)** There was an upward trend in the CPI in the United States over the 42-year period. The rate of increase became faster in the late 1970s and mid-1980s, but the rate of increase tapered off in the early 1980s and early 1990s.

**16.14 (b)** $\hat{Y} = 294.5076 + 67.0012X$ where $X =$ years relative to 1978. **(c)** $X = 2007 - 1978 = 29$, $\hat{Y} = 294.5076 + 67.0012(29) = \$2,237.5419$ billion $X = 2008 - 1978 = 30$, $\hat{Y} = 294.5076 + 67.0012(30) = \$2,304.5431$ billion. **(d)** There is an upward trend in federal receipts between 1978 and 2006. The trend appears to be nonlinear. A quadratic trend or exponential trend model could be explored.

**16.16 (b)** Linear trend: $\hat{Y} = 1.1330 + 0.7295X$ where $X$ is relative to 1975. **(c)** Quadratic trend: $\hat{Y} = 2.1123 + 0.5337X + 0.0063X^2$ where $X$ is relative to 1975. **(d)** Exponential trend: $\log_{10} \hat{Y} = 0.5512 + 0.0298X$ where $X$ is relative to 1975. **(e)** Linear trend: $\hat{Y}_{2007} = 1.1330 + 0.7295(32) = \$24.4778$ billion $\hat{Y}_{2008} = 1.1330 + 0.7295(33) = \$25.2073$ billion Quadratic trend $\hat{Y}_{2007} = 2.1123 + 0.5337(32) + 0.0063(32)^2 = \$25.6594$ billion $\hat{Y}_{2008} = 2.1123 + 0.5337(33) + 0.0063(33)^2 = \$26.6037$ billion Exponential trend: $\hat{Y}_{2007} = 10^{0.5512+0.0298(32)} = \$32.0682$ billion $\hat{Y}_{2008} = 10^{0.5512+0.0298(33)} = \$34.3490$ billion

**16.18 (b)** Linear trend: $\hat{Y} = -2.9639 + 2.1727X$ where $X$ is relative to 1987. **(c)** Quadratic trend: $\hat{Y} = -3.2905 + 2.2758X - 0.0052X^2$ where $X$ is relative to 1987. **(d)** Exponential trend: $\log_{10} \hat{Y} = 0.3537 + 0.0718X$ where $X$ is relative to 1987. **(e)** Investigating the 1st, 2nd, and percentage differences suggests that the linear and quadratic trend models have about the same fit whereas the exponential trend model seems to fit the early years' data better. **(f)** $X = 2008 - 1987 = 21$. Using the exponential trend model, $\hat{Y}_{2008} = 10^{0.3537+0.0718(21)} = 72.6437$. Using the linear trend model, $\hat{Y}_{2008} = -2.9639 + 2.1727(21) = 42.6623$. Using the quadratic trend model, $\hat{Y}_{2008} = -3.2905 + 2.2758(21) - 0.0052(21)^2 = 42.2274$. The exponential trend fits the data in the earlier years better than the linear or quadratic model. However, the economy went into a recession in 2000 and the exponential trend was no longer able to forecast the stock price accurately in 2008. If the trend of the latter years continues, the linear and quadratic models appear to be able to forecast the stock price more accurately in 2008.

**16.20 (a)** For Time Series I, the graph of $Y$ vs. $X$ appears to be more linear than the graph of log $Y$ vs. $X$, so a linear model appears to be more appropriate. For Time Series II, the graph of log $Y$ vs. $X$ appears to be more linear than the graph of $Y$ vs. $X$, so an exponential model appears to be more appropriate. **(b)** Time Series I: $\hat{Y} = 100.082 + 14.9752X$, where $X =$ years relative to 1997. Time Series II: $\hat{Y} = 99.704(1.1501)^X$, where $X =$ years relative to 1997. **(c)** Forecasts for 2007: Time Series I: 249.834; Time Series II: 403.709.

**16.22 (b)** Linear trend: $\hat{Y} = -94.6750 + 62.0964X$, where $X$ is relative to 1993. **(c)** Quadratic trend: $\hat{Y} = 26.8176 + 6.0229X + 4.0053X^2$, where $X$ is relative to 1993. **(d)** Exponential trend: $\log_{10} \hat{Y} = 1.6118 + 0.1034 X$, where $X$ is relative to 1993. **(e)** Linear trend: $\hat{Y}_{2008} = -94.6750 + 62.0964(15) = 836.7714 = 837$ stores; $\hat{Y}_{2009} = -94.6750 + 62.0964(16) = 898.8679 = 899$ stores. Quadratic trend: $\hat{Y}_{2008} = 26.8176 + 6.0229(15) + 4.0053(15)^2 = 1018.3429 = 1018$ stores; $\hat{Y}_{2009} = 26.8176 + 6.0229(16) + 4.0053(16)^2 = 1148.5286 = 1149$ stores. **(f)** Both the quadratic trend model and the exponential trend model are capable of capturing the increasing rate of growth of the number of stores open. The rate of growth estimated by the exponential trend model is the highest followed by the quadratic trend model and, finally, the linear trend model. The quadratic trend model appears to be tracking the growth rate of the real data closer than the exponential trend model so it should be used to forecast the number of stores open for 2008 and 2009.

**16.24** $t_{STAT} = 2.40 > 2.2281$; reject $H_0$.

**16.26 (a)** $t_{STAT} = 1.60 < 2.2281$; do not reject $H_0$.

**16.28 (a)** Because the $p$-value $= 0.9280 > 0.05$ level of significance, the third-order term can be dropped. **(b)** Because the $p$-value $= 0.1015 > 0.05$ level of significance, the second-order term can be dropped. **(c)** Because the $p$-value is virtually zero, the first-order term cannot be dropped. **(d)** The most appropriate model for forecasting is the first-order autoregressive model: $\hat{Y}_i = 0.5347 + 1.0124Y_{i-1}$. The forecast for 2007 is 24.9327 and for 2008 is 25.7757.

**16.30 (a)** Because the $p$-value $= 0.5302 > 0.05$ level of significance, the third-order term can be dropped. **(b)** Because the $p$-value $= 0.1523 > 0.05$ level of significance, the second-order term can be dropped. **(c)** Because the $p$-value is virtually zero, the first-order term cannot be dropped. **(d)** The most appropriate model for forecasting is the first-order autoregressive model: $\hat{Y}_i = 2.9354 + 0.93344Y_{i-1}$. The forecast for 2008 is 37.6698.

**16.32 (a)** 2.121. **(b)** 1.515.

**16.34 (b)** $S_{YX} = 424.0941$. **(c)** $MAD = 319.2461$. **(d)** The residuals in the linear trend model show strings of consecutive positive and negative values. The linear trend model is inadequate in capturing the nonlinear trend.

**16.36 (b),(c)** Linear: $SSE = 52.8088$, $S_{YX} = 1.3268$, $MAD = 1.0509$. Quadratic: $SSE = 45.4029$, $S_{YX} = 1.2512$, $MAD = 0.9410$. Exponential: $SSE = 156.2702$, $S_{YX} = 2.2823$, $MAD = 1.5593$. First-order autoregressive: $SSE = 12.4133$, $S_{YX} = 0.6543$, $MAD = 0.4550$. **(d)** The residuals in the three trend models show strings of consecutive positive and negative values. The autoregressive model performs well for the historical data and has a fairly random pattern of residuals. The autoregressive model also has the smallest values in $MAD$ and $S_{YX}$. Based on the principle of parsimony, the autoregressive model would be the best model for forecasting.

**16.38 (b),(c)** Linear: $SSE = 1{,}066.3301$, $S_{YX} = 7.4915$, $MAD = 5.4534$. Quadratic: $SSE = 1{,}065.7336$, $S_{YX} = 7.6946$, $MAD = 5.4802$. Exponential: $SSE = 2{,}488.4585$, $S_{YX} = 11.4442$, $MAD = 7.1611$. First-order autoregressive: $SSE = 629.97723$, $S_{YX} = 5.9160$, $MAD = 4.1224$. **(d)** The residuals in the linear and quadratic trend models show strings of consecutive positive and negative values. The exponential trend model and the autoregressive model perform well for the historical data and have a fairly random pattern of residuals. The autoregressive model also has the smallest values in $MAD$ and $S_{YX}$. Based on the principle of parsimony, the autoregressive model would be the best model for forecasting.

**16.40 (a)** $\log \hat{\beta}_0 = 2$, $\hat{\beta}_0 = 10^2 = 100$. This is the fitted value for January 2003 prior to adjustment with the January multiplier. **(b)** $\log \hat{\beta}_1 = 0.01$. The estimated average monthly compound growth rate is 2.33%. **(c)** $\log \hat{\beta}_2 = 0.1$, $\hat{\beta}_2 = 10^{0.1} = 1.2589$. The January values in the time series are estimated to have a mean 25.89% higher than the December values.

**16.42 (a)** $\log \hat{\beta}_0 = 3.0$, $\hat{\beta}_0 = 10^{3.0} = 1{,}000$. This is the fitted value for January 2003 prior to adjustment by the quarterly multiplier. **(b)** $\log \hat{\beta}_1 = 0.1$, $\hat{\beta}_1 = 10^{0.1} = 1.2589$. The estimated average quarterly compound growth rate is $(\hat{\beta}_1 - 1)100\% = 25.89\%$. **(c)** $\log \hat{\beta}_3 = 0.2$, $\hat{\beta}_3 = 10^{0.2} = 1.5849$.

**16.44** $\log_{10} \hat{Y} = 3.0842 + 1.02711 \cdot (10)^{-5} X - 0.007097Q_1 - 0.01055Q_2 - 0.03302Q_3$. **(c)** $\log_{10} \hat{\beta}_1 = 1.02711 \cdot (10)^{-5}$; $\hat{\beta}_1 = 10^{1.02711 \cdot (10)^{-5}} = 1.00002365$; $(\hat{\beta}_1 - 1)100\% = 0.002365\%$. The estimated *quarterly* compound growth rate in the S&P Composite Stock Price Index is 0.002365%, after adjusting for the seasonal component. **(d)** $\log_{10} \hat{\beta}_2 = -0.007097$; $\hat{\beta}_2 = 10^{-0.007097} = 0.9838$; $(\hat{\beta}_2 - 1)100\% = -1.6209\%$. The first quarter values in the time series are estimated to have a mean 1.6209% below the fourth quarter values. **(e)** First quarter, 2007: $\hat{Y}_{36} = 1195.2381$. **(f)** 1,185.201, 1,126.028, 1,215.017.

**16.46 (b)**

$$\log \hat{Y} = 0.6742 + 0.0007213X - 0.001806M_1 + 0.002615M_2 - 0.001933M_3$$
$$- 0.003444M_4 - 0.00266M_5 + 0.0002119M_6 + 0.001384M_7$$
$$+ 0.0003286M_8 - 0.001094M_9 - 0.004466M_{10} + 0.0008555M_{11}$$

**(c)** $\hat{Y}_{83} = 5.42\%$. **(d)** Forecasts for all 12 months of 2007 are 5.4074, 5.4718, 5.4238, 5.4140, 5.4328, 5.4779, 5.5019, 5.4976, 5.4888, 5.4554, 5.5318, and 5.5301. **(e)** $\log_{10} \hat{\beta}_1 = 0.0007213$; $\hat{\beta}_1 = 10^{0.0007213} = 1.001662$. The estimated monthly compound growth rate is $(\hat{\beta}_1 - 1) 100\% = 0.1662\%$. **(f)** $\log_{10} \hat{\beta}_8 = 0.001384$; $\hat{\beta}_8 = 10^{0.001384} = 1.0032$. $(\hat{\beta}_8 - 1) 100\% = 0.32\%$. The July values in the time series are estimated to have a mean 0.32% above the December values.

**16.48 (a)** The retail industry is heavily subject to seasonal variation due to the holiday seasons, and so are the revenues for Toys Я Us. **(b)** There is an obvious seasonal effect in the time series. **(c)** The exponential trend forecasting equation with seasonal components is: $\log_{10} \hat{Y} = 3.6435 + 0.0020X - 0.3789Q_1 - 0.3846Q_2 - 0.3525Q_3$. **(d)** The estimated quarterly compound growth rate is 0.46%. **(e)** $\log_{10} \hat{\beta}_2 = -0.3789$. $\hat{\beta}_2 = 10^{-0.3789} = 0.4179$. $(\hat{\beta}_2 - 1)100\% = -58.21\%$. The first-quarter values in the time series are estimated to have a mean 58.21% below the fourth-quarter values. $\log_{10} \hat{\beta}_3 = -0.3846$. $\hat{\beta}_3 = 10^{-0.3846} = 0.4124$. $(\hat{\beta}_3 - 1) 100\% = -58.76\%$. The second-quarter values in the time series are estimated to have a mean 58.76% below the fourth-quarter values. $\log_{10} \hat{\beta}_4 = -0.3525$. $\hat{\beta}_4 = 10^{-0.3525}$. $(\hat{\beta}_4 - 1)100\% = -55.59\%$. The third-quarter values in the time series are estimated to have a mean 55.59% below the fourth-quarter values. **(f)** Forecasts for 2006: $\hat{Y}_{41} = \$2{,}209.4155$ millions; $\hat{Y}_{42} = \$2{,}190.6572$ millions; $\hat{Y}_{43} = \$2{,}369.9104$ millions; $\hat{Y}_{44} = \$5{,}360.4578$ millions.

**16.50** The price of the commodity in 2007 was 75% higher than in 1995.

**16.52 (a)** 186.96. **(b)** 162.16. **(c)** 154.42.

**16.54 (a) and (c)**

| Year | Price | Price Index (base = 1980) | Price Index (base = 1990) | Year | Price | Price Index (base = 1980) | Price Index (base = 1990) |
|------|-------|------|------|------|-------|------|------|
| 1980 | 3.208 | 100.00 | 109.98 | 1994 | 2.530 | 78.87 | 86.73 |
| 1981 | 2.777 | 86.56 | 95.20 | 1995 | 4.398 | 137.09 | 150.77 |
| 1982 | 2.475 | 77.15 | 84.85 | 1996 | 3.577 | 111.50 | 122.63 |
| 1983 | 2.528 | 78.80 | 86.66 | 1997 | 3.300 | 102.87 | 113.13 |
| 1984 | 2.495 | 77.77 | 85.53 | 1998 | 4.025 | 125.47 | 137.98 |
| 1985 | 2.585 | 80.58 | 88.62 | 1999 | 3.435 | 107.08 | 117.76 |
| 1986 | 2.737 | 85.32 | 93.83 | 2000 | 3.540 | 110.35 | 121.36 |
| 1987 | 3.192 | 99.50 | 109.43 | 2001 | 3.224 | 100.50 | 110.52 |
| 1988 | 2.635 | 82.14 | 90.33 | 2002 | 2.936 | 91.52 | 100.65 |
| 1989 | 2.964 | 92.39 | 101.61 | 2003 | 2.999 | 93.49 | 102.81 |
| 1990 | 2.917 | 90.93 | 100.00 | 2004 | 2.892 | 90.15 | 99.14 |
| 1991 | 2.945 | 91.80 | 100.96 | 2005 | 3.049 | 95.04 | 104.53 |
| 1992 | 2.668 | 83.17 | 91.46 | 2006 | 3.232 | 100.75 | 110.80 |
| 1993 | 2.352 | 73.32 | 80.63 | | | | |

**(b)** The price of coffee in 2006 was 0.75% higher than it was in 1980. **(d)** The price of coffee in 2006 was 10.80% higher than it was in 1990. **(e)** It would not be a good idea to use 1995 as the base year because that was when the coffee price was at its peak. **(f)** There was a slight upward trend in coffee costs from 1980 to 2006, with a prominent cyclical component.

**16.56 (a)**

| Year | Electricity | Natural Gas | Fuel oil | Electricity Price Index (base = 1992) | Natural Gas Price Index (base = 1992) | Fuel Oil Price Index (base = 1992) |
|---|---|---|---|---|---|---|
| 1992 | 44.501 | 26.376 | 0.985 | 100.00 | 100.00 | 100.00 |
| 1993 | 16.959 | 28.749 | 0.969 | 38.11 | 109.00 | 98.38 |
| 1994 | 48.200 | 30.236 | 0.919 | 108.31 | 114.63 | 93.30 |
| 1995 | 48.874 | 29.872 | 0.913 | 109.83 | 113.25 | 92.69 |
| 1996 | 48.538 | 29.570 | 1.007 | 109.07 | 112.11 | 102.23 |
| 1997 | 49.245 | 32.904 | 1.136 | 110.66 | 124.75 | 115.33 |
| 1998 | 46.401 | 31.438 | 0.966 | 104.27 | 119.19 | 98.07 |
| 1999 | 45.061 | 30.699 | 0.834 | 101.26 | 116.39 | 84.67 |
| 2000 | 45.207 | 31.664 | 1.189 | 101.59 | 120.05 | 120.71 |
| 2001 | 47.472 | 49.734 | 1.509 | 106.68 | 188.56 | 153.20 |
| 2002 | 47.868 | 36.316 | 1.123 | 107.57 | 137.69 | 114.01 |
| 2003 | 47.663 | 40.227 | 1.396 | 107.11 | 152.51 | 141.73 |
| 2004 | 49.159 | 46.048 | 1.508 | 110.47 | 174.58 | 153.10 |
| 2005 | 50.847 | 50.932 | 1.859 | 114.26 | 193.10 | 188.73 |
| 2006 | 57.223 | 66.402 | 2.418 | 128.59 | 251.75 | 245.48 |

**(b)**

| Year | Electricity | Natural Gas | Fuel oil | Electricity Price Index (base = 1996) | Natural Gas Price Index (base = 1996) | Fuel Oil Price Index (base = 1996) |
|---|---|---|---|---|---|---|
| 1992 | 44.501 | 26.376 | 0.985 | 91.68 | 89.20 | 97.82 |
| 1993 | 16.959 | 28.749 | 0.969 | 34.94 | 97.22 | 96.23 |
| 1994 | 48.200 | 30.236 | 0.919 | 99.30 | 102.25 | 91.26 |
| 1995 | 48.874 | 29.872 | 0.913 | 100.69 | 101.02 | 90.67 |
| 1996 | 48.538 | 29.570 | 1.007 | 100.00 | 100.00 | 100.00 |
| 1997 | 49.245 | 32.904 | 1.136 | 101.46 | 111.27 | 112.81 |
| 1998 | 46.401 | 31.438 | 0.966 | 95.60 | 106.32 | 95.93 |
| 1999 | 45.061 | 30.699 | 0.834 | 92.84 | 103.82 | 82.82 |
| 2000 | 45.207 | 31.664 | 1.189 | 93.14 | 107.08 | 118.07 |
| 2001 | 47.472 | 49.734 | 1.509 | 97.80 | 168.19 | 149.85 |
| 2002 | 47.868 | 36.316 | 1.123 | 98.62 | 122.81 | 111.52 |
| 2003 | 47.663 | 40.227 | 1.396 | 98.20 | 136.04 | 138.63 |
| 2004 | 49.159 | 46.048 | 1.508 | 101.28 | 155.73 | 149.75 |
| 2005 | 50.847 | 50.932 | 1.859 | 104.76 | 172.24 | 184.61 |
| 2006 | 57.223 | 66.402 | 2.418 | 117.89 | 224.56 | 240.12 |

**(c)**

| Year | Electricity | Natural Gas | Fuel Oil | Unweighted |
|---|---|---|---|---|
| 1992 | 44.501 | 26.376 | 0.985 | 100.00 |
| 1993 | 16.959 | 28.749 | 0.969 | 64.95 |
| 1994 | 48.200 | 30.236 | 0.919 | 110.43 |
| 1995 | 48.874 | 29.872 | 0.913 | 110.85 |
| 1996 | 48.538 | 29.570 | 1.007 | 110.09 |
| 1997 | 49.245 | 32.904 | 1.136 | 115.90 |
| 1998 | 46.401 | 31.438 | 0.966 | 109.66 |
| 1999 | 45.061 | 30.699 | 0.834 | 106.58 |
| 2000 | 45.207 | 31.664 | 1.189 | 108.62 |
| 2001 | 47.472 | 49.734 | 1.509 | 137.37 |
| 2002 | 47.868 | 36.316 | 1.123 | 118.71 |

| 2003 | 47.663 | 40.227 | 1.396 | 124.25 |
|---|---|---|---|---|
| 2004 | 49.159 | 46.048 | 1.508 | 134.58 |
| 2005 | 50.847 | 50.932 | 1.859 | 144.22 |
| 2006 | 57.223 | 66.402 | 2.418 | 175.40 |

**(d)** 212.84. **(e)** 203.15.

**16.70 (b)** Linear trend: $\hat{Y} = 174{,}576.6087 + 2{,}364.2727X$, where $X$ is relative to 1984. **(c)** 2007: $\hat{Y}_{2007} = 174{,}576.6087 + 2{,}364.2727(23) = 228{,}954.8814$ thousands. 2008: $\hat{Y}_{2008} = 174{,}576.6087 + 2{,}364.2727(24) = 231{,}319.1542$ thousands. **(d)(b)** Linear trend: $\hat{Y} = 114512.3804 + 1677.5820X$, where $X$ is relative to 1984. **(c)** 2007: $\hat{Y}_{2007} = 114512.3804 + 1677.5820(23) = 153{,}096.7668$ thousands. 2008: $\hat{Y}_{2007} = 114512.3804 + 1677.5820(24) = 154{,}774.3488$ thousands.

**16.72 (b)** Linear trend: $\hat{Y} = -1.5028 + 0.6226X$, where $X$ is relative to 1975. **(c)** Quadratic trend: $\hat{Y} = 1.3859 + 0.0448X + 0.0186X^2$, where $X$ is relative to 1975. **(d)** Exponential trend: $\log_{10}\hat{Y} = 0.1368 + 0.0408X$, where $X$ is relative to 1975. **(e)** Third-order autoregressive model: $\hat{Y}_i = 0.1444 + 1.2884Y_{i-1} - 0.4681Y_{i-2} + 0.2485Y_{i-3}$. Test of $A_3$: $p$-value = $0.2572 > 0.05$. Do not reject $H_0$ that $A_3 = 0$. Third-order term can be deleted. Second-order autoregressive model: $\hat{Y}_i = 0.1196 + 1.2423Y_{i-1} -0.1864Y_{i-2}$. Test of $A_2$: $p$-value $0.3739 > 0.05$. Do not reject $H_0$ that $A_2 = 0$. Second-order term can be deleted. First-order autoregressive model: $\hat{Y}_i = 0.1440 + 1.0675Y_{i-1}$. $p$-value is virtually 0. Reject $H_0$ that $A_1 = 0$. A first-order autoregressive model is appropriate. **(f)** The residuals in the first three models show strings of consecutive positive and negative values. The autoregressive model performs well for the historical data and has a fairly random pattern of residuals. **(g)** $S_{YX}$ is 2.3649 for the linear model, 0.4092 for the quadratic model, 1.2115 for the exponential model, and 0.3201 for the first-order autoregressive model. $MAD$ is 1.9100 for the linear model, 0.2921 for the quadratic model, 0.7691 for the exponential model, and 0.2111 for the first-order autoregressive model. **(h)** The autoregressive model is the best model for forecasting because it has the smallest values in the standard error of the estimate and $MAD$. **(i)** 23.2017 billions.

**16.74 (b)** Variable A: $\hat{Y} = 9.6331 + 2.6625X$, where $X =$ years relative to 1984. Variable B: $\hat{Y} = 11.9123 + 0.4069X$, where $X =$ years relative to 1984. **(c)** Variable A: $\hat{Y} = 7.4700 + 3.2524X - 0.02565X^2$, where $X =$ years relative to 1984. Variable B: $\hat{Y} = 10.2222 + 0.8679X - 0.02004X^2$, where $X =$ years relative to 1984. **(d)** Variable A: $\log_{10}\hat{Y} = 1.1602 + 0.03322X$, where $X =$ years relative to 1984. Variable B: $\log_{10}\hat{Y} = 1.0810 + 0.01141X$, where $X =$ years relative to 1984. **(e)** Variable A: Third-order autoregressive model: $\hat{Y}_i = 4.5486 + 1.2365Y_{i-1} - 0.3920Y_{i-2} + 0.09585Y_{i-3}$. Test of $A_3$: $p$-value $0.7007 > 0.05$. Do not reject $H_0$ that $A_3 = 0$. Third-order term can be deleted. Second-order autoregressive model: $\hat{Y}_i = 4.5857 + 1.2104Y_{i-1} - 0.2754Y_{i-2}$. Test of $A_2$: $p$-value $0.2313 > 0.05$. Do not reject $H_0$ that $A_2 = 0$. Second-order term can be deleted. First-order autoregressive model: $\hat{Y}_i = 4.0543 + 0.9599Y_{i-1}$. $p$-value is virtually 0. Reject $H_0$ that $A_1 = 0$. A first-order autoregressive model is appropriate. Variable B: Third-order autoregressive model: $\hat{Y}_i = 0.6371 + 2.0048Y_{i-1} - 1.4271Y_{i-2} + 0.3917Y_{i-3}$. $p$-value = $0.0605 > 0.05$. Do not reject $H_0$ that $A_3 = 0$. Third-order term can be deleted. Second-order autoregressive model: $\hat{Y}_i = 0.6561 + 1.6450Y_{i-1} - 0.6782Y_{i-2}$. $p$-value = $0.0000 < 0.05$. Reject $H_0$ that $A_2 = 0$. A second-order autoregressive model is appropriate. **(f)** Variable A: The residuals in the linear and quadratic trend models show strings of consecutive positive and negative values. There is no apparent pattern in the residuals of the exponential trend and first-order autoregressive model. Variable B: The residuals in the linear and exponential trend models show strings of consecutive positive and negative values. There is no apparent pattern in the residuals of the quadratic trend and second-order autoregressive model. **(g)** Variable A: $S_{YX}$

is 8.1264 for the linear model, 8.2346 for the quadratic model, 10.4380 for the exponential model, and 6.4050 for the first-order autoregressive model. *MAD* is 5.5059 for the linear model, 5.7344 for the quadratic model, 7.0218 for the exponential model, and 4.8869 for the first-order autoregressive model. Variable B: $S_{YX}$ is 0.9040 for the linear model, 0.1319 for the quadratic model, 1.1705 for the exponential model, and 0.0876 for the second-order autoregressive model. *MAD* is 0.7413 for the linear model, 0.0969 for the quadratic model, 0.9441 for the exponential model, and 0.0665 for the second-order autoregressive model. **(h)** The first-order autoregressive model has the smallest values in the standard error of the estimate and *MAD*. Thus, the first-order autoregressive model would probably be the best model for forecasting Variable A. The second-order autoregressive model has the smallest values in the standard error of the estimate and *MAD*. Thus, the second-order autoregressive model would probably be the best model for forecasting Variable B. **(i)** Variable A: 71.6411, Variable B: 19.4435. **(j)** You would recommend Variable A, which consists of investments that are primarily made in stocks, for a member of Teachers' Retirement System of New York City because it had a higher return than Variable B over the past 24-year period.

# CHAPTER 17

**17.2 (a)**

| Event | A | B |
|-------|---|---|
| 1 | 0 | 40 |
| 2 | 0 | 200 |
| 3 | 0 | 300 |

**17.4 (a)** and **(b)** Payoff table:

| Event | Company A | Company B |
|-------|-----------|-----------|
| | **Action** | |
| 1 | $10,000 + $2 × 1,000 = $12,000 | $2,000 + $4 × 1,000 = $6,000 |
| 2 | $10,000 + $2 × 2,000 = $14,000 | $2,000 + $4 × 2,000 = $10,000 |
| 3 | $10,000 + $2 × 5,000 = $20,000 | $2,000 + $4 × 5,000 = $22,000 |
| 4 | $10,000 + $2 × 10,000 = $30,000 | $2,000 + $4 × 10,000 = $42,000 |
| 5 | $10,000 + $2 × 50,000 = $110,000 | $2,000 + $4 × 50,000 = $202,000 |

**(d)** Opportunity loss table:

| Event | Optimum Action | Profit of Optimum Action | Alternative Courses of Action A | B |
|-------|---------------|--------------------------|-------|-------|
| 1 | A | 12,000 | 0 | 6,000 |
| 2 | A | 14,000 | 0 | 4,000 |
| 3 | B | 22,000 | 2,000 | 0 |
| 4 | B | 42,000 | 12,000 | 0 |
| 5 | B | 202,000 | 92,000 | 0 |

**17.6 (a)** Action A. **(b)** Action B. **(c)** 125, 112.5. **(d)** 25, 37.5. **(f)** Action A. **(g)** 60%, 11.11%. **(h)** 1.667, 9.0. **(i)** Action B. **(j)** Expected monetary value leads to a different decision than the return-to-risk criteria.

**17.8 (a)** 10%. **(b)** 25%. **(c)** 4.0.

**17.10** Stock A. It has a higher expected value and an equal standard deviation.

**17.12 (a)** Maximum of sell soft drinks = $60, Maximum of sell ice cream = $90; Sell ice cream. **(b)** Minimum of sell soft drinks = $50, Minimum of sell ice cream = $30; Sell soft drinks. **(c)** EMV(Soft drinks) = 50(0.4) + 60(0.6) = 56, EMV(Ice cream) = 30(0.4) + 90(0.6) = 66. **(d)** EOL(Soft drinks) = 0(0.4) + 30(0.6) = 18, EOL(Ice cream) = 20(0.4) + 0(0.6) = 8. **(e)** EVPI is the maximum amount of money the vendor is willing to pay for information about which event will occur. **(f)** Based on (c) and (d), choose to sell ice cream because you will earn a higher expected monetary value and incur a lower opportunity loss than choosing to sell soft drinks. **(g)** $CV(\text{Soft drinks}) = \frac{4.899}{56} \times 100\% = 8.7482\%$, $CV(\text{Ice cream}) = \frac{29.394}{66} \times 100\% = 44.536\%$. **(h)** Return-to-risk ratio for soft drinks $= \frac{56}{4.899} = 11.431$; Return-to-risk ratio for ice cream $= \frac{66}{29.394} = 2.245$. **(i)** Sell soft drinks because it has the smallest coefficient of variation and the largest return-to-risk ratio. **(j)** There are no differences.

**17.14 (a)** Investment C. **(b)** Investment A. **(c)** 1,050, 1,400, 1,400. **(d)** 522.02, 2498.00, 9656.09. **(e)** 4,100, 3,750, 3,750. **(f)** EVPI = 3,750. **(g)** 49.72%, 178.43%, 689.72%. **(h)** 2.01, .56, .14. **(i)** and **(j)** Actions B and C maximize expected monetary value, but action A minimizes the coefficient of variation and maximizes the return-to-risk ratio. **(k)** Maximum EMV: (1) C: 4,700 (2) C: 11,000 (3) A or B: 800 (4) A: 800 Maximum return-to-risk ratio: (1) A: 2.4398 (2) A: 2.7294 (3) A: 1.8257 (4) A: 1.7457.

**17.16 (a)** Company B. **(b)** Company A. **(c)** 25,200, 32,400. **(d)** 10,700, 3,500. **(e)** EVPI = 3,500. **(f)** Sign with Company B. **(g)** 114.25%, 177.73%. **(h)** 0.875, 0.563. **(i)** Sign with Company B if not risk averse. **(j)** Company B has a higher EMV, but a lower return-to-risk ratio. **(k)** A: EMV = 35,400; Return-to-risk ratio = 0.9397; B: EMV = 52,800 Return-to-risk ratio = 0.70. The decision is unchanged.

**17.18 (a)** $P(E_1 \mid F) = .6$, $P(E_2 \mid F) = .4$. **(b)** 110, 110. **(c)** 30, 30. **(d)** EVPI = 30. **(e)** Choose either one. **(f)** 66.8%, 11.1%. **(g)** 1.497, 8.981. **(h)** Action B.

**17.20** P(Forecast cool | Cool weather) = 0.80, P(Forecast warm | Warm weather) = 0.70. **(a)** Revised probabilities: $P(\text{Cool} \mid \text{Forecast cool}) = \frac{0.32}{0.5} = 0.64$, $P(\text{Warm} \mid \text{Forecast cool}) = \frac{0.18}{0.5} = 0.36$. **(b)** EMV(Soft drinks) = 50(0.64) + 60(0.36) = 53.6, EMV(Ice cream) = 30(0.64) + 90(0.36) = 51.6, EOL(Soft drinks) = 0(0.64) + 30(0.36) = 10.8, EOL(Ice cream) = 20(0.64) + 0(0.36) = 12.8, EMV with perfect information = 50(0.64) + 90(0.36) = 64.4, EVPI = EMV, perfect information $-EMV_A$ = 64.4 − 53.6 = 10.8. The vendor should not be willing to pay more than $10.80 for a perfect forecast of the weather. The vendor should sell soft drinks to maximize value and minimize loss. $CV(\text{Soft drinks}) = \frac{4.8}{53.6} 100\% = 8.96\%$, $CV(\text{Ice cream}) = \frac{28.8}{51.6} 100\% = 55.81\%$, return-to-risk ratio for soft drinks $= \frac{53.6}{4.8} = 11.1667$, return-to-risk ratio for ice cream $= \frac{51.6}{28.8} = 1.7917$. Based on these revised probabilities, the vendor's decision changes because of the increased likelihood of cool weather given a forecast for cool. Under these conditions, she should sell soft drinks to maximize the expected monetary value and minimize her expected opportunity loss.

**17.22 (a)** 0.5590, 0.2484, 0.1412, 0.0502, 0.0013. **(b)** EMV: 14,658.60, 11,315.4; EOL: 1004.4, 4347.6; CV: 38.42%, 99.55%; RTRR: 2.603, 1.005. **(c)** Under new circumstances, sign with Company A.

**17.36 (c)** 2,100, 2,660, 2,520, 1,960. **(d)** 980, 420, 560, 1,120. **(e)** $EVPI =$ $420. **(f)** Buy 8,000 loaves. **(g)** 0%, 15.79%, 35.57%, 57.14%. **(h)** Undefined, 6.333, 2.811, 1.750. **(i)** Buy 8,000 loaves. **(k)(c)** 2,100, 2,380, 2,100, 1,540. **(d)** 700, 490, 770, 1,330. **(e)** $EVPI =$ $490. **(f)** Buy 8,000 loaves. **(g)** 0%, 26.96%, 51.64%, 85.76%. **(h)** Undefined, 3.7097, 1.9365, 1.1660. **(i)** Buy 8,000 loaves.

**17.38 (c)** –$100,000 **(d)** 1,200,000, 1,100,000. **(e)** $EVPI =$ $1,100,000. **(f)** –0.0356, undefined. **(g)** Continue using old packaging. **(h)(c)** –1,600,0000, 0. **(d)** 2,400,000, 800,000. **(e)** $EVPI =$ $800,000. **(f)** –0.5101, undefined. **(g)** Continue using old packaging. **(j)** 0.2466, 0.6575, 0.0959. **(k)(c)** 150,600, 0. **(d)** 986,400, 1,137,000. **(e)** $EVPI =$ $986,400. **(f)** 0.0570, undefined. **(g)** Use new packaging. **(l)** 0.5902, 0.3934, 0.0164. **(m)(c)** –1,885,400, 0. **(d)** 2,360,800, 475,400. **(e)** $EVPI =$ $475,400. **(f)** –0.7288, undefined. **(g)** Use old packaging.

**17.40 (c)** 180, 100. **(d)** 20, 100. **(e)** $EVPI =$ $20. **(f)** 1.2665, undefined. **(g)** Call the mechanic. **(h)** 0.0143, 0.2100, 0.4159, 0.3598. **(i)(c)** 248.386, 100. **(d)** 1.144, 149.53. **(e)** $EVPI =$ 1.144. **(f)** 2.055, undefined. **(g)** Call the mechanic.

# CHAPTER 18

**18.2 (a)** Day 4, Day 3. **(b)** LCL = 0.0397, UCL = 0.2460. **(c)** No, proportions are within control limits.

**18.4 (a)** $n = 500$, $\bar{p} = 761/16{,}000 = 0.0476$

$$UCL = \bar{p} + 3\sqrt{\frac{\bar{p}(1-\bar{p})}{n}}$$

$$= 0.0476 + 3\sqrt{\frac{0.0476(1-0.0476)}{500}} = 0.0761$$

$$LCL = \bar{p} - 3\sqrt{\frac{\bar{p}(1-\bar{p})}{n}}$$

$$= 0.0476 - 3\sqrt{\frac{0.0476(1-0.0476)}{500}} = 0.0190$$

**(b)** Because the individual points are distributed around $\bar{p}$ without any pattern and all the points are within the control limits, the process is in a state of statistical control.

**18.6 (a)** UCL = 0.0176, LCL = 0.0082. The proportion of unacceptable cans is below the LCL on Day 4. There is evidence of a pattern over time because the last eight points are all above the mean and most of the earlier points are below the mean. Therefore, this process is out of control.

**18.8 (a)** UCL = 0.1431, LCL = 0.0752. Days 9, 26, and 30 are above the UCL. Therefore, this process is out of control.

**18.12 (a)** UCL = 21.6735, LCL = 1.3265. **(b)** Yes, time 1 is above the UCL.

**18.14 (a)** The twelve errors committed by Gina appear to be much higher than all others, and Gina would need to explain her performance. **(b)** $\bar{c} = 66/12 = 5.5$, UCL $= 5.5 + 3\sqrt{5.5} = 12.5356$, LCL does not exist. The number of errors is in a state of statistical control since none of the tellers are outside the UCL. **(c)** Because Gina is within the control limits, she is operating within the system and should not be singled out for further scrutiny. **(d)** The process needs to be studied and potentially changed using principles of Six Sigma and/or total quality management.

**18.16 (a)** $\bar{c} = 3.0566$. **(b)** LCL does not exist, UCL = 8.3015. **(c)** There are no weeks outside the control limits. Therefore, this process is in control. **(d)** Because these weeks are within the control limits, the results are explainable by common cause variation.

**18.18 (a)** $d_2 = 2.2059$. **(b)** $d_3 = 0.880$. **(c)** $D_3 = 0$. **(d)** $D_4 = 2.282$. **(e)** $A_2 = 0.729$.

**18.20 (a)** $\bar{R} = 0.247$, $R$ chart: UCL = 0.636; LCL does not exist. **(b)** According to the $R$-charts, the process appears to be in control with all points lying inside the control limits without any pattern and no evidence of special cause variation. **(c)** $\bar{\bar{X}} = 47.998$, $\bar{X}$ chart: UCL = 48.2507; LCL = 47.7453. **(d)** According to the $\bar{X}$ charts, the process appears to be in control with all points lying inside the control limits without any pattern and no evidence of special cause variation.

**18.22 (a)** $\bar{R} = \dfrac{\sum\limits_{i=1}^{k} R_i}{k} = 3.275$, $\bar{\bar{X}} = \dfrac{\sum\limits_{i=1}^{k} \bar{X}_i}{k} = 5.9413$.

$R$ chart: UCL $= D_4\bar{R} = 2.282(3.275) = 7.4736$. LCL does not exist. $\bar{X}$ chart: UCL $= \bar{\bar{X}} + A_2\bar{R} = 5.9413 + 0.729(3.275) = 8.3287$. LCL $= \bar{\bar{X}} - A_2\bar{R} = 5.9413 - 0.729(3.275) = 3.5538$. **(b)** The process appears to be in control because there are no points outside the control limits and there is no evidence of a pattern in the range chart, and there are no points outside the control limits and there is no evidence of a pattern in the $\bar{X}$ chart.

**18.24 (a)** $\bar{R} = 0.8794$, LCL does not exist, UCL = 2.0068. **(b)** $\bar{\bar{X}} = 20.1065$, LCL = 19.4654, UCL = 20.7475. **(c)** The process is in control.

**18.26 (a)** $\bar{R} = 8.145$, LCL does not exist, UCL = 18.5869; $\bar{\bar{X}} = 18.12$, UCL = 24.0577, LCL = 12.1823. **(b)** There are no sample ranges outside the control limits and there does not appear to be a pattern in the range chart. The mean is above the UCL on Day 15 and below the LCL on Day 16. Therefore, the process is not in control.

**18.28 (a)** $\bar{R} = 0.3022$, LCL does not exist, UCL = 0.6389; $\bar{\bar{X}} = 90.1312$, UCL = 90.3060, LCL = 89.9573. **(b)** On Days 5 and 6, the sample ranges were above the UCL. The mean chart may be erroneous because the range is out of control. The process is out of control.

**18.30 (a)** $P(98 < X < 102) = P(-1 < Z < 1) = 0.6826$. **(b)** $P(93 < X < 107.5) = P(-3.5 < Z < 3.75) = 0.99968$. **(c)** $P(X > 93.8) = P(Z > -3.1) = 0.99903$. **(d)** $P(X < 110) = P(Z < 5) = 0.999999713$.

**18.32 (a)** $P(18 < X < 22)$

$$= P\left(\frac{18 - 20.1065}{0.8794/2.059} < Z < \frac{22 - 20.1065}{0.8794/2.059}\right)$$

$$= P(-4.932 < Z < 4.4335) = 0.9999$$

**(b)** $$C_p = \frac{(USL - LSL)}{6(\bar{R}/d_2)} = \frac{(22-18)}{6(0.8794/2.059)}$$

$$= 1.56$$

$$CPL = \frac{(\bar{\bar{X}} - LSL)}{3(\bar{R}/d_2)} = \frac{(20.1065 - 18)}{3(0.8794/2.059)}$$

$$= 1.644$$

$$CPU = \frac{(USL - \bar{\bar{X}})}{3(\bar{R}/d_2)} = \frac{(22 - 20.1065)}{3(0.8794/2.059)}$$

$$= 1.477$$

$$C_{pk} = \min(CPL, CPU) = 1.477$$

**18.34** $\bar{R} = 0.2248$, $\bar{\bar{X}} = 5.509$, $n = 4$, $d_2 = 2.059$. **(a)** $P(5.2 < X < 5.8) = P(-2.83 < Z < 2.67) = 0.9962 - 0.0023 = 0.9939$. **(b)** Because only 99.39% of the tea bags are within the specification limits, this process is not capable of meeting the goal of 99.7%.

**18.46 (a)** The main reason that service quality is lower than product quality is because the former involves human interaction, which is prone to variation. Also, the most critical aspects of a service are often timeliness and professionalism, and customers can always perceive that the service could be done quicker and with greater professionalism. For products, customers often cannot perceive a better or more ideal product than the one they are getting. For example, a new laptop is better and contains more interesting features than any laptop the owner has ever imagined. **(b)** Both services and products are the results of processes. However, measuring services is often harder because of the dynamic variation due to the human interaction between the service provider and the customer. Product quality is often a straightforward measurement of a static physical characteristic like the amount of sugar in a can of soda. Categorical data are also more common in service quality. **(c)** Yes. **(d)** Yes.

**18.48 (a)** $\bar{p} = 0.2702$, LCL $= 0.1700$, UCL $= 0.3703$. **(b)** Yes, RudyBird's market share is in control before the in-store promotion. **(c)** All seven days of the in-store promotion are above the UCL. The promotion increased market share.

**18.50 (a)** $\bar{p} = 0.75175$, LCL $= 0.62215$, UCL $= 0.88135$. Although none of the points are outside the control limits, there is a clear pattern over time, with the last 13 points above the center line. Therefore, this process is not in control. **(b)** Because the increasing trend begins around Day 20, this change in method would be the assignable cause. **(c)** The control chart would have been developed using the first 20 days, and then a different control chart would be used for the final twenty points because they represent a different process.

**18.52 (a)** $\bar{p} = 0.1198$, LCL $= 0.0205$, UCL $= 0.2191$. **(b)** Day 24 is below the LCL; therefore, the process is out of control. **(c)** Special causes of variation should be investigated to improve the process. Next, the process should be improved to decrease the proportion of undesirable trades.

# Index

# SITE LICENSE AGREEMENT AND LIMITED WARRANTY

**READ THIS LICENSE CAREFULLY BEFORE OPENING THIS PACKAGE.** BY OPENING THIS PACKAGE, YOU ARE AGREEING TO THE TERMS AND CONDITIONS OF THIS LICENSE. IF YOU DO NOT AGREE, DO NOT OPEN THE PACKAGE. PROMPTLY RETURN THE UNOPENED PACKAGE AND ALL ACCOMPANYING ITEMS TO THE PLACE YOU OBTAINED THEM. *THESE TERMS APPLY TO ALL LICENSED SOFTWARE ON THE DISK EXCEPT THAT THE TERMS FOR USE OF ANY SHAREWARE OR FREE-WARE ON THE DISKETTES ARE AS SET FORTH IN THE ELECTRONIC LICENSE LOCATED ON THE DISK:*

**1. GRANT OF LICENSE and OWNERSHIP**: The enclosed computer programs and data ("Software") are licensed, not sold, to you by Pearson Education, Inc. ("We" or the "Company") in consideration of your purchase or adoption of the accompanying Company textbooks and/or other materials, and your agreement to these terms. We reserve any rights not granted to you. You own only the disk(s) but we and/or licensors own the Software itself. This license allows you to use and display the enclosed copy of the Software on up to 1 computer at a single campus or branch or geographic location of an educational institution, for academic use only, so long as you
comply with the terms of this Agreement. You may make one copy for back up only.

**2. RESTRICTIONS**: You may <u>not</u> transfer or distribute the Software or documentation to anyone else. Except for backup, you may <u>not</u> copy the documentation or the Software. You may <u>not</u> reverse engineer, disassemble, decompile, modify, adapt, translate, or create derivative works based on the Software or the Documentation. You may be held legally responsible for any copying or copyright infringement that is caused by your failure to abide by the terms of these restrictions.

**3. TERMINATION**: This license is effective until terminated. This license will terminate automatically without notice from the Company if you fail to comply with any provisions or limitations of this license. Upon termination, you shall destroy the Documentation and all copies of the Software. All provisions of this Agreement as to limitation and disclaimer of warranties, limitation of liability, remedies or damages, and our ownership rights shall survive termination.

**4. LIMITED WARRANTY AND DISCLAIMER OF WARRANTY**: Company warrants that for a period of 60 days from the date you purchase this Software (or purchase or adopt the accompanying textbook), the Software, when properly installed and used in accordance with the Documentation, will operate in substantial conformity with the description of the Software set forth in the Documentation, and that for a period of 30 days the disk(s) on which the Software is delivered shall be free from defects in materials and workmanship under normal use. The Company does <u>not</u> warrant that the Software will meet your requirements or that the operation of the Software will be uninterrupted or error-free. Your only remedy and the Company's only obligation under these limited warranties is, at the Company's option, return of the disk for a refund of any amounts paid for it by you or replacement of the disk. THIS LIMITED WARRANTY IS THE ONLY WARRANTY PROVIDED BY THE COMPANY AND ITS LICENSORS, AND THE COMPANY AND ITS LICENSORS DISCLAIM ALL OTHER WARRANTIES, EXPRESS OR IMPLIED, INCLUDING WITHOUT LIMITATION, THE IMPLIED WARRANTIES OF MERCHANTABILITY AND FITNESS FOR A PARTICULAR PURPOSE. THE COMPANY DOES NOT WARRANT, GUARANTEE OR MAKE ANY REPRESENTATION REGARDING THE ACCURACY, RELIABILITY, CURRENTNESS, USE, OR RESULTS OF USE, OF THE SOFTWARE.

**5. LIMITATION OF REMEDIES AND DAMAGES**: IN NO EVENT, SHALL THE COMPANY OR ITS EMPLOYEES, AGENTS, LICENSORS, OR CONTRACTORS BE LIABLE FOR ANY INCIDENTAL, INDIRECT, SPECIAL, OR CONSEQUENTIAL DAMAGES ARISING OUT OF OR IN CONNECTION WITH THIS LICENSE OR THE SOFTWARE, INCLUDING FOR LOSS OF USE, LOSS OF DATA, LOSS OF INCOME OR PROFIT, OR OTHER LOSSES, SUSTAINED AS A RESULT OF INJURY TO ANY PERSON, OR LOSS OF OR DAMAGE TO PROPERTY, OR CLAIMS OF THIRD PARTIES, EVEN IF THE COMPANY OR AN AUTHORIZED REPRESENTATIVE OF THE COMPANY HAS BEEN ADVISED OF THE POSSIBILITY OF SUCH DAMAGES. IN NO EVENT SHALL THE LIABILITY OF THE COMPANY FOR DAMAGES WITH RESPECT TO THE SOFTWARE EXCEED THE AMOUNTS ACTUALLY PAID BY YOU, IF ANY, FOR THE SOFTWARE OR THE ACCOMPANYING TEXTBOOK. SOME JURISDICTIONS DO NOT ALLOW THE LIMITATION OF LIABILITY IN CERTAIN CIRCUMSTANCES, THE ABOVE LIMITATIONS MAY NOT ALWAYS APPLY.

**6. GENERAL**: THIS AGREEMENT SHALL BE CONSTRUED IN ACCORDANCE WITH THE LAWS OF THE UNITED STATES OF AMERICA AND THE STATE OF NEW YORK, APPLICABLE TO CONTRACTS MADE IN NEW YORK, AND SHALL BENEFIT THE COMPANY, ITS AFFILIATES AND ASSIGNEES. This Agreement is the complete and exclusive statement of the agreement between you and the Company and supersedes all proposals, prior agreements, oral or written, and any other communications between you and the company or any of its representatives relating to the subject matter. If you are a U.S. Government user, this Software is licensed with "restricted rights" as set forth in subparagraphs (a)-(d) of the Commercial Computer-Restricted Rights clause at FAR 52.227-19 or in subparagraphs (c)(1)(ii) of the Rights in Technical Data and Computer Software clause at DFARS 252.227-7013, and similar clauses, as applicable.

Should you have any questions concerning this agreement or if you wish to contact the Company for any reason, please contact in writing:

Director of New Media
Higher Education Division
Prentice Hall, Inc.
1 Lake Street
Upper Saddle River, NJ 07458